CUSTOMIZED FOR
SAN DIEGO MESA COLLEGE

CHEMISTRY

VOLUME 1

With Selected Material from

Chemistry
The Molecular Nature of Matter and Change
Sixth Edition
Martin S. Silberberg

McGraw Hill Learning Solutions

Boston Burr Ridge, IL Dubuque, IA New York San Francisco St. Louis
Bangkok Bogotá Caracas Lisbon London Madrid
Mexico City Milan New Delhi Seoul Singapore Sydney Taipei Toronto

The McGraw-Hill Companies

Chemistry, Volume 1
Customized for San Diego Mesa College
Sixth Edition

This book is a McGraw-Hill Learning Solutions textbook and contains select material from *Chemistry: The Molecular Nature of Matter and Change*, Sixth Edition by Martin S. Silberberg. Copyright © 2012, 2009, 2006, 2003 by The McGraw-Hill Companies, Inc. Reprinted with permission of the publisher. Many custom published texts are modified versions or adaptations of our best-selling textbooks. Some adaptations are printed in black and white to keep prices at a minimum, while others are in color.

1 2 3 4 5 6 7 8 9 0 KNG KNG 13 12 11

ISBN-13: 978-0-07-754266-5
ISBN-10: 0-07-754266-5
PART OF:
ISBN-13: 978-0-07-754866-7
ISBN-10: 0-07-754866-3

Learning Solutions Representative: James Doepke
Production Editor: Nichole Birkenholz
Cover Design: Caitlin Anderson
Printer/Binder: King Printing
Cover Photo Credits: © 2011 JupiterImages Corporation

To Ruth and Daniel, with all my love,
and
In Memory of my Mother,
Gert Mazur,
Whose unfailing belief in me, I have finally come to realize,
has been a driving force in my life.

BRIEF CONTENTS

DETAILED CONTENTS

CHAPTER 1 • Keys to the Study of Chemistry 2

CHAPTER 2 • The Components of Matter 36

CHAPTER 6 • Thermochemistry: Energy Flow and Chemical Change 228

CHAPTER 7 • Quantum Theory and Atomic Structure 260

CHAPTER 8 • Electron Configuration and Chemical Periodicity 294

CHAPTER 9 • Models of Chemical Bonding 328

CHAPTER 10 • The Shapes of Molecules 362

CHAPTER 11 • Theories of Covalent Bonding 394

CHAPTER 12 • Intermolecular Forces: Liquids, Solids, and Phase Changes 418

CHAPTER 13 • The Properties of Mixtures: Solutions and Colloids 476

LIST OF SAMPLE PROBLEMS (Molecular-scene problems are shown in color.)

Chapter 6

Chapter 7

Chapter 8

Chapter 9

Chapter 10

Chapter 11

Chapter 12

Chapter 13

Chapter 15

Chapter 16

Chapter 17

Chapter 18

Chapter 19

Chapter 20

Chapter 21

Chapter 23

Chapter 24

About the Author

Martin S. Silberberg received a B.S. in Chemistry from the City University of New York and a Ph.D. in Chemistry from the University of Oklahoma. He then accepted a position as research associate in analytical biochemistry at the Albert Einstein College of Medicine in New York City, where he developed methods to study neurotransmitter metabolism in Parkinson's disease and other neurological disorders. Following six years as research associate, Dr. Silberberg joined the faculty of Bard College at Simon's Rock, a liberal arts college known for its excellence in teaching small classes of highly motivated students. As head of the Natural Sciences Major and Director of Premedical Studies, he taught courses in general chemistry, organic chemistry, biochemistry, and liberal-arts chemistry. The small class size and close student contact afforded him insights into how students learn chemistry, where they have difficulties, and what strategies can help them succeed. Dr. Silberberg decided to apply these insights in a broader context and established a textbook writing, editing, and consulting company. Before writing his own texts, he worked as a consulting and development editor on chemistry, biochemistry, and physics texts for several major college publishers. He resides with his wife Ruth and son in the Pioneer Valley near Amherst, Massachusetts, where he enjoys the rich cultural and academic life of the area and relaxes by cooking and singing.

Preface

At the core of natural science, chemistry is so crucial to an understanding of medicine, molecular biology, genetics, pharmacology, ecology, atmospheric science, engineering, nuclear studies, materials science, and many other fields that it has become a central requirement for an increasing number of academic majors. Furthermore, chemical principles are at the core of many key societal issues, including climate change, energy options, materials recycling, diet and nutrition, and medicine and disease. Clearly, the study of chemistry plays an essential role in our world.

WHAT SETS THIS BOOK APART

For five editions, *Chemistry: The Molecular Nature of Matter and Change* has been recognized for setting the standard among general chemistry textbooks. This sixth edition maintains that unparalleled reputation by keeping pace with the evolution of student learning. The text still contains the most accurate macroscopic-to-molecular illustrations, consistent step-by-step worked problems, and an extensive collection of end-of-chapter problems, with a wide range of difficulties and applications targeting student interests in engineering, medicine, materials, and environmental studies. Changes throughout the text have made it more succinct, the artwork more teachable and modern, and the design more open and inviting. And, while the content has certainly been updated to reflect chemistry's growing impact in the world, the mechanisms of the text—the teaching approaches that are so admired and emulated—have remained the same. Three hallmarks make this text a market leader.

Visualizing Chemical Models—Macroscopic to Molecular

Chemistry deals with observable changes caused by unobservable atomic-scale events, requiring an understanding of a size gap of mind-boggling proportions. One of the text's goals coincides with that of so many instructors: to help the student visualize chemical events on the molecular scale. Thus, concepts are explained first at the macroscopic level and then from a molecular point of view, with the text's groundbreaking illustrations always placed next to the discussion to bring the point home for today's visually oriented students.

Thinking Logically to Solve Problems

The problem-solving approach, based on the four-step method widely accepted by experts in chemical education, is introduced in Chapter 1 and employed *consistently* throughout the text. It encourages students to *plan* a logical approach to a problem, and only then proceed to *solve* it. Each sample problem includes a *check,* which fosters the habit of "taking a breath" to assess the reasonableness and magnitude of the answer. Finally, for *practice* and reinforcement, each sample problem is followed immediately by a similar follow-up problem, for which an abbreviated solution, not merely a numerical answer, is given at the end of the chapter. In this edition, solving problems and visualizing models have been married through an increasing number of molecular-scene problems in both worked examples and homework sets.

Applying Ideas to the Real World

An understanding of modern chemistry influences attitudes about climate change and health care, while also explaining the spring in a running shoe and the display of a laptop screen. Today's students may enter one of the emerging chemistry-related hybrid fields—biomaterials science or planetary geochemistry, for example—and their text should point out the relevance of chemical concepts to such career directions. The *Chemical Connections* and *Tools of the Laboratory* boxed essays (which now include problems to reinforce learning), the fewer but more pedagogic margin notes, and the many applications woven into the chapter content are up-to-date, student-friendly features that complement the text content.

REFINING THE STANDARD: AN EVOLVING LEARNING SYSTEM

Just as the field of chemistry is addressing major changes in the world, the student learning experience is changing as well—different math and reading preparation, less time for traditional studying, electronic media as part of daily lectures and homework, new challenges and options in career choices, and so on. To address these dynamic times, a modern general chemistry text supported by a suite of robust electronic tools for professor and student must continue to evolve, as this text has through all previous editions. From first to second edition, a major emphasis was placed on creating more molecular art to help students visualize chemistry at that level. The third edition incorporated many revised sample problems and a plethora of new end-of-chapter problems. The fourth edition gave birth to molecular-scene sample problems to help students understand concepts through simple molecular depictions. Molecular scenes became so popular that the fifth edition tripled the number of sample problems and doubled the number of end-of-chapter problems using them. During these revisions, major content improvements took place in limiting-reactant stoichiometry, green chemistry, biomolecular structure, kinetics and equilibrium, entropy and free energy, and nuclear chemistry, among many other areas.

With each edition, students and instructors alike have been involved in refining the text. Especially in preparation for the sixth edition, the author, together with key members of the editorial, sales, and marketing teams, consulted extensively with student and faculty users. From chapter reviews, focus groups, symposia, class tests, and one-on-one interviews with instructors, we were gratified to learn that everyone loved the pioneering, and still the most accurate, molecular art; the stepwise problem-solving approach, time-honored and consistent with decades of education research; the abundant mix of qualitative, basic quantitative, and applied end-of-chapter problems; and the thorough, student-friendly coverage of mainstream topics.

Based on this feedback, our revision for this edition focuses on "refining the standard" set earlier: distilling the writing to be concise and direct, opening up the overall appearance of pages, and improving illustrations by shortening legends and adding explanations into the art. We are delighted to introduce the sixth edition of *Chemistry: The Molecular Nature of Matter and Change,* which moves further toward perfecting content and approach in these ways:

Chapter openings, simplified. A familiar application and photo engage the student, followed by a bulleted list of main topics covered in the chapter.

Writing style and content presentation. Every line of every discussion has been revised to optimize clarity, readability, and a more direct presentation of ideas. The use of additional subheads, numbered (and titled) paragraphs, and bulleted (and titled) lists has eliminated long unbroken paragraphs. Main ideas are delineated and highlighted, making for more efficient study and lectures. As a result, the text is over 70 pages shorter, yet no key topics have been removed.

Problem-solving format. The much admired and duplicated four-part (plan, solution, check, practice) *Sample Problems* are displayed cleanly. Both data-based and molecular-scene problems occur throughout, and, to deepen understanding, most *Follow-Up Problems* have worked-out solutions at the back of each chapter, with a road map when appropriate, effectively doubling the number of worked problems. This edition has 15 more sample problems—many in the earlier chapters, where students need the most practice and confidence.

Art and figure legends. The innovative art that raised the bar in chemistry textbooks is still present, with many figures made more realistic and modern. Moreover, figure legends have been greatly shortened and their explanations added to neighboring text and the figures themselves for greater comprehension and less redundancy.

Page design and layout. A more open look invites the reader with cleaner margins and more white space, yet with the same attention to keeping text, figures, and tables near each other for easier viewing and studying.

Incorporating relevance. Applications make chemistry meaningful, so many exciting ideas from the margin notes and galleries of the fifth edition have been incorporated directly into the text, where they are more likely to be read. The boxed essays—*Chemical Connections* and *Tools of the Laboratory*—are more concise and are now accompanied by several homework problems to make them more useful for student and teacher.

Section Summaries. This universally approved feature is even easier to use in its new bulleted format.

Chapter review. Our unique *Chapter Review Guide* aids study by presenting concepts to understand and skills to master, key terms, key equations, and the multistep *Brief Solutions to Follow-Up Problems* (rather than simple numerical answers).

End-of-chapter problem sets. With an enhanced design to improve readability and traditional and molecular-scene problems updated and revised, these problem sets, more extensive than in most other texts, provide students and teachers with abundant choices in a wide range of difficulty and set in real-life scenarios.

Content Changes to Individual Chapters

- Chapter 2 presents a new figure and table on molecular modeling.
- Discussion of empirical formulas has been moved from Chapter 2 to Chapter 3 so it appears just before molecular formulas.
- Within Chapter 3, some sample problems have been segmented and seven new sample problems introduced to better focus problem-solving on distinct concepts.
- Chapter 3 contains more extensive use of stoichiometry reaction tables in limiting-reactant problems.
- Chapter 4 presents a new molecular-scene sample problem on depicting an ionic compound in aqueous solution.
- Chapter 5 includes a new subsection on how gas laws apply to breathing.
- Chapter 5 also contains new short discussions on the relevance of gas density.
- Also in Chapter 5, coverage of reaction stoichiometry has been more logically grouped with other rearrangements of the ideal gas law.
- Chapter 5 contains new illustrations of diffusion and origin of pressure.
- In Chapter 5, *Chemical Connections to Atmospheric Science* uses the gas laws to explain why the troposphere has a uniform composition.
- Chapter 7 includes a new sample problem on using the Rydberg equation.
- Chapter 8 contains a new subsection covering electron configuration, chemical reactivity, and redox behavior.

- In Chapter 9, *Tools of the Laboratory: Infrared Spectroscopy* contains a new discussion of carbon dioxide in global warming.
- Chapter 11 includes a new discussion of limitations to *d*-orbital hybridization.
- Chapter 12 presents new short discussions of everyday applications of surface tension, capillarity, and viscosity.
- Chapter 13 presents everyday applications of freezing point depression and osmotic pressure.
- The fifth edition's *Interchapter* has been deleted, but key figures have been placed in relevant locations within other chapters.
- Chapter 14 provides a thorough, focused survey of main-group descriptive chemistry.
- Chapter 15 contains new art for the molecular biology of protein synthesis and DNA replication.
- Chapter 16 incorporates two of the fifth edition's boxed features—on measuring reaction rates and on enzymes—into the chapter text.
- Chapter 17 makes consistent use of benchmarks for determining when an assumption is valid.
- Chapter 17 incorporates the fifth edition's boxed feature on ammonia production into the chapter text.
- Chapter 19 incorporates the fifth edition's boxed feature on cave formation into the chapter text.

Flexibility in Topic and Chapter Presentation

Chemistry: The Molecular Nature of Matter and Change has been revised to keep the mainstream topic sequence working optimally for teacher and student. But every course is unique, so flexibility has been built in: many section and subsection breaks allow topics to be rearranged with minimal loss of continuity. For example, redox balancing can be covered in Chapter 4, in Chapter 21, or, as done in the text, in both Chapter 4 (oxidation-number method) *and* Chapter 21 (half-reaction method, in preparation for electrochemistry). Likewise, several chapters can be taught in different orders. For instance, gases (Chapter 5) can be covered in sequence to explore the mathematical modeling of physical behavior or, with no loss of continuity, just before liquids and solids (Chapter 12) to show the effects of intermolecular forces on the three states of matter. In fact, feedback has indicated that many instructors move chapters, sections, and topics around, for example, covering descriptive chemistry (Chapter 14) and organic chemistry (Chapter 15) in the more traditional placement at the end of the course. Because the topic sequence is so flexible, any instructor can feel comfortable making such changes to suit his or her course.

KEEPING PACE WITH THE EVOLUTION OF STUDENT LEARNING

Many of us don't have the same cell phones, computers, or cars that we did just a few years ago—because technology is improving. In much the same way, the Silberberg Learning System has also been improving. The fifth edition of this text was accompanied by an online homework program called ARIS. Through careful observation of students and collaboration with instructors, the online homework tool has evolved into an online learning and engagement tool: **Connect:™ Chemistry.** The goal of Connect: Chemistry is to usher in a new era of meaningful online learning that balances the conceptual and quantitative aspect of this most vital discipline.

With this sixth edition, McGraw-Hill is offering students and instructors a greatly enhanced digital homework experience through Connect: Chemistry. Each problem formerly in the ARIS system has been carefully converted into the new program. Within Connect: Chemistry, each problem retains Silberberg's problem-solving methodology and is enhanced with specific hints, as well as feedback for common incorrect answers—all authored and accuracy-checked by teams of dedicated chemistry professors with many years of classroom experience. Several rounds of editorial revising and more expert checking, in addition to numerous instructor and student tests of all problems, ensure the accuracy and pedagogic soundness of all content.

In addition to the specific hints and feedback, many problems offer students the opportunity to engage in chemical drawing that can be assessed directly within their homework. To provide this important pedagogic experience, Connect: Chemistry has partnered with CambridgeSoft's® ChemDraw, widely considered the "gold standard" of scientific drawing programs and *the* cornerstone application for drawing and annotating molecules, reactions, and pathways. This collaboration of Connect: Chemistry and ChemDraw features an easy-to-use, intuitive, and comprehensive course management and homework system with professional-grade drawing capabilities.

THE SILBERBERG LEARNING SYSTEM

Many pedagogic tools are woven throughout the chapters to guide students on their learning journey.

Chapter Openers

Each chapter introduces a familiar application and photo relating to the main topic of the chapter, followed by a bulleted list of main topics. The chapter outline shows the sequence of topics and subtopics. At the top of the opposite page, *Concepts and Skills to Review* lists key material from earlier chapters that students should understand before starting to read the current one.

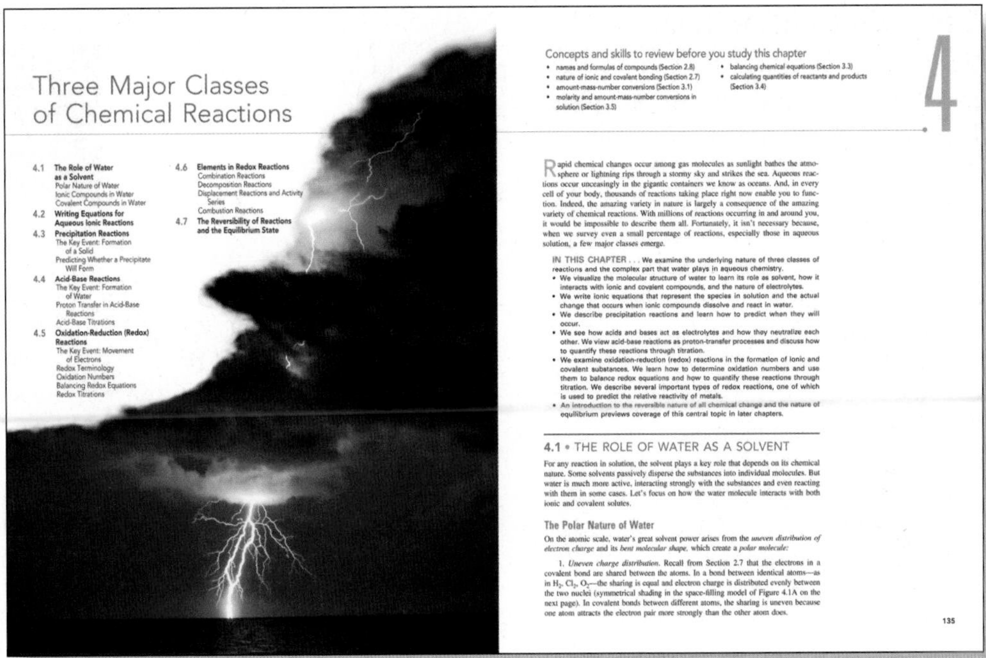

Three Major Classes of Chemical Reactions

4.1 **The Role of Water as a Solvent**
Polar Nature of Water
Ionic Compounds in Water
Covalent Compounds in Water
4.2 **Writing Equations for Aqueous Ionic Reactions**
4.3 **Precipitation Reactions**
The Key Event: Formation of a Solid
Predicting Whether a Precipitate Will Form
4.4 **Acid-Base Reactions**
The Key Event: Formation of Water
Proton Transfer in Acid-Base Reactions
Acid-Base Titrations
4.5 **Oxidation-Reduction (Redox) Reactions**
The Key Event: Movement of Electrons
Redox Terminology
Oxidation Numbers
Balancing Redox Equations
Redox Titrations
4.6 **Elements in Redox Reactions**
Combination Reactions
Decomposition Reactions
Displacement Reactions and Activity Series
Combustion Reactions
4.7 **The Reversibility of Reactions and the Equilibrium State**

Concepts and skills to review before you study this chapter
- names and formulas of compounds (Section 2.8)
- nature of ionic and covalent bonding (Section 2.7)
- amount-mass-number conversions (Section 3.1)
- molarity and amount-mass-number conversions in solution (Section 3.5)
- balancing chemical equations (Section 3.3)
- calculating quantities of reactants and products (Section 3.4)

4

Rapid chemical changes occur among gas molecules as sunlight bathes the atmosphere or lightning rips through a stormy sky and strikes the sea. Aqueous reactions occur unceasingly in the gigantic containers we know as oceans. And, in every cell of your body, thousands of reactions taking place right now enable you to function. Indeed, the amazing variety in nature is largely a consequence of the amazing variety of chemical reactions. With millions of reactions occurring in and around you, it would be impossible to describe them all. Fortunately, it isn't necessary because, when we survey even a small percentage of reactions, especially those in aqueous solution, a few major classes emerge.

IN THIS CHAPTER . . . We examine the underlying nature of three classes of reactions and the complex part that water plays in aqueous chemistry.
- We visualize the molecular structure of water to learn its role as solvent, how it interacts with ionic and covalent compounds, and the nature of electrolytes.
- We write ionic equations that represent the species in solution and the actual change that occurs when ionic compounds dissolve and react in water.
- We describe precipitation reactions and learn how to predict when they will occur.
- We see how acids and bases act as electrolytes and how they neutralize each other. We view acid-base reactions as proton-transfer processes and discuss how to quantify these reactions through titration.
- We examine oxidation-reduction (redox) reactions in the formation of ionic and covalent substances. We learn how to determine oxidation numbers and use them to balance redox equations and how to quantify these reactions through titration. We describe several important types of redox reactions, one of which is used to predict the relative reactivity of metals.
- An introduction to the reversible nature of all chemical change and the nature of equilibrium previews coverage of this central topic in later chapters.

4.1 • THE ROLE OF WATER AS A SOLVENT

For any reaction in solution, the solvent plays a key role that depends on its chemical nature. Some solvents passively disperse the substances into individual molecules. But water is much more active, interacting strongly with the substances and even reacting with them in some cases. Let's focus on how the water molecule interacts with both ionic and covalent solutes.

The Polar Nature of Water

On the atomic scale, water's great solvent power arises from the *uneven distribution of electron charge* and its *bent molecular shape*, which create a *polar molecule*:

1. *Uneven charge distribution*. Recall from Section 2.7 that the electrons in a covalent bond are shared between the atoms. In a bond between identical atoms—as in H_2, Cl_2, O_2—the sharing is equal and electron charge is distributed evenly between the two nuclei (symmetrical shading in the space-filling model of Figure 4.1A on the next page). In covalent bonds between different atoms, the sharing is uneven because one atom attracts the electron pair more strongly than the other atom does.

135

Problem Solving

A worked-out *Sample Problem* appears whenever an important new concept or skill is introduced. The problem-solving step helps students think through chemistry problems logically and systematically. The universally accepted four-step approach of plan, solve, check, and practice is used consistently for every sample problem in the text. The steps are:

- **Plan** analyzes the problem so that students can use what is known to find what is unknown. This step develops the habit of thinking through the solution before performing calculations. Most quantitative problems are accompanied in the margin by a *Road Map*, a block diagram that is specific to the problem and leads students visually through the planned steps.
- **Solution** presents the calculation steps *in the same order* as they appear in the plan and in the road map.
- **Check** fosters the habit of going over one's work with a rough calculation to make sure the answer is both chemically and mathematically reasonable—a great way to avoid careless errors. In many cases, this step is followed by a *Comment* that identifies an additional insight, alternative approach, or common mistake to avoid.
- **Follow-Up Problem** presents a similar problem to provide immediate practice, with an abbreviated multistep solution appearing at the end of the chapter. Where appropriate in the first several chapters, students are asked to draw their own road map to solve the follow-up problem.

Sample Problem 3.13 **Balancing an Equation from a Molecular Scene**

Problem The following molecular scenes depict an important reaction in nitrogen chemistry (nitrogen is blue; oxygen is red):

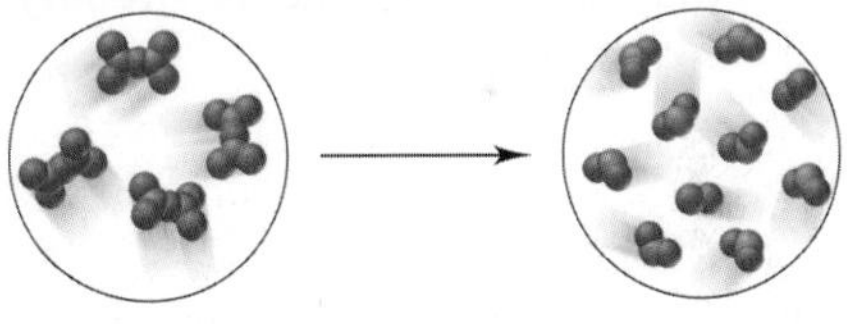

Write a balanced equation for this reaction.

Plan To write a balanced equation, we first have to determine the formulas of the molecules and obtain coefficients by counting the number of each molecule. Then, we arrange this information in the correct equation format, using the smallest whole-number coefficients and including states of matter.

Solution The reactant circle shows only one type of molecule. It has two N and five O atoms, so the formula is N_2O_5; there are four of these molecules. The product circle shows two different molecules, one with one N and two O atoms, and the other with two O atoms; there are eight NO_2 and two O_2. Thus, we have:

$$4N_2O_5 \longrightarrow 8NO_2 + 2O_2$$

Writing the balanced equation with the smallest whole-number coefficients and all substances as gases:

$$2N_2O_5(g) \longrightarrow 4NO_2(g) + O_2(g)$$

Check Reactant (4 N, 10 O) ⟶ products (4 N, 8 + 2 = 10 O)

Follow-Up Problem 3.13 Write a balanced equation for the important atmospheric reaction depicted below (carbon is black; oxygen is red):

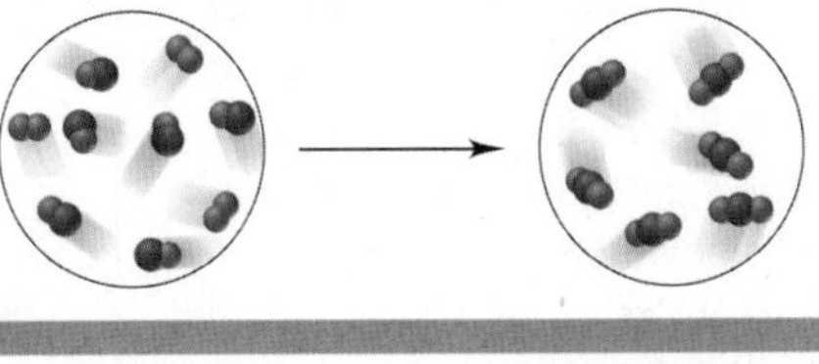

Three-Level Illustrations

As the art that set the standard for chemistry textbooks, these illustrations connect the macroscopic and molecular levels of reality with the symbolic level in the form of a chemical equation.

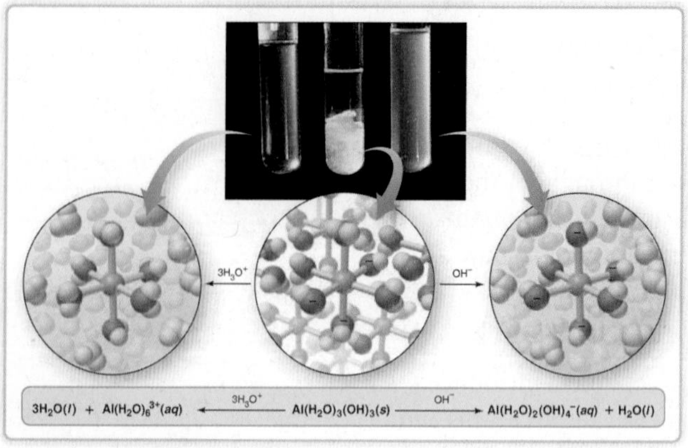

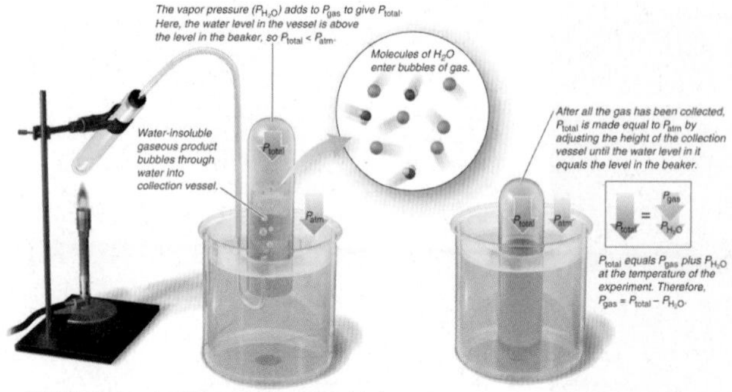

Figure 5.12 Collecting a water-insoluble gaseous product and determining its pressure.

Annotated Figures

Modern, explanatory figures describe chemical processes through instructional labeling and realistic, three-dimensional art.

Optimized Presentation

Text paragraphs have been made more concise, with presentation of content optimized through the use of subheads, numbered paragraphs, and lists. Main ideas are delineated, resulting in a more student-friendly study format.

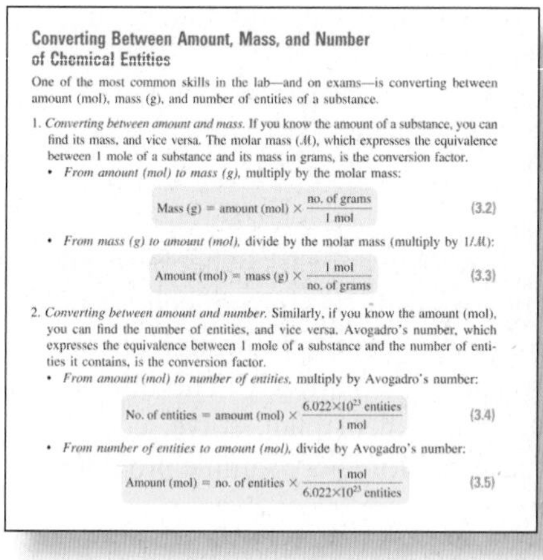

Converting Between Amount, Mass, and Number of Chemical Entities

One of the most common skills in the lab—and on exams—is converting between amount (mol), mass (g), and number of entities of a substance.

1. *Converting between amount and mass.* If you know the amount of a substance, you can find its mass, and vice versa. The molar mass ($\mathcal{M}$), which expresses the equivalence between 1 mole of a substance and its mass in grams, is the conversion factor.
   - *From amount (mol) to mass (g),* multiply by the molar mass:

$$\text{Mass (g)} = \text{amount (mol)} \times \frac{\text{no. of grams}}{1 \text{ mol}} \quad (3.2)$$

   - *From mass (g) to amount (mol),* divide by the molar mass (multiply by $1/\mathcal{M}$):

$$\text{Amount (mol)} = \text{mass (g)} \times \frac{1 \text{ mol}}{\text{no. of grams}} \quad (3.3)$$

2. *Converting between amount and number.* Similarly, if you know the amount (mol), you can find the number of entities, and vice versa. Avogadro's number, which expresses the equivalence between 1 mole of a substance and the number of entities it contains, is the conversion factor.
   - *From amount (mol) to number of entities,* multiply by Avogadro's number:

$$\text{No. of entities} = \text{amount (mol)} \times \frac{6.022\times10^{23} \text{ entities}}{1 \text{ mol}} \quad (3.4)$$

   - *From number of entities to amount (mol),* divide by Avogadro's number:

$$\text{Amount (mol)} = \text{no. of entities} \times \frac{1 \text{ mol}}{6.022\times10^{23} \text{ entities}} \quad (3.5)$$

Applications

Chemical Connections essays show the interdisciplinary nature of chemistry by applying chemical principles directly to related scientific fields, including physiology, geology, biochemistry, engineering, and environmental science. *Tools of the Laboratory* essays describe the key instruments and techniques that chemists use in modern practice to obtain the data that underlie their theories. Both essay features now include several problems to enhance learning and relevance.

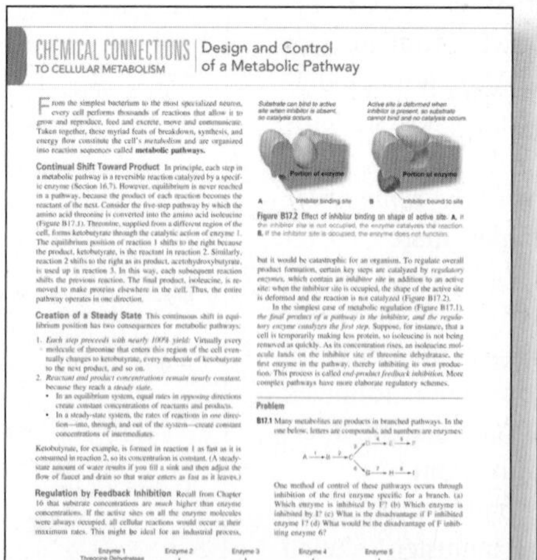

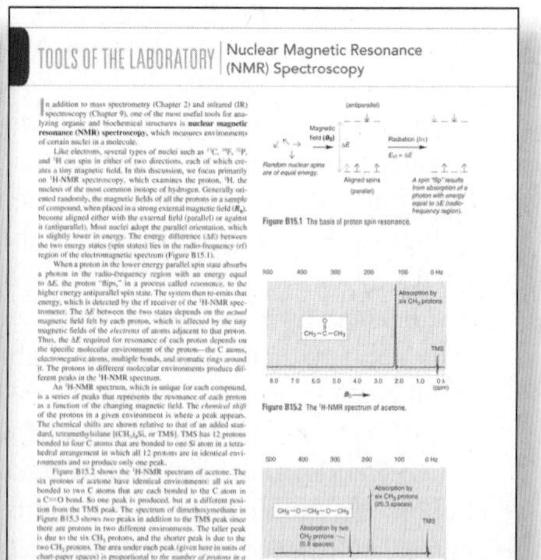

Section Summaries

Concise, bulleted summary lists conclude each section, restating the major ideas just covered.

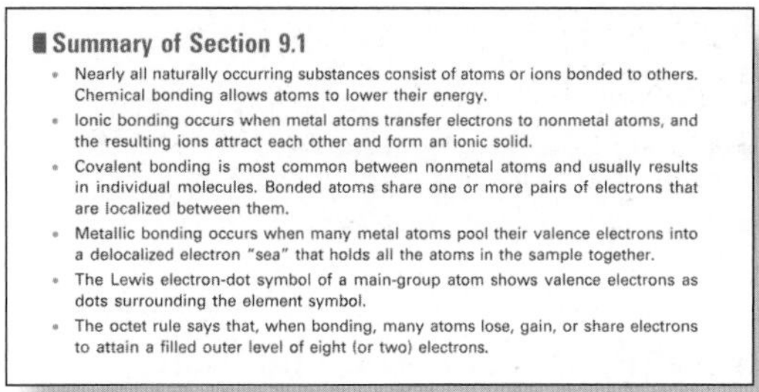

Summary of Section 9.1

- Nearly all naturally occurring substances consist of atoms or ions bonded to others. Chemical bonding allows atoms to lower their energy.
- Ionic bonding occurs when metal atoms transfer electrons to nonmetal atoms, and the resulting ions attract each other and form an ionic solid.
- Covalent bonding is most common between nonmetal atoms and usually results in individual molecules. Bonded atoms share one or more pairs of electrons that are localized between them.
- Metallic bonding occurs when many metal atoms pool their valence electrons into a delocalized electron "sea" that holds all the atoms in the sample together.
- The Lewis electron-dot symbol of a main-group atom shows valence electrons as dots surrounding the element symbol.
- The octet rule says that, when bonding, many atoms lose, gain, or share electrons to attain a filled outer level of eight (or two) electrons.

Chapter Review Guide

A rich catalog of study aids ends each chapter to help students review its content.

- **Learning Objectives,** with section and/or sample problem numbers, focus on key concepts and skills.
- **Key Terms** are boldfaced and defined within the chapter and listed here by section (with page numbers), as well as being defined again in the *Glossary*.
- **Key Equations and Relationships** are screened and numbered within the chapter and listed here with page numbers.
- **Brief Solutions to Follow-Up Problems** double the number of worked problems by providing multistep calculations at the ends of the chapters, rather than just a numerical answer at the back of the book. Road maps are supplied for those follow-up problems that ask students to prepare one in planning their solution.

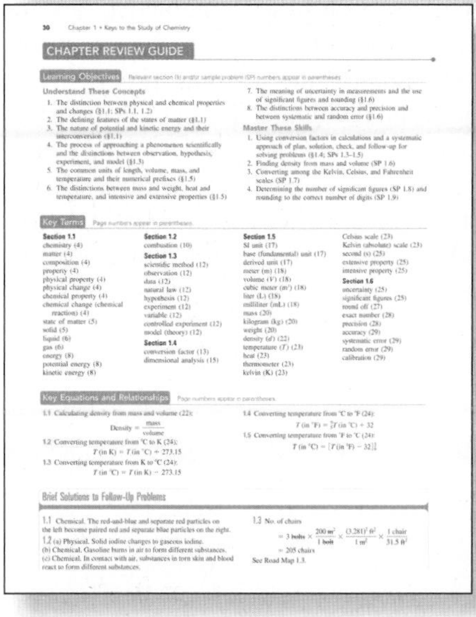

End-of-Chapter Problems

An exceptionally large number of qualitative, quantitative, and molecular-scene homework problems end each chapter. Three types of problems are keyed by chapter section, with comprehensive problems following:

- **Concept Review Questions** test students' qualitative understanding of key ideas.
- **Skill-Building Exercises** are grouped in pairs that cover a similar idea, with one of each pair answered in the back of the book. These exercises begin with simple questions and increase in difficulty, gradually eliminating students' need for multistep directions.
- **Problems in Context** apply the skills learned in the skill-building exercises to interesting scenarios, including examples from industry, medicine, and the environment.
- **Comprehensive Problems,** most based on realistic applications, are more challenging and rely on concepts and skills from any section of the current chapter or from previous chapters.

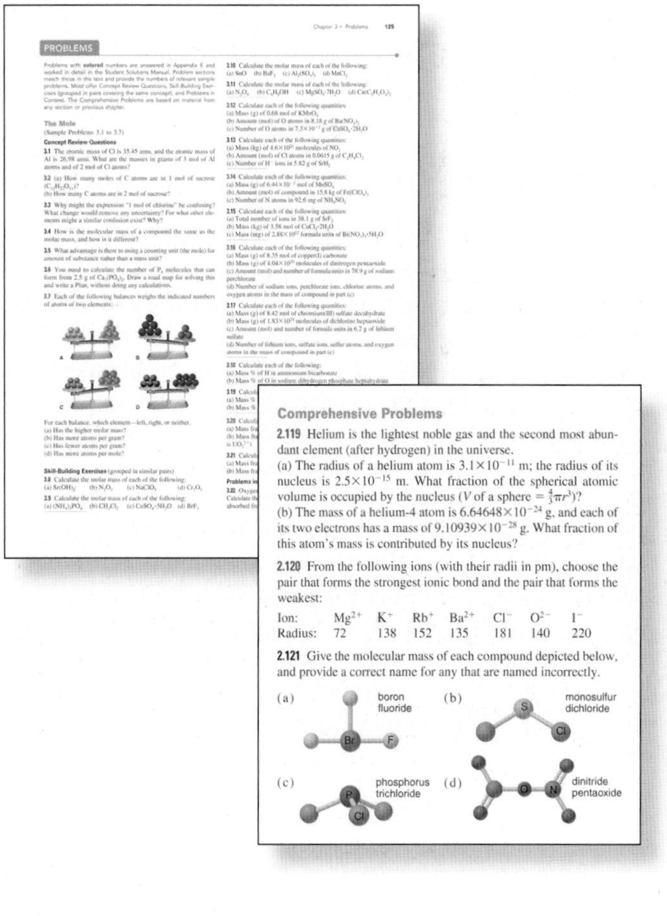

Comprehensive Problems

2.119 Helium is the lightest noble gas and the second most abundant element (after hydrogen) in the universe.
(a) The radius of a helium atom is 3.1×10^{-11} m; the radius of its nucleus is 2.5×10^{-15} m. What fraction of the spherical atomic volume is occupied by the nucleus (V of a sphere $= \frac{4}{3}\pi r^3$)?
(b) The mass of a helium-4 atom is 6.64648×10^{-24} g, and each of its two electrons has a mass of 9.10939×10^{-28} g. What fraction of this atom's mass is contributed by its nucleus?

2.120 From the following ions (with their radii in pm), choose the pair that forms the strongest ionic bond and the pair that forms the weakest:

Ion:	Mg^{2+}	K^+	Rb^+	Ba^{2+}	Cl^-	O^{2-}	I^-
Radius:	72	138	152	135	181	140	220

2.121 Give the molecular mass of each compound depicted below, and provide a correct name for any that are named incorrectly.

LEARNING SYSTEM RESOURCES FOR INSTRUCTORS

McGraw-Hill connect™ | CHEMISTRY

www.mcgrawhillconnect.com/chemistry

McGraw-Hill Connect is a web-based, interactive assignment and assessment platform that incorporates cognitive science principles to customize the learning process. The chemical drawing tool found within Connect: Chemistry is CambridgeSoft's ChemDraw, which is widely considered the "gold standard" of scientific drawing programs and the cornerstone application for drawing and annotating molecules, reactions, and pathways. This combination of Connect and ChemDraw is an easy-to-use, intuitive, and comprehensive course management and homework system with professional-grade drawing capabilities.

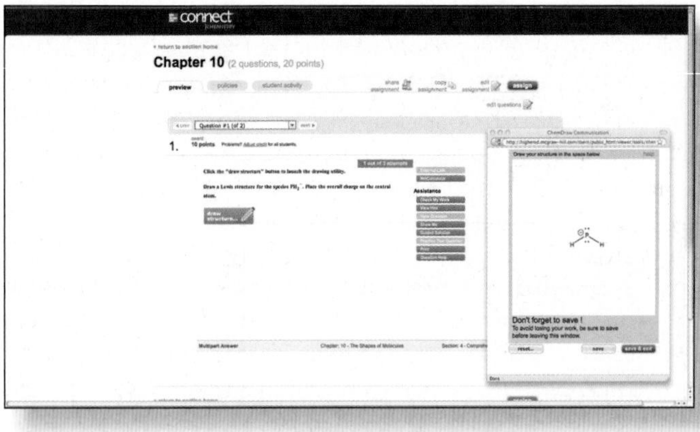

End-of-chapter problems from this textbook are available in Connect: Chemistry for instructors to build assignments that are automatically graded and tracked through reports that export easily to Excel. Instructors can edit existing problems and write entirely new problems; track individual student performance—by problem, assignment, concept, or in relation to the class overall—with automatic grading; provide instant feedback to students; and store detailed grade reports securely online. Grade reports can be easily integrated with learning management systems such as WebCT and Blackboard. Single sign-on integration is available with the Blackboard course management system. Within Connect, instructors can also create and share materials with colleagues. Ask your McGraw-Hill representative for more information, and then check it out at www.mcgrawhillconnect.com/chemistry.

Blackboard Course Management Integration with McGraw-Hill Content

McGraw-Hill Blackboard Do More

McGraw-Hill Higher Education and Blackboard, the Web-based course-management system, have teamed up to allow students and faculty to easily use online materials and activities to complement face-to-face teaching. Blackboard features exciting social learning and teaching tools that foster more logical, visually impactful, and active learning opportunities for students. This partnership transforms closed-door classrooms into communities where students remain connected to their educational experience 24 hours a day.

This partnership allows instructors and students access to McGraw-Hill's Connect™ and Create™ from within Blackboard—with a single sign-on.

Instructors also get deep integration of McGraw-Hill content and content engines into Blackboard. Whether choosing a book for your course or building Connect™ assignments, all the tools you need are right where you want them—inside Blackboard.

Gradebooks are now seamless. When a student completes an integrated Connect™ assignment, the grade for that assignment is automatically (and instantly) fed to the Blackboard grade center.

McGraw-Hill and Blackboard now offer easy access to industry-leading technology and content, whether your campus hosts it, or we do. Be sure to ask your local McGraw-Hill representative for details.

Presentation Center Accessed from your textbook's Connect website, Presentation Center is an online digital library containing McGraw-Hill owned photos, artwork, animations, and other types of media that can be used to create customized lectures, visually enhanced tests and quizzes, compelling course websites, or attractive printed support materials for classroom purposes. The visual resources in this collection include the following:

- **Art** Full-color digital files of all illustrations in the book can be readily incorporated into lecture presentations, exams, or custom-made classroom materials. In addition, all files have been inserted into PowerPoint slides for ease of lecture preparation.
- **Photos** The photo collection contains digital files of photographs from the text, which can be reproduced for multiple classroom uses.
- **Tables** Every table that appears in the text has been saved in electronic form for use in classroom presentations and/or classroom materials.

- **Animations** Numerous full-color animations illustrating important processes are also provided. Harness the visual impact of concepts in motion by importing these files into classroom presentations or online course materials.

PowerPoint materials can also be accessed through your textbook's Connect website:

- **PowerPoint Lecture Outlines** Ready-made presentations that combine art and lecture notes are provided for each chapter of the text.
- **PowerPoint Slides** For instructors who prefer to create their lectures from scratch, all illustrations, photos, sample problems, and tables have been inserted into blank PowerPoint slides, arranged by chapter.

The Presentation Center library includes thousands of assets from many McGraw-Hill titles. This ever-growing resource gives instructors the power to utilize assets specific to an adopted textbook as well as content from all other books in the library. Accessed through the instructor side of your textbook's Connect website, Presentation Center's dynamic search engine allows you to explore by discipline, course, textbook chapter, asset type, or keyword. Simply browse, select, and download the files you need to build engaging course materials. To access Connect, request registration information from your McGraw-Hill sales representative.

Mc Graw Hill tegrity campus

Digital Lecture Capture: Tegrity McGraw-Hill *Tegrity Campus* records and distributes your lecture with just a click of a button. Students can view anytime/anywhere via computer, iPod, or mobile device. *Tegrity* indexes as it records your slideshow presentations and anything shown on your computer, so students can use keywords to find exactly what they want to study.

Computerized Test Bank Prepared by Walter Orchard, Professor Emeritus of Tacoma Community College, over 2300 test questions to accompany *Chemistry: The Molecular Nature of Matter and Change* are available utilizing Brownstone's Diploma testing software. *Diploma's* software allows you to quickly create a customized test using McGraw-Hill's supplied questions or by authoring your own. *Diploma* allows you to create your tests without an Internet connection—just download the software and question files directly to your computer.

Instructor's Solutions Manual This supplement, prepared by Patricia Amateis of Virginia Tech, contains complete, worked-out solutions for *all* the end-of-chapter problems in the text. It can be found within the Instructors Resources, on the Connect: Chemistry site.

Content Delivery Flexibility *Chemistry: The Molecular Nature of Matter and Change,* by Martin Silberberg, is available in other formats in addition to the traditional textbook, giving instructors and students more choices for the format of their chemistry text.

Mc Graw Hill create

- **Customizable Textbooks: Create** McGraw-Hill Create™ is a new, self-service website that allows you to create custom course materials—print or eBook—by drawing on McGraw-Hill's comprehensive, cross-disciplinary content. Add your own content quickly and easily. Tap into other rights-secured third-party sources as well. Then, arrange the content in a way that makes the most sense for your course. Even personalize your book with your course name and information. Choose the best format for your course: color print, black-and-white print, or ebook (which is viewable on an iPad). And when you are finished customizing, you will receive a free PDF review copy in just minutes. Visit McGraw-Hill Create at www.mcgrawhillcreate.com today and begin building your perfect book.
- **ConnectPlus eBook** McGraw-Hill's ConnectPlus eBook takes digital texts beyond a simple PDF. With the same content as the printed book, but optimized for the screen, the ConnectPlus eBook has embedded media, including animations and videos, which bring concepts to life and provide "just in time" learning for students. Additionally, fully integrated homework problems allow students to interact with the problems to determine if they're gaining mastery of the content, and the problems can also be assigned by the instructor.

Cooperative Chemistry Laboratory Manual Prepared by Melanie Cooper of Clemson University, this innovative manual features open-ended problems designed to simulate experience in a research lab. Working in groups, students investigate one problem over a period of several weeks, so they might complete three or four projects during the semester, rather than one preprogrammed experiment per class. The emphasis is on experimental design, analytic problem solving, and communication.

LEARNING SYSTEM RESOURCES FOR STUDENTS

Student Study Guide This valuable study guide, prepared by Libby Bent Weberg, is designed to help you recognize your learning style; understand how to read, classify, and create a plan for solving a problem; and practice your problem-solving skills. For each section of each chapter, the guide provides study objectives and a summary of the corresponding text. Following the summary are sample problems with detailed solutions. Each chapter has true-false questions and a self-test, with all answers provided at the end of the chapter.

Student Solutions Manual This supplement, prepared by Patricia Amateis of Virginia Tech, contains detailed solutions and explanations for all problems in the main text that have colored numbers.

Mc Graw Hill connect™ CHEMISTRY

Connect: Chemistry With Connect: Chemistry, you can practice solving assigned homework problems using the Silberberg problem-solving methodology applied in the textbook. Algorithmic problems serve up multiple versions of similar problems for mastery of content, with hints and feedback for common incorrect answers to help you stay on track. Where appropriate, you engage in accurate, professional-grade chemical drawing through the use of CambridgeSoft's ChemDraw tool, which is implemented directly into homework problems. Check it out at www.mcgraw-hillconnect.com/chemistry.

Mc Graw Hill LearnSmart™

LearnSmart™ This adaptive diagnostic learning system, powered by Connect: Chemistry and based on artificial intelligence, constantly assesses your knowledge of the course material. As you work within the system, LearnSmart develops a personal learning path adapted to what you have actively learned and retained. This innovative study tool also has features to allow your instructor to see exactly what you have accomplished, with a built-in assessment tool for graded assignments. You can access LearnSmart for general chemistry by going to www.mcgraw-hillconnect.com/chemistry.

Animations for MP3/iPod A number of animations are available for download to your MP3/iPod through the textbook's Connect website.

Acknowledgments

The sixth edition and its associated learning system are the culmination of numerous chapter reviews, insightful suggestions, brainstorming sessions, focus groups, interviews, and class tests. Each person involved played an important part in the revision of the text and its ancillaries.

I feel very fortunate to have a relationship with my publisher based on mutual respect, shared goals, and warm friendship. Heading the McGraw-Hill Higher Education team with their advice and support were Publisher Ryan Blankenship and Executive Editor Jeff Huettman, Developmental Editor Donna Nemmers, Director of Digital Content David Spurgeon, Digital Project Manager Daryl Bruflodt, Project Manager Peggy Selle, Designer David Hash, and Marketing Manager Tami Hodge.

Patricia Amateis, Virginia Tech, helped revise several chapters and prepared Appendix E as well as the Instructor's and Student Solutions Manuals. Krishnan Rajeshwar, University of Texas–Arlington, updated the discussion of the future of energy use.

I am very grateful to the Board of Advisors, who helped me make this text the optimum teaching tool: Debra Feakes, Texas State University–San Marcos, Derek Gragson, California Polytechnic State University–San Luis Obispo, and James Reeves, University of North Carolina–Wilmington. Also, my deepest gratitude extends to the following individuals, who attended focus groups or symposia, provided content reviews, and class-tested materials in preparation for the Sixth Edition and its associated learning system:

Patricia Amateis, *Virginia Tech*
Margaret Asirvatham, *University of Colorado—Boulder*
Yiyan Bai, *Houston Community College–Central*
Laurance Beauvais, *San Diego State University*
Thomas Bertolini, *University of Southern California*
Fereshteh Billiot, *Texas A&M University–Corpus Christi*
Deborah Booth, *University of Southern Mississippi*
Simon Bott, *University of Houston*
Stacey Lowery Bretz, *Miami University of Ohio*
Karen Brewer, *Virginia Tech*
Les Butler, *Louisiana State University*
Bindu Chakravarty, *Houston Community College–Northeast Campus*
Chris Cheatum, *University of Iowa*
Liwei Chen, *Ohio University*
Tom Clausen, *University of Alaska–Fairbanks*
Erin Dahlke, *Loras College*
Michelle Driessen, *University of Minnesota*
Jack Duff, *Southern Polytechnic State University*
Bill Durham, *University of Arkansas*
Emmanuel Ewane, *Houston Community College–Northwest*
Deborah Exton, *University of Oregon*
Paul Fazen, *Villanova University*
David Frank, *California State University–Fresno*
John Gelder, *Oklahoma State University*
Greg Gellene, *Texas Tech University*
Dimitri Giarikos, *Nova Southeastern University*
Michael Greenlief, *University of Missouri–Columbia*
Todor Gounev, *University of Missouri–Kansas City*
John Hagen, *California Polytechnic State University–San Luis Obispo*
Michael Hailu, *Columbus State Community College*
John Halpin, *New York University*
Narayan Hosmane, *Northern Illinois University*
Larry Houk, *University of Memphis*
Eihab Jaber, *Worcester State University*
Heiko Jacobsen, *Tulane University*
Richard Jarman, *College of DuPage*
Steve Keller, *University of Missouri*
San Kim, *Northern Virginia Community College*
Chuck Kirkpatrick, *St. Louis University*
Marina Koether, *Kennesaw State University*
Patric Kolniak, *Louisiana State University*
Pamela Kraemer, *Northern Virginia Community College*
Jothi Kumar, *North Carolina A&T State University*
Dorothy B. Kurland, *Emeritus, West Virginia Institute of Technology*
Anna Larsen, *Ithaca College*
Allison Long, *Georgia Southern University*
Jeanette Madea, *Broward Community College*
Diana Malone, *Clarke University*
Lisa McGaw, *University of Central Oklahoma*
Thomas McGrath, *Baylor University*
Danny McGuire, *Cameron University*
Bill McLaughlin, *Montana State University*
Lauren McMills, *Ohio University*
Joyce Miller, *San Jacinto College–South*
Kristine Miller, *Anne Arundel Community College*
Jeremy Mitchell-Koch, *Emporia State University*
Debbie Mohler, *James Madison University*
Kereen Monteyne, *University of Northern Kentucky*
Mahesh Narayan, *University of Texas–El Paso*
Jessica Orvis, *Georgia Southern University*
Jason Overby, *College of Charleston*
Richard Paselk, *Humboldt State University*
Louis Pignolet, *Emeritus, University of Minnesota*
John Pollard, *The University of Arizona*
Bernard Powell, *University of Texas–San Antonio*
William Quintana, *New Mexico State University*
Edward Quitevis, *Texas Tech University*
Jeff Rack, *Ohio University*
Lisa Reece, *Ozarks Technical Community College*
Michelle Richards-Babb, *West Virginia University*
Dawn Rickey, *Colorado State University*
Thomas Ridgway, *University of Cincinnati*
Steven Rowley, *Middlesex County College*
Raymond Sadeghi, *University of Texas–San Antonio*
Issa Salame, *The City College of New York*
Jim Satterlee, *Washington State University*
Colleen Scott, *Southern Illinois University–Carbondale*
Thomas Selegue, *Pima Community College*
Steve Shore, *Oklahoma City Community College*
Michael Sommer, *University of Wyoming*
Jie Song, *University of Michigan–Flint*

David Speckhard, *Loras College*
Rick Spinney, *Ohio State University*
Emelyn S. Q. Tan, *National University of Singapore*
Kimberly Trick, *University of Dayton*
Cyriacus Uzomba, *Austin Community College*
Debbie Warnaar, *James Madison University*
Lyle Wescott, *University of Mississippi*
Wayne Wesolowski, *The University of Arizona*
Daniel Williams, *Kennesaw State University*
Stephanie Wunder, *Temple University*
Timothy Zauche, *University of Wisconsin–Platteville*
Lin Zhu, *IUPUI*

Connect: Chemistry has been greatly enhanced by the efforts of Kereen Monteyne, University of Northern Kentucky; MaryKay Orgill, University of Nevada–Las Vegas; and Yasmin Patell, Kansas State University; who did a masterful job of authoring hints and feedback to augment all of the system's homework problems. The following individuals helped write and review learning goal–oriented content for **LearnSmart for General Chemistry:** Margaret Asirvatham, University of Colorado–Boulder; William Burns, Arkansas State University; Cabot-Ann Christofferson, South Dakota School of Mines; Christina Johnson, University of California–San Diego; Adam I. Keller, Columbus State Community College; Willem R. Leenstra, University of Vermont; Margaret Ruth Leslie, Kent State University; Benjamin R. Martin, Texas State University–San Marcos; Kathy Thrush Shaginaw, Particular Solutions, Inc.; and Erin Whitteck.

Several expert freelancers contributed as well. As always, Jane Hoover did an excellent copyediting of the textbook, and Francine Banwarth and Rose Kramer followed with meticulous proofreading. John Murdzek and LaurelTech exercised careful skill in accuracy-checking content within Connect: Chemistry.

Over the years and editions, I've always had the great benefit of the expertise of my "in-home" team. This time around, my son, Daniel, offered his keen artist's eye to the figures revised, the photos selected, and the cover devised. And my wife, Ruth, made this text come to fruition—literally. She worked closely with the McGraw-Hill production team and provided indispensable, detailed input to the compositor, copy editor, and proof readers. And, of course, they both kept the author going with their love and support.

CHEMISTRY

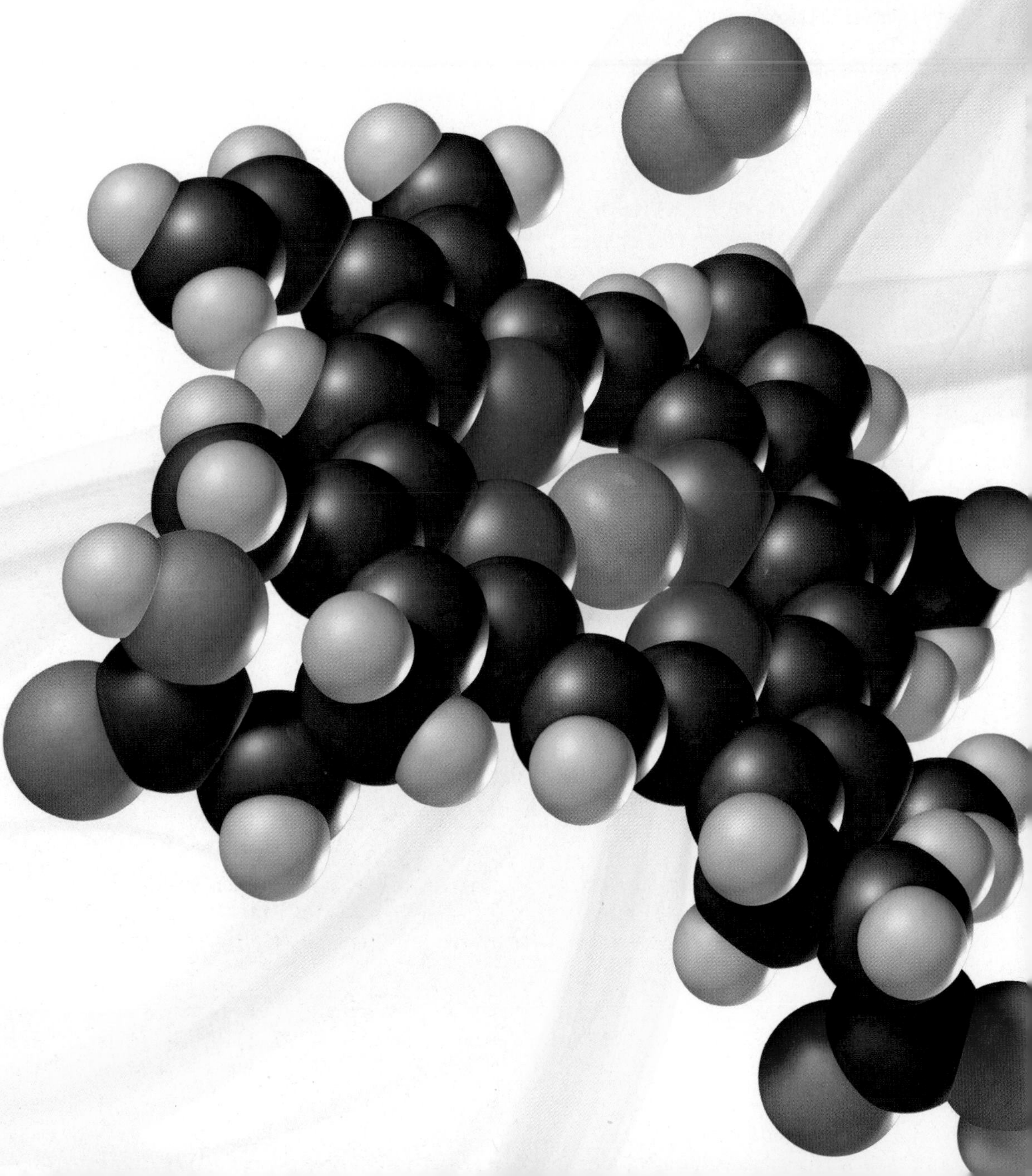

Keys to the Study of Chemistry

1

Concepts and skills to review before you study this chapter

- exponential (scientific) notation (Appendix A)

Maybe you're taking this course because chemistry is fundamental to understanding other natural sciences. Maybe it's required for your medical or engineering major. Or maybe you just want to learn more about the impact of chemistry on society or even on a personal, everyday level. For example, did you have cereal, fruit, and coffee for breakfast today? In chemical terms, you enjoyed nutrient-enriched, spoilage-retarded carbohydrate flakes mixed in a white emulsion of fats, proteins, and monosaccharides, with a piece of fertilizer-grown, pesticide-treated fruit, and a cup of hot aqueous extract of stimulating alkaloid. Earlier, you may have been awakened by the sound created as molecules aligned in the liquid-crystal display of your clock and electrons flowed to create a noise. You might have thrown off a thermal insulator of manufactured polymer and jumped in the shower to emulsify fatty substances on your skin and hair with purified water and formulated detergents. Perhaps you next adorned yourself in an array of pleasant-smelling pigmented gels, dyed polymeric fibers, synthetic footwear, and metal-alloy jewelry. After breakfast, you probably abraded your teeth with a colloidal dispersion of artificially flavored, dental-hardening agents, grabbed your laptop (an electronic device containing ultrathin, microetched semiconductor layers powered by a series of voltaic cells), collected some books (processed cellulose and plastic, electronically printed with light- and oxygen-resistant inks), hopped in your hydrocarbon-fueled, metal-vinyl-ceramic vehicle, electrically ignited a synchronized series of controlled gaseous explosions, and took off for class!

But the true impact of chemistry extends much farther than the commercial products of daily life. The truth is the most profound biological and environmental questions ultimately have chemical answers: How does an organism reproduce, grow, and age? What are the underlying explanations for health and disease? How can we sustain a planetary ecosystem in which plant, animal, and human populations thrive? Is there life on other worlds?

So, no matter what your reason for studying chemistry, you're going to learn some amazing ideas. And, this course comes with a bonus for developing two mental skills. The first, common to all science courses, is the ability to solve problems systematically. The second is specific to chemistry, for as you comprehend its ideas, you begin to view a hidden reality, one filled with incredibly minute particles moving at fantastic speeds, colliding billions of times a second, and interacting in ways that allow your brain to translate fluxes of electric charge into thoughts and that determine how all the matter inside and outside of you behaves. This chapter holds the keys to unlock and enter this new world.

IN THIS CHAPTER . . . We discuss some central ideas about matter and energy, the process of science, units of measurement, and how scientists handle data.

- We begin with fundamental concepts about matter and energy and their changes.
- A brief discussion of chemistry's origins, including some major missteps, leads to an overview of how scientists build models to study nature.
- We consider systematic chemical problem solving, including unit conversion and modern unit systems for mass, length, volume, density, and temperature.
- We see that data collection always includes some uncertainty and examine the distinction between accuracy and precision.

1.1 • SOME FUNDAMENTAL DEFINITIONS

A good place to begin our exploration of chemistry is to define it and a few central concepts. **Chemistry** is *the study of matter and its properties, the changes that matter undergoes, and the energy associated with those changes.*

The Properties of Matter

Matter is the "stuff" of the universe: air, glass, planets, students—*anything that has mass and volume.* (In Section 1.5, we discuss the meanings of mass and volume in terms of how they are measured.) Chemists want to know the **composition** of matter, *the types and amounts of simpler substances that make it up.* A *substance* is a type of matter that has a defined, fixed composition.

We learn about matter by observing its **properties,** *the characteristics that give each substance its unique identity.* To identify a person, we might observe height, weight, hair and eye color, fingerprints, and, now, even DNA pattern, until we arrive at a unique identification. To identify a substance, we observe two types of properties, physical and chemical, which are closely related to two types of change that matter undergoes:

- **Physical properties** are characteristics a substance shows *by itself, without changing into or interacting with another substance.* These properties include melting point, electrical conductivity, and density. A **physical change** occurs when a substance *alters its physical properties,* ***not*** *its composition.* For example, when ice melts, several physical properties change, such as hardness, density, and ability to flow. But the composition of the sample does *not* change: it is still water. The photograph in Figure 1.1A shows what this change looks like in everyday life. The "blow-up" circles depict a magnified view of the particles making up the sample. In the icicle, the particles lie in a repeating pattern, whereas they are jumbled in the droplet, but *the particles are the same* in both forms of water.

  Physical change (same substance before and after):

  $$\text{Water (solid form)} \longrightarrow \text{water (liquid form)}$$

- **Chemical properties** are characteristics a substance shows *as it changes into or interacts with another substance (or substances).* Chemical properties include flammability, corrosiveness, and reactivity with acids. A **chemical change,** also called a **chemical reaction,** occurs when *a substance (or substances) is converted into a different substance (or substances).* Figure 1.1B shows the chemical change (reaction) that occurs when you pass an electric current through water: the water decomposes

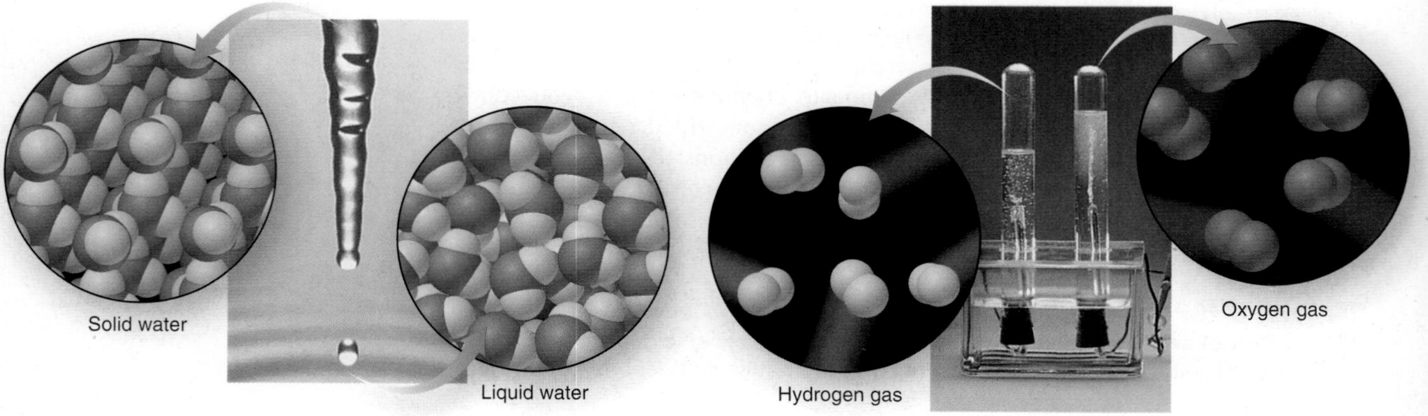

A Physical change:
*Solid form of water becomes liquid form. Particles before and after remain the same, which means composition did **not** change.*

B Chemical change:
*Electric current decomposes water into different substances (hydrogen and oxygen). Particles before and after are different, which means composition **did** change.*

Figure 1.1 The distinction between physical and chemical change.

(breaks down) into two other substances, hydrogen and oxygen, that bubble into the tubes. The composition *has* changed: the final sample is no longer water.

Chemical change (different substances before and after):

$$\text{Water} \xrightarrow{\text{electric current}} \text{hydrogen} + \text{oxygen}$$

Let's work through a sample problem that uses atomic-scale scenes to distinguish between physical and chemical change.

Sample Problem 1.1 Visualizing Change on the Atomic Scale

Problem The scenes below represent an atomic-scale view of a sample of matter, A, undergoing two different changes, left to B and right to C:

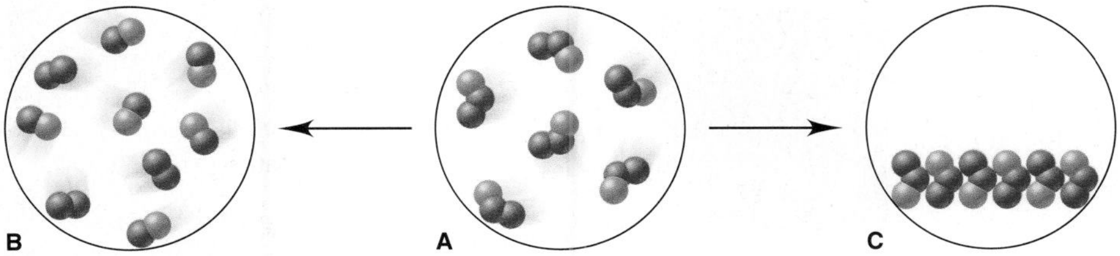

Decide whether each depiction shows a physical or a chemical change.

Plan Given depictions of the changes, we have to determine whether each represents a physical or a chemical change. The number and colors of the little spheres that make up each particle tell its "composition." Samples with particles of the *same* composition but in a different arrangement depict a *physical* change, whereas samples with particles of a *different* composition depict a *chemical* change.

Solution In A, each particle consists of one blue and two red spheres. The particles in A change into two types in B, one made of red and blue spheres and the other made of two red spheres; therefore, they have undergone a chemical change to form different particles. The particles in C are the same as those in A, but they are closer together and arranged differently; therefore, they have undergone a physical change.

Follow-Up Problem 1.1 Is the following change chemical or physical? (Compare your answer with the one in Brief Solutions to Follow-Up Problems at the end of the chapter.)

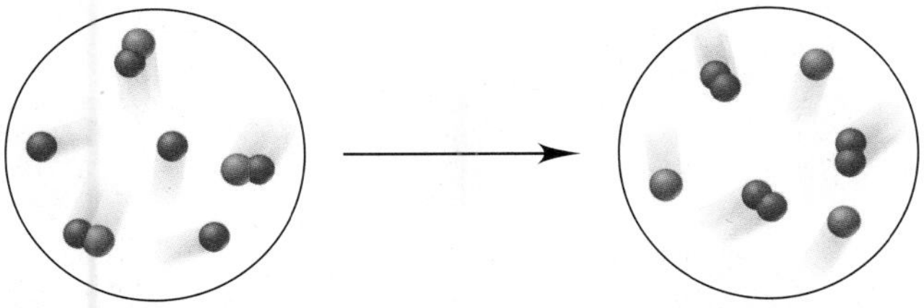

Like water, hydrogen, oxygen, or any other real substance, copper is also identified by *its own set* of physical and chemical properties (Table 1.1 on the next page).

The States of Matter

Matter occurs commonly in *three physical forms* called **states:** solid, liquid, and gas. We'll define the states and see how temperature can change them.

Defining the States On the macroscopic scale, each state of matter is defined by the way the sample fills a container (Figure 1.2, next page, *flasks at top*):

- A **solid** has a fixed shape that does not conform to the container shape. Solids are *not* defined by rigidity or hardness: solid iron is rigid and hard, but solid lead is flexible, and solid wax is soft.

Table 1.1 Some Characteristic Properties of Copper

Physical Properties		Chemical Properties	
Easily shaped into sheets (malleable) and wires (ductile)		Slowly forms a blue-green carbonate in moist air	
Can be melted and mixed with zinc to form brass		Reacts with nitric or sulfuric acid	
Density = 8.95 g/cm^3 Melting point = 1083°C Boiling point = 2570°C		Slowly forms deep-blue solution in aqueous ammonia	

- A **liquid** has a varying shape that conforms to the container shape, but only to the extent of the liquid's volume; that is, a liquid has *an upper surface.*
- A **gas** also has a varying shape that conforms to the container shape, but it fills the entire container and, thus, does *not* have a surface.

On the atomic scale, each state is defined by the relative positions of its particles (Figure 1.2, *circles at bottom*):

- In a *solid,* the particles lie next to each other in a regular, three-dimensional *array.*
- In a *liquid,* the particles also lie close together but move randomly around each other.
- In a *gas,* the particles have large distances between them and move randomly throughout the container.

Figure 1.2 The physical states of matter.

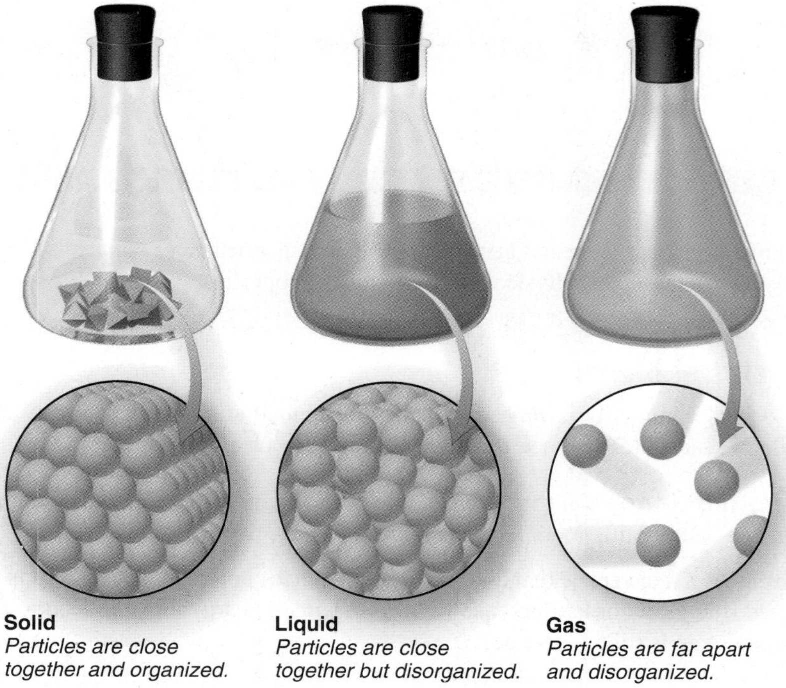

Temperature and Changes of State Depending on the temperature and pressure of the surroundings, many substances can exist in each of the three physical states and undergo changes in state as well. For example, as the temperature increases, solid water melts to liquid water, which boils to gaseous water (also called *water vapor*). Similarly, as the temperature drops, water vapor condenses to liquid water, and with further cooling, the liquid freezes to ice. In a steel plant, solid iron melts to liquid (molten) iron and then cools to the solid again. And, far beyond the confines of a laboratory or steel plant, lakes of molten sulfur lie on Jupiter's moon Io (*see photo*), which is capped by poles of frozen hydrogen sulfide, a gas on Earth.

The main point is that *a physical change caused by heating can generally be reversed by cooling*. This is *not* generally true for a chemical change. For example, heating iron in moist air causes a chemical reaction that yields the brown, crumbly substance known as rust. Cooling does not reverse this change; rather, another chemical change (or series of them) is required.

The following sample problem provides practice in distinguishing some familiar examples of physical and chemical change.

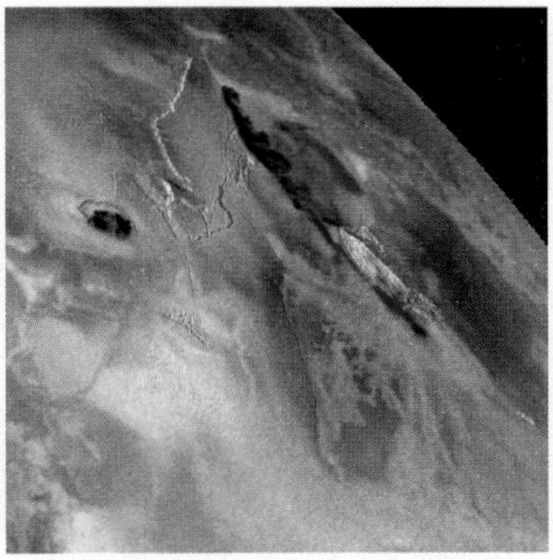

What common substances occur in unusual states on other worlds?

Sample Problem 1.2 Distinguishing Between Physical and Chemical Change

Problem Decide whether each of the following processes is primarily a physical or a chemical change, and explain briefly:
(a) Frost forms as the temperature drops on a humid winter night.
(b) A cornstalk grows from a seed that is watered and fertilized.
(c) A match ignites to form ash and a mixture of gases.
(d) Perspiration evaporates when you relax after jogging.
(e) A silver fork tarnishes slowly in air.

Plan The basic question we ask to decide whether a change is chemical or physical is, "Does the substance change composition or just change form?"

Solution **(a)** Frost forming is a physical change: the drop in temperature changes water vapor (gaseous water) in humid air to ice crystals (solid water).
(b) A seed growing involves chemical change: the seed uses water, substances from air, fertilizer, and soil, and energy from sunlight to make complex changes in composition.
(c) The match burning is a chemical change: the combustible substances in the match head are converted into other substances.
(d) Perspiration evaporating is a physical change: the water in sweat changes its form, from liquid to gas, but not its composition.
(e) Tarnishing is a chemical change: silver changes to silver sulfide by reacting with sulfur-containing substances in the air.

Follow-Up Problem 1.2 Decide whether each of the following processes is primarily a physical or a chemical change, and explain briefly (see Brief Solutions at the end of the chapter):
(a) Purple iodine vapor appears when solid iodine is warmed.
(b) Gasoline fumes are ignited by a spark in an automobile engine's cylinder.
(c) A scab forms over an open cut.

The Central Theme in Chemistry

Understanding the properties of a substance and the changes it undergoes leads to the central theme in chemistry: *macroscopic-scale* properties and behavior, those we can see, are the results of *atomic-scale* properties and behavior that we cannot see. The distinction between chemical and physical change is defined by composition, which we study macroscopically. But composition ultimately depends on the makeup of substances at the atomic scale. Similarly, macroscopic properties of substances in any of the three states arise from atomic-scale behavior of their particles. Picturing a chemical event on the molecular scale, even one as common as the flame of a laboratory burner (*see margin*), helps clarify what is taking place. What is happening when water boils or copper melts? What events occur in the invisible world of minute particles that cause a seed to grow, a neon light to glow, or a nail to rust? Throughout the text, we return to this central idea:

*We study **observable** changes in matter to understand their **unobservable** causes.*

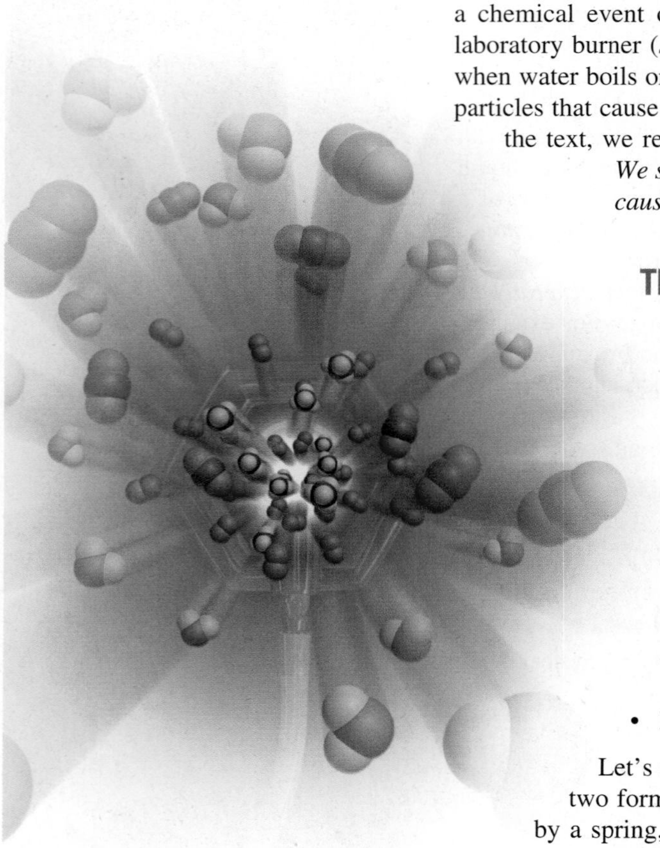

Methane and oxygen form carbon dioxide and water in the flame of a lab burner. (Carbon is black, oxygen red, and hydrogen blue.)

The Importance of Energy in the Study of Matter

Physical and chemical changes are accompanied by energy changes. **Energy** is often defined as *the ability to do work.* Essentially, all work involves moving something. Work is done when your arm lifts a book, when a car's engine moves the wheels, or when a falling rock moves the ground as it lands. The object doing the work (arm, engine, rock) transfers some of the energy it possesses to the object on which the work is done (book, wheels, ground).

The total energy an object possesses is the sum of its potential energy and its kinetic energy.

- **Potential energy** is *the energy due to the **position** of the object relative to other objects.*
- **Kinetic energy** is *the energy due to the **motion** of the object.*

Let's examine four systems that illustrate the relationship between these two forms of energy: a weight raised above the ground, two balls attached by a spring, two electrically charged particles, and a fuel and its waste products. Two concepts central to all these cases are

1. *When energy is converted from one form to the other, it is conserved, not destroyed.*
2. *Situations of lower energy are more stable, and therefore favored, over situations of higher energy (less stable).*

The four cases are

- *A weight raised above the ground* (Figure 1.3A). The energy you exert to lift a weight against gravity, increases the weight's potential energy (energy due to its position). When you drop the weight, that additional potential energy is converted to kinetic energy (energy due to motion). The situation with the weight elevated and higher in potential energy is *less stable,* so the weight will fall when released to result in a situation that is lower in potential energy and *more stable.*
- *Two balls attached by a spring* (Figure 1.3B). When you pull the balls apart, the energy you exert to stretch the relaxed spring increases the system's potential energy. This change in potential energy is converted to kinetic energy when you release the balls. The system of balls and spring is less stable (has more potential energy) when the spring is stretched than when it is relaxed.
- *Two electrically charged particles* (Figure 1.3C). Due to interactions known as *electrostatic forces, opposite charges attract each other, and like charges repel each other.* When energy is exerted to move a positive particle away from a negative one, the potential energy of the system increases, and that increase is converted to kinetic energy when the particles are pulled together by the electrostatic attraction. Similarly, when energy is used to move two positive (or two negative) particles together, their potential energy increases and changes to kinetic energy when they are pushed apart by the electrostatic repulsion. Charged particles move naturally to a more stable situation (lower energy).
- *A fuel and its waste products* (Figure 1.3D). Matter is composed of positively and negatively charged particles. *The chemical potential energy of a substance results from the relative positions of and the attractions and repulsions among its particles.*

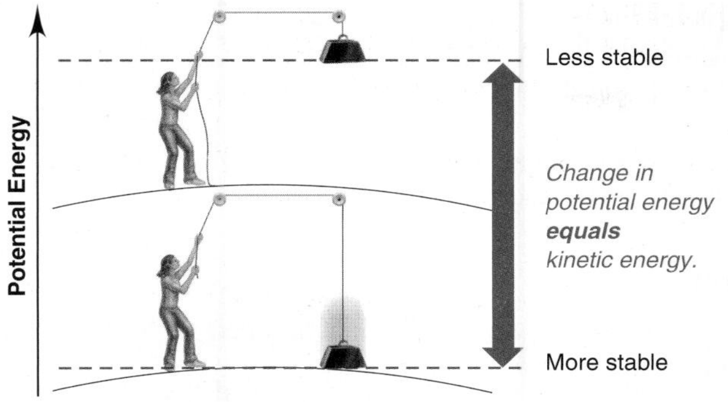

A A gravitational system. *Potential energy is gained when a weight is lifted. It is converted to kinetic energy as the weight falls.*

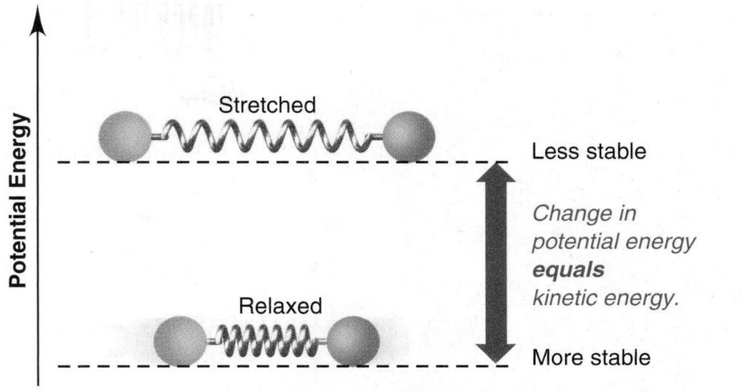

B A system of two balls attached by a spring. *Potential energy is gained when the spring is stretched. It is converted to the kinetic energy of the moving balls as the spring relaxes.*

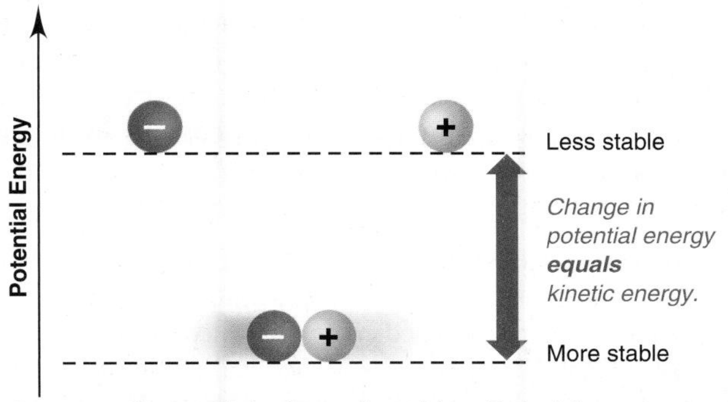

C A system of oppositely charged particles. *Potential energy is gained when the charges are separated. It is converted to kinetic energy as the attraction pulls the charges together.*

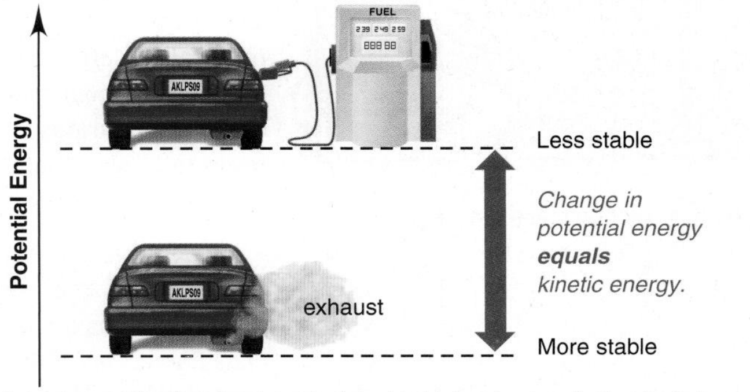

D A system of fuel and exhaust. *A fuel is higher in chemical potential energy than the exhaust. As the fuel burns, some of its potential energy is converted to the kinetic energy of the moving car.*

Figure 1.3 Potential energy is converted to kinetic energy. The dashed horizontal lines indicate the potential energy of each system before and after the change.

Some substances are higher in potential energy than others. For example, gasoline and oxygen have more chemical potential energy than the exhaust gases they form. This difference is converted into kinetic energy, which moves the car, heats the interior, makes the lights shine, and so on. Similarly, the difference in potential energy between the food and air we take in and the wastes we excrete enables us to move, grow, keep warm, study chemistry, and so on.

Summary of Section 1.1

- Chemists study the composition and properties of matter and how they change.
- Each substance has a unique set of *physical* properties (attributes of the substance itself) and *chemical properties* (attributes of the substance as it interacts with or changes to other substances). Changes in matter can be *physical* (different form of the same substance) or *chemical* (different substance).
- Matter exists in three physical states—solid, liquid, and gas. The behavior of each state is due to the arrangement of the particles.
- A physical change caused by heating may be reversed by cooling. But a chemical change caused by heating can be reversed only by other chemical changes.
- Macroscopic changes result from submicroscopic changes.
- Changes in matter are accompanied by changes in energy.
- An object's potential energy is due to its position; an object's kinetic energy is due to its motion. Energy used to lift a weight, stretch a spring, or separate opposite charges increases the system's potential energy, which is converted to kinetic energy as the system returns to its original condition. Energy changes form but is conserved.
- Chemical potential energy arises from the positions and interactions of a substance's particles. When a higher energy (less stable) substance is converted into a more stable (lower energy) substance, some potential energy is converted into kinetic energy.

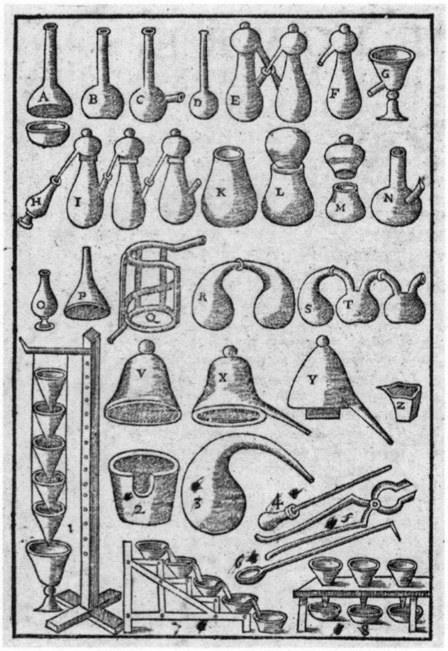

Figure 1.4 Alchemical apparatus.

1.2 • CHEMICAL ARTS AND THE ORIGINS OF MODERN CHEMISTRY

This brief overview of early breakthroughs, and a few false directions, describes how the modern science of chemistry arose and progressed.

Prechemical Traditions

Chemistry had its origin in a prescientific past that incorporated three overlapping traditions—alchemy, medicine, and technology:

1. *The alchemical tradition. Alchemy* was an occult study of nature that began in the 1st century AD and dominated thinking for over 1500 years. Originally influenced by the Greek idea that matter strives for "perfection," alchemists later became obsessed with converting "baser" metals, such as lead, into "purer" ones, such as gold. The alchemists' names for substances and their belief that matter could be altered magically were very difficult to correct over the centuries. Their legacy to chemistry was in technical methods. They invented distillation, percolation, and extraction and devised apparatus still used routinely today (Figure 1.4). But perhaps even more important was that alchemists encouraged observation and experimentation, which replaced the Greek approach of explaining nature solely through reason.

2. *The medical tradition.* Alchemists also influenced medical practice in medieval Europe. And ever since the 13th century, distillates and extracts of roots, herbs, and other plant matter have been used as sources of medicines. The alchemist and physician Paracelsus (1493–1541) considered the body to be a chemical system and illness an imbalance that could be restored by treatment with drugs. Although many early prescriptions were useless, later ones had increasing success. Thus began the alliance between medicine and chemistry that thrives today.

3. *The technological tradition.* For thousands of years, pottery making, dyeing, and especially metallurgy contributed greatly to people's experience with materials. During the Middle Ages and the Renaissance, books were published that described how to purify, assay, and coin silver and gold, how to use balances, furnaces, and crucibles, and how to make glass and gunpowder. Some introduced quantitative measurement, which was lacking in alchemical writings. Many creations from those times are still marveled at throughout the world. Nevertheless, the skilled artisans showed little interest in *why* a substance changes or *how to predict* its behavior.

The Phlogiston Fiasco and the Impact of Lavoisier

Chemical investigation in the modern sense—inquiry into the causes of changes in matter—began in the late 17th century. At that time, most scientists explained **combustion,** the process of burning, with the *phlogiston theory*. It proposed that combustible materials contain *phlogiston,* an undetectable substance released when the material burns. Highly combustible materials like charcoal were thought to contain a lot of phlogiston, and slightly combustible materials like metals only a little.

But inconsistencies continuously arose.

Phlogiston critics: Why is air needed for combustion, and why does charcoal stop burning in a closed vessel?
Phlogiston supporters: Air "attracts" phlogiston out of the charcoal, and burning stops when the air in the vessel is "saturated" with phlogiston.

Critics also noted that when a metal burns, it forms its *calx,* which weighs more than the metal, leading them to ask,

Critics: How can the *loss* of phlogiston cause a *gain* in mass?
Supporters: Phlogiston has negative mass.

As ridiculous as these responses seem now, it's important to remember that, even today, scientists may dismiss conflicting evidence rather than abandon an accepted idea.

The conflict over phlogiston was resolved when the young French chemist Antoine Lavoisier (1743–1794) performed several experiments:

1. Heating mercury calx decomposed it into two products—mercury and a gas—whose *total mass equaled the starting mass of the calx.*
2. Heating mercury with the gas reformed the calx, yielded mercury and, again, *the total mass remained constant.*
3. Heating mercury in a measured volume of air yielded mercury calx and left four-fifths of the air remaining.
4. A burning candle placed in the remaining air was extinguished.

Lavoisier named the gas *oxygen* and gave metal calxes the name *metal oxides.* His explanation of his results made the phlogiston theory irrelevant:

- Oxygen, a normal component of air, combines with a substance when it burns.
- In a closed container, a combustible substance stops burning when it has combined with all the available oxygen.
- A metal calx (metal oxide) weighs more than the metal because its mass includes the mass of the oxygen.

This new theory triumphed because it relied on *quantitative, reproducible measurements,* not on strange properties of undetectable substances. Because this approach is at the heart of science, many propose that the *science* of chemistry began with Lavoisier.

Summary of Section 1.2

- Alchemy, medicine, and technology placed little emphasis on objective experimentation, focusing instead on mystical explanations or practical experience, but these traditions contributed some apparatus and methods that are still important today.
- Lavoisier overthrew the phlogiston theory by showing quantitatively that oxygen, a component of air, is required for combustion and combines with a burning substance.

1.3 • THE SCIENTIFIC APPROACH: DEVELOPING A MODEL

Unlike our prehistoric ancestors, who survived through *trial and error*—gradually learning which types of stone were hard enough to shape others, which plants were edible and which poisonous—we employ the *quantitative theories* of chemistry to understand materials, make better use of them, and create new ones: specialized drugs, advanced composites, synthetic polymers, and countless others (Figure 1.5).

Figure 1.5 **Modern materials in a variety of applications.** **A,** High-tension polymers in synthetic hip joints. **B,** Specialized polymers in clothing and sports gear. **C,** Liquid crystals and semiconductors in electronic devices. **D,** Medicinal agents in pills.

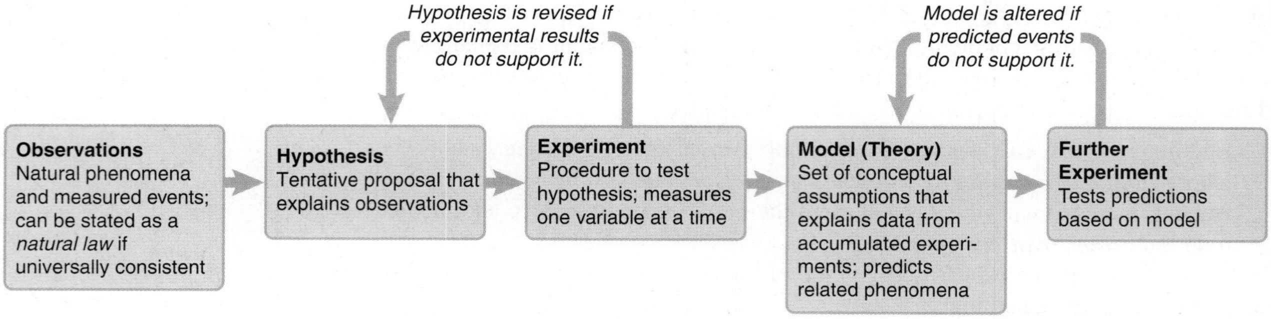

Figure 1.6 The scientific approach to understanding nature. Hypotheses and models are mental pictures that are revised to match observations and experimental results, *not* the other way around.

To understand nature, scientists use an approach called the **scientific method.** It is not a stepwise checklist, but rather a process involving creative propositions and tests aimed at objective, verifiable discoveries. There is no single procedure, and luck often plays a key role in discovery. In general terms, the scientific approach includes the following parts (Figure 1.6):

- ***Observations.*** These are the facts our ideas must explain. The most useful observations are quantitative because they can be analyzed to reveal trends. Pieces of quantitative information are **data.** When the same observation is made by many investigators in many situations with no clear exceptions, it is summarized, often in mathematical terms, as a **natural law.** The observation that mass remains constant during chemical change—made by Lavoisier and numerous experimenters since—is known as the law of mass conservation (Chapter 2).
- ***Hypothesis.*** Whether derived from observation or from a "spark of intuition," a hypothesis is a proposal made to explain an observation. A sound hypothesis need not be correct, but it must be *testable by experiment.* Indeed, a hypothesis is often the reason for performing an experiment: if the results do not support it, the hypothesis must be revised or discarded. Hypotheses can be altered, but experimental results cannot.
- ***Experiment.*** A set of procedural steps that tests a hypothesis, an experiment often leads to a revised hypothesis and new experiments to test it. An experiment typically contains at least two **variables,** quantities that can have more than one value. A well-designed experiment is **controlled** in that it measures the effect of one variable on another while keeping all other variables constant. Experimental results must be *reproducible* by others. Both skill and creativity play a part in experimental design.
- ***Model.*** Formulating conceptual models, or **theories,** based on *experiments* that test *hypotheses* about *observations* distinguishes scientific thinking from speculation. As hypotheses are revised according to experimental results, a model emerges to explain how the phenomenon occurs. A model is a *simplified,* not an exact, representation of some aspect of nature that we use to *predict* related phenomena. Ongoing experimentation refines the model to account for new facts.

Lavoisier's overthrow of the phlogiston theory demonstrates the scientific method of thinking. *Observations* of burning and smelting led to the *hypothesis* that combustion involved the loss of phlogiston. *Experiments* showing that air is required for burning and that a metal gains mass during combustion led Lavoisier to propose a new *hypothesis,* which he tested repeatedly with quantitative *experiments.* Accumulating evidence supported his developing *model (theory)* that combustion involves combination with a component of air (oxygen). Innumerable *predictions* based on this theory have supported its validity, and Lavoisier himself extended the theory to account for animal respiration and metabolism.

Summary of Section 1.3

- The scientific method is a process designed to explain and predict phenomena.
- Observations lead to hypotheses about how or why a phenomenon occurs. When repeated with no exceptions, observations may be expressed as a natural law.
- Hypotheses are tested by controlled experiments and revised when necessary.
- If reproducible data support a hypothesis, a model (theory) can be developed to explain the observed phenomenon. A good model predicts related phenomena but must be refined whenever conflicting data appear.

1.4 • CHEMICAL PROBLEM SOLVING

In many ways, learning chemistry is learning how to solve chemistry problems, not only those in exams or homework, but the more complex ones in life and society. The sample problems in this book are designed to strengthen your skills for solving problems. In this section, we describe the problem-solving approach. Most problems include calculations, so let's first discuss how to handle measured quantities.

Units and Conversion Factors in Calculations

All measured quantities consist of a number *and* a unit: a person's height is "5 feet, 10 inches," not "5, 10." Ratios of quantities have ratios of units, such as miles/hour. (We discuss some important units in Section 1.5.) To minimize errors, make it a habit to *include units in all calculations.*

The arithmetic operations used with quantities are the same as those used with pure numbers; that is, units can be multiplied, divided, and canceled:

- A carpet measuring 3 feet by 4 feet (ft) has an area of

$$\text{Area} = 3\ \text{ft} \times 4\ \text{ft} = (3 \times 4)(\text{ft} \times \text{ft}) = 12\ \text{ft}^2$$

- A car traveling 350 miles (mi) in 7 hours (h) has a speed of

$$\text{Speed} = \frac{350\ \text{mi}}{7\ \text{h}} = \frac{50\ \text{mi}}{1\ \text{h}}\ \text{(often written 50 mi}\cdot\text{h}^{-1}\text{)}$$

- In 3 hours, the car travels a distance of

$$\text{Distance} = 3\ \cancel{\text{h}} \times \frac{50\ \text{mi}}{1\ \cancel{\text{h}}} = 150\ \text{mi}$$

Constructing a Conversion Factor **Conversion factors** are *ratios used to express a quantity in different units.* Suppose we want to know the distance of that 150-mile car trip in feet. To convert miles to feet, we use *equivalent quantities,*

$$1\ \text{mi} = 5280\ \text{ft}$$

from which we can construct two conversion factors. Dividing both sides by 5280 ft gives one conversion factor (shown in blue):

$$\frac{1\ \text{mi}}{5280\ \text{ft}} = \frac{5280\ \cancel{\text{ft}}}{5280\ \cancel{\text{ft}}} = 1$$

And, dividing both sides by 1 mi gives the other conversion factor (the inverse):

$$\frac{1\ \cancel{\text{mi}}}{1\ \cancel{\text{mi}}} = \frac{5280\ \text{ft}}{1\ \text{mi}} = 1$$

Since the numerator and denominator of a conversion factor are equal, multiplying a quantity by a conversion factor is the same as multiplying by 1. Thus, *even though the number and unit change, the size of the quantity remains the same.*

To convert the distance from miles to feet, we choose the conversion factor with miles in the denominator, because it cancels miles and gives the answer in feet:

$$\text{Distance (ft)} = 150\ \cancel{\text{mi}} \times \frac{5280\ \text{ft}}{1\ \cancel{\text{mi}}} = 792{,}000\ \text{ft}$$

$$\text{mi} \Rightarrow \text{ft}$$

Choosing the Correct Conversion Factor It is easier to convert if you first decide whether the answer expressed in the new units should have a larger or smaller number. In the previous case, we know that a foot is *smaller* than a mile, so the distance in feet should have a *larger* number (792,000) than the distance in miles (150). The conversion factor has the larger number (5280) in the numerator, so it gave a larger number in the answer.

Most importantly, the *conversion factor you choose must cancel all units except those you want in the answer.* Therefore, set the unit you are converting *from* (beginning unit) in the *opposite position in the conversion factor* (numerator or denominator) so that it cancels and you are left with the unit you are converting *to* (final unit):

$$\cancel{\text{beginning unit}} \times \frac{\text{final unit}}{\cancel{\text{beginning unit}}} = \text{final unit} \qquad \text{as in} \qquad \cancel{\text{mi}} \times \frac{\text{ft}}{\cancel{\text{mi}}} = \text{ft}$$

Or, in cases that involve units raised to a power:

$$(\cancel{\text{beginning unit}} \times \cancel{\text{beginning unit}}) \times \frac{\text{final unit}^2}{\cancel{\text{beginning unit}^2}} = \text{final unit}^2$$

$$\text{as in} \qquad (\cancel{\text{ft}} \times \cancel{\text{ft}}) \times \frac{\text{mi}^2}{\cancel{\text{ft}^2}} = \text{mi}^2$$

Or, in cases that involve a ratio of units:

$$\frac{\cancel{\text{beginning unit}}}{\text{final unit}_1} \times \frac{\text{final unit}_2}{\cancel{\text{beginning unit}}} = \frac{\text{final unit}_2}{\text{final unit}_1} \qquad \text{as in} \qquad \frac{\cancel{\text{mi}}}{\text{h}} \times \frac{\text{ft}}{\cancel{\text{mi}}} = \frac{\text{ft}}{\text{h}}$$

Converting Between Unit Systems We use the same procedure to convert between systems of units, for example, between the English (or American) unit system and the International System (a revised metric system; Section 1.5). Suppose we know that the height of Angel Falls in Venezuela (the world's highest) is 3212 ft, and we find its height in miles as

$$\text{Height (mi)} = 3212\ \cancel{\text{ft}} \times \frac{1\ \text{mi}}{5280\ \cancel{\text{ft}}} = 0.6083\ \text{mi}$$

ft ⇒ mi

Now, we want its height in kilometers (km). The equivalent quantities are

$$1.609\ \text{km} = 1\ \text{mi}$$

Because we are converting *from* miles *to* kilometers, we use the conversion factor with miles in the denominator in order to cancel miles:

$$\text{Height (km)} = 0.6083\ \cancel{\text{mi}} \times \frac{1.609\ \text{km}}{1\ \cancel{\text{mi}}} = 0.9788\ \text{km}$$

mi ⇒ km

Notice that kilometers are *smaller* than miles, so this conversion factor gave us an answer with a *larger* number (0.9788 is larger than 0.6083).

If we want the height of Angel Falls in meters (m), we use the equivalent quantities 1 km = 1000 m to construct the conversion factor:

$$\text{Height (m)} = 0.9788\ \cancel{\text{km}} \times \frac{1000\ \text{m}}{1\ \cancel{\text{km}}} = 978.8\ \text{m}$$

km ⇒ m

In longer calculations, we often string together several conversion steps:

$$\text{Height (m)} = 3212\ \cancel{\text{ft}} \times \frac{1\ \cancel{\text{mi}}}{5280\ \cancel{\text{ft}}} \times \frac{1.609\ \cancel{\text{km}}}{1\ \cancel{\text{mi}}} \times \frac{1000\ \text{m}}{1\ \cancel{\text{km}}} = 978.8\ \text{m}$$

ft ⇒ mi ⇒ km ⇒ m

The use of conversion factors in calculations is also referred to as the factor-label method or **dimensional analysis** (because units represent physical dimensions). We use this approach throughout the text.

A Systematic Approach to Solving Chemistry Problems

The approach used in this book to solve problems emphasizes reasoning, not memorizing, and is based on a simple idea: plan how to solve the problem *before* you try to solve it, then check your answer, and practice with a similar follow-up problem. In general, the sample problems consist of several parts:

1. **Problem.** This part states all the information you need to solve the problem, usually framed in some interesting context.
2. **Plan.** This part helps you *think* about the solution *before* juggling numbers and pressing calculator buttons. There is often more than one way to solve a problem, and the given plan is one possibility. The plan will
   - Clarify the known and unknown: what information do you have, and what are you trying to find?
   - Suggest the steps from known to unknown: what ideas, conversions, or equations are needed?
   - Present a road map (especially in early chapters), a flow diagram of the plan. The road map has a box for each intermediate result and an arrow showing the step (conversion factor or operation) used to get to the next box.
3. **Solution.** This part shows the calculation steps in the same order as in the plan (and the road map).
4. **Check.** This part helps you check that your final answer makes sense: Are the units correct? Did the change occur in the expected direction? Is it reasonable chemically? To avoid a large math error, we also often do a rough calculation and see if we get an answer "in the same ballpark" as the actual result. Here's a typical "ballpark" calculation from everyday life. You are at a music store and buy three CDs at $14.97 each. With a 5% sales tax, the bill comes to $47.16. In your mind, you know that $14.97 is about $15, and 3 times $15 is $45; with the sales tax, the cost should be a bit more. So, your quick mental calculation *is* in the same ballpark as the actual cost.
5. **Comment.** This part appears occasionally to provide an application, an alternative approach, a common mistake to avoid, or an overview.
6. **Follow-Up Problem.** This part presents a similar problem that requires you to apply concepts and/or methods used in solving the sample problem.

Of course, you can't learn to solve chemistry problems, any more than you can learn to swim, by reading about it, so here are a few suggestions:

- Follow along in the sample problem with pencil, paper, and calculator.
- Try the follow-up problem as soon as you finish the sample problem. A feature called Brief Solutions to Follow-Up Problems appears at the end of each chapter, allowing you to compare your solution steps and answer.
- Read the sample problem and text again if you have trouble.
- Try the practice quizzes in the Online Learning Center at www.mhhe.com/silberberg. For each chapter, two interactive quizzes provide conceptual and problem-solving practice and offer feedback for review.
- The end-of-chapter problems review and extend the concepts and skills in the chapter, so work as many as you can. (Answers are given in the back of the book for problems with a colored number.)

Let's apply this systematic approach in a unit-conversion problem.

Sample Problem 1.3 Converting Units of Length

Problem To wire your stereo equipment, you need 325 centimeters (cm) of speaker wire that sells for \$0.15/ft. How much does the wire cost?

Road Map

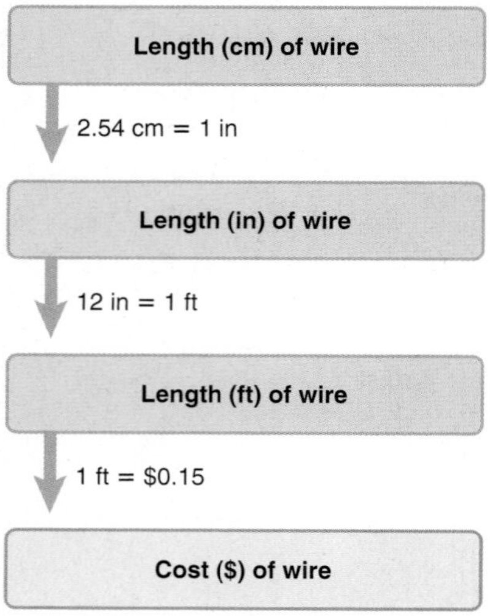

Plan We know the length of wire in centimeters (325 cm) and the price in dollars per foot (\$0.15/ft). We can find the unknown cost of the wire by converting the length from centimeters to inches (in) and from inches to feet. The price gives us the equivalent quantities (1 ft = \$0.15) to convert feet of wire to cost in dollars. The road map starts with the known and moves through the calculation steps to the unknown.

Solution Converting the known length from centimeters to inches: The equivalent quantities alongside the road map arrow are needed to construct the conversion factor. We choose 1 in/2.54 cm, rather than the inverse, because it gives an answer in inches:

$$\text{Length (in)} = \text{length (cm)} \times \text{conversion factor} = 325\ \cancel{\text{cm}} \times \frac{1\ \text{in}}{2.54\ \cancel{\text{cm}}} = 128\ \text{in}$$

Converting the length from inches to feet:

$$\text{Length (ft)} = \text{length (in)} \times \text{conversion factor} = 128\ \cancel{\text{in}} \times \frac{1\ \text{ft}}{12\ \cancel{\text{in}}} = 10.7\ \text{ft}$$

Converting the length in feet to cost in dollars:

$$\text{Cost (\$)} = \text{length (ft)} \times \text{conversion factor} = 10.7\ \cancel{\text{ft}} \times \frac{\$0.15}{1\ \cancel{\text{ft}}} = \boxed{\$1.60}$$

Check The units are correct for each step. The conversion factors make sense in terms of the relative unit sizes: the number of inches is *smaller* than the number of centimeters (an inch is *larger* than a centimeter), and the number of feet is *smaller* than the number of inches. The total cost seems reasonable: a little more than 10 ft of wire at \$0.15/ft should cost a little more than \$1.50.

Comment **1.** We could also have strung the three steps together:

$$\text{Cost (\$)} = 325\ \cancel{\text{cm}} \times \frac{1\ \cancel{\text{in}}}{2.54\ \cancel{\text{cm}}} \times \frac{1\ \cancel{\text{ft}}}{12\ \cancel{\text{in}}} \times \frac{\$0.15}{1\ \cancel{\text{ft}}} = \boxed{\$1.60}$$

2. There are usually alternative sequences in unit-conversion problems. Here, for example, we would get the same answer if we first converted the cost of wire from \$/ft to \$/cm and kept the wire length in cm. Try it yourself.

Follow-Up Problem 1.3 A furniture factory needs 31.5 ft^2 of fabric to upholster one chair. Its Dutch supplier sends the fabric in bolts of exactly 200 m^2. How many chairs can be upholstered with 3 bolts of fabric (1 m = 3.281 ft)? Draw a road map to show how you plan the solution. (See Brief Solutions.)

Summary of Section 1.4

- A measured quantity consists of a number and a unit.
- A conversion factor is a ratio of equivalent quantities (and, thus, equal to 1) that is used to express a quantity in different units.
- The problem-solving approach used in this book has four parts: (1) plan the steps to the solution, which often includes a flow diagram (road map) of the steps, (2) perform the calculations according to the plan, (3) check to see if the answer makes sense, and (4) practice with a similar problem and compare your solution with the one at the end of the chapter.

1.5 • MEASUREMENT IN SCIENTIFIC STUDY

Measurement has a rich history characterized by the search for *exact, invariable standards.* Measuring for purposes of trade, building, and surveying began thousands of years ago, but for most of that time, it was based on standards that could vary: a yard was the distance from the king's nose to the tip of his outstretched arm, and an acre was the area tilled in one day by a man with a pair of oxen. Our current system of measurement began in 1790 in France, when a committee, of which Lavoisier was a member, developed the *metric system.* Then, in 1960, another committee in France revised the metric system and established the universally accepted **SI units** (from the French **S**ystème **I**nternational d'Unités).

General Features of SI Units

The SI system is based on seven **fundamental units,** or **base units,** each identified with a physical quantity (Table 1.2). All other units are **derived units,** combinations of the seven base units. For example, the derived unit for speed, meters per second (m/s), is the base unit for length (m) divided by the base unit for time (s). (Derived units that are a ratio of base units can be used as conversion factors.) For quantities much smaller or larger than the base unit, we use decimal prefixes and exponential (scientific) notation (Table 1.3). (If you need a review of exponential notation, see Appendix A.) Because the prefixes are based on powers of 10, SI units are easier to use in calculations than English units.

Some Important SI Units in Chemistry

Here, we discuss units for length, volume, mass, density, temperature, and time; other units are presented in later chapters. Table 1.4 (*on the next page*) shows some SI quantities for length, volume, and mass, along with their English-system equivalents.

Table 1.2 SI Base Units

Physical Quantity (Dimension)	Unit Name	Unit Abbreviation
Mass	kilogram	kg
Length	meter	m
Time	second	s
Temperature	kelvin	K
Electric current	ampere	A
Amount of substance	mole	mol
Luminous intensity	candela	cd

Table 1.3 Common Decimal Prefixes Used with SI Units

Prefix*	Prefix Symbol	Word	Conventional Notation	Exponential Notation
tera	T	trillion	1,000,000,000,000	1×10^{12}
giga	G	billion	1,000,000,000	1×10^{9}
mega	M	million	1,000,000	1×10^{6}
kilo	k	thousand	1,000	1×10^{3}
hecto	h	hundred	100	1×10^{2}
deka	da	ten	10	1×10^{1}
—	—	one	1	1×10^{0}
deci	d	tenth	0.1	1×10^{-1}
centi	c	hundredth	0.01	1×10^{-2}
milli	m	thousandth	0.001	1×10^{-3}
micro	μ	millionth	0.000001	1×10^{-6}
nano	n	billionth	0.000000001	1×10^{-9}
pico	p	trillionth	0.000000000001	1×10^{-12}
femto	f	quadrillionth	0.000000000000001	1×10^{-15}

*The prefixes most frequently used by chemists appear in bold type.

Table 1.4 Common SI-English Equivalent Quantities

Quantity	SI	SI Equivalents	English Equivalents	English to SI Equivalent
Length	1 kilometer (km)	1000 (10^3) meters	0.6214 mile (mi)	1 mile = 1.609 km
	1 meter (m)	100 (10^2) centimeters	1.094 yards (yd)	1 yard = 0.9144 m
		1000 millimeters (mm)	39.37 inches (in)	1 foot (ft) = 0.3048 m
	1 centimeter (cm)	0.10 (10^{-2}) meter	0.3937 inch	1 inch = 2.54 cm (exactly)
Volume	1 cubic meter (m^3)	1,000,000 (10^6) cubic centimeters	35.31 cubic feet (ft^3)	1 cubic foot = 0.02832 m^3
	1 cubic decimeter (dm^3)	1000 cubic centimeters	0.2642 gallon (gal)	1 gallon = 3.785 dm^3
			1.057 quarts (qt)	1 quart = 0.9464 dm^3
				1 quart = 946.4 cm^3
	1 cubic centimeter (cm^3)	0.001 dm^3	0.03381 fluid ounce	1 fluid ounce = 29.57 cm^3
Mass	1 kilogram (kg)	1000 grams	2.205 pounds (lb)	1 pound = 0.4536 kg

Length The SI base unit of length is the **meter (m).** In the metric system, it was originally defined as 1/10,000,000 of the distance from the equator to the North Pole, and later as the distance between two fine lines engraved on a corrosion-resistant metal bar. More recently, the first exact, unchanging standard was adopted: 1,650,763.73 wavelengths of orange-red light from electrically excited krypton atoms. The current standard is exact and invariant: 1 meter is the distance light travels in a vacuum in 1/299,792,458 of a second.

A meter is a little longer than a yard (1 m = 1.094 yd); a centimeter (10^{-2} m) is about two-fifths of an inch (1 cm = 0.3937 in; 1 in = 2.54 cm). Biological cells are often measured in micrometers (1 μm = 10^{-6} m). On the atomic scale, nanometers (10^{-9} m) and picometers (10^{-12} m) are used. Many proteins have diameters of about 2 nm; atomic diameters are about 200 pm (0.2 nm). An older unit still in use is the angstrom (1 Å = 10^{-10} m = 0.1 nm = 100 pm).

Volume Any sample of matter has a certain **volume (*V*),** the amount of space it occupies. The SI unit of volume is the **cubic meter (m^3).** In chemistry, we often use non-SI units, the **liter (L)** and the **milliliter (mL)** (note the uppercase L). Physicians and other medical practitioners measure body fluids in cubic decimeters (dm^3), which are equivalent to liters:

$$1\ \text{L} = 1\ \text{dm}^3 = 10^{-3}\ \text{m}^3$$

And 1 mL, or $\frac{1}{1000}$ of a liter, is equivalent to 1 cubic centimeter (cm^3):

$$1\ \text{mL} = 1\ \text{cm}^3 = 10^{-3}\ \text{dm}^3 = 10^{-3}\ \text{L} = 10^{-6}\ \text{m}^3$$

A liter is slightly larger than a quart (qt) (1 L = 1.057 qt; 1 qt = 946.4 mL); 1 fluid ounce ($\frac{1}{32}$ of a quart) equals 29.57 mL (29.57 cm^3).

Figure 1.7 is a life-size depiction of the two 1000-fold decreases in volume from 1 dm^3 to 1 cm^3 and then to 1 mm^3. The edge of a 1-m^3 cube would be about 2.5 times the width of this text opened flat.

Figure 1.8A shows some laboratory glassware for working with volumes. Erlenmeyer flasks and beakers are used to contain liquids. Graduated cylinders, pipets, and burets are used to measure and transfer them. Volumetric flasks and pipets have a fixed volume indicated by a mark on the neck. Solutions are prepared quantitatively in volumetric flasks, and specific amounts are put into cylinders, pipets, or burets to transfer to beakers or flasks for further steps. In Figure 1.8B, an automatic pipet transfers liquid accurately *and* quickly.

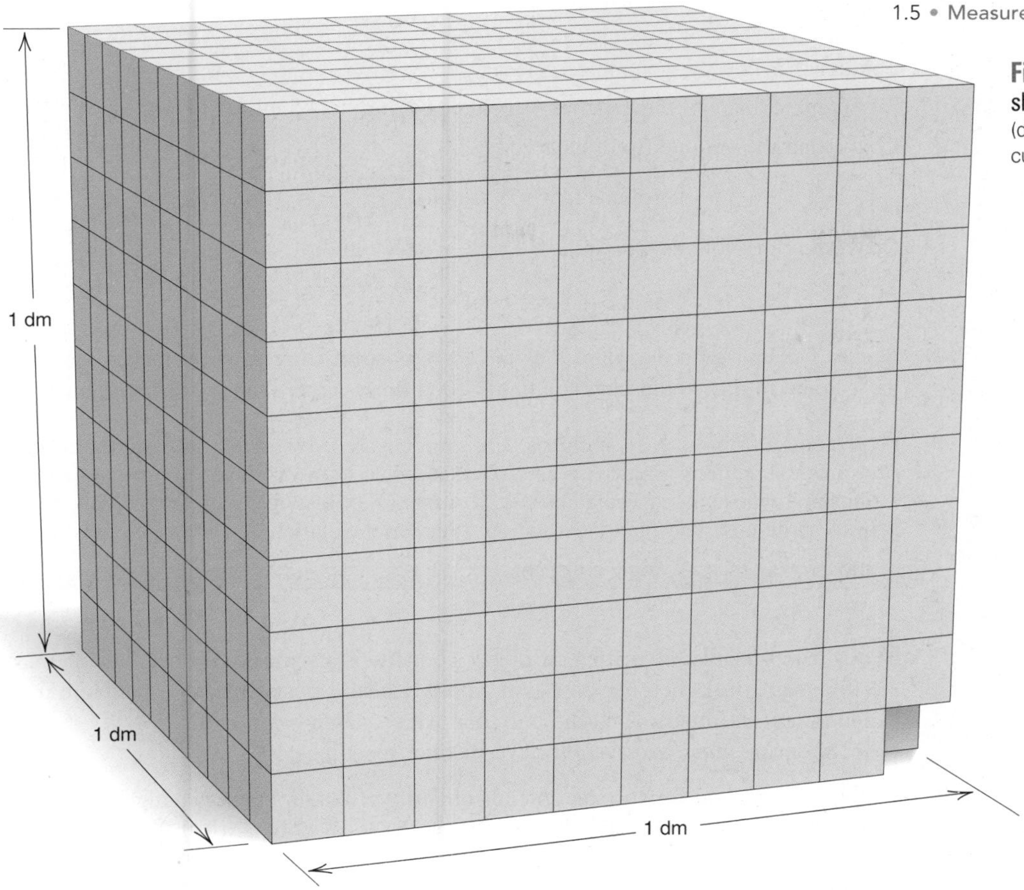

Figure 1.7 Some volume relationships in SI: From cubic decimeter (dm^3) to cubic centimeter (cm^3) to cubic millimeter (mm^3).

Some volume equivalents:

$1\ m^3 = 1000\ dm^3$

$1\ dm^3 = 1000\ cm^3$
$= 1\ L = 1000\ mL$

$1\ cm^3 = 1000\ mm^3$
$= 1\ mL = 1000\ \mu L$

$1\ mm^3 = 1\ \mu L$

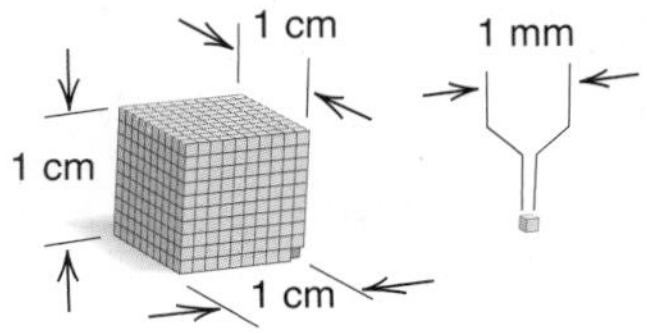

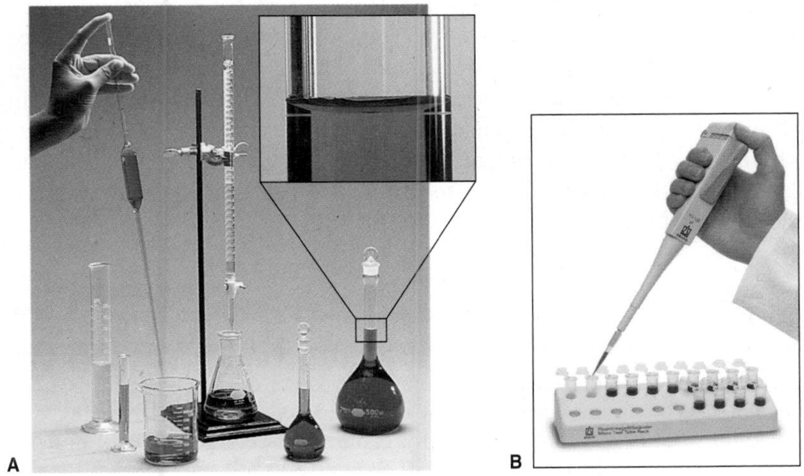

Figure 1.8 Common laboratory volumetric glassware. **A,** From left to right are two graduated cylinders, a pipet being emptied into a beaker, a buret delivering liquid to an Erlenmeyer flask, and two volumetric flasks. **Inset,** In contact with the glass neck of the flask, the liquid forms a concave meniscus (curved surface). **B,** An automatic pipet delivers a given volume of liquid to each test tube.

Sample Problem 1.4 Converting Units of Volume

Problem The volume of an irregularly shaped solid can be determined from the volume of water it displaces. A graduated cylinder contains 19.9 mL of water. When a small piece of galena, an ore of lead, is added, it sinks and the volume increases to 24.5 mL. What is the volume of the piece of galena in cm^3 and in L?

Plan We have to find the volume of the galena from the change in volume of the cylinder contents. The volume of galena in mL is the difference before (19.9 mL) and after (24.5 mL) adding it. Since mL and cm^3 represent identical volumes, the volume in mL equals the volume in cm^3. We then use equivalent quantities ($1\ mL = 10^{-3}\ L$) to convert mL to L. The road map shows these steps.

Road Map

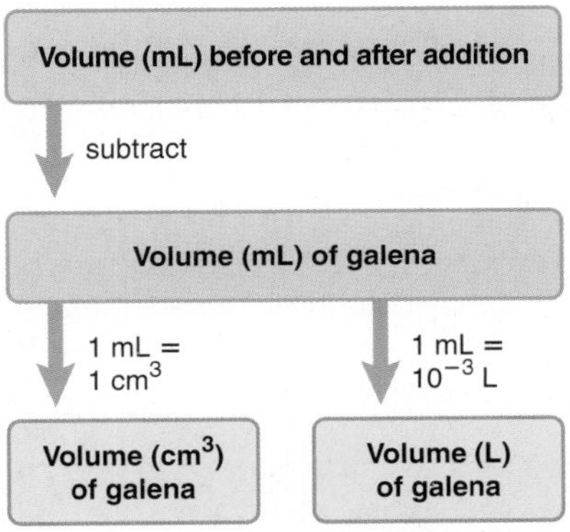

Solution Finding the volume of galena:

$$\text{Volume (mL)} = \text{volume after} - \text{volume before} = 24.5\ \text{mL} - 19.9\ \text{mL} = 4.6\ \text{mL}$$

Converting the volume from mL to cm^3:

$$\text{Volume (cm}^3\text{)} = 4.6\ \cancel{\text{mL}} \times \frac{1\ \text{cm}^3}{1\ \cancel{\text{mL}}} = 4.6\ \text{cm}^3$$

Converting the volume from mL to L:

$$\text{Volume (L)} = 4.6\ \cancel{\text{mL}} \times \frac{10^{-3}\ \text{L}}{1\ \cancel{\text{mL}}} = 4.6\times10^{-3}\ \text{L}$$

Check The units and magnitudes of the answers seem correct, and it makes sense that the volume in mL would have a number 1000 times larger than the same volume in L.

Follow-Up Problem 1.4 Within a cell, proteins are synthesized on particles called ribosomes. Assuming ribosomes are spherical, what is the volume (in dm^3 and μL) of a ribosome whose average diameter is 21.4 nm (V of a sphere $= \frac{4}{3}\pi r^3$)? Draw a road map to show how you plan the solution. (See Brief Solutions.)

Mass The quantity of matter an object contains is its **mass.** The SI unit of mass is the **kilogram (kg),** the only base unit whose standard is an object—a platinum-iridium cylinder kept in France—and the only one whose name has a prefix.*

The terms *mass* and *weight* have distinct meanings:

- *Mass is constant* because an object's quantity of matter cannot change.
- ***Weight*** *is variable* because it depends on the local gravitational field acting on the object.

Because the strength of the gravitational field varies with altitude, you (and other objects) weigh slightly less on a high mountain than at sea level.

Does this mean that a sample weighed on laboratory balances in Miami (sea level) and in Denver (about 1.7 km above sea level) give different results? No, because these balances measure mass, not weight. (We actually "mass" an object when we weigh it on a balance, but we don't use that term.) Mechanical balances compare the object's mass with masses built into the balance, so the local gravitational field pulls on them equally. Electronic (analytical) balances generate an electric field that counteracts the local field, and the current needed to restore the pan to zero is converted to the equivalent mass and displayed.

Sample Problem 1.5 Converting Units of Mass

Problem Many international computer communications are carried by optical fibers in cables laid along the ocean floor. If one strand of optical fiber weighs 1.19×10^{-3} lb/m, what is the mass (in kg) of a cable made of six strands of optical fiber, each long enough to link New York and Paris (8.84×10^3 km)?

Plan We have to find the mass of cable (in kg) from the given mass/length of fiber (1.19×10^{-3} lb/m), number of fibers/cable (6), and length of cable (8.84×10^3 km). Let's first find the mass of one fiber and then the mass of cable. As shown in the road map, we convert the length of one fiber from km to m and then find its mass (in lb) by converting m to lb. Then we multiply the fiber mass by 6 to get the cable mass, and finally convert lb to kg.

Road Map

Length (km) of fiber

↓ $1\ \text{km} = 10^3\ \text{m}$

Length (m) of fiber

↓ $1\ \text{m} = 1.19\times10^{-3}\ \text{lb}$

Mass (lb) of fiber

↓ 6 fibers = 1 cable

Mass (lb) of cable

↓ 2.205 lb = 1 kg

Mass (kg) of cable

Solution Converting the fiber length from km to m:

$$\text{Length (m) of fiber} = 8.84\times10^3\ \cancel{\text{km}} \times \frac{10^3\ \text{m}}{1\ \cancel{\text{km}}} = 8.84\times10^6\ \text{m}$$

*The names of the other base units are used as the root words, but for units of mass we attach prefixes to the word "gram," as in "microgram" and "kilogram"; thus, we say "milligram", never "microkilogram."

Converting the length of one fiber to mass (lb):

$$\text{Mass (lb) of fiber} = 8.84\times10^6\ \cancel{\text{m}} \times \frac{1.19\times10^{-3}\ \text{lb}}{1\ \cancel{\text{m}}} = 1.05\times10^4\ \text{lb}$$

Finding the mass of the cable (lb):

$$\text{Mass (lb) of cable} = \frac{1.05\times10^4\ \text{lb}}{1\ \cancel{\text{fiber}}} \times \frac{6\ \cancel{\text{fibers}}}{1\ \text{cable}} = 6.30\times10^4\ \text{lb/cable}$$

Converting the mass of cable from lb to kg:

$$\text{Mass (kg) of cable} = \frac{6.30\times10^4\ \cancel{\text{lb}}}{1\ \text{cable}} \times \frac{1\ \text{kg}}{2.205\ \cancel{\text{lb}}} = 2.86\times10^4\ \text{kg/cable}$$

Check The units are correct. Let's think through the relative sizes of the answers to see if they make sense: The number of m should be 10^3 larger than the number of km. If 1 m of fiber weighs about 10^{-3} lb, about 10^7 m should weigh about 10^4 lb. The cable mass should be six times as much, or about 6×10^4 lb. Since 1 lb is about $\frac{1}{2}$ kg, the number of kg should be about half the number of lb.

Follow-Up Problem 1.5 An intravenous nutrient solution is delivered to a hospital patient at a rate of 1.5 drops per second. If a drop of solution weighs 65 mg on average, how many kilograms are delivered in 8.0 h? Draw a road map to show how you plan the solution. (See Brief Solutions.)

Figure 1.9 shows the ranges of some common lengths, volumes, and masses.

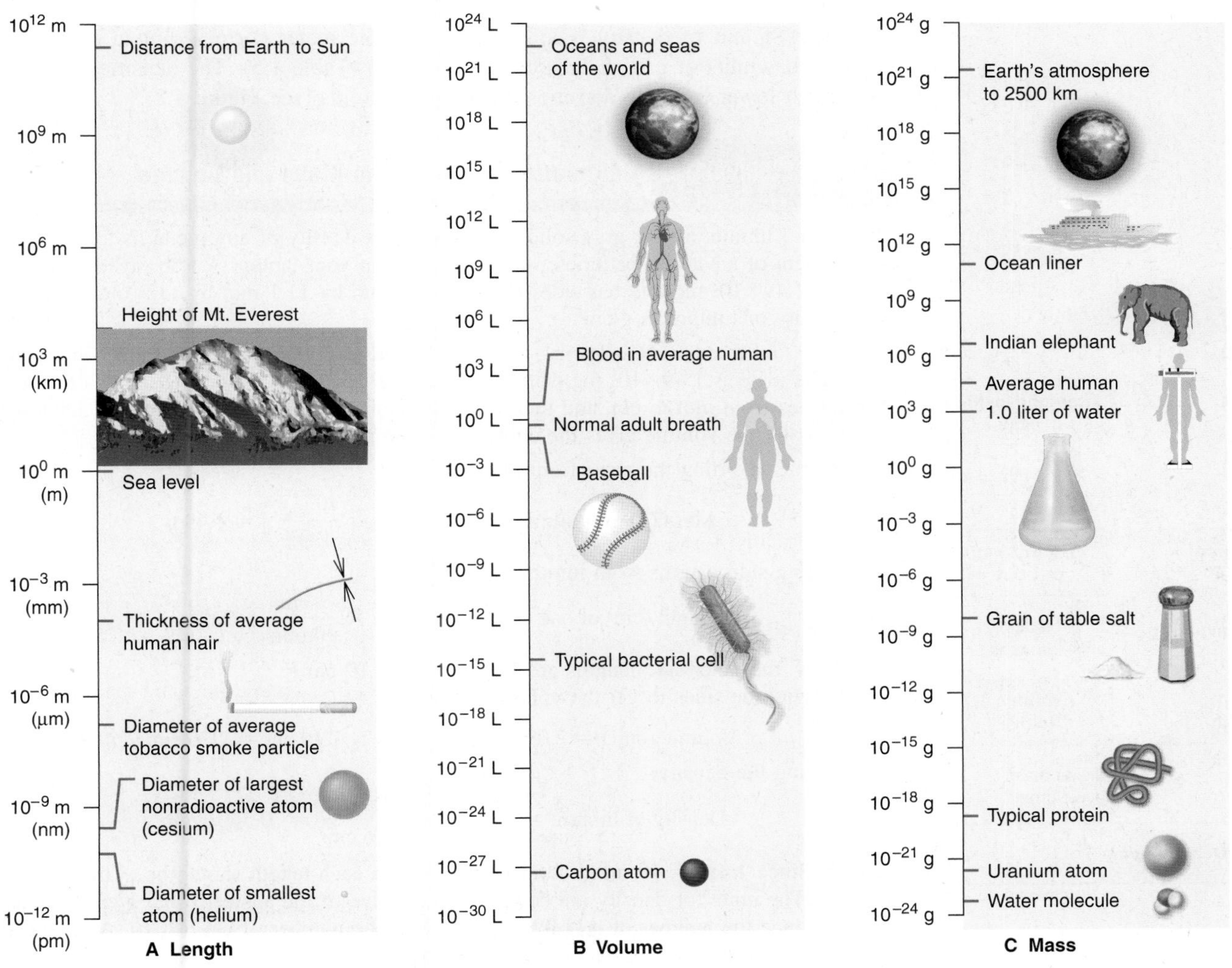

Figure 1.9 Some interesting quantities of length (**A**), volume (**B**), and mass (**C**). The vertical scales are exponential.

Table 1.5 Densities of Some Common Substances*

Substance	Physical State	Density (g/cm³)
Hydrogen	gas	0.0000899
Oxygen	gas	0.00133
Grain alcohol	liquid	0.789
Water	liquid	0.998
Table salt	solid	2.16
Aluminum	solid	2.70
Lead	solid	11.3
Gold	solid	19.3

*At room temperature (20°C) and normal atmospheric pressure (1 atm).

Density The **density (*d*)** of an object is its mass divided by its volume:

$$\text{Density} = \frac{\text{mass}}{\text{volume}} \tag{1.1}$$

We isolate each of these variables by treating density as a conversion factor:

$$\text{Mass} = \text{volume} \times \text{density} = \cancel{\text{volume}} \times \frac{\text{mass}}{\cancel{\text{volume}}}$$

or,

$$\text{Volume} = \text{mass} \times \frac{1}{\text{density}} = \cancel{\text{mass}} \times \frac{\text{volume}}{\cancel{\text{mass}}}$$

Because volume can change with temperature, so can density. But, at a given temperature and pressure, the *density of a substance is a characteristic physical property and, thus, has a specific value.*

The SI unit of density is kilograms per cubic meter (kg/m^3), but in chemistry, density has units of g/L (g/dm^3) or g/mL (g/cm^3) (Table 1.5). The densities of gases are much lower than the densities of liquids or solids (see Figure 1.2).

Sample Problem 1.6 Calculating Density from Mass and Volume

Problem Lithium, a soft, gray solid with the lowest density of any metal, is a key component of advanced batteries, such as the one in your laptop. A slab of lithium weighs 1.49×10^3 mg and has sides that are 20.9 mm by 11.1 mm by 11.9 mm. Find the density of lithium in g/cm^3.

Plan To find the density in g/cm^3, we need the mass of lithium in g and the volume in cm^3. The mass is 1.49×10^3 mg, so we convert mg to g. We convert the lengths of the three sides from mm to cm, and then multiply them to find the volume in cm^3. Dividing the mass by the volume gives the density (see the road map).

Road Map

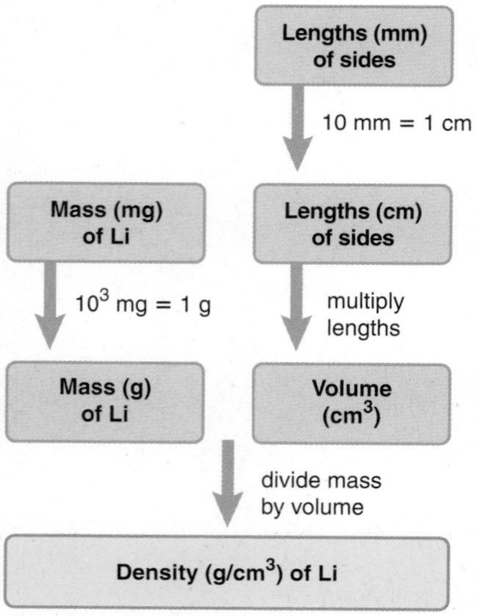

Solution Converting the mass from mg to g:

$$\text{Mass (g) of lithium} = 1.49\times10^3\ \cancel{\text{mg}}\left(\frac{10^{-3}\ \text{g}}{1\ \cancel{\text{mg}}}\right) = 1.49\ \text{g}$$

Converting side lengths from mm to cm:

$$\text{Length (cm) of one side} = 20.9\ \cancel{\text{mm}} \times \frac{1\ \text{cm}}{10\ \cancel{\text{mm}}} = 2.09\ \text{cm}$$

Similarly, the other side lengths are 1.11 cm and 1.19 cm.
Multiplying the sides to get the volume:

$$\text{Volume (cm}^3) = 2.09\ \text{cm} \times 1.11\ \text{cm} \times 1.19\ \text{cm} = 2.76\ \text{cm}^3$$

Calculating the density:

$$\text{Density of lithium} = \frac{\text{mass}}{\text{volume}} = \frac{1.49\ \text{g}}{2.76\ \text{cm}^3} = 0.540\ \text{g/cm}^3$$

Check Since 1 cm = 10 mm, the number of cm in each length should be $\frac{1}{10}$ the number of mm. The units for density are correct, and the size of the answer (~0.5 g/cm^3) seems correct since the number of g (1.49) is about half the number of cm^3 (2.76). Also, the problem states that lithium has a very low density, so this answer makes sense.

Follow-Up Problem 1.6 The piece of galena in Sample Problem 1.4 has a volume of 4.6 cm^3. If the density of galena is 7.5 g/cm^3, what is the mass (in kg) of that piece of galena? Draw a road map to show how you plan the solution. (See Brief Solutions.)

Temperature There is a noteworthy distinction between temperature and heat:

- **Temperature (T)** is *a measure* of how hot or cold one object is relative to another.
- **Heat** is *the energy* that flows from the object with the higher temperature to the object with the lower temperature. When you hold an ice cube, it feels like the "cold" flows into your hand, but actually, heat flows from your hand to the ice.

In the laboratory, we measure temperature with a **thermometer,** a narrow tube containing a fluid that expands when heated. When the thermometer is immersed in a substance hotter than itself, heat flows from the substance through the glass into the fluid, which expands and rises in the thermometer tube. If a substance is colder than the thermometer, heat flows to the substance from the fluid, which contracts and falls within the tube.

We'll consider three temperature scales: the Celsius (°C, formerly called centigrade), the Kelvin (K), and the Fahrenheit (°F) scales. The SI base unit of temperature is the **kelvin** (**K,** with no degree sign, °). Figure 1.10 shows some interesting temperatures in the Kelvin scale, which is preferred in scientific work (although the Celsius scale is still used frequently). In the United States, the Fahrenheit scale is used for weather reporting, body temperature, and so forth.

The three scales differ in the size of the unit and/or the temperature of the zero point. Figure 1.11 shows the freezing and boiling points of water in the three scales. The **Celsius scale** sets water's freezing point at 0°C and its boiling point (at normal atmospheric pressure) at 100°C. The **Kelvin (absolute) scale** uses the *same size degree* as the Celsius scale—$\frac{1}{100}$ of the difference between the freezing and boiling points of water—but it has a *different zero point;* that is, 0 K, or *absolute zero,* equals −273.15°C. Thus, in the Kelvin scale, *all temperatures are positive;* for example, water freezes at +273.15 K (0°C) and boils at +373.15 K (100°C).

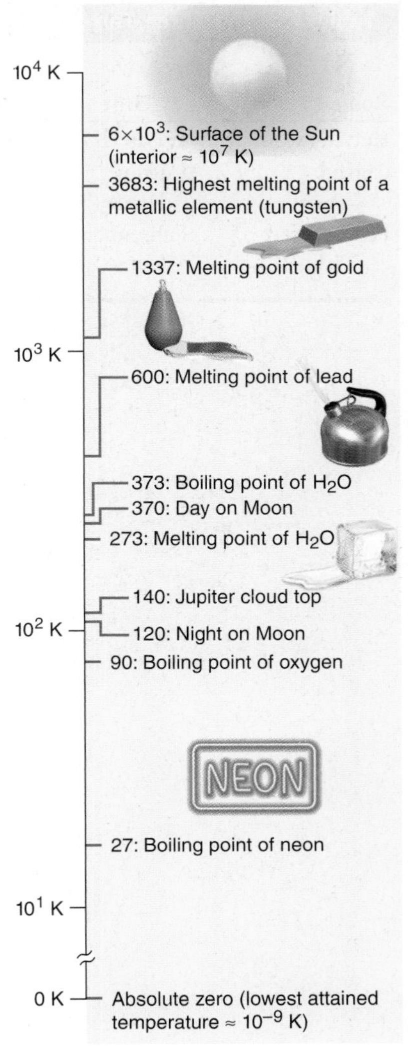

Figure 1.10 Some interesting temperatures.

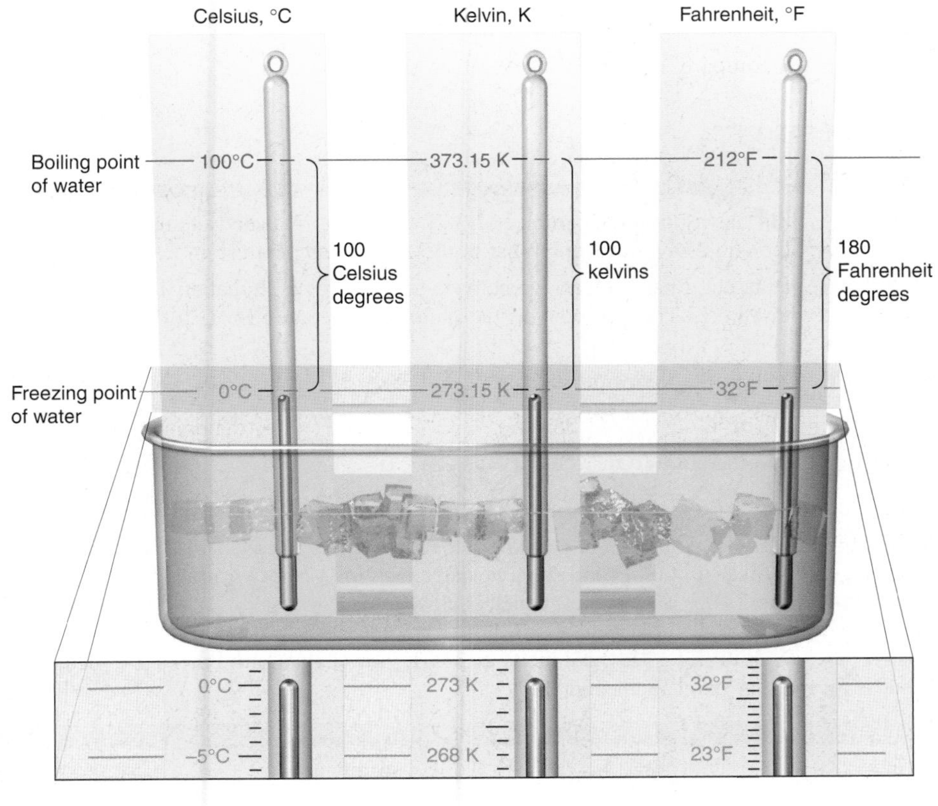

Figure 1.11 Freezing and boiling points of water in the Celsius, Kelvin (absolute), and Fahrenheit scales. At the bottom of the figure, a portion of each of the three thermometer scales is expanded to show the sizes of the units.

Table 1.6 The Three Temperature Scales

Scale	Unit	Size of Degree (Relative to K)	Freezing Point of H_2O	Boiling Point of H_2O	*T* at Absolute Zero	Conversion
Kelvin (absolute)	kelvin (K)	—	273.15 K	373.15 K	0 K	to °C (Equation 1.2)
Celsius	Celsius degree (°C)	1	0°C	100°C	−273.15°C	to K (Equation 1.3) to °F (Equation 1.4)
Fahrenheit	Fahrenheit degree (°F)	$\frac{5}{9}$	32°F	212°F	−459.67°F	to °C (Equation 1.5)

We convert between the Celsius and Kelvin scales by remembering the different zero points: 0°C = 273.15 K, so

$$T\text{ (in K)} = T\text{ (in °C)} + 273.15 \tag{1.2}$$

And, therefore,

$$T\text{ (in °C)} = T\text{ (in K)} - 273.15 \tag{1.3}$$

The Fahrenheit scale differs from the other scales in its zero point *and* in the size of its degree. Water freezes at 32°F and boils at 212°F. Therefore, 180 Fahrenheit degrees (212°F − 32°F) represents the same temperature change as 100 Celsius degrees (or 100 kelvins). Because 100 Celsius degrees equal 180 Fahrenheit degrees,

$$1\text{ Celsius degree} = \tfrac{180}{100}\text{ Fahrenheit degrees} = \tfrac{9}{5}\text{ Fahrenheit degrees}$$

To convert a temperature from °C to °F, first change the degree size and then adjust the zero point:

$$T\text{ (in °F)} = \tfrac{9}{5}T\text{ (in °C)} + 32 \tag{1.4}$$

To convert a temperature from °F to °C, do the two steps in the opposite order: adjust the zero point and then change the degree size. In other words, solve Equation 1.4 for *T* (in °C):

$$T\text{ (in °C)} = [T\text{ (in °F)} - 32]\tfrac{5}{9} \tag{1.5}$$

Table 1.6 compares the three temperature scales.

Sample Problem 1.7 Converting Units of Temperature

Problem A child has a body temperature of 38.7°C, and normal body temperature is 98.6°F. Does the child have a fever? What is the child's temperature in kelvins?

Plan To see if the child has a fever, we convert from °C to °F (Equation 1.4) and compare it with 98.6°F. Then, to convert the child's temperature in °C to K, we use Equation 1.2.

Solution Converting the temperature from °C to °F:

$$T\text{ (in °F)} = \tfrac{9}{5}T\text{ (in °C)} + 32 = \tfrac{9}{5}(38.7\text{°C}) + 32 = 101.7\text{°F};\ \text{yes, the child has a fever.}$$

Converting the temperature from °C to K:

$$T\text{ (in K)} = T\text{ (in °C)} + 273.15 = 38.7\text{°C} + 273.15 = 311.8\text{ K}$$

Check From everyday experience, you know that 101.7°F is a reasonable temperature for someone with a fever. In the second step, we can check for a large error as follows: 38.7°C is almost 40°C, and 40 + 273 = 313, which is close to our answer.

Follow-Up Problem 1.7 Mercury melts at 234 K, lower than any other pure metal. What is its melting point in °C and °F?

Time The SI base unit of time is the **second (s),** which is now based on an atomic standard. The best pendulum clock is accurate to within 3 seconds per year, and the best quartz clock is 1000 times more accurate. The most recent version of the atomic clock is over 6000 times more accurate than that—within 1 second in 20 million years! Rather than the oscillations of a pendulum, the atomic clock measures the oscillations of microwave radiation absorbed by gaseous cesium atoms cooled to around 10^{-6} K: 1 second is defined as 9,192,631,770 of these oscillations. Chemists now use lasers to measure the speed of extremely fast reactions that occur in a few picoseconds (10^{-12} s) or femtoseconds (10^{-15} s).

Extensive and Intensive Properties Some variables are *dependent* on the amount of substance present; these are called **extensive properties.** On the other hand, **intensive properties** are *independent* of the amount of substance. Mass and volume, for example, are extensive properties, but density is an intensive property. Thus, a gallon of water has four times the mass of a quart of water, but it also has four times the volume, so the density, the *ratio* of mass to volume, is the same for both samples.

Another important example concerns heat, an extensive property, and temperature, an intensive property: a vat of boiling water has more heat, that is, more energy, than a cup of boiling water, but both samples have the same temperature.

Summary of Section 1.5

- The SI unit system consists of seven base units and numerous derived units.
- Exponential notation and prefixes based on powers of 10 are used to express very small and very large numbers.
- The SI base unit of length is the meter (m); on the atomic scale, the nanometer (nm) and picometer (pm) are used commonly.
- Volume (V) units are derived from length units, and the most important volume units are the cubic meter (m^3) and the liter (L).
- The *mass* of an object—the quantity of matter in it—is constant. The SI unit of mass is the kilogram (kg). The *weight* of an object varies with the gravitational field.
- Density (d) is a characteristic physical property of a substance and is the ratio of its mass to its volume.
- Temperature (T) is a measure of the relative hotness of an object. Heat is energy that flows from an object at higher T to one at lower T.
- Temperature scales differ in the size of the degree unit and/or the zero point. For scientific uses, temperature is measured in kelvins (K) or degrees Celsius (°C).
- Extensive properties, such as mass, volume, and energy, depend on the amount of a substance. Intensive properties, such as density and temperature, do not.

1.6 • UNCERTAINTY IN MEASUREMENT: SIGNIFICANT FIGURES

All measuring devices—balances, pipets, thermometers, and so forth—are made to limited specifications, and we use our imperfect senses and skills to read them. Therefore, we can *never* measure a quantity exactly; put another way, every measurement includes some **uncertainty.** The device we choose depends on how much uncertainty is acceptable. When you buy potatoes, a supermarket scale that measures in 0.1-kg increments is acceptable; it tells you that the mass is, for example, 2.0 ± 0.1 kg. The "± 0.1 kg" term expresses the uncertainty: the potatoes weigh between 1.9 and 2.1 kg. Needing more certainty than that to weigh a substance, a chemist uses a balance that measures in 0.001-kg increments and finds the substance weighs 2.036 ± 0.001 kg, that is, between 2.035 and 2.037 kg. The greater number of digits in this measurement means we know the mass of the substance with *more certainty* than we know the mass of potatoes.

We *always estimate the rightmost digit* of a measurement. The uncertainty can be expressed with the ± sign, but generally we drop the sign and *assume an uncertainty of one unit in the rightmost digit.* The digits we record, both the certain and the uncertain ones, are called **significant figures.** There are four significant figures in 2.036 kg

Figure 1.12 The number of significant figures in a measurement. The thermometer on the left is graduated in increments of 0.1°C; the one on the right is graduated in increments of 1°C.

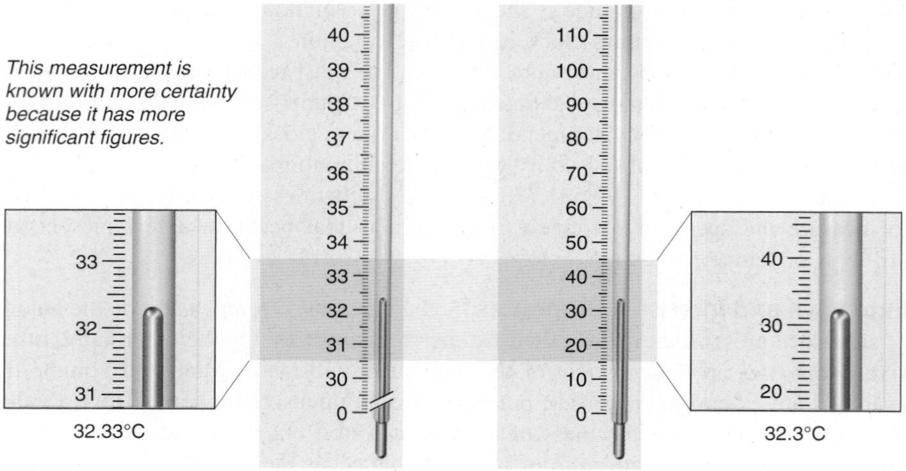

and two in 2.0 kg. *The greater the number of significant figures, the greater is the certainty of a measurement.* Figure 1.12 shows this point for two thermometers.

Determining Which Digits Are Significant

When you take a measurement or use one in a calculation, you must know the number of digits that are significant: *all digits are significant, except zeros used only to position the decimal point.* The following procedure applies this point:

1. Make sure the measurement has a decimal point.
2. Start at the left, and move right until you reach the first nonzero digit.
3. Count that digit and every digit to its right as significant.

A complication can arise when zeros end a number:

- If there *is* a decimal point and the zeros lie either after or before it, they *are* significant: 1.1300 g has five significant figures and 6500. has four.
- If there is *no* decimal point, we assume that the zeros are *not* significant, unless exponential notation clarifies the quantity: 5300 L is *assumed* to have two significant figures, but 5.300×10^3 L has four, 5.30×10^3 L has three, and 5.3×10^3 L has two.
- A terminal decimal point indicates that zeros are significant: 500 mL has one significant figure, but 500. mL has three (as do 5.00×10^2 mL and 0.500 L).

Sample Problem 1.8 Determining the Number of Significant Figures

Problem For each of the following quantities, underline the zeros that are significant figures (sf) and determine the total number of significant figures. For (d) to (f), express each quantity in exponential notation first.

(a) 0.0030 L **(b)** 0.1044 g **(c)** 53,069 mL
(d) 0.00004715 m **(e)** 57,600. s **(f)** 0.0000007160 cm^3

Plan We determine the number of significant figures by counting digits, as just presented, paying particular attention to the position of zeros in relation to the decimal point, and underline the zeros that are significant.

Solution (a) $0.003\underline{0}$ L has 2 sf
(b) $0.1\underline{0}44$ g has 4 sf
(c) $53,\underline{0}69$ mL has 5 sf
(d) 0.00004715 m, or 4.715×10^{-5} m, has 4 sf
(e) $57,6\underline{00}.$ s, or $5.76\underline{00}\times10^4$ s, has 5 sf
(f) $0.000000716\underline{0}$ cm^3, or $7.16\underline{0}\times10^{-7}$ cm^3, has 4 sf

Check Be sure that every zero counted as significant comes after nonzero digit(s) in the number.

Follow-Up Problem 1.8 For each of the following quantities, underline the zeros that are significant figures and determine the total number of significant figures (sf). For (d) to (f), express each quantity in exponential notation first.
(a) 31.070 mg **(b)** 0.06060 g **(c)** 850.°C
(d) 200.0 mL **(e)** 0.0000039 m **(f)** 0.000401 L

Significant Figures: Calculations and Rounding Off

Measuring several quantities typically results in data with differing numbers of significant figures. In a calculation, we keep track of the number in each quantity so that we don't have more significant figures (more certainty) in the answer than in the data. If we do have too many significant figures, we must **round off** the answer.

The general rule for rounding is that *the least certain measurement sets the limit on certainty for the entire calculation and determines the number of significant figures in the final answer.* Suppose you want to find the density of a new ceramic. You measure the mass of a piece of it on a precise laboratory balance and obtain 3.8056 g; you measure the volume as 2.5 mL by displacement of water in a graduated cylinder. The mass has five significant figures, but the volume has only two. Should you report the density as 3.8056 g/2.5 mL = 1.5222 g/mL or as 1.5 g/mL? The answer with five significant figures implies more certainty than the answer with two. But you didn't measure the volume to five significant figures, so you can't possibly know the density with that much certainty. Therefore, you report 1.5 g/mL, the answer with two significant figures.

Rules for Arithmetic Operations The two rules in arithmetic calculations are

1. *For multiplication and division.* The answer contains the same number of significant figures as there are in the measurement with the *fewest significant figures.* Suppose you want to find the volume of a sheet of a new graphite composite. The length (9.2 cm) and width (6.8 cm) are obtained with a ruler, and the thickness (0.3744 cm) with a set of calipers. The calculation is

$$\text{Volume (cm}^3) = 9.2\ \text{cm} \times 6.8\ \text{cm} \times 0.3744\ \text{cm} = 23.4225\ \text{cm}^3 = 23\ \text{cm}^3$$

Even though your calculator may show 23.4225 cm^3, you report 23 cm^3, the answer with two significant figures, the same as in the measurements with the lower number of significant figures. After all, if the length and width have two significant figures, you can't possibly know the volume with more certainty.

2. *For addition and subtraction.* The answer has the same number of decimal places as there are in the measurement with the *fewest decimal places.* Suppose you want the total volume after adding water to a protein solution: you have 83.5 mL of solution in a graduated cylinder and add 23.28 mL of water from a buret. The calculation is shown in the margin. Here the calculator shows 106.78 mL, but you report the volume as 106.8 mL, because the measurement with fewer decimal places (83.5 mL) has one decimal place (*see margin*).

$$\begin{array}{r} 83.5\ \text{mL} \\ +\ 23.28\ \text{mL} \\ \hline 106.78\ \text{mL} \end{array}$$

Answer: Volume = 106.8 mL

Rules for Rounding Off You usually need to round off the final answer to the proper number of significant figures or decimal places. Notice that in calculating the volume of the graphite composite above, we removed the extra digits, but in calculating the total volume of the protein solution, we removed the extra digit and increased the last digit by one. The general rule for rounding is that *the least certain measurement sets the limit on the certainty of the final answer.* Here are detailed rules for rounding off:

1. If the digit removed is *more than 5,* the preceding number increases by 1: 5.379 rounds to 5.38 if you need three significant figures and to 5.4 if you need two.
2. If the digit removed is *less than 5,* the preceding number remains the same: 0.2413 rounds to 0.241 if you need three significant figures and to 0.24 if you need two.
3. If the digit removed *is 5,* the preceding number increases by 1 if it is odd and remains the same if it is even: 17.75 rounds to 17.8, but 17.65 rounds to 17.6. If the 5 is followed only by zeros, rule 3 is followed; if the 5 is followed by nonzeros, rule 1 is followed: 17.6500 rounds to 17.6, but 17.6513 rounds to 17.7.

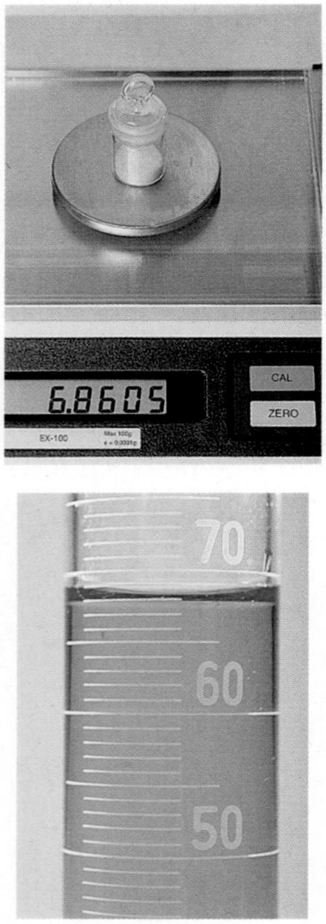

Figure 1.13 Significant figures and measuring devices. The mass measurement (6.8605 g) has more significant figures than the volume measurement (68.2 mL).

4. *Always carry one or two additional significant figures through a multistep calculation and round off the final answer* ***only.*** Don't be concerned if you string together a calculation to check a sample or follow-up problem and find that your answer differs in the last decimal place from the one in the book. To show you the correct number of significant figures in text calculations, *we round off intermediate steps,* and that process may sometimes change the last digit.

Note that, unless you set a limit on your calculator, it gives answers with too many figures and you must round the displayed result.

Significant Figures in the Lab The measuring device you choose determines the number of significant figures you can obtain. Suppose an experiment requires a solution made by dissolving a solid in a liquid. You weigh the solid on an analytical balance and obtain a mass with five significant figures. It would make sense to measure the liquid with a buret or a pipet, which measures volumes to more significant figures than a graduated cylinder. If you do choose the cylinder, you would have to round off more digits, and some certainty in the mass value would be wasted (Figure 1.13). With experience, you'll choose a measuring device based on the number of significant figures you need in the final answer.

Exact Numbers **Exact numbers** have no uncertainty associated with them. Some are part of a unit conversion: by definition, there are exactly 60 minutes in 1 hour, 1000 micrograms in 1 milligram, and 2.54 centimeters in 1 inch. Other exact numbers result from actually counting items: there are exactly 3 coins in my hand, 26 letters in the English alphabet, and so forth. Therefore, unlike a measured quantity, *exact numbers do not limit the number of significant figures in a calculation.*

Sample Problem 1.9 Significant Figures and Rounding

Problem Perform the following calculations and round the answers to the correct number of significant figures:

(a) $$\frac{16.3521\ \text{cm}^2 - 1.448\ \text{cm}^2}{7.085\ \text{cm}}$$

(b) $$\frac{(4.80\times10^4\ \text{mg})\left(\dfrac{1\ \text{g}}{1000\ \text{mg}}\right)}{11.55\ \text{cm}^3}$$

Plan We use the rules just presented in the text: **(a)** We subtract before we divide. **(b)** We note that the unit conversion involves an exact number.

Solution (a) $$\frac{16.3521\ \text{cm}^2 - 1.448\ \text{cm}^2}{7.085\ \text{cm}} = \frac{14.904\ \text{cm}^{\not 2}}{7.085\ \not{\text{cm}}} = 2.104\ \text{cm}$$

(b) $$\frac{(4.80\times10^4\ \not{\text{mg}})\left(\dfrac{1\ \text{g}}{1000\ \not{\text{mg}}}\right)}{11.55\ \text{cm}^3} = \frac{48.0\ \text{g}}{11.55\ \text{cm}^3} = 4.16\ \text{g/cm}^3$$

Check Note that in (a) we lose a decimal place in the numerator, and in (b) we retain 3 sf in the answer because there are 3 sf in 4.80. Rounding to the nearest whole number is always a good way to check: **(a)** $(16 - 1)/7 \approx 2$; **(b)** $(5\times10^4/1\times10^3)/12 \approx 4$.

Follow-Up Problem 1.9 Perform the following calculation and round the answer to the correct number of significant figures: $$\frac{25.65\ \text{mL} + 37.4\ \text{mL}}{73.55\ \text{s}\left(\dfrac{1\ \text{min}}{60\ \text{s}}\right)}$$

Precision, Accuracy, and Instrument Calibration

We may use the words "precision" and "accuracy" interchangeably in everyday speech, but for scientific measurements they have distinct meanings. **Precision,** or *reproducibility,* refers to how close the measurements in a series are to each other,

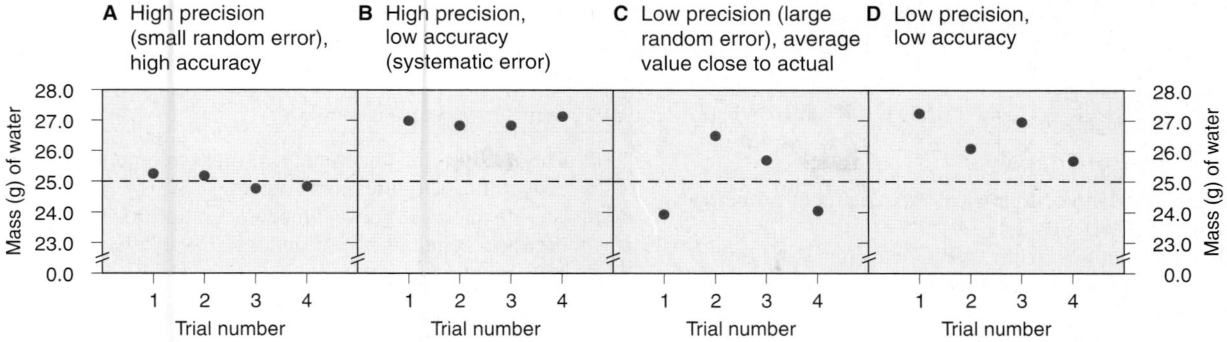

Figure 1.14 Precision and accuracy in a laboratory calibration.

and **accuracy** refers to how close each measurement is to the actual value. These terms are related to two widespread types of error:

1. **Systematic error** produces values that are *either* all higher or all lower than the actual value. This type of error is part of the experimental system, often caused by a faulty device or by a consistent mistake in taking a reading.
2. **Random error,** in the absence of systematic error, produces values that are higher *and* lower than the actual value. Random error *always* occurs, but its size depends on the measurer's skill and the instrument's precision.

Precise measurements have low random error, that is, small deviations from the average. *Accurate measurements have low systematic error and, generally, low random error.* In some cases, when many measurements have a high random error, the *average* may still be accurate.

Suppose each of four students measures 25.0 mL of water in a preweighed graduated cylinder and then weighs the water *plus* cylinder on a balance. If the density of water is 1.00 g/mL at the temperature of the experiment, the *actual* mass of 25.0 mL of water is 25.0 g. Each student performs the operation four times, subtracts the mass of the empty cylinder, and obtains one of four graphs (Figure 1.14). In graphs A and B, random error is small; that is, precision is high (the weighings are reproducible). In A, however, the accuracy is high as well (all the values are close to 25.0 g), whereas in B the accuracy is low (there is a systematic error). In graphs C and D, random error is large; that is, precision is low. Note, however, that in D there is also a systematic error (all the values are high), whereas in C the average of the values is close to the actual value.

Systematic error can be taken into account through **calibration,** comparing the measuring device with a known standard. The systematic error in graph B, for example, might be caused by a poorly manufactured cylinder that reads "25.0" when it actually contains about 27 mL. If that cylinder had been calibrated, the student could have adjusted all volumes measured with it. The students also should calibrate the balance with standardized masses.

Summary of Section 1.6

- The final digit of a measurement is always estimated. Thus, all measurements have some uncertainty, which is expressed by the number of significant figures.
- The certainty of a calculated result depends on the certainty of the data, so the answer has as many significant figures as in the least certain measurement.
- Excess digits are rounded off in the final answer with a set of rules.
- The choice of laboratory device depends on the certainty needed.
- Exact numbers have as many significant figures as the calculation requires.
- Precision refers to how close values are to each other, and accuracy refers to how close values are to the actual value.
- Systematic errors give values that are either all higher or all lower than the actual value. Random errors give some values that are higher and some that are lower than the actual value.
- Precise measurements have low random error; accurate measurements have low systematic error and low random error.
- A systematic error is often caused by faulty equipment and can be compensated for by calibration.

CHAPTER REVIEW GUIDE

Learning Objectives

Relevant section (§) and/or sample problem (SP) numbers appear in parentheses.

Understand These Concepts

1. The distinction between physical and chemical properties and changes (§1.1; SPs 1.1, 1.2)
2. The defining features of the states of matter (§1.1)
3. The nature of potential and kinetic energy and their interconversion (§1.1)
4. The process of approaching a phenomenon scientifically and the distinctions between observation, hypothesis, experiment, and model (§1.3)
5. The common units of length, volume, mass, and temperature and their numerical prefixes (§1.5)
6. The distinctions between mass and weight, heat and temperature, and intensive and extensive properties (§1.5)
7. The meaning of uncertainty in measurements and the use of significant figures and rounding (§1.6)
8. The distinctions between accuracy and precision and between systematic and random error (§1.6)

Master These Skills

1. Using conversion factors in calculations and a systematic approach of plan, solution, check, and follow-up for solving problems (§1.4; SPs 1.3–1.5)
2. Finding density from mass and volume (SP 1.6)
3. Converting among the Kelvin, Celsius, and Fahrenheit scales (SP 1.7)
4. Determining the number of significant figures (SP 1.8) and rounding to the correct number of digits (SP 1.9)

Key Terms

Page numbers appear in parentheses.

Section 1.1
chemistry (4)
matter (4)
composition (4)
property (4)
physical property (4)
physical change (4)
chemical property (4)
chemical change (chemical reaction) (4)
state of matter (5)
solid (5)
liquid (6)
gas (6)
energy (8)
potential energy (8)
kinetic energy (8)

Section 1.2
combustion (10)

Section 1.3
scientific method (12)
observation (12)
data (12)
natural law (12)
hypothesis (12)
experiment (12)
variable (12)
controlled experiment (12)
model (theory) (12)

Section 1.4
conversion factor (13)
dimensional analysis (15)

Section 1.5
SI unit (17)
base (fundamental) unit (17)
derived unit (17)
meter (m) (18)
volume (V) (18)
cubic meter (m^3) (18)
liter (L) (18)
milliliter (mL) (18)
mass (20)
kilogram (kg) (20)
weight (20)
density (d) (22)
temperature (T) (23)
heat (23)
thermometer (23)
kelvin (K) (23)
Celsius scale (23)
Kelvin (absolute) scale (23)
second (s) (25)
extensive property (25)
intensive property (25)

Section 1.6
uncertainty (25)
significant figures (25)
round off (27)
exact number (28)
precision (28)
accuracy (29)
systematic error (29)
random error (29)
calibration (29)

Key Equations and Relationships

Page numbers appear in parentheses.

1.1 Calculating density from mass and volume (22):

$$\text{Density} = \frac{\text{mass}}{\text{volume}}$$

1.2 Converting temperature from °C to K (24):

$$T\text{ (in K)} = T\text{ (in °C)} + 273.15$$

1.3 Converting temperature from K to °C (24):

$$T\text{ (in °C)} = T\text{ (in K)} - 273.15$$

1.4 Converting temperature from °C to °F (24):

$$T\text{ (in °F)} = \tfrac{9}{5}T\text{ (in °C)} + 32$$

1.5 Converting temperature from °F to °C (24):

$$T\text{ (in °C)} = [T\text{ (in °F)} - 32]\tfrac{5}{9}$$

Brief Solutions to Follow-Up Problems

1.1 Chemical. The red-and-blue and separate red particles on the left become paired red and separate blue particles on the right.

1.2 (a) Physical. Solid iodine changes to gaseous iodine.
(b) Chemical. Gasoline burns in air to form different substances.
(c) Chemical. In contact with air, substances in torn skin and blood react to form different substances.

1.3 No. of chairs

$$= 3\ \cancel{\text{bolts}} \times \frac{200\ \cancel{\text{m}^2}}{1\ \cancel{\text{bolt}}} \times \frac{(3.281)^2\ \cancel{\text{ft}^2}}{1\ \cancel{\text{m}^2}} \times \frac{1\text{ chair}}{31.5\ \cancel{\text{ft}^2}}$$

$$= 205\text{ chairs}$$

See Road Map 1.3.

Road Map 1.3

Fabric (bolts)
↓ $200\ m^2 = 1$ bolt
Fabric (m^2)
↓ $(3.281)^2\ ft^2 = 1\ m^2$
Fabric (ft^2)
↓ 1 chair = $31.5\ ft^2$
No. of chairs

Road Map 1.4

Diameter (dm)
↓ diameter = $2r$
r (dm)
↓ $V = \frac{4}{3}\pi r^3$
V (dm^3)
↓ $1\ dm^3 = 1$ L; 1 L = $10^6\ \mu$L
V (μL)

1.4 Radius of ribosome (dm) $= \frac{21.4\ \cancel{nm}}{2} \times \frac{1\ dm}{10^8\ \cancel{nm}}$

$= 1.07 \times 10^{-7}$ dm

Volume of ribosome (dm^3) $= \frac{4}{3}\pi r^3 = \frac{4}{3}(3.14)(1.07 \times 10^{-7}\ dm)^3$

$= 5.13 \times 10^{-21}\ dm^3$

Volume of ribosome (μL) $= (5.13 \times 10^{-21}\ \cancel{dm^3})\left(\frac{1\ \cancel{L}}{1\ \cancel{dm^3}}\right)\left(\frac{10^6\ \mu L}{1\ \cancel{L}}\right)$

$= 5.13 \times 10^{-15}\ \mu$L

See Road Map 1.4.

1.5 Mass (kg) of solution

$= 8.0\ \cancel{h} \times \frac{60\ \cancel{min}}{1\ \cancel{h}} \times \frac{60\ \cancel{s}}{1\ \cancel{min}} \times \frac{1.5\ \cancel{drops}}{1\ \cancel{s}}$

$\times \frac{65\ \cancel{mg}}{1\ \cancel{drop}} \times \frac{1\ \cancel{g}}{10^3\ \cancel{mg}} \times \frac{1\ kg}{10^3\ \cancel{g}}$

$= 2.8$ kg

See Road Map 1.5.

Road Map 1.5

Time (hr)
↓ 1 hr = 60 min
Time (min)
↓ 1 min = 60 s
Time (s)
↓ 1 s = 1.5 drops
No. of drops
↓ 1 drop = 65 mg
Mass (mg) of solution
↓ 10^3 mg = 1 g
Mass (g) of solution
↓ 10^3 g = 1 kg
Mass (kg) of solution

Road Map 1.6

V (cm^3)
↓ multiply by density
Mass (g)
↓ 10^3 g = 1 kg
Mass (kg)

1.6 Mass (kg) of sample $= 4.6\ \cancel{cm^3} \times \frac{7.5\ \cancel{g}}{1\ \cancel{cm^3}} \times \frac{1\ kg}{10^3\ \cancel{g}}$

$= 0.034$ kg

See Road Map 1.6.

1.7 T (in °C) = 234 K − 273.15 = −39°C
T (in °F) = $\frac{9}{5}$(−39°C) + 32 = −38°F
Answer contains two significant figures (see Section 1.6).

1.8 (a) 31.0̲7̲0̲ mg, 5 sf (b) 0.060̲6̲0̲ g, 4 sf
(c) 850̲.°C, 3 sf (d) $2.\underline{000} \times 10^2$ mL, 4 sf
(e) 3.9×10^{-6} m, 2 sf (f) $4.\underline{0}1 \times 10^{-4}$ L, 3 sf

1.9 $\dfrac{25.65\ mL + 37.4\ mL}{73.55\ \cancel{s}\left(\frac{1\ min}{60\ \cancel{s}}\right)} = 51.4$ mL/min

PROBLEMS

Problems with **colored** numbers are answered in Appendix E and worked in detail in the Student Solutions Manual. Problem sections match those in the text and provide the numbers of relevant sample problems. Most offer Concept Review Questions, Skill-Building Exercises (grouped in pairs covering the same concept), and Problems in Context. The Comprehensive Problems are based on material from any section.

Some Fundamental Definitions

(Sample Problems 1.1 and 1.2)

Concept Review Question

1.1 Scenes A–D represent atomic-scale views of different samples of substances:

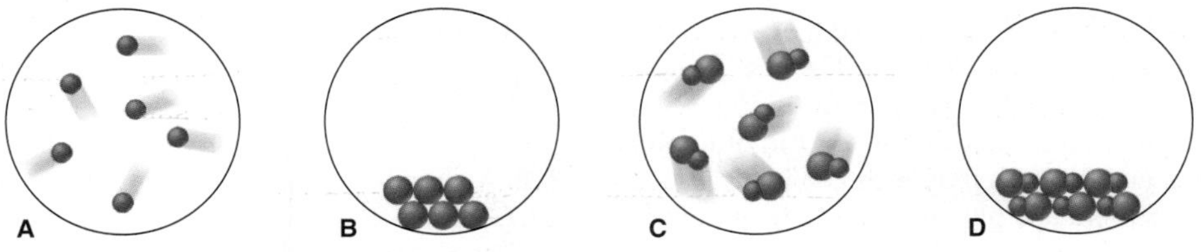

(a) Under one set of conditions, the substances in A and B mix, and the result is depicted in C. Does this represent a chemical or a physical change?
(b) Under a second set of conditions, the same substances mix, and the result is depicted in D. Does this represent a chemical or a physical change?
(c) Under a third set of conditions, the sample depicted in C changes to that in D. Does this represent a chemical or a physical change?
(d) After the change in part (c) has occurred, does the sample have different chemical properties? Physical properties?

Skill-Building Exercises (grouped in similar pairs)

1.2 Describe solids, liquids, and gases in terms of how they fill a container. Use your descriptions to identify the physical state (at room temperature) of the following: (a) helium in a toy balloon; (b) mercury in a thermometer; (c) soup in a bowl.

1.3 Use your descriptions from Problem 1.2 to identify the physical state (at room temperature) of the following: (a) the air in your room; (b) tablets in a bottle of vitamins; (c) sugar in a packet.

1.4 Define *physical property* and *chemical property*. Identify each type of property in the following statements:
(a) Yellow-green chlorine gas attacks silvery sodium metal to form white crystals of sodium chloride (table salt).
(b) A magnet separates a mixture of black iron shavings and white sand.

1.5 Define *physical change* and *chemical change*. State which type of change occurs in each of the following statements:
(a) Passing an electric current through molten magnesium chloride yields molten magnesium and gaseous chlorine.
(b) The iron in discarded automobiles slowly forms reddish brown, crumbly rust.

1.6 Which of the following is a chemical change? Explain your reasoning: (a) boiling canned soup; (b) toasting a slice of bread; (c) chopping a log; (d) burning a log.

1.7 Which of the following changes can be reversed by changing the temperature: (a) dew condensing on a leaf; (b) an egg turning hard when it is boiled; (c) ice cream melting; (d) a spoonful of batter cooking on a hot griddle?

1.8 For each pair, which has higher potential energy?
(a) The fuel in your car or the gaseous products in its exhaust
(b) Wood in a fire or the ashes after the wood burns

1.9 For each pair, which has higher kinetic energy?
(a) A sled resting at the top of a hill or a sled sliding down the hill
(b) Water above a dam or water falling over the dam

Chemical Arts and the Origins of Modern Chemistry

Concept Review Questions

1.10 The alchemical, medical, and technological traditions were precursors to chemistry. State a contribution that each made to the development of the science of chemistry.

1.11 How did the phlogiston theory explain combustion?

1.12 One important observation that supporters of the phlogiston theory had trouble explaining was that the calx of a metal weighs more than the metal itself. Why was that observation important? How did the phlogistonists respond?

1.13 Lavoisier developed a new theory of combustion that overturned the phlogiston theory. What measurements were central to his theory, and what key discovery did he make?

The Scientific Approach: Developing a Model

Concept Review Questions

1.14 How are the key elements of scientific thinking used in the following scenario? While making toast, you notice it fails to pop out of the toaster. Thinking the spring mechanism is stuck, you notice that the bread is unchanged. Assuming you forgot to plug in the toaster, you check and find it is plugged in. When you take the toaster into the dining room and plug it into a different outlet, you find the toaster works. Returning to the kitchen, you turn on the switch for the overhead light and nothing happens.

1.15 Why is a quantitative observation more useful than a nonquantitative one? Which of the following is (are) quantitative? (a) The Sun rises in the east. (b) A person weighs one-sixth as much on the Moon as on Earth. (c) Ice floats on water. (d) A hand pump cannot draw water from a well more than 34 ft deep.

1.16 Describe the essential features of a well-designed experiment.

1.17 Describe the essential features of a scientific model.

Chemical Problem Solving

(Sample Problem 1.3)

Concept Review Question

1.18 When you convert feet to inches, how do you decide which part of the conversion factor should be in the numerator and which in the denominator?

Skill-Building Exercises (grouped in similar pairs)

1.19 Write the conversion factor(s) for
(a) in^2 to m^2 (b) km^2 to cm^2
(c) mi/h to m/s (d) lb/ft^3 to g/cm^3

1.20 Write the conversion factor(s) for
(a) cm/min to in/s (b) m^3 to in^3
(c) m/s^2 to km/h^2 (d) gal/h to L/min

Measurement in Scientific Study

(Sample Problems 1.4 to 1.7)

Concept Review Questions

1.21 Describe the difference between intensive and extensive properties. Which of the following properties are intensive: (a) mass; (b) density; (c) volume; (d) melting point?

1.22 Explain the difference between mass and weight. Why is your weight on the Moon one-sixth that on Earth?

1.23 For each of the following cases, state whether the density of the object increases, decreases, or remains the same:
(a) A sample of chlorine gas is compressed.
(b) A lead weight is carried up a high mountain.
(c) A sample of water is frozen.
(d) An iron bar is cooled.
(e) A diamond is submerged in water.

1.24 Explain the difference between heat and temperature. Does 1 L of water at 65°F have more, less, or the same quantity of energy as 1 L of water at 65°C?

1.25 A one-step conversion is sufficient to convert a temperature in the Celsius scale to the Kelvin scale, but not to the Fahrenheit scale. Explain.

Skill-Building Exercises (grouped in similar pairs)

1.26 The average radius of a molecule of lysozyme, an enzyme in tears, is 1430 pm. What is its radius in nanometers (nm)?

1.27 The radius of a barium atom is 2.22×10^{-10} m. What is its radius in angstroms (Å)?

1.28 What is the length in inches (in) of a 100.-m soccer field?

1.29 The center on your basketball team is 6 ft 10 in tall. How tall is the player in millimeters (mm)?

1.30 A small hole in the wing of a space shuttle requires a 20.7-cm^2 patch. (a) What is the patch's area in square kilometers (km^2)? (b) If the patching material costs NASA \$3.25/in^2, what is the cost of the patch?

1.31 The area of a telescope lens is 7903 mm^2. (a) What is the area in square feet (ft^2)? (b) If it takes a technician 45 s to polish 135 mm^2, how long does it take her to polish the entire lens?

1.32 Express your body weight in kilograms (kg).

1.33 There are 2.60×10^{15} short tons of oxygen in the atmosphere (1 short ton = 2000 lb). How many metric tons of oxygen are present (1 metric ton = 1000 kg)?

1.34 The average density of Earth is 5.52 g/cm^3. What is its density in (a) kg/m^3; (b) lb/ft^3?

1.35 The speed of light in a vacuum is 2.998×10^8 m/s. What is its speed in (a) km/h; (b) mi/min?

1.36 The volume of a certain bacterial cell is 2.56 μm^3. (a) What is its volume in cubic millimeters (mm^3)? (b) What is the volume of 10^5 cells in liters (L)?

1.37 (a) How many cubic meters of milk are in 1 qt (946.4 mL)? (b) How many liters of milk are in 835 gal (1 gal = 4 qt)?

1.38 An empty vial weighs 55.32 g. (a) If the vial weighs 185.56 g when filled with liquid mercury (d = 13.53 g/cm^3), what is its volume? (b) How much would the vial weigh if it were filled with water (d = 0.997 g/cm^3 at 25°C)?

1.39 An empty Erlenmeyer flask weighs 241.3 g. When filled with water (d = 1.00 g/cm^3), the flask and its contents weigh 489.1 g. (a) What is the flask's volume? (b) How much does the flask weigh when filled with chloroform (d = 1.48 g/cm^3)?

1.40 A small cube of aluminum measures 15.6 mm on a side and weighs 10.25 g. What is the density of aluminum in g/cm^3?

1.41 A steel ball-bearing with a circumference of 32.5 mm weighs 4.20 g. What is the density of the steel in g/cm^3 (V of a sphere = $\frac{4}{3}\pi r^3$; circumference of a circle = $2\pi r$)?

1.42 Perform the following conversions:
(a) 68°F (a pleasant spring day) to °C and K
(b) −164°C (the boiling point of methane, the main component of natural gas) to K and °F
(c) 0 K (absolute zero, theoretically the coldest possible temperature) to °C and °F

1.43 Perform the following conversions:
(a) 106°F (the body temperature of many birds) to K and °C
(b) 3410°C (the melting point of tungsten, the highest for any metallic element) to K and °F
(c) 6.1×10^3 K (the surface temperature of the Sun) to °F and °C

Problems in Context

1.44 A 25.0-g sample of each of three unknown metals is added to 25.0 mL of water in graduated cylinders A, B, and C, and the final volumes are depicted in the circles below. Given their densities, identify the metal in each cylinder: zinc (7.14 g/mL), iron (7.87 g/mL), or nickel (8.91 g/mL).

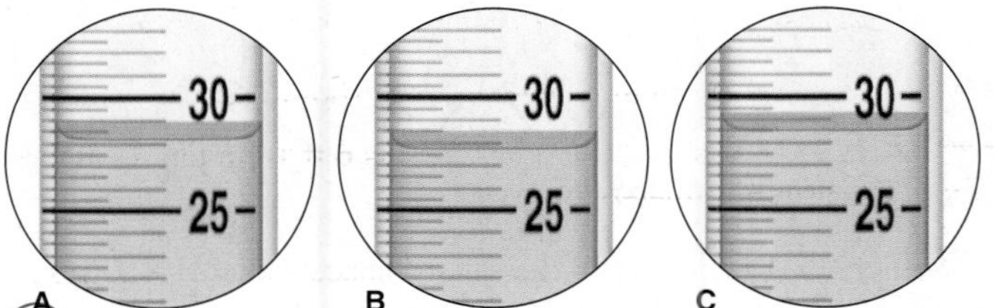

1.45 The distance between two adjacent peaks on a wave is called the *wavelength.*
(a) The wavelength of a beam of ultraviolet light is 2 meters (nm). What is its wavelength in meters?
(b) The wavelength of a beam of red light is 6760 pm. What is its wavelength in angstroms (Å)?

1.46 Each of the beakers depicted below contains two liquids that do not dissolve in each other. Three of the liquids are designated A, B, and C, and water is designated W.

(a) Which of the liquids is (are) more dense than water and which less dense?
(b) If the densities of W, C, and A are 1.0 g/mL, 0.88 g/mL, and 1.4 g/mL, respectively, which of the following densities is possible for liquid B: 0.79 g/mL, 0.86 g/mL, 0.94 g/mL, or 1.2 g/mL?

1.47 A cylindrical tube 9.5 cm high and 0.85 cm in diameter is used to collect blood samples. How many cubic decimeters (dm^3) of blood can it hold (V of a cylinder = $\pi r^2 h$)?

1.48 Copper can be drawn into thin wires. How many meters of 34-gauge wire (diameter = 6.304×10^{-3} in) can be produced from the copper in 5.01 lb of covellite, an ore of copper that is 66% copper by mass? (*Hint:* Treat the wire as a cylinder: V of cylinder = $\pi r^2 h$; d of copper = 8.95 g/cm^3.)

Uncertainty in Measurement: Significant Figures

(Sample Problems 1.8 and 1.9)

Concept Review Questions

1.49 What is an exact number? How are exact numbers treated differently from other numbers in a calculation?

1.50 Which procedure(s) decrease(s) the random error of a measurement: (1) taking the average of more measurements; (2) calibrating the instrument; (3) taking fewer measurements? Explain.

1.51 A newspaper reported that the attendance at Slippery Rock's home football game was 16,532. (a) How many significant figures does this number contain? (b) Was the actual number of people counted? (c) After Slippery Rock's next home game, the newspaper reported an attendance of 15,000. If you assume that this number contains two significant figures, how many people could actually have been at the game?

Skill-Building Exercises (grouped in similar pairs)

1.52 Underline the significant zeros in the following numbers:
(a) 0.41 (b) 0.041 (c) 0.0410 (d) 4.0100×10^4

1.53 Underline the significant zeros in the following numbers:
(a) 5.08 (b) 508 (c) 5.080×10^3 (d) 0.05080

1.54 Round off each number to the indicated number of significant figures (sf): (a) 0.0003554 (to 2 sf); (b) 35.8348 (to 4 sf); (c) 22.4555 (to 3 sf).

1.55 Round off each number to the indicated number of significant figures (sf): (a) 231.554 (to 4 sf); (b) 0.00845 (to 2 sf); (c) 144,000 (to 2 sf).

1.56 Round off each number in the following calculation to one fewer significant figure, and find the answer:

$$\frac{19 \times 155 \times 8.3}{3.2 \times 2.9 \times 4.7}$$

1.57 Round off each number in the following calculation to one fewer significant figure, and find the answer:

$$\frac{10.8 \times 6.18 \times 2.381}{24.3 \times 1.8 \times 19.5}$$

1.58 Carry out the following calculations, making sure that your answer has the correct number of significant figures:

(a) $\frac{2.795 \text{ m} \times 3.10 \text{ m}}{6.48 \text{ m}}$

(b) $V = \frac{4}{3}\pi r^3$, where $r = 17.282$ mm

(c) 1.110 cm + 17.3 cm + 108.2 cm + 316 cm

1.59 Carry out the following calculations, making sure that your answer has the correct number of significant figures:

(a) $\frac{2.420 \text{ g} + 15.6 \text{ g}}{4.8 \text{ g}}$ (b) $\frac{7.87 \text{ mL}}{16.1 \text{ mL} - 8.44 \text{ mL}}$

(c) $V = \pi r^2 h$, where $r = 6.23$ cm and $h = 4.630$ cm

1.60 Write the following numbers in scientific notation:
(a) 131,000.0 (b) 0.00047 (c) 210,006 (d) 2160.5

1.61 Write the following numbers in scientific notation:
(a) 282.0 (b) 0.0380 (c) 4270.8 (d) 58,200.9

1.62 Write the following numbers in standard notation. Use a terminal decimal point when needed:
(a) 5.55×10^3 (b) 1.0070×10^4 (c) 8.85×10^{-7} (d) 3.004×10^{-3}

1.63 Write the following numbers in standard notation. Use a terminal decimal point when needed:
(a) 6.500×10^3 (b) 3.46×10^{-5} (c) 7.5×10^2 (d) 1.8856×10^2

1.64 Convert the following into correct scientific notation:
(a) 802.5×10^2 (b) 1009.8×10^{-6} (c) 0.077×10^{-9}

1.65 Convert the following into correct scientific notation:
(a) 14.3×10^1 (b) 851×10^{-2} (c) 7500×10^{-3}

1.66 Carry out each calculation, paying special attention to significant figures, rounding, and units (J = joule, the SI unit of energy; mol = mole, the SI unit for amount of substance):

(a) $\frac{(6.626\times10^{-34} \text{ J·s})(2.9979\times10^8 \text{ m/s})}{489\times10^{-9} \text{ m}}$

(b) $\frac{(6.022\times10^{23} \text{ molecules/mol})(1.23\times10^2 \text{ g})}{46.07 \text{ g/mol}}$

(c) $(6.022\times10^{23} \text{ atoms/mol})(2.18\times10^{-18} \text{ J/atom})\left(\frac{1}{2^2} - \frac{1}{3^2}\right)$, where the numbers 2 and 3 in the last term are exact

1.67 Carry out each calculation, paying special attention to significant figures, rounding, and units:

(a) $\frac{4.32\times10^7 \text{ g}}{\frac{4}{3}(3.1416)(1.95\times10^2 \text{ cm})^3}$ (The term $\frac{4}{3}$ is exact.)

(b) $\frac{(1.84\times10^2 \text{ g})(44.7 \text{ m/s})^2}{2}$ (The term 2 is exact.)

(c) $\frac{(1.07\times10^{-4} \text{ mol/L})^2(3.8\times10^{-3} \text{ mol/L})}{(8.35\times10^{-5} \text{ mol/L})(1.48\times10^{-2} \text{ mol/L})^3}$

1.68 Which statements include exact numbers?
(a) Angel Falls is 3212 ft high.
(b) There are 8 known planets in the Solar System.
(c) There are 453.59 g in 1 lb.
(d) There are 1000 mm in 1 m.

1.69 Which of the following include exact numbers?
(a) The speed of light in a vacuum is a physical constant; to six significant figures, it is 2.99792×10^8 m/s.
(b) The density of mercury at 25°C is 13.53 g/mL.
(c) There are 3600 s in 1 h.
(d) In 2003, the United States had 50 states.

Problems in Context

1.70 How long is the metal strip shown below? Be sure to answer with the correct number of significant figures.

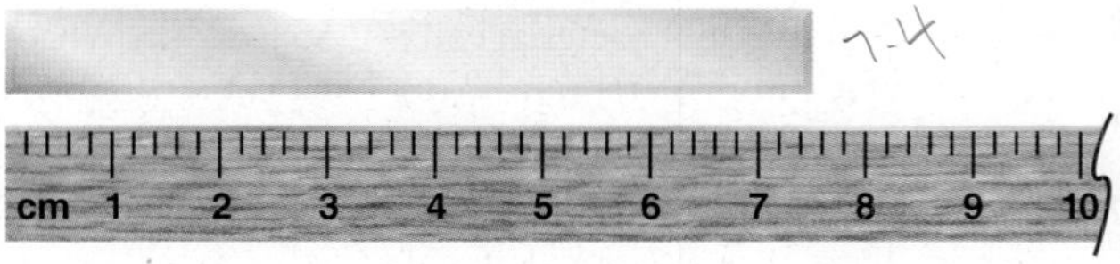

1.71 These organic solvents are used to clean compact discs:

Solvent	Density (g/mL) at 20°C
Chloroform	1.492
Diethyl ether	0.714
Ethanol	0.789
Isopropanol	0.785
Toluene	0.867

(a) If a 15.00-mL sample of CD cleaner weighs 11.775 g at 20°C, which solvent does the sample most likely contain?
(b) The chemist analyzing the cleaner calibrates her equipment and finds that the pipet is accurate to ±0.02 mL, and the balance is accurate to ±0.003 g. Is this equipment precise enough to distinguish between ethanol and isopropanol?

1.72 A laboratory instructor gives a sample of amino-acid powder to each of four students, I, II, III, and IV, and they weigh the samples. The true value is 8.72 g. Their results for three trials are
I: 8.72 g, 8.74 g, 8.70 g II: 8.56 g, 8.77 g, 8.83 g
III: 8.50 g, 8.48 g, 8.51 g IV: 8.41 g, 8.72 g, 8.55 g
(a) Calculate the average mass from each set of data, and tell which set is the most accurate.
(b) Precision is a measure of the average of the deviations of each piece of data from the average value. Which set of data is the most precise? Is this set also the most accurate?
(c) Which set of data is both the most accurate and the most precise?
(d) Which set of data is both the least accurate and the least precise?

1.73 The following dartboards illustrate the types of errors often seen in measurements. The bull's-eye represents the actual value, and the darts represent the data.

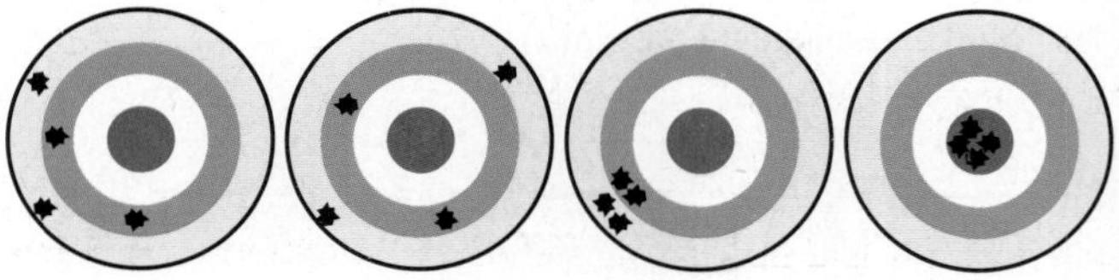

Exp. I Exp. II Exp. III Exp. IV

(a) Which experiments yield the same average result?
(b) Which experiment(s) display(s) high precision?
(c) Which experiment(s) display(s) high accuracy?
(d) Which experiment(s) show(s) a systematic error?

Comprehensive Problems

1.74 Two blank potential energy diagrams appear below. Beneath each diagram are objects to place in the diagram. Draw the objects on the dashed lines to indicate higher or lower potential energy and label each case as more or less stable:

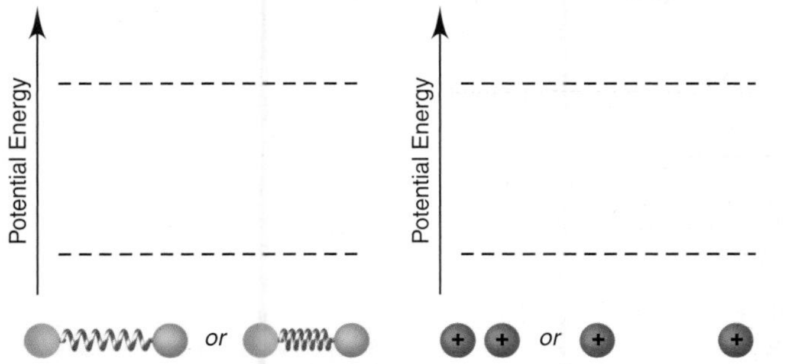

(a) Two balls attached to a relaxed *or* a compressed spring

(b) Two positive charges near *or* apart from each other

1.75 The scenes below illustrate two different mixtures. When mixture A at 273 K is heated to 473 K, mixture B results.

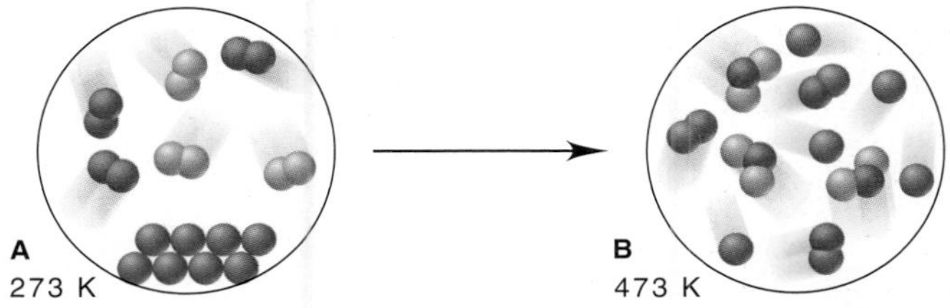

(a) How many different chemical changes occur?
(b) How many different physical changes occur?

1.76 Bromine is used to prepare the pesticide methyl bromide and flame retardants for plastic electronic housings. It is recovered from seawater, underground brines, and the Dead Sea. The average concentrations of bromine in seawater (d = 1.024 g/mL) and the Dead Sea (d = 1.22 g/mL) are 0.065 g/L and 0.50 g/L, respectively. What is the mass ratio of bromine in the Dead Sea to that in seawater?

1.77 An Olympic-size pool is 50.0 m long and 25.0 m wide. (a) How many gallons of water (d = 1.0 g/mL) are needed to fill the pool to an average depth of 4.8 ft? (b) What is the mass (in kg) of water in the pool?

1.78 At room temperature (20°C) and pressure, the density of air is 1.189 g/L. An object will float in air if its density is less than that of air. In a buoyancy experiment with a new plastic, a chemist creates a rigid, thin-walled ball that weighs 0.12 g and has a volume of 560 cm^3.
(a) Will the ball float if it is evacuated?
(b) Will it float if filled with carbon dioxide (d = 1.830 g/L)?
(c) Will it float if filled with hydrogen (d = 0.0899 g/L)?
(d) Will it float if filled with oxygen (d = 1.330 g/L)?
(e) Will it float if filled with nitrogen (d = 1.165 g/L)?
(f) For any case in which the ball will float, how much weight must be added to make it sink?

1.79 Asbestos is a fibrous silicate mineral with remarkably high tensile strength. But it is no longer used because airborne asbestos particles can cause lung cancer. Grunerite, a type of asbestos, has a tensile strength of 3.5×10^2 kg/mm^2 (thus, a strand of grunerite with a 1-mm^2 cross-sectional area can hold up to 3.5×10^2 kg). The tensile strengths of aluminum and Steel No. 5137 are 2.5×10^4 lb/in^2 and 5.0×10^4 lb/in^2, respectively. Calculate the cross-sectional areas (in mm^2) of wires of aluminum and of Steel No. 5137 that have the same tensile strength as a fiber of grunerite with a cross-sectional area of 1.0 μm^2.

1.80 Earth's oceans have an average depth of 3800 m, a total surface area of 3.63×10^8 km^2, and an average concentration of dissolved gold of 5.8×10^{-9} g/L. (a) How many grams of gold are in the oceans? (b) How many cubic meters of gold are in the oceans? (c) Assuming the price of gold is \$370.00/troy oz, what is the value of gold in the oceans (1 troy oz = 31.1 g; d of gold = 19.3 g/cm^3)?

1.81 Brass is an alloy of copper and zinc. Varying the mass percentages of the two metals produces brasses with different properties. A brass called *yellow zinc* has high ductility and strength and is 34%–37% zinc by mass. (a) Find the mass range (in g) of copper in 185 g of yellow zinc. (b) What is the mass range (in g) of zinc in a sample of yellow zinc that contains 46.5 g of copper?

1.82 Liquid nitrogen is obtained from liquefied air and is used industrially to prepare frozen foods. It boils at 77.36 K. (a) What is this temperature in °C? (b) What is this temperature in °F? (c) At the boiling point, the density of the liquid is 809 g/L and that of the gas is 4.566 g/L. How many liters of liquid nitrogen are produced when 895.0 L of nitrogen gas is liquefied at 77.36 K?

1.83 A jogger runs at an average speed of 5.9 mi/h. (a) How fast is she running in m/s? (b) How many kilometers does she run in 98 min? (c) If she starts a run at 11:15 am, what time is it after she covers 4.75×10^4 ft?

1.84 Scenes A and B depict changes in matter at the atomic scale:

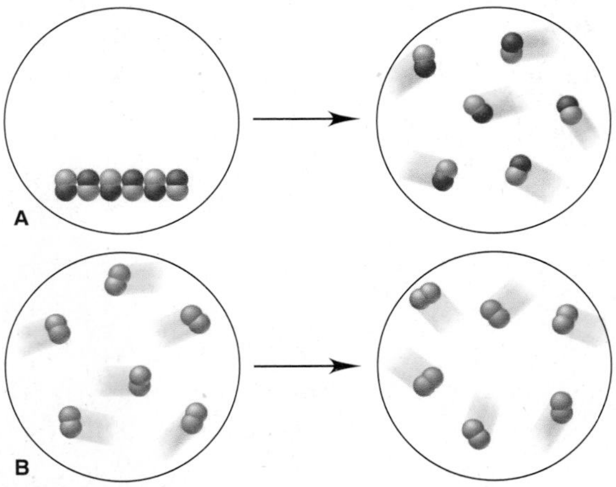

(a) Which show(s) a physical change? (b) Which show(s) a chemical change? (c) Which result(s) in different physical properties? (d) Which result(s) in different chemical properties? (e) Which result(s) in a change in state?

1.85 If a temperature scale were based on the freezing point (5.5°C) and boiling point (80.1°C) of benzene and the temperature difference between these points was divided into 50 units (called °X), what would be the freezing and boiling points of water in °X? (See Figure 1.11, p. 23.)

1.86 Earth's surface area is 5.10×10^8 km^2; its crust has a mean thickness of 35 km and a mean density of 2.8 g/cm^3. The two most abundant elements in the crust are oxygen (4.55×10^5 g/t, where t stands for "metric ton"; 1 t = 1000 kg) and silicon (2.72×10^5 g/t), and the two rarest nonradioactive elements are ruthenium and rhodium, each with an abundance of 1×10^{-4} g/t. What is the total mass of each of these elements in Earth's crust?

The Components of Matter

Concepts and skills to review before you study this chapter

- physical and chemical change (Section 1.1)
- states of matter (Section 1.1)
- attraction and repulsion between charged particles (Section 1.1)
- meaning of a scientific model (Section 1.3)
- SI units and conversion factors (Section 1.5)
- significant figures in calculations (Section 1.6)

2

Look closely at almost any sample of matter—a rock, a piece of wood, a butterfly wing—and you'll see that it's made of smaller parts. With a microscope, you'll see still smaller parts. And, if you could zoom in a billion times closer, you'd find, on the atomic scale, the ultimate particles that make up all things.

Modern scientists are certainly not the first to wonder what things are made of. The philosophers of ancient Greece did too, and most believed that everything was made of one or, at most, a few elemental substances (elements), whose hotness, wetness, hardness, and other properties gave rise to the properties of everything else. Democritus (c. 460–370 BC), the father of atomism, took a different approach, and his reasoning went something like this: if you cut a piece of, say, aluminum foil smaller and smaller, you must eventually reach a particle of aluminum so small that it can no longer be cut. Therefore, matter is ultimately composed of indivisible particles with nothing but empty space between them. He called the particles *atoms* (Greek *atomos,* "uncuttable") and proclaimed: "According to convention, there is a sweet and a bitter, a hot and a cold, and . . . there is order. In truth, there are atoms and a void." But, Aristotle, one of the greatest and most influential philosophers of Western culture, said it was impossible for "nothing" to exist, and the concept of atoms was suppressed for 2000 years.

Finally, in the 17th century, the English scientist Robert Boyle argued that, by definition, an element is composed of "simple Bodies, not made of any other Bodies, of which all mixed Bodies are compounded, and into which they are ultimately resolved," a description remarkably close to our idea of an element, with atoms being the "simple Bodies." The next two centuries saw rapid progress in chemistry and the development of a "billiard-ball" image of the atom. Then, an early 20th-century burst of creativity led to our current model of an atom with a complex internal structure.

IN THIS CHAPTER . . . We examine the properties and composition of matter on the macroscopic and atomic scales.

- We relate the three types of matter—elements, compounds, and mixtures—to the chemical entities they consist of—atoms, ions, and molecules.
- We see how the defining properties of the types of matter relate to laws discovered in the 18th century concerning the masses of substances that react with each other.
- We examine the 19th-century atomic model proposed to explain these laws.
- We describe some 20th-century experiments that led to our current understanding of atomic structure and atomic mass.
- We focus on how the elements are organized in the periodic table and introduce the two major ways that elements combine.
- We derive names and formulas of compounds and calculate their masses.
- We examine the models chemists use to depict molecules.
- We classify mixtures and see how to separate them.
- We present a final overview of the components of matter.

2.1 • ELEMENTS, COMPOUNDS, AND MIXTURES: AN ATOMIC OVERVIEW

Matter can be classified into three types based on its composition—elements, compounds, and mixtures. Elements and compounds are the two kinds of substances: a **substance** is matter whose composition is fixed. Mixtures are not substances because they have a variable composition.

1. *Elements.* An **element** is the simplest type of matter with unique physical and chemical properties. *It consists of only one kind of atom* and, therefore, cannot be broken down into a simpler type of matter by any physical or chemical methods. Each element has a name, such as silicon, oxygen, or copper. A sample of silicon contains only silicon atoms. The *macroscopic* properties of a piece of silicon, such as color, density, and combustibility, are different from those of a piece of copper because the *submicroscopic* properties of silicon atoms are different from those of copper atoms; that is, *each element is unique because the properties of its atoms are unique.*

In nature, most elements exist as populations of atoms, either separated or in contact with each other, depending on the physical state. Figure 2.1A shows atoms of an element in its gaseous state. Several elements occur in molecular form: a **molecule** is an independent structure of two or more atoms bound together (Figure 2.1B). Oxygen, for example, occurs in air as *diatomic* (two-atom) molecules.

2. *Compounds.* A **compound** consists of *two or more different elements that are bonded chemically* (Figure 2.1C). That is, the elements in a compound are not just mixed together: their atoms have joined in a chemical reaction. Many compounds, such as ammonia, water, and carbon dioxide, consist of molecules. But many others, like sodium sulfate (which we'll discuss shortly) and silicon dioxide, do not. No matter what the compound, however, one defining feature is that *the elements are present in fixed parts by mass* (fixed mass ratio). This is so because *each unit of the compound consists of a fixed number of atoms of each element.* For example, consider a sample of ammonia. It is 14 parts nitrogen by mass and 3 parts hydrogen by mass *because* 1 nitrogen atom has 14 times the mass of 1 hydrogen atom, and each ammonia molecule consists of 1 nitrogen atom and 3 hydrogen atoms:

Ammonia gas is 14 parts N by mass and 3 parts H by mass.
1 N atom has 14 times the mass of 1 H atom.
Each ammonia molecule consists of 1 N atom and 3 H atoms.

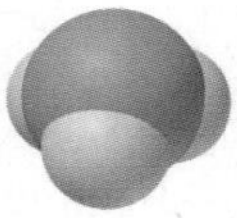

Another defining feature of a compound is that *its properties are different from the properties of its component elements.* Table 2.1 shows a striking example: soft, silvery sodium metal and yellow-green, poisonous chlorine gas are very different from the compound they form—white, crystalline sodium chloride, common table salt!

Unlike an element, a compound *can* be broken down into simpler substances—its component elements. For example, an electric current breaks down molten sodium chloride into metallic sodium and chlorine gas. By definition, this breakdown is a *chemical change,* not a physical one.

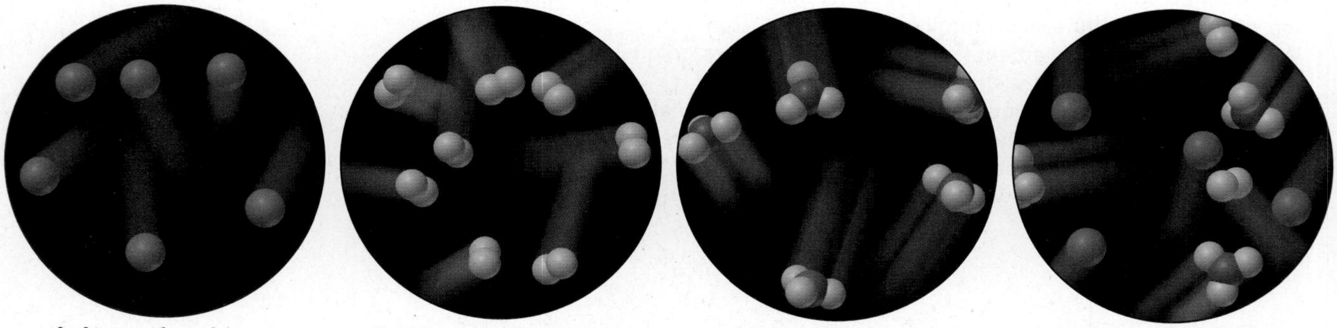

A Atoms of an element | **B** Molecules of an element | **C** Molecules of a compound | **D** Mixture of two elements and a compound

Figure 2.1 Elements, compounds, and mixtures on the atomic scale. The samples depicted here are gases, but the three types of matter also occur as liquids and solids.

Table 2.1 Some Properties of Sodium, Chlorine, and Sodium Chloride

Property	Sodium	+	Chlorine	⟶	Sodium Chloride
Melting point	97.8°C		−101°C		801°C
Boiling point	881.4°C		−34°C		1413°C
Color	Silvery		Yellow-green		Colorless (white)
Density	0.97 g/cm^3		0.0032 g/cm^3		2.16 g/cm^3
Behavior in water	Reacts		Dissolves slightly		Dissolves freely

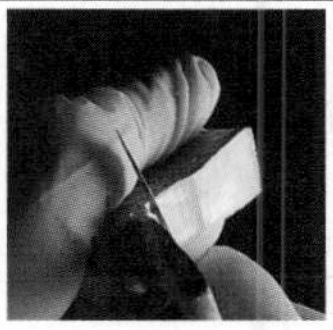

3. *Mixtures.* A **mixture** consists of two or more substances (elements and/or compounds) that are physically intermingled. Because a mixture is *not* a substance, in contrast to a compound, *the components of a mixture* ***can*** *vary in their parts by mass.* A mixture of the compounds sodium chloride and water, for example, can have many different parts by mass of salt to water. On the atomic scale, a mixture consists of the individual units that make up its component elements and/or compounds (Figure 2.1D). It makes sense, then, that *a mixture retains many of the properties of its components.* Saltwater, for instance, is colorless like water and tastes salty like sodium chloride.

Unlike compounds, mixtures can be separated into their components by *physical changes;* chemical changes are not needed. For example, the water in saltwater can be boiled off, a physical process that leaves behind solid sodium chloride. The following sample problem will help differentiate these types of matter.

Sample Problem 2.1 Distinguishing Elements, Compounds, and Mixtures at the Atomic Scale

Problem The scenes below represent atomic-scale views of three samples of matter:

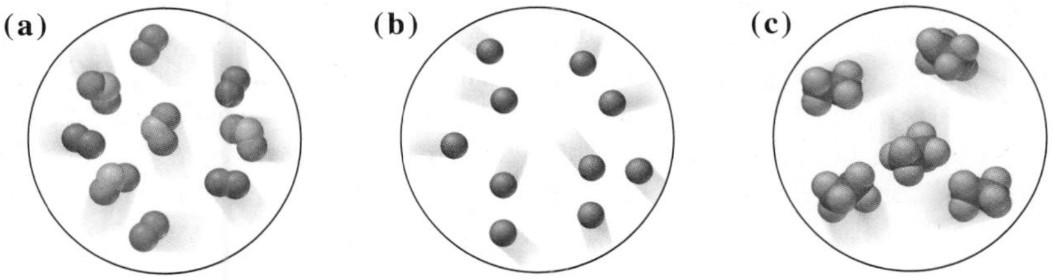

Describe each sample as an element, compound, or mixture.

Plan We have to determine the type of matter by examining the component particles. If a sample contains only one type of particle, it is either an element or a compound; if it contains more than one type, it is a mixture. Particles of an element have only one kind of atom (one color), and particles of a compound have two or more kinds of atoms.

Solution **(a)** Mixture: there are three different types of particles. Two types contain only one kind of atom, either green or purple, so they are elements, and the third type contains two red atoms for every one yellow, so it is a compound.

(b) Element: the sample consists of only blue atoms.

(c) Compound: the sample consists of molecules that each have two black and six blue atoms.

Follow-Up Problem 2.1 Describe the following reaction in terms of elements, compounds, and mixtures. (See Brief Solutions at the end of the chapter.)

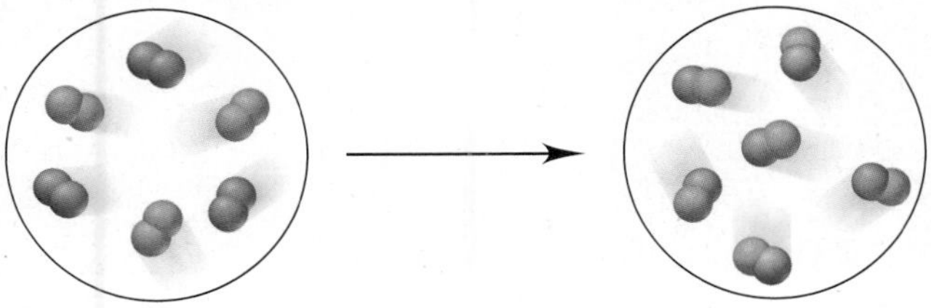

Summary of Section 2.1

- All matter exists as either elements, compounds, or mixtures.
- Elements and compounds are substances, types of matter with a fixed composition.
- An element consists of only one type of atom and occurs as collections of individual atoms or molecules.
- A compound contains two or more elements chemically combined and exhibits different properties from its component elements. The elements occur in fixed parts by mass because each unit of the compound has a fixed number of each type of atom. Only a chemical change can break down a compound into its elements.
- A mixture consists of two or more substances mixed together, not chemically combined. The components retain their individual properties, can be present in any proportion, and can be separated by physical changes.

2.2 • THE OBSERVATIONS THAT LED TO AN ATOMIC VIEW OF MATTER

Any model of the composition of matter had to explain the *law of mass conservation* and the *law of definite (or constant) composition.* As you'll see, an atomic theory developed by John Dalton in the early 19th century explained these mass laws and another now known as the *law of multiple proportions.*

Mass Conservation

The most fundamental chemical observation of the 18th century was the **law of mass conservation:** *the total mass of substances does not change during a chemical reaction.* The *number* of substances may change and, by definition, their properties must, but the *total amount* of matter remains constant. (Lavoisier had first stated this law on the basis of his combustion experiments.) Figure 2.2 illustrates mass conservation because the lead nitrate and sodium chromate solutions (*left*) have the same mass as the solid lead chromate in sodium nitrate solution (*right*) that forms when they react.

Even in a complex biochemical change, such as the metabolism of the sugar glucose, which involves many reactions, mass is conserved:

$$\begin{aligned} \text{180 g glucose} + \text{192 g oxygen gas} &\longrightarrow \text{264 g carbon dioxide} + \text{108 g water} \\ \text{372 g material before} &\longrightarrow \text{372 g material after} \end{aligned}$$

Mass conservation means that, based on all chemical experience, *matter cannot be created or destroyed.*

To be precise about it, we now know, based on the work of Albert Einstein (1879–1955), that the mass before and after a reaction is not *exactly* the same. Some

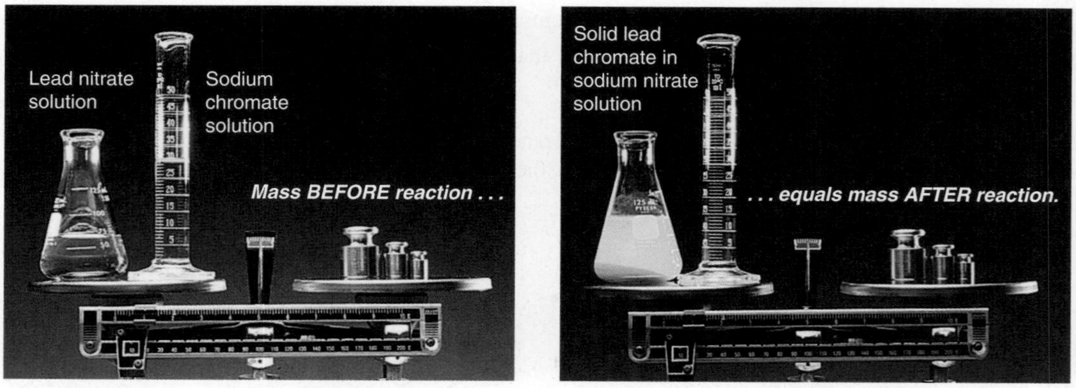

Figure 2.2 The law of mass conservation.

mass is converted to energy, or vice versa, but the difference is too small to measure, even with the best balance. For example, when 100 g of carbon burns, the carbon dioxide formed weighs 0.000000036 g (3.6×10^{-8} g) less than the carbon and oxygen that reacted. Because the energy changes of *chemical* reactions are so small, for all practical purposes, mass *is* conserved. Later in the text, you'll see that energy changes in *nuclear* reactions are so large that mass changes are easy to measure.

Definite Composition

The sodium chloride in your salt shaker is the same substance whether it comes from a salt mine, a salt flat, or any other source. This fact is expressed in the **law of definite (or constant) composition,** which states that *no matter what its source, a particular compound is composed of the same elements in the same parts (fractions) by mass.* The **fraction by mass (mass fraction)** is the part of the compound's mass that each element contributes. It is obtained by dividing the mass of each element by the mass of the compound. The **percent by mass (mass percent, mass %)** is the fraction by mass expressed as a percentage (multiplied by 100).

For an everyday example, consider a box that contains three types of marbles (*right*): yellow ones weigh 1.0 g each, purple 2.0 g each, and red 3.0 g each. Each type makes up a fraction of the total mass of marbles, 16.0 g. The *mass fraction* of yellow marbles is their number times their mass divided by the total mass: (3 × 1.0 g)/16.0 g = 0.19. The *mass percent* (parts per 100 parts) of yellow marbles is 0.19 × 100 = 19% by mass. The purple marbles have a mass fraction of 0.25 and are 25% by mass of the total, and the red marbles have a mass fraction of 0.56 and are 56% by mass.

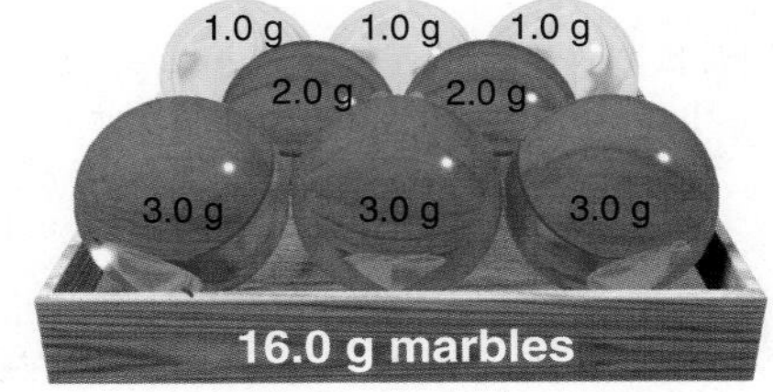

Similarly, in a compound, each element has a *fixed* mass fraction (and mass percent). For example, calcium carbonate, the major compound in seashells, marble, and coral is composed of three elements—calcium, carbon, and oxygen. The following results are obtained from a mass analysis of 20.0 g of calcium carbonate:

Analysis by Mass (grams/20.0 g)	Mass Fraction (parts/1.00 part)	Percent by Mass (parts/100 parts)
8.0 g calcium	0.40 calcium	40% calcium
2.4 g carbon	0.12 carbon	12% carbon
9.6 g oxygen	0.48 oxygen	48% oxygen
20.0 g	1.00 part by mass	100% by mass

The mass of each element depends on the mass of the sample—that is, more than 20.0 g of compound would contain more than 8.0 g of calcium—but *the mass fraction is fixed no matter what the size of the sample.* The sum of the mass fractions (or mass percents) equals 1.00 part (or 100%) by mass. The law of definite composition tells us that pure samples of calcium carbonate, no matter where they come from, always contain 40% calcium, 12% carbon, and 48% oxygen by mass (Figure 2.3).

Because a given element always constitutes the same mass fraction of a given compound, we can use that mass fraction to find the actual mass of the element in any sample of the compound:

$$\text{Mass of element} = \text{mass of compound} \times \frac{\text{part by mass of element}}{\text{one part by mass of compound}}$$

Or, more simply, we can skip the need to find the mass fraction first and use the results of mass analysis directly:

$$\text{Mass of element in sample} = \text{mass of compound in sample} \times \frac{\text{mass of element in compound}}{\text{mass of compound}} \quad (2.1)$$

Figure 2.3 The law of definite composition. Calcium carbonate occurs in many forms (such as marble, *top,* and coral, *bottom*), but the mass percents of its elements are always the same.

Sample Problem 2.2 Calculating the Mass of an Element in a Compound

Problem Pitchblende is the most important compound of uranium. Mass analysis of an 84.2-g sample shows that it contains 71.4 g of uranium, with oxygen the only other element. How many grams of uranium are in 102 kg of pitchblende?

Road Map

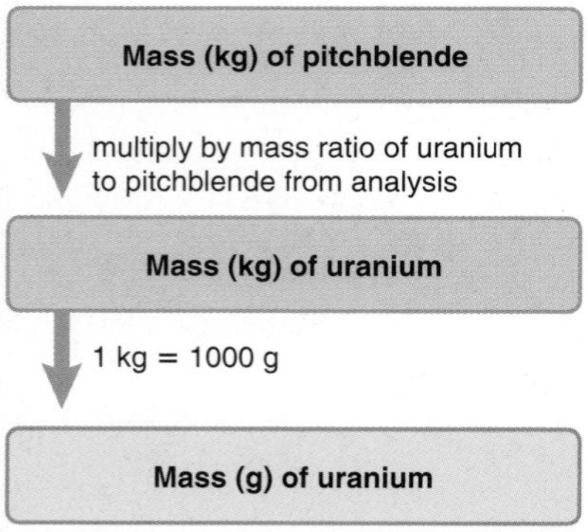

Plan We have to find the mass of uranium in a known mass (102 kg) of pitchblende, given the mass of uranium (71.4 g) in a different mass of pitchblende (84.2 g). The mass ratio of uranium to pitchblende is the same for any sample of pitchblende. Therefore, using Equation 2.1, we multiply the mass (in kg) of the pitchblende sample by the ratio of uranium to pitchblende from the mass analysis. This gives the mass (in kg) of uranium, and we convert kilograms to grams.

Solution Finding the mass (kg) of uranium in 102 kg of pitchblende:

$$\text{Mass (kg) of uranium} = \text{mass (kg) of pitchblende} \times \frac{\text{mass (kg) of uranium in pitchblende}}{\text{mass (kg) of pitchblende}}$$

$$= 102\ \cancel{\text{kg pitchblende}} \times \frac{71.4\ \text{kg uranium}}{84.2\ \cancel{\text{kg pitchblende}}} = 86.5\ \text{kg uranium}$$

Converting the mass of uranium from kg to g:

$$\text{Mass (g) of uranium} = 86.5\ \cancel{\text{kg}}\ \text{uranium} \times \frac{1000\ \text{g}}{1\ \cancel{\text{kg}}} = 8.65\times10^4\ \text{g uranium}$$

Check The analysis showed that most of the mass of pitchblende is due to uranium, so the large mass of uranium makes sense. Rounding off to check the math gives:

$$\sim 100\ \text{kg pitchblende} \times \frac{70}{85} = 82\ \text{kg uranium}$$

Follow-Up Problem 2.2 How many metric tons (t) of oxygen are combined in a sample of pitchblende that contains 2.3 t of uranium? (*Hint:* Remember that oxygen is the only other element present.) See Brief Solutions.

Multiple Proportions

An observation that applies when two elements form more than one compound is now called the **law of multiple proportions:** *if elements A and B react to form two compounds, the different masses of B that combine with a fixed mass of A can be expressed as a ratio of small whole numbers.* Consider two compounds, let's call them I and II, that carbon and oxygen form. These compounds have very different properties: the density of carbon oxide I is 1.25 g/L, whereas that of II is 1.98 g/L; I is poisonous and flammable, but II is not. Mass analysis shows that

Carbon oxide I is 57.1 mass % oxygen and 42.9 mass % carbon
Carbon oxide II is 72.7 mass % oxygen and 27.3 mass % carbon

To see the phenomenon of multiple proportions, we use the mass percents of oxygen and of carbon to find their masses in a given mass, say 100 g, of each compound. Then we divide the mass of oxygen by the mass of carbon in each compound to obtain the mass of oxygen that combines with a fixed mass of carbon:

	Carbon Oxide I	Carbon Oxide II
g oxygen/100 g compound	57.1	72.7
g carbon/100 g compound	42.9	27.3
g oxygen/g carbon	$\frac{57.1}{42.9} = 1.33$	$\frac{72.7}{27.3} = 2.66$

If we then divide the grams of oxygen per gram of carbon in II by that in I, we obtain a ratio of small whole numbers:

$$\frac{2.66\ \text{g oxygen/g carbon in II}}{1.33\ \text{g oxygen/g carbon in I}} = \frac{2}{1}$$

The law of multiple proportions tells us that in two compounds of the same elements, the mass fraction of one element relative to the other element changes in *increments based on ratios of small whole numbers.* In this case, the ratio is 2/1—for a given mass of carbon, compound II contains *2 times* as much oxygen as I, not 1.583 times, 1.716 times, or any other intermediate amount. In the next section, we'll explain the mass laws on the atomic scale.

Summary of Section 2.2

- The law of mass conservation states that the total mass remains constant during a chemical reaction.
- The law of definite composition states that any sample of a given compound has the same elements present in the same parts by mass.
- The law of multiple proportions states that, in different compounds of the same elements, the masses of one element that combine with a fixed mass of the other can be expressed as a ratio of small whole numbers.

2.3 • DALTON'S ATOMIC THEORY

With 200 years of hindsight, it may be easy to see how the mass laws could be explained by an atomic model—matter existing in indestructible units, each with a particular mass—but it was a major breakthrough in 1808 when John Dalton (1766–1844) presented his atomic theory of matter in *A New System of Chemical Philosophy.*

Despite having no formal education, Dalton began teaching science at age 12 and then studied color blindness, a personal affliction still known as *daltonism.* At 21, he started recording daily weather data and continued this project for the rest of his life. His results on humidity and dew point led to a key discovery about gases (Section 5.4) and eventually to his atomic theory.

Postulates of the Atomic Theory

Dalton expressed his theory in a series of postulates. Like most great thinkers, he integrated the ideas of others into his own. As we go through the postulates, presented here in modern terms, let's see which were original and which came from others.

1. All matter consists of **atoms,** tiny indivisible particles of an element that cannot be created or destroyed. (This derives from the "eternal, indestructible atoms" proposed by Democritus more than 2000 years earlier and reflects mass conservation as stated by Lavoisier.)
2. Atoms of one element *cannot* be converted into atoms of another element. In chemical reactions, the atoms of the original substances recombine to form different substances. (This rejects the alchemical belief in the magical transmutation of elements.)
3. Atoms of an element are identical in mass and other properties and are different from atoms of any other element. (This contains Dalton's major new ideas: *unique mass and properties* for the atoms of a given element.)
4. Compounds result from the chemical combination of a specific ratio of atoms of different elements. (This follows directly from the law of definite composition.)

How the Theory Explains the Mass Laws

Let's see how Dalton's postulates explain the mass laws:

- *Mass conservation.* Atoms cannot be created or destroyed (postulate 1) or converted into other types of atoms (postulate 2). Therefore, a chemical reaction, in which atoms are combined differently, cannot possibly result in a mass change.
- *Definite composition.* A compound is a combination of a *specific* ratio of different atoms (postulate 4), each of which has a particular mass (postulate 3). Thus, each element in a compound constitutes a fixed fraction of the total mass.
- *Multiple proportions.* Atoms of an element have the same mass (postulate 3) and are indivisible (postulate 1). The masses of element B that combine with a fixed mass of element A give a small, whole-number ratio because different numbers of B atoms combine with each A atom in different compounds.

The *simplest* arrangement consistent with the mass data for carbon oxides I and II in our earlier example is that one atom of oxygen combines with one atom of carbon in compound I (carbon monoxide) and that two atoms of oxygen combine with one atom of carbon in compound II (carbon dioxide):

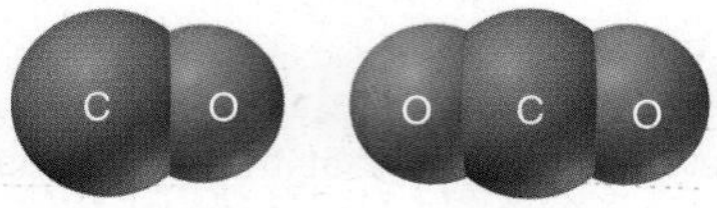

Let's work through a sample problem that reviews the mass laws.

Sample Problem 2.3 Visualizing the Mass Laws

Problem The scenes below represent an atomic-scale view of a chemical reaction:

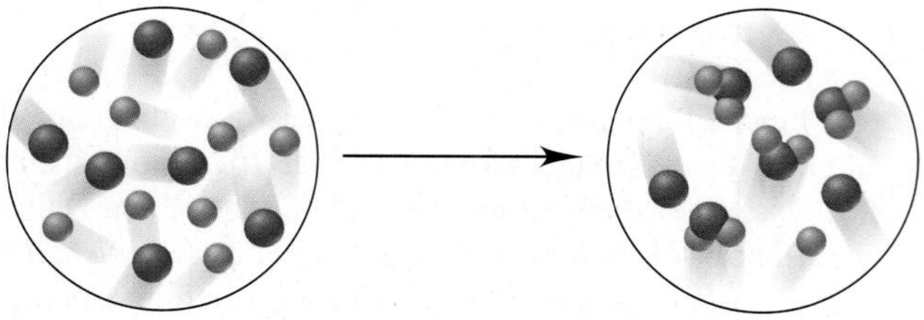

Which of the mass laws—mass conservation, definite composition, or multiple proportions—is (are) illustrated?

Plan From the depictions, we note the numbers, colors, and combinations of atoms (spheres) to see which mass laws pertain. If the numbers of each atom are the same before and after the reaction, the total mass did not change (mass conservation). If a compound forms that always has the same atom ratio, the elements are present in fixed parts by mass (definite composition). When the same elements form different compounds and the ratio of the atoms of one element that combine with one atom of the other element is a small whole number, the ratio of their masses is a small whole number as well (multiple proportions).

Solution There are seven purple and nine green atoms in each circle, so mass is conserved. The compound formed has one purple and two green atoms, so it has definite composition. Only one compound forms, so the law of multiple proportions does not pertain.

Follow-Up Problem 2.3 Which sample(s) best display(s) the fact that compounds of bromine (orange) and fluorine (yellow) exhibit the law of multiple proportions? Explain.

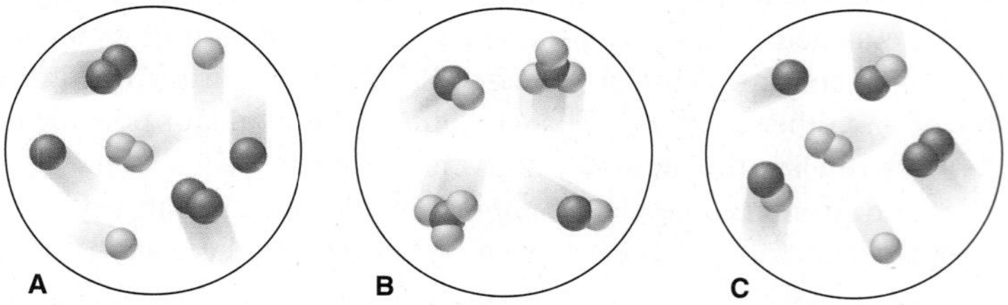

Summary of Section 2.3

- Dalton's atomic theory explained the mass laws by proposing that all matter consists of indivisible, unchangeable atoms of fixed, unique mass.
- Mass is conserved during a reaction because the atoms retain their identities but are combined differently.
- Each compound has a fixed mass fraction of each of its elements because it is composed of a fixed number of each type of atom.
- Different compounds of the same elements exhibit multiple proportions because they each consist of whole atoms.

2.4 • THE OBSERVATIONS THAT LED TO THE NUCLEAR ATOM MODEL

Dalton's model established that masses of reacting elements could be explained in terms of atoms but not why atoms bond as they do: why, for example, do two, and not three, hydrogen atoms bond with one oxygen atom in a water molecule?

Moreover, Dalton's "billiard ball" model of the atom did not predict the existence of subatomic charged particles, which were observed in later experiments that led to the discovery of *electrons* and the atomic *nucleus.* Let's examine some of these experiments and the more complex atomic model that emerged from them.

Discovery of the Electron and Its Properties

For many years, scientists had known that matter and electric charge were related. When amber is rubbed with fur, or glass with silk, positive and negative charges form—the same charges that make your hair crackle and cling to your comb on a dry day. They also knew that an electric current could decompose certain compounds into their elements. But they did not know what a current was made of.

Cathode Rays To discover the nature of an electric current, some investigators tried passing current through nearly evacuated glass tubes fitted with metal electrodes. When the electric power source was turned on, a "ray" could be seen striking the phosphor-coated end of the tube and emitting a glowing spot of light. The rays were called **cathode rays** because they originated at the negative electrode (cathode) and moved to the positive electrode (anode).

Figure 2.4 shows some properties of cathode rays based on these observations. The main conclusion was that *cathode rays consist of negatively charged particles found in all matter.* The rays appear when these particles collide with the few remaining gas molecules in the evacuated tube. Cathode ray particles were later named *electrons.* There are many familiar cases of the effects of charged particles colliding with gases or hitting a phosphor-coated screen:

- In a "neon" sign, electrons collide with the gas particles in the tube, causing them to give off light.
- The aurora borealis, or northern lights (*see photo*), occurs when Earth's magnetic field bends streams of charged particles coming from the Sun, which then collide with gas particles in the atmosphere to give off light.
- In older televisions and computer monitors, the cathode ray passes back and forth over the coated screen, creating a pattern that we see as a picture.

Why do the northern lights glow?

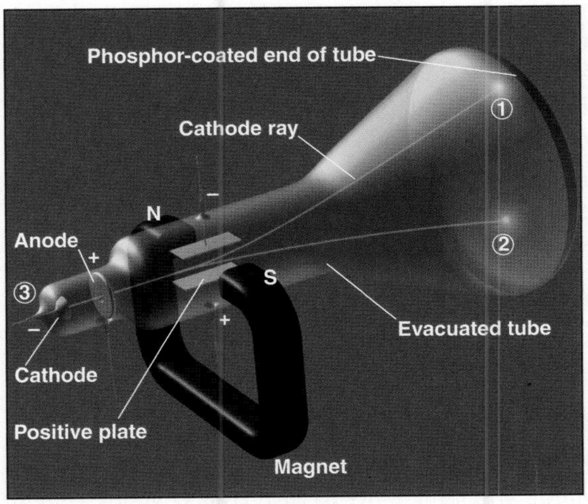

OBSERVATION	CONCLUSION
1. Ray bends in magnetic field.	Consists of charged particles
2. Ray bends toward positive plate in electric field.	Consists of negative particles
3. Ray is identical for any cathode.	Particles found in all matter

Figure 2.4 Observations that established the properties of cathode rays.

Mass and Charge of the Electron Two classic experiments and their conclusion revealed the mass and charge of the electron:

1. *Mass/charge ratio.* In 1897, the British physicist J. J. Thomson (1856–1940) measured the ratio of the mass of a cathode ray particle to its charge. By comparing this value with the mass/charge ratio for the lightest charged particle in solution, Thomson estimated that the cathode ray particle weighed less than $\frac{1}{1000}$ as much as hydrogen, the lightest atom! He was shocked because this implied that, contrary to Dalton's atomic theory, *atoms contain even smaller particles.* Fellow scientists reacted with disbelief to Thomson's conclusion, thinking he was joking.

2. *Charge.* In 1909, the American physicist Robert Millikan (1868–1953) measured the *charge* of the electron. He did so by observing the movement of oil droplets in an apparatus that contained electrically charged plates and an x-ray source (Figure 2.5). X-rays knocked electrons from gas molecules in the air within the apparatus, and the electrons stuck to an oil droplet falling through a hole in a positively charged plate. With the electric field off, Millikan measured the mass of the droplet from its rate of fall. Then, by adjusting the field's strength, he made the droplet hang suspended in the air and, thus, measured its total charge.

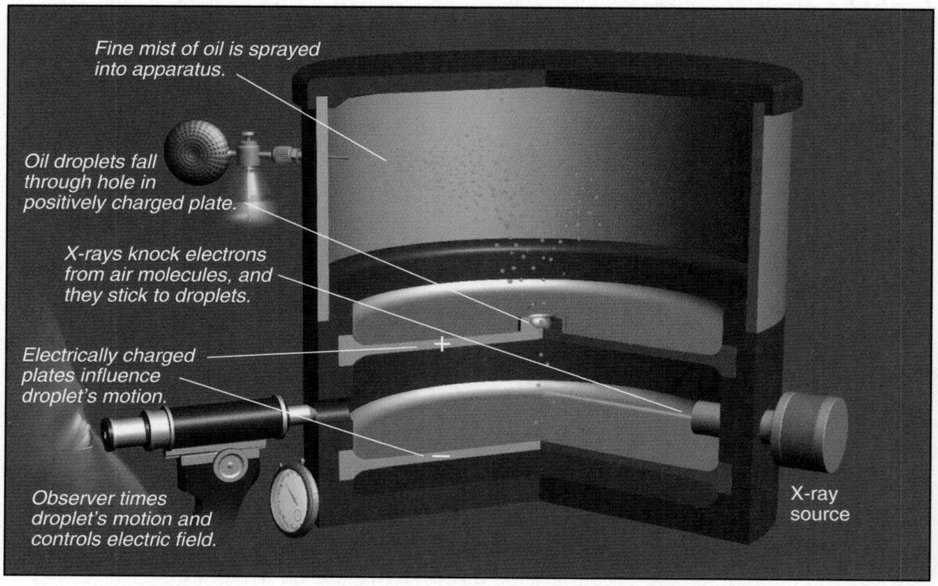

Figure 2.5 **Millikan's oil-drop experiment for measuring an electron's charge.** The total charge on an oil droplet is some whole-number multiple of the charge of the electron.

After many tries, Millikan found that the total charge of the various droplets was always some *whole-number multiple of a minimum charge.* If different oil droplets picked up different numbers of electrons, he reasoned that this minimum charge must be the charge of the electron itself. Remarkably, the value that he calculated over a century ago was within 1% of the modern value of the electron's charge, -1.602×10^{-19} C (C stands for *coulomb,* the SI unit of charge).

3. *Conclusion: calculating the electron's mass.* The electron's mass/charge ratio from work by Thomson and others and the value for the electron's charge can be used to find the electron's mass, which is *extremely* small:

$$\text{Mass of electron} = \frac{\text{mass}}{\cancel{\text{charge}}} \times \cancel{\text{charge}} = \left(-5.686\times10^{-12}\,\frac{\text{kg}}{\cancel{\text{C}}}\right)(-1.602\times10^{-19}\,\cancel{\text{C}})$$
$$= 9.109\times10^{-31}\text{ kg} = 9.109\times10^{-28}\text{ g}$$

Discovery of the Atomic Nucleus

The presence of electrons in all matter posed some major questions about the structure of atoms. Matter is electrically neutral, so atoms must be also. But if atoms contain negatively charged electrons, what positive charges balance them? And if an electron has such a tiny mass, what accounts for an atom's much larger mass? To address these issues, Thomson proposed his "plum-pudding" model—a spherical atom composed of diffuse, positively charged matter with electrons embedded like "raisins in a plum pudding."

In 1910, New Zealand–born physicist Ernest Rutherford (1871–1937) tested this model and obtained an unexpected result (Figure 2.6):

1. *Experimental design.* Figure 2.6B shows the experimental setup, in which tiny, dense, positively charged alpha (α) particles emitted from radium are aimed at gold foil. A circular, zinc-sulfide screen registers the deflection (scattering) of the α particles by emitting light flashes when the particles strike it.
2. *Expected results.* With Thomson's model in mind (Figure 2.6A), Rutherford expected only minor, if any, deflections of the α particles because they should act as bullets and go right through the gold atoms. After all, an electron would not deflect an α particle any more than a Ping-Pong ball would deflect a baseball.
3. *Actual results.* Initial results were consistent with this idea, but then the unexpected happened (Figure 2.6C). As Rutherford recalled: "I remember two or three days later Geiger [one of his coworkers] coming to me in great excitement and saying, 'We have been able to get some of the α particles coming backwards . . .' It was quite the most incredible event that has ever happened to me in my life. It was almost as incredible as if you fired a 15-inch shell at a piece of tissue paper and it came back and hit you." In fact, very few α particles were deflected at all, and only 1 in 20,000 was deflected by more than 90° ("coming backwards").
4. *Rutherford's conclusion.* Rutherford concluded that these few α particles were being repelled by something small, dense, and positive within the gold atoms. Calculations based on the mass, charge, and velocity of the α particles and the proportion of these large-angle deflections showed that
   - An atom is mostly space occupied by electrons.
   - In the center is a tiny region, which Rutherford called the **nucleus,** that contains all the positive charge and essentially all the mass of the atom.

   He proposed that positive particles lay within the nucleus and called them *protons.*

Rutherford's model explained the charged nature of matter, but it could not account for all the atom's mass. After more than 20 years, in 1932, James Chadwick discovered the *neutron,* an uncharged dense particle that also resides in the nucleus.

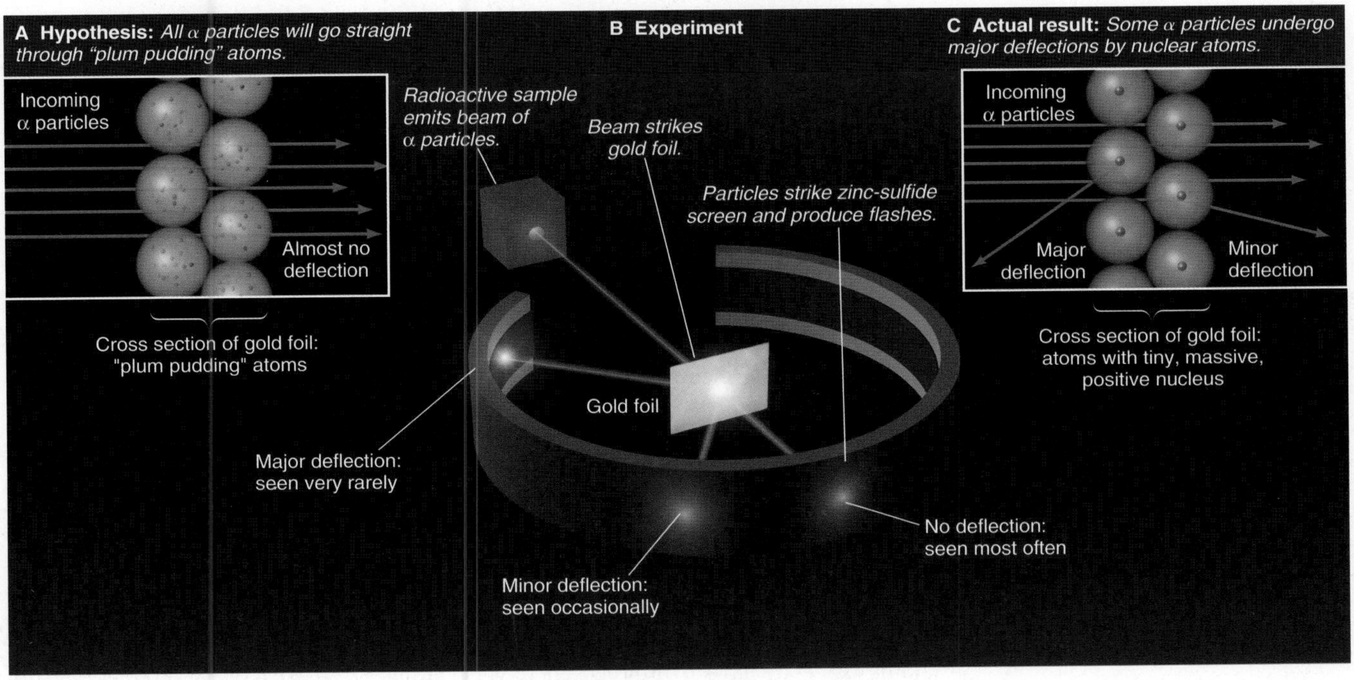

Figure 2.6 Rutherford's α-scattering experiment and discovery of the atomic nucleus.

Summary of Section 2.4

- Several major discoveries at the turn of the 20th century resolved questions about Dalton's model and led to our current model of atomic structure.
- Cathode rays were shown to consist of negative particles (electrons) that exist in all matter. J. J. Thomson measured their mass/charge ratio and concluded that they are much smaller and lighter than atoms.
- Robert Millikan determined the charge of the electron, which he combined with other data to calculate its mass.
- Ernest Rutherford proposed that atoms consist of a tiny, massive, positive nucleus surrounded by electrons.

2.5 • THE ATOMIC THEORY TODAY

Dalton's model of an indivisible particle has given way to our current model of an atom with an elaborate internal architecture of subatomic particles. In this section, we examine that model and see how Dalton's theory stands up today.

The Tiny, Massive Nucleus A few analogies can help you grasp the incredible properties of the atomic nucleus. A nucleus the size of the period at the end of a sentence would weigh about 100 tons, as much as 50 cars! An atom the size of the Houston Astrodome would have a nucleus the size of a green pea that would contain virtually all its mass. If the nucleus were the size depicted at the right in Figure 2.7 (about 1 cm across), the atom would be about 200 m across, or more than the length of two football fields!

Structure of the Atom

An *atom* is an electrically neutral, spherical entity composed of a positively charged central nucleus surrounded by one or more negatively charged electrons (Figure 2.7). The electrons move rapidly within the available volume, held there by the attraction of the nucleus. An atom's diameter ($\sim 1 \times 10^{-10}$ m) is about 20,000 times the diameter of its nucleus ($\sim 5 \times 10^{-15}$ m). The nucleus contributes 99.97% of the atom's mass, occupies only about 1 quadrillionth of its volume, and is incredibly dense: about 10^{14} g/mL!

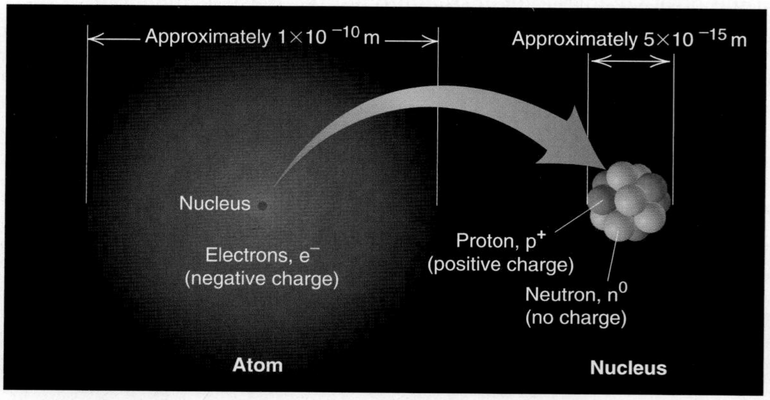

Figure 2.7 General features of the atom.

An atomic nucleus consists of protons and neutrons (the only exception is the simplest hydrogen nucleus, which is a single proton). The **proton (p^+)** has a positive charge, and the **neutron (n^0)** has no charge; thus, the positive charge of the nucleus results from its protons. The *magnitudes* of the charges possessed by a proton and by an **electron (e^-)** are equal, but the *signs* of the charges are opposite. *An atom is neutral because the number of protons in the nucleus equals the number of electrons surrounding the nucleus.* Some properties of these three subatomic particles are listed in Table 2.2 on the next page.

Atomic Number, Mass Number, and Atomic Symbol

The **atomic number (Z)** of an element equals the number of protons in the nucleus of each of its atoms. *All atoms of an element have the same atomic number, and the atomic number of each element is different from that of any other element.* All carbon atoms ($Z = 6$) have 6 protons, all oxygen atoms ($Z = 8$) have 8 protons, and all

Table 2.2 Properties of the Three Key Subatomic Properties

	Charge		Mass		
Name (Symbol)	**Relative**	**Absolute (C)***	**Relative (amu)†**	**Absolute (g)**	**Location in Atom**
Proton (p^+)	1+	$+1.60218\times10^{-19}$	1.00727	1.67262×10^{-24}	Nucleus
Neutron (n^0)	0	0	1.00866	1.67493×10^{-24}	Nucleus
Electron (e^-)	1−	-1.60218×10^{-19}	0.00054858	9.10939×10^{-24}	Outside nucleus

*The coulomb (C) is the SI unit of charge.
†The atomic mass unit (amu) equals 1.66054×10^{-24} g; discussed later in this section.

uranium atoms (Z = 92) have 92 protons. There are currently 117 known elements, of which 90 occur in nature and 27 have been synthesized by nuclear scientists.

The **mass number (*A*)** is the total number of protons and neutrons in the nucleus of an atom. Each proton and each neutron contributes one unit to the mass number. Thus, a carbon atom with 6 protons and 6 neutrons in its nucleus has a mass number of 12, and a uranium atom with 92 protons and 146 neutrons in its nucleus has a mass number of 238.

The **atomic symbol** (or *element symbol*) of an element is based on its English, Latin, or Greek name, such as C for carbon, S for sulfur, and Na for sodium (Latin *natrium*). Often written with the symbol are the atomic number (Z) as a left *sub*script and the mass number (A) as a left *super*script, so element X would be $^{A}_{Z}X$. Since the mass number is the sum of protons and neutrons, the number of neutrons (N) equals the mass number minus the atomic number:

$$\text{Number of neutrons} = \text{mass number} - \text{atomic number}, \quad \text{or} \quad N = A - Z \qquad (2.2)$$

Thus, a chlorine atom, symbolized $^{35}_{17}Cl$, has A = 35, Z = 17, and N = 35 − 17 = 18. Because each element has its own atomic number, we also know the atomic number given the symbol. For example, instead of writing $^{12}_{6}C$ for carbon with mass number 12, we can write ^{12}C (spoken "carbon twelve"), with Z = 6 understood. Another way to name this atom is carbon-12.

Isotopes

All atoms of an element have the same atomic number but not the same mass number. **Isotopes** of an element are atoms that have *different numbers of neutrons* and therefore different mass numbers. For example, all carbon atoms (Z = 6) have 6 protons and 6 electrons, but only 98.89% of naturally occurring carbon atoms have 6 neutrons (A = 12). A small percentage (1.11%) have 7 neutrons (A = 13), and even fewer (less than 0.01%) have 8 (A = 14). These are carbon's three naturally occurring isotopes—^{12}C, ^{13}C, and ^{14}C. *A natural sample of carbon has these three isotopes in these relative proportions.* Five other carbon isotopes—^{9}C, ^{10}C, ^{11}C, ^{15}C, and ^{16}C—have been created in the laboratory. Figure 2.8 depicts the atomic number, mass number, and symbol for four atoms, two of which are isotopes of the element uranium.

The chemical properties of an element are primarily determined by the number of electrons, so *all isotopes of an element have nearly identical chemical behavior,* even though they have different masses.

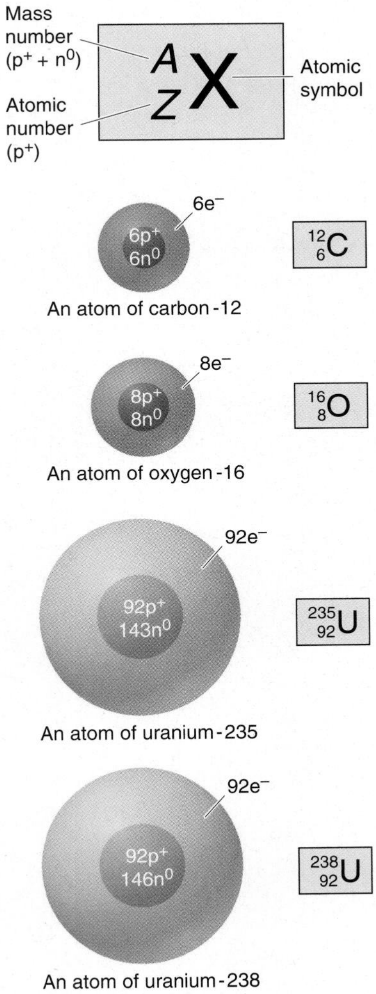

Figure 2.8 The $^{A}_{Z}X$ notations and spherical representations for four atoms. (The nuclei are not drawn to scale.)

Sample Problem 2.4 Determining the Number of Subatomic Particles in the Isotopes of an Element

Problem Silicon (Si) is a major component of semiconductor chips. It has three naturally occurring isotopes: ^{28}Si, ^{29}Si, and ^{30}Si. Determine the numbers of protons, neutrons, and electrons in each silicon isotope.

Plan The mass number (*A;* left superscript) of each of the three isotopes is given, which is the sum of protons and neutrons. From the elements list on the text's inside front cover, we find the atomic number (*Z,* number of protons), which equals the number of electrons. We obtain the number of neutrons by subtracting *Z* from *A* (Equation 2.2).

Solution From the elements list, the atomic number of silicon is 14. Therefore,

$$^{28}Si \text{ has } 14p^+,\ 14e^-,\text{ and } 14n^0\,(28 - 14)$$
$$^{29}Si \text{ has } 14p^+,\ 14e^-,\text{ and } 15n^0\,(29 - 14)$$
$$^{30}Si \text{ has } 14p^+,\ 14e^-,\text{ and } 16n^0\,(30 - 14)$$

Follow-Up Problem 2.4 How many protons, neutrons, and electrons are in **(a)** $^{11}_{5}Q$? **(b)** $^{41}_{20}R$? **(c)** $^{131}_{53}X$? What elements do Q, R, and X represent?

Atomic Masses of the Elements

The mass of an atom is measured *relative* to the mass of an atomic standard. The modern standard is the carbon-12 atom, whose mass is defined as *exactly* 12 atomic mass units. Thus, the **atomic mass unit (amu)** is $\frac{1}{12}$ the mass of a carbon-12 atom. Based on this standard, the ^1H atom has a mass of 1.008 amu; in other words, a ^{12}C atom has almost 12 times the mass of an ^1H atom. We will continue to use the term *atomic mass unit* in the text, although the name of the unit has been changed to the **dalton (Da);** thus, one ^{12}C atom has a mass of 12 daltons (12 Da, or 12 amu). The atomic mass unit is a unit of relative mass, but it has an absolute mass of 1.66054×10^{-24} g.

The isotopic makeup of an element is determined by **mass spectrometry,** a method for measuring the relative masses and abundances of atomic-scale particles very precisely (which we discuss in the Tools of the Laboratory essay). For example, using a mass spectrometer, we measure the mass ratio of ^{28}Si to ^{12}C as

$$\frac{\text{Mass of }^{28}\text{Si atom}}{\text{Mass of }^{12}\text{C standard}} = 2.331411$$

From this mass ratio, we find the **isotopic mass** of the ^{28}Si atom, the relative mass of this silicon isotope:

$$\begin{aligned}\text{Isotopic mass of }^{28}\text{Si} &= \text{measured mass ratio} \times \text{mass of }^{12}\text{C}\\ &= 2.331411 \times 12 \text{ amu} = 27.97693 \text{ amu}\end{aligned}$$

Along with the isotopic mass, the mass spectrometer gives the relative abundance as a percentage (or fraction) of each isotope in a sample of the element. For example, the relative abundance of ^{28}Si is 92.23% (or 0.9223).

From such data, we can obtain the **atomic mass** (also called *atomic weight*) of an element, the *average* of the masses of its naturally occurring isotopes weighted according to their abundances. Each naturally occurring isotope of an element contributes a certain portion to the atomic mass. For instance, multiplying the isotopic mass of ^{28}Si by its fractional abundance gives the portion of the atomic mass of Si contributed by ^{28}Si:

$$\text{Portion of Si atomic mass from }^{28}\text{Si} = 27.97693 \text{ amu} \times 0.9223 = 25.8031 \text{ amu}$$
(retaining two additional significant figures)

Similar calculations give the portions contributed by ^{29}Si (28.976495 amu × 0.0467 = 1.3532 amu) and by ^{30}Si (29.973770 amu × 0.0310 = 0.9292 amu). Adding the three portions together (rounding to two decimal places at the end) gives the atomic mass of silicon:

$$\begin{aligned}\text{Atomic mass of Si} &= 25.8031 \text{ amu} + 1.3532 \text{ amu} + 0.9292 \text{ amu}\\ &= 28.0855 \text{ amu} = 28.09 \text{ amu}\end{aligned}$$

The atomic mass is an average value; thus, while no individual silicon atom has a mass of 28.09 amu, in the laboratory, we consider a sample of silicon to consist of atoms with this average mass.

TOOLS OF THE LABORATORY | Mass Spectrometry

Mass spectrometry is a powerful technique for measuring the mass and abundance of charged particles from their mass/charge ratio (*m/e*). When a high-energy electron collides with a particle, say, an atom of neon-20, one of the atom's electrons is knocked away and the resulting particle has one positive charge, Ne^+ (Figure B2.1). Thus, its *m/e* equals the mass divided by 1+.

Figure B2.2, part A, depicts the core of one type of mass spectrometer. The sample is introduced (and vaporized if liquid or solid), then bombarded by high-energy electrons to form positively charged particles, in this case, of the different neon isotopes. These are attracted toward a series of negatively charged plates with slits in them. Some particles pass through the slits into an evacuated tube exposed to a magnetic field. As the particles enter this region, their paths are bent, the lightest particles (lowest *m/e*) are deflected most and the heaviest particles (highest *m/e*) least. At the end of the magnetic region, the particles strike a detector, which records their relative positions and abundances (Figure B2.2, parts B and C).

Mass spectrometry is now employed to measure the mass of virtually any atom, molecule, or molecular fragment. The technique is being used to study catalyst surfaces, forensic materials, fuel mixtures, medicinal agents, and many other samples, especially proteins (Figure B2.2, part D); in fact, John B. Fenn and Koichi Tanaka shared part of the 2002 Nobel Prize in chemistry for developing methods to study proteins by mass spectrometry.

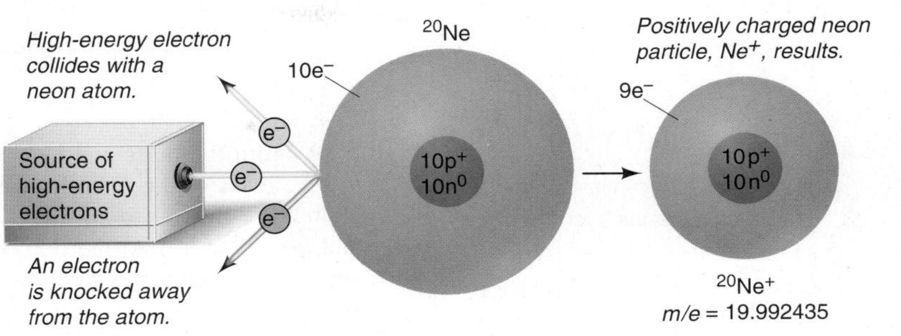

Figure B2.1 Formation of a positively charged neon particle (Ne^+).

Problems

B2.1 Chlorine has two naturally occurring isotopes, ^{35}Cl (abundance 76%) and ^{37}Cl (abundance 24%), and it occurs as diatomic (two-atom) molecules. In a mass spectrum, peaks are seen for the molecule and for the separated atoms.
(a) How many peaks are in the mass spectrum?
(b) What is the *m/e* value of the heaviest particle and of the lightest particle?

B2.2 When a sample of pure carbon is analyzed by mass spectrometry, peaks X, Y, and Z are obtained. Peak Y is taller than X and Z, and Z is taller than X. What is the *m/e* value of the isotope responsible for peak Z?

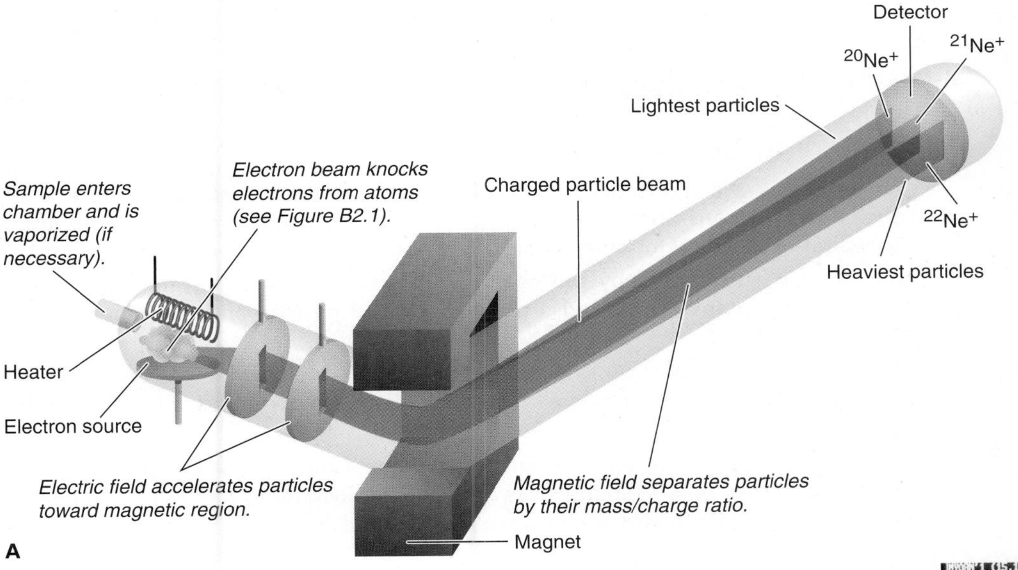

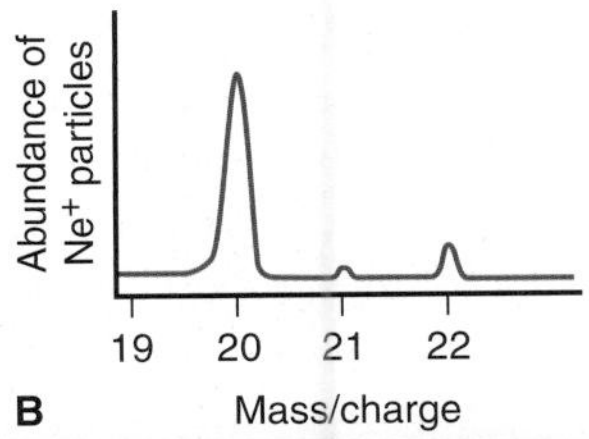

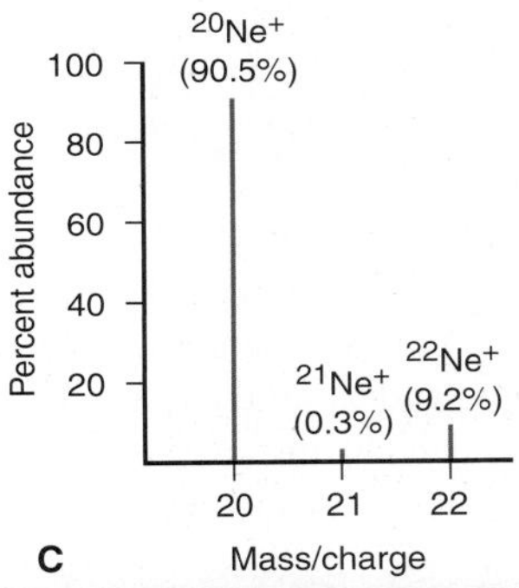

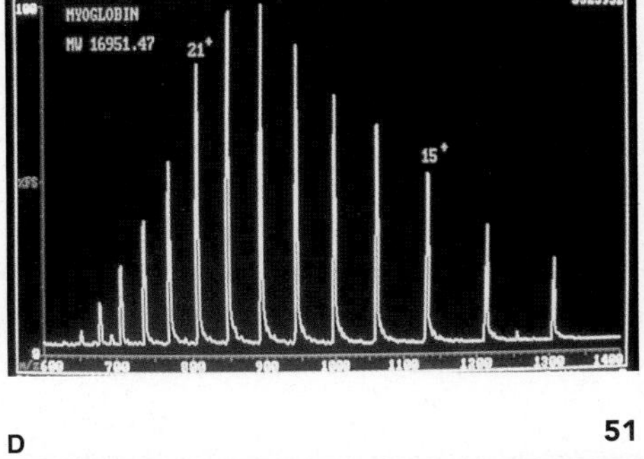

Figure B2.2 The mass spectrometer and its data. **A,** Particles are separated by their *m/e* values. **B,** The relative abundances of three Ne isotopes. **C,** The percent abundance of each isotope. **D,** The mass spectrum of a protein molecule. Each peak represents a molecular fragment.

Sample Problem 2.5 Calculating the Atomic Mass of an Element

Problem Silver (Ag; $Z = 47$) has 46 known isotopes, but only two occur naturally, ^{107}Ag and ^{109}Ag. Given the following data, calculate the atomic mass of Ag:

Isotope	Mass (amu)	Abundance (%)
^{107}Ag	106.90509	51.84
^{109}Ag	108.90476	48.16

Road Map

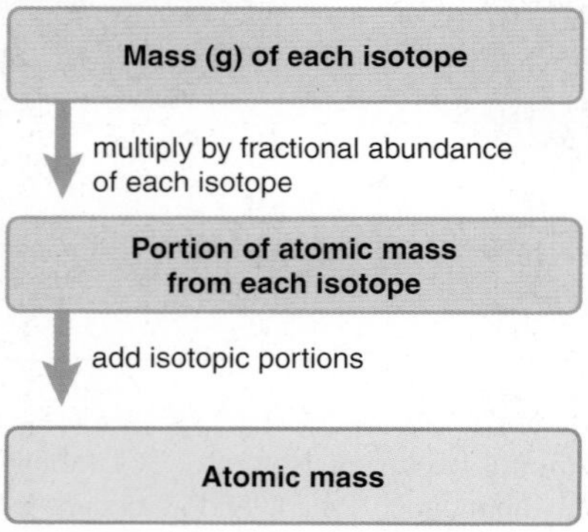

Plan From the mass and abundance of the two Ag isotopes, we have to find the atomic mass of Ag (weighted average of the isotopic masses). We divide each percent abundance by 100 to get the fractional abundance and then multiply that by each isotopic mass to find the portion of the atomic mass contributed by each isotope. The sum of the isotopic portions is the atomic mass.

Solution Finding the fractional abundances:

$$\text{Fractional abundance of } ^{107}\text{Ag} = 51.84/100 = 0.5184; \text{ similarly, } ^{109}\text{Ag} = 0.4816$$

Finding the portion of the atomic mass from each isotope:

$$\begin{aligned}\text{Portion of atomic mass from } ^{107}\text{Ag} &= \text{isotopic mass} \times \text{fractional abundance}\\ &= 106.90509 \text{ amu} \times 0.5184 = 55.42 \text{ amu}\\ \text{Portion of atomic mass from } ^{109}\text{Ag} &= 108.90476 \text{ amu} \times 0.4816 = 52.45 \text{ amu}\end{aligned}$$

Finding the atomic mass of silver:

$$\text{Atomic mass of Ag} = 55.42 \text{ amu} + 52.45 \text{ amu} = 107.87 \text{ amu}$$

Check The individual portions seem right: ~ 100 amu $\times$ 0.50 = 50 amu. The portions should be almost the same because the two isotopic abundances are almost the same. We rounded each portion to four significant figures because that is the number of significant figures in the abundance values. This is the correct atomic mass (to two decimal places); in the list of elements (inside front cover), it is rounded to 107.9 amu.

Follow-Up Problem 2.5 Boron (B; $Z = 5$) has two naturally occurring isotopes. Find the percent abundances of ^{10}B and ^{11}B given these data: atomic mass of B = 10.81 amu, isotopic mass of ^{10}B = 10.0129 amu, and isotopic mass of ^{11}B = 11.0093 amu. (*Hint:* The sum of the fractional abundances is 1. If x = abundance of ^{10}B, then $1 - x$ = abundance of ^{11}B.)

Summary of Section 2.5

- An atom has a central nucleus, which contains positively charged protons and uncharged neutrons and is surrounded by negatively charged electrons. An atom is neutral because the number of electrons equals the number of protons.
- An atom is represented by the notation $^{A}_{Z}X$, in which Z is the atomic number (number of protons), A the mass number (sum of protons and neutrons), and X the atomic symbol.
- An element occurs naturally as a mixture of isotopes, atoms with the same number of protons but different numbers of neutrons. Each isotope has a mass relative to the ^{12}C mass standard.
- The atomic mass of an element is the average of its isotopic masses weighted according to their natural abundances and is determined using modern instruments, especially the mass spectrometer.

2.6 • ELEMENTS: A FIRST LOOK AT THE PERIODIC TABLE

At the end of the 18th century, Lavoisier compiled a list of the 23 elements known at that time; by 1870, 65 were known; by 1925, 88; today, there are 117 and still counting! By the mid-19th century, enormous amounts of information concerning reactions, properties, and atomic masses of the elements had been accumulated. Several researchers noted recurring, or *periodic,* patterns of behavior and proposed schemes to organize the elements according to some fundamental property.

In 1871, the Russian chemist Dmitri Mendeleev (1836–1907) published the most successful of these organizing schemes as a table of the elements listed by increasing atomic mass and arranged so that elements with similar chemical properties fell in the same column. The modern **periodic table of the elements,** based on Mendeleev's version (but arranged by *atomic number,* not mass), is one of the great classifying schemes in science and an indispensable tool to chemists—and chemistry students.

Organization of the Periodic Table One common version of the modern periodic table appears in Figure 2.9 (and inside the front cover). It is formatted as follows:

1. Each element has a box that contains its atomic number, atomic symbol, and atomic mass. (A mass in parentheses is the mass number of the most stable isotope of that element.) The boxes lie, from left to right, in order of *increasing atomic number* (number of protons in the nucleus).
2. The boxes are arranged into a grid of **periods** (horizontal rows) and **groups** (vertical columns). Each period has a number from 1 to 7. Each group has a number from 1 to 8 *and* either the letter A or B. A newer system, with group numbers from 1 to 18 but no letters, appears in parentheses under the number-letter designations. (The text uses the number-letter system and shows the newer numbering system in parentheses.)
3. The eight A groups (two on the left and six on the right) contain the *main-group elements.* The ten B groups, located between Groups 2A(2) and 3A(13), contain the *transition elements.* Two horizontal series of *inner transition elements,* the lanthanides and the actinides, fit *between* the elements in Group 3B(3) and Group 4B(4) and are placed below the main body of the table.

Figure 2.9 The modern periodic table. As of mid-2010, elements 113–116 and 118 had not been named.

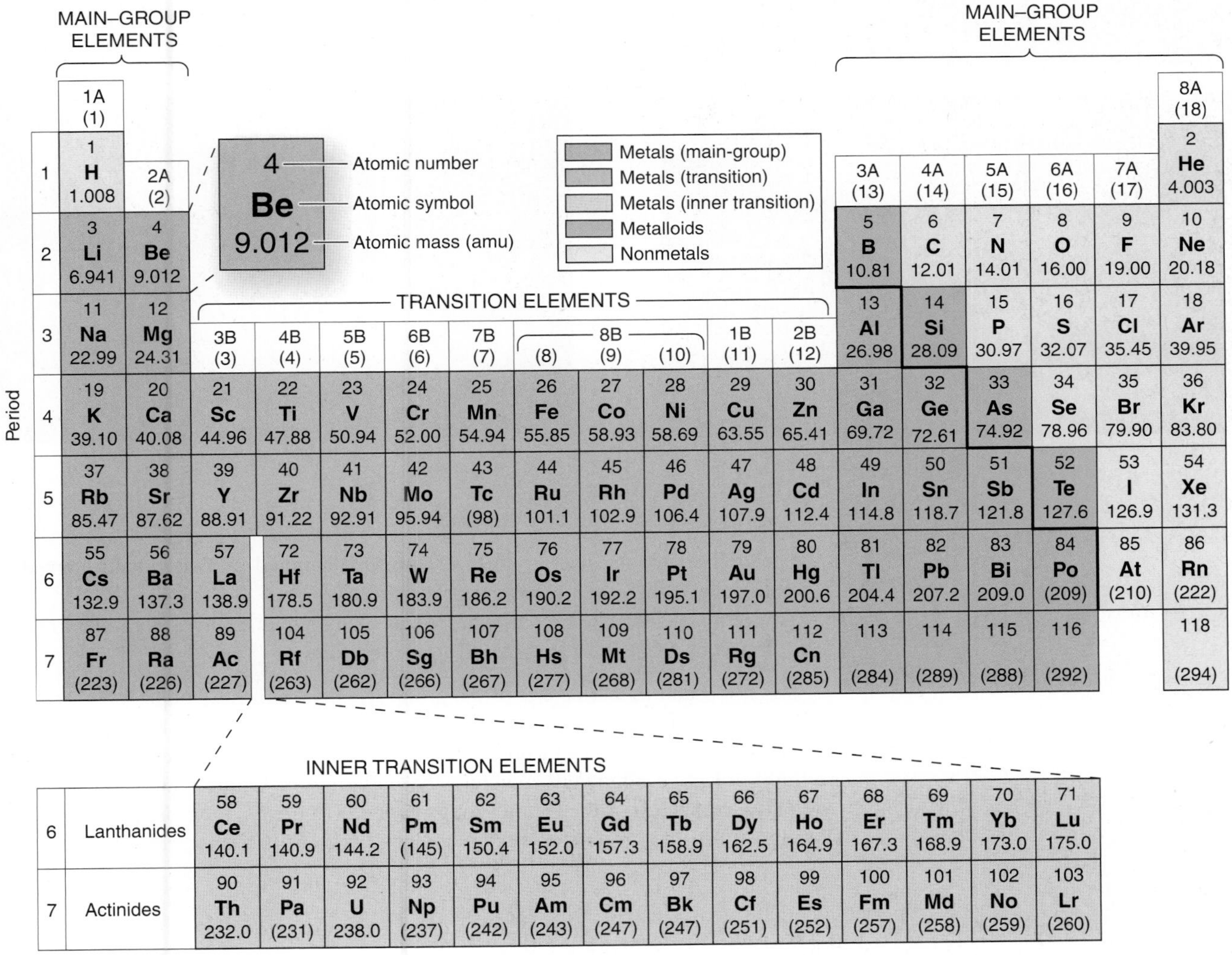

Classifying the Elements One of the clearest ways to classify the elements is as metals, nonmetals, and metalloids. The "staircase" line that runs from the top of Group 3A(13) to the bottom of Group 6A(16) is a dividing line:

- The **metals** (three shades of blue in Figure 2.9) lie in the large lower-left portion of the table. About three-quarters of the elements are metals, including many main-group elements and all the transition and inner transition elements. They are generally shiny solids at room temperature (mercury is the only liquid) that conduct heat and electricity well. They can be tooled into sheets (are malleable) and wires (are ductile).
- The **nonmetals** (yellow) lie in the small upper-right portion of the table. They are generally gases or dull, brittle solids at room temperature (bromine is the only liquid) and conduct heat and electricity poorly.
- The **metalloids** (green; also called **semimetals**), which lie along the staircase line, have properties between those of metals and nonmetals.

Figure 2.10 shows examples of these three classes of elements.

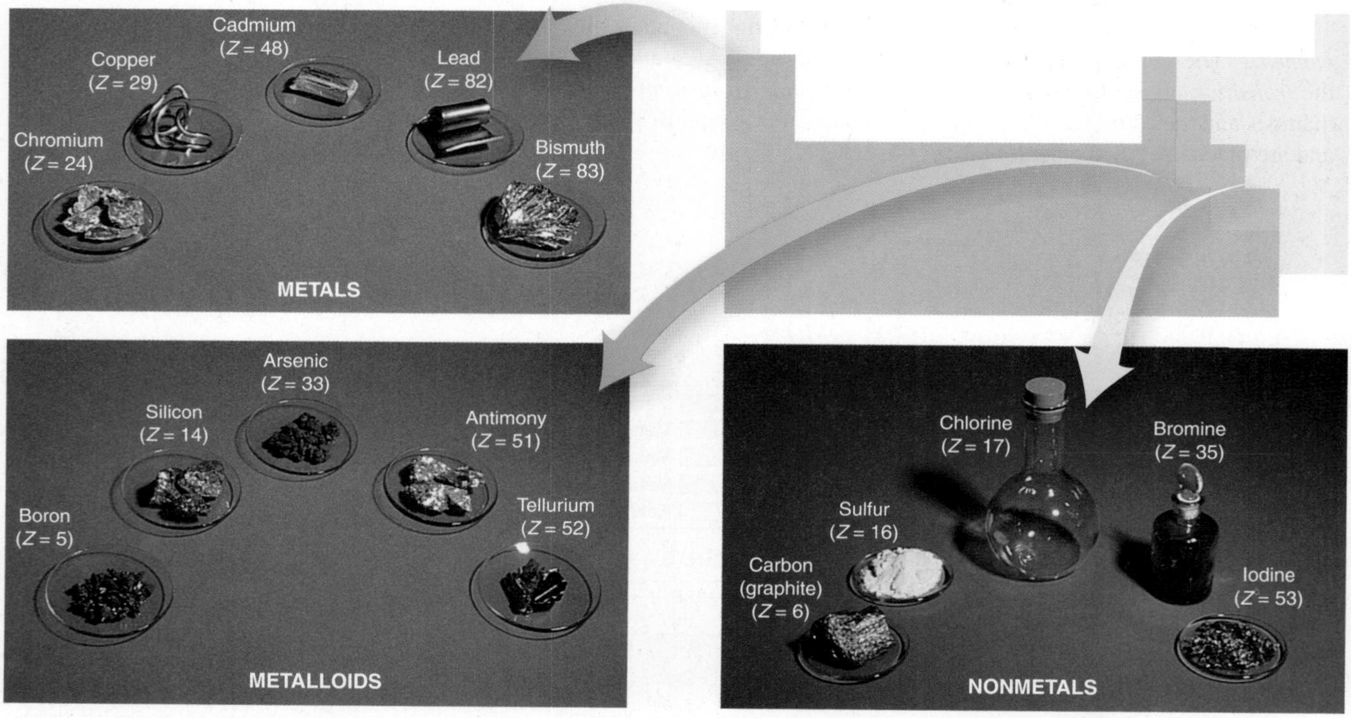

Figure 2.10 Some metals, metalloids, and nonmetals.

Two major points to keep in mind:

1. In general, elements in a group have **similar** chemical properties and elements in a period have **different** chemical properties.
2. Despite this classification of three types of elements, in reality, there is a gradation in properties from left to right and top to bottom.

It is important to learn some of the group (family) names. Group 1A(1), except for hydrogen, consists of the *alkali metals,* and Group 2A(2) consists of the *alkaline earth metals.* Both groups consist of highly reactive elements. The *halogens,* Group 7A(17), are highly reactive nonmetals, whereas the *noble gases,* Group 8A(18), are relatively unreactive nonmetals. Other main groups [3A(13) to 6A(16)] are often named for the first element in the group; for example, Group 6A(16) is the *oxygen family.*

Two of the major branches of chemistry have traditionally been defined by the elements that each studies. *Organic chemistry* studies the compounds of carbon, specifically those that contain hydrogen and often oxygen, nitrogen, and a few other elements. This branch is concerned with fuels, drugs, dyes, and the like. *Inorganic chemistry,* on the other hand, focuses on the compounds of all the other elements and is concerned with catalysts, electronic materials, metal alloys, mineral salts, and the like. With the explosive growth in biomedical and materials sciences, the line between these branches has all but disappeared.

Summary of Section 2.6

- In the periodic table, the elements are arranged by atomic number into horizontal periods and vertical groups.
- Nonmetals appear in the upper-right portion of the table, metalloids lie along a staircase line, and metals fill the rest of the table.
- Elements within a group have similar behavior, whereas elements within a period have dissimilar behavior.

2.7 • COMPOUNDS: INTRODUCTION TO BONDING

Only a few elements occur free in nature. The noble gases—helium (He), neon (Ne), argon (Ar), krypton (Kr), xenon (Xe), and radon (Rn)—occur in air as separate atoms. In addition to occurring in compounds, oxygen (O), nitrogen (N), and sulfur (S) occur in their most common elemental form as the molecules O_2, N_2, and S_8, and carbon (C) occurs in vast, nearly pure deposits of coal. And some metals—copper (Cu), silver (Ag), gold (Au), and platinum (Pt)—are also sometimes found uncombined. But, aside from these few exceptions, *the overwhelming majority of elements occur in compounds combined with other elements.*

Elements combine in two general ways and both involve *the electrons of the atoms of interacting elements:*

1. *Transferring electrons* from one element to another to form **ionic compounds**
2. *Sharing electrons* between atoms of different elements to form **covalent compounds**

These processes generate **chemical bonds,** the forces that hold the atoms together in a compound. This section introduces compound formation, which we'll discuss in much more detail in later chapters.

The Formation of Ionic Compounds

Ionic compounds are composed of **ions,** charged particles that form when an atom (or small group of atoms) gains or loses one or more electrons. The simplest type of ionic compound is a **binary ionic compound,** one composed of two elements. It typically forms *when a metal reacts with a nonmetal:*

- Each metal atom *loses* one or more electrons and becomes a **cation,** a positively charged ion.
- Each nonmetal atom *gains* one or more of the electrons lost by the metal atom and becomes an **anion,** a negatively charged ion.

In effect, the metal atoms *transfer electrons* to the nonmetal atoms. The resulting large numbers of cations and anions attract each other and form the ionic compound. A cation or anion derived from a single atom is called a **monatomic ion;** we'll discuss polyatomic ions, those derived from a small group of atoms, later.

The Case of Sodium Chloride *All binary ionic compounds are solid arrays of oppositely charged ions.* The formation of the binary ionic compound sodium chloride, common table salt, from its elements is depicted in Figure 2.11. In the electron transfer, a sodium atom *loses* one electron and forms a sodium cation, Na^+. (The charge on the ion is written as a *right superscript.*) A chlorine atom *gains* the electron and becomes a chloride anion, Cl^-. (The name change when the nonmetal atom becomes an anion is discussed in the next section.) The oppositely charged ions (Na^+ and Cl^-) attract each other, and the similarly charged ions (Na^+ and Na^+, or Cl^- and Cl^-) repel each other. The resulting solid aggregation is a regular array of alternating Na^+ and Cl^- ions that extends in all three dimensions. Even the tiniest visible grain of table salt contains an enormous number of sodium and chloride ions.

Coulomb's Law The strength of the ionic bonding depends to a great extent on the net strength of these attractions and repulsions and is described by *Coulomb's law,* which can be expressed as follows: *the energy of attraction (or repulsion) between two particles is directly proportional to the product of the charges and inversely proportional to the distance between them.*

$$\text{Energy} \propto \frac{\text{charge 1} \times \text{charge 2}}{\text{distance}}$$

In other words, as is summarized in Figure 2.12,

- Ions with higher charges attract (or repel) each other more strongly than ions with lower charges.
- Smaller ions attract (or repel) each other more strongly than larger ions, because their charges are closer together.

Predicting the Number of Electrons Lost or Gained *Ionic compounds are neutral* because they contain equal numbers of positive and negative *charges.* Thus, there are equal numbers of Na^+ and Cl^- ions in sodium chloride, because both ions are singly charged. But there are two Na^+ ions for each oxide ion, O^{2-}, in sodium oxide because two 1+ ions balance one 2− ion.

Can we predict the number of electrons a given atom will lose or gain when it forms an ion? For A-group elements, we usually find that metal atoms lose electrons and nonmetal atoms gain electrons to *form ions with the same number of electrons as in an atom of the nearest noble gas* [Group 8A(18)]. Noble gases have a stability that is related to their number (and arrangement) of electrons. Thus, a sodium atom ($11e^-$) can attain the stability of a neon atom ($10e^-$), the nearest noble gas, by

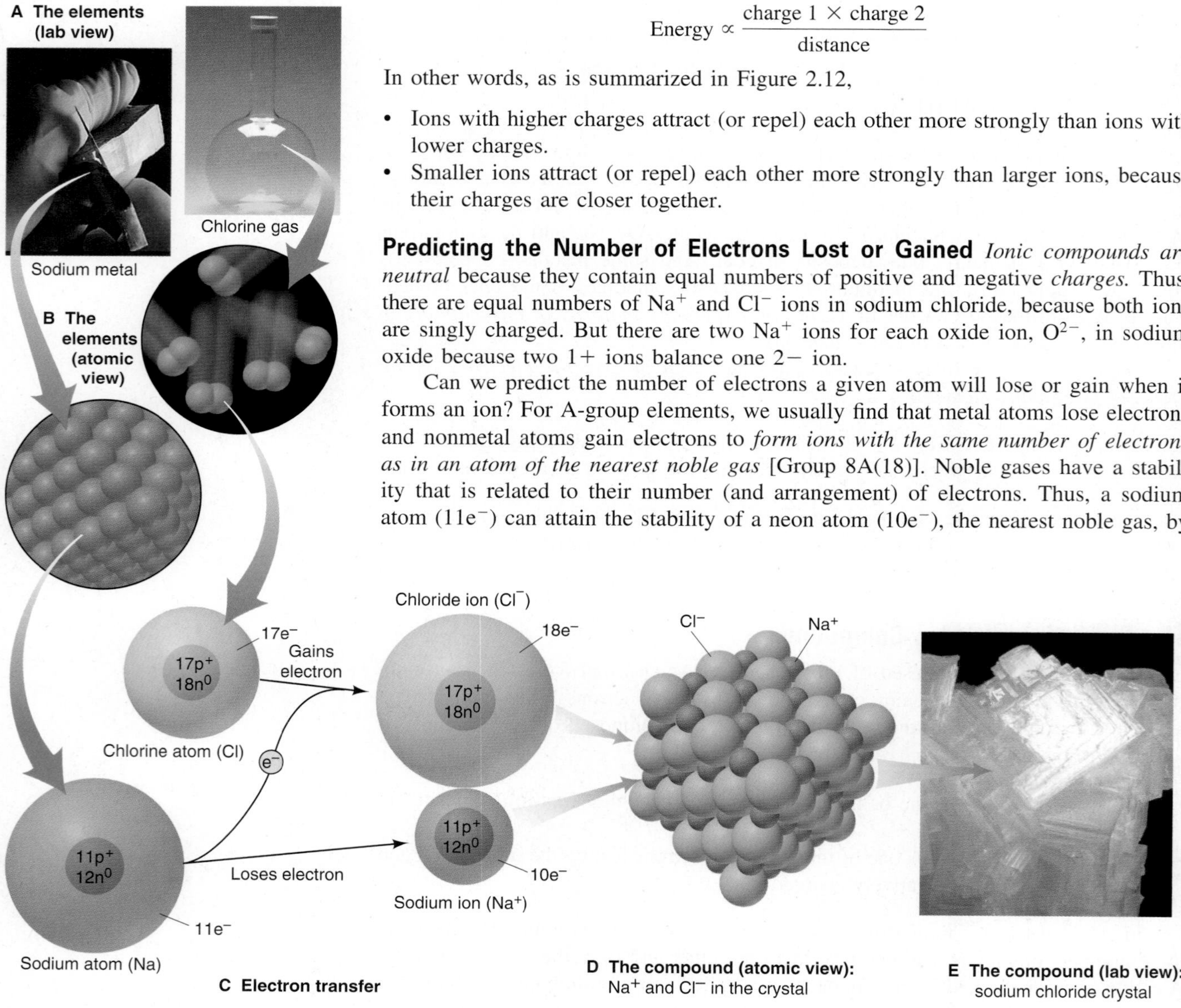

Figure 2.11 The formation of an ionic compound. **A,** The two elements as seen in the laboratory. **B,** The elements on the atomic scale. **C,** The electron transfer from Na atom to Cl atom to form Na^+ and Cl^- ions. **D,** Countless Na^+ and Cl^- ions attract each other and form a regular three-dimensional array. **E,** Crystalline NaCl occurs naturally as the mineral halite.

losing one electron. Similarly, a chlorine atom ($17e^-$) attains the stability of an argon atom ($18e^-$), its nearest noble gas, by gaining one electron. Thus, in general, when an element located near a noble gas forms a monatomic ion,

- *Metals lose electrons:* elements in Group 1A(1) lose one electron, elements in Group 2A(2) lose two, and aluminum in Group 3A(13) loses three.
- *Nonmetals gain electrons:* elements in Group 7A(17) gain one electron, oxygen and sulfur in Group 6A(16) gain two, and nitrogen in Group 5A(15) gains three.

In the periodic table in Figure 2.9, it looks like the elements in Group 7A(17) are "closer" to the noble gases than the elements in Group 1A(1). In truth, both groups are only one electron away from the number of electrons in the nearest noble gas. Figure 2.13 shows a periodic table of monatomic ions that is cut and rejoined as a cylinder. Note that fluorine (F; Z = 9) has one electron *fewer* than the noble gas neon (Ne; Z = 10) and sodium (Na; Z = 11) has one electron *more;* thus, they form the F^- and Na^+ ions. Similarly, oxygen (O; Z = 8) gains two electrons and magnesium (Mg; Z = 12) loses two to form the O^{2-} and Mg^{2+} ions and attain the same number of electrons as neon. In Figure 2.13, species in a row have the same number of electrons.

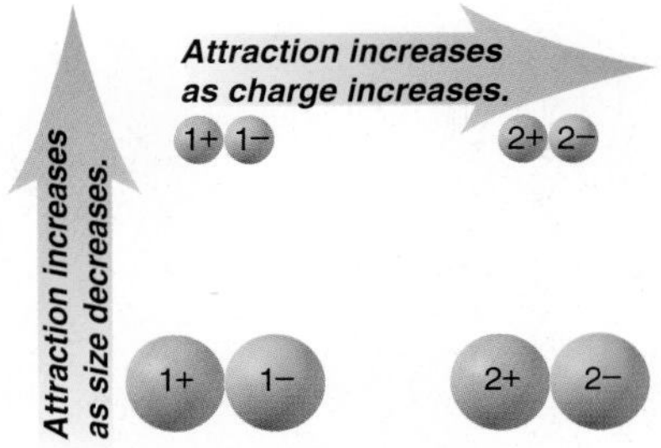

Figure 2.12 Factors that influence the strength of ionic bonding.

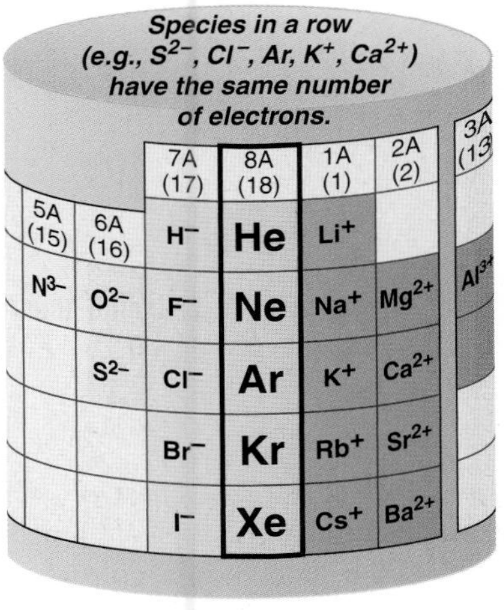

Figure 2.13 The relationship between ion formed and the nearest noble gas.

Sample Problem 2.6 Predicting the Ion an Element Forms

Problem What monatomic ions do the following elements form?
(a) Iodine (Z = 53) **(b)** Calcium (Z = 20) **(c)** Aluminum (Z = 13)

Plan We use the given Z value to find the element in the periodic table and see where its group lies relative to the noble gases. Elements in Groups 1A, 2A, and 3A *lose* electrons to attain the same number as the nearest noble gas and become positive ions; those in Groups 5A, 6A, and 7A *gain* electrons and become negative ions.

Solution (a) I^- Iodine ($_{53}I$) is in Group 7A(17), the halogens. Like any member of this group, it gains 1 electron to attain the same number as the nearest Group 8A(18) member, in this case, $_{54}Xe$.
(b) Ca^{2+} Calcium ($_{20}Ca$) is in Group 2A(2), the alkaline earth metals. Like any Group 2A member, it loses 2 electrons to attain the same number as the nearest noble gas, $_{18}Ar$.
(c) Al^{3+} Aluminum ($_{13}Al$) is a metal in the boron family [Group 3A(13)] and thus loses 3 electrons to attain the same number as its nearest noble gas, $_{10}Ne$.

Follow-Up Problem 2.6 What monatomic ion does each of the following elements form: **(a)** $_{16}S$; **(b)** $_{37}Rb$; **(c)** $_{56}Ba$?

Atoms far apart: *No interactions.*

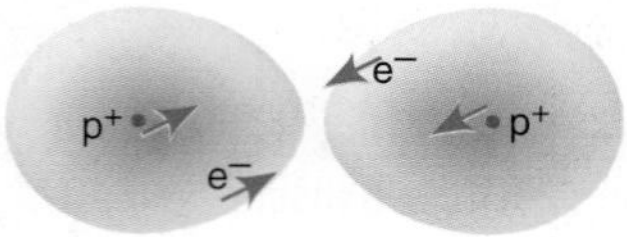

Atoms closer: *Attractions* (green arrows) *between nucleus of one atom and electron of the other increase. Repulsions between nuclei and between electrons are very weak.*

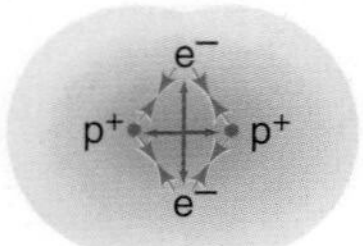

Optimum distance: *H_2 molecule forms because attractions* (green arrows) *balance repulsions* (red arrows).

Figure 2.14 Formation of a covalent bond between two H atoms.

The Formation of Covalent Compounds

Covalent compounds form when elements share electrons, which usually occurs between nonmetals. The simplest case of electron sharing occurs not in a compound but between two hydrogen atoms (H; $Z = 1$). Imagine two separated H atoms approaching each other (Figure 2.14). As they get closer, the nucleus of each atom attracts the electron of the other atom more and more strongly. As the separated atoms begin to interpenetrate each other, repulsions between the nuclei and between the electrons begin to increase. At some optimum distance between the nuclei, the two atoms form a **covalent bond,** a pair of electrons mutually attracted by the two nuclei. The result is a hydrogen molecule, in which each electron no longer "belongs" to a particular H atom: the two electrons are *shared* by the two nuclei. A sample of hydrogen gas consists of these diatomic molecules (H_2)—pairs of atoms that are chemically bound and behave as an independent unit—*not* separate H atoms. Figure 2.15 shows other nonmetals that exist as molecules at room temperature.

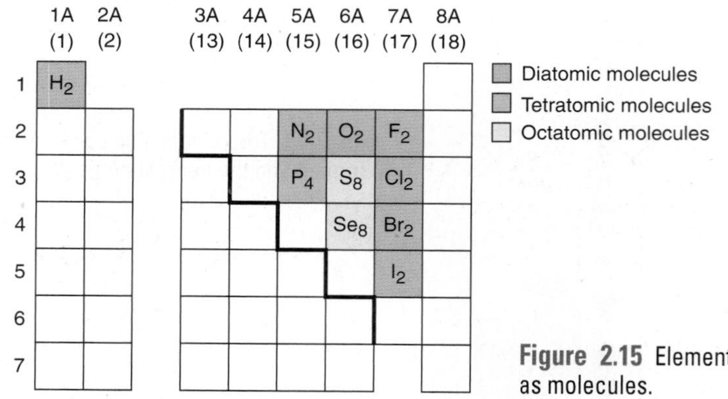

Figure 2.15 Elements that occur as molecules.

Atoms of different elements share electrons to form the molecules of a covalent compound. A sample of hydrogen fluoride, for example, consists of molecules in which one H atom forms a covalent bond with one F atom; water consists of molecules in which one O atom forms covalent bonds with two H atoms:

Hydrogen fluoride, HF 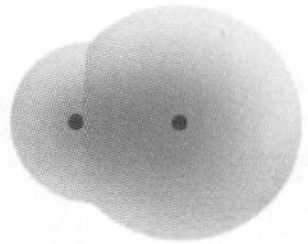

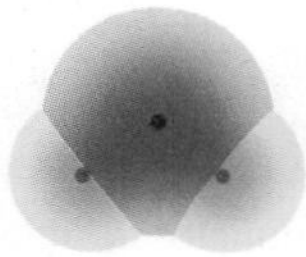 Water, H_2O

Distinguishing the Entities in Covalent and Ionic Substances There is a key distinction between the chemical entities in covalent substances and in ionic substances. *Most covalent substances consist of molecules.* A cup of water, for example, consists of individual water molecules lying near each other. In contrast, under ordinary conditions, *there are no molecules in an ionic compound.* A piece of sodium chloride, for example, is a continuous array in three dimensions of oppositely charged sodium and chloride ions, *not* a collection of individual sodium chloride "molecules."

Another key distinction between covalent and ionic substances concerns the nature of the particles attracting each other. Covalent bonding involves the mutual attraction between two (positively charged) nuclei and the two (negatively charged) electrons that reside between them. Ionic bonding involves the mutual attraction between positive and negative ions.

Polyatomic Ions: Covalent Bonds Within Ions Many ionic compounds contain **polyatomic ions,** which consist of two or more atoms bonded *covalently* and have a net positive or negative charge. For example, Figure 2.16 shows that a crystalline form of calcium carbonate (*left*) occurs on the atomic scale as an array of polyatomic carbonate anions and monatomic calcium cations (*center*). The carbonate ion (*right*) consists of a carbon atom covalently bonded to three oxygen atoms, and two additional electrons give the ion its 2− charge. In many reactions, the polyatomic ion stays together as a unit.

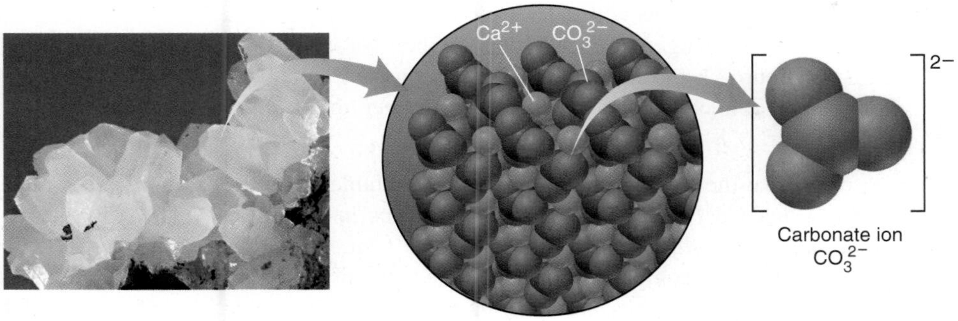

Figure 2.16 The carbonate ion in calcium carbonate.

Summary of Section 2.7

- Although a few elements occur uncombined in nature, the great majority exist in compounds.
- Ionic compounds form when a metal *transfers* electrons to a nonmetal, and the resulting positive and negative ions attract each other to form a three-dimensional array. In many cases, metal atoms lose and nonmetal atoms gain enough electrons to attain the same number of electrons as in atoms of the nearest noble gas.
- Covalent compounds form when elements, usually nonmetals, *share* electrons. Each covalent bond is an electron pair mutually attracted by two atomic nuclei.
- Monatomic ions are derived from single atoms. Polyatomic ions consist of two or more covalently bonded atoms that have a net positive or negative charge due to a deficit or excess of electrons.

2.8 • FORMULAS, NAMES, AND MASSES OF COMPOUNDS

In a **chemical formula,** element symbols and, often, numerical subscripts show the type and number of each atom in the smallest unit of the substance. In this section, you'll learn how to write the names and formulas of ionic and simple covalent compounds, how to calculate the mass of a compound from its formula, and how to visualize molecules with three-dimensional models. To make learning the names and formula of compounds easier, we'll rely on various rules, so be prepared for a bit of memorization and a lot of practice.

Binary Ionic Compounds

Let's begin with two general rules:

- For *all* ionic compounds, *names and formulas give the positive ion (cation) first and the negative ion (anion) second.*
- For all *binary* ionic compounds, *the name of the cation is the name of the metal, and the name of the anion has the suffix -ide added to the root of the name of the nonmetal.*

For example, the anion formed from brom*ine* is named brom*ide* (brom+ide). Therefore, the compound formed from the metal calcium and the nonmetal bromine is named *calcium bromide.*

Table 2.3 Common Monatomic Ions*

Charge	Formula	Name
Cations		
1+	H^+	hydrogen
	Li^+	**lithium**
	Na^+	**sodium**
	K^+	**potassium**
	Cs^+	cesium
	Ag^+	**silver**
2+	**Mg^{2+}**	**magnesium**
	Ca^{2+}	**calcium**
	Sr^{2+}	strontium
	Ba^{2+}	**barium**
	Zn^{2+}	**zinc**
	Cd^{2+}	cadmium
3+	Al^{3+}	aluminum
Anions		
1−	H^-	hydride
	F^-	**fluoride**
	Cl^-	**chloride**
	Br^-	**bromide**
	I^-	**iodide**
2−	**O^{2-}**	**oxide**
	S^{2-}	**sulfide**
3−	N^{3-}	nitride

*Listed by charge; those in **boldface** are most common.

In general, if the metal of a binary ionic compound is a main-group element (A groups) it usually forms a single type of ion; if it is a transition element (B groups), it often forms more than one. We discuss each case in turn.

Compounds of Elements That Form One Ion The periodic table presents some key points about the formulas of main-group monatomic ions:

- Monatomic ions of main-group elements have the same ionic charge; the alkali metals—Li, Na, K, Rb, Cs, and Fr—form ions with a 1+ charge; the halogens—F, Cl, Br, and I—form ions with a 1− charge; and so forth.
- For cations, ion charge equals A-group number: Na is in Group 1A and forms Na^+, Ba is in Group 2A and forms Ba^{2+}. (Exceptions in Figure 2.17 are Sn^{2+} and Pb^{2+}.)
- For anions, ion charge equals A-group number minus 8; for example, S is in Group 6A ($6 - 8 = -2$) and thus forms S^{2-}.

Try to memorize the A-group monatomic ions in Table 2.3 (all of these listed except Ag^+, Zn^{2+}, and Cd^{2+}) according to their positions in Figure 2.17. These ions have *the same number of electrons as an atom of the nearest noble gas.*

Because an ionic compound consists of an array of ions rather than separate molecules, its formula represents the **formula unit,** the *relative* numbers of cations and anions in the compound. The compound has zero net charge, so the positive charges of the cations balance the negative charges of the anions. For example, calcium bromide is composed of Ca^{2+} ions and Br^- ions, so two Br^- balance each Ca^{2+}. The formula is $CaBr_2$, not Ca_2Br. In this and all other formulas,

- The subscript refers to the element *preceding* it.
- The *subscript 1 is understood* from the presence of the element symbol alone (that is, we do not write Ca_1Br_2).
- The charge (without the sign) of one ion becomes the subscript of the other:

$$Ca^{2+}\ Br^{1-} \quad \text{gives} \quad Ca_1Br_2 \quad \text{or} \quad CaBr_2$$

- Reduce the subscripts to the smallest whole numbers that retain the ratio of ions. Thus, for example, for the Ca^{2+} and O^{2-} ions in calcium oxide, we get Ca_2O_2, which we reduce to the formula CaO.*

*Compounds of the mercury(I) ion, such as Hg_2Cl_2, and peroxides of the alkali metals, such as Na_2O_2, are the only two common exceptions to this step; in fact, reducing the subscripts for these compounds would give the incorrect formulas HgCl and NaO.

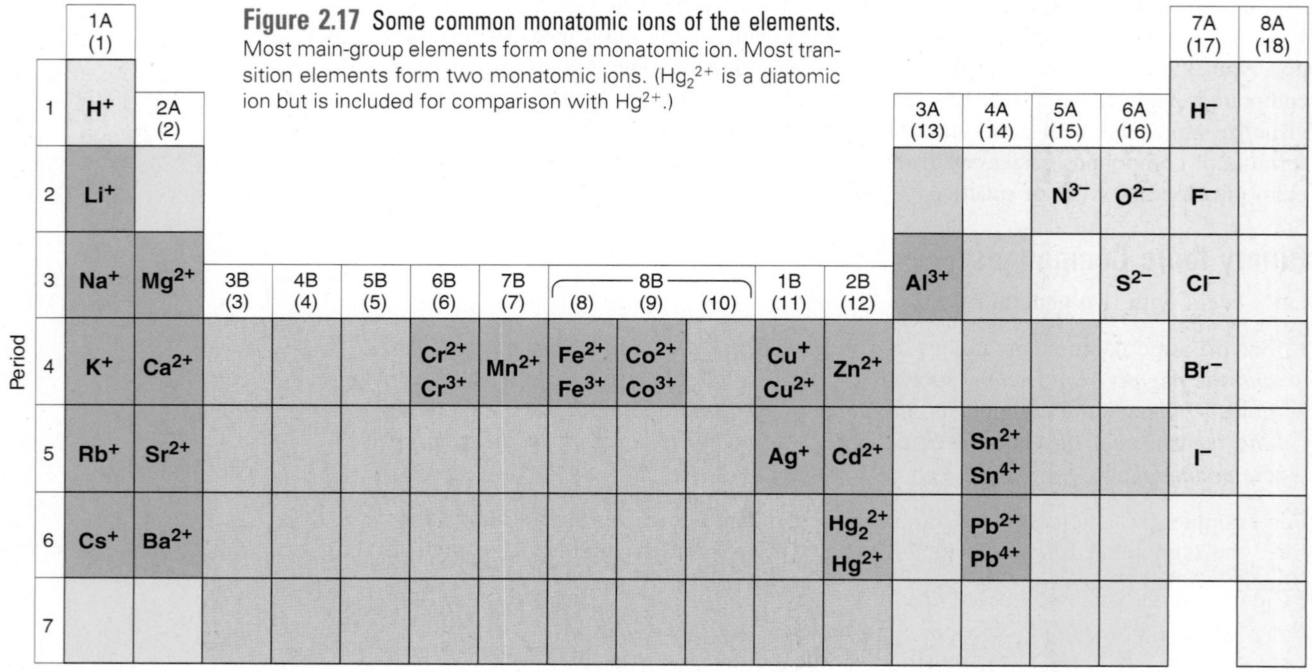

Figure 2.17 Some common monatomic ions of the elements. Most main-group elements form one monatomic ion. Most transition elements form two monatomic ions. (Hg_2^{2+} is a diatomic ion but is included for comparison with Hg^{2+}.)

The following two sample problems apply these rules. In Sample Problem 2.7, we name the compound from its elements, and in Sample Problem 2.8, we find the formula.

Sample Problem 2.7 Naming Binary Ionic Compounds

Problem Name the ionic compound formed from the following pairs of elements:
(a) Magnesium and nitrogen
(b) Iodine and cadmium
(c) Strontium and fluorine
(d) Sulfur and cesium

Plan The key to naming a binary ionic compound is to recognize which element is the metal and which is the nonmetal. When in doubt, check the periodic table. We place the cation name first, add the suffix *-ide* to the nonmetal root, and place the anion name last.

Solution **(a)** Magnes*ium* is the metal; *nitr-* is the nonmetal root: magnesium nitride
(b) Cadm*ium* is the metal; *iod-* is the nonmetal root: cadmium iodide
(c) Stront*ium* is the metal; *fluor-* is the nonmetal root: strontium fluoride (Note the spelling is fl*uo*ride, not fl*ou*ride.)
(d) Ces*ium* is the metal; *sulf-* is the nonmetal root: cesium sulfide

Follow-Up Problem 2.7 For the following ionic compounds, give the name and periodic table group number of each element present:
(a) Zinc oxide
(b) Silver bromide
(c) Lithium chloride
(d) Aluminum sulfide

Sample Problem 2.8 Determining Formulas of Binary Ionic Compounds

Problem Write formulas for the compounds named in Sample Problem 2.7.

Plan We write the formula by finding the smallest number of each ion that gives the neutral compound. These numbers appear as *right subscripts* to the element symbol.

Solution
(a) Mg^{2+} and N^{3-}; three Mg^{2+} ions (6+) balance two N^{3-} ions (6−): Mg_3N_2
(b) Cd^{2+} and I^-; one Cd^{2+} ion (2+) balances two I^- ions (2−): CdI_2
(c) Sr^{2+} and F^-; one Sr^{2+} ion (2+) balances two F^- ions (2−): SrF_2
(d) Cs^+ and S^{2-}; two Cs^+ ions (2+) balance one S^{2-} ion (2−): Cs_2S

Comment **1.** The subscript 1 is understood and so not written; thus, in (b), we do *not* write Cd_1I_2.
2. Ion charges do *not* appear in the compound formula; thus, in (c), we do *not* write $Sr^{2+}F_2{}^-$.

Follow-Up Problem 2.8 Write the formulas of the compounds named in Follow-Up Problem 2.7.

Compounds with Metals That Form More Than One Ion As noted earlier, many metals, particularly the transition elements (B groups), can form more than one ion. Table 2.4 on the next page lists some examples; see Figure 2.17 for their placement in the periodic table. Names of compounds containing these elements include a *Roman numeral within parentheses* immediately after the metal ion's name to indicate its ionic charge. For example, iron can form Fe^{2+} and Fe^{3+} ions. The two compounds that iron forms with chlorine are $FeCl_2$, named iron(II) chloride (spoken "iron two chloride"), and $FeCl_3$, named iron(III) chloride.

Table 2.4 Some Metals That Form More Than One Monatomic Ion*

Element	Ion Formula	Systematic Name	Common (Trivial) Name
Chromium	Cr^{2+}	chromium(II)	chromous
	Cr^{3+}	**chromium(III)**	chromic
Cobalt	Co^{2+}	cobalt(II)	
	Co^{3+}	cobalt(III)	
Copper	**Cu^{+}**	**copper(I)**	cuprous
	Cu^{2+}	**copper(II)**	cupric
Iron	**Fe^{2+}**	**iron(II)**	ferrous
	Fe^{3+}	**iron(III)**	ferric
Lead	**Pb^{2+}**	**lead(II)**	
	Pb^{4+}	lead(IV)	
Mercury	Hg_2^{2+}	mercury(I)	mercurous
	Hg^{2+}	**mercury(II)**	mercuric
Tin	**Sn^{2+}**	**tin(II)**	stannous
	Sn^{4+}	tin(IV)	stannic

*Listed alphabetically by metal name; the ions in **boldface** are most common.

We are focusing here on systematic names, but some common (trivial) names are still used. In common names for certain metal ions, the Latin root of the metal is followed by either of two suffixes (see Table 2.4):

- The suffix *-ous* for the ion with the lower charge
- The suffix *-ic* for the ion with the higher charge

Thus, iron(II) chloride is also called ferr*ous* chloride and iron(III) chloride is ferr*ic* chloride. (Memory aid: there is an ***o*** in *-ous* and *lower,* and an ***i*** in *-ic* and *higher.*)

Table 2.5 Common Polyatomic Ions*

Formula	Name
Cations	
NH_4^+	**ammonium**
H_3O^+	**hydronium**
Anions	
CH_3COO^- (or $C_2H_3O_2^-$)	**acetate**
CN^-	cyanide
OH^-	**hydroxide**
ClO^-	hypochlorite
ClO_2^-	chlorite
ClO_3^-	**chlorate**
ClO_4^-	**perchlorate**
NO_2^-	nitrite
NO_3^-	**nitrate**
MnO_4^-	**permanganate**
CO_3^{2-}	**carbonate**
HCO_3^-	**hydrogen carbonate** (or **bicarbonate**)
CrO_4^{2-}	chromate
$Cr_2O_7^{2-}$	**dichromate**
O_2^{2-}	peroxide
PO_4^{3-}	**phosphate**
HPO_4^{2-}	hydrogen phosphate
$H_2PO_4^-$	dihydrogen phosphate
SO_3^{2-}	sulfite
SO_4^{2-}	**sulfate**
HSO_4^-	hydrogen sulfate (or bisulfate)

*Boldface ions are most common.

Sample Problem 2.9 Determining Names and Formulas of Ionic Compounds of Metals That Form More Than One Ion

Problem Give the systematic names for the formulas or the formulas for the names of the following compounds:
(a) Tin(II) fluoride **(b)** CrI_3 **(c)** Ferric oxide **(d)** CoS

Solution **(a)** Tin(II) ion is Sn^{2+}; fluoride is F^-. Two F^- ions balance one Sn^{2+} ion: tin(II) fluoride is SnF_2. (The common name is stannous fluoride.)
(b) The anion is I^-, iodide, and the formula shows three I^-. Therefore, the cation must be Cr^{3+}, chromium(III) ion: CrI_3 is chromium(III) iodide. (The common name is chromic iodide.)
(c) *Ferric* is the common name for iron(III) ion, Fe^{3+}; oxide ion is O^{2-}. To balance the charges, the formula is Fe_2O_3. [The systematic name is iron(III) oxide.]
(d) The anion is sulfide, S^{2-}, which requires that the cation be Co^{2+}. The name is cobalt(II) sulfide.

Follow-Up Problem 2.9 Give the systematic names for the formulas or the formulas for the names of the following compounds:
(a) Lead(IV) oxide **(b)** Cu_2S **(c)** $FeBr_2$ **(d)** Mercuric chloride

Compounds That Contain Polyatomic Ions

Many ionic compounds contain polyatomic ions. Table 2.5 shows some common polyatomic ions. Remember that *the polyatomic ion stays together as a charged unit.* The formula for potassium nitrate is KNO_3: each K^+ balances one NO_3^-. The formula for sodium carbonate is Na_2CO_3: two Na^+ balance one CO_3^{2-}. *When two or more of the same polyatomic ion are present in the formula unit, that ion appears in parentheses with the subscript written outside.* For example, calcium nitrate contains one Ca^{2+} and two NO_3^- ions and has the formula $Ca(NO_3)_2$. Parentheses and a subscript are *only* used if *more than one* of a given polyatomic ion is present; thus, sodium nitrate is $NaNO_3$, *not* $Na(NO_3)$.

Families of Oxoanions As Table 2.5 shows, most polyatomic ions are **oxoanions** (or *oxyanions*), those in which an element, usually a nonmetal, is bonded to one or more oxygen atoms. There are several families of two or four oxoanions that differ only in the number of oxygen atoms. The following simple naming conventions are used with these ions.

With two oxoanions in the family:

- The ion with *more* O atoms takes the nonmetal root and the suffix *-ate*.
- The ion with *fewer* O atoms takes the nonmetal root and the suffix *-ite*.

For example, SO_4^{2-} is the sulf*ate* ion, and SO_3^{2-} is the sulf*ite* ion; similarly, NO_3^- is nitr*ate*, and NO_2^- is nitr*ite*.

With four oxoanions in the family (a halogen bonded to O) (Figure 2.18):

- The ion with *most* O atoms has the prefix *per-*, the nonmetal root, and the suffix *-ate*.
- The ion with *one fewer* O atom has just the root and the suffix *-ate*.
- The ion with *two fewer* O atoms has just the root and the suffix *-ite*.
- The ion with *least (three fewer)* O atoms has the prefix *hypo-*, the root, and the suffix *-ite*.

For example, for the four chlorine oxoanions,

ClO_4^- is *per*chlor*ate*, ClO_3^- is chlor*ate*, ClO_2^- is chlor*ite*, ClO^- is *hypo*chlor*ite*

No. of O atoms (increasing ↑)	Prefix	Root	Suffix
	per	*root*	ate
		root	ate
		root	ite
	hypo	*root*	ite

Figure 2.18 Naming oxoanions. Prefixes and suffixes indicate the number of O atoms in the anion.

Hydrated Ionic Compounds Ionic compounds called **hydrates** have a specific number of water molecules in each formula unit, which is shown after a centered dot in the formula and noted in the name by a Greek numerical prefix before the word *hydrate.* Table 2.6 shows these prefixes. For example, Epsom salt has seven water molecules in each formula unit: the formula is $MgSO_4{\cdot}7H_2O$, and the name is magnesium sulfate *hepta*hydrate. Similarly, the mineral gypsum has the formula $CaSO_4{\cdot}2H_2O$ and the name calcium sulfate *di*hydrate. The water molecules, referred to as "waters of hydration," are part of the hydrate's structure. Heating can remove some or all of them, leading to a different substance. For example, when heated strongly, blue copper(II) sulfate pentahydrate ($CuSO_4{\cdot}5H_2O$) is converted to white copper(II) sulfate ($CuSO_4$).

Table 2.6 Numerical Prefixes for Hydrates and Binary Covalent Compounds

Number	Prefix
1	mono-
2	di-
3	tri-
4	tetra-
5	penta-
6	hexa-
7	hepta-
8	octa-
9	nona-
10	deca-

Sample Problem 2.10 Determining Names and Formulas of Ionic Compounds Containing Polyatomic Ions

Problem Give the systematic names for the formulas or the formulas for the names of the following compounds:
(a) $Fe(ClO_4)_2$ **(b)** Sodium sulfite **(c)** $Ba(OH)_2{\cdot}8H_2O$

Solution (a) ClO_4^- is perchlorate, which has a 1− charge, so the cation must be Fe^{2+}. The name is iron(II) perchlorate. (The common name is ferrous perchlorate.)
(b) Sodium is Na^+; sulfite is SO_3^{2-}, and two Na^+ ions balance one SO_3^{2-} ion. The formula is Na_2SO_3.
(c) Ba^{2+} is barium; OH^- is hydroxide. There are eight (*octa-*) water molecules in each formula unit. The name is barium hydroxide octahydrate.

Follow-Up Problem 2.10 Give the systematic names for the formulas or the formulas for the names of the following compounds:
(a) Cupric nitrate trihydrate **(b)** Zinc hydroxide **(c)** LiCN

Sample Problem 2.11 Recognizing Incorrect Names and Formulas of Ionic Compounds

Problem Explain what is wrong with the name or formula at the end of each statement, and correct it:
(a) $Ba(C_2H_3O_2)_2$ is called barium diacetate.
(b) Sodium sulfide has the formula $(Na)_2SO_3$.
(c) Iron(II) sulfate has the formula $Fe_2(SO_4)_3$.
(d) Cesium carbonate has the formula $Cs_2(CO_3)$.

Solution **(a)** The charge of the Ba^{2+} ion *must* be balanced by *two* $C_2H_3O_2^-$ ions, so the prefix *di-* is unnecessary. For ionic compounds, we do not indicate the number of ions with numerical prefixes. The correct name is barium acetate.
(b) Two mistakes occur here. The sodium ion is monatomic, so it does *not* require parentheses. The sulfide ion is S^{2-}, *not* SO_3^{2-} (which is sulfite). The correct formula is Na_2S.
(c) The Roman numeral refers to the charge of the ion, *not* the number of ions in the formula. Fe^{2+} is the cation, so it requires one SO_4^{2-} to balance its charge. The correct formula is $FeSO_4$. [$Fe_2(SO_4)_3$ is the formula for iron(III) sulfate.]
(d) Parentheses are *not* required when only one polyatomic ion of a kind is present. The correct formula is Cs_2CO_3.

Follow-Up Problem 2.11 State why the formula or name at the end of each statement is incorrect, and correct it:
(a) Ammonium phosphate is $(NH_3)_4PO_4$.
(b) Aluminum hydroxide is $AlOH_3$.
(c) $Mg(HCO_3)_2$ is manganese(II) carbonate.
(d) $Cr(NO_3)_3$ is chromic(III) nitride.
(e) $Ca(NO_2)_2$ is cadmium nitrate.

Acid Names from Anion Names

Acids are an important group of hydrogen-containing compounds that have been used in chemical reactions since before alchemical times. In the laboratory, acids are typically used in water solution. When naming them and writing their formulas, we consider acids as anions that are connected to the number of hydrogen ions (H^+) needed for charge neutrality. The two common types of acids are binary acids and oxoacids:

1. *Binary acid* solutions form when certain gaseous compounds dissolve in water. For example, when gaseous hydrogen chloride (HCl) dissolves in water, it forms hydrochloric acid, that is,

   Prefix *hydro-* + nonmetal *root* + suffix *-ic* + separate word *acid*
   hydro + chlor + ic + acid

   or *hydrochloric acid.* This naming pattern holds for many compounds in which hydrogen combines with an anion that has an *-ide* suffix.

2. *Oxoacid* names are similar to those of the oxoanions, except for two suffix changes:
   - *-ate* in the anion becomes *-ic* in the acid
   - *-ite* in the anion becomes *-ous* in the acid

   The oxoanion prefixes *hypo-* and *per-* are retained. Thus,

   BrO_4^- is *per*brom*ate*, and $HBrO_4$ is *per*brom*ic* acid.
   IO_2^- is iod*ite*, and HIO_2 is iod*ous* acid.

Sample Problem 2.12 Determining Names and Formulas of Anions and Acids

Problem Name each of the following anions and give the name and formula of the acid derived from it: **(a)** Br^- **(b)** IO_3^- **(c)** CN^- **(d)** SO_4^{2-} **(e)** NO_2^-.

Solution (a) The anion is bromide; the acid is hydrobromic acid, HBr.
(b) The anion is iodate; the acid is iodic acid, HIO_3.
(c) The anion is cyanide; the acid is hydrocyanic acid, HCN.
(d) The anion is sulfate; the acid is sulfuric acid, H_2SO_4. (In this case, the suffix is added to the element name *sulfur,* not to the root, *sulf-*.)
(e) The anion is nitrite; the acid is nitrous acid, HNO_2.

Comment We must add *two* H^+ ions to the sulfate ion to obtain sulfuric acid because SO_4^{2-} has a 2− charge.

Follow-Up Problem 2.12 Write the formula for the name or name for the formula of each acid: **(a)** chloric acid **(b)** HF **(c)** acetic acid **(d)** sulfurous acid **(e)** HBrO.

Binary Covalent Compounds

Binary covalent compounds are typically formed by the combination of two nonmetals. Some are so familiar that we use their common names, such as ammonia (NH_3), methane (CH_4), and water (H_2O), but most are named systematically:

- The element with the lower group number in the periodic table comes first in the name. The element with the higher group number comes second and is named with its root and the suffix *-ide*. For example, nitrogen [Group 5A(15)] and fluorine [Group 7A(17)] form a compound that has three fluorine atoms for every nitrogen atom. The name and formula are nitrogen trifluoride, NF_3 (*Exception:* When the compound contains oxygen and any of the halogens chlorine, bromine, or iodine, the halogen is named first.)
- If both elements are in the same group, the one with the higher period number is named first. Thus, the Group 6A(16) elements sulfur (Period 3) and oxygen (Period 2) form sulfur dioxide, SO_2.
- Covalent compounds use Greek numerical prefixes (see Table 2.6) to indicate the number of atoms of each element. The first element in the name has a prefix *only* when more than one atom of it is present; the second element *usually* has a prefix.

Sample Problem 2.13 Determining Names and Formulas of Binary Covalent Compounds

Problem (a) What is the formula of carbon disulfide?
(b) What is the name of PCl_5?
(c) Give the name and formula of the compound whose molecules each consist of two N atoms and four O atoms.

Solution (a) The prefix *di-* means "two." The formula is CS_2.
(b) P is the symbol for phosphorus; there are five chlorine atoms, which is indicated by the prefix *penta-*. The name is phosphorus pentachloride.
(c) Nitrogen (N) comes first in the name (lower group number). The compound is dinitrogen tetraoxide, N_2O_4.

Follow-Up Problem 2.13 Give the name or formula for **(a)** SO_3; **(b)** SiO_2; **(c)** dinitrogen monoxide; **(d)** selenium hexafluoride.

Sample Problem 2.14 Recognizing Incorrect Names and Formulas of Binary Covalent Compounds

Problem Explain what is wrong with the name or formula at the end of each statement, and correct it: **(a)** SF_4 is monosulfur pentafluoride. **(b)** Dichlorine heptaoxide is Cl_2O_6. **(c)** N_2O_3 is dinitrotrioxide.

Solution **(a)** There are two mistakes. *Mono-* is not needed if there is only one atom of the first element, and the prefix for four is *tetra-*, not *penta-*. The correct name is sulfur tetrafluoride.

(b) The prefix *hepta-* indicates seven, not six. The correct formula is Cl_2O_7.

(c) The full name of the first element is needed, and a space separates the two element names. The correct name is dinitrogen trioxide.

Follow-Up Problem 2.14 Explain what is wrong with the name or formula at the end of each statement, and correct it: **(a)** S_2Cl_2 is disulfurous dichloride. **(b)** Nitrogen monoxide is N_2O. **(c)** $BrCl_3$ is trichlorine bromide.

Table 2.7 The First 10 Straight-Chain Alkanes

Name (Formula)	Model
Methane (CH_4)	
Ethane (C_2H_6)	
Propane (C_3H_8)	
Butane (C_4H_{10})	
Pentane (C_5H_{12})	
Hexane (C_6H_{14})	
Heptane (C_7H_{16})	
Octane (C_8H_{18})	
Nonane (C_9H_{20})	
Decane ($C_{10}H_{22}$)	

The Simplest Organic Compounds: Straight-Chain Alkanes

Organic compounds typically have complex structures that consist of chains, branches, and/or rings of carbon atoms bonded to hydrogen atoms and, often, to atoms of oxygen, nitrogen, and a few other elements. At this point, we'll lay the groundwork for naming organic compounds by focusing on the simplest ones. Rules for naming more complex ones are detailed in Chapter 15.

Hydrocarbons, the simplest type of organic compound, contain *only* carbon and hydrogen. *Alkanes* are the simplest type of hydrocarbon; many function as important fuels, such as methane, propane, butane, and the mixture that makes up gasoline. The simplest alkanes to name are the *straight-chain alkanes* because the carbon chains have no branches. Alkanes are named with a *root,* based on the number of C atoms in the chain, followed by the suffix *-ane.* Table 2.7 gives the names, molecular formulas, and space-filling models (discussed shortly) of the first 10 straight-chain alkanes. Note that the roots of the four smallest ones are new, but those for the larger ones are the same as the Greek prefixes shown in Table 2.6.

Molecular Masses from Chemical Formulas

In Section 2.5, we calculated the atomic mass of an element. Using the periodic table and the formula of a compound, we calculate the **molecular mass** (also called *molecular weight*) of a formula unit of the compound as the sum of the atomic masses:

$$\text{Molecular mass} = \text{sum of atomic masses} \tag{2.3}$$

The molecular mass of a water molecule (using atomic masses to four significant figures from the periodic table) is

$$\begin{aligned}\text{Molecular mass of } H_2O &= (2 \times \text{atomic mass of H}) + (1 \times \text{atomic mass of O}) \\ &= (2 \times 1.008 \text{ amu}) + 16.00 \text{ amu} = 18.02 \text{ amu}\end{aligned}$$

Ionic compounds don't consist of molecules, so the mass of a formula unit is termed the **formula mass** instead of *molecular mass.* To calculate the formula mass of a compound with a polyatomic ion, *the number of atoms of each element inside the parentheses is multiplied by the subscript outside the parentheses.* For barium nitrate, $Ba(NO_3)_2$,

Formula mass of $Ba(NO_3)_2$

$$\begin{aligned}&= (1 \times \text{atomic mass of Ba}) + (2 \times \text{atomic mass of N}) + (6 \times \text{atomic mass of O}) \\ &= 137.3 \text{ amu} + (2 \times 14.01 \text{ amu}) + (6 \times 16.00 \text{ amu}) = 261.3 \text{ amu}\end{aligned}$$

We can use atomic masses, not ionic masses, because electron loss equals electron gain, so electron mass is balanced. In the next two sample problems, the name or molecular depiction is used to find a compound's molecular or formula mass.

Sample Problem 2.15 Calculating the Molecular Mass of a Compound

Problem Using the periodic table, calculate the molecular (or formula) mass of
(a) Tetraphosphorus trisulfide **(b)** Ammonium nitrate

Plan We first write the formula, then multiply the number of atoms (or ions) of each element by its atomic mass (from the periodic table), and find the sum.

Solution **(a)** The formula is P_4S_3.

$$\begin{aligned}\text{Molecular mass} &= (4 \times \text{atomic mass of P}) + (3 \times \text{atomic mass of S}) \\ &= (4 \times 30.97 \text{ amu}) + (3 \times 32.07 \text{ amu}) = \boxed{220.09 \text{ amu}}\end{aligned}$$

(b) The formula is NH_4NO_3. We count the total number of N atoms even though they belong to different ions:

Formula mass

$$\begin{aligned}&= (2 \times \text{atomic mass of N}) + (4 \times \text{atomic mass of H}) + (3 \times \text{atomic mass of O}) \\ &= (2 \times 14.01 \text{ amu}) + (4 \times 1.007 \text{ amu}) + (3 \times 16.00 \text{ amu}) = \boxed{80.05 \text{ amu}}\end{aligned}$$

Check You can often find large errors by rounding atomic masses to the nearest 5 and adding: **(a)** $(4 \times 30) + (3 \times 30) = 210 \approx 220.09$. The sum has two decimal places because the atomic masses have two. **(b)** $(2 \times 15) + 4 + (3 \times 15) = 79 \approx 80.05$.

Follow-Up Problem 2.15 What is the molecular (or formula) mass of
(a) Hydrogen peroxide **(b)** Cesium chloride
(c) Sulfuric acid **(d)** Potassium sulfate?

Sample Problem 2.16 Using Molecular Depictions to Determine Formula, Name, and Mass

Problem Each scene represents a binary compound. Determine its formula, name, and molecular (or formula) mass.

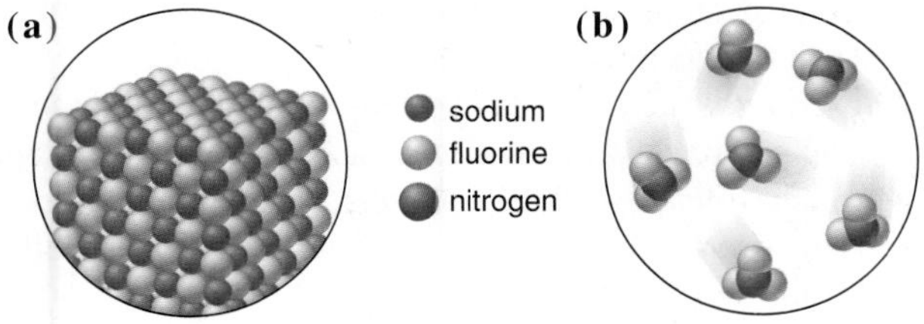

Plan Each of the compounds contains only two elements, so to find the formula, we find the simplest whole-number ratio of one atom to the other. From the formula, we determine the name and the molecular (or formula) mass.

Solution **(a)** There is one brown sphere (sodium) for each green sphere (fluorine), so the formula is NaF. A metal and nonmetal form an ionic compound, in which the metal is named first: sodium fluoride.

$$\begin{aligned}\text{Formula mass} &= (1 \times \text{atomic mass of Na}) + (1 \times \text{atomic mass of F}) \\ &= 22.99 \text{ amu} + 19.00 \text{ amu} = \boxed{41.99 \text{ amu}}\end{aligned}$$

(b) There are three green spheres (fluorine) for each blue sphere (nitrogen), so the formula is NF_3. Two nonmetals form a covalent compound. Nitrogen has a lower group number, so it is named first: nitrogen trifluoride.

$$\begin{aligned}\text{Molecular mass} &= (1 \times \text{atomic mass of N}) + (3 \times \text{atomic mass of F}) \\ &= 14.01 \text{ amu} + (3 \times 19.00) = \boxed{71.01 \text{ amu}}\end{aligned}$$

Check **(a)** For binary ionic compounds, we predict ionic charges from the periodic table (see Figure 2.13). Na forms a 1+ ion, and F forms a 1− ion, so the charges balance with one Na^+ per F^-. Also, ionic compounds are solids, consistent with the picture. **(b)** Covalent compounds often occur as individual molecules, as in the picture. Rounding in (a) gives $25 + 20 = 45$; in (b), we get $15 + (3 \times 20) = 75$, so there are no large errors.

Follow-Up Problem 2.16 Each scene represents a binary compound. Determine its name, formula, and molecular (or formula) mass.

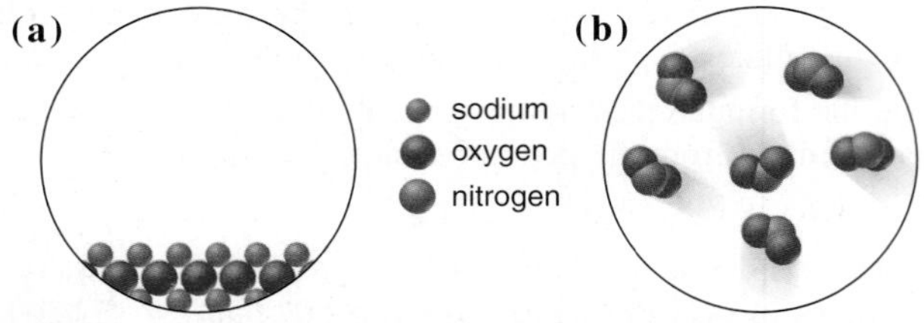

Representing Molecules with Formulas and Models

In order to represent objects too small to see, chemists employ a variety of formulas and models. Each conveys different information, as shown for water below:

- A **molecular formula** uses element symbols and, often, numerical subscripts to give the *actual* number of atoms of each element in a molecule of the compound. (Recall that, for ionic compounds, the *formula unit* gives the *relative* number of each type of ion.) The molecular formula of water is H_2O: there are two H atoms and one O atom in each molecule.

  H_2O

- A **structural formula** shows the relative placement and connections of atoms in the molecule. It uses symbols for the atoms *and* either a pair of dots *(electron-dot formula)* or a line *(bond-line formula)* to show the bonds between the atoms. In water, each H atom is bonded to the O atom, but not to the other H atom.

  H:O:H

  H–O–H

In models, colored balls represent atoms (*see margin*).

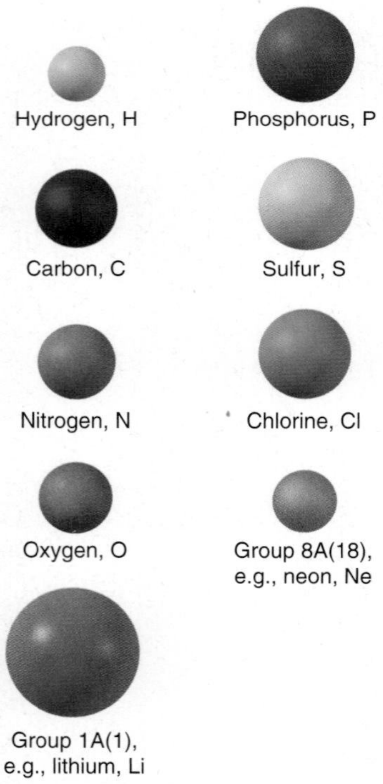

- A *ball-and-stick model* shows atoms as balls and bonds as sticks, and the angles between the bonds are accurate. Note that water is a bent molecule (with a bond angle of 104.5°). This type of model doesn't show the bonded atoms overlapping (see Figure 2.14) or their relative sizes, so it exaggerates the distance between them.

- A *space-filling model* is an accurately scaled-up image of the molecule, so it shows the relative sizes of the atoms, the relative distances between the nuclei (centers of the spheres), and the angles between the bonds. However, bonds are not shown, and it can be difficult to see each atom in a complex molecule.

Every molecule is minute, but the range of molecular sizes, and thus molecular masses, is enormous. Table 2.8 shows some diatomic and small polyatomic molecules, and, at the other end of the size range two extremely large molecules, called *macromolecules,* deoxyribonucleic acid (DNA) and nylon.

Summary of Section 2.8

- An ionic compound is named with cation first and anion second. For metals that can form more than one ion, the charge is shown with a Roman numeral.
- Oxoanions have suffixes, and sometimes prefixes, attached to the root of the element name to indicate the number of oxygen atoms.
- Names of hydrates have a numerical prefix indicating the number of associated water molecules.
- Acid names are based on anion names.
- For binary covalent compounds, the first word of the name is the element farther left or lower down in the periodic table, and prefixes show the numbers of each atom.
- The molecular (or formula) mass of a compound is the sum of the atomic masses.
- Chemical formulas give the number of atoms (molecular) or the arrangement of atoms (structural) of one unit of a compound.
- Molecular models convey information about bond angles (ball-and-stick) and relative atomic sizes and distances between atoms (space-filling).

Table 2.8 Representing Molecules

Name	Molecular Formula (Molecular Mass, in amu)	Bond-Line Formula	Ball-and-Stick Model	Space-Filling Model
Carbon monoxide	CO (28.01)	C≡O		
Nitrogen dioxide	NO_2 (46.01)	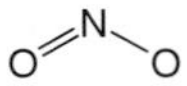		
Butane	C_4H_{10} (58.12)	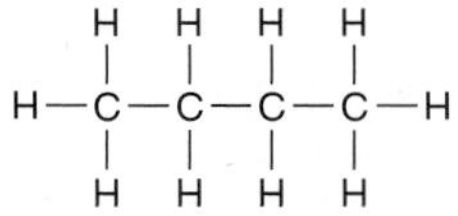	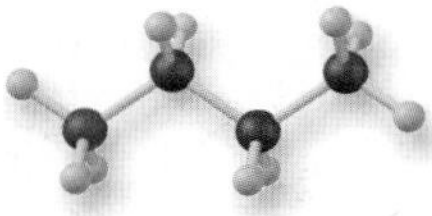	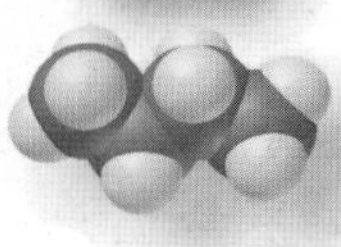
Aspirin (acetylsalicylic acid)	$C_9H_8O_4$ (180.15)	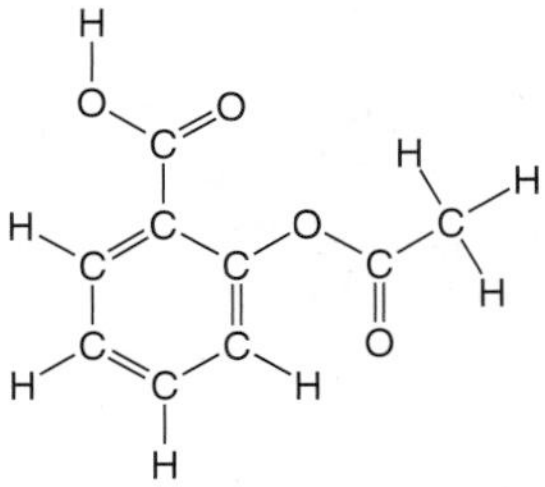	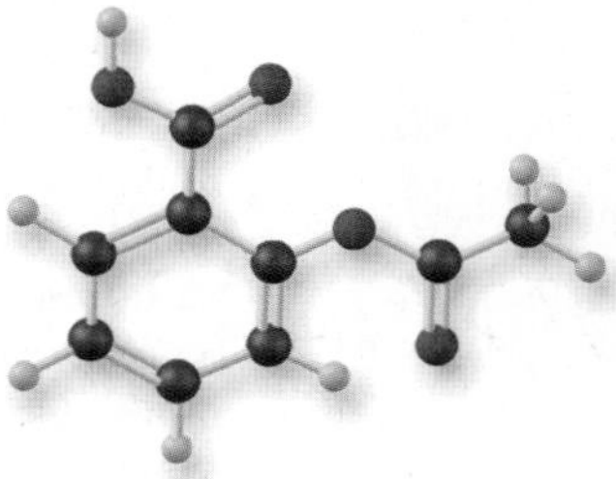	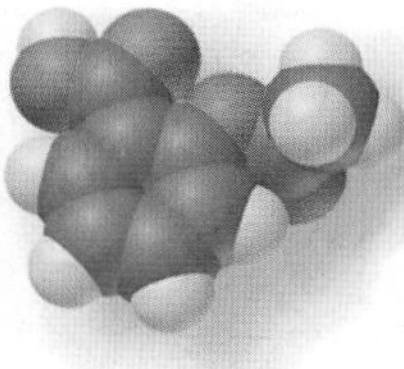

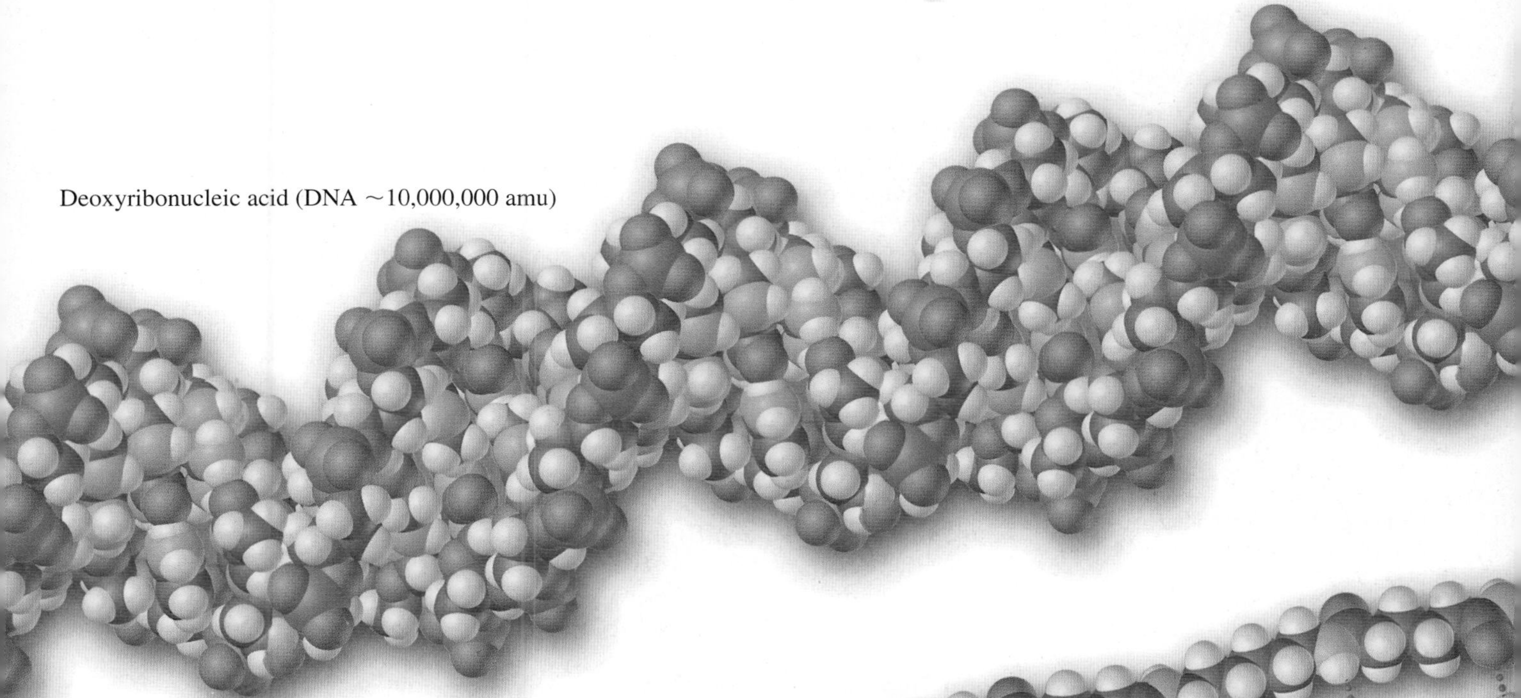

Deoxyribonucleic acid (DNA ~10,000,000 amu)

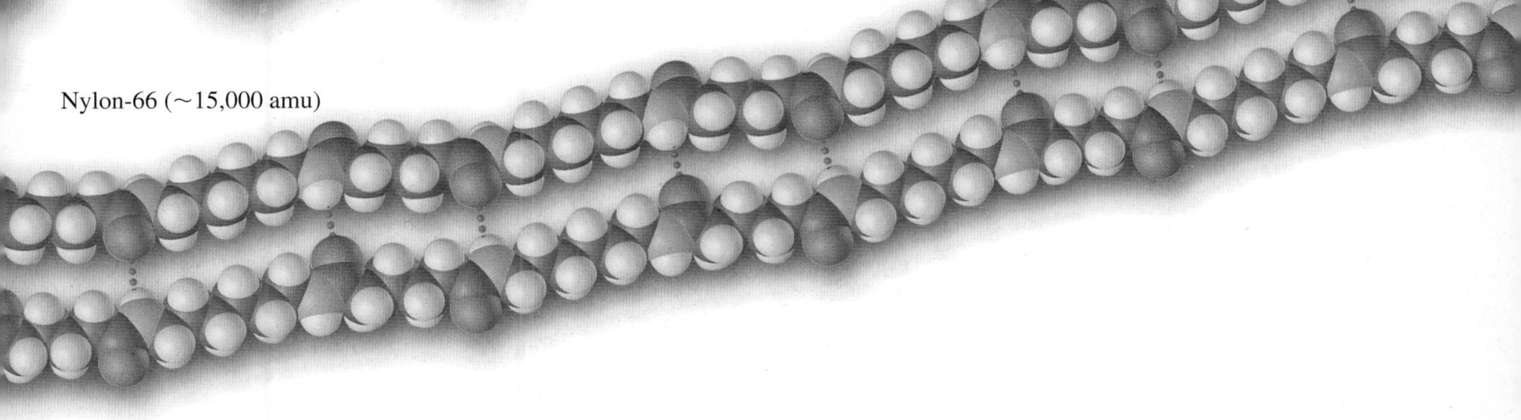

Nylon-66 (~15,000 amu)

2.9 • MIXTURES: CLASSIFICATION AND SEPARATION

In the natural world, *matter usually occurs as mixtures.* A sample of clean air, for example, consists of many elements and compounds physically mixed together, including O_2, N_2, CO_2, the noble gases [Group 8A(18)], and water vapor (H_2O). The oceans are complex mixtures of dissolved ions and covalent substances, including Na^+, Mg^{2+}, Cl^-, SO_4^{2-}, O_2, CO_2, and of course H_2O. Rocks and soils are mixtures of numerous compounds, including calcium carbonate ($CaCO_3$), silicon dioxide (SiO_2), aluminum oxide (Al_2O_3), and iron(III) oxide (Fe_2O_3). And living things contain thousands of substances—carbohydrates, lipids, proteins, nucleic acids, and many simpler ionic and covalent compounds.

There are two broad classes of mixtures:

- A **heterogeneous mixture** has one or more visible boundaries between the components. Thus, its composition is *not* uniform, but rather varies from one region to another. Many rocks are heterogeneous, having individual grains of different minerals. In some heterogeneous mixtures, such as milk and blood, the boundaries can be seen only with a microscope.
- A **homogeneous mixture** (or **solution**) has no visible boundaries because the components are individual atoms, ions, or molecules. Thus, its composition *is* uniform. A mixture of sugar dissolved in water is homogeneous, for example, because the sugar molecules and water molecules are uniformly intermingled on the molecular level. We have no way to tell visually whether a sample of matter is a substance (element or compound) or a homogeneous mixture.

Although we usually think of solutions as liquid, they can exist in all three physical states. For example, air is a gaseous solution of mostly oxygen and nitrogen molecules, and wax is a solid solution of several fatty substances. Solutions in water, called **aqueous solutions,** are especially important in the chemistry lab and comprise a major portion of the environment and of all organisms.

Recall that mixtures differ from compounds in three major ways:

1. The proportions of the components can vary.
2. The individual properties of the components are observable.
3. The components can be separated by physical means.

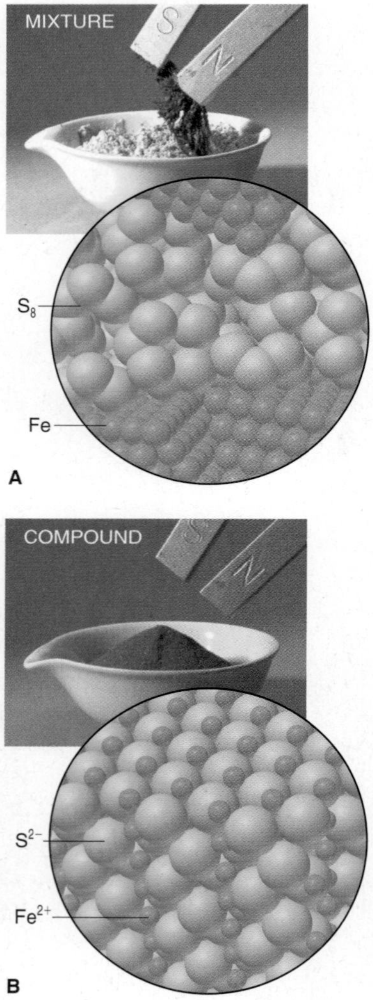

Figure 2.19 The distinction between mixtures and compounds. A, A *mixture* of iron and sulfur consists of the two elements. **B,** The *compound* iron(II) sulfide consists of an array of Fe^{2+} and S^{2-} ions.

The difference between a mixture and a compound is well illustrated using iron and sulfur as components (Figure 2.19). Any proportion of iron metal filings and powdered sulfur forms a mixture. The components can be separated with a magnet because iron metal is magnetic. But if we heat the container strongly, the components form the compound iron(II) sulfide (FeS). The magnet can no longer remove the iron because it exists as Fe^{2+} ions chemically bound to S^{2-} ions.

Chemists have devised many procedures for separating a mixture into its components, and the Tools of the Laboratory essay describes some common ones.

An Overview of the Components of Matter

Understanding matter at the observable and atomic scales is the essence of chemistry. Figure 2.20 is a visual overview of many key terms and ideas in this chapter.

Summary of Section 2.9

- Heterogeneous mixtures have visible boundaries between the components.
- Homogeneous mixtures (solutions) have no visible boundaries because mixing occurs at the molecular level. They can occur in any physical state.
- Components of mixtures (unlike those of compounds) can have variable proportions, can be separated physically, and retain their properties.
- Separation methods are based on differences in physical properties and include filtration (particle size), crystallization (solubility), distillation (volatility), and chromatography (solubility).

TOOLS OF THE LABORATORY | Basic Separation Techniques

Some of the most challenging laboratory procedures involve separating mixtures and purifying the components. All of the techniques described here depend on the *physical properties* of the substances in the mixture; no chemical changes occur.

Filtration is based on *differences in particle size* and is often used to separate a solid from a liquid, which flows through the tiny holes in filter paper as the solid is retained. In vacuum filtration, reduced pressure speeds the flow of the liquid through the filter. Filtration is used in the purification of tap water.

Crystallization is based on *differences in solubility*. The *solubility* of a substance is the amount that dissolves in a fixed volume of solvent at a given temperature. Since solubility often increases with temperature, the impure solid is dissolved in hot solvent and when the solution cools, the purified compound crystallizes. A key component of computer chips is purified by a type of crystallization.

Distillation separates components through *differences in* ***volatility,*** the tendency of a substance to become a gas. *Simple* distillation separates components with *large* differences in volatility, such as water from dissolved ionic compounds (Figure B2.3). As the mixture boils, the vapor is richer in the more volatile component, in this case, water, which is condensed and collected separately. *Fractional* distillation uses many vaporization-condensation steps to separate components with small volatility differences, such as those in petroleum (discussed in Chapter 13).

Chromatography is also based on *differences in solubility*. The mixture is dissolved in a gas or liquid, and the components are separated as this solution, called the *mobile phase,* flows through a solid (or viscous liquid) called the *stationary phase.* A component with lower solubility in the stationary phase moves through it faster than a component with a higher solubility. Figure B2.4 depicts the separation of inks by *column chromatography*.

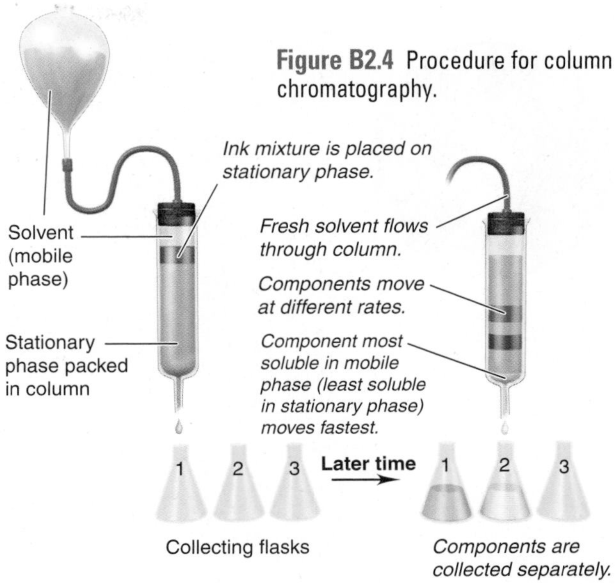

Figure B2.4 Procedure for column chromatography.

In a related technique called *gas-liquid chromatography (GLC),* the mobile phase is an inert gas, such as helium, that carries a gaseous mixture of components into a long tube packed with the stationary phase (Figure B2.5, part A). The components emerge separately and reach a detector. A chromatogram has numerous peaks, each representing the amount of a specific component (Figure B2.5, part B). *High-performance (high-pressure) liquid chromatography (HPLC)* is similar to GLC, but the mixture need not be vaporized, so more diverse mixtures can be separated.

Problem

B2.3 Name the technique(s) and briefly describe the procedure for separating each of the following mixtures into pure components: (a) table salt and pepper; (b) drinking water contaminated with soot; (c) crushed ice and crushed glass; (d) table sugar dissolved in ethanol; (e) two pigments (chlorophyll *a* and chlorophyll *b*) from spinach leaves.

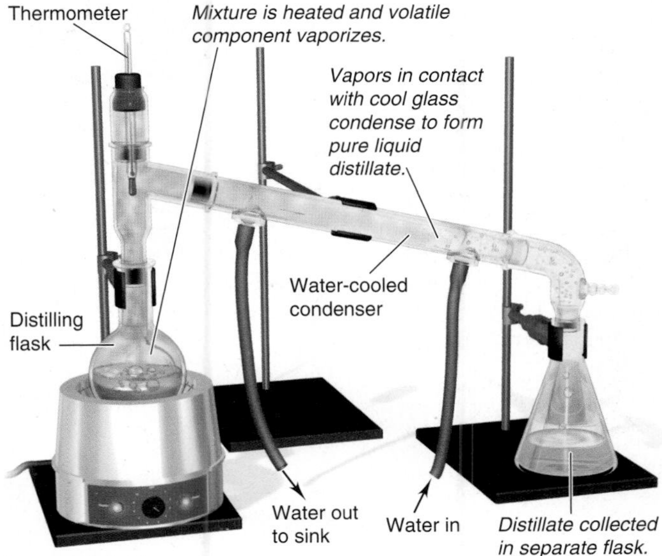

Figure B2.3 Distillation.

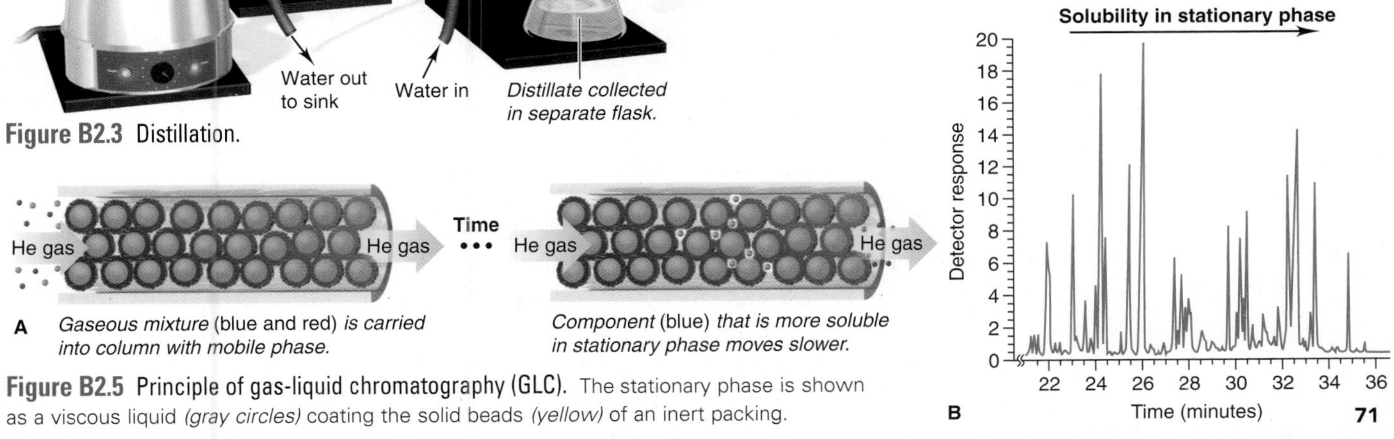

Figure B2.5 Principle of gas-liquid chromatography (GLC). The stationary phase is shown as a viscous liquid *(gray circles)* coating the solid beads *(yellow)* of an inert packing.

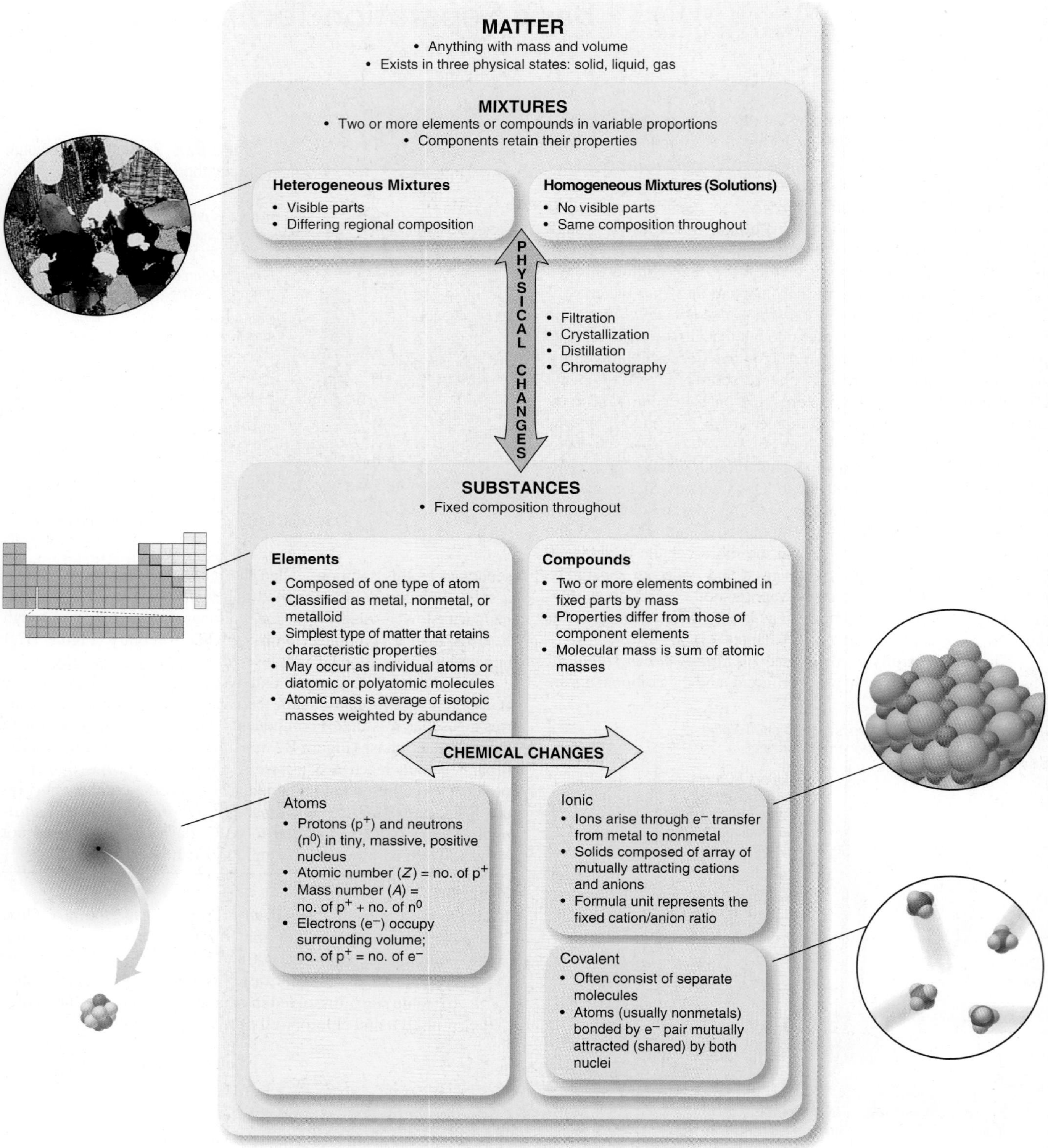

Figure 2.20 The classification of matter from a chemical point of view.

CHAPTER REVIEW GUIDE

Learning Objectives

Relevant section (§) and/or sample problem (SP) numbers appear in parentheses.

Understand These Concepts

1. The defining characteristics of the three types of matter—element, compound, and mixture—on the macroscopic and atomic levels (§2.1)
2. The significance of the three mass laws—mass conservation, definite composition, and multiple proportions (§2.2)
3. The postulates of Dalton's atomic theory and how it explains the mass laws (§2.3)
4. The major contribution of experiments by Thomson, Millikan, and Rutherford to our understanding of atomic structure (§2.4)
5. The structure of the atom, the main features of the subatomic particles, and the importance of isotopes (§2.5)
6. The format of the periodic table and general location and characteristics of metals, metalloids, and nonmetals (§2.6)
7. The essential features of ionic and covalent compounds and the distinction between them (§2.7)
8. The types of mixtures and their properties (§2.9)

Master These Skills

1. Distinguishing elements, compounds, and mixtures at the atomic scale (SP 2.1)
2. Using the mass ratio of element to compound to find the mass of an element in a compound (SP 2.2)
3. Visualizing the mass laws (SP 2.3)
4. Using atomic notation to express the subatomic makeup of an isotope (SP 2.4)
5. Calculating an atomic mass from isotopic composition (SP 2.5)
6. Predicting the monatomic ion formed from a main-group element (SP 2.6)
7. Naming and writing the formula of an ionic compound formed from the ions in Tables 2.3 to 2.5 (SPs 2.7–2.12, 2.16)
8. Naming and writing the formula of a binary covalent compound (SPs 2.13, 2.14, 2.16)
9. Calculating the molecular or formula mass of a compound (SP 2.15)

Key Terms

Page numbers appear in parentheses.

Section 2.1
substance (38)
element (38)
molecule (38)
compound (38)
mixture (39)

Section 2.2
law of mass conservation (40)
law of definite (or constant) composition (41)
fraction by mass (mass fraction) (41)
percent by mass (mass percent, mass %) (41)
law of multiple proportions (42)

Section 2.3
atom (43)

Section 2.4
cathode ray (45)
nucleus (47)

Section 2.5
proton (p^+) (48)
neutron (n^0) (48)
electron (e^-) (48)
atomic number (Z) (48)
mass number (A) (49)
atomic symbol (49)
isotope (49)
atomic mass unit (amu) (50)
dalton (Da) (50)
mass spectrometry (50)
isotopic mass (50)
atomic mass (50)

Section 2.6
periodic table of the elements (53)
period (53)
group (53)
metal (54)
nonmetal (54)
metalloid (semimetal) (54)

Section 2.7
ionic compound (55)
covalent compound (55)
chemical bond (55)
ion (55)
binary ionic compound (55)
cation (55)
anion (55)
monatomic ion (55)
covalent bond (58)
polyatomic ion (59)

Section 2.8
chemical formula (59)
formula unit (60)
oxoanion (63)
hydrate (63)
binary covalent compound (65)
molecular mass (66)
formula mass (66)
molecular formula (68)
structural formula (68)

Section 2.9
heterogeneous mixture (70)
homogeneous mixture (solution) (70)
aqueous solution (70)
filtration (71)
crystallization (71)
distillation (71)
volatility (71)
chromatography (71)

Key Equations and Relationships

Page numbers appear in parentheses.

2.1 Finding the mass of an element in a given mass of compound (41):

Mass of element in sample

$$= \text{mass of compound in sample} \times \frac{\text{mass of element}}{\text{mass of compound}}$$

2.2 Calculating the number of neutrons in an atom (49):

$$\text{Number of neutrons} = \text{mass number} - \text{atomic number}$$

or

$$N = A - Z$$

2.3 Determining the molecular mass of a formula unit of a compound (66):

$$\text{Molecular mass} = \text{sum of atomic masses}$$

Brief Solutions to Follow-Up Problems

2.1 There are two types of particles reacting (left circle), one with two blue atoms and the other with two orange; the depiction shows a mixture of two elements. In the product (right circle), all the particles have one blue atom and one orange; this is a compound.

2.2 Mass (t) of pitchblende

$$= 2.3 \text{ \sout{t uranium}} \times \frac{84.2 \text{ t pitchblende}}{71.4 \text{ \sout{t uranium}}} = 2.7 \text{ t pitchblende}$$

Mass (t) of oxygen

$$= 2.7 \text{ \sout{t pitchblende}} \times \frac{(84.2 - 71.4 \text{ t oxygen})}{84.2 \text{ \sout{t pitchblend}}} = 0.41 \text{ t oxygen}$$

2.3 Sample B. Two bromine-fluorine compounds appear. In one, there are three fluorine atoms for each bromine; in the other, there is one fluorine for each bromine. Therefore, in the two compounds, the ratio of fluorines combining with one bromine is 3/1.

2.4 (a) $5p^+$, $6n^0$, $5e^-$; Q = B
(b) $20p^+$, $21n^0$, $20e^-$; R = Ca
(c) $53p^+$, $78n^0$, $53e^-$; X = I

2.5 $10.0129x + [11.0093(1 - x)] = 10.81$; $0.9964x = 0.1993$; $x = 0.2000$ and $1 - x = 0.8000$; % abundance of ^{10}B = 20.00%; % abundance of ^{11}B = 80.00%

2.6 (a) S^{2-}; (b) Rb^+; (c) Ba^{2+}

2.7 (a) Zinc [Group 2B(12)] and oxygen [Group 6A(16)]
(b) Silver [Group 1B(11)] and bromine [Group 7A(17)]
(c) Lithium [Group 1A(1)] and chlorine [Group 7A(17)]
(d) Aluminum [Group 3A(13)] and sulfur [Group 6A(16)]

2.8 (a) ZnO; (b) AgBr; (c) LiCl; (d) Al_2S_3

2.9 (a) PbO_2; (b) copper(I) sulfide (cuprous sulfide); (c) iron(II) bromide (ferrous bromide); (d) $HgCl_2$

2.10 (a) $Cu(NO_3)_2{\cdot}3H_2O$; (b) $Zn(OH)_2$; (c) lithium cyanide

2.11 (a) $(NH_4)_3PO_4$; ammonium is NH_4^+ and phosphate is PO_4^{3-}.
(b) $Al(OH)_3$; parentheses are needed around the polyatomic ion OH^-.
(c) Magnesium hydrogen carbonate; Mg^{2+} is magnesium and can have only a 2+ charge, so it does not need (II); HCO_3^- is hydrogen carbonate (or bicarbonate).
(d) Chromium(III) nitrate; the *-ic* ending is not used with Roman numerals; NO_3^- is nitr*ate*.
(e) Calcium nitrite; Ca^{2+} is calcium and NO_2^- is nitr*ite*.

2.12 (a) $HClO_3$; (b) hydrofluoric acid; (c) CH_3COOH (or $HC_2H_3O_2$); (d) H_2SO_3; (e) hypobromous acid

2.13 (a) Sulfur trioxide; (b) silicon dioxide; (c) N_2O; (d) SeF_6

2.14 (a) Disulfur dichloride; the *-ous* suffix is not used.
(b) NO; the name indicates one nitrogen.
(c) Bromine trichloride; Br is in a higher period in Group 7A(17), so it is named first.

2.15 (a) H_2O_2, 34.02 amu; (b) CsCl, 168.4 amu; (c) H_2SO_4, 98.09 amu; (d) K_2SO_4, 174.27 amu

2.16 (a) Na_2O. This is an ionic compound, so the name is sodium oxide.

Formula mass

$$= (2 \times \text{atomic mass of Na}) + (1 \times \text{atomic mass of O})$$
$$= (2 \times 22.99 \text{ amu}) + 16.00 \text{ amu} = 61.98 \text{ amu}$$

(b) NO_2. This is a covalent compound, and N has the lower group number, so the name is nitrogen dioxide.

Molecular mass

$$= (1 \times \text{atomic mass of N}) + (2 \times \text{atomic mass of O})$$
$$= 14.01 \text{ amu} + (2 \times 16.00 \text{ amu}) = 46.01 \text{ amu}$$

PROBLEMS

Problems with **colored** numbers are answered in Appendix E and worked in detail in the Student Solutions Manual. Problem sections match those in the text and provide the numbers of relevant sample problems. Most offer Concept Review Questions, Skill-Building Exercises (grouped in pairs covering the same concept), and Problems in Context. The Comprehensive Problems are based on material from any section or previous chapter.

Elements, Compounds, and Mixtures: An Atomic Overview

(Sample Problem 2.1)

Concept Review Questions

2.1 What is the key difference between an element and a compound?

2.2 List two differences between a compound and a mixture.

2.3 Which of the following are pure substances? Explain.
(a) Calcium chloride, used to melt ice on roads, consists of two elements, calcium and chlorine, in a fixed mass ratio.
(b) Sulfur consists of sulfur atoms combined into octatomic molecules.
(c) Baking powder, a leavening agent, contains 26% to 30% sodium hydrogen carbonate and 30% to 35% calcium dihydrogen phosphate by mass.
(d) Cytosine, a component of DNA, consists of H, C, N, and O atoms bonded in a specific arrangement.

2.4 Classify each substance in Problem 2.3 as an element, compound, or mixture, and explain your answers.

2.5 Explain the following statement: The smallest particles unique to an element may be atoms or molecules.

2.6 Explain the following statement: The smallest particles unique to a compound cannot be atoms.

2.7 Can the relative amounts of the components of a mixture vary? Can the relative amounts of the components of a compound vary? Explain.

Problems in Context

2.8 The tap water found in many areas of the United States leaves white deposits when it evaporates. Is this tap water a mixture or a compound? Explain.

2.9 Each scene below represents a mixture. Describe each one in terms of the number(s) of elements and/or compounds present.

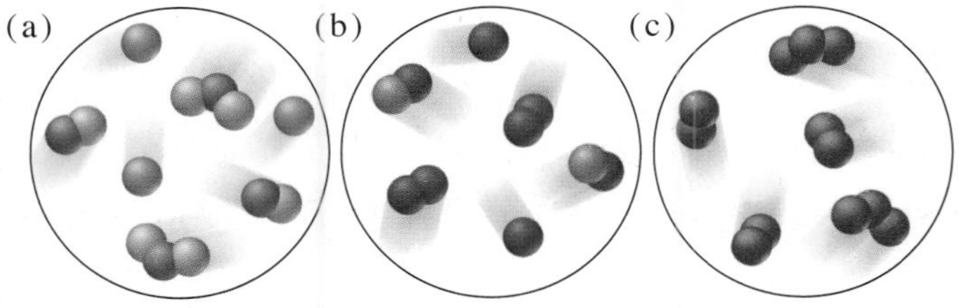

2.10 Samples of illicit "street" drugs often contain an inactive component, such as ascorbic acid (vitamin C). After obtaining a sample of cocaine, government chemists calculate the mass of vitamin C per gram of drug sample, and use it to track the drug's distribution. For example, if different samples of cocaine obtained on the streets of New York, Los Angeles, and Paris all contain 0.6384 g of vitamin C per gram of sample, they very likely come from a common source. Do these street samples consist of a compound, element, or mixture? Explain.

The Observations That Led to an Atomic View of Matter

(Sample Problem 2.2)

Concept Review Questions

2.11 Why was it necessary for separation techniques and methods of chemical analysis to be developed before the laws of definite composition and multiple proportions could be formulated?

2.12 To which classes of matter—element, compound, and/or mixture—do the following apply: (a) law of mass conservation; (b) law of definite composition; (c) law of multiple proportions?

2.13 In our modern view of matter and energy, is the law of mass conservation still relevant to chemical reactions? Explain.

2.14 Identify the mass law that each of the following observations demonstrates, and explain your reasoning:
(a) A sample of potassium chloride from Chile contains the same percent by mass of potassium as one from Poland.
(b) A flashbulb contains magnesium and oxygen before use and magnesium oxide afterward, but its mass does not change.
(c) Arsenic and oxygen form one compound that is 65.2 mass % arsenic and another that is 75.8 mass % arsenic.

2.15 Which of the following scenes illustrate(s) the fact that compounds of chlorine (green) and oxygen (red) exhibit the law of multiple proportions? Name the compounds.

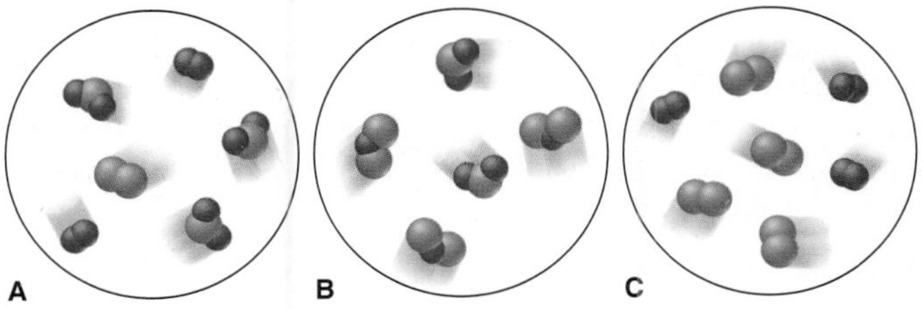

2.16 (a) Does the percent by mass of each element in a compound depend on the amount of compound? Explain.
(b) Does the mass of each element in a compound depend on the amount of compound? Explain.

2.17 Does the percent by mass of each element in a compound depend on the amount of that element used to make the compound? Explain.

Skill-Building Exercises (grouped in similar pairs)

2.18 State the mass law(s) demonstrated by the following experimental results, and explain your reasoning:

Experiment 1: A student heats 1.00 g of a blue compound and obtains 0.64 g of a white compound and 0.36 g of a colorless gas.

Experiment 2: A second student heats 3.25 g of the same blue compound and obtains 2.08 g of a white compound and 1.17 g of a colorless gas.

2.19 State the mass law(s) demonstrated by the following experimental results, and explain your reasoning:

Experiment 1: A student heats 1.27 g of copper and 3.50 g of iodine to produce 3.81 g of a white compound; 0.96 g of iodine remains.

Experiment 2: A second student heats 2.55 g of copper and 3.50 g of iodine to form 5.25 g of a white compound, and 0.80 g of copper remains.

2.20 Fluorite, a mineral of calcium, is a compound of the metal with fluorine. Analysis shows that a 2.76-g sample of fluorite contains 1.42 g of calcium. Calculate the (a) mass of fluorine in the sample; (b) mass fractions of calcium and fluorine in fluorite; (c) mass percents of calcium and fluorine in fluorite.

2.21 Galena, a mineral of lead, is a compound of the metal with sulfur. Analysis shows that a 2.34-g sample of galena contains 2.03 g of lead. Calculate the (a) mass of sulfur in the sample; (b) mass fractions of lead and sulfur in galena; (c) mass percents of lead and sulfur in galena.

2.22 Magnesium oxide (MgO) forms when the metal burns in air.
(a) If 1.25 g of MgO contains 0.754 g of Mg, what is the mass ratio of magnesium to oxide?
(b) How many grams of Mg are in 534 g of MgO?

2.23 Zinc sulfide (ZnS) occurs in the zinc blende crystal structure.
(a) If 2.54 g of ZnS contains 1.70 g of Zn, what is the mass ratio of zinc to sulfide?
(b) How many kilograms of Zn are in 3.82 kg of ZnS?

2.24 A compound of copper and sulfur contains 88.39 g of metal and 44.61 g of nonmetal. How many grams of copper are in 5264 kg of compound? How many grams of sulfur?

2.25 A compound of iodine and cesium contains 63.94 g of metal and 61.06 g of nonmetal. How many grams of cesium are in 38.77 g of compound? How many grams of iodine?

2.26 Show, with calculations, how the following data illustrate the law of multiple proportions:
Compound 1: 47.5 mass % sulfur and 52.5 mass % chlorine
Compound 2: 31.1 mass % sulfur and 68.9 mass % chlorine

2.27 Show, with calculations, how the following data illustrate the law of multiple proportions:
Compound 1: 77.6 mass % xenon and 22.4 mass % fluorine
Compound 2: 63.3 mass % xenon and 36.7 mass % fluorine

Problems in Context

2.28 Dolomite is a carbonate of magnesium and calcium. Analysis shows that 7.81 g of dolomite contains 1.70 g of Ca. Calculate the mass percent of Ca in dolomite. On the basis of the mass percent of Ca, and neglecting all other factors, which is the richer source of Ca, dolomite or fluorite (see Problem 2.20)?

2.29 The mass percent of sulfur in a sample of coal is a key factor in the environmental impact of the coal because the sulfur combines with oxygen when the coal is burned and the oxide can then be incorporated into acid rain. Which of the following coals would have the smallest environmental impact?

	Mass (g) of Sample	Mass (g) of Sulfur in Sample
Coal A	378	11.3
Coal B	495	19.0
Coal C	675	20.6

Dalton's Atomic Theory

(Sample Problem 2.3)

Concept Review Questions

2.30 Which of Dalton's postulates about atoms are inconsistent with later observations? Do these inconsistencies mean that Dalton was wrong? Is Dalton's model still useful? Explain.

2.31 Use Dalton's theory to explain why potassium nitrate from India or Italy has the same mass percents of K, N, and O.

The Observations That Led to the Nuclear Atom Model

Concept Review Questions

2.32 Thomson was able to determine the mass/charge ratio of the electron but not its mass. How did Millikan's experiment allow determination of the electron's mass?

2.33 The following charges on individual oil droplets were obtained during an experiment similar to Millikan's. Determine a charge for the electron (in C, coulombs), and explain your answer: -3.204×10^{-19} C; -4.806×10^{-19} C; -8.010×10^{-19} C; -1.442×10^{-18} C.

2.34 Describe Thomson's model of the atom. How might it account for the production of cathode rays?

2.35 When Rutherford's coworkers bombarded gold foil with α particles, they obtained results that overturned the existing (Thomson) model of the atom. Explain.

The Atomic Theory Today

(Sample Problems 2.4 and 2.5)

Concept Review Questions

2.36 Define *atomic number* and *mass number*. Which can vary without changing the identity of the element?

2.37 Choose the correct answer. The difference between the mass number of an isotope and its atomic number is (a) directly related to the identity of the element; (b) the number of electrons; (c) the number of neutrons; (d) the number of isotopes.

2.38 Even though several elements have only one naturally occurring isotope and all atomic nuclei have whole numbers of protons and neutrons, no atomic mass is a whole number. Use the data from Table 2.2 to explain this fact.

Skill-Building Exercises (grouped in similar pairs)

2.39 Argon has three naturally occurring isotopes, ^{36}Ar, ^{38}Ar, and ^{40}Ar. What is the mass number of each? How many protons, neutrons, and electrons are present in each?

2.40 Chlorine has two naturally occurring isotopes, ^{35}Cl and ^{37}Cl. What is the mass number of each isotope? How many protons, neutrons, and electrons are present in each?

2.41 Do both members of the following pairs have the same number of protons? Neutrons? Electrons?
(a) $^{16}_{8}O$ and $^{17}_{8}O$ (b) $^{40}_{18}Ar$ and $^{41}_{19}K$ (c) $^{60}_{27}Co$ and $^{60}_{28}Ni$

Which pair(s) consist(s) of atoms with the same *Z* value? *N* value? *A* value?

2.42 Do both members of the following pairs have the same number of protons? Neutrons? Electrons?
(a) $^{3}_{1}H$ and $^{3}_{2}He$ (b) $^{14}_{6}C$ and $^{15}_{7}N$ (c) $^{19}_{9}F$ and $^{18}_{9}F$

Which pair(s) consist(s) of atoms with the same *Z* value? *N* value? *A* value?

2.43 Write the $^{A}_{Z}X$ notation for each atomic depiction:

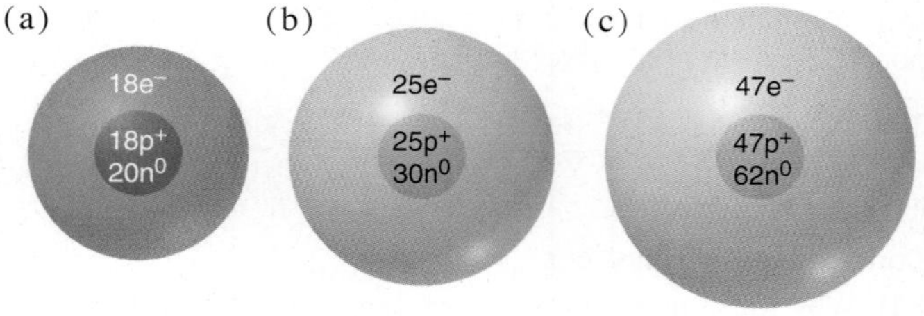

2.44 Write the $^{A}_{Z}X$ notation for each atomic depiction:

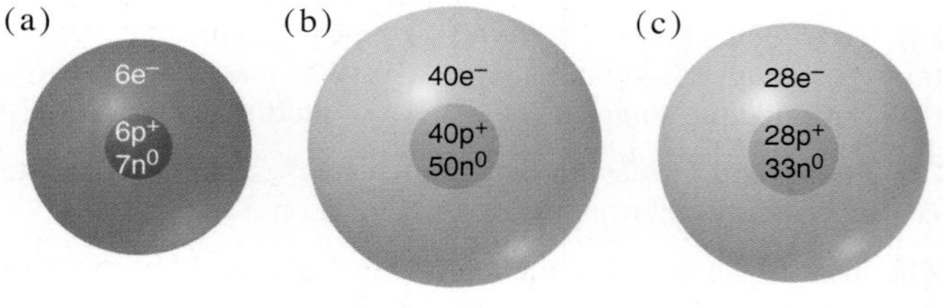

2.45 Draw atomic depictions similar to those in Problem 2.43 for (a) $^{48}_{22}Ti$; (b) $^{79}_{34}Se$; (c) $^{11}_{5}B$.

2.46 Draw atomic depictions similar to those in Problem 2.43 for (a) $^{207}_{82}Pb$; $^{9}_{4}Be$; $^{75}_{33}As$.

2.47 Gallium has two naturally occurring isotopes, ^{69}Ga (isotopic mass = 68.9256 amu, abundance = 60.11%) and ^{71}Ga (isotopic mass = 70.9247 amu, abundance = 39.89%). Calculate the atomic mass of gallium.

2.48 Magnesium has three naturally occurring isotopes, ^{24}Mg (isotopic mass = 23.9850 amu, abundance = 78.99%), ^{25}Mg (isotopic mass = 24.9858 amu, abundance = 10.00%), and ^{26}Mg (isotopic mass = 25.9826 amu, abundance = 11.01%). Calculate the atomic mass of magnesium.

2.49 Chlorine has two naturally occurring isotopes, ^{35}Cl (isotopic mass = 34.9689 amu) and ^{37}Cl (isotopic mass = 36.9659 amu). If chlorine has an atomic mass of 35.4527 amu, what is the percent abundance of each isotope?

2.50 Copper has two naturally occurring isotopes, ^{63}Cu (isotopic mass = 62.9396 amu) and ^{65}Cu (isotopic mass = 64.9278 amu). If copper has an atomic mass of 63.546 amu, what is the percent abundance of each isotope?

Elements: A First Look at the Periodic Table

Concept Review Questions

2.51 How can iodine (Z = 53) have a higher atomic number yet a lower atomic mass than tellurium (Z = 52)?

2.52 Correct each of the following statements:
(a) In the modern periodic table, the elements are arranged in order of increasing atomic mass.
(b) Elements in a period have similar chemical properties.
(c) Elements can be classified as either metalloids or nonmetals.

2.53 What class of elements lies along the "staircase" line in the periodic table? How do the properties of these elements compare with those of metals and nonmetals?

2.54 What are some characteristic properties of elements to the left of the elements along the "staircase"? To the right?

2.55 The elements in Groups 1A(1) and 7A(17) are all quite reactive. What is a major difference between them?

Skill-Building Exercises (grouped in similar pairs)

2.56 Give the name, atomic symbol, and group number of the element with each Z value, and classify it as a metal, metalloid, or nonmetal:
(a) $Z = 32$ (b) $Z = 15$ (c) $Z = 2$ (d) $Z = 3$ (e) $Z = 42$

2.57 Give the name, atomic symbol, and group number of the element with each Z value, and classify it as a metal, metalloid, or nonmetal:
(a) $Z = 33$ (b) $Z = 20$ (c) $Z = 35$ (d) $Z = 19$ (e) $Z = 13$

2.58 Fill in the blanks:
(a) The symbol and atomic number of the heaviest alkaline earth metal are ______ and ______.
(b) The symbol and atomic number of the lightest metalloid in Group 4A(14) are ______ and ______.
(c) Group 1B(11) consists of the *coinage metals.* The symbol and atomic mass of the coinage metal whose atoms have the fewest electrons are ______ and ______.
(d) The symbol and atomic mass of the halogen in Period 4 are ______ and ______.

2.59 Fill in the blanks:
(a) The symbol and atomic number of the heaviest nonradioactive noble gas are ______ and ______.
(b) The symbol and group number of the Period 5 transition element whose atoms have the fewest protons are ______ and ______.
(c) The elements in Group 6A(16) are sometimes called the *chalcogens.* The symbol and atomic number of the first metallic chalcogen are ______ and ______.
(d) The symbol and number of protons of the Period 4 alkali metal atom are ______ and ______.

Compounds: Introduction to Bonding

(Sample Problem 2.6)

Concept Review Questions

2.60 Describe the type and nature of the bonding that occurs between reactive metals and nonmetals.

2.61 Describe the type and nature of the bonding that often occurs between two nonmetals.

2.62 How can ionic compounds be neutral if they consist of positive and negative ions?

2.63 Given that the ions in LiF and in MgO are of similar size, which compound has stronger ionic bonding? Use Coulomb's law in your explanation.

2.64 Are molecules present in a sample of BaF_2? Explain.

2.65 Are ions present in a sample of P_4O_6? Explain.

2.66 The monatomic ions of Groups 1A(1) and 7A(17) are all singly charged. In what major way do they differ? Why?

2.67 Describe the formation of solid magnesium chloride ($MgCl_2$) from large numbers of magnesium and chlorine atoms.

2.68 Describe the formation of solid potassium sulfide (K_2S) from large numbers of potassium and sulfur atoms.

2.69 Does potassium nitrate (KNO_3) incorporate ionic bonding, covalent bonding, or both? Explain.

Skill-Building Exercises (grouped in similar pairs)

2.70 What monatomic ions do potassium (Z = 19) and iodine (Z = 53) form?

2.71 What monatomic ions do barium (Z = 56) and selenium (Z = 34) form?

2.72 For each ionic depiction, give the name of the parent atom, its mass number, and its group and period numbers:

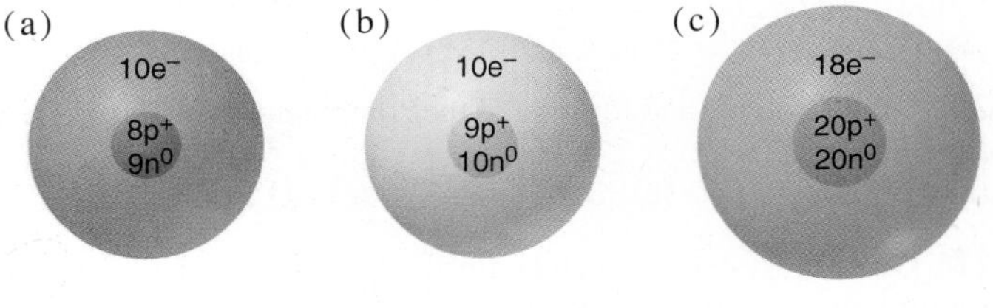

2.73 For each ionic depiction, give the name of the parent atom, its mass number, and its group and period numbers:

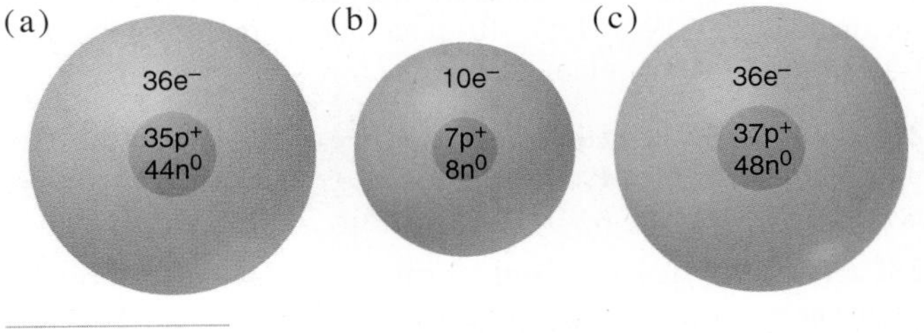

2.74 An ionic compound forms when lithium (Z = 3) reacts with oxygen (Z = 8). If a sample of the compound contains 8.4×10^{21} lithium ions, how many oxide ions does it contain?

2.75 An ionic compound forms when calcium (Z = 20) reacts with iodine (Z = 53). If a sample of the compound contains 7.4×10^{21} calcium ions, how many iodide ions does it contain?

2.76 The radii of the sodium and potassium ions are 102 pm and 138 pm, respectively. Which compound has stronger ionic attractions, sodium chloride or potassium chloride?

2.77 The radii of the lithium and magnesium ions are 76 pm and 72 pm, respectively. Which compound has stronger ionic attractions, lithium oxide or magnesium oxide?

Formulas, Names, and Masses of Compounds

(Sample Problems 2.7 to 2.16)

Concept Review Questions

2.78 What information about the relative numbers of ions and the percent mass of elements is in the formula MgF_2?

2.79 How is a structural formula similar to a molecular formula? How is it different?

2.80 Consider a mixture of 10 billion O_2 molecules and 10 billion H_2 molecules. In what way is this mixture similar to a sample containing 10 billion hydrogen peroxide (H_2O_2) molecules? In what way is it different?

2.81 For what type(s) of compound do we use Roman numerals in the names?

2.82 For what type(s) of compound do we use Greek numerical prefixes in the names?

2.83 For what type of compound are we unable to write a molecular formula?

Skill-Building Exercises (grouped in similar pairs)

2.84 Give the name and formula of the compound formed from the following elements: (a) sodium and nitrogen; (b) oxygen and strontium; (c) aluminum and chlorine.

2.85 Give the name and formula of the compound formed from the following elements: (a) cesium and bromine; (b) sulfur and barium; (c) calcium and fluorine.

2.86 Give the name and formula of the compound formed from the following elements:
(a) $_{12}L$ and $_{9}M$ (b) $_{30}L$ and $_{16}M$ (c) $_{17}L$ and $_{38}M$

2.87 Give the name and formula of the compound formed from the following elements:
(a) $_{37}Q$ and $_{35}R$ (b) $_{8}Q$ and $_{13}R$ (c) $_{20}Q$ and $_{53}R$

2.88 Give the systematic names for the formulas or the formulas for the names: (a) tin(IV) chloride; (b) $FeBr_3$; (c) cuprous bromide; (d) Mn_2O_3.

2.89 Give the systematic names for the formulas or the formulas for the names: (a) Na_2HPO_4; (b) potassium carbonate dihydrate; (c) $NaNO_2$; (d) ammonium perchlorate.

2.90 Give the systematic names for the formulas or the formulas for the names: (a) CoO; (b) mercury(I) chloride; (c) $Pb(C_2H_3O_2)_2{\cdot}3H_2O$; (d) chromic oxide.

2.91 Give the systematic names for the formulas or the formulas for the names: (a) $Sn(SO_3)_2$; (b) potassium dichromate; (c) $FeCO_3$; (d) copper(II) nitrate.

2.92 Correct each of the following formulas:
(a) Barium oxide is BaO_2
(b) Iron(II) nitrate is $Fe(NO_3)_3$
(c) Magnesium sulfide is $MnSO_3$

2.93 Correct each of the following names:
(a) CuI is cobalt(II) iodide
(b) $Fe(HSO_4)_3$ is iron(II) sulfate
(c) $MgCr_2O_7$ is magnesium dichromium heptaoxide

2.94 Give the name and formula for the acid derived from each of the following anions:
(a) hydrogen sulfate (b) IO_3^- (c) cyanide (d) HS^-

2.95 Give the name and formula for the acid derived from each of the following anions:
(a) perchlorate (b) NO_3^- (c) bromite (d) F^-

2.96 Many chemical names are similar at first glance. Give the formulas of the species in each set:
(a) Ammonium ion and ammonia
(b) Magnesium sulfide, magnesium sulfite, and magnesium sulfate
(c) Hydrochloric acid, chloric acid, and chlorous acid
(d) Cuprous bromide and cupric bromide

2.97 Give the formulas of the compounds in each set:
(a) Lead(II) oxide and lead(IV) oxide
(b) Lithium nitride, lithium nitrite, and lithium nitrate
(c) Strontium hydride and strontium hydroxide
(d) Magnesium oxide and manganese(II) oxide

2.98 Give the name and formula of the compound whose molecules consist of two sulfur atoms and four fluorine atoms.

2.99 Give the name and formula of the compound whose molecules consist of two chlorine atoms and one oxygen atom.

2.100 Correct the name to match the formula of the following compounds: (a) calcium(II) dichloride, $CaCl_2$; (b) Copper(II) oxide, Cu_2O; (c) Stannous tetrafluoride, SnF_4; (d) Hydrogen chloride acid, HCl.

2.101 Correct the formula to match the name of the following compounds: (a) iron(III) oxide, Fe_3O_4; (b) chloric acid, HCl; (c) mercuric oxide, Hg_2O; (d) dichlorine heptaoxide, Cl_2O_6.

2.102 Give the number of atoms of the specified element in a formula unit of each of the following compounds, and calculate the molecular (formula) mass:
(a) Oxygen in aluminum sulfate, $Al_2(SO_4)_3$
(b) Hydrogen in ammonium hydrogen phosphate, $(NH_4)_2HPO_4$
(c) Oxygen in the mineral azurite, $Cu_3(OH)_2(CO_3)_2$

2.103 Give the number of atoms of the specified element in a formula unit of each of the following compounds, and calculate the molecular (formula) mass:
(a) Hydrogen in ammonium benzoate, $C_6H_5COONH_4$
(b) Nitrogen in hydrazinium sulfate, $N_2H_6SO_4$
(c) Oxygen in the mineral leadhillite, $Pb_4SO_4(CO_3)_2(OH)_2$

2.104 Write the formula of each compound, and determine its molecular (formula) mass: (a) ammonium sulfate; (b) sodium dihydrogen phosphate; (c) potassium bicarbonate.

2.105 Write the formula of each compound, and determine its molecular (formula) mass: (a) sodium dichromate; (b) ammonium perchlorate; (c) magnesium nitrite trihydrate.

2.106 Calculate the molecular (formula) mass of each compound: (a) dinitrogen pentaoxide; (b) lead(II) nitrate; (c) calcium peroxide.

2.107 Calculate the molecular (formula) mass of each compound: (a) iron(II) acetate tetrahydrate; (b) sulfur tetrachloride; (c) potassium permanganate.

2.108 Give the formula, name, and molecular mass of the following molecules:

(a)

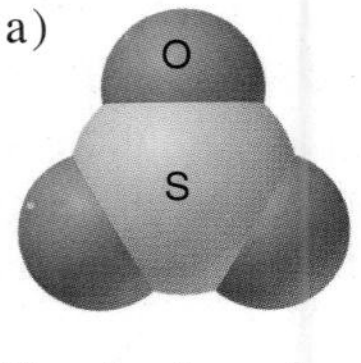

(b)

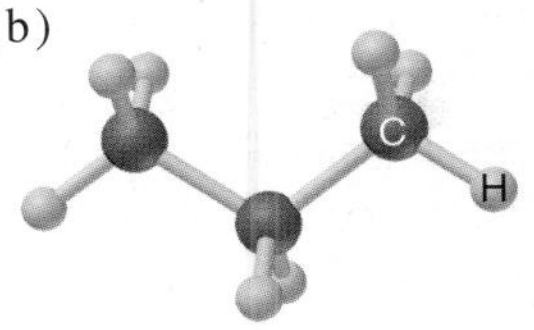

2.109 Give the formula, name, and molecular mass of the following molecules:

(a)

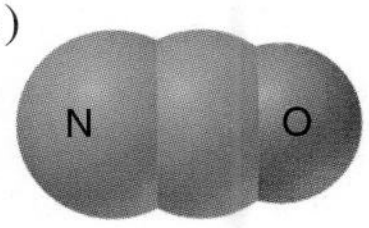

(b)

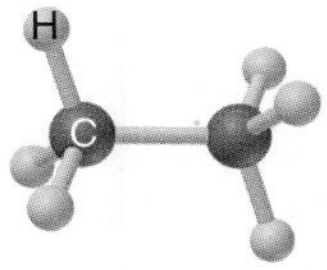

Problems in Context

2.110 Before the use of systematic names, many compounds had common names. Give the systematic name for each of the following:
(a) Blue vitriol, $CuSO_4{\cdot}5H_2O$
(b) Slaked lime, $Ca(OH)_2$
(c) Oil of vitriol, H_2SO_4
(d) Washing soda, Na_2CO_3
(e) Muriatic acid, HCl
(f) Epsom salt, $MgSO_4{\cdot}7H_2O$
(g) Chalk, $CaCO_3$
(h) Dry ice, CO_2
(i) Baking soda, $NaHCO_3$
(j) Lye, NaOH

2.111 Each circle contains a representation of a binary compound. Determine its name, formula, and molecular (formula) mass.

(a)

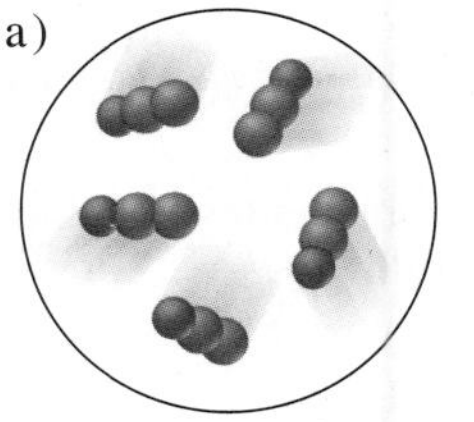

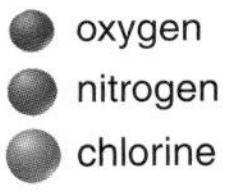

(b)

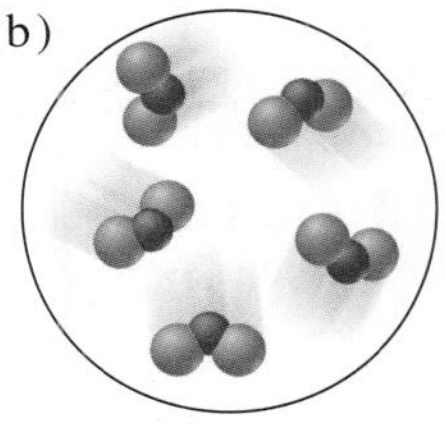

Mixtures: Classification and Separation

Concept Review Questions

2.112 In what main way is separating the components of a mixture different from separating the components of a compound?

2.113 What is the difference between a homogeneous and a heterogeneous mixture?

2.114 Is a solution a homogeneous or a heterogeneous mixture? Give an example of an aqueous solution.

Skill-Building Exercises (grouped in similar pairs)

2.115 Classify each of the following as a compound, a homogeneous mixture, or a heterogeneous mixture: (a) distilled water; (b) gasoline; (c) beach sand; (d) wine; (e) air.

2.116 Classify each of the following as a compound, a homogeneous mixture, or a heterogeneous mixture: (a) orange juice; (b) vegetable soup; (c) cement; (d) calcium sulfate; (e) tea.

Problems in Context

2.117 Which separation method is operating in each of the following procedures?
(a) Pouring a mixture of cooked pasta and boiling water into a colander
(b) Removing colored impurities from raw sugar to make refined sugar

2.118 A quality-control laboratory analyzes a product mixture using gas-liquid chromatography. The separation of components is more than adequate, but the process takes too long. Suggest two ways, other than changing the stationary phase, to shorten the analysis time.

Comprehensive Problems

2.119 Helium is the lightest noble gas and the second most abundant element (after hydrogen) in the universe.
(a) The radius of a helium atom is 3.1×10^{-11} m; the radius of its nucleus is 2.5×10^{-15} m. What fraction of the spherical atomic volume is occupied by the nucleus (V of a sphere $= \frac{4}{3}\pi r^3$)?
(b) The mass of a helium-4 atom is 6.64648×10^{-24} g, and each of its two electrons has a mass of 9.10939×10^{-28} g. What fraction of this atom's mass is contributed by its nucleus?

2.120 From the following ions (with their radii in pm), choose the pair that forms the strongest ionic bond and the pair that forms the weakest:

Ion:	Mg^{2+}	K^+	Rb^+	Ba^{2+}	Cl^-	O^{2-}	I^-
Radius:	72	138	152	135	181	140	220

2.121 Give the molecular mass of each compound depicted below, and provide a correct name for any that are named incorrectly.

(a)

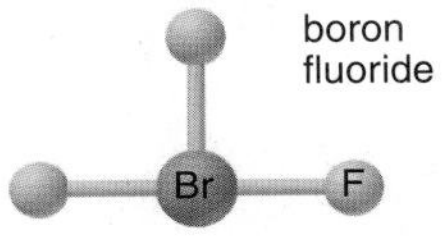

(b)

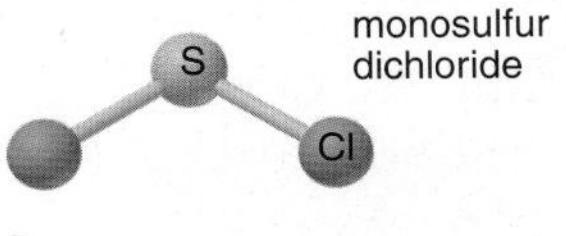

(c)

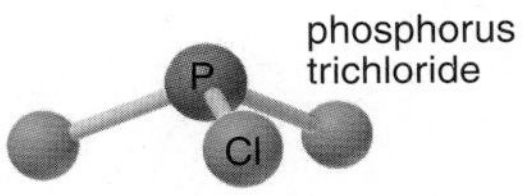

(d)

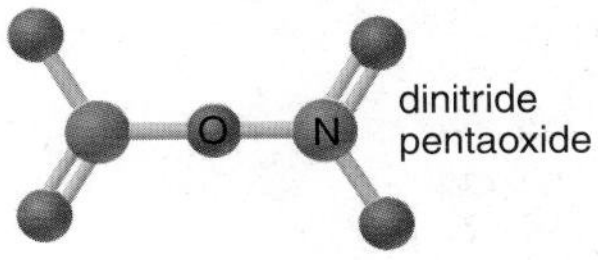

2.122 Polyatomic ions are named by patterns that apply to elements in a given group. Using the periodic table and Table 2.5, give the name of each of the following: (a) SeO_4^{2-}; (b) AsO_4^{3-}; (c) BrO_2^-; (d) $HSeO_4^-$; (e) TeO_3^{2-}.

2.123 Ammonium dihydrogen phosphate, formed from the reaction of phosphoric acid with ammonia, is used as a crop fertilizer as well as a component of some fire extinguishers. (a) What are the mass percentages of N and P in the compound? (b) How much ammonia is incorporated into 100. g of the compound?

2.124 Nitrogen forms more oxides than any other element. The percents by mass of N in three different nitrogen oxides are (I) 46.69%; (II) 36.85%; (III) 25.94%. For each compound, determine (a) the simplest whole-number ratio of N to O, and (b) the number of grams of oxygen per 1.00 g of nitrogen.

2.125 The number of atoms in 1 dm^3 of aluminum is nearly the same as the number of atoms in 1 dm^3 of lead, but the densities of these metals are very different (see Table 1.5). Explain.

2.126 You are working in the laboratory preparing sodium chloride. Consider the following results for three preparations of the compound:

Case 1: 39.34 g Na + 60.66 g Cl_2 $\longrightarrow$ 100.00 g NaCl
Case 2: 39.34 g Na + 70.00 g Cl_2 $\longrightarrow$ 100.00 g NaCl + 9.34 g Cl_2
Case 3: 50.00 g Na + 50.00 g Cl_2 $\longrightarrow$ 82.43 g NaCl + 17.57 g Na

Explain these results in terms of the laws of conservation of mass and definite composition.

2.127 Scenes A–I depict various types of matter on the atomic scale. Choose the correct scene(s) for each of the following:
(a) A mixture that fills its container
(b) A substance that cannot be broken down into simpler ones
(c) An element with a very high resistance to flow
(d) A homogeneous mixture
(e) An element that conforms to the walls of its container and displays an upper surface
(f) A gas consisting of diatomic particles
(g) A gas that can be broken down into simpler substances
(h) A substance with a 2/1 ratio of its component atoms
(i) Matter that can be separated into its component substances by physical means
(j) A heterogeneous mixture
(k) Matter that obeys the law of definite composition

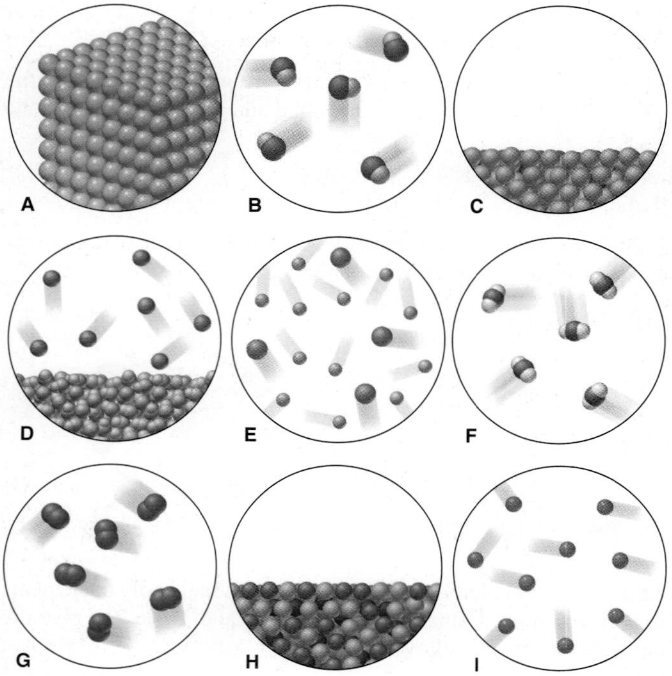

2.128 The seven most abundant ions in seawater make up more than 99% by mass of the dissolved compounds. Here are their abundances in units of mg ion/kg seawater: chloride 18,980; sodium 10,560; sulfate 2650; magnesium 1270; calcium 400; potassium 380; hydrogen carbonate 140.
(a) What is the mass % of each ion in seawater?
(b) What percent of the total mass of ions is sodium ion?
(c) How does the total mass % of alkaline earth metal ions compare with the total mass % of alkali metal ions?
(d) Which make up the larger mass fraction of dissolved components, anions or cations?

2.129 The scenes below represent a mixture of two monatomic gases undergoing a reaction when heated. Which mass law(s) is (are) illustrated by this change?

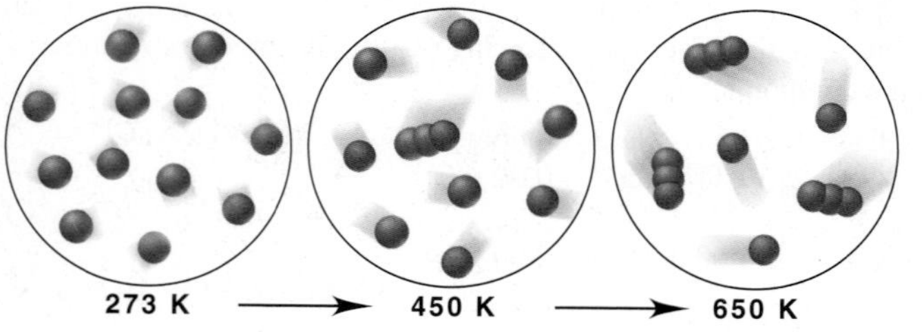

2.130 When barium (Ba) reacts with sulfur (S) to form barium sulfide (BaS), each Ba atom reacts with an S atom. If 2.50 cm^3 of Ba reacts with 1.75 cm^3 of S, are there enough Ba atoms to react with the S atoms (d of Ba = 3.51 g/cm^3; d of S = 2.07 g/cm^3)?

2.131 Succinic acid (*below*) is an important metabolite in biological energy production. Give the molecular formula, molecular mass, and the mass percent of each element in succinic acid.

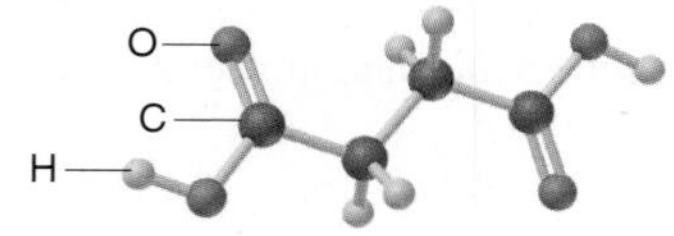

2.132 Fluoride ion is poisonous in relatively low amounts: 0.2 g of F^- per 70 kg of body weight can cause death. Nevertheless, in order to prevent tooth decay, F^- ions are added to drinking water at a concentration of 1 mg of F^- ion per L of water. How many liters of fluoridated drinking water would a 70-kg person have to consume in one day to reach this toxic level? How many kilograms of sodium fluoride would be needed to treat a 8.50×10^7-gal reservoir?

2.133 Antimony has many uses, for example, in infrared devices and as part of an alloy in lead storage batteries. The element has two naturally occurring isotopes, one with mass 120.904 amu, the other with mass 122.904 amu. (a) Write the ${}^{A}_{Z}X$ notation for each isotope. (b) Use the atomic mass of antimony from the periodic table to calculate the natural abundance of each isotope.

2.134 Dinitrogen monoxide (N_2O; nitrous oxide) is a greenhouse gas that enters the atmosphere principally from natural fertilizer breakdown. Some studies have shown that the isotope ratios of ${}^{15}N$ to ${}^{14}N$ and of ${}^{18}O$ to ${}^{16}O$ in N_2O depend on the source, which can thus be determined by measuring the relative abundance of molecular masses in a sample of N_2O.
(a) What different molecular masses are possible for N_2O?
(b) The percent abundance of ${}^{14}N$ is 99.6%, and that of ${}^{16}O$ is 99.8%. Which molecular mass of N_2O is least common, and which is most common?

2.135 Use the box color(s) in the periodic table below to identify the element(s) described by each of the following:

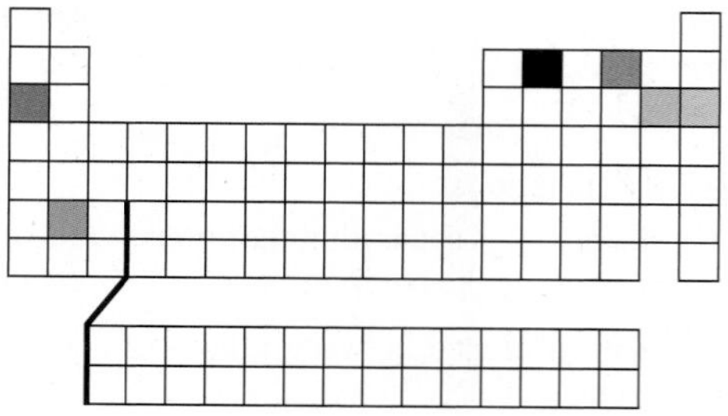

(a) Four elements that are nonmetals
(b) Two elements that are metals
(c) Three elements that are gases at room temperature
(d) Three elements that are solid at room temperature
(e) One pair of elements likely to form a covalent compound
(f) Another pair of elements likely to form a covalent compound
(g) One pair of elements likely to form an ionic compound with formula MX
(h) Another pair of elements likely to form an ionic compound with formula MX
(i) Two elements likely to form an ionic compound with formula M_2X
(j) Two elements likely to form an ionic compound with formula MX_2

(k) An element that forms no compounds
(l) A pair of elements whose compounds exhibit the law of multiple proportions

2.136 The two isotopes of potassium with significant abundance in nature are ^{39}K (isotopic mass 38.9637 amu, 93.258%) and ^{41}K (isotopic mass 40.9618 amu, 6.730%). Fluorine has only one naturally occurring isotope, ^{19}F (isotopic mass 18.9984 amu). Calculate the formula mass of potassium fluoride.

2.137 Boron trifluoride is used as a catalyst in the synthesis of organic compounds. When this compound is analyzed by mass spectrometry (see Tools of the Laboratory, p. 51), several different 1+ ions form, including ions representing the whole molecule as well as molecular fragments formed by the loss of one, two, and three F atoms. Given that boron has two naturally occurring isotopes, ^{10}B and ^{11}B, and fluorine has one, ^{19}F, calculate the masses of all possible 1+ ions.

2.138 Nitrogen monoxide (NO) is a bioactive molecule in blood. Low NO concentrations cause respiratory distress and the formation of blood clots. Doctors prescribe nitroglycerin, $C_3H_5N_3O_9$, and isoamyl nitrate, $(CH_3)_2CHCH_2CH_2ONO_2$, to increase NO. If each compound releases one molecule of NO per atom of N it contains, calculate the mass percent of NO in each.

2.139 TNT (trinitrotoluene; *below*) is used as an explosive in construction. Calculate the mass of each element in 1.00 lb of TNT.

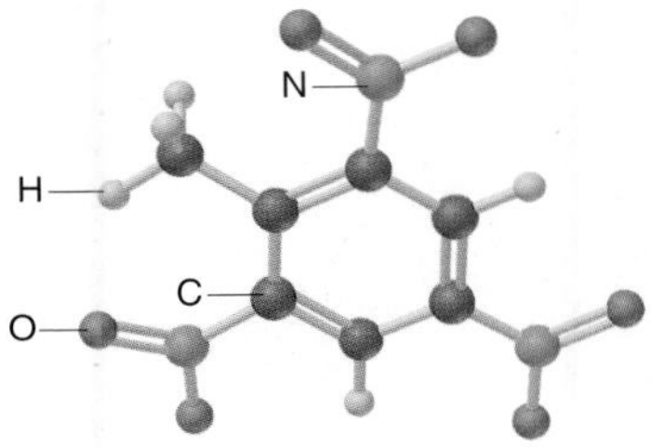

2.140 Nuclei differ in their stability, and some are so unstable that they undergo radioactive decay. The ratio of the number of neutrons to number of protons (*N/Z*) in a nucleus correlates with its stability. Calculate the *N/Z* ratio for (a) ^{144}Sm; (b) ^{56}Fe; (c) ^{20}Ne; (d) ^{107}Ag. (e) The radioactive isotope ^{238}U decays in a series of nuclear reactions that includes another uranium isotope, ^{234}U, and three lead isotopes, ^{214}Pb, ^{210}Pb, and ^{206}Pb. How many neutrons, protons, and electrons are in each of these five isotopes?

2.141 The anticancer drug Platinol (Cisplatin), $Pt(NH_3)_2Cl_2$, reacts with the cancer cell's DNA and interferes with its growth. (a) What is the mass % of platinum (Pt) in Platinol? (b) If Pt costs \$32/g, how many grams of Platinol can be made for \$1.00 million (assume that the cost of Pt determines the cost of the drug)?

2.142 In the periodic table below, give the name, symbol, atomic number, atomic mass, period number, and group number of (a) the *building-block elements (red)*, which occur in nearly every biological molecule, and (b) the *macronutrients (green)*, which are either essential ions in cell fluids or are part of many biomolecules.

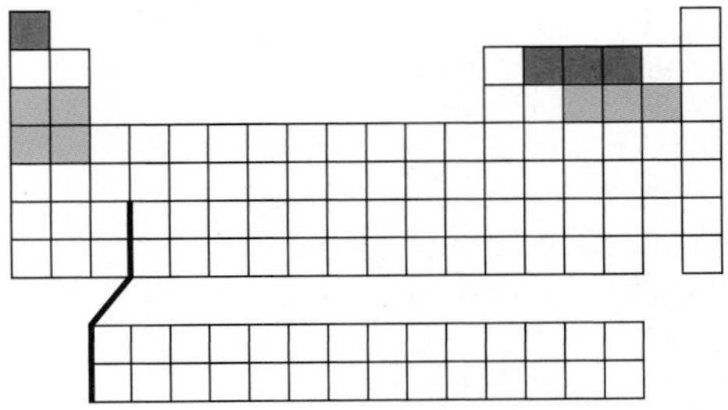

2.143 The block diagram below classifies the components of matter on the macroscopic scale. Identify blocks (a)–(d).

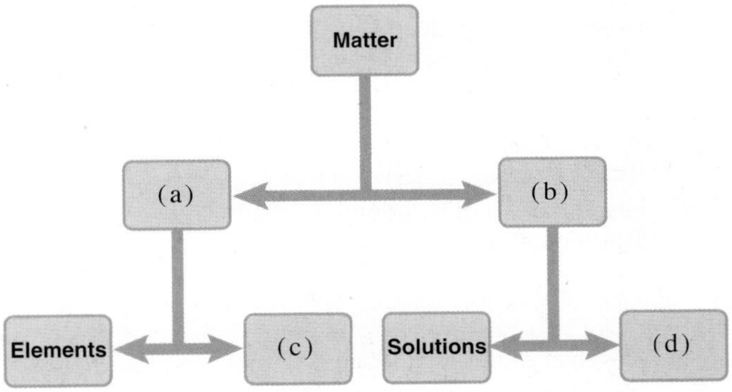

2.144 Which of the following steps in an overall process involve(s) a physical change and which involve(s) a chemical change?

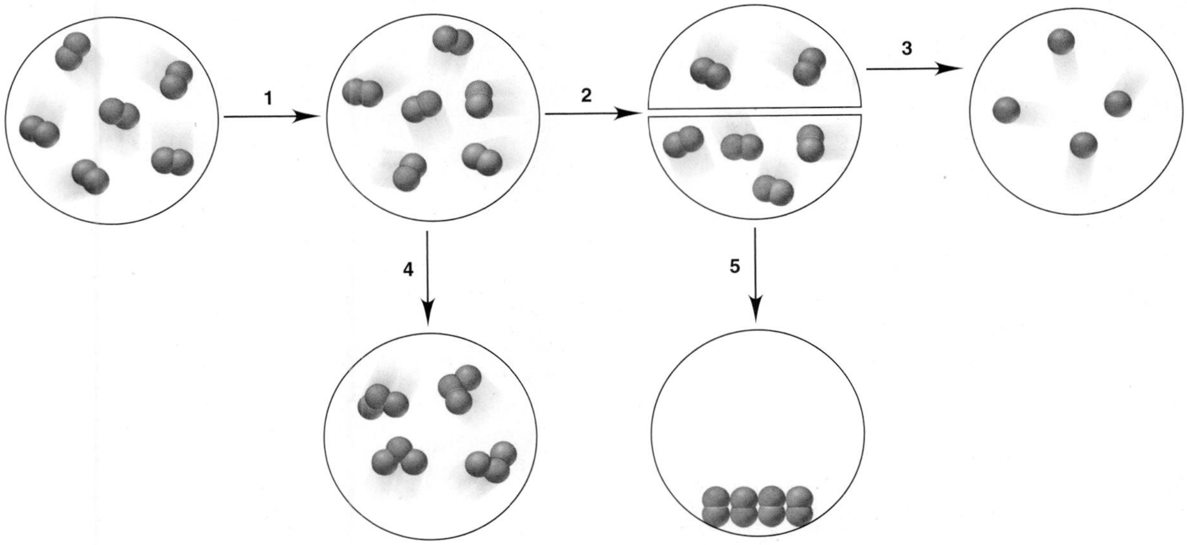

Stoichiometry of Formulas and Equations

3

Concepts and skills to review before you study this chapter

- atomic mass (Section 2.5)
- names and formulas of compounds (Section 2.8)
- molecular (or formula) mass (Section 2.8)
- molecular and structural formulas, and ball-and-stick and space-filling models (Section 2.8)

Chemistry is, above all, a practical science. Imagine that you're a biochemist who has extracted a substance with medicinal activity from a tropical plant: what is its formula, and what quantity of metabolic products will establish a safe dosage level? In 1785, the cardiac drug digitoxin was extracted from the foxglove (*photo*). (Since then, thousands of other biologically active compounds have been found in plants and many are used in modern medicines.) Or, suppose you're a chemical engineer studying rocket-fuel thrust: what amount of propulsive gases will a fuel produce? Perhaps you're on a team of environmental chemists examining coal samples: what quantity of air pollutants will a sample produce when burned? Or, maybe you're a polymer chemist preparing a plastic with unusual properties: how much of this new material will the polymerization reaction yield? You can answer countless questions like these with a knowledge of **stoichiometry** (pronounced "stoy-key-AHM-uh-tree"; from the Greek *stoicheion,* "element or part," and *metron,* "measure"), the study of the quantitative aspects of formulas and reactions.

IN THIS CHAPTER . . . We relate the mass of a substance to the number of chemical entities comprising it (atoms, ions, molecules, or formula units) and apply this relationship to formulas and equations.

- We discuss the *mole*, the chemist's unit for amount of a substance, and use it to convert between mass and number of entities.
- We also use it to derive a chemical formula from the results of mass analysis.
- We see whether two key types of formulas relate to molecular structures.
- We learn how to write chemical equations and how to balance them in terms of the amounts of substances reacting and produced.
- We calculate the amounts of reactants and products in a reaction and see why one of the reactants limits the amount of product that can form and, thus, the reaction yield.
- We discuss concentration and apply stoichiometry to reactions in solution.

3.1 • THE MOLE

In daily life, we often measure things by counting or by weighing: we weigh beans or rice, but we count eggs or pencils. And we use counting units (a dozen pencils) or mass units (a kilogram of beans) to express the amount. Similarly, daily life in the laboratory involves measuring substances. We want to know the numbers of chemical entities—atoms, ions, molecules, or formula units—that react with each other, but how can we possibly count or weigh such minute objects? As you'll see, chemists have devised a unit, called the *mole,* to *count chemical entities by weighing them.*

Imagine a Mole of . . . A mole of any ordinary object is a staggering amount: a mole of periods (.) lined up side by side would equal the radius of our galaxy; a mole of marbles stacked tightly together would cover the United States 70 miles deep. However, atoms and molecules are not ordinary objects: you can swallow a mole of water molecules (about 18 mL) in one gulp!

Defining the Mole

The **mole** (abbreviated **mol**) is the SI unit for *amount of substance*. It is defined as *the amount of a substance that contains the same number of entities as the number of atoms in 12 g of carbon-12.* This number, called **Avogadro's number** (in honor of the 19th-century Italian physicist Amedeo Avogadro), is enormous:

One mole (1 mol) contains 6.022×10^{23} entities (to four significant figures) (3.1)

A counting unit, like *dozen,* tells you the number of objects but not their mass; a mass unit, like *kilogram,* tells you the mass of the objects but not their number. The mole tells you both—the *number* of objects in a given *mass* of substance:

1 mol of carbon-12 contains 6.022×10^{23} carbon-12 atoms *and* has a mass of 12 g

What does it mean that the mole unit allows you to count entities by weighing the sample? Suppose you have a sample of carbon-12 and want to know the number of atoms present. You find that the sample weighs 6 g, so it is 0.5 mol of carbon-12 and contains 3.011×10^{23} atoms:

6 g of carbon-12 is 0.5 mol of carbon-12 and contains 3.011×10^{23} atoms

16
S
32.07

Knowing the amount (in moles), the mass (in grams), and the number of entities becomes very important when we mix different substances to run a reaction. The central relationship between masses on the atomic scale and on the macroscopic scale is the same for elements and compounds:

- *Elements.* The mass in **atomic mass units (amu)** of one atom of an element is the *same numerically* as the mass in **grams (g)** of 1 mole of atoms of the element. Recall from Chapter 2 that each atom of an element is considered to have the *atomic mass* given in the periodic table *(see margin)*. Thus,

1 atom of S	has a mass of	32.07 amu	and	1 mol (6.022×10^{23} atoms) of S	has a mass of	32.07 g
1 atom of Fe	has a mass of	55.85 amu	and	1 mol (6.022×10^{23} atoms) of Fe	has a mass of	55.85 g

Note, also, that since atomic masses are relative, 1 Fe atom weighs 55.85/32.07 as much as 1 S atom, and 1 mol of Fe weighs 55.85/32.07 as much as 1 mol of S.

- *Compounds.* The mass in **atomic mass units (amu)** of one molecule (or formula unit) of a compound is the *same numerically* as the mass in **grams (g)** of 1 mole of the compound. Thus, for example,

1 molecule of H_2O	has a mass of	18.02 amu	and	1 mol (6.022×10^{23} molecules) of H_2O	has a mass of	18.02 g
1 formula unit of NaCl	has a mass of	58.44 amu	and	1 mol (6.022×10^{23} formula units) of NaCl	has a mass of	58.44 g

Here, too, because masses are relative, 1 H_2O molecule weighs 18.02/58.44 as much as 1 NaCl formula unit, and 1 mol of H_2O weighs 18.02/58.44 as much as 1 mol of NaCl.

The two key points to remember about the importance of the mole unit are

- The *mole* lets us relate the *number* of entities to the *mass* of a sample of those entities.
- The mole maintains the *same numerical relationship* between mass on the atomic scale (atomic mass units, amu) and mass on the macroscopic scale (grams, g).

In everyday terms, a grocer *does not* know there are 1 dozen eggs from their weight or that there is 1 kilogram of beans from their count, because eggs and beans do not have fixed masses. But, by weighing out 63.55 g (1 mol) of copper, a chemist *does* know that there are 6.022×10^{23} copper atoms, because all copper atoms have an atomic mass of 63.55 amu. Figure 3.1 shows 1 mole of some familiar elements and compounds.

Figure 3.1 One mole (6.022×10^{23} entities) of some familiar substances. From left to right: 1 mol of copper (63.55 g), of liquid H_2O (18.02 g), of sodium chloride (table salt, 58.44 g), of sucrose (table sugar, 342.3 g), and of aluminum (26.98 g).

Determining Molar Mass

The **molar mass** ($\mathcal{M}$) of a substance is the mass per mole of its entities (atoms, molecules, or formula units) and has units of grams per mole (g/mol). The periodic table is indispensable for calculating molar mass:

1. *Elements.* To find the molar mass, look up the atomic mass and note whether the element is monatomic or molecular.

- *Monatomic elements.* The molar mass is the periodic-table value in grams per mole.* For example, the molar mass of neon is 20.18 g/mol, and the molar mass of gold is 197.0 g/mol.

*The mass value in the periodic table has no units because it is a *relative* atomic mass, given by the atomic mass (in amu) divided by 1 amu ($\frac{1}{12}$ mass of one ^{12}C atom in amu):

$$\text{Relative atomic mass} = \frac{\text{atomic mass } (\cancel{\text{amu}})}{\frac{1}{12}\text{ mass of } ^{12}\text{C } (\cancel{\text{amu}})}$$

Therefore, you use the same number for the atomic mass and for the molar mass.

- *Molecular elements.* You must know the formula to determine the molar mass (see Figure 2.15). For example, in air, oxygen exists most commonly as diatomic molecules, so the molar mass of O_2 is twice that of O:

$$\text{Molar mass } (\mathcal{M}) \text{ of } O_2 = 2 \times \mathcal{M} \text{ of O} = 2 \times 16.00 \text{ g/mol} = 32.00 \text{ g/mol}$$

The most common form of sulfur exists as octatomic molecules, S_8:

$$\mathcal{M} \text{ of } S_8 = 8 \times \mathcal{M} \text{ of S} = 8 \times 32.07 \text{ g/mol} = 256.6 \text{ g/mol}$$

2. *Compounds. The molar mass is the sum of the molar masses of the atoms in the formula.* Thus, from the formula of sulfur dioxide, SO_2, we know that 1 mol of SO_2 molecules contains 1 mol of S atoms and 2 mol of O atoms:

$$\mathcal{M} \text{ of } SO_2 = \mathcal{M} \text{ of S} + (2 \times \mathcal{M} \text{ of O}) = 32.07 \text{ g/mol} + (2 \times 16.00 \text{ g/mol}) = 64.07 \text{ g/mol}$$

Similarly, for ionic compounds, such as potassium sulfide (K_2S), we have

$$\mathcal{M} \text{ of } K_2S = (2 \times \mathcal{M} \text{ of K}) + \mathcal{M} \text{ of S} = (2 \times 39.10 \text{ g/mol}) + 32.07 \text{ g/mol} = 110.27 \text{ g/mol}$$

Thus, *subscripts in a formula refer to individual atoms (or ions) as well as to moles of atoms (or ions).* Table 3.1 summarizes these ideas for glucose, $C_6H_{12}O_6$ *(see margin),* the essential sugar in energy metabolism.

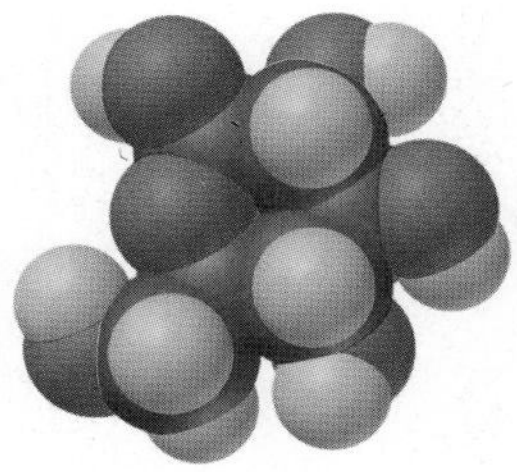

Glucose

Table 3.1 Information Contained in the Chemical Formula of Glucose, $C_6H_{12}O_6$ ($\mathcal{M}$ = 180.16 g/mol)

	Carbon (C)	Hydrogen (H)	Oxygen (O)
Atoms/molecule of compound	6 atoms	12 atoms	6 atoms
Moles of atoms/mole of compound	6 mol of atoms	12 mol of atoms	6 mol of atoms
Atoms/mole of compound	$6(6.022\times10^{23})$ atoms	$12(6.022\times10^{23})$ atoms	$6(6.022\times10^{23})$ atoms
Mass/molecule of compound	6(12.01 amu) = 72.06 amu	12(1.008 amu) = 12.10 amu	6(16.00 amu) = 96.00 amu
Mass/mole of compound	72.06 g	12.10 g	96.00 g

Converting Between Amount, Mass, and Number of Chemical Entities

One of the most common skills in the lab—and on exams—is converting between amount (mol), mass (g), and number of entities of a substance.

1. *Converting between amount and mass.* If you know the amount of a substance, you can find its mass, and vice versa. The molar mass ($\mathcal{M}$), which expresses the equivalence between 1 mole of a substance and its mass in grams, is the conversion factor.
   - *From amount (mol) to mass (g),* multiply by the molar mass:

$$\text{Mass (g)} = \text{amount (mol)} \times \frac{\text{no. of grams}}{1 \text{ mol}} \tag{3.2}$$

   - *From mass (g) to amount (mol),* divide by the molar mass (multiply by $1/\mathcal{M}$):

$$\text{Amount (mol)} = \text{mass (g)} \times \frac{1 \text{ mol}}{\text{no. of grams}} \tag{3.3}$$

2. *Converting between amount and number.* Similarly, if you know the amount (mol), you can find the number of entities, and vice versa. Avogadro's number, which expresses the equivalence between 1 mole of a substance and the number of entities it contains, is the conversion factor.
   - *From amount (mol) to number of entities,* multiply by Avogadro's number:

$$\text{No. of entities} = \text{amount (mol)} \times \frac{6.022\times10^{23} \text{ entities}}{1 \text{ mol}} \tag{3.4}$$

   - *From number of entities to amount (mol),* divide by Avogadro's number:

$$\text{Amount (mol)} = \text{no. of entities} \times \frac{1 \text{ mol}}{6.022\times10^{23} \text{ entities}} \tag{3.5}$$

Amount-Mass-Number Conversions Involving Elements We begin with amount-mass-number relationships of elements. As Figure 3.2 shows, *convert mass or number of entities to amount (mol) first.*

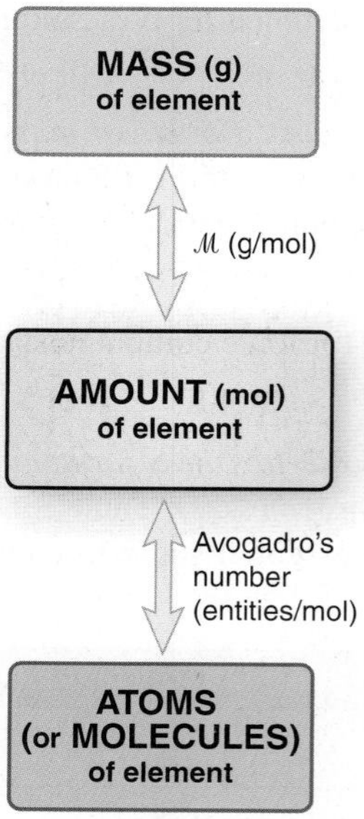

Figure 3.2 Mass-mole-number relationships for elements. To find the number of atoms (or molecules) in a given mass, or vice versa, convert to amount (mol) first. For molecular elements, Avogadro's number gives *molecules* per mole.

Let's work through a series of sample problems that show these conversions for both elements and compounds.

Sample Problem 3.1 Calculating the Mass of a Given Amount of an Element

Problem Silver (Ag) is used in jewelry and tableware but no longer in U.S. coins. How many grams of Ag are in 0.0342 mol of Ag?

Plan We know the amount of Ag (0.0342 mol) and have to find the mass (g). To convert units of *moles* of Ag to *grams* of Ag, we multiply by the *molar mass* of Ag, which we find in the periodic table (see the road map).

Road Map

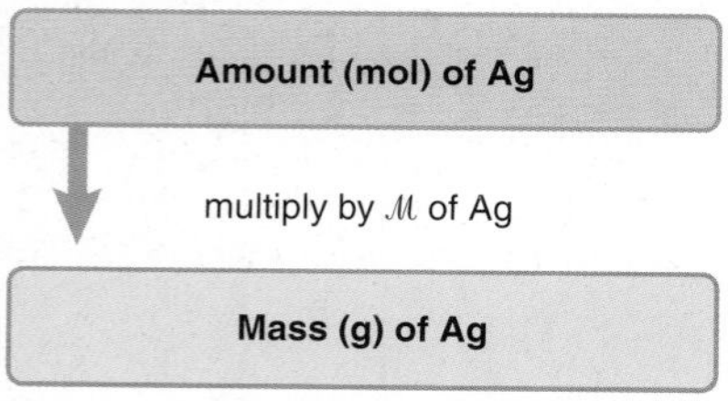

Solution Converting from amount (mol) of Ag to mass (g):

$$\text{Mass (g) of Ag} = 0.0342 \cancel{\text{mol Ag}} \times \frac{107.9 \text{ g Ag}}{1 \cancel{\text{mol Ag}}} = \boxed{3.69 \text{ g Ag}}$$

Check We rounded the mass to three significant figures because the amount (mol) has three. The units are correct. About 0.03 mol × 100 g/mol gives 3 g; the small mass makes sense because 0.0342 is a small fraction of a mole.

Follow-Up Problem 3.1 Graphite is the crystalline form of carbon used in "lead" pencils. How many moles of carbon are in 315 mg of graphite? Include a road map that shows how you planned the solution. (See Brief Solutions at the end of the chapter for solutions to this and all other follow-up problems.)

Sample Problem 3.2 Calculating the Number of Entities in a Given Amount of an Element

Problem Gallium (Ga) is a key element in solar panels, calculators, and other light-sensitive electronic devices. How many Ga atoms are in 2.85×10^{-3} mol of gallium?

Plan We know the amount of gallium (2.85×10^{-3} mol) and need the number of Ga atoms. We multiply amount (mol) by Avogadro's number to find number of atoms (see the road map).

Solution Converting from amount (mol) of Ga to number of atoms:

$$\text{No. of Ga atoms} = 2.85\times10^{-3}\ \cancel{\text{mol Ga}} \times \frac{6.022\times10^{23}\ \text{Ga atoms}}{1\ \cancel{\text{mol Ga}}}$$

$$= 1.72\times10^{21}\ \text{Ga atoms}$$

Road Map

Amount (mol) of Ga

↓ multiply by 6.022×10^{23} atoms/mol

Number of Ga atoms

Check The number of atoms has three significant figures because the number of moles does. When we round amount (mol) of Ga and Avogadro's number, we have $\sim(3\times10^{-3}\ \text{mol})(6\times10^{23}\ \text{atoms/mol}) = 18\times10^{20}$, or 1.8×10^{21} atoms, so our answer seems correct.

Follow-Up Problem 3.2 At rest, a person inhales 9.72×10^{21} nitrogen molecules in an average breath of air. How many moles of nitrogen atoms are inhaled? (*Hint:* In air, nitrogen occurs as a diatomic molecule.) Include a road map that shows how you planned the solution.

For the next problem, note that mass and number of entities relate directly to amount (mol), but *not* to each other. Therefore, *to convert between mass and number, first convert to amount.*

Sample Problem 3.3 Calculating the Number of Entities in a Given Mass of an Element

Problem Iron (Fe) is the main component of steel and, thus, the most important metal in industrial society; it is also essential in the body. How many Fe atoms are in 95.8 g of Fe?

Plan We know the mass of Fe (95.8 g) and need the number of Fe atoms. We cannot convert directly from mass to number, so we first convert to amount (mol) by dividing mass of Fe by its molar mass. Then, we multiply amount (mol) by Avogadro's number to find number of atoms (see the road map).

Road Map

Mass (g) of Fe

↓ divide by $\mathcal{M}$ of Fe

Amount (mol) of Fe

↓ multiply by 6.022×10^{23} atoms/mol

Number of Fe atoms

Solution Converting from mass (g) of Fe to amount (mol):

$$\text{Moles of Fe} = 95.8\ \cancel{\text{g Fe}} \times \frac{1\ \text{mol Fe}}{55.85\ \cancel{\text{g Fe}}} = 1.72\ \text{mol Fe}$$

Converting from amount (mol) of Fe to number of Fe atoms:

$$\text{No. of Fe atoms} = 1.72\ \cancel{\text{mol Fe}} \times \frac{6.022\times10^{23}\ \text{atoms Fe}}{1\ \cancel{\text{mol Fe}}}$$

$$= 10.4\times10^{23}\ \text{atoms Fe}$$

$$= 1.04\times10^{24}\ \text{atoms Fe}$$

Check Rounding the mass and the molar mass of Fe, we have $\sim100\ \text{g}/(\sim60\ \text{g/mol}) = 1.7$ mol. Therefore, the number of atoms should be a bit less than twice Avogadro's number: $<2(6\times10^{23}) = <1.2\times10^{24}$, so the answer seems correct.

Follow-Up Problem 3.3 Manganese (Mn) is a transition element essential for the growth of bones. What is the mass in grams of 3.22×10^{20} Mn atoms, the number found in 1 kg of bone? Include a road map that shows how you planned the solution.

Amount-Mass-Number Conversions Involving Compounds Only one new step is needed to solve amount-mass-number problems involving compounds: we need the chemical formula to find the molar mass and the amount of each element in the compound. The relationships are shown in Figure 3.3 on the next page, and Sample Problems 3.4 and 3.5 apply them to compounds with simple and more complicated formulas, respectively.

Figure 3.3 Amount-mass-number relationships for compounds. Use the chemical formula to find the amount (mol) of each element in a compound.

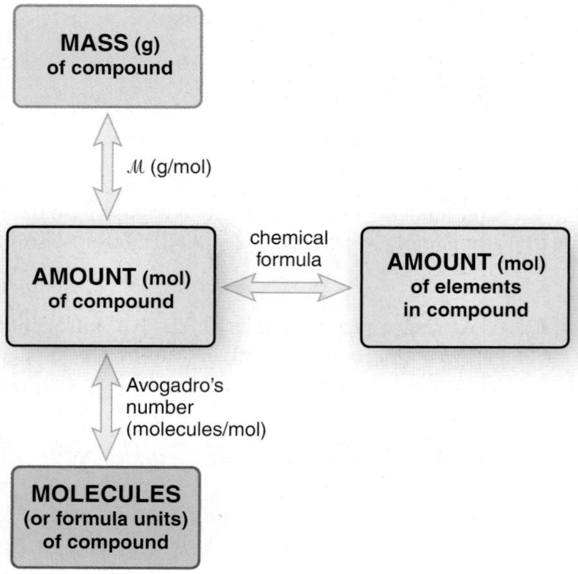

Sample Problem 3.4 Calculating the Number of Chemical Entities in a Given Mass of a Compound I

Problem Nitrogen dioxide is a component of urban smog that forms from gases in car exhaust. How many molecules are in 8.92 g of nitrogen dioxide?

Plan We know the mass of compound (8.92 g) and need to find the number of molecules. As you just saw in Sample Problem 3.3, to convert mass to number of entities, we have to find the amount (mol). To do so, we divide the mass by the molar mass ($\mathcal{M}$), which we calculate from the molecular formula (see Sample Problem 2.15). Once we have the amount (mol), we multiply by Avogadro's number to find the number of molecules (see the road map).

Road Map

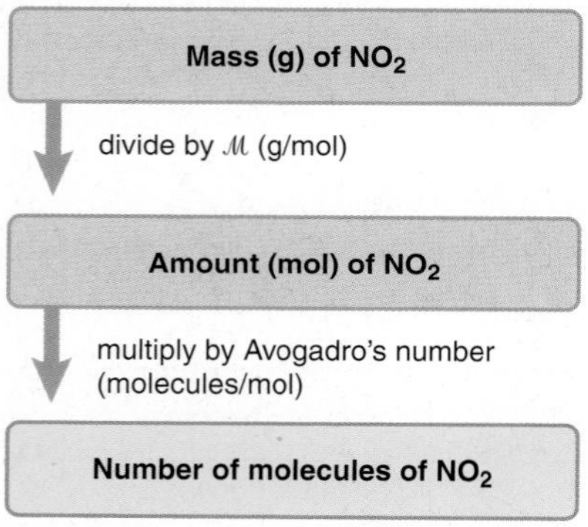

Solution The formula is NO_2. Calculating the molar mass:

$$\begin{aligned}\mathcal{M} &= (1 \times \mathcal{M} \text{ of N}) + (2 \times \mathcal{M} \text{ of O})\\ &= 14.01 \text{ g/mol} + (2 \times 16.00 \text{ g/mol})\\ &= 46.01 \text{ g/mol}\end{aligned}$$

Converting from mass (g) of NO_2 to amount (mol):

$$\begin{aligned}\text{Amount (mol) of } NO_2 &= 8.92 \cancel{\text{g } NO_2} \times \frac{1 \text{ mol } NO_2}{46.01 \cancel{\text{g } NO_2}}\\ &= 0.194 \text{ mol } NO_2\end{aligned}$$

Converting from amount (mol) of NO_2 to number of molecules:

$$\begin{aligned}\text{No. of molecules} &= 0.194 \cancel{\text{mol } NO_2} \times \frac{6.022\times10^{23} \text{ } NO_2 \text{ molecules}}{1 \cancel{\text{mol } NO_2}}\\ &= 1.17\times10^{23} \text{ } NO_2 \text{ molecules}\end{aligned}$$

Check Rounding, we get $(\sim0.2 \text{ mol})(6\times10^{23}) = 1.2\times10^{23}$, so the answer seems correct.

Follow-Up Problem 3.4 Fluoride ion is added to drinking water to prevent tooth decay. What is the mass (g) of sodium fluoride in a liter of water that contains 1.19×10^{19} formula units of the compound? Include a road map that shows how you planned the solution.

Sample Problem 3.5 Calculating the Number of Chemical Entities in a Given Mass of a Compound II

Problem Ammonium carbonate is a white solid that decomposes with warming. It has many uses, for example, as a component in baking powder, fire extinguishers, and smelling salts.
(a) How many formula units are in 41.6 g of ammonium carbonate?
(b) How many O atoms are in this sample?

Plan **(a)** We know the mass of compound (41.6 g) and need to find the number of formula units. As in Sample Problem 3.4, we find the amount (mol) and then multiply by Avogadro's number to find the number of formula units. [The road map shows the steps for part (a).] **(b)** To find the number of O atoms, we multiply the number of formula units by the number of O atoms in one formula unit.

Road Map

Mass (g) of $(NH_4)_2CO_3$

↓ divide by $\mathcal{M}$ (g/mol)

Amount (mol) of $(NH_4)_2CO_3$

↓ multiply by 6.022×10^{23} formula units/mol

Number of formula units of $(NH_4)_2CO_3$

Solution **(a)** The formula is $(NH_4)_2CO_3$ (see Table 2.5). Calculating the molar mass:

$$\begin{aligned}\mathcal{M} &= (2 \times \mathcal{M} \text{ of N}) + (8 \times \mathcal{M} \text{ of H}) + (1 \times \mathcal{M} \text{ of C}) + (3 \times \mathcal{M} \text{ of O}) \\ &= (2 \times 14.01 \text{ g/mol N}) + (8 \times 1.008 \text{ g/mol H}) + 12.01 \text{ g/mol C} \\ &\quad + (3 \times 16.00 \text{ g/mol O}) \\ &= 96.09 \text{ g/mol } (NH_4)_2CO_3\end{aligned}$$

Converting from mass (g) to amount (mol):

$$\begin{aligned}\text{Amount (mol) of } (NH_4)_2CO_3 &= 41.6 \cancel{\text{g } (NH_4)_2CO_3} \times \frac{1 \text{ mol } (NH_4)_2CO_3}{96.09 \cancel{\text{g } (NH_4)_2CO_3}} \\ &= 0.433 \text{ mol } (NH_4)_2CO_3\end{aligned}$$

Converting from amount (mol) to formula units:

$$\begin{aligned}\text{Formula units of } (NH_4)_2CO_3 &= 0.433 \cancel{\text{mol } (NH_4)_2CO_3} \\ &\quad \times \frac{6.022\times10^{23} \text{ formula units } (NH_4)_2CO_3}{1 \cancel{\text{mol } (NH_4)_2CO_3}} \\ &= 2.61\times10^{23} \text{ formula units } (NH_4)_2CO_3\end{aligned}$$

(b) Finding the number of O atoms:

$$\begin{aligned}\text{No. of O atoms} &= 2.61\times10^{23} \cancel{\text{formula units } (NH_4)_2CO_3} \times \frac{3 \text{ O atoms}}{1 \cancel{\text{formula unit } (NH_4)_2CO_3}} \\ &= 7.83\times10^{23} \text{ O atoms}\end{aligned}$$

Check In (a), the units are correct. Since the mass is less than half the molar mass ($\sim42/96 < 0.5$), the number of formula units should be less than half Avogadro's number ($\sim2.6\times10^{23}/6.0\times10^{23} < 0.5$).

Comment A *common mistake* is to forget the subscript 2 outside the parentheses in $(NH_4)_2CO_3$, which would give a much lower molar mass.

Follow-Up Problem 3.5 Tetraphosphorus decaoxide reacts with water to form phosphoric acid, a major industrial acid. In the laboratory, the oxide is a drying agent.
(a) What is the mass (g) of 4.65×10^{22} molecules of tetraphosphorus decaoxide?
(b) How many P atoms are present in this sample?

The Importance of Mass Percent

For many purposes, it is important to know how much of an element is present in a given amount of compound. A biochemist may want the ionic composition of a mineral nutrient; an atmospheric chemist may be studying the amount of carbon in a fuel; a materials scientist may want the metalloid composition of a semiconductor. In this section, we find the composition of a compound in terms of mass percent and use it to find the mass of each element in the compound.

Determining Mass Percent from a Chemical Formula Each element contributes a fraction of a compound's mass, and that fraction multiplied by 100 gives the element's mass percent. Finding the mass percent is similar on the molecular and molar scales:

- *For a molecule (or formula unit) of compound,* use the molecular (or formula) mass and chemical formula to find the mass percent of any element X in the compound:

$$\text{Mass \% of element X} = \frac{\text{atoms of X in formula} \times \text{atomic mass of X(amu)}}{\text{molecular (or formula) mass of compound (amu)}} \times 100$$

- *For a mole of compound,* use the molar mass and formula to find the mass percent of each element on a mole basis:

$$\text{Mass \% of element X} = \frac{\text{moles of X in formula} \times \text{molar mass of X (g/mol)}}{\text{mass (g) of 1 mol of compound}} \times 100 \quad (3.6)$$

As always, the individual mass percents add up to 100% (within rounding). In Sample Problem 3.6, we determine the mass percent of each element in a compound.

Sample Problem 3.6 Calculating the Mass Percent of Each Element in a Compound from the Formula

Problem In mammals, lactose (milk sugar) is metabolized to glucose ($C_6H_{12}O_6$), the key nutrient for generating chemical potential energy. What is the mass percent of each element in glucose?

Road Map

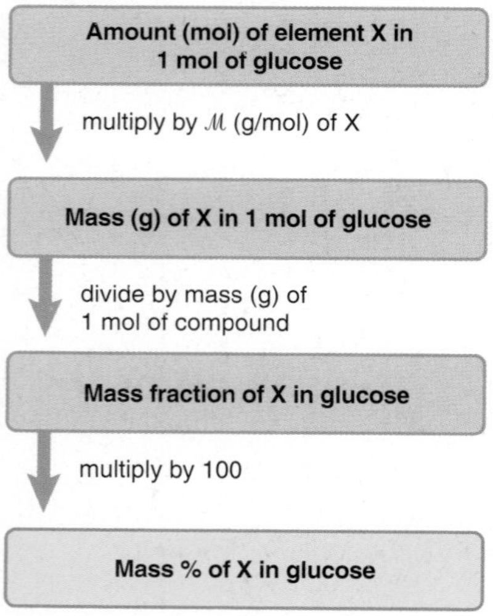

Plan We know the relative amounts (mol) of the elements from the formula (6 C, 12 H, 6 O), and we have to find the mass % of each element. We multiply the amount of each by its molar mass to find its mass. Dividing each mass by the mass of 1 mol of glucose gives the mass fraction of each element, and multiplying by 100 gives each mass %. The calculation steps for any element (X) are shown in the road map.

Solution Converting amount (mol) of C to mass (g):
We have 6 mol of C in 1 mol of glucose, so

$$\text{Mass (g) of C} = 6\ \cancel{\text{mol C}} \times \frac{12.01\ \text{g C}}{1\ \cancel{\text{mol C}}} = 72.06\ \text{g C}$$

Calculating the mass of 1 mol of glucose ($C_6H_{12}O_6$):

$$\begin{aligned}\mathcal{M} &= (6 \times \mathcal{M}\text{ of C}) + (12 \times \mathcal{M}\text{ of H}) + (6 \times \mathcal{M}\text{ of O})\\ &= (6 \times 12.01\ \text{g/mol C}) + (12 \times 1.008\ \text{g/mol H}) + (6 \times 16.00\ \text{g/mol O})\\ &= 180.16\ \text{g/mol}\ C_6H_{12}O_6\end{aligned}$$

Finding the mass fraction of C in glucose:

$$\text{Mass fraction of C} = \frac{\text{total mass of C}}{\text{mass of 1 mol glucose}} = \frac{72.06\ \text{g C}}{180.16\ \text{g glucose}} = 0.4000$$

Changing to mass %:

$$\text{Mass \% of C} = \text{mass fraction of C} \times 100 = 0.4000 \times 100$$

$$= 40.00\ \text{mass \% C}$$

Combining the steps for each of the other elements in glucose:

$$\text{Mass \% of H} = \frac{\text{mol H} \times \mathcal{M}\text{ of H}}{\text{mass of 1 mol glucose}} \times 100 = \frac{12\ \cancel{\text{mol H}} \times \frac{1.008\ \text{g H}}{1\ \cancel{\text{mol H}}}}{180.16\ \text{g glucose}} \times 100$$

$$= 6.714\ \text{mass \% H}$$

$$\text{Mass \% of O} = \frac{\text{mol O} \times \mathcal{M}\text{ of O}}{\text{mass of 1 mol glucose}} \times 100 = \frac{6\ \cancel{\text{mol O}} \times \frac{16.00\ \text{g O}}{1\ \cancel{\text{mol O}}}}{180.16\ \text{g glucose}} \times 100$$

$$= 53.29\ \text{mass \% O}$$

Check The answers make sense: even though there are equal numbers of moles of O and of C in the compound, the mass % of O is greater than the mass % of C because the molar mass of O is greater than the molar mass of C. The mass % of H is small because the molar mass of H is small. The sum of the mass percents is 100.00%.

Comment From here on, you should be able to determine the molar mass of a compound, so that calculation will no longer be shown.

Follow-Up Problem 3.6 Agronomists base the effectiveness of fertilizers on their nitrogen content. Ammonium nitrate is a common fertilizer. Calculate the mass percent of N in ammonium nitrate.

Determining the Mass of an Element from Its Mass Percent Sample Problem 3.6 shows that *an element always constitutes the same fraction of the mass of a given compound.* We obtained that fraction by dividing the total mass of element in a formula unit by the mass of one mole of the compound (see Equation 3.6). We can use that ratio directly to find the mass of element in any mass of a compound:

$$\text{Mass of element} = \text{mass of compound} \times \frac{\text{mass of element in 1 mol of compound}}{\text{mass of 1 mol of compound}} \quad (3.7)$$

For example, to find the mass of oxygen in 15.5 g of nitrogen dioxide, we have

$$\text{Mass (g) of O} = 15.5 \text{ g } NO_2 \times \frac{2 \text{ mol} \times \mathcal{M} \text{ of O (g/mol)}}{\text{mass (g) of 1 mol } NO_2}$$

$$= 15.5 \cancel{\text{g } NO_2} \times \frac{32.00 \text{ g O}}{46.01 \cancel{\text{g } NO_2}} = 10.8 \text{ g O}$$

Sample Problem 3.7 Calculating the Mass of an Element in a Compound

Problem Use the information in Sample Problem 3.6 to determine the mass (g) of carbon in 16.55 g of glucose.

Plan To find the mass of C in the sample of glucose, we multiply the mass of the sample by the mass of 6 mol of C divided by the mass of 1 mol of glucose.

Solution Finding the mass of C in a given mass of glucose:

$$\text{Mass (g) of C} = \text{mass (g) of glucose} \times \frac{6 \text{ mol C} \times \mathcal{M} \text{ of C (g/mol)}}{\text{mass (g) of 1 mol glucose}}$$

$$= 16.55 \cancel{\text{g glucose}} \times \frac{72.06 \text{ g C}}{180.16 \cancel{\text{g glucose}}} = 6.620 \text{ g C}$$

Check Rounding shows that the answer is "in the right ballpark": 16 g times less than 0.5 parts by mass should be less than 8 g.

Follow-Up Problem 3.7 Use the information in Follow-Up Problem 3.6 to find the mass (g) of N in 35.8 kg of ammonium nitrate.

Summary of Section 3.1

- A mole of substance is the amount that contains Avogadro's number (6.022×10^{23}) of chemical entities (atoms, molecules, or formula units).
- The mass (in grams) of a mole of the entity has the same numerical value as the mass (in amu) of the individual entity. Thus, the mole allows us to count entities by weighing them.
- Using the molar mass ($\mathcal{M}$, g/mol) of an element (or compound) and Avogadro's number as conversion factors, we can convert among amount (mol), mass (g), and number of entities.
- The mass fraction of element X in a compound is used to find the mass of X in a given amount of the compound.

3.2 • DETERMINING THE FORMULA OF AN UNKNOWN COMPOUND

In Sample Problems 3.6 and 3.7, we used a compound's formula to find the mass percent (or mass fraction) of each element in it *and* the mass of each element in any size sample of it. In this section, we do the reverse: we use the masses of elements in a compound to find the formula. Then, we look briefly at the relationship between molecular formula and molecular structure.

Let's compare three common types of formula, using hydrogen peroxide as an example:

- The **empirical formula** is derived from mass analysis. It shows the *lowest* whole number of moles, and thus the *relative* number of atoms, of each element in the compound. For example, in hydrogen peroxide, there is 1 part by mass of hydrogen for every 16 parts by mass of oxygen. Because the atomic mass of hydrogen is 1.008 amu and that of oxygen is 16.00 amu, there is one H atom for every O atom. Thus, the empirical formula is HO.

Recall from Section 2.8, p. 59, that

- The **molecular formula** shows the *actual* number of atoms of each element in a molecule: the molecular formula is H_2O_2, twice the empirical formula.
- The **structural formula** shows the relative *placement and connections of atoms* in the molecule: the structural formula is H—O—O—H.

Let's see how to determine empirical and molecular formulas.

Empirical Formulas

A chemist studying an unknown compound goes through a three-step process to find the empirical formula:

1. Determine the mass (g) of each component element.
2. Convert each mass (g) to amount (mol), and write a preliminary formula.
3. Convert the amounts (mol) mathematically to whole-number (integer) subscripts. To accomplish this math conversion,
   - Divide each subscript by the smallest subscript, and
   - If necessary, multiply through by the *smallest integer* that turns all subscripts into integers.

Sample Problem 3.8 demonstrates these math steps.

Sample Problem 3.8 Determining an Empirical Formula from Amounts of Elements

Road Map

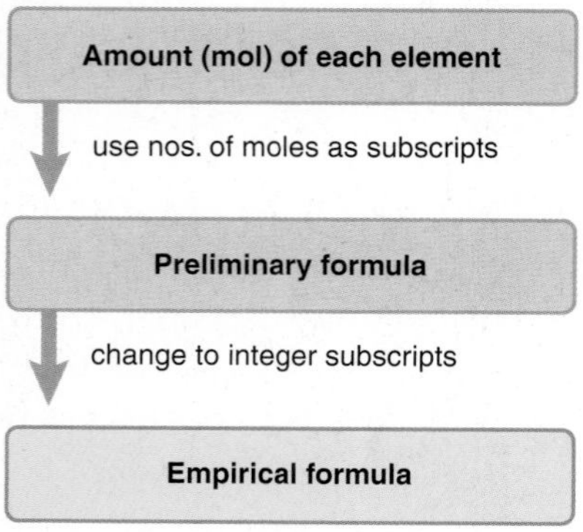

Problem A sample of an unknown compound contains 0.21 mol of zinc, 0.14 mol of phosphorus, and 0.56 mol of oxygen. What is the empirical formula?

Plan We are given the amount (mol) of each element as fractions. We use these fractional amounts directly in a preliminary formula as subscripts of the element symbols. Then, we convert the fractions to whole numbers.

Solution Using the fractions to write a preliminary formula, with the symbols Zn for zinc, P for phosphorus, and O for oxygen:

$$Zn_{0.21}P_{0.14}O_{0.56}$$

Converting the fractions to whole numbers:

1. Divide each subscript by the smallest one, which in this case is 0.14:

$$Zn_{\frac{0.21}{0.14}}P_{\frac{0.14}{0.14}}O_{\frac{0.56}{0.14}} \longrightarrow Zn_{1.5}P_{1.0}O_{4.0}$$

2. Multiply through by the *smallest integer* that turns all subscripts into integers. We multiply by 2 to make 1.5 (the subscript for Zn) into an integer:

$$Zn_{(1.5\times2)}P_{(1.0\times2)}O_{(4.0\times2)} \longrightarrow Zn_{3.0}P_{2.0}O_{8.0}, \quad \text{or} \quad Zn_3P_2O_8$$

Check The integer subscripts must be the smallest integers with the same ratio as the original fractional numbers of moles: 3/2/8 is *the same ratio* as 0.21/0.14/0.56.

Comment A more conventional way to write this formula is $Zn_3(PO_4)_2$; this compound is zinc phosphate, formerly used widely as a dental cement.

Follow-Up Problem 3.8 A sample of a white solid contains 0.170 mol of boron and 0.255 mol of hydrogen. What is the empirical formula?

Sample Problems 3.9–3.11 show how other types of compositional data are used to determine chemical formulas.

Sample Problem 3.9 Determining an Empirical Formula from Masses of Elements

Problem Analysis of a sample of an ionic compound yields 2.82 g of Na, 4.35 g of Cl, and 7.83 g of O. What is the empirical formula and the name of the compound?

Plan This problem is similar to Sample Problem 3.8, except that we are given element *masses* that we must convert into integer subscripts. We first divide each mass by the element's molar mass to find amount (mol). Then we construct a preliminary formula and convert the amounts (mol) to integers.

Solution Finding amount (mol) of each element:

$$\text{Amount (mol) of Na} = 2.82 \cancel{\text{g Na}} \times \frac{1 \text{ mol Na}}{22.99 \cancel{\text{g Na}}} = 0.123 \text{ mol Na}$$

$$\text{Amount (mol) of Cl} = 4.35 \cancel{\text{g Cl}} \times \frac{1 \text{ mol Cl}}{35.45 \cancel{\text{g Cl}}} = 0.123 \text{ mol Cl}$$

$$\text{Amount (mol) of O} = 7.83 \cancel{\text{g O}} \times \frac{1 \text{ mol O}}{16.00 \cancel{\text{g O}}} = 0.489 \text{ mol O}$$

Constructing a preliminary formula: $Na_{0.123}Cl_{0.123}O_{0.489}$

Converting to integer subscripts (dividing all by the smallest subscript):

$$Na_{\frac{0.123}{0.123}}Cl_{\frac{0.123}{0.123}}O_{\frac{0.489}{0.123}} \longrightarrow Na_{1.00}Cl_{1.00}O_{3.98} \approx Na_1Cl_1O_4, \quad \text{or} \quad NaClO_4$$

The empirical formula is $NaClO_4$; the name is sodium perchlorate.

Check The numbers of moles seem correct because the masses of Na and Cl are slightly more than 0.1 of their molar masses. The mass of O is greatest and its molar mass is smallest, so it should have the greatest number of moles. The ratio of subscripts, 1/1/4, is the same as the ratio of moles, 0.123/0.123/0.489 (within rounding).

Follow-Up Problem 3.9 An unknown metal M reacts with sulfur to form a compound with the formula M_2S_3. If 3.12 g of M reacts with 2.88 g of S, what are the names of M and M_2S_3? [*Hint:* Determine the amount (mol) of S and use the formula to find the amount (mol) of M.]

Molecular Formulas

If we know the molar mass of a compound, we can use the empirical formula to obtain the molecular formula, which uses as subscripts the *actual* numbers of moles of each element in 1 mol of compound. For some compounds, such as water (H_2O), ammonia (NH_3), and methane (CH_4), the empirical and molecular formulas are identical, but for many others, the molecular formula is a *whole-number multiple* of the empirical formula. As you saw, hydrogen peroxide has the empirical formula HO. Dividing the molar mass of hydrogen peroxide (34.02 g/mol) by the empirical formula mass of HO (17.01 g/mol) gives the whole-number multiple:

$$\text{Whole-number multiple} = \frac{\text{molar mass (g/mol)}}{\text{empirical formula mass (g/mol)}} = \frac{34.02\ \cancel{\text{g/mol}}}{17.01\ \cancel{\text{g/mol}}} = 2.000 = 2$$

Multiplying the empirical formula subscripts by 2 gives the molecular formula:

$$H_{(1\times2)}O_{(1\times2)} \text{ gives } H_2O_2$$

Instead of giving compositional data as masses of each element, analytical laboratories provide mass percents. To find the molecular formula, we first determine the empirical formula and then the whole-number multiple:

1. Assume 100.0 g of compound to express each mass percent directly as mass (g).
2. Convert each mass (g) to amount (mol).
3. Derive the empirical formula.
4. Divide the compound's molar mass by the empirical formula mass to find the whole-number multiple.
5. Multiply each subscript in the empirical formula by the multiple.

Sample Problem 3.10 Determining a Molecular Formula from Elemental Analysis and Molar Mass

Problem During excessive physical activity, lactic acid ($\mathcal{M}$ = 90.08 g/mol) forms in muscle tissue and is responsible for muscle soreness. Elemental analysis shows that this compound contains 40.0 mass % C, 6.71 mass % H, and 53.3 mass % O.
(a) Determine the empirical formula of lactic acid.
(b) Determine the molecular formula.

(a) Determining the empirical formula

Plan We know the mass % of each element and must convert each to an integer subscript. The mass of the sample of lactic acid is not given, but the mass percents are the same for any sample of it. Therefore, we assume there is 100.0 g of lactic acid and express each mass % as a number of grams. Then, we construct the empirical formula as in Sample Problem 3.9.

Solution Expressing mass % as mass (g) by assuming 100.0 g of lactic acid:

$$\text{Mass (g) of C} = \frac{40.0 \text{ parts C by mass}}{100 \text{ parts by mass}} \times 100.0 \text{ g} = 40.0 \text{ g C}$$

Similarly, we have 6.71 g of H and 53.3 g of O.

Converting from mass (g) of each element to amount (mol):

$$\text{Amount (mol) of C} = \text{mass of C} \times \frac{1}{\mathcal{M} \text{ of C}} = 40.0\ \cancel{\text{g C}} \times \frac{1 \text{ mol C}}{12.01\ \cancel{\text{g C}}} = 3.33 \text{ mol C}$$

Similarly, we have 6.66 mol of H and 3.33 mol of O.

Constructing the preliminary formula: $C_{3.33}H_{6.66}O_{3.33}$

Converting to integer subscripts:

$$C_{\frac{3.33}{3.33}}H_{\frac{6.66}{3.33}}O_{\frac{3.33}{3.33}} \longrightarrow C_{1.00}H_{2.00}O_{1.00} = C_1H_2O_1, \text{ the empirical formula is } CH_2O$$

Check The numbers of moles seem correct: the masses of C and O are each slightly more than 3 times their molar masses (e.g., for C, 40 g/(12 g/mol) > 3 mol), and the mass of H is over 6 times its molar mass of 1.

(b) Determining the molecular formula

Plan The molecular formula subscripts are whole-number multiples of the empirical formula subscripts. To find this multiple, we divide the given molar mass (90.08 g/mol) by the empirical formula mass, which we find from the sum of the elements' molar masses. Then we multiply each subscript in the empirical formula by the multiple.

Solution The empirical formula mass is 30.03 g/mol. Finding the whole-number multiple:

$$\text{Whole-number multiple} = \frac{\mathcal{M} \text{ of lactic acid}}{\mathcal{M} \text{ of empirical formula}} = \frac{90.08\ \cancel{\text{g/mol}}}{30.03\ \cancel{\text{g/mol}}} = 3.000 = 3$$

Determining the molecular formula:

$$C_{(1\times3)}H_{(2\times3)}O_{(1\times3)} = C_3H_6O_3$$

Check The calculated molecular formula has the same ratio of moles of elements (3/6/3) as the empirical formula (1/2/1) and corresponds to the given molar mass:

$$\mathcal{M} \text{ of lactic acid} = (3 \times \mathcal{M} \text{ of C}) + (6 \times \mathcal{M} \text{ of H}) + (3 \times \mathcal{M} \text{ of O})$$
$$= (3 \times 12.01 \text{ g/mol}) + (6 \times 1.008 \text{ g/mol}) + (3 \times 16.00 \text{ g/mol})$$
$$= 90.08 \text{ g/mol}$$

Follow-Up Problem 3.10 One of the most widespread environmental carcinogens (cancer-causing agents) is benzo[*a*]pyrene ($\mathcal{M}$ = 252.30 g/mol). It is found in coal dust, cigarette smoke, and even charcoal-grilled meat. Analysis of this hydrocarbon shows 95.21 mass % C and 4.79 mass % H. What is the molecular formula of benzo[*a*]pyrene?

Combustion Analysis of Organic Compounds Still another type of compositional data is obtained through **combustion analysis,** used to measure the amounts of carbon and hydrogen in a combustible organic compound. The unknown compound is burned in an excess of pure O_2, and the H_2O and CO_2 that form are absorbed in separate containers (Figure 3.4). By weighing the absorbers before and after combustion, we find the masses of CO_2 and H_2O and use them to find the masses of C and H in the compound; from these results, we find the empirical formula. Many organic compounds also contain oxygen, nitrogen, or a halogen. As long as the third element doesn't interfere with the absorption of H_2O and CO_2, we calculate its mass by subtracting the masses of C and H from the original mass of the compound.

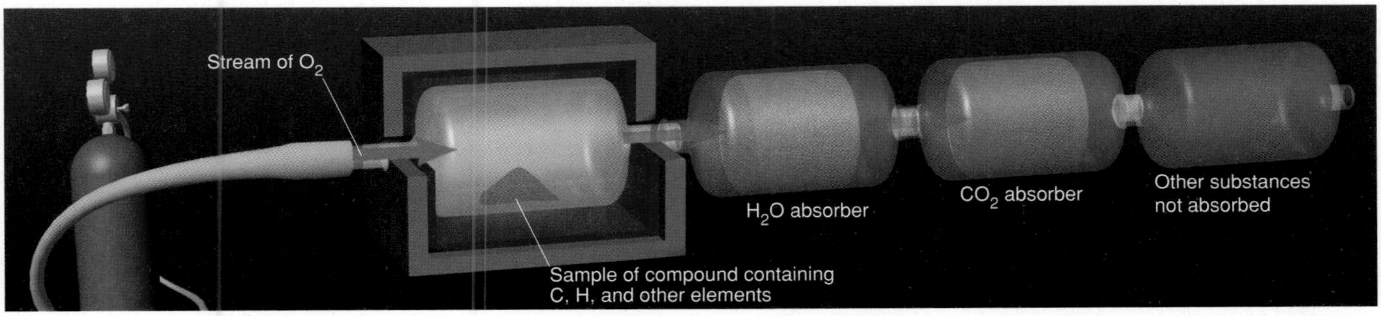

Figure 3.4 Combustion apparatus for determining formulas of organic compounds. A sample of an organic compound is burned in a stream of O_2. The resulting H_2O is absorbed by $Mg(ClO_4)_2$, and the CO_2 is absorbed by NaOH on asbestos.

Sample Problem 3.11 Determining a Molecular Formula from Combustion Analysis

Problem Vitamin C ($\mathcal{M}$ = 176.12 g/mol) is a compound of C, H, and O found in many natural sources, especially citrus fruits. When a 1.000-g sample of vitamin C is burned in a combustion apparatus, the following data are obtained:

$$\text{Mass of } CO_2 \text{ absorber after combustion} = 85.35 \text{ g}$$
$$\text{Mass of } CO_2 \text{ absorber before combustion} = 83.85 \text{ g}$$
$$\text{Mass of } H_2O \text{ absorber after combustion} = 37.96 \text{ g}$$
$$\text{Mass of } H_2O \text{ absorber before combustion} = 37.55 \text{ g}$$

What is the molecular formula of vitamin C?

Plan We find the masses of CO_2 and H_2O by subtracting the masses of the absorbers before and after the combustion. From the mass of CO_2, we use Equation 3.7 to find the mass of C. Similarly, we find the mass of H from the mass of H_2O. The mass of vitamin C (1.000 g) minus the sum of the masses of C and H gives the mass of O, the third element present. Then, we proceed as in Sample Problem 3.10: calculate amount (mol) of each element using its molar mass, construct the empirical formula, determine the whole-number multiple from the given molar mass, and construct the molecular formula.

Solution Finding the masses of combustion products:

$$\text{Mass (g) of } CO_2 = \text{mass of } CO_2 \text{ absorber after} - \text{mass before}$$
$$= 85.35\text{ g} - 83.85\text{ g} = 1.50\text{ g } CO_2$$
$$\text{Mass (g) of } H_2O = \text{mass of } H_2O \text{ absorber after} - \text{mass before}$$
$$= 37.96\text{ g} - 37.55\text{ g} = 0.41\text{ g } H_2O$$

Calculating masses (g) of C and H using Equation 3.7:

$$\text{Mass of element} = \text{mass of compound} \times \frac{\text{mass of element in 1 mol of compound}}{\text{mass of 1 mol of compound}}$$

$$\text{Mass (g) of C} = \text{mass of } CO_2 \times \frac{1\text{ mol C} \times \mathcal{M}\text{ of C}}{\text{mass of 1 mol } CO_2} = 1.50\ \cancel{\text{g } CO_2} \times \frac{12.01\text{ g C}}{44.01\ \cancel{\text{g } CO_2}}$$
$$= 0.409\text{ g C}$$

$$\text{Mass (g) of H} = \text{mass of } H_2O \times \frac{2\text{ mol H} \times \mathcal{M}\text{ of H}}{\text{mass of 1 mol } H_2O} = 0.41\ \cancel{\text{g } H_2O} \times \frac{2.016\text{ g H}}{18.02\ \cancel{\text{g } H_2O}}$$
$$= 0.046\text{ g H}$$

Calculating mass (g) of O:

$$\text{Mass (g) of O} = \text{mass of vitamin C sample} - (\text{mass of C} + \text{mass of H})$$
$$= 1.000\text{ g} - (0.409\text{ g} + 0.046\text{ g}) = 0.545\text{ g O}$$

Finding the amounts (mol) of elements: Dividing the mass (g) of each element by its molar mass gives 0.0341 mol of C, 0.046 mol of H, and 0.0341 mol of O.

Constructing the preliminary formula: $C_{0.0341}H_{0.046}O_{0.0341}$

Determining the empirical formula: Dividing through by the smallest subscript gives

$$C_{\frac{0.0341}{0.0341}}H_{\frac{0.046}{0.0341}}O_{\frac{0.0341}{0.0341}} = C_{1.00}H_{1.3}O_{1.00}$$

We find that 3 is the smallest integer that makes all subscripts into integers:

$$C_{(1.00\times3)}H_{(1.3\times3)}O_{(1.00\times3)} = C_{3.00}H_{3.9}O_{3.00} \approx C_3H_4O_3$$

Determining the molecular formula:

$$\text{Whole-number multiple} = \frac{\mathcal{M}\text{ of vitamin C}}{\mathcal{M}\text{ of empirical formula}} = \frac{176.12\ \cancel{\text{g/mol}}}{88.06\ \cancel{\text{g/mol}}} = 2.000 = 2$$

$$C_{(3\times2)}H_{(4\times2)}O_{(3\times2)} = C_6H_8O_6$$

Check The element masses seem correct: carbon makes up slightly more than 0.25 of the mass of CO_2 (12 g/44 g > 0.25), as do the masses in the problem (0.409 g/1.50 g > 0.25). Hydrogen makes up slightly more than 0.10 of the mass of H_2O (2 g/18 g > 0.10), as do the masses in the problem (0.046 g/0.41 g > 0.10). The molecular formula has the same ratio of subscripts (6/8/6) as the empirical formula (3/4/3) and the preliminary formula (0.0341/0.046/0.0341), and it gives the known molar mass:

$$(6 \times \mathcal{M}\text{ of C}) + (8 \times \mathcal{M}\text{ of H}) + (6 \times \mathcal{M}\text{ of O}) = \mathcal{M}\text{ of vitamin C}$$
$$(6 \times 12.01\text{ g/mol}) + (8 \times 1.008\text{ g/mol}) + (6 \times 16.00\text{ g/mol}) = 176.12\text{ g/mol}$$

Comment The subscript we calculated for H was 3.9, which we rounded to 4. But, if we had strung the calculation steps together, we would have obtained 4.0:

$$\text{Subscript of H} = 0.41\text{ g } H_2O \times \frac{2.016\text{ g H}}{18.02\text{ g } H_2O} \times \frac{1\text{ mol H}}{1.008\text{ g H}} \times \frac{1}{0.0341\text{ mol}} \times 3 = 4.0$$

Follow-Up Problem 3.11 A dry-cleaning solvent ($\mathcal{M}$ = 146.99 g/mol) that contains C, H, and Cl is suspected to be a cancer-causing agent. When a 0.250-g sample was studied by combustion analysis, 0.451 g of CO_2 and 0.0617 g of H_2O formed. Find the molecular formula.

Chemical Formulas and Molecular Structures; Isomers

A formula represents a real, three-dimensional object. The structural formula makes this point, with its relative placement of atoms, but do empirical and molecular formulas contain structural information?

Table 3.2 Some Compounds with Empirical Formula CH_2O (Composition by Mass: 40.0% C, 6.71% H, 53.3% O)

Name	Molecular Formula	Whole-Number Multiple	$\mathcal{M}$ (g/mol)	Use or Function
Formaldehyde	CH_2O	1	30.03	Disinfectant; biological preservative
Acetic acid	$C_2H_4O_2$	2	60.05	Acetate polymers; vinegar (5% solution)
Lactic acid	$C_3H_6O_3$	3	90.08	Causes milk to sour; forms in muscles during exercise
Erythrose	$C_4H_8O_4$	4	120.10	Forms during sugar metabolism
Ribose	$C_5H_{10}O_5$	5	150.13	Component of many nucleic acids and vitamin B_2
Glucose	$C_6H_{12}O_6$	6	180.16	Major nutrient for energy in cells

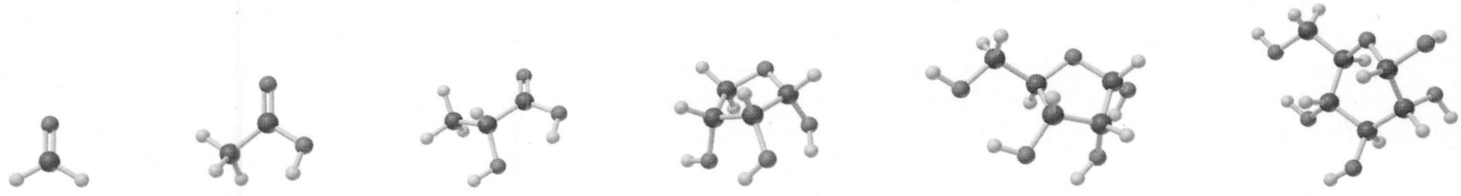

CH_2O $C_2H_4O_2$ $C_3H_6O_3$ $C_4H_8O_4$ $C_5H_{10}O_5$ $C_6H_{12}O_6$

1. *Different compounds with the same empirical formula.* The empirical formula tells nothing about molecular structure because it is based solely on mass analysis. In fact, different compounds can have the *same* empirical formula. NO_2 and N_2O_4 are inorganic cases, and there are numerous organic ones. For example, many compounds have the empirical formula CH_2 (the general formula is C_nH_{2n}, with n an integer greater than or equal to 2), such as ethylene (C_2H_4) and propylene (C_3H_6), starting materials for two common plastics. Table 3.2 shows some biological compounds with the same empirical formula.

2. *Isomers: Different compounds with the same molecular formula.* A molecular formula also tells nothing about structure. Different compounds can have the *same* molecular formula because their atoms can bond in different arrangements to give more than one *structural formula.* **Isomers** are compounds with the same molecular formula, and thus molar mass, but different properties. *Constitutional,* or *structural, isomers,* occur when the atoms link together in different arrangements. Table 3.3 shows two pairs of examples. The left pair, butane and 2-methylpropane, share the molecular formula C_4H_{10}. One has a four-C chain and the other a one-C branch off a three-C chain. Both are small alkanes, so their properties are similar, but not identical. The two compounds with the molecular formula C_2H_6O have very different properties; indeed, they are different classes of organic compound—one is an alcohol and the other an ether.

Table 3.3 Two Pairs of Constitutional Isomers

	C_4H_{10}		C_2H_6O	
Property	**Butane**	**2-Methylpropane**	**Ethanol**	**Dimethyl Ether**
$\mathcal{M}$ (g/mol)	58.12	58.12	46.07	46.07
Boiling point	−0.5°C	−11.6°C	78.5°C	−25°C
Density (at 20°C)	0.579 g/mL (gas)	0.549 g/mL	0.789 g/mL (liquid)	0.00195 g/mL (gas)
Structural formula	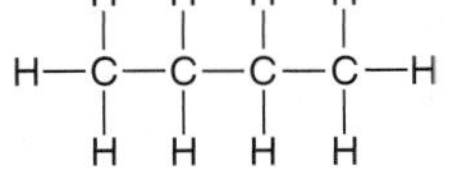	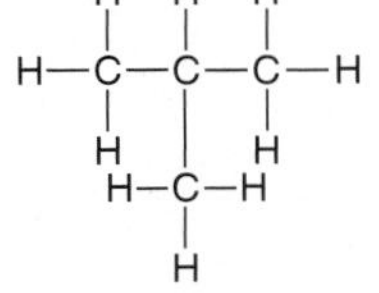	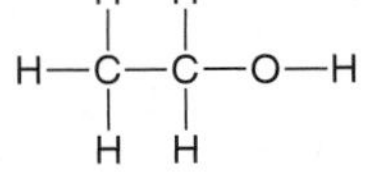	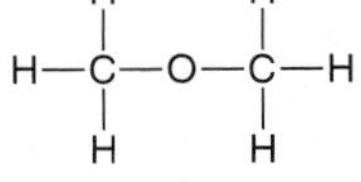
Space-filling model	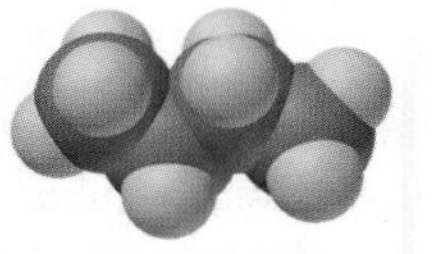			

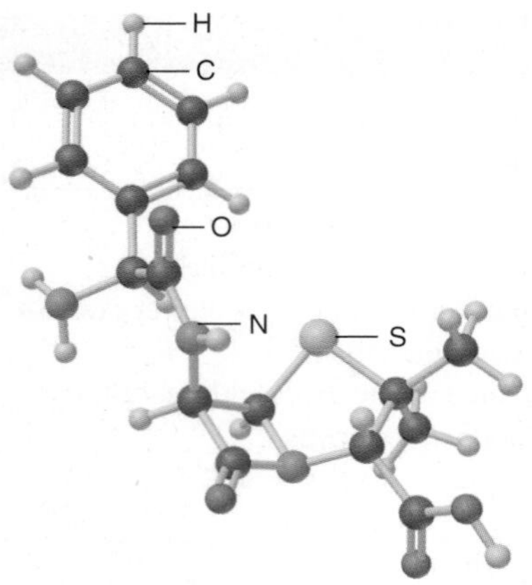

Figure 3.5 The antibiotic ampicillin.

As the number and kinds of atoms increase, the number of constitutional isomers—that is, the number of structural formulas that can be written for a given molecular formula—also increases: C_2H_6O has two structural formulas (Table 3.3), C_3H_8O has three, and $C_4H_{10}O$ seven. Imagine how many there are for $C_{16}H_{19}N_3O_4S$! Of all the possible isomers, only one is the antibiotic ampicillin (Figure 3.5). We'll discuss these and other types of isomerism fully later in the text.

Summary of Section 3.2

- From the masses of elements in a compound, their relative numbers of moles are found, which gives the empirical formula.
- If the molar mass of the compound is known, the molecular formula, the actual numbers of moles of each element, can also be determined.
- Combustion analysis provides data on the masses of C and H in an organic compound, which are used to obtain the formula.
- Atoms can bond in different arrangements (structural formulas). Two or more compounds with the same molecular formula are constitutional isomers.

3.3 • WRITING AND BALANCING CHEMICAL EQUATIONS

Thinking in terms of amounts, rather than masses, allows us to view reactions as large populations of interacting particles rather than as grams of material. For example, for the formation of HF from H_2 and F_2, if we weigh the substances, we find that

Macroscopic level (grams): 2.016 g of H_2 and 38.00 g of F_2 react to form 40.02 g of HF

This information tells us little except that mass is conserved. However, if we convert these masses (g) to amounts (mol), we find that

Macroscopic level (moles): 1 mol of H_2 and 1 mol of F_2 react to form 2 mol of HF

This information reveals that an enormous number of H_2 molecules react with just as many F_2 molecules to form twice as many HF molecules. Dividing by Avogadro's number shows the reaction between individual molecules:

Molecular level: 1 molecule of H_2 and 1 molecule of F_2 react to form 2 molecules of HF

Thus, *the macroscopic (molar) change corresponds to the submicroscopic (molecular) change* (Figure 3.6). This information forms the essence of a **chemical equation,** a statement that uses formulas to express the identities and quantities of substances in a chemical or physical change.

Figure 3.6 The formation of HF on the macroscopic and molecular levels.

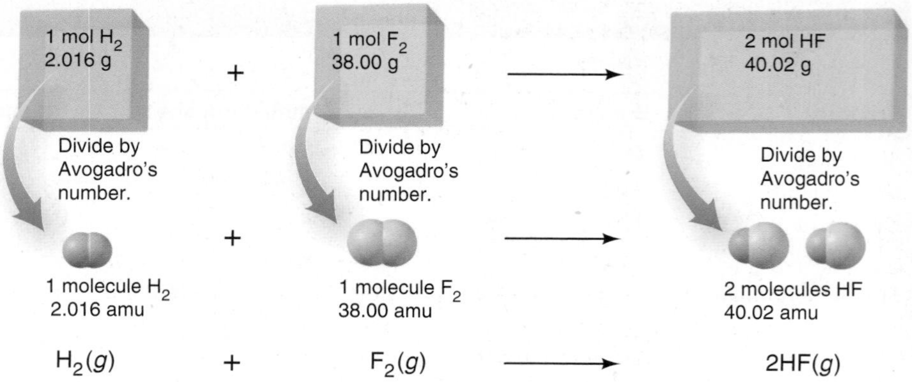

Steps for Balancing an Equation To present a chemical change quantitatively, the equation must be *balanced: the same number of each type of atom must appear on both sides.* As an example, here is a description of a chemical change that occurs in many fireworks and in a common lecture demonstration: a magnesium strip burns in oxygen gas to yield powdery magnesium oxide. (Light and heat are also produced, but we are concerned here only with substances.) Converting this description into a balanced equation involves the following steps:

1. *Translating the statement.* We first translate the chemical statement into a "skeleton" equation: the substances present *before* the change, called **reactants,** are placed to the left of a yield arrow, which points to the substances produced *during* the change, called **products:**

$$\underbrace{\_Mg + \_O_2}_{\text{reactants}} \xrightarrow{\text{yield}} \underbrace{\_MgO}_{\text{product}}$$

magnesium and oxygen yield magnesium oxide

   At the beginning of the balancing process, we put a blank *in front of* each formula to remind us that we have to account for its atoms.

2. *Balancing the atoms.* By shifting our attention back and forth, we *match the numbers of each type of atom on the left and the right of the yield arrow.* In each blank, we place a **balancing (stoichiometric) coefficient,** a numerical multiplier of *all the atoms* in the formula that follows it. In general, balancing is easiest when we
   - Start with the most complex substance, the one with the largest number of different types of atoms.
   - End with the least complex substance, such as an element by itself.

   In this case, MgO is the most complex, so we place a coefficient 1 in that blank:

$$\_Mg + \_O_2 \longrightarrow \underline{1}\,MgO$$

   To balance the Mg in MgO, we place a 1 in front of Mg on the left:

$$\underline{1}\,Mg + \_O_2 \longrightarrow \underline{1}\,MgO$$

   The O atom in MgO must be balanced by one O atom on the left. One-half an O_2 molecule provides one O atom:

$$\underline{1}\,Mg + \underline{\tfrac{1}{2}}\,O_2 \longrightarrow \underline{1}\,MgO$$

   In terms of numbers of each type of atom, the equation is balanced.

3. *Adjusting the coefficients.* There are several conventions about the final coefficients:
   - In most cases, *the smallest whole-number coefficients are preferred.* In this case, one-half of an O_2 molecule cannot exist, so we multiply the equation by 2:

$$2Mg + 1O_2 \longrightarrow 2MgO$$

   - We used the coefficient 1 to remind us to balance each substance. But, a coefficient of 1 is implied by the presence of the formula, so we don't write it:

$$2Mg + O_2 \longrightarrow 2MgO$$

   (This convention is similar to not writing a subscript 1 in a formula.)

4. *Checking.* After balancing and adjusting the coefficients, always check that the equation is balanced:

$$\text{Reactants (2 Mg, 2 O)} \longrightarrow \text{products (2 Mg, 2 O)}$$

5. *Specifying the states of matter.* The final equation also indicates the physical state of each substance or whether it is dissolved in water. The abbreviations used for these states are shown in the margin. From the original statement, we know that a Mg "strip" is solid, O_2 is a gas, and "powdery" MgO is also solid. The balanced equation, therefore, is

$$2Mg(s) + O_2(g) \longrightarrow 2MgO(s)$$

g for gas
l for liquid
s for solid
aq for aqueous solution

As you saw in Figure 3.6, *balancing coefficients refer to both individual chemical entities and moles of entities*. Thus,

2 atoms of Mg and 1 molecule of O_2 yield 2 formula units of MgO
2 moles of Mg and 1 mole of O_2 yield 2 moles of MgO

Figure 3.7 depicts this reaction on three levels:

- *Macroscopic level (photos),* as it appears in the laboratory
- *Molecular level (blow-up circles),* as chemists imagine it (with darker colored atoms representing the stoichiometry)
- *Symbolic level,* in the form of the balanced chemical equation

Keep in mind several key points about the balancing process:

- A coefficient operates on *all* the atoms in the formula that follows it:

  2MgO *means* $2 \times (MgO)$, or 2 Mg atoms + 2 O atoms
  $2Ca(NO_3)_2$ *means* $2 \times [Ca(NO_3)_2]$, or 2 Ca atoms + 4 N atoms + 12 O atoms

- Chemical formulas *cannot* be altered. In step 2 of the example, we *cannot* balance the O atoms by changing MgO to MgO_2 because MgO_2 is a different compound.
- Other reactants or products *cannot* be added. Thus, we *cannot* balance the O atoms by changing the reactant from O_2 molecules to O atoms or by adding an O atom to the products. The description of the reaction mentions oxygen gas, which consists of O_2 molecules, *not* separate O atoms.
- A balanced equation remains balanced if you multiply all the coefficients by the same number. For example,

$$4Mg(s) + 2O_2(g) \longrightarrow 4MgO(s)$$

  is also balanced because the coefficients have just been multiplied by 2. However, *by convention,* we balance an equation with the *smallest* whole-number coefficients.

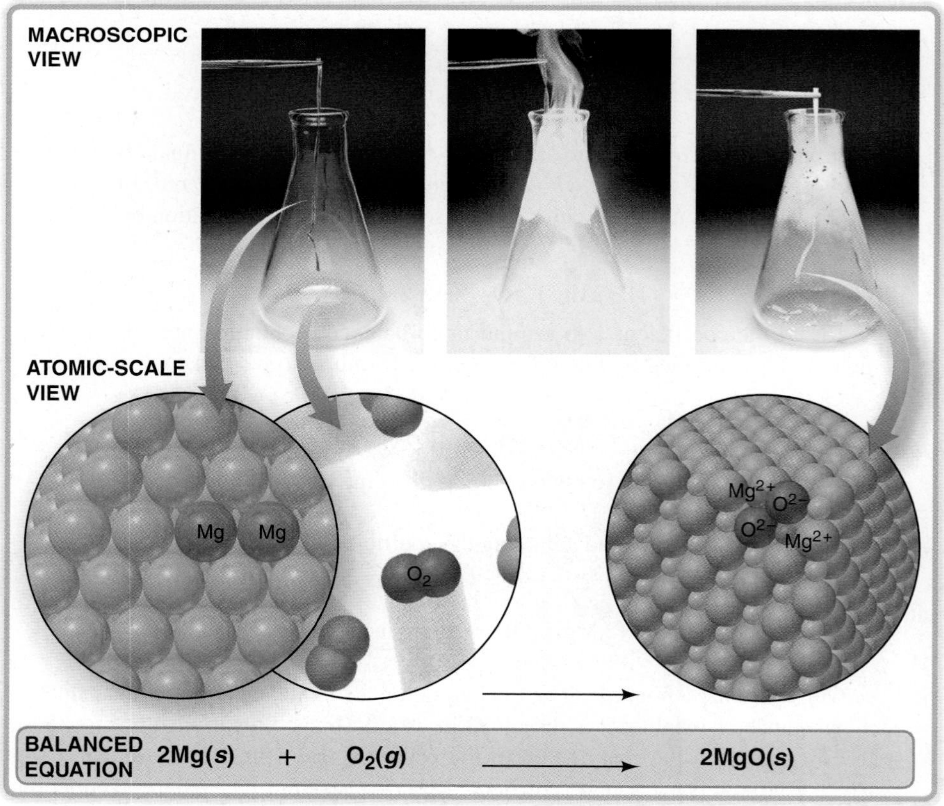

Figure 3.7 A three-level view of the reaction between magnesium and oxygen.

Sample Problem 3.12 Balancing Chemical Equations

Problem Within the cylinders of a car's engine, the hydrocarbon octane (C_8H_{18}), one of many components of gasoline, mixes with oxygen from the air and burns to form carbon dioxide and water vapor. Write a balanced equation for this reaction.

Solution 1. *Translate* the statement into a skeleton equation (with coefficient blanks). Octane and oxygen are reactants; "oxygen from the air" implies molecular oxygen, O_2. Carbon dioxide and water vapor are products:

$$\_C_8H_{18} + \_O_2 \longrightarrow \_CO_2 + \_H_2O$$

2. *Balance the atoms.* Start with the most complex substance, C_8H_{18}, and balance O_2 last:

$$\underline{1}\,C_8H_{18} + \_O_2 \longrightarrow \_CO_2 + \_H_2O$$

The C atoms in C_8H_{18} end up in CO_2. Each CO_2 contains one C atom, so 8 molecules of CO_2 are needed to balance the 8 C atoms in each C_8H_{18}:

$$\underline{1}\,C_8H_{18} + \_O_2 \longrightarrow \underline{8}\,CO_2 + \_H_2O$$

The H atoms in C_8H_{18} end up in H_2O. The 18 H atoms in C_8H_{18} require the coefficient 9 in front of H_2O:

$$\underline{1}\,C_8H_{18} + \_O_2 \longrightarrow \underline{8}\,CO_2 + \underline{9}\,H_2O$$

There are 25 atoms of O on the right (16 in $8CO_2$ plus 9 in $9H_2O$), so we place the coefficient $\frac{25}{2}$ in front of O_2:

$$\underline{1}\,C_8H_{18} + \underline{\tfrac{25}{2}}\,O_2 \longrightarrow \underline{8}\,CO_2 + \underline{9}\,H_2O$$

3. *Adjust the coefficients.* Multiply through by 2 to obtain whole numbers:

$$2C_8H_{18} + 25O_2 \longrightarrow 16CO_2 + 18H_2O$$

4. *Check* that the equation is balanced:

$$\text{Reactants (16 C, 36 H, 50 O)} \longrightarrow \text{products (16 C, 36 H, 50 O)}$$

5. *Specify* states of matter. C_8H_{18} is liquid; O_2, CO_2, and H_2O vapor are gases:

$$2C_8H_{18}(l) + 25O_2(g) \longrightarrow 16CO_2(g) + 18H_2O(g)$$

Comment This is an example of a combustion reaction. *Any* compound containing C and H that burns in an excess of air produces CO_2 and H_2O.

Follow-Up Problem 3.12

Write a balanced equation for each of the following:

(a) A characteristic reaction of Group 1A(1) elements: chunks of sodium react violently with water to form hydrogen gas and sodium hydroxide solution.
(b) The destruction of marble statuary by acid rain: aqueous nitric acid reacts with calcium carbonate to form carbon dioxide, water, and aqueous calcium nitrate.
(c) Halogen compounds exchanging bonding partners: phosphorus trifluoride is prepared by the reaction of phosphorus trichloride and hydrogen fluoride; hydrogen chloride is the other product. The reaction involves gases only.
(d) Explosive decomposition of dynamite: liquid nitroglycerine ($C_3H_5N_3O_9$) explodes to produce a mixture of gases—carbon dioxide, water vapor, nitrogen, and oxygen.

Visualizing a Reaction with a Molecular Scene A great way to focus on the rearrangement of atoms from reactants to products is by visualizing an equation as a molecular scene. Here's a representation of the combustion of octane we just balanced:

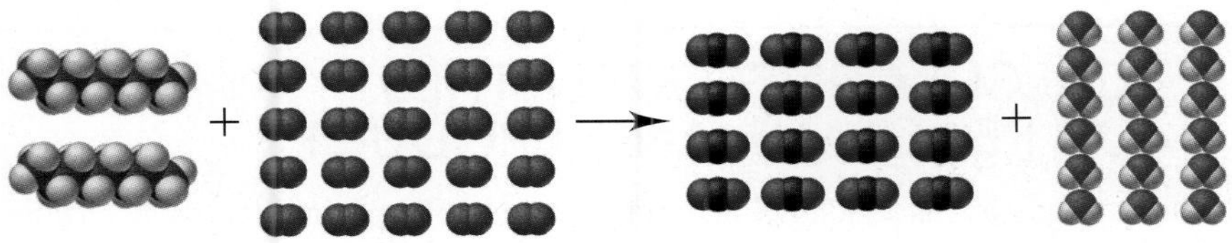

$$2C_8H_{18}(l) + 25O_2(g) \longrightarrow 16CO_2(g) + 18H_2O(g)$$

Now let's work through a sample problem to do the reverse—derive a balanced equation from a molecular scene.

Sample Problem 3.13 **Balancing an Equation from a Molecular Scene**

Problem The following molecular scenes depict an important reaction in nitrogen chemistry (nitrogen is blue; oxygen is red):

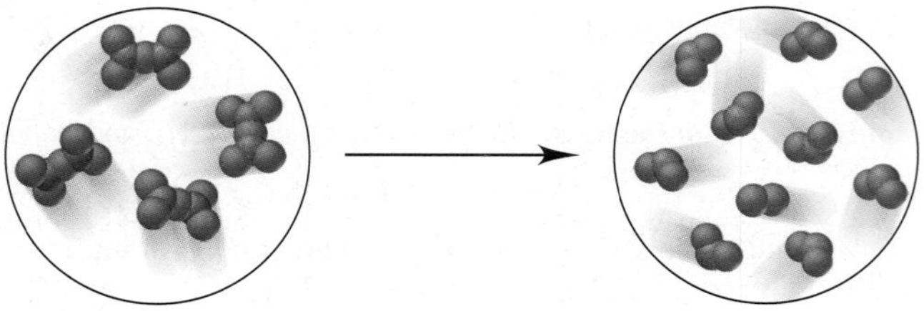

Write a balanced equation for this reaction.

Plan To write a balanced equation, we first have to determine the formulas of the molecules and obtain coefficients by counting the number of each molecule. Then, we arrange this information in the correct equation format, using the smallest whole-number coefficients and including states of matter.

Solution The reactant circle shows only one type of molecule. It has two N and five O atoms, so the formula is N_2O_5; there are four of these molecules. The product circle shows two different molecules, one with one N and two O atoms, and the other with two O atoms; there are eight NO_2 and two O_2. Thus, we have:

$$4N_2O_5 \longrightarrow 8NO_2 + 2O_2$$

Writing the balanced equation with the smallest whole-number coefficients and all substances as gases:

$$2N_2O_5(g) \longrightarrow 4NO_2(g) + O_2(g)$$

Check Reactant (4 N, 10 O) $\longrightarrow$ products (4 N, 8 + 2 = 10 O)

Follow-Up Problem 3.13 Write a balanced equation for the important atmospheric reaction depicted below (carbon is black; oxygen is red):

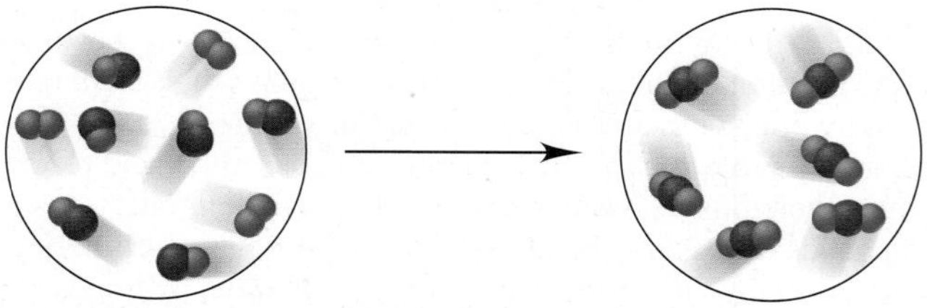

Summary of Section 3.3

- A chemical equation has reactant formulas on the left of a yield arrow and product formulas on the right.
- A balanced equation has the same number of each type of atom on both sides.
- Balancing coefficients are integer multipliers for *all* the atoms in a formula and apply to the individual entity or to moles of entities.

3.4 • CALCULATING QUANTITIES OF REACTANT AND PRODUCT

A balanced equation is essential for all calculations involving chemical change: *if you know the number of moles of one substance, the balanced equation tells you the number of moles of the others.*

Stoichiometrically Equivalent Molar Ratios from the Balanced Equation

In a balanced equation, *the amounts (mol) of substances are stoichiometrically equivalent to each other,* which means that a specific amount of one substance is formed from, produces, or reacts with a specific amount of the other. The quantitative relationships are expressed as *stoichiometrically equivalent molar ratios* that we use as conversion factors to calculate the amounts. For example, consider the equation for the combustion of propane, a hydrocarbon fuel used in cooking and water heating:

$$C_3H_8(g) + 5O_2(g) \longrightarrow 3CO_2(g) + 4H_2O(g)$$

If we view the reaction quantitatively in terms of C_3H_8, we see that

1 mol of C_3H_8 reacts with 5 mol of O_2
1 mol of C_3H_8 produces 3 mol of CO_2
1 mol of C_3H_8 produces 4 mol of H_2O

Therefore, in this reaction,

1 mol of C_3H_8 is stoichiometrically equivalent to 5 mol of O_2
1 mol of C_3H_8 is stoichiometrically equivalent to 3 mol of CO_2
1 mol of C_3H_8 is stoichiometrically equivalent to 4 mol of H_2O

We chose to look at C_3H_8, but any two of the substances are stoichiometrically equivalent to each other. Thus,

3 mol of CO_2 is stoichiometrically equivalent to 4 mol of H_2O
5 mol of O_2 is stoichiometrically equivalent to 3 mol of CO_2

and so on. A balanced equation contains a wealth of quantitative information relating individual chemical entities, amounts (mol) of substances, and masses of substances, and Table 3.4 presents the quantitative information contained in this equation.

Here's a typical problem that shows how stoichiometric equivalence is used to create conversion factors: in the combustion of propane, how many moles of O_2 are consumed when 10.0 mol of H_2O are produced? To solve this problem, we have to find the molar ratio between O_2 and H_2O. From the balanced equation, we see that for every 5 mol of O_2 consumed, 4 mol of H_2O is formed:

5 mol of O_2 is stoichiometrically equivalent to 4 mol of H_2O

Table 3.4 Information Contained in a Balanced Equation

Viewed in Terms of	**Reactants** $C_3H_8(g)$ + $5O_2(g)$		**Products** $3CO_2(g)$ + $4H_2O(g)$
Molecules	1 molecule C_3H_8 + 5 molecules O_2	$\longrightarrow$	3 molecules CO_2 + 4 molecules H_2O
	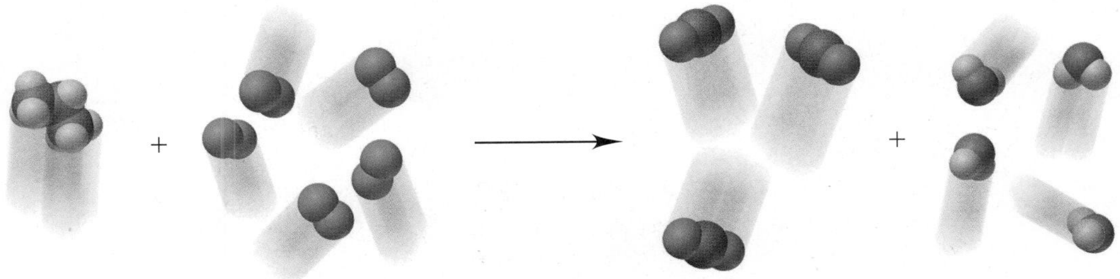		
Amount (mol)	1 mol C_3H_8 + 5 mol O_2	$\longrightarrow$	3 mol CO_2 + 4 mol H_2O
Mass (amu)	44.09 amu C_3H_8 + 160.00 amu O_2	$\longrightarrow$	132.03 amu CO_2 + 72.06 amu H_2O
Mass (g)	44.09 g C_3H_8 + 160.00 g O_2	$\longrightarrow$	132.03 g CO_2 + 72.06 g H_2O
Total mass (g)	204.09 g	$\longrightarrow$	204.09 g

As with any equivalent quantities, we can construct two conversion factors, depending on the quantity we want to find:

$$\frac{5 \text{ mol } O_2}{4 \text{ mol } H_2O} \quad \text{or} \quad \frac{4 \text{ mol } H_2O}{5 \text{ mol } O_2}$$

Since we want to find amount (mol) of O_2 and we know amount (mol) of H_2O, we choose "5 mol O_2/4 mol H_2O" to cancel "mol H_2O":

$$\text{Amount (mol) of } O_2 \text{ consumed} = 10.0 \cancel{\text{mol } H_2O} \times \frac{5 \text{ mol } O_2}{4 \cancel{\text{mol } H_2O}} = 12.5 \text{ mol } O_2$$

$$\text{mol } H_2O \xrightarrow[\text{conversion factor}]{\text{molar ratio as}} \text{mol } O_2$$

*You **cannot** solve this type of problem without the balanced equation.* Here is an approach for solving *any* stoichiometry problem that involves a reaction:

1. Write the balanced equation.
2. When necessary, convert the known mass (or number of entities) of one substance to amount (mol) using its molar mass (or Avogadro's number).
3. Use the molar ratio to calculate the unknown amount (mol) of the other substance.
4. When necessary, convert the amount of that other substance to the desired mass (or number of entities) using its molar mass (or Avogadro's number).

Figure 3.8 summarizes the possible relationships among quantities of substances in a reaction, and Sample Problems 3.14–3.16 apply three of them in the first chemical step of converting copper ore to copper metal.

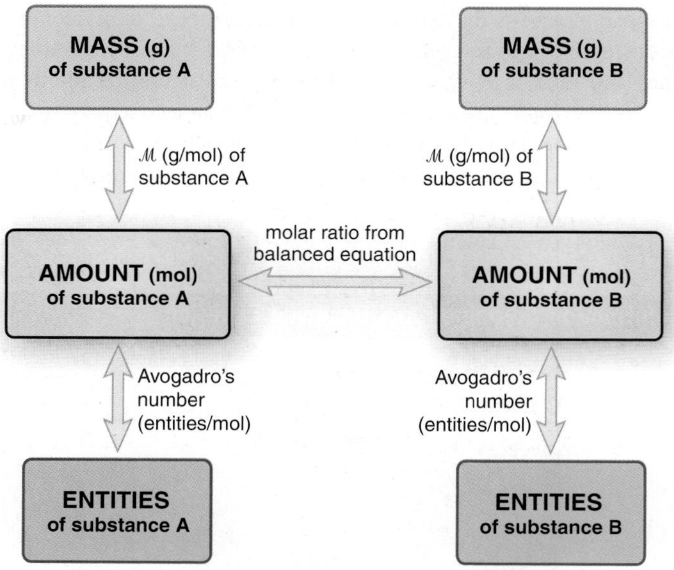

Figure 3.8 Summary of amount-mass-number relationships in a chemical equation. Start at any box (known) and move to any other (unknown) by using the conversion factor on the arrow. As always, convert to amount (mol) first.

Sample Problem 3.14 Calculating Quantities of Reactants and Products: Amount (mol) to Amount (mol)

Problem In a lifetime, the average American uses 1750 lb (794 kg) of copper in coins, plumbing, and wiring. Copper is obtained from sulfide ores, such as chalcocite [copper(I) sulfide] by a multistep process. After grinding the ore, it is "roasted" (heated strongly with oxygen gas) to form powdered copper(I) oxide and gaseous sulfur dioxide. How many moles of oxygen are required to roast 10.0 mol of copper(I) sulfide?

Plan We *always* write the balanced equation first. The formulas of the reactants are Cu_2S and O_2, and the formulas of the products are Cu_2O and SO_2, so we have

$$2Cu_2S(s) + 3O_2(g) \longrightarrow 2Cu_2O(s) + 2SO_2(g)$$

We know the amount of Cu_2S (10.0 mol) and must find the amount (mol) of O_2 that is needed to roast it. The balanced equation shows that 3 mol of O_2 is needed for 2 mol of Cu_2S, so the conversion factor for finding amount (mol) of O_2 is "3 mol O_2/2 mol Cu_2S" (see the road map).

Road Map

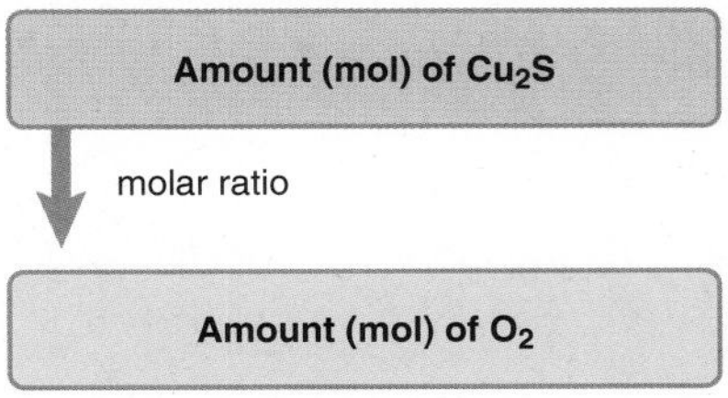

Solution Calculating the amount of O_2:

$$\text{Amount (mol) of } O_2 = 10.0\ \cancel{\text{mol } Cu_2S} \times \frac{3 \text{ mol } O_2}{2\ \cancel{\text{mol } Cu_2S}} = 15.0 \text{ mol } O_2$$

Check The units are correct, and the answer is reasonable because this molar ratio of O_2 to Cu_2S (15/10) is identical to the ratio in the balanced equation (3/2).

Comment A *common mistake* is to invert the conversion factor; that calculation would be

$$\text{Amount (mol) of } O_2 = 10.0 \text{ mol } Cu_2S \times \frac{2 \text{ mol } Cu_2S}{3 \text{ mol } O_2} = \frac{6.67 \text{ mol}^2\ Cu_2S}{1 \text{ mol } O_2}$$

The strange units should alert you that an error was made in setting up the conversion factor. Also note that this answer, 6.67, is *less* than 10.0, whereas the equation shows that there should be *more* moles of O_2 (3 mol) than moles of Cu_2S (2 mol). Be sure to think through the calculation when setting up the conversion factor and canceling units.

Follow-Up Problem 3.14 Thermite is a mixture of iron(III) oxide and aluminum powders that was once used to weld railroad tracks. It undergoes a spectacular reaction to yield solid aluminum oxide and molten iron. How many moles of iron(III) oxide are needed to form 3.60×10^3 mol of iron? Include a road map that shows how you planned the solution.

Sample Problem 3.15 Calculating Quantities of Reactants and Products: Amount (mol) to Mass (g)

Problem During the roasting process, how many grams of sulfur dioxide form when 10.0 mol of copper(I) sulfide reacts?

Plan Referring to the balanced equation in Sample Problem 3.14, here we are given amount of reactant (10.0 mol of Cu_2S) and need the mass (g) of product (SO_2) that forms. We find the amount (mol) of SO_2 using the molar ratio (2 mol SO_2/2 mol Cu_2S) and then multiply by its molar mass (64.07 g/mol) to find mass (g) of SO_2 (see the road map).

Road Map

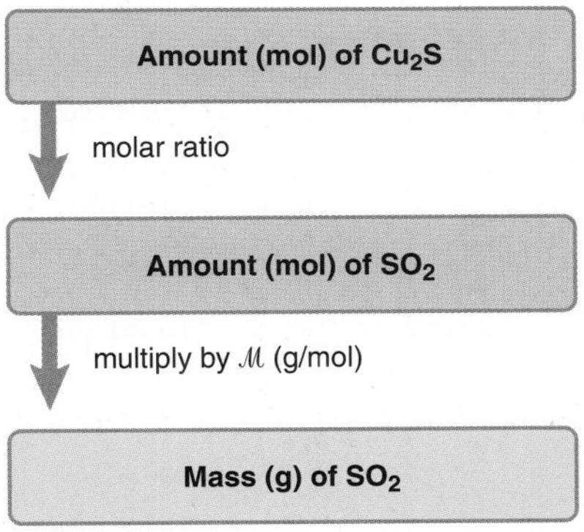

Solution Combining the two conversion steps into one calculation, we have

$$\text{Mass (g) of } SO_2 = 10.0\ \cancel{\text{mol } Cu_2S} \times \frac{2\ \cancel{\text{mol } SO_2}}{2\ \cancel{\text{mol } Cu_2S}} \times \frac{64.07 \text{ g } SO_2}{1\ \cancel{\text{mol } SO_2}} = 641 \text{ g } SO_2$$

Check The answer makes sense, since the molar ratio shows that 10.0 mol of SO_2 is formed and each mole weighs about 64 g. We rounded to three significant figures.

Follow-Up Problem 3.15 In the thermite reaction, what amount (mol) of iron forms when 1.85×10^{25} formula units of aluminum oxide reacts? Write a road map to show how to plan the solution.

Sample Problem 3.16 Calculating Quantities of Reactants and Products: Mass to Mass

Problem During the roasting of chalcocite, how many kilograms of oxygen are required to form 2.86 kg of copper(I) oxide?

Plan In this problem, we know the mass of the product, Cu_2O (2.86 kg), and we need the mass (kg) of O_2 that reacts to form it. Therefore, we must convert from mass of product to amount of product to amount of reactant to mass of reactant. We convert the mass of Cu_2O from kg to g and then to amount (mol). Then, we use the molar ratio (3 mol O_2/2 mol Cu_2O) to find the amount (mol) of O_2 required. Finally, we convert amount of O_2 to g and then kg (see the road map on the next page).

Road Map

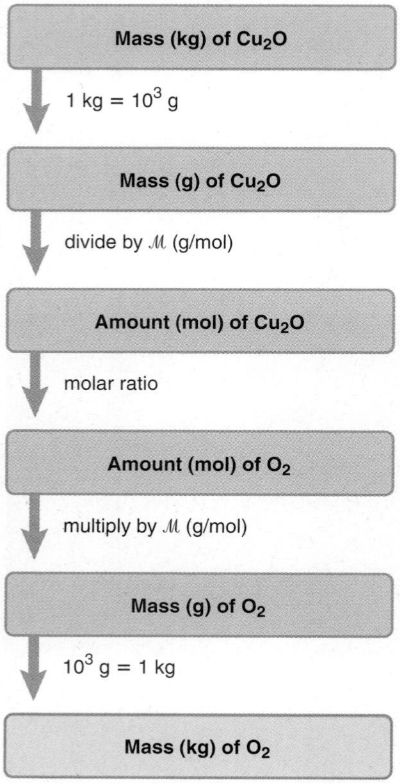

Solution Converting from kilograms of Cu_2O to moles of Cu_2O: Combining the mass unit conversion with the mass-to-amount conversion gives

$$\text{Amount (mol) of } Cu_2O = 2.86\ \cancel{\text{kg } Cu_2O} \times \frac{10^3\ \cancel{\text{g}}}{1\ \cancel{\text{kg}}} \times \frac{1\ \text{mol } Cu_2O}{143.10\ \cancel{\text{g } Cu_2O}} = 20.0\ \text{mol } Cu_2O$$

Converting from moles of Cu_2O to moles of O_2:

$$\text{Amount (mol) of } O_2 = 20.0\ \cancel{\text{mol } Cu_2O} \times \frac{3\ \text{mol } O_2}{2\ \cancel{\text{mol } Cu_2O}} = 30.0\ \text{mol } O_2$$

Converting from moles of O_2 to kilograms of O_2: Combining the amount-to-mass conversion with the mass unit conversion gives

$$\text{Mass (kg) of } O_2 = 30.0\ \cancel{\text{mol } O_2} \times \frac{32.00\ \cancel{\text{g}}\ O_2}{1\ \cancel{\text{mol } O_2}} \times \frac{1\ \text{kg}}{10^3\ \cancel{\text{g}}} = 0.960\ \text{kg } O_2$$

Check The units are correct. Rounding to check the math, for example, in the final step, $\sim$30 mol × 30 g/mol × 1 kg/10^3 g = 0.90 kg. The answer seems reasonable: even though the amount (mol) of O_2 is greater than the amount (mol) of Cu_2O, the mass of O_2 is less than the mass of Cu_2O because $\mathcal{M}$ of O_2 is less than $\mathcal{M}$ of Cu_2O.

Comment The three related sample problems (3.14–3.16) highlight the main point for solving stoichiometry problems: *convert the information given into amount (mol).* Then, use the appropriate molar ratio and any other conversion factors to complete the solution.

Follow-Up Problem 3.16 During the thermite reaction, how many atoms of aluminum react for every 1.00 g of aluminum oxide that forms? Include a road map that shows how you planned the solution.

Reactions That Occur in a Sequence

In many situations, a product of one reaction becomes a reactant for the next in a sequence of reactions. For stoichiometric purposes, when the same (common) substance forms in one reaction and reacts in the next, we eliminate it in an **overall (net) equation.** The steps to writing the overall equation are

1. Write the sequence of balanced equations.
2. Adjust the equations arithmetically to cancel the common substance.
3. Add the adjusted equations together to obtain the overall balanced equation.

Sample Problem 3.17 shows the approach by continuing with the copper recovery process that started in Sample Problem 3.14.

Sample Problem 3.17 Writing an Overall Equation for a Reaction Sequence

Problem Roasting is the first step in extracting copper from chalcocite. In the next step, copper(I) oxide reacts with powdered carbon to yield copper metal and carbon monoxide gas. Write a balanced overall equation for the two-step sequence.

Plan To obtain the overall equation, we write the individual equations in sequence, adjust coefficients to cancel the common substance (or substances), and add the equations together. In this case, only Cu_2O appears as a product in one equation and a reactant in the other, so it is the common substance.

Solution Writing the individual balanced equations:

$$2Cu_2S(s) + 3O_2(g) \longrightarrow 2Cu_2O(s) + 2SO_2(g) \quad \text{[equation 1; see Sample Problem 3.14]}$$
$$Cu_2O(s) + C(s) \longrightarrow 2Cu(s) + CO(g) \quad \text{[equation 2]}$$

Adjusting the coefficients: Since 2 mol of Cu_2O forms in equation 1 but 1 mol of Cu_2O reacts in equation 2, we double *all* the coefficients in equation 2 to use up the Cu_2O:

$$2Cu_2S(s) + 3O_2(g) \longrightarrow 2Cu_2O(s) + 2SO_2(g) \quad \text{[equation 1]}$$
$$2Cu_2O(s) + 2C(s) \longrightarrow 4Cu(s) + 2CO(g) \quad \text{[equation 2, doubled]}$$

Adding the two equations and canceling the common substance: We keep the reactants of both equations on the left and the products of both equations on the right:

$$2Cu_2S(s) + 3O_2(g) + \cancel{2Cu_2O(s)} + 2C(s) \longrightarrow \cancel{2Cu_2O(s)} + 2SO_2(g) + 4Cu(s) + 2CO(g)$$

or,

$$2Cu_2S(s) + 3O_2(g) + 2C(s) \longrightarrow 2SO_2(g) + 4Cu(s) + 2CO(g)$$

Check Reactants (4 Cu, 2 S, 6 O, 2 C) $\longrightarrow$ products (4 Cu, 2 S, 6 O, 2 C)

Comment 1. Even though Cu_2O *does* participate in the chemical change, it is not involved in the reaction stoichiometry. An overall equation *may not* show which substances actually react; for example, C(*s*) and $Cu_2S(s)$ do not interact directly in this reaction sequence, even though both are shown as reactants.
2. The SO_2 formed in copper recovery contributes to acid rain, so chemists have devised microbial and electrochemical methods to extract metals without roasting sulfide ores. Such methods are examples of *green chemistry;* we'll discuss another on page 113.
3. These reactions were shown to explain how to obtain an overall equation. The actual extraction of copper is more complex, as you'll see in Chapter 22.

Follow-Up Problem 3.17 The SO_2 formed in copper recovery reacts in air with oxygen and forms sulfur trioxide. This gas, in turn, reacts with water to form a sulfuric acid solution that falls in rain. Write a balanced overall equation for this process.

Reaction Sequences in Organisms Multistep reaction sequences called *metabolic pathways* occur throughout biological systems. (We discuss them again in Chapter 17.) For example, in most cells, the chemical energy in glucose is released through a sequence of about 30 individual reactions. The product of each reaction step is the reactant of the next, so that all the common substances cancel, and the overall equation is

$$C_6H_{12}O_6(aq) + 6O_2(g) \longrightarrow 6CO_2(g) + 6H_2O(l)$$

We eat food that contains glucose, inhale O_2, and excrete CO_2 and H_2O. In our cells, these reactants and products are many steps apart: O_2 never reacts *directly* with glucose, and CO_2 and H_2O are formed at various, often distant, steps along the sequence of reactions. Even so, the molar ratios in the overall equation are the same as if the glucose burned in a combustion chamber filled with O_2 and formed CO_2 and H_2O directly (Figure 3.9).

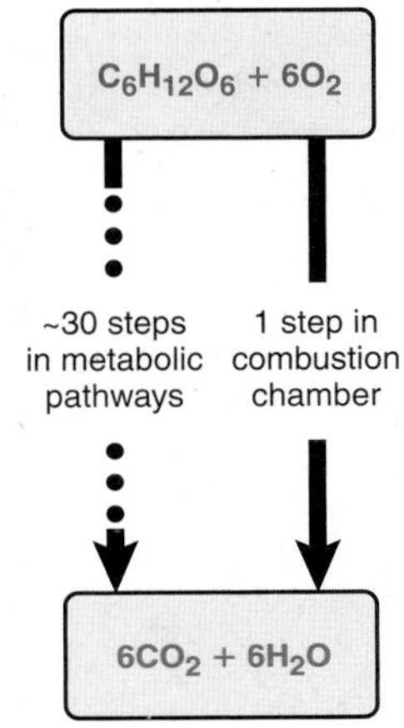

Figure 3.9 An overall equation equals the sum of the individual steps.

Reactions That Involve a Limiting Reactant

In problems up to now, the amount of *one* reactant was given, and we assumed there was enough of the other reactants to react with it completely. For example, suppose we want the amount (mol) of SO_2 that forms when 5.2 mol of Cu_2S reacts with O_2:

$$2Cu_2S(s) + 3O_2(g) \longrightarrow 2Cu_2O(s) + 2SO_2(g) \text{ [equation 1; see Sample Problem 3.14]}$$

We assume the 5.2 mol of Cu_2S reacts with as much O_2 as needed. Because all the Cu_2S reacts, its initial amount of 5.2 mol determines, or *limits,* the amount of SO_2 that can form, no matter how much more O_2 is present. In this situation, we call Cu_2S the **limiting reactant** (or *limiting reagent*).

Suppose, however, you know the amounts of both Cu_2S *and* O_2 and need to find out how much SO_2 forms. You first have to determine whether Cu_2S *or* O_2 is the limiting reactant—that is, which one is completely used up—because it limits how much SO_2 can form. The reactant that is *not* limiting is present *in excess,* which means the amount that doesn't react is left over. ● To determine which is the limiting reactant, we use the molar ratios in the balanced equation to perform a series of calculations to see *which reactant forms less product.*

● Limiting "Reactants" in Everyday Life Limiting-"reactant" situations arise in business all the time. A car assembly-plant manager must order more tires if there are 1500 car bodies and only 4000 tires, and a clothes manufacturer must cut more sleeves if there are 320 sleeves for 170 shirt bodies. You've probably faced such situations in daily life as well. A muffin recipe calls for 2 cups of flour and 1 cup of sugar, but you have 3 cups of flour and only $\frac{3}{4}$ cup of sugar. Clearly, the flour is in excess and the sugar limits the number of muffins you can make. Or, you're in charge of making cheeseburgers for a picnic, and you have 10 buns, 12 meat patties, and 15 slices of cheese. Here, the number of buns limits how many cheeseburgers you can make. Or, there are 26 students and only 23 microscopes in a cell biology lab. You'll find that limiting-"reactant" situations are almost limitless.

Determining the Limiting Reactant Let's clarify these ideas in a much more appetizing situation. Suppose you have a job making ice cream sundaes. Each sundae requires two scoops (12 oz) of ice cream, one cherry, and 50 mL of syrup:

$$\text{2 scoops (12 oz)} + \text{1 cherry} + \text{50 mL syrup} \longrightarrow \text{1 sundae}$$

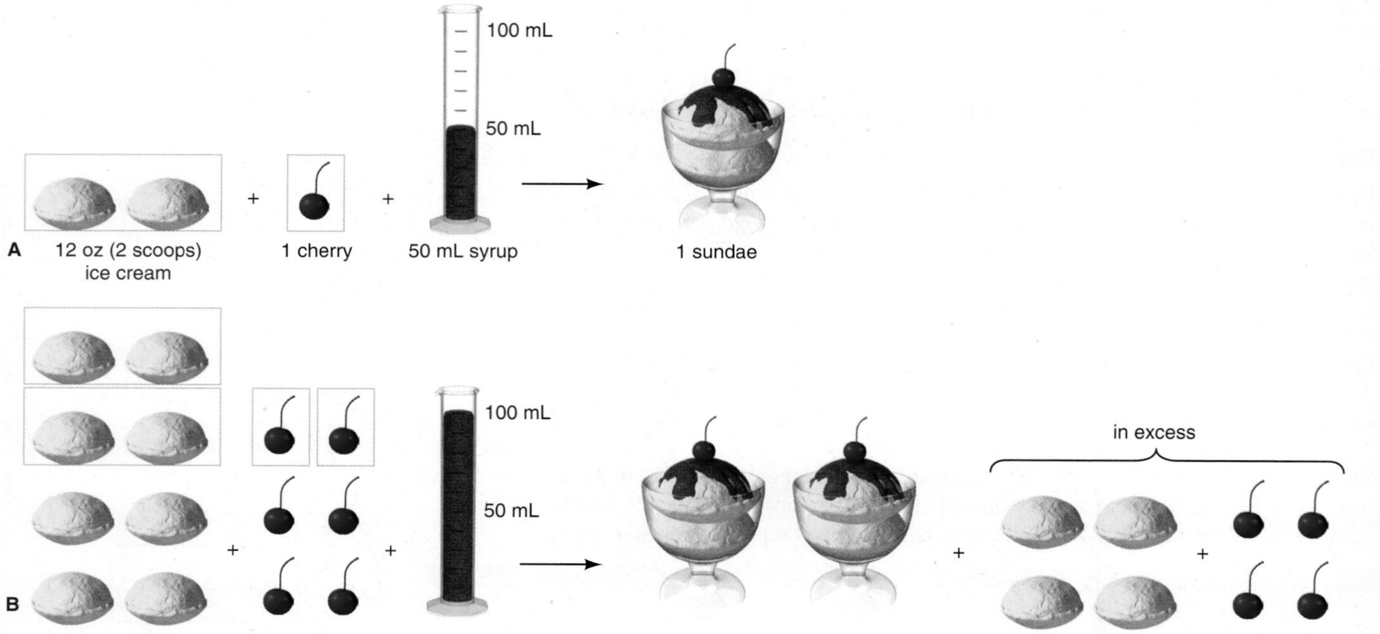

Figure 3.10 An ice cream sundae analogy for limiting reactants. **A,** The "reactants" form the "product" (sundae). **B,** Only two sundaes can be made before all the syrup is used up, so syrup is the limiting "reactant"; four scoops of ice cream and four cherries are "in excess."

A mob of 25 ravenous school kids enters, and each one wants a sundae with vanilla ice cream and chocolate syrup. You have 300 oz of vanilla ice cream (at 6 oz per scoop), 30 cherries, and 1 L of syrup: can you feed them all? A series of calculations based on the balanced equation shows the number of sundaes you can make from each ingredient:

$$\text{Ice cream: No. of sundaes} = 300\ \cancel{\text{oz}} \times \frac{1\ \cancel{\text{scoop}}}{6\ \cancel{\text{oz}}} \times \frac{1\ \text{sundae}}{2\ \cancel{\text{scoops}}} = 25\ \text{sundaes}$$

$$\text{Cherries: No. of sundaes} = 30\ \cancel{\text{cherries}} \times \frac{1\ \text{sundae}}{1\ \cancel{\text{cherry}}} = 30\ \text{sundaes}$$

$$\text{Syrup: No. of sundaes} = 1000\ \cancel{\text{mL syrup}} \times \frac{1\ \text{sundae}}{50\ \cancel{\text{mL syrup}}} = 20\ \text{sundaes}$$

Of the reactants (ice cream, cherry, syrup), the syrup forms the *least* product (sundaes), so it is the limiting "reactant." When all the syrup has been used up, some ice cream and cherries are "unreacted" so they are in excess:

300 oz (50 scoops) + 30 cherries + 1 L syrup ⟶
20 sundaes + 60 oz (10 scoops) + 10 cherries

Figure 3.10 shows a similar example with different initial (starting) quantities.

Using Reaction Tables in Limiting-Reactant Problems A good way to keep track of the quantities in a limiting-reactant problem is with a *reaction table*. The balanced equation appears at the top for the column heads. The table shows the

- *Initial* quantities of reactants and products *before* the reaction
- *Change* in the quantities of reactants and products *during* the reaction
- *Final* quantities of reactants and products remaining *after* the reaction

For example, for the ice-cream sundae "reaction," the reaction table would be

Quantity	12 oz (2 scoops)	+	1 cherry	+	50 mL syrup	⟶	1 sundae
Initial	300 oz (50 scoops)		30 cherries		1000 mL syrup		0 sundaes
Change	−240 oz (40 scoops)		−20 cherries		−1000 mL syrup		+20 sundaes
Final	60 oz (10 scoops)		10 cherries		0 mL syrup		20 sundaes

The body of the table shows the following important points:

- In the Initial line, "product" has not yet formed, so the entry is "0 sundaes."
- In the Change line, since the reactants (ice cream, cherries, syrup) are used during the reaction, their quantities decrease, so the changes in their quantities have a *negative* sign. At the same time, the quantity of product (sundaes) increases, so the change in its quantity has a *positive* sign.
- For the Final line, we *add* the Change and Initial lines. Notice that some reactants (ice cream and cherries) are in excess, while the limiting reactant (syrup) is used up.

Solving Limiting-Reactant Problems In limiting-reactant problems, *the quantities of two (or more) reactants are given, and we first determine which is limiting.* To do this, just as we did with the ice cream sundaes, we use the balanced equation to solve a series of calculations to see how much product forms from the given quantity of each reactant: the limiting reactant is the one that yields the *least* quantity of product.

The following problems examine these ideas from several aspects. In Sample Problem 3.18, we solve the problem by looking at a molecular scene; in Sample Problem 3.19, we start with the amounts (mol) of two reactants, and in Sample Problem 3.20, we start with masses of two reactants.

Sample Problem 3.18 Using Molecular Depictions in a Limiting-Reactant Problem

Problem Nuclear engineers use chlorine trifluoride to prepare uranium fuel for power plants. The compound is formed as a gas by the reaction of elemental chlorine and fluorine. The circle in the margin shows a representative portion of the reaction mixture before the reaction starts (chlorine is *green;* fluorine is *yellow*).

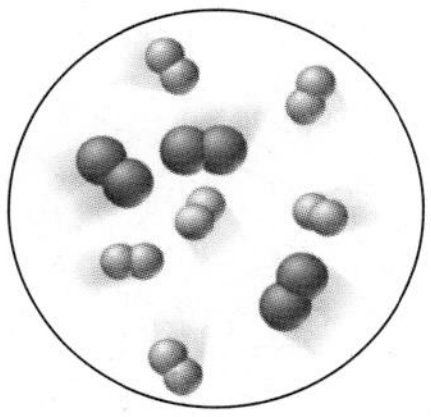

(a) Find the limiting reactant.
(b) Write a reaction table for the process.
(c) Draw a representative portion of the mixture after the reaction is complete. (*Hint:* The ClF_3 molecule has Cl bonded to three individual F atoms.)

Plan **(a)** We have to find the limiting reactant. The first step is to write the balanced equation, so we need the formulas and states of matter. From the name, chlorine trifluoride, we know the product consists of one Cl atom bonded to three F atoms, or ClF_3. Elemental chlorine and fluorine are the diatomic molecules Cl_2 and F_2, and all three substances are gases. To find the limiting reactant, we find the number of molecules of product that would form from the numbers of molecules of each reactant: whichever forms less product is the limiting reactant. **(b)** We use these numbers of molecules to write a reaction table. **(c)** We use the numbers in the Final line of the table to draw the scene.

Solution **(a)** The balanced equation is

$$Cl_2(g) + 3F_2(g) \longrightarrow 2ClF_3(g)$$

$$\text{For } Cl_2\text{: Molecules of } ClF_3 = 3\ \cancel{\text{molecules of } Cl_2} \times \frac{2 \text{ molecules of } ClF_3}{1\ \cancel{\text{molecule of } Cl_2}}$$
$$= 6 \text{ molecules of } ClF_3$$

$$\text{For } F_2\text{: Molecules of } ClF_3 = 6\ \cancel{\text{molecules of } F_2} \times \frac{2 \text{ molecules of } ClF_3}{3\ \cancel{\text{molecules of } F_2}}$$
$$= \tfrac{12}{3} \text{ molecules of } ClF_3 = 4 \text{ molecules of } ClF_3$$

Because it forms less product, F_2 is the limiting reactant.

(b) Since F_2 is the limiting reactant, all of it (6 molecules) is used in the "Change" line of the reaction table:

Molecules	$Cl_2(g)$	+	$3F_2(g)$	$\longrightarrow$	$2ClF_3(g)$
Initial	3		6		0
Change	−2		−6		+4
Final	1		0		4

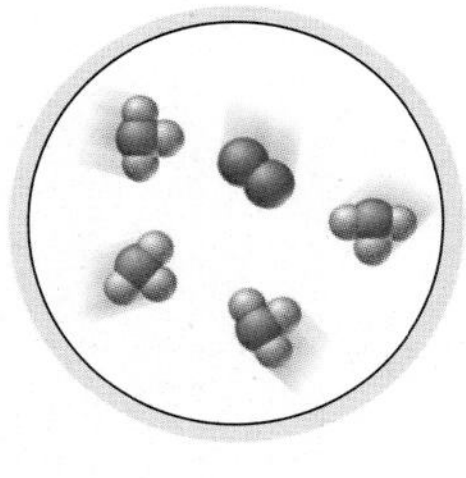

(c) The representative portion of the final reaction mixture *(see margin)* includes 1 molecule of Cl_2 (the reactant in excess) and 4 molecules of product ClF_3.

Check The equation is balanced: reactants (2 Cl, 6 F) $\longrightarrow$ products (2 Cl, 6 F). And, as shown in the circles, the numbers of each type of atom before and after the reaction are equal. Let's think through our choice of limiting reactant. From the equation, one Cl_2 needs three F_2 to form two ClF_3. Therefore, the three Cl_2 molecules in the circle depicting reactants need nine (3×3) F_2. But there are only six F_2, so there is not enough F_2 to react with the available Cl_2; or put the other way, there is too much Cl_2 to react with the available F_2. From either point of view, F_2 is the limiting reactant.

Follow-Up Problem 3.18 B_2 (B is *red*) reacts with AB as shown below:

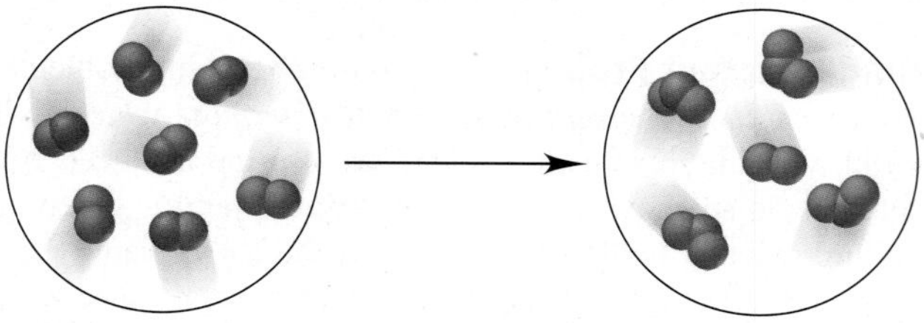

Write a balanced equation for the reaction, and determine the limiting reactant.

Sample Problem 3.19 Calculating Quantities in a Limiting-Reactant Problem: Amount to Amount

Problem In another preparation of ClF_3 (see Sample Problem 3.18), 0.750 mol of Cl_2 reacts with 3.00 mol of F_2. **(a)** Find the limiting reactant. **(b)** Write a reaction table.

Plan (a) We find the limiting reactant by calculating the amount (mol) of ClF_3 formed from the amount (mol) of each reactant: the reactant that forms fewer moles of ClF_3 is limiting. **(b)** We enter those values into the reaction table.

Solution (a) Determining the limiting reactant:
Finding amount (mol) of ClF_3 from amount (mol) of Cl_2:

$$\text{Amount (mol) of ClF}_3 = 0.750\ \cancel{\text{mol Cl}_2} \times \frac{2\ \text{mol ClF}_3}{1\ \cancel{\text{mol Cl}_2}} = 1.50\ \text{mol ClF}_3$$

Finding amount (mol) of ClF_3 from amount (mol) of F_2:

$$\text{Amount (mol) of ClF}_3 = 3.00\ \cancel{\text{mol F}_2} \times \frac{2\ \text{mol ClF}_3}{3\ \cancel{\text{mol F}_2}} = 2.00\ \text{mol ClF}_3$$

In this case, Cl_2 is limiting because it forms fewer moles of ClF_3.
(b) Writing the reaction table, with Cl_2 limiting:

Amount (mol)	$Cl_2(g)$	+	$3F_2(g)$	$\longrightarrow$	$2ClF_3(g)$
Initial	0.750		3.00		0
Change	−0.750		−2.25		+1.50
Final	0		0.75		1.50

Check Let's check that Cl_2 is the limiting reactant by assuming, for the moment, that F_2 is limiting. If that were true, all 3.00 mol of F_2 would react to form 2.00 mol of ClF_3. However, based on the balanced equation, obtaining 2.00 mol of ClF_3 would require 1.00 mol of Cl_2, and only 0.750 mol of Cl_2 is present. Thus, Cl_2 must be the limiting reactant.

Comment A major point to note from Sample Problems 3.18 and 3.19 is that the relative quantities of reactants *do not* determine which is limiting, but rather the quantity of product formed, which is based on the *molar ratio in the balanced equation.* In both problems, there is more F_2 than Cl_2. However,

- Sample Problem 3.18 has an F_2/Cl_2 ratio of 6/3, or 2/1, which is less than the required molar ratio of 3/1, so F_2 is limiting and Cl_2 is in excess.
- Sample Problem 3.19 has an F_2/Cl_2 ratio of 3.00/0.750, which is greater than the required molar ratio of 3/1, so Cl_2 is limiting and F_2 is in excess.

Follow-Up Problem 3.19 For the reaction in Follow-Up Problem 3.18, how many moles of product form from 1.5 mol of each reactant?

Sample Problem 3.20 Calculating Quantities in a Limiting-Reactant Problem: Mass to Mass

Problem A fuel mixture used in the early days of rocketry consisted of two liquids, hydrazine (N_2H_4) and dinitrogen tetraoxide (N_2O_4), which ignite on contact to form nitrogen gas and water vapor.
(a) How many grams of nitrogen gas form when 1.00×10^2 g of N_2H_4 and 2.00×10^2 g of N_2O_4 are mixed?
(b) Write a reaction table for this process.

Plan The amounts of two reactants are given, which means this is a limiting-reactant problem. **(a)** To determine the mass of product formed, we must find the limiting reactant by calculating which of the given masses of reactant forms *less* nitrogen gas. As always, we first write the balanced equation. We convert the grams of each reactant to moles using its molar mass and then use the molar ratio from the balanced equation to find the number of moles of N_2 each reactant forms. Next, we convert the lower amount of N_2 to mass (see the road map). **(b)** We use the values based on the limiting reactant for the reaction table.

Road Map

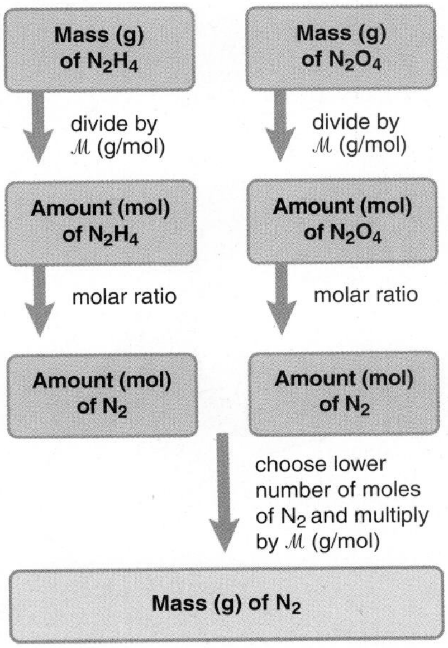

Solution (a) Writing the balanced equation:

$$2N_2H_4(l) + N_2O_4(l) \longrightarrow 3N_2(g) + 4H_2O(g)$$

Finding the amount (mol) of N_2 from the amount (mol) of each reactant

For N_2H_4: $$\text{Amount (mol) of } N_2H_4 = 1.00\times10^2\ \cancel{\text{g } N_2H_4} \times \frac{1 \text{ mol } N_2H_4}{32.05\ \cancel{\text{g } N_2H_4}} = 3.12 \text{ mol } N_2H_4$$

$$\text{Amount (mol) of } N_2 = 3.12\ \cancel{\text{mol } N_2H_4} \times \frac{3 \text{ mol } N_2}{2\ \cancel{\text{mol } N_2H_4}} = 4.68 \text{ mol } N_2$$

For N_2O_4: $$\text{Amount (mol) of } N_2O_4 = 2.00\times10^2\ \cancel{\text{g } N_2O_4} \times \frac{1 \text{ mol } N_2O_4}{92.02\ \cancel{\text{g } N_2O_4}} = 2.17 \text{ mol } N_2O_4$$

$$\text{Amount (mol) of } N_2 = 2.17\ \cancel{\text{mol } N_2O_4} \times \frac{3 \text{ mol } N_2}{1\ \cancel{\text{mol } N_2O_4}} = 6.51 \text{ mol } N_2$$

Thus, N_2H_4 is the limiting reactant because it yields less N_2.

Converting from amount (mol) of N_2 to mass (g):

$$\text{Mass (g) of } N_2 = 4.68\ \cancel{\text{mol } N_2} \times \frac{28.02 \text{ g } N_2}{1\ \cancel{\text{mol } N_2}} = 131 \text{ g } N_2$$

(b) With N_2H_4 as the limiting reactant, the reaction table is

Amount (mol)	$2N_2H_4(g)$	+	$N_2O_4(g)$	$\longrightarrow$	$3N_2(g)$	+	$4H_2O(g)$
Initial	3.12		2.17		0		0
Change	−3.12		−1.56		+4.68		+6.24
Final	0		0.61		4.68		6.24

Check The number of grams of N_2O_4 is more than that of N_2H_4, but there are fewer moles of N_2O_4 because its $\mathcal{M}$ is much higher. Rounding for N_2H_4: 100 g N_2H_4 × 1 mol/32 g ≈ 3 mol; ~3 mol × $\frac{3}{2}$ ≈ 4.5 mol N_2; ~4.5 mol × 30 g/mol ≈ 135 g N_2.

Comment 1. Recall this *common mistake* in solving limiting-reactant problems: The limiting reactant is not the *reactant* present in fewer moles (or grams). Rather, it is the reactant that forms fewer moles (or grams) of *product.*

2. An *alternative approach* to finding the limiting reactant compares "How much is needed?" with "How much is given?" That is, based on the balanced equation,

- Find the amount (mol) of each reactant needed to react with the other reactant.
- Compare that *needed* amount with the *given* amount in the problem statement. There will be *more* than enough of one reactant (excess) and *less* than enough of the other (limiting).

For example, the balanced equation for this problem shows that 2 mol of N_2H_4 reacts with 1 mol of N_2O_4. The amount (mol) of N_2O_4 needed to react with the given 3.12 mol of N_2H_4 is

$$\text{Amount (mol) of } N_2O_4 \text{ needed} = 3.12\ \cancel{\text{mol } N_2H_4} \times \frac{1 \text{ mol } N_2O_4}{2\ \cancel{\text{mol } N_2H_4}} = 1.56 \text{ mol } N_2O_4$$

The amount of N_2H_4 needed to react with the given 2.17 mol of N_2O_4 is

$$\text{Amount (mol) of } N_2H_4 \text{ needed} = 2.17\ \cancel{\text{mol } N_2O_4} \times \frac{2 \text{ mol } N_2H_4}{1\ \cancel{\text{mol } N_2O_4}} = 4.34 \text{ mol } N_2H_4$$

We are given 2.17 mol of N_2O_4, which is *more* than the 1.56 mol of N_2O_4 needed, and we are given 3.12 mol of N_2H_4, which is *less* than the 4.34 mol of N_2H_4 needed. Therefore, N_2H_4 is limiting, and N_2O_4 is in excess.

Follow-Up Problem 3.20 How many grams of solid aluminum sulfide can be prepared by the reaction of 10.0 g of aluminum and 15.0 g of sulfur? How many grams of the nonlimiting reactant are in excess?

Theoretical, Actual, and Percent Reaction Yields

Up until now, we've assumed that 100% of the limiting reactant becomes product, that ideal methods exist for isolating the product, and that we have perfect lab technique and collect all the product. In theory, this may happen, but in reality, it doesn't, and chemists recognize three types of reaction yield:

1. *Theoretical yield.* The amount of product calculated from the molar ratio in the balanced equation is the **theoretical yield.** But, there are several reasons why the theoretical yield is *never* obtained:
   - Reactant mixtures often proceed through **side reactions** that form different products (Figure 3.11). In the rocket fuel reaction in Sample Problem 3.20, for example, the reactants might form some NO in the following side reaction:
     $$N_2H_4(l) + 2N_2O_4(l) \longrightarrow 6NO(g) + 2H_2O(g)$$
     This reaction decreases the amounts of reactants available for N_2 production.
   - Even more important, many reactions seem to stop before they are complete, so some limiting reactant is unused. (We'll see why in Chapter 4.)
   - Physical losses occur in every step of a separation (see Tools of the Laboratory, Section 2.9): some solid clings to filter paper, some distillate evaporates, and so forth. With careful technique, you can minimize, but never eliminate, such losses.

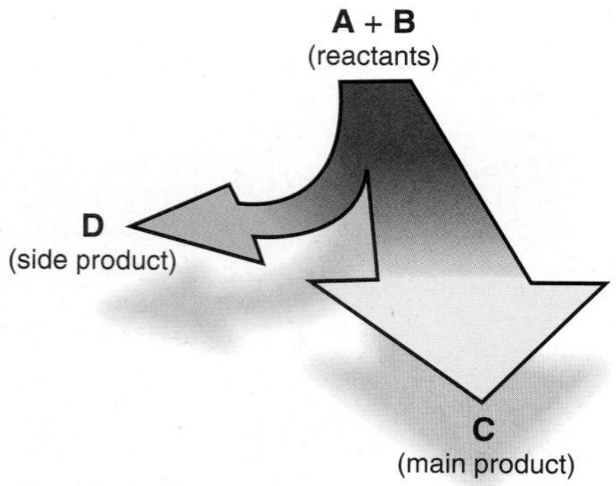

Figure 3.11 The effect of a side reaction on the yield of the main product.

2. *Actual yield.* Given these reasons for obtaining less than the theoretical yield, the amount of product actually obtained is the **actual yield.** Theoretical and actual yields are expressed in units of amount (moles) or mass (grams).

3. *Percent yield.* The **percent yield (% yield)** is the actual yield expressed as a percentage of the theoretical yield:

$$\%\ \text{yield} = \frac{\text{actual yield}}{\text{theoretical yield}} \times 100 \qquad \textbf{(3.8)}$$

By definition, the actual yield is less than the theoretical yield, so the percent yield is *always* less than 100%.

Road Map

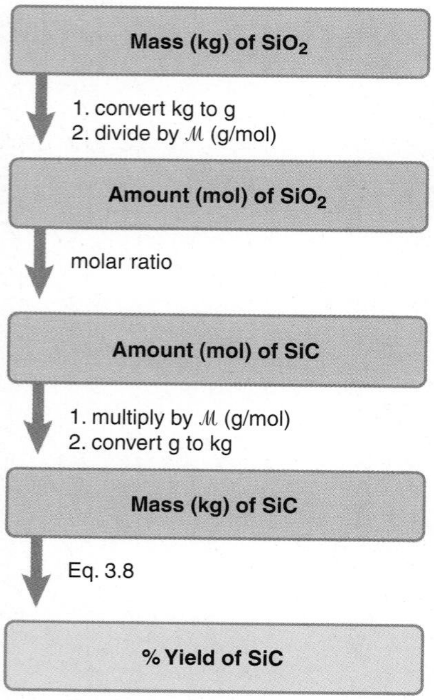

Sample Problem 3.21 Calculating Percent Yield

Problem Silicon carbide (SiC) is an important ceramic material made by reacting sand (silicon dioxide, SiO_2) with powdered carbon at a high temperature. Carbon monoxide is also formed. When 100.0 kg of sand is processed, 51.4 kg of SiC is recovered. What is the percent yield of SiC from this process?

Plan We are given the actual yield of SiC (51.4 kg), so we need the theoretical yield to calculate the percent yield. After writing the balanced equation, we convert the given mass of SiO_2 (100.0 kg) to amount (mol). We use the molar ratio to find the amount of SiC formed and convert it to mass (kg) to obtain the theoretical yield. Then, we use Equation 3.8 to find the percent yield (see the road map).

Solution Writing the balanced equation:

$$SiO_2(s) + 3C(s) \longrightarrow SiC(s) + 2CO(g)$$

Converting from mass (kg) of SiO_2 to amount (mol):

$$\text{Amount (mol) of } SiO_2 = 100.0\ \cancel{\text{kg } SiO_2} \times \frac{1000\ \cancel{\text{g}}}{1\ \cancel{\text{kg}}} \times \frac{1\ \text{mol } SiO_2}{60.09\ \cancel{\text{g } SiO_2}} = 1664\ \text{mol } SiO_2$$

Converting from amount (mol) of SiO_2 to amount (mol) of SiC:
The molar ratio is 1 mol SiC/1 mol SiO_2, so

$$\text{Amount (mol) of } SiO_2 = \text{moles of SiC} = 1664 \text{ mol SiC}$$

Converting from amount (mol) of SiC to mass (kg):

$$\text{Mass (kg) of SiC} = 1664 \cancel{\text{mol SiC}} \times \frac{40.10 \cancel{\text{g}} \text{ SiC}}{1 \cancel{\text{mol SiC}}} \times \frac{1 \text{ kg}}{1000 \cancel{\text{g}}} = 66.73 \text{ kg SiC}$$

Calculating the percent yield:

$$\% \text{ yield of SiC} = \frac{\text{actual yield}}{\text{theoretical yield}} \times 100 = \frac{51.4 \cancel{\text{kg SiC}}}{66.73 \cancel{\text{kg SiC}}} \times 100 = 77.0\%$$

Check Rounding shows that the mass of SiC seems correct: ~1500 mol × 40 g/mol × 1 kg/1000 g = 60 kg. The molar ratio of SiC/SiO_2 is 1/1, and $\mathcal{M}$ of SiC is about two-thirds ($\sim\frac{40}{60}$) of $\mathcal{M}$ of SiO_2, so 100 kg of SiO_2 should form about 66 kg of SiC.

Follow-Up Problem 3.21 Marble (calcium carbonate) reacts with hydrochloric acid solution to form calcium chloride solution, water, and carbon dioxide. Find the percent yield of carbon dioxide if 3.65 g is collected when 10.0 g of marble reacts.

Yields in Multistep Syntheses In the multistep synthesis of a complex compound, the overall yield can be surprisingly low, even if the yield of each step is high. For example, suppose a six-step synthesis has a 90.0% yield for each step. To find the overall percent yield, *express the yield of each step as a decimal, multiply them together, and then convert back to percent.* The overall recovery is only slightly more than 50%:

$$\text{Overall \% yield} = (0.900 \times 0.900 \times 0.900 \times 0.900 \times 0.900 \times 0.900) \times 100 = 53.1\%$$

Such multistep sequences are common in laboratory syntheses of medicines, dyes, pesticides, and many other organic compounds. For example, the antidepressant Sertraline is prepared from a simple starting compound in six steps, with yields of 80%, 80%, 50%, 100%, 48%, and 30%, respectively, and an overall percent yield of only 4.6% (Figure 3.12). Because a typical synthesis begins with large amounts of inexpensive, simple reactants and ends with small amounts of expensive, complex products, the overall yield greatly influences the commercial potential of a product.

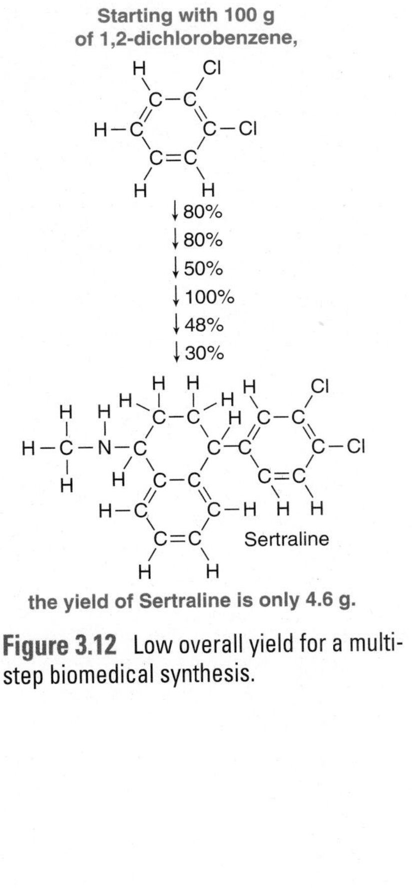

Figure 3.12 Low overall yield for a multistep biomedical synthesis.

Atom Economy: A Green Chemistry Perspective on Yield In the relatively new field of **green chemistry,** academic, industrial, and government chemists develop methods that reduce or prevent the release of harmful substances into the environment and the wasting of energy resources.

One way that green chemists evaluate a synthetic route is to focus on its *atom economy,* the proportion of reactant atoms that end up in the desired product. The efficiency of a synthesis is quantified in terms of the *percent atom economy:*

$$\% \text{ atom economy} = \frac{\text{no. of moles} \times \text{molar mass of desired product}}{\text{sum of (no. of moles} \times \text{molar mass) for all products}} \times 100$$

Consider two synthetic routes—one starting with benzene (C_6H_6), the other with butane (C_4H_{10})—for the production of maleic anhydride ($C_4H_2O_3$), a key substance in the manufacture of polymers, dyes, medicines, pesticides, and other products:

Route 1. $2C_6H_6(l) + 9O_2(g) \rightarrow \cdots \rightarrow 2C_4H_2O_3(l) + 4H_2O(l) + 4CO_2(g)$

Route 2. $2C_4H_{10}(g) + 7O_2(g) \rightarrow \cdots \rightarrow 2C_4H_2O_3(l) + 8H_2O(l)$

Let's compare the efficiency of these routes in terms of percent atom economy:

Route 1.

$$\% \text{ atom economy} = \frac{2 \times \mathcal{M} \text{ of } C_4H_2O_3}{(2 \times \mathcal{M} \text{ of } C_4H_2O_3) + (4 \times \mathcal{M} \text{ of } H_2O) + (4 \times \mathcal{M} \text{ of } CO_2)} \times 100$$

$$= \frac{2 \times 98.06 \cancel{\text{g}}}{(2 \times 98.06 \cancel{\text{g}}) + (4 \times 18.02 \cancel{\text{g}}) + (4 \times 44.01 \cancel{\text{g}})} \times 100$$

$$= 44.15\%$$

Route 2.

$$\% \text{ atom economy} = \frac{2 \times \mathcal{M} \text{ of } C_4H_2O_3}{(2 \times \mathcal{M} \text{ of } C_4H_2O_3) + (8 \times \mathcal{M} \text{ of } H_2O)} \times 100$$
$$= \frac{2 \times 98.06 \text{ g}}{(2 \times 98.06 \text{ g}) + (8 \times 18.02 \text{ g})} \times 100$$
$$= 57.63\%$$

From the perspective of atom economy, route 2 is preferable because a larger percentage of reactant atoms end up in the desired product. It is also a "greener" approach than route 1 because it avoids the use of the toxic reactant benzene and does not produce CO_2, a gas that contributes to global warming.

Summary of Section 3.4

- The substances in a balanced equation are related to each other by stoichiometrically equivalent molar ratios, which are used as conversion factors to find the amount (mol) of one substance given the amount of another.
- In limiting-reactant problems, the quantities of two (or more) reactants are given, and the limiting reactant is the one that forms the lower quantity of product. Reaction tables show the initial and final quantities of all reactants and products, as well as the changes in those quantities.
- In practice, side reactions, incomplete reactions, and physical losses result in an actual yield of product that is less than the theoretical yield (the quantity based on the molar ratio from the balanced equation), giving a percent yield less than 100%. In multistep reaction sequences, the overall yield is found by multiplying the yields for each step.
- Atom economy, or the proportion of reactant atoms found in the product, is one criterion for choosing a "greener" reaction process.

3.5 • FUNDAMENTALS OF SOLUTION STOICHIOMETRY

In popular media, you may see a chemist in a lab coat, surrounded by glassware, mixing colored solutions that froth and give off billowing fumes. Most reactions in solution are not this dramatic, and good technique requires safer mixing procedures; however, it is true that aqueous solution chemistry is central to laboratory chemistry. Liquid solutions are easier to store than gases and easier to mix than solids, and the amounts of substances in solution can be measured precisely. Many environmental reactions and almost all biochemical reactions occur in solution.

We know the amounts of pure substances by converting their masses into number of moles. But for dissolved substances, we need the *concentration*—the number of moles per volume of solution—to find the volume that contains a given number of moles. In this section, we first discuss *molarity,* the most common way to express concentration (Chapter 13 covers others). Then, we see how to prepare a solution of a specific molarity and how to use solutions in stoichiometric calculations.

Expressing Concentration in Terms of Molarity

A solution consists of a smaller quantity of one substance, the **solute,** dissolved in a larger quantity of another, the **solvent.** When it dissolves, the solute's chemical entities become evenly dispersed throughout the solvent. The **concentration** of a solution is often expressed as *the quantity of solute dissolved in a given quantity of solution.*

Concentration is an *intensive* property (like density or temperature; Section 1.5) and thus is independent of the solution volume: a 50-L tank of a solution has the *same concentration* (solute quantity/solution quantity) as a 50-mL beaker of the solution. **Molarity (*M*)** expresses the concentration in units of *moles of solute per liter of solution:*

$$\text{Molarity} = \frac{\text{moles of solute}}{\text{liters of solution}} \quad \text{or} \quad M = \frac{\text{mol solute}}{\text{L soln}} \tag{3.9}$$

Sample Problem 3.22 Calculating the Molarity of a Solution

Problem Glycine has the simplest structure of the 20 amino acids that make up proteins. What is the molarity of a solution that contains 0.715 mol of glycine in 495 mL?

Plan The molarity is the number of moles of solute in each liter of solution. We divide the number of moles (0.715 mol) by the volume (495 mL) and convert the volume to liters to find the molarity (see the road map).

Road Map

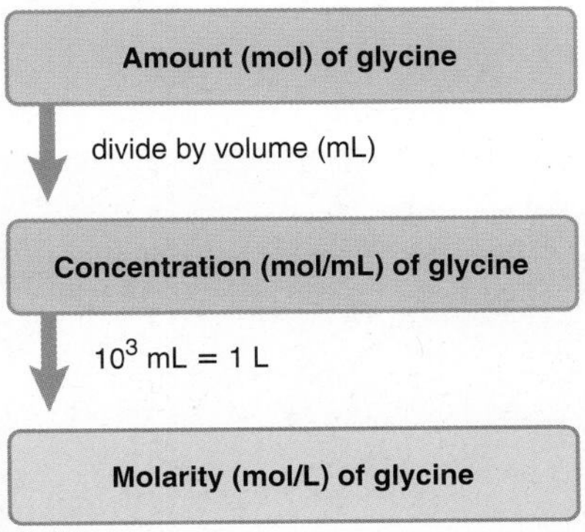

Solution

$$\text{Molarity} = \frac{0.715 \text{ mol glycine}}{495 \text{ }\cancel{\text{mL soln}}} \times \frac{1000 \text{ }\cancel{\text{mL}}}{1 \text{ L}} = 1.44\ M \text{ glycine}$$

Check A quick look at the math shows about 0.7 mol of glycine in about 0.5 L of solution, so the concentration should be about 1.4 mol/L, or 1.4 *M*.

Follow-Up Problem 3.22 How many moles of KI are in 84 mL of 0.50 *M* KI? Include a road map that shows how you planned the solution.

Amount-Mass-Number Conversions Involving Solutions

Like many intensive properties, molarity can be used as a *conversion factor* between volume (L) of solution and amount (mol) of solute, from which we can find the mass or the number of entities of solute (Figure 3.13), as applied in Sample Problem 3.23.

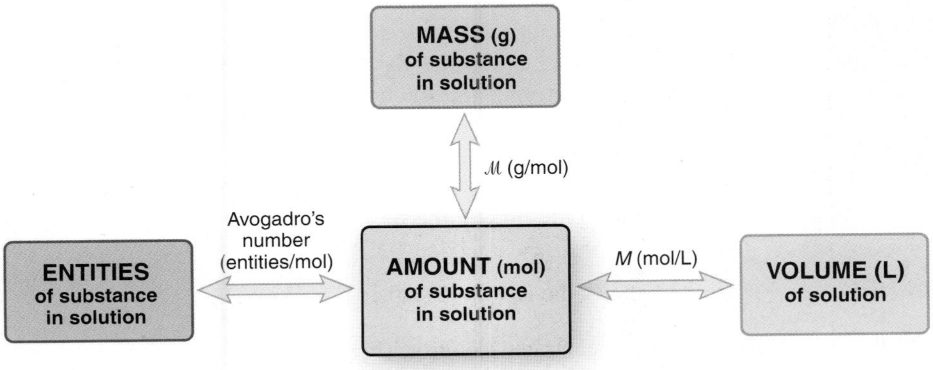

Figure 3.13 Summary of amount-mass-number relationships in solution. The amount (mol) of a substance in solution is related to the volume (L) of solution through the molarity (*M*; mol/L). As always, convert the given quantity to amount (mol) first.

Sample Problem 3.23 Calculating Mass of Solute in a Given Volume of Solution

Problem Biochemists often study reactions in solutions containing phosphate ion, commonly found in cells. How many grams of solute are in 1.75 L of 0.460 *M* sodium hydrogen phosphate?

Plan We need the mass (g) of solute, so we multiply the known solution volume (1.75 L) by the known molarity (0.460 *M*) to find the amount (mol) of solute and convert it to mass (g) using the solute's molar mass (see the road map).

Road Map

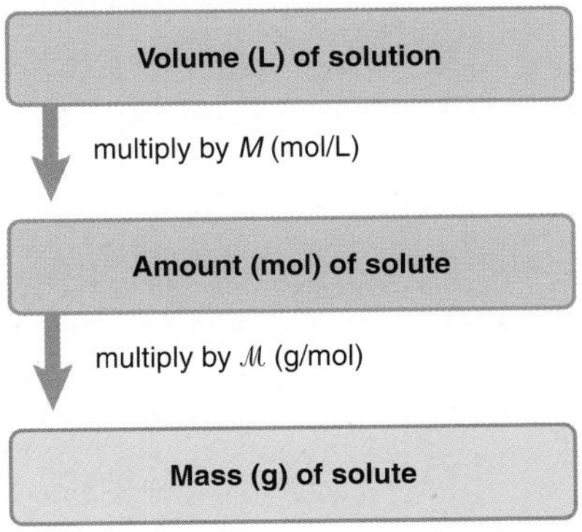

Solution Calculating amount (mol) of solute in solution:

$$\text{Amount (mol) of } Na_2HPO_4 = 1.75 \text{ }\cancel{\text{L soln}} \times \frac{0.460 \text{ mol } Na_2HPO_4}{1 \text{ }\cancel{\text{L soln}}} = 0.805 \text{ mol } Na_2HPO_4$$

Converting from amount (mol) of solute to mass (g):

$$\text{Mass (g) } Na_2HPO_4 = 0.805 \text{ }\cancel{\text{mol } Na_2HPO_4} \times \frac{141.96 \text{ g } Na_2HPO_4}{1 \text{ }\cancel{\text{mol } Na_2HPO_4}} = 114 \text{ g } Na_2HPO_4$$

Check The answer seems to be correct: ~1.8 L of 0.5 mol/L solution contains 0.9 mol, and 150 g/mol × 0.9 mol = 135 g, which is close to 114 g of solute.

Follow-Up Problem 3.23 In biochemistry laboratories, solutions of sucrose (table sugar, $C_{12}H_{22}O_{11}$) are used in high-speed centrifuges to separate the parts of a biological cell. How many liters of 3.30 *M* sucrose contain 135 g of solute? Include a road map that shows how you planned the solution.

Preparing and Diluting Molar Solutions

Notice that the volume term in the denominator of the molarity expression in Equation 3.9 is the *solution* volume, **not** the *solvent* volume. This means that you *cannot* dissolve 1 mol of solute in 1 L of solvent to make a 1 *M* solution. Because the solute volume adds to the solvent volume, the total volume (solute + solvent) would be *more* than 1 L, so the concentration would be *less* than 1 *M*.

Figure 3.14 Laboratory preparation of molar solutions.

Preparing a Solution Correctly preparing a solution of a solid solute requires four steps. Let's prepare 0.500 L of 0.350 *M* nickel(II) nitrate hexahydrate [$Ni(NO_3)_2 \cdot 6H_2O$]:

1. *Weigh the solid.* Calculate the mass of solid needed by converting from volume (L) to amount (mol) and then to mass (g):

$$\text{Mass (g) of solute} = 0.500\ \cancel{\text{L soln}} \times \frac{0.350\ \cancel{\text{mol Ni(NO}_3)_2\cdot 6\text{H}_2\text{O}}}{1\ \cancel{\text{L soln}}} \times \frac{290.82\text{ g Ni(NO}_3)_2\cdot 6\text{H}_2\text{O}}{1\ \cancel{\text{mol Ni(NO}_3)_2\cdot 6\text{H}_2\text{O}}}$$
$$= 50.9\text{ g Ni(NO}_3)_2\cdot 6\text{H}_2\text{O}$$

2. *Transfer the solid.* We need 0.500 L of solution, so we choose a 500-mL volumetric flask, add enough distilled water to fully dissolve the solute (usually about half the final volume, or 250 mL of distilled water in this case), and transfer the solute. Wash down any solid clinging to the neck with some solvent.
3. *Dissolve the solid.* Swirl the flask until all the solute is dissolved. If necessary, wait until the solution is at room temperature. (As we discuss in Chapter 13, the solution process may be accompanied by heating or cooling.)
4. *Add solvent to the final volume.* Add distilled water to bring the solution volume to the line on the flask neck; cover and mix thoroughly again.

Figure 3.14 shows the last three steps.

Diluting a Solution A concentrated solution (higher molarity) is converted to a dilute solution (lower molarity) by adding solvent, which means the solution volume increases but the amount (mol) of solute stays the same. As a result, the dilute solution contains *fewer solute particles per unit volume* and, thus, has a lower concentration than the concentrated solution (Figure 3.15). If you need several different dilute solutions, prepare a concentrated solution *(stock solution)* and store it and dilute it as needed.

Figure 3.15 Converting a concentrated solution to a dilute solution.

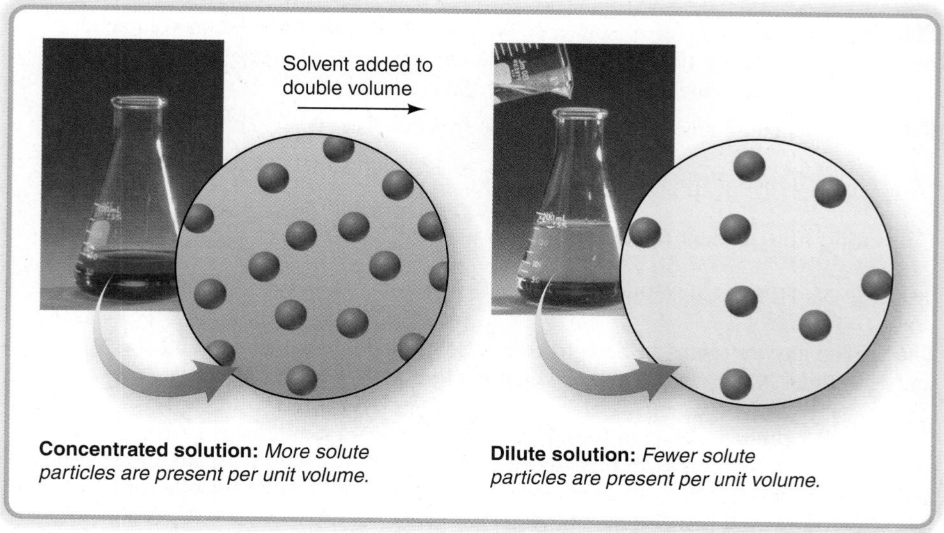

Sample Problem 3.24 Preparing a Dilute Solution from a Concentrated Solution

Problem Isotonic saline is 0.15 *M* aqueous NaCl. It simulates the total concentration of ions in many cellular fluids, and its uses range from cleaning contact lenses to washing red blood cells. How would you prepare 0.80 L of isotonic saline from a 6.0 *M* stock solution?

Plan To dilute a concentrated solution, we add only solvent, so the *moles of solute are the same in both solutions.* We know the volume (0.80 L) and molarity (0.15 *M*) of the dilute (dil) NaCl solution needed, so we find the amount (mol) of NaCl it contains. Then, we find the volume (L) of concentrated (conc; 6.0 *M*) NaCl solution that contains the same amount (mol). We add solvent *up to* the final volume (see the road map).

Road Map

Volume (L) of dilute solution

↓ multiply by *M* (mol/L) of dilute solution

Amount (mol) of NaCl in dilute solution = Amount (mol) of NaCl in concentrated solution

↓ divide by *M* (mol/L) of concentrated solution

Volume (L) of concentrated solution

Solution Finding amount (mol) of solute in dilute solution:

$$\text{Amount (mol) of NaCl in dil soln} = 0.80\ \cancel{\text{L soln}} \times \frac{0.15\ \text{mol NaCl}}{1\ \cancel{\text{L soln}}}$$
$$= 0.12\ \text{mol NaCl}$$

Finding amount (mol) of solute in concentrated solution:

Because we add only solvent to dilute the solution,

$$\text{Amount (mol) of NaCl in dil soln} = \text{amount (mol) of NaCl in conc soln}$$
$$= 0.12\ \text{mol NaCl}$$

Finding the volume (L) of concentrated solution that contains 0.12 mol of NaCl:

$$\text{Volume (L) of conc NaCl soln} = 0.12\ \cancel{\text{mol NaCl}} \times \frac{1\ \text{L soln}}{6.0\ \cancel{\text{mol NaCl}}}$$
$$= 0.020\ \text{L soln}$$

To prepare 0.80 L of dilute solution, place 0.020 L of 6.0 *M* NaCl in a 1.0-L graduated cylinder, add distilled water (~780 mL) to the 0.80-L mark, and stir thoroughly.

Check The answer seems reasonable because a small volume of concentrated solution is used to prepare a large volume of dilute solution. Also, the ratio of volumes (0.020 L/0.80 L) is the same as the ratio of concentrations (0.15 *M*/6.0 *M*).

Follow-Up Problem 3.24 A chemical engineer dilutes a stock solution of sulfuric acid by adding 25.0 m^3 of 7.50 *M* acid to enough water to make 500. m^3. What is the concentration of sulfuric acid in the diluted solution in g/mL?

Solving Dilution Problems To solve dilution problems and others involving a change in concentration, apply the following relationship:

$$M_{\text{dil}} \times V_{\text{dil}} = \text{amount (mol)} = M_{\text{conc}} \times V_{\text{conc}} \qquad (3.10)$$

where *M* and *V* are the molarity and volume of the *dil*ute (subscript "dil") and *conc*entrated (subscript "conc") solutions. Using the values in Sample Problem 3.24, for example, and solving Equation 3.10 for V_{conc} gives

$$V_{\text{conc}} = \frac{M_{\text{dil}} \times V_{\text{dil}}}{M_{\text{conc}}} = \frac{0.15\ \cancel{M} \times 0.80\ \text{L}}{6.0\ \cancel{M}}$$
$$= 0.020\ \text{L}$$

Notice that Sample Problem 3.24 had the same calculation broken into two parts:

$$V_{\text{conc}} = 0.80\ \cancel{\text{L}} \times \frac{0.15\ \cancel{\text{mol NaCl}}}{1\ \cancel{\text{L}}} \times \frac{1\ \text{L}}{6.0\ \cancel{\text{mol NaCl}}}$$
$$= 0.020\ \text{L}$$

In the next sample problem, we use a variation of this relationship, with molecular scenes showing numbers of particles, to visualize changes in concentration.

Sample Problem 3.25 Visualizing Changes in Concentration

(a)

(b)

Problem The top circle at left represents a unit volume of a solution. Draw a circle representing a unit volume of the solution after each of these changes:
(a) For every 1 mL of solution, 1 mL of solvent is added.
(b) One-third of the solvent is boiled off.

Plan Given the starting solution, we have to find the number of solute particles in a unit volume after each change. The number of particles per unit volume, N, is directly related to the number of moles per unit volume, M, so we can use a relationship similar to Equation 3.10 to find the number of particles. **(a)** The volume increases, so the final solution is more dilute—fewer particles per unit volume. **(b)** Some solvent is lost, so the final solution is more concentrated—more particles per unit volume.

Solution (a) Finding the number of particles in the dilute solution, N_{dil}:

$$N_{\text{dil}} \times V_{\text{dil}} = N_{\text{conc}} \times V_{\text{conc}}$$

thus,

$$N_{\text{dil}} = N_{\text{conc}} \times \frac{V_{\text{conc}}}{V_{\text{dil}}} = 8 \text{ particles} \times \frac{1 \text{ mL}}{2 \text{ mL}} = 4 \text{ particles}$$

(b) Finding the number of particles in the concentrated solution, N_{conc}:

$$N_{\text{dil}} \times V_{\text{dil}} = N_{\text{conc}} \times V_{\text{conc}}$$

thus,

$$N_{\text{conc}} = N_{\text{dil}} \times \frac{V_{\text{dil}}}{V_{\text{conc}}} = 8 \text{ particles} \times \frac{1 \text{ mL}}{\frac{2}{3} \text{ mL}} = 12 \text{ particles}$$

Check In (a), the volume is doubled (from 1 mL to 2 mL), so the number of particles should be halved; $\frac{1}{2}$ of 8 is 4. In (b), the volume is $\frac{2}{3}$ of the original, so the number of particles should be $\frac{3}{2}$ of the original; $\frac{3}{2}$ of 8 is 12.

Comment In (b), we assumed that only solvent boils off. This is true with nonvolatile solutes, such as ionic compounds, but in Chapter 13, we'll encounter solutions in which both solvent *and* solute are volatile.

Follow-Up Problem 3.25 The circle labeled A represents a unit volume of a solution. Explain the changes that must be made to A to obtain the unit volumes in B and C.

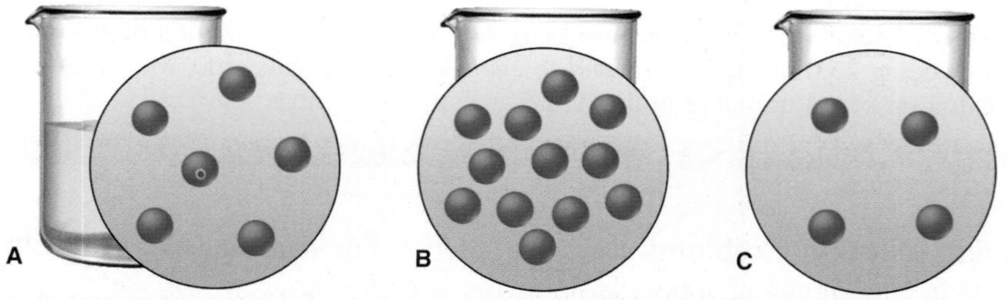

Stoichiometry of Reactions in Solution

Solving stoichiometry problems for reactions in solution requires the additional step of converting the volume of reactant or product in solution to amount (mol):

1. Balance the equation.
2. Find the amount (mol) of one substance from the volume and molarity.
3. Relate it to the stoichiometrically equivalent amount of another substance.
4. Convert to the desired units.

Sample Problem 3.26 Calculating Quantities of Reactants and Products for a Reaction in Solution

Problem Specialized cells in the stomach release HCl to aid digestion. If they release too much, the excess can be neutralized with an antacid. A common antacid contains magnesium hydroxide, which reacts with the acid to form water and magnesium chloride solution. As a government chemist testing commercial antacids, you use 0.10 M HCl to simulate the acid concentration in the stomach. How many liters of "stomach acid" react with a tablet containing 0.10 g of magnesium hydroxide?

Plan We are given the mass (0.10 g) of magnesium hydroxide, $Mg(OH)_2$, that reacts with the acid. We also know the acid concentration (0.10 *M*) and must find the acid volume. After writing the balanced equation, we convert the mass (g) of $Mg(OH)_2$ to amount (mol) and use the molar ratio to find the amount (mol) of HCl that reacts with it. Then, we use the molarity of HCl to find the volume (L) that contains this amount (see the road map).

Road Map

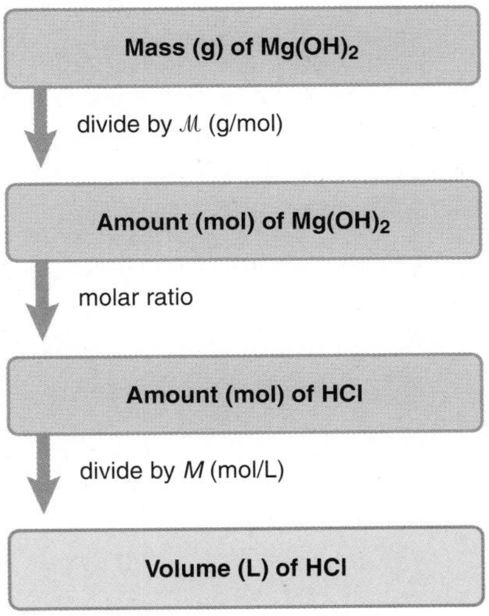

Solution Writing the balanced equation:

$$Mg(OH)_2(s) + 2HCl(aq) \longrightarrow MgCl_2(aq) + 2H_2O(l)$$

Converting from mass (g) of $Mg(OH)_2$ to amount (mol):

$$\text{Amount (mol) of } Mg(OH)_2 = 0.10\ \cancel{g\ Mg(OH)_2} \times \frac{1\ mol\ Mg(OH)_2}{58.33\ \cancel{g\ Mg(OH)_2}} = 1.7\times10^{-3}\ mol\ Mg(OH)_2$$

Converting from amount (mol) of $Mg(OH)_2$ to amount (mol) of HCl:

$$\text{Amount (mol) of HCl} = 1.7\times10^{-3}\ \cancel{mol\ Mg(OH)_2} \times \frac{2\ mol\ HCl}{1\ \cancel{mol\ Mg(OH)_2}} = 3.4\times10^{-3}\ mol\ HCl$$

Converting from amount (mol) of HCl to volume (L):

$$\text{Volume (L) of HCl} = 3.4\times10^{-3}\ \cancel{mol\ HCl} \times \frac{1\ L}{0.10\ \cancel{mol\ HCl}} = 3.4\times10^{-2}\ L$$

Check The size of the answer seems reasonable: a small volume of dilute acid (0.034 L of 0.10 *M*) reacts with a small amount of antacid (0.0017 mol).

Comment In Chapter 4, you'll see that this equation is an oversimplification, because HCl and $MgCl_2$ exist in solution as separated ions.

Follow-Up Problem 3.26 Another active ingredient in some antacids is aluminum hydroxide. Which is more effective at neutralizing stomach acid, magnesium hydroxide or aluminum hydroxide? [*Hint:* "Effectiveness" refers to the amount of acid that reacts with a given mass of antacid. You already know the effectiveness of 0.10 g of $Mg(OH)_2$.]

Except for the additional step of finding amounts (mol) in solution, limiting-reactant problems for reactions in solution are handled just like other such problems.

Sample Problem 3.27 Solving Limiting-Reactant Problems for Reactions in Solution

Problem Mercury and its compounds have uses from fillings for teeth (as a mixture with silver, copper, and tin) to the production of chlorine. Because of their toxicity, however, soluble mercury compounds, such as mercury(II) nitrate, must be removed from industrial wastewater. One removal method reacts the wastewater with sodium sulfide solution to produce solid mercury(II) sulfide and sodium nitrate solution. In a laboratory simulation, 0.050 L of 0.010 *M* mercury(II) nitrate reacts with 0.020 L of 0.10 *M* sodium sulfide. **(a)** How many grams of mercury(II) sulfide form? **(b)** Write a reaction table for this process.

Plan This is a limiting-reactant problem because *the quantities of two reactants are given.* After balancing the equation, we determine the limiting reactant. From the molarity and volume of each solution, we calculate the amount (mol) of each reactant. Then, we use the molar ratio to find the amount of product (HgS) that each reactant forms. The limiting reactant forms fewer moles of HgS, which we convert to mass (g) of HgS using its molar mass (see the road map). We use the amount of HgS formed from the limiting reactant in the reaction table.

Road Map

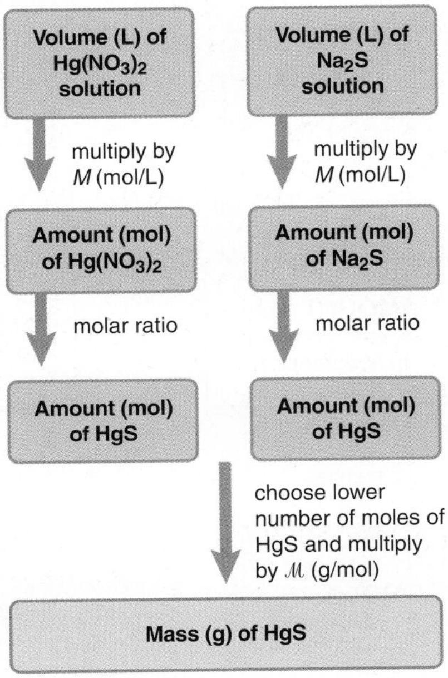

Solution (a) Writing the balanced equation:

$$Hg(NO_3)_2(aq) + Na_2S(aq) \longrightarrow HgS(s) + 2NaNO_3(aq)$$

Finding the amount (mol) of HgS formed from $Hg(NO_3)_2$: Combining the steps gives

$$\text{Amount (mol) of HgS} = 0.050\ \cancel{L\ soln} \times \frac{0.010\ \cancel{mol\ Hg(NO_3)_2}}{1\ \cancel{L\ soln}} \times \frac{1\ mol\ HgS}{1\ \cancel{mol\ Hg(NO_3)_2}}$$

$$= \mathbf{5.0\times10^{-4}\ mol\ HgS}$$

Finding the amount (mol) of HgS from Na_2S: Combining the steps gives

$$\text{Amount (mol) of HgS} = 0.020\ \cancel{\text{L soln}} \times \frac{0.10\ \cancel{\text{mol Na}_2\text{S}}}{1\ \cancel{\text{L soln}}} \times \frac{1\ \text{mol HgS}}{1\ \cancel{\text{mol Na}_2\text{S}}} = \mathbf{2.0{\times}10^{-3}\ mol\ HgS}$$

$Hg(NO_3)_2$ is the limiting reactant because it forms fewer moles of HgS.
Converting the amount (mol) of HgS formed from $Hg(NO_3)_2$ to mass (g):

$$\text{Mass (g) of HgS} = 5.0{\times}10^{-4}\ \cancel{\text{mol HgS}} \times \frac{232.7\ \text{g HgS}}{1\ \cancel{\text{mol HgS}}} = 0.12\ \text{g HgS}$$

(b) With $Hg(NO_3)_2$ as the limiting reactant, the reaction table is

Amount (mol)	$Hg(NO_3)_2(aq)$	+	$Na_2S(aq)$	⟶	$HgS(s)$	+	$2NaNO_3(aq)$
Initial	$5.0{\times}10^{-4}$		$2.0{\times}10^{-3}$		0		0
Change	$-5.0{\times}10^{-4}$		$-5.0{\times}10^{-4}$		$+5.0{\times}10^{-4}$		$+1.0{\times}10^{-3}$
Final	0		$1.5{\times}10^{-3}$		$5.0{\times}10$		$1.0{\times}10^{-3}$

A large excess of Na_2S remains after the reaction. Note that the amount of $NaNO_3$ formed is twice the amount of $Hg(NO_3)_2$ consumed, as the balanced equation shows.

Check As a check on our choice of the limiting reactant, let's use the alternative method in Sample Problem 3.20 (see Comment, p. 111).

Finding amount (mol) of reactants given:

$$\text{Amount (mol) of Hg(NO}_3)_2 = 0.050\ \cancel{\text{L soln}} \times \frac{0.010\ \text{mol Hg(NO}_3)_2}{1\ \cancel{\text{L soln}}} = 5.0{\times}10^{-4}\ \text{mol Hg(NO}_3)_2$$

$$\text{Amount (mol) of Na}_2\text{S} = 0.020\ \cancel{\text{L soln}} \times \frac{0.10\ \text{mol Na}_2\text{S}}{1\ \cancel{\text{L soln}}} = 2.0{\times}10^{-3}\ \text{mol Na}_2\text{S}$$

The molar ratio of the reactants is 1 $Hg(NO_3)_2$/1 Na_2S. Therefore, $Hg(NO_3)_2$ is limiting because there is less of it than we would need to react with all of the available Na_2S.

Follow-Up Problem 3.27 Despite the toxicity of lead, many of its compounds are still used to make pigments. **(a)** When 268 mL of 1.50 *M* lead(II) acetate reacts with 130. mL of 3.40 *M* sodium chloride, how many grams of solid lead(II) chloride can form? (Sodium acetate solution also forms.) **(b)** Using the abbreviation "Ac" for the acetate ion, write a reaction table for the process.

Figure 3.16 provides a visual review of all the stoichiometric relationships we've discussed in this chapter.

Figure 3.16 An overview of amount-mass-number stoichiometric relationships.

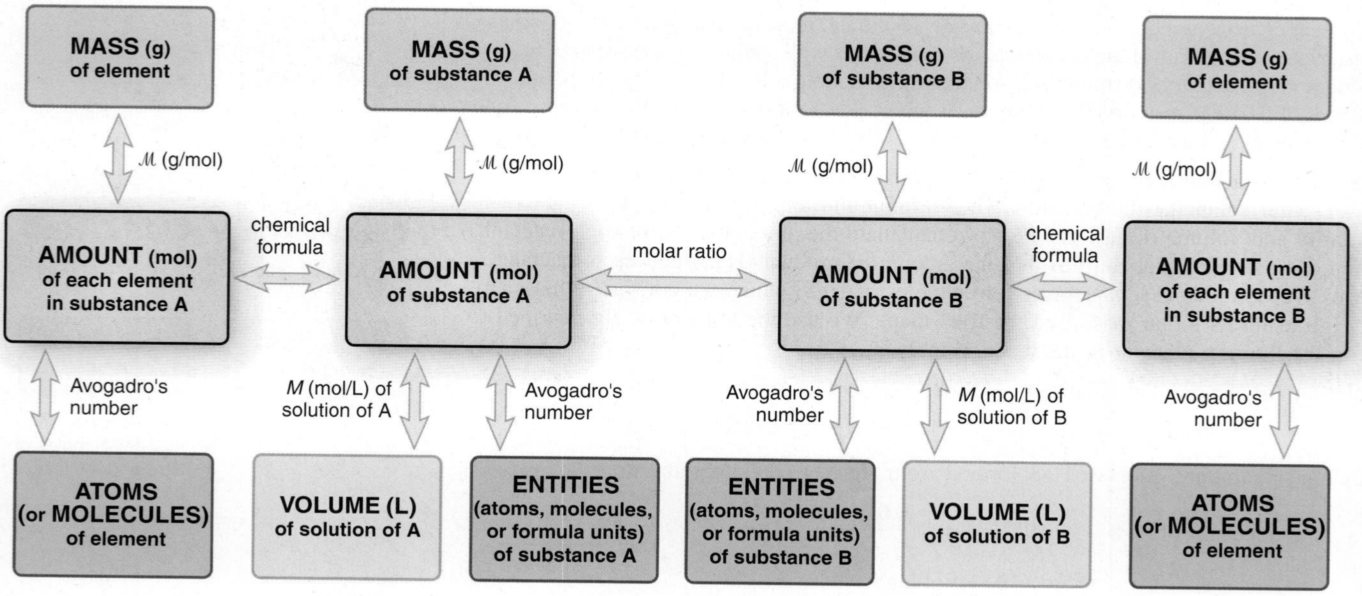

Summary of Section 3.5

- When reactions occur in solution, amounts of reactants and products are given in terms of concentration and volume.
- Molarity is the number of moles of solute dissolved in one liter of solution. A concentrated solution (higher molarity) is converted to a dilute solution (lower molarity) by adding solvent.
- By using molarity as a conversion factor, we can apply the principles of stoichiometry to reactions in solution.

CHAPTER REVIEW GUIDE

Learning Objectives

Relevant section (§) and/or sample problem (SP) numbers appear in parentheses.

Understand These Concepts

1. The definition of the mole unit (§3.1)
2. Relation between the mass of a chemical entity (in amu) and the mass of a mole of the entities (in g) (§3.1)
3. The relations among amount of substance (in mol), mass (in g), and number of chemical entities (§3.1)
4. Mole-mass-number information in a chemical formula (§3.1)
5. The difference between empirical and molecular formulas of a compound (§3.2)
6. How more than one substance can have the same empirical formula and the same molecular formula (isomers) (§3.2)
7. The importance of balancing equations for the quantitative study of chemical reactions (§3.3)
8. Mole-mass-number information in a balanced equation (§3.4)
9. The relation between amounts of reactants and amounts of products (§3.4)
10. Why one reactant limits the amount of product (§3.4)
11. The causes of lower-than-expected yields and the distinction between theoretical and actual yields (§3.4)
12. The meanings of concentration and molarity (§3.5)
13. The effect of dilution on the concentration of solute (§3.5)
14. How reactions in solution differ from reactions of pure reactants (§3.5)

Master These Skills

1. Calculating the molar mass of any substance (§3.1; SPs 3.5, 3.6)
2. Converting between amount of substance (in moles), mass (in grams), and number of chemical entities (SPs 3.1–3.5)
3. Using mass percent to find the mass of an element in a given mass of compound (SPs 3.6, 3.7)
4. Determining empirical and molecular formulas of a compound from mass percents and molar masses of elements (SPs 3.8–3.10)
5. Determining a molecular formula from combustion analysis (SP 3.11)
6. Converting a chemical statement or a molecular depiction into a balanced equation (SPs 3.12, 3.13)
7. Using stoichiometrically equivalent molar ratios to convert between amounts of reactants and products in reactions of pure and dissolved substances (SPs 3.14–3.16, 3.26)
8. Writing an overall equation from a series of equations (SP 3.17)
9. Solving limiting-reactant problems for reactions of pure and dissolved substances (SPs 3.18–3.20, 3.27)
10. Calculating percent yield (SP 3.21)
11. Calculating molarity and mass of solute in solution (SPs 3.22, 3.23)
12. Preparing a dilute solution from a concentrated one (SP 3.24)
13. Using molecular depictions to understand changes in concentration (SP 3.25)

Key Terms

Page numbers appear in parentheses.

stoichiometry (83)

Section 3.1
mole (mol) (83)
Avogadro's number (83)
molar mass ($\mathcal{M}$) (84)

Section 3.2
empirical formula (92)
molecular formula (92)
structural formula (92)
combustion analysis (95)
isomer (97)

Section 3.3
chemical equation (98)
reactant (99)
product (99)
balancing (stoichiometric) coefficient (99)

Section 3.4
overall (net) equation (106)
limiting reactant (107)
theoretical yield (112)
side reaction (112)
actual yield (112)
percent yield (% yield) (112)
green chemistry (113)

Section 3.5
solute (114)
solvent (114)
concentration (114)
molarity (M) (114)

Key Equations and Relationships

Page numbers appear in parentheses.

3.1 Number of entities in one mole (83):

1 mol contains 6.022×10^{23} entities (to 4 sf)

3.2 Converting amount (mol) to mass (g) using $\mathcal{M}$ (85):

$$\text{Mass (g)} = \text{amount (mol)} \times \frac{\text{no. of grams}}{1\ \text{mol}}$$

3.3 Converting mass (g) to amount (mol) using $1/\mathcal{M}$ (85):

$$\text{Amount (mol)} = \text{mass (g)} \times \frac{1\ \text{mol}}{\text{no. of grams}}$$

3.4 Converting amount (mol) to number of entities (85):

$$\text{No. of entities} = \text{amount (mol)} \times \frac{6.022\times10^{23}\ \text{entities}}{1\ \text{mol}}$$

3.5 Converting number of entities to amount (mol) (85):

$$\text{Amount (mol)} = \text{no. of entities} \times \frac{1\ \text{mol}}{6.022\times10^{23}\ \text{entities}}$$

3.6 Calculating mass % (90):

Mass % of element X

$$= \frac{\text{moles of X in formula} \times \text{molar mass of X (g/mol)}}{\text{mass (g) of 1 mol of compound}} \times 100$$

3.7 Finding the mass of an element in any mass of compound (91):

$$\text{Mass of element} = \text{mass of compound} \times \frac{\text{mass of element in 1 mol of compound}}{\text{mass of 1 mol of compound}}$$

3.8 Calculating percent yield (112):

$$\%\ \text{yield} = \frac{\text{actual yield}}{\text{theoretical yield}} \times 100$$

3.9 Defining molarity (114):

$$\text{Molarity} = \frac{\text{moles of solute}}{\text{liters of solution}} \quad \text{or} \quad M = \frac{\text{mol solute}}{\text{L soln}}$$

3.10 Diluting a concentrated solution (117):

$$M_{\text{dil}} \times V_{\text{dil}} = \text{amount (mol)} = M_{\text{conc}} \times V_{\text{conc}}$$

Brief Solutions to Follow-Up Problems

3.1

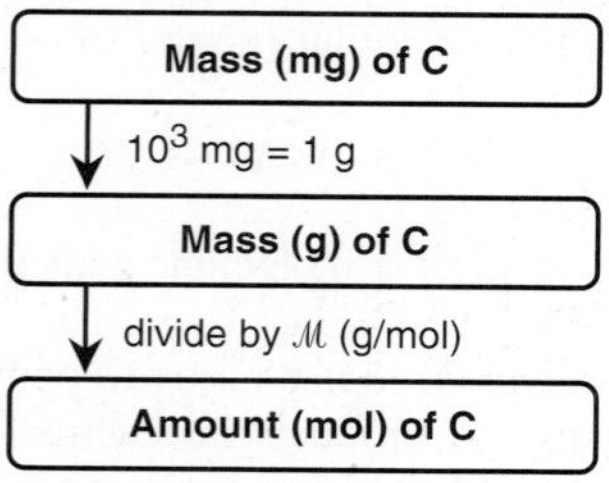

$$\text{Amount (mol) of C} = 315\ \cancel{\text{mg C}} \times \frac{1\ \cancel{\text{g}}}{10^3\ \cancel{\text{mg}}} \times \frac{1\ \text{mol C}}{12.01\ \cancel{\text{g C}}}$$
$$= 2.62\times10^{-2}\ \text{mol C}$$

3.2

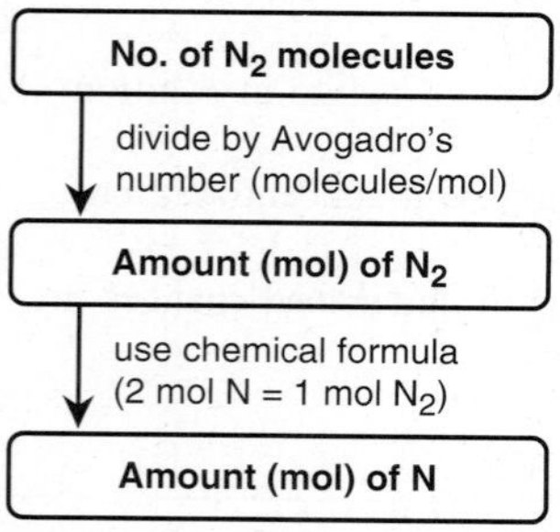

$$\text{Amount (mol) of N} = 9.72\times10^{21}\ \cancel{N_2\ \text{molecules}} \times \frac{1\ \cancel{\text{mol}\ N_2}}{6.022\times10^{23}\ \cancel{N_2\ \text{molecules}}} \times \frac{2\ \text{mol N}}{1\ \cancel{\text{mol}\ N_2}}$$
$$= 3.23\times10^{-2}\ \text{mol N}$$

3.3

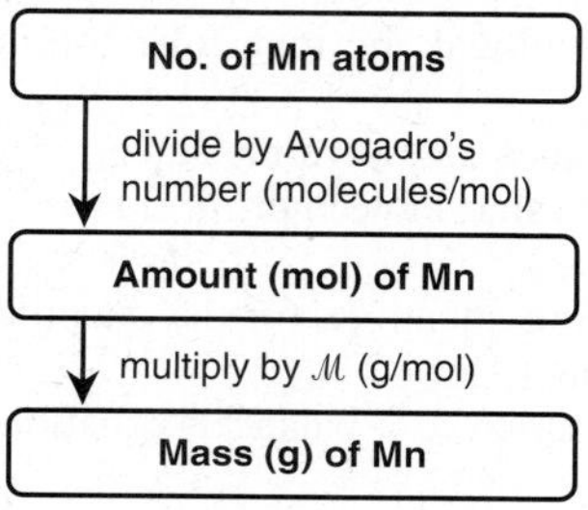

$$\text{Mass (g) of Mn} = 3.22\times10^{20}\ \cancel{\text{Mn atoms}} \times \frac{1\ \cancel{\text{mol Mn}}}{6.022\times10^{23}\ \cancel{\text{Mn atoms}}} \times \frac{54.94\ \text{g Mn}}{\cancel{1\ \text{mol Mn}}}$$
$$= 2.94\times10^{-2}\ \text{g Mn}$$

3.4

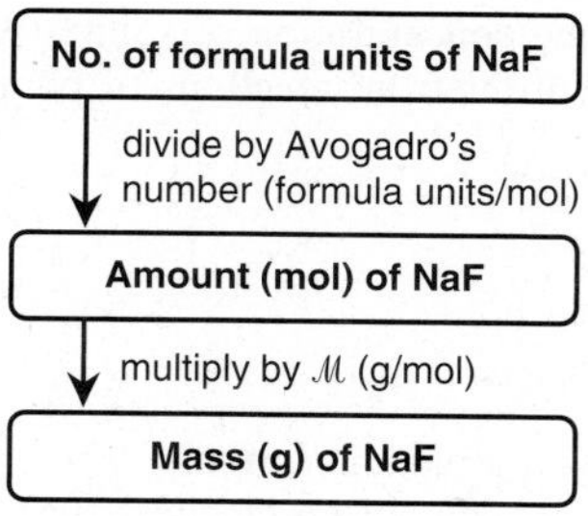

$$\mathcal{M} = (1 \times \mathcal{M}\ \text{of Na}) + (1 \times \mathcal{M}\ \text{of F})$$
$$= 22.99\ \text{g/mol} + 19.00\ \text{g/mol} = 41.99\ \text{g/mol}$$

$$\text{Mass (g) of NaF} = 1.19\times10^{19}\ \cancel{\text{NaF formula units}} \times \frac{1\ \cancel{\text{mol NaF}}}{6.022\times10^{23}\ \cancel{\text{NaF formula units}}} \times \frac{41.99\ \text{g NaF}}{1\ \cancel{\text{mol NaF}}} = 8.30\times10^{-4}\ \text{NaF}$$

3.5 (a) Mass (g) of P_4O_{10}

$$= 4.65\times10^{22}\ \cancel{\text{molecules } P_4O_{10}} \times \frac{1\ \cancel{\text{mol } P_4O_{10}}}{6.022\times10^{23}\ \cancel{\text{molecules } P_4O_{10}}} \times \frac{283.88\ \text{g } P_4O_{10}}{1\ \cancel{\text{mol } P_4O_{10}}}$$

$$= 21.9\ \text{g } P_4O_{10}$$

(b) No. of P atoms $= 4.65\times10^{22}\ \cancel{\text{molecules } P_4O_{10}} \times \frac{4\ \text{atoms P}}{1\ \cancel{\text{molecule } P_4O_{10}}}$

$$= 1.86\times10^{23}\ \text{P atoms}$$

3.6 Mass % of N $= \dfrac{2\ \cancel{\text{mol N}} \times \dfrac{14.01\ \cancel{\text{g N}}}{1\ \cancel{\text{mol N}}}}{80.05\ \cancel{\text{g } NH_4NO_3}} \times 100$

$$= 35.00\ \text{mass \% N}$$

3.7 Mass (g) of N $= 35.8\ \cancel{\text{kg } NH_4NO_3} \times \dfrac{10^3\ \cancel{\text{g}}}{1\ \cancel{\text{kg}}} \times \dfrac{0.3500\ \text{g N}}{1\ \cancel{\text{g } NH_4NO_3}}$

$$= 1.25\times10^4\ \text{g N}$$

3.8 Preliminary formula: $B_{0.170}O_{0.255}$

Divide by smaller subscript: $B_{\frac{0.170}{0.170}}O_{\frac{0.255}{0.170}} = B_{1.00}O_{1.50}$

Multiply by 2: $B_{2\times1.00}O_{2\times1.50} = B_{2.00}O_{3.00} = B_2O_3$

3.9 Amount (mol) of S $= 2.88\ \cancel{\text{g S}} \times \dfrac{1\ \text{mol S}}{32.07\ \cancel{\text{g S}}} = 0.0898\ \text{mol S}$

Amount (mol) of M $= 0.0898\ \cancel{\text{mol S}} \times \dfrac{2\ \text{mol M}}{3\ \cancel{\text{mol S}}} = 0.0599\ \text{mol M}$

Molar mass of M $= \dfrac{3.12\ \text{g M}}{0.0599\ \text{mol M}} = 52.1\ \text{g/mol}$

M is chromium, and M_2S_3 is chromium(III) sulfide.

3.10 Assuming 100.00 g of compound, we have 95.21 g of C and 4.79 g of H:

Amount (mol) of C $= 95.21\ \cancel{\text{g C}} \times \dfrac{1\ \text{mol C}}{12.01\ \cancel{\text{g C}}} = 7.928\ \text{mol C}$

Similarly, there is 4.75 mol H.

Preliminary formula: $C_{7.928}H_{4.75} \approx C_{1.67}H_{1.00}$

Empirical formula: C_5H_3

Whole-number multiple $= \dfrac{252.30\ \cancel{\text{g/mol}}}{63.07\ \cancel{\text{g/mol}}} = 4$

Molecular formula: $C_{20}H_{12}$

3.11 Mass (g) of C $= 0.451\ \cancel{\text{g } CO_2} \times \dfrac{12.01\ \text{g C}}{44.01\ \cancel{\text{g } CO_2}}$

$$= 0.123\ \text{g C}$$

Similarly, there is 0.00690 g H.

Mass (g) of Cl = 0.250 g − (0.123 g + 0.00690 g) = 0.120 g Cl

Amount (mol) of elements: 0.0102 mol C; 0.00685 mol H; 0.00339 mol Cl

Empirical formula: C_3H_2Cl

Whole-number multiple = 2

Molecular formula: $C_6H_4Cl_2$

3.12 (a) $2Na(s) + 2H_2O(l) \longrightarrow H_2(g) + 2NaOH(aq)$

(b) $2HNO_3(aq) + CaCO_3(s) \longrightarrow CO_2(g) + H_2O(l) + Ca(NO_3)_2(aq)$

(c) $PCl_3(g) + 3HF(g) \longrightarrow PF_3(g) + 3HCl(g)$

(d) $4C_3H_5N_3O_9(l) \longrightarrow 12CO_2(g) + 10H_2O(g) + 6N_2(g) + O_2(g)$

3.13 From the depiction, we have

$$6CO + 3O_2 \longrightarrow 6CO_2$$

Or,

$$2CO(g) + O_2(g) \longrightarrow 2CO_2(g)$$

3.14

Amount (mol) of Fe

↓ molar ratio

Amount (mol) of Fe_2O_3

$Fe_2O_3(s) + 2Al(s) \longrightarrow Al_2O_3(s) + 2Fe(l)$

Amount (mol) of Fe_2O_3 $= 3.60\times10^3\ \cancel{\text{mol Fe}} \times \dfrac{1\ \text{mol } Fe_2O_3}{2\ \cancel{\text{mol Fe}}}$

$$= 1.80\times10^3\ \text{mol } Fe_2O_3$$

3.15

No. of formula units of Al_2O_3

↓ divide by Avogadro's number (formula units/mol)

Amount (mol) of Al_2O_3

↓ molar ratio

Amount (mol) of Fe

Amount (mol) of Fe $= 1.85\times10^{25}\ \cancel{Al_2O_3\ \text{f.u.}} \times \dfrac{1\ \cancel{\text{mol } Al_2O_3}}{6.022\times10^{23}\ \cancel{Al_2O_3\ \text{f.u.}}} \times \dfrac{2\ \text{mol Fe}}{1\ \cancel{\text{mol } Al_2O_3}}$

$$= 61.4\ \text{mol Fe}$$

3.16

Mass (g) of Al_2O_3

↓ divide by $\mathcal{M}$ (g/mol)

Amount (mol) of Al_2O_3

↓ molar ratio

Amount (mol) of Al

↓ multiply by Avogadro's number (atoms/mol)

No. of Al atoms

No. of Al atoms $= 1.00\ \cancel{\text{g } Al_2O_3} \times \dfrac{1\ \cancel{\text{mol } Al_2O_3}}{101.96\ \cancel{\text{g } Al_2O_3}} \times \dfrac{2\ \cancel{\text{mol Al}}}{1\ \cancel{\text{mol } Al_2O_3}} \times \dfrac{6.022\times10^{23}\ \text{Al atoms}}{1\ \cancel{\text{mol Al}}}$

$$= 1.18\times10^{22}\ \text{Al atoms}$$

3.17

$$2SO_2(g) + O_2(g) \longrightarrow \cancel{2SO_3(g)}$$
$$\cancel{2SO_3(g)} + 2H_2O(l) \longrightarrow 2H_2SO_4(aq)$$
$$\overline{2SO_2(g) + O_2(g) + 2H_2O(l) \longrightarrow 2H_2SO_4(aq)}$$

3.18 $4AB + 2B_2 \longrightarrow 4AB_2$, or $2AB(g) + B_2(g) \longrightarrow 2AB_2(g)$

For AB: $\text{Molecules of } AB_2 = 4\cancel{AB} \times \dfrac{2AB_2}{2\cancel{AB}} = 4AB_2$

For B_2: $\text{Molecules of } AB_2 = 3\cancel{B_2} \times \dfrac{2AB_2}{1\cancel{B_2}} = 6AB_2$

Thus, AB_2 is the limiting reactant; one B_2 molecule is in excess.

3.19

$\text{Amount (mol) of } AB_2 = 1.5\ \cancel{\text{mol AB}} \times \dfrac{2\text{ mol }AB_2}{2\ \cancel{\text{mol AB}}} = 1.5\text{ mol }AB_2$

$\text{Amount (mol) of } AB_2 = 1.5\ \cancel{\text{mol }B_2} \times \dfrac{2\text{ mol }AB_2}{1\ \cancel{\text{mol }B_2}} = 3.0\text{ mol }AB_2$

Therefore, 1.5 mol of AB_2 can form.

3.20 $2Al(s) + 3S(s) \longrightarrow Al_2S_3(s)$

Mass (g) of Al_2S_3 formed from 10.0 g of Al

$= 10.0\ \cancel{\text{g Al}} \times \dfrac{1\ \cancel{\text{mol Al}}}{26.98\ \cancel{\text{g Al}}} \times \dfrac{1\ \cancel{\text{mol }Al_2S_3}}{2\ \cancel{\text{mol Al}}} \times \dfrac{150.17\text{ g }Al_2S_3}{1\ \cancel{\text{mol }Al_2S_3}}$

$= 27.8\text{ g }Al_2S_3$

Similarly, mass (g) of Al_2S_3 formed from 15.0 g of S = 23.4 g Al_2S_3. Thus, S is the limiting reactant, and 23.4 g of Al_2S_3 forms.

Mass (g) of Al in excess

= total mass of Al − mass of Al used

= 10.0 g Al

$-\left(15.0\ \cancel{\text{g S}} \times \dfrac{1\ \cancel{\text{mol S}}}{32.07\ \cancel{\text{g S}}} \times \dfrac{2\ \cancel{\text{mol Al}}}{3\ \cancel{\text{mol S}}} \times \dfrac{26.98\text{ g Al}}{1\ \cancel{\text{mol Al}}}\right)$

= 1.6 g Al

(We would obtain the same answer if sulfur were shown more correctly as S_8.)

3.21 $CaCO_3(s) + 2HCl(aq) \longrightarrow CaCl_2(aq) + H_2O(l) + CO_2(g)$

$\text{Theoretical yield (g) of } CO_2 = 10.0\ \cancel{\text{g }CaCO_3} \times \dfrac{1\ \cancel{\text{mol }CaCO_3}}{100.09\ \cancel{\text{g }CaCO_3}} \times \dfrac{1\ \cancel{\text{mol }CO_2}}{1\ \cancel{\text{mol }CaCO_3}} \times \dfrac{44.01\text{ g }CO_2}{1\ \cancel{\text{mol }CO_2}} = 4.40\text{ g }CO_2$

$\%\text{ yield} = \dfrac{3.65\ \cancel{\text{g }CO_2}}{4.40\ \cancel{\text{g }CO_2}} \times 100 = 83.0\%$

3.22

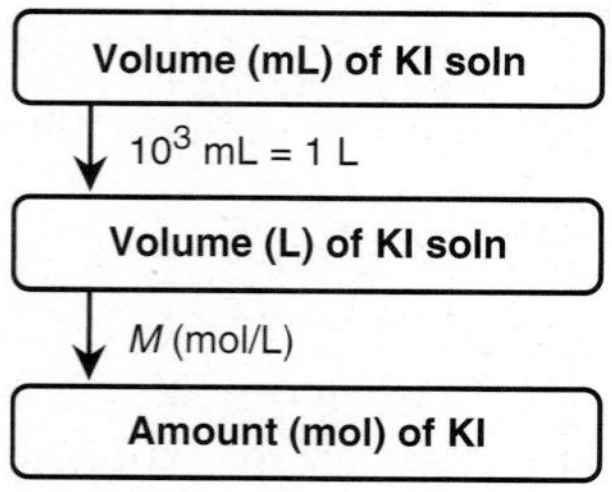

$\text{Amount (mol) of KI} = 84\ \cancel{\text{mL soln}} \times \dfrac{1\ \cancel{\text{L}}}{10^3\ \cancel{\text{mL}}} \times \dfrac{0.50\text{ mol KI}}{1\ \cancel{\text{L soln}}}$

= 0.042 mol KI

3.23

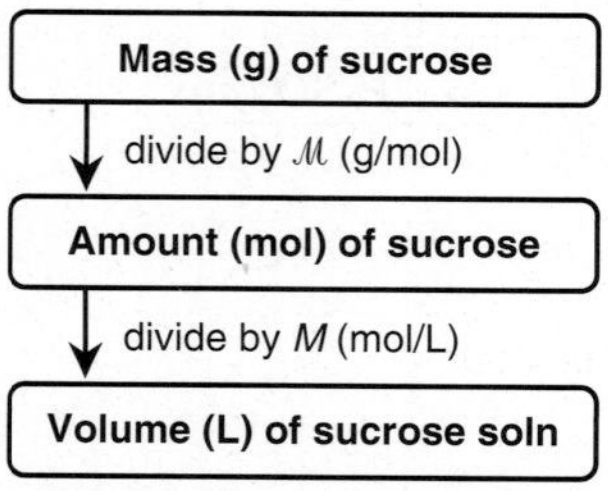

Volume (L) of sucrose soln

$= 135\ \cancel{\text{g sucrose}} \times \dfrac{1\ \cancel{\text{mol sucrose}}}{342.30\ \cancel{\text{g sucrose}}} \times \dfrac{1\text{ L soln}}{3.30\ \cancel{\text{mol sucrose}}}$

= 0.120 L soln

3.24 $M_{dil}\text{ of } H_2SO_4 = \dfrac{7.50\ M \times 25.0\ \cancel{\text{m}^3}}{500.\ \cancel{\text{m}^3}} = 0.375\ M\ H_2SO_4$

Mass (g) of H_2SO_4/mL soln

$= \dfrac{0.375\ \cancel{\text{mol }H_2SO_4}}{1\ \cancel{\text{L soln}}} \times \dfrac{1\ \cancel{\text{L}}}{10^3\text{ mL}} \times \dfrac{98.09\text{ g }H_2SO_4}{1\ \cancel{\text{mol }H_2SO_4}}$

$= 3.68\times10^{-2}$ g/mL soln

3.25 To obtain B, the total volume of sol A was reduced by half:

$V_{conc} = V_{dil} \times \dfrac{N_{dil}}{N_{conc}} = 1.0\text{ mL} \times \dfrac{6\ \cancel{\text{particles}}}{12\ \cancel{\text{particles}}} = 0.50\text{ mL}$

To obtain C, $\frac{1}{2}$ of a volume of solvent was added for every volume of A:

$V_{dil} = V_{conc} \times \dfrac{N_{conc}}{N_{dil}} = 1.0\text{ mL} \times \dfrac{6\ \cancel{\text{particles}}}{4\ \cancel{\text{particles}}} = 1.5\text{ mL}$

3.26 $Al(OH)_3(s) + 3HCl(aq) \longrightarrow AlCl_3(aq) + 3H_2O(l)$

Volume (L) of HCl neutralized

$= 0.10\ \cancel{\text{g }Al(OH)_3} \times \dfrac{1\ \cancel{\text{mol }Al(OH)_3}}{78.00\ \cancel{\text{g }Al(OH)_3}} \times \dfrac{3\ \cancel{\text{mol HCl}}}{1\ \cancel{\text{mol }Al(OH)_3}} \times \dfrac{1\text{ L soln}}{0.10\ \cancel{\text{mol HCl}}}$

$= 3.8\times10^{-2}$ L soln

Therefore, $Al(OH)_3$ is more effective than $Mg(OH)_2$.

3.27 (a) For $Pb(C_2H_3O_2)_2$:

$\text{Amount (mol) of } Pb(C_2H_3O_2)_2 = 0.268\ \cancel{\text{L}} \times \dfrac{1.50\text{ mol }Pb(C_2H_3O_2)_2}{1\ \cancel{\text{L}}}$

$= 0.402\text{ mol }Pb(C_2H_3O_2)_2$

$\text{Amount (mol) of } PbCl_2 = 0.402\ \cancel{\text{mol }Pb(C_2H_3O_2)_2} \times \dfrac{1\text{ mol }PbCl_2}{1\ \cancel{\text{mol }Pb(C_2H_3O_2)_2}} = 0.402\text{ mol }PbCl_2$

For NaCl: $\text{Amount (mol) of NaCl} = \dfrac{3.40\text{ mol NaCl}}{1\ \cancel{\text{L}}} \times 0.130\ \cancel{\text{L}}$

= 0.442 mol NaCl

$\text{Amount (mol) of } PbCl_2 = 0.442\ \cancel{\text{mol NaCl}} \times \dfrac{1\text{ mol }PbCl_2}{2\ \cancel{\text{mol NaCl}}}$

$= 0.221\text{ mol }PbCl_2$

Thus, NaCl is the limiting reactant.

$\text{Mass (g) of } PbCl_2 = 0.22\ \cancel{\text{mol }PbCl_2} \times \dfrac{278.1\text{ g }PbCl_2}{1\ \cancel{\text{mol }PbCl_2}}$

$= 61.5\text{ g }PbCl_2$

(b) Using "Ac" for acetate ion and with NaCl limiting:

Amount (mol)	$Pb(Ac)_2$	+	2NaCl	⟶	$PbCl_2$	+	2NaAc
Initial	0.402		0.442		0		0
Change	−0.221		−0.442		+0.221		+0.442
Final	0.181		0		0.221		0.442

PROBLEMS

Problems with **colored** numbers are answered in Appendix E and worked in detail in the Student Solutions Manual. Problem sections match those in the text and provide the numbers of relevant sample problems. Most offer Concept Review Questions, Skill-Building Exercises (grouped in pairs covering the same concept), and Problems in Context. The Comprehensive Problems are based on material from any section or previous chapter.

The Mole

(Sample Problems 3.1 to 3.7)

Concept Review Questions

3.1 The atomic mass of Cl is 35.45 amu, and the atomic mass of Al is 26.98 amu. What are the masses in grams of 3 mol of Al atoms and of 2 mol of Cl atoms?

3.2 (a) How many moles of C atoms are in 1 mol of sucrose ($C_{12}H_{22}O_{11}$)?
(b) How many C atoms are in 2 mol of sucrose?

3.3 Why might the expression "1 mol of chlorine" be confusing? What change would remove any uncertainty? For what other elements might a similar confusion exist? Why?

3.4 How is the molecular mass of a compound the same as the molar mass, and how is it different?

3.5 What advantage is there to using a counting unit (the mole) for amount of substance rather than a mass unit?

3.6 You need to calculate the number of P_4 molecules that can form from 2.5 g of $Ca_3(PO_4)_2$. Draw a road map for solving this and write a Plan, without doing any calculations.

3.7 Each of the following balances weighs the indicated numbers of atoms of two elements:

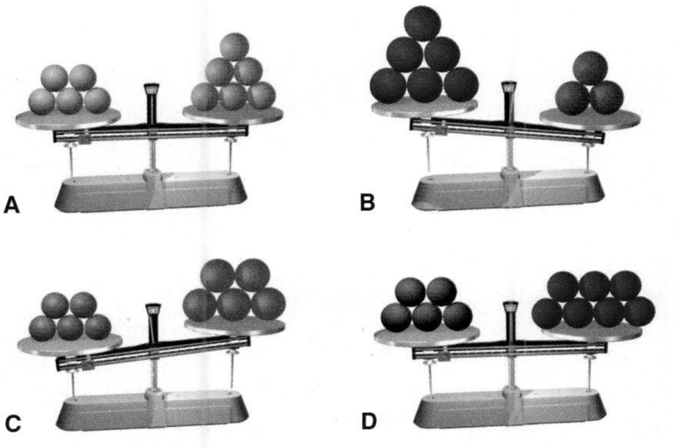

For each balance, which element—left, right, or neither,
(a) Has the higher molar mass?
(b) Has more atoms per gram?
(c) Has fewer atoms per gram?
(d) Has more atoms per mole?

Skill-Building Exercises (grouped in similar pairs)

3.8 Calculate the molar mass of each of the following:
(a) $Sr(OH)_2$ (b) N_2O_3 (c) $NaClO_3$ (d) Cr_2O_3

3.9 Calculate the molar mass of each of the following:
(a) $(NH_4)_3PO_4$ (b) CH_2Cl_2 (c) $CuSO_4 \cdot 5H_2O$ (d) BrF_3

3.10 Calculate the molar mass of each of the following:
(a) SnO (b) BaF_2 (c) $Al_2(SO_4)_3$ (d) $MnCl_2$

3.11 Calculate the molar mass of each of the following:
(a) N_2O_4 (b) C_4H_9OH (c) $MgSO_4 \cdot 7H_2O$ (d) $Ca(C_2H_3O_2)_2$

3.12 Calculate each of the following quantities:
(a) Mass (g) of 0.68 mol of $KMnO_4$
(b) Amount (mol) of O atoms in 8.18 g of $Ba(NO_3)_2$
(c) Number of O atoms in 7.3×10^{-3} g of $CaSO_4 \cdot 2H_2O$

3.13 Calculate each of the following quantities:
(a) Mass (kg) of 4.6×10^{21} molecules of NO_2
(b) Amount (mol) of Cl atoms in 0.0615 g of $C_2H_4Cl_2$
(c) Number of H^- ions in 5.82 g of SrH_2

3.14 Calculate each of the following quantities:
(a) Mass (g) of 6.44×10^{-2} mol of $MnSO_4$
(b) Amount (mol) of compound in 15.8 kg of $Fe(ClO_4)_3$
(c) Number of N atoms in 92.6 mg of NH_4NO_2

3.15 Calculate each of the following quantities:
(a) Total number of ions in 38.1 g of SrF_2
(b) Mass (kg) of 3.58 mol of $CuCl_2 \cdot 2H_2O$
(c) Mass (mg) of 2.88×10^{22} formula units of $Bi(NO_3)_3 \cdot 5H_2O$

3.16 Calculate each of the following quantities:
(a) Mass (g) of 8.35 mol of copper(I) carbonate
(b) Mass (g) of 4.04×10^{20} molecules of dinitrogen pentaoxide
(c) Amount (mol) and number of formula units in 78.9 g of sodium perchlorate
(d) Number of sodium ions, perchlorate ions, chlorine atoms, and oxygen atoms in the mass of compound in part (c)

3.17 Calculate each of the following quantities:
(a) Mass (g) of 8.42 mol of chromium(III) sulfate decahydrate
(b) Mass (g) of 1.83×10^{24} molecules of dichlorine heptaoxide
(c) Amount (mol) and number of formula units in 6.2 g of lithium sulfate
(d) Number of lithium ions, sulfate ions, sulfur atoms, and oxygen atoms in the mass of compound in part (c)

3.18 Calculate each of the following:
(a) Mass % of H in ammonium bicarbonate
(b) Mass % of O in sodium dihydrogen phosphate heptahydrate

3.19 Calculate each of the following:
(a) Mass % of I in strontium periodate
(b) Mass % of Mn in potassium permanganate

3.20 Calculate each of the following:
(a) Mass fraction of C in cesium acetate
(b) Mass fraction of O in uranyl sulfate trihydrate (the uranyl ion is UO_2^{2+})

3.21 Calculate each of the following:
(a) Mass fraction of Cl in calcium chlorate
(b) Mass fraction of N in dinitrogen trioxide

Problems in Context

3.22 Oxygen is required for the metabolic combustion of foods. Calculate the number of atoms in 38.0 g of oxygen gas, the amount absorbed from the lungs at rest in about 15 min.

3.23 Cisplatin (*right*), or Platinol, is used in the treatment of certain cancers. Calculate (a) the amount (mol) of compound in 285.3 g of cisplatin; (b) the number of hydrogen atoms in 0.98 mol of cisplatin.

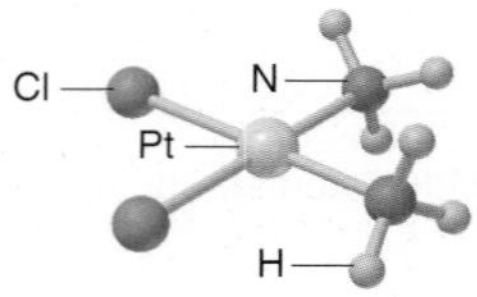

3.24 Allyl sulfide (*below*) gives garlic its characteristic odor. Calculate (a) the mass (g) of 2.63 mol of allyl sulfide; (b) the number of carbon atoms in 35.7 g of allyl sulfide.

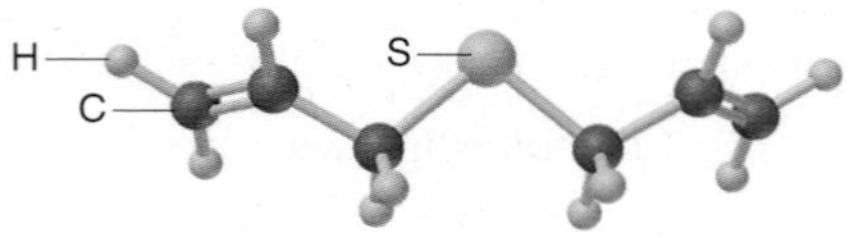

3.25 Iron reacts slowly with oxygen and water to form a compound commonly called rust ($Fe_2O_3 \cdot 4H_2O$). For 45.2 kg of rust, calculate (a) moles of compound; (b) moles of Fe_2O_3; (c) grams of Fe.

3.26 Propane is widely used in liquid form as a fuel for barbecue grills and camp stoves. For 85.5 g of propane, calculate (a) moles of compound; (b) grams of carbon.

3.27 The effectiveness of a nitrogen fertilizer is determined mainly by its mass % N. Rank the following fertilizers, most effective first: potassium nitrate; ammonium nitrate; ammonium sulfate; urea, $CO(NH_2)_2$.

3.28 The mineral galena is composed of lead(II) sulfide and has an average density of 7.46 g/cm^3. (a) How many moles of lead(II) sulfide are in 1.00 ft^3 of galena? (b) How many lead atoms are in 1.00 dm^3 of galena?

3.29 Hemoglobin, a protein in red blood cells, carries O_2 from the lungs to the body's cells. Iron (as ferrous ion, Fe^{2+}) makes up 0.33 mass % of hemoglobin. If the molar mass of hemoglobin is 6.8×10^4 g/mol, how many Fe^{2+} ions are in one molecule?

Determining the Formula of an Unknown Compound

(Sample Problems 3.8 to 3.11)

Concept Review Questions

3.30 What is the difference between an empirical formula and a molecular formula? Can they ever be the same?

3.31 List three ways compositional data may be given in a problem that involves finding an empirical formula.

3.32 Which of the following sets of information allows you to obtain the molecular formula of a covalent compound? In each case that allows it, explain how you would proceed (draw a road map and write a Plan for a solution).
(a) Number of moles of each type of atom in a given sample of the compound
(b) Mass % of each element and the total number of atoms in a molecule of the compound
(c) Mass % of each element and the number of atoms of one element in a molecule of the compound
(d) Empirical formula and mass % of each element
(e) Structural formula

3.33 Is $MgCl_2$ an empirical or a molecular formula for magnesium chloride? Explain.

Skill-Building Exercises (grouped in similar pairs)

3.34 What is the empirical formula and empirical formula mass for each of the following compounds?
(a) C_2H_4 (b) $C_2H_6O_2$ (c) N_2O_5 (d) $Ba_3(PO_4)_2$ (e) Te_4I_{16}

3.35 What is the empirical formula and empirical formula mass for each of the following compounds?
(a) C_4H_8 (b) $C_3H_6O_3$ (c) P_4O_{10} (d) $Ga_2(SO_4)_3$ (e) Al_2Br_6

3.36 Give the name, empirical formula, and molar mass of the compound depicted in Figure P3.36.

3.37 Give the name, empirical formula, and molar mass of the compound depicted in Figure P3.37.

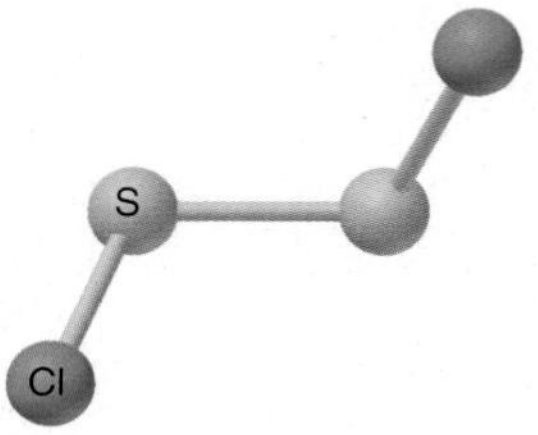

Figure P3.36

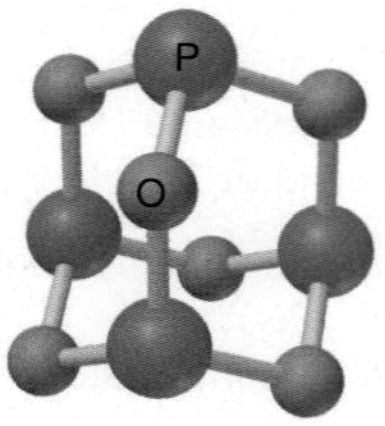

Figure P3.37

3.38 What is the molecular formula of each compound?
(a) Empirical formula CH_2 ($\mathcal{M}$ = 42.08 g/mol)
(b) Empirical formula NH_2 ($\mathcal{M}$ = 32.05 g/mol)
(c) Empirical formula NO_2 ($\mathcal{M}$ = 92.02 g/mol)
(d) Empirical formula CHN ($\mathcal{M}$ = 135.14 g/mol)

3.39 What is the molecular formula of each compound?
(a) Empirical formula CH ($\mathcal{M}$ = 78.11 g/mol)
(b) Empirical formula $C_3H_6O_2$ ($\mathcal{M}$ = 74.08 g/mol)
(c) Empirical formula HgCl ($\mathcal{M}$ = 472.1 g/mol)
(d) Empirical formula $C_7H_4O_2$ ($\mathcal{M}$ = 240.20 g/mol)

3.40 Find the empirical formula of the following compounds:
(a) 0.063 mol of chlorine atoms combined with 0.22 mol of oxygen atoms
(b) 2.45 g of silicon combined with 12.4 g of chlorine
(c) 27.3 mass % carbon and 72.7 mass % oxygen

3.41 Find the empirical formula of the following compounds:
(a) 0.039 mol of iron atoms combined with 0.052 mol of oxygen atoms
(b) 0.903 g of phosphorus combined with 6.99 g of bromine
(c) A hydrocarbon with 79.9 mass % carbon

3.42 An oxide of nitrogen contains 30.45 mass % N. (a) What is the empirical formula of the oxide? (b) If the molar mass is 90 ± 5 g/mol, what is the molecular formula?

3.43 A chloride of silicon contains 79.1 mass % Cl. (a) What is the empirical formula of the chloride? (b) If the molar mass is 269 g/mol, what is the molecular formula?

3.44 A sample of 0.600 mol of a metal M reacts completely with excess fluorine to form 46.8 g of MF_2.
(a) How many moles of F are in the sample of MF_2 that forms?
(b) How many grams of M are in this sample of MF_2?
(c) What element is represented by the symbol M?

3.45 A 0.370-mol sample of a metal oxide (M_2O_3) weighs 55.4 g.
(a) How many moles of O are in the sample?
(b) How many grams of M are in the sample?
(c) What element is represented by the symbol M?

Problems in Context

3.46 Nicotine is a poisonous, addictive compound found in tobacco. A sample of nicotine contains 6.16 mmol of C, 8.56 mmol of H, and 1.23 mmol of N [1 mmol (1 millimole) = 10^{-3} mol]. What is the empirical formula of nicotine?

3.47 Cortisol ($\mathcal{M}$ = 362.47 g/mol) is a steroid hormone involved in protein synthesis. Medically, it has a major use in reducing inflammation from rheumatoid arthritis. Cortisol is 69.6% C, 8.34% H, and 22.1% O by mass. What is its molecular formula?

3.48 Acetaminophen (*below*) is a popular nonaspirin pain reliever. What is the mass % of each element in acetaminophen?

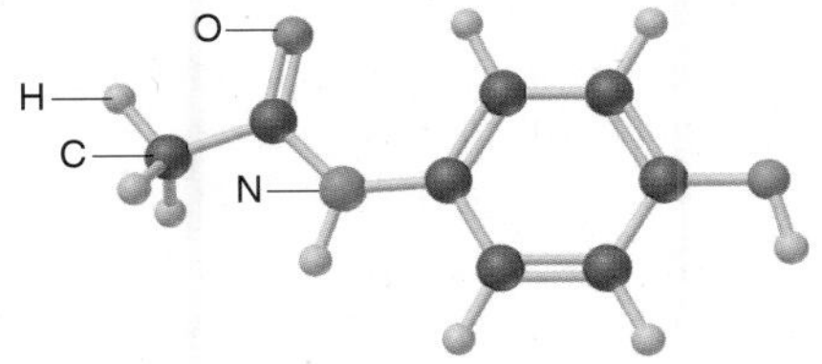

3.49 Menthol ($\mathcal{M}$ = 156.3 g/mol), the strong-smelling substance in many cough drops, is a compound of carbon, hydrogen, and oxygen. When 0.1595 g of menthol was burned in a combustion apparatus, 0.449 g of CO_2 and 0.184 g of H_2O formed. What is menthol's molecular formula?

Writing and Balancing Chemical Equations

(Sample Problems 3.12 and 3.13)

Concept Review Questions

3.50 What three types of information does a balanced chemical equation provide? How?

3.51 How does a balanced chemical equation apply the law of conservation of mass?

3.52 In the process of balancing the equation

$$Al + Cl_2 \longrightarrow AlCl_3$$

Student I writes: $Al + Cl_2 \longrightarrow AlCl_2$
Student II writes: $Al + Cl_2 + Cl \longrightarrow AlCl_3$
Student III writes: $2Al + 3Cl_2 \longrightarrow 2AlCl_3$
Is the approach of Student I valid? Student II? Student III? Explain.

3.53 The scenes below represent a chemical reaction between elements A (red) and B (green):

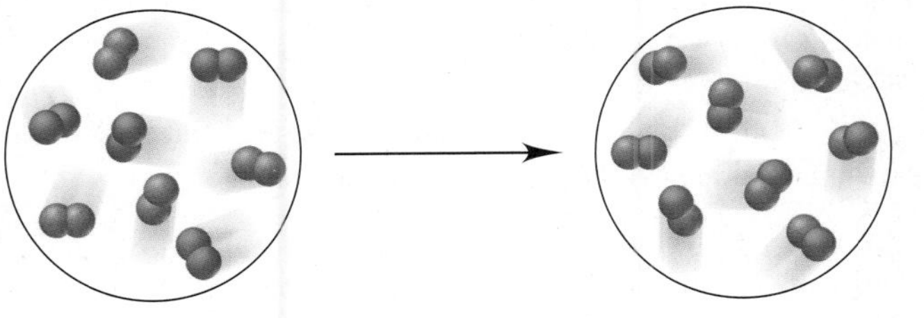

Which best represents the balanced equation for the reaction?
(a) $2A + 2B \longrightarrow A_2 + B_2$ (b) $A_2 + B_2 \longrightarrow 2AB$
(c) $B_2 + 2AB \longrightarrow 2B_2 + A_2$ (d) $4A_2 + 4B_2 \longrightarrow 8AB$

Skill-Building Exercises (grouped in similar pairs)

3.54 Write balanced equations for each of the following by inserting the correct coefficients in the blanks:
(a) $\_Cu(s) + \_S_8(s) \longrightarrow \_Cu_2S(s)$
(b) $\_P_4O_{10}(s) + \_H_2O(l) \longrightarrow \_H_3PO_4(l)$
(c) $\_B_2O_3(s) + \_NaOH(aq) \longrightarrow \_Na_3BO_3(aq) + \_H_2O(l)$
(d) $\_CH_3NH_2(g) + \_O_2(g) \longrightarrow \_CO_2(g) + \_H_2O(g) + \_N_2(g)$

3.55 Write balanced equations for each of the following by inserting the correct coefficients in the blanks:
(a) $\_Cu(NO_3)_2(aq) + \_KOH(aq) \longrightarrow \_Cu(OH)_2(s) + \_KNO_3(aq)$
(b) $\_BCl_3(g) + \_H_2O(l) \longrightarrow \_H_3BO_3(s) + \_HCl(g)$
(c) $\_CaSiO_3(s) + \_HF(g) \longrightarrow \_SiF_4(g) + \_CaF_2(s) + \_H_2O(l)$
(d) $\_(CN)_2(g) + \_H_2O(l) \longrightarrow \_H_2C_2O_4(aq) + \_NH_3(g)$

3.56 Write balanced equations for each of the following by inserting the correct coefficients in the blanks:
(a) $\_SO_2(g) + \_O_2(g) \longrightarrow \_SO_3(g)$
(b) $\_Sc_2O_3(s) + \_H_2O(l) \longrightarrow \_Sc(OH)_3(s)$
(c) $\_H_3PO_4(aq) + \_NaOH(aq) \longrightarrow \_Na_2HPO_4(aq) + \_H_2O(l)$
(d) $\_C_6H_{10}O_5(s) + \_O_2(g) \longrightarrow \_CO_2(g) + \_H_2O(g)$

3.57 Write balanced equations for each of the following by inserting the correct coefficients in the blanks:
(a) $\_As_4S_6(s) + \_O_2(g) \longrightarrow \_As_4O_6(s) + \_SO_2(g)$
(b) $\_Ca_3(PO_4)_2(s) + \_SiO_2(s) + \_C(s) \longrightarrow \_P_4(g) + \_CaSiO_3(l) + \_CO(g)$
(c) $\_Fe(s) + \_H_2O(g) \longrightarrow \_Fe_3O_4(s) + \_H_2(g)$
(d) $\_S_2Cl_2(l) + \_NH_3(g) \longrightarrow \_S_4N_4(s) + \_S_8(s) + \_NH_4Cl(s)$

3.58 Convert the following into balanced equations:
(a) When gallium metal is heated in oxygen gas, it melts and forms solid gallium(III) oxide.
(b) Liquid hexane burns in oxygen gas to form carbon dioxide gas and water vapor.
(c) When solutions of calcium chloride and sodium phosphate are mixed, solid calcium phosphate forms and sodium chloride remains in solution.

3.59 Convert the following into balanced equations:
(a) When lead(II) nitrate solution is added to potassium iodide solution, solid lead(II) iodide forms and potassium nitrate solution remains.
(b) Liquid disilicon hexachloride reacts with water to form solid silicon dioxide, hydrogen chloride gas, and hydrogen gas.
(c) When nitrogen dioxide is bubbled into water, a solution of nitric acid forms and gaseous nitrogen monoxide is released.

Problem in Context

3.60 Loss of atmospheric ozone has led to an ozone "hole" over Antarctica. The loss occurs in part through three consecutive steps:
(1) Chlorine atoms react with ozone (O_3) to form chlorine monoxide and molecular oxygen.
(2) Chlorine monoxide forms ClOOCl.
(3) ClOOCl absorbs sunlight and breaks into chlorine atoms and molecular oxygen.
(a) Write a balanced equation for each step.
(b) Write an overall balanced equation for the sequence.

Calculating Quantities of Reactant and Product

(Sample Problems 3.14 to 3.21)

Concept Review Questions

3.61 What does the term *stoichiometrically equivalent molar ratio* mean, and how is it applied in solving problems?

3.62 The circle below represents a mixture of A_2 and B_2 before they react to form AB_3.

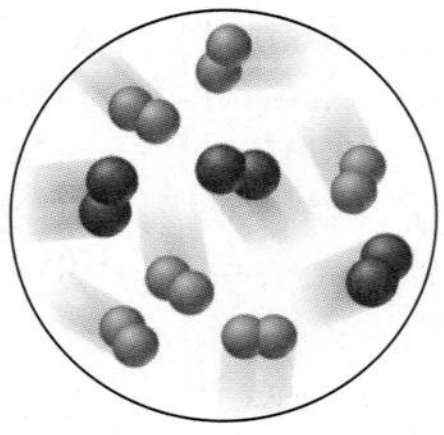

(a) What is the limiting reactant?
(b) How many molecules of product can form?

3.63 Percent yields are generally calculated from masses. Would the result be the same if amounts (mol) were used instead? Why?

Skill-Building Exercises (grouped in similar pairs)

3.64 Reactants A and B form product C. Draw a road map and write a Plan to find the mass (g) of C when 25 g of A reacts with excess B.

3.65 Reactants D and E form product F. Draw a road map and write a Plan to find the mass (g) of F when 27 g of D reacts with 31 g of E.

3.66 Chlorine gas can be made in the laboratory by the reaction of hydrochloric acid and manganese(IV) oxide:

$$4HCl(aq) + MnO_2(s) \longrightarrow MnCl_2(aq) + 2H_2O(g) + Cl_2(g)$$

When 1.82 mol of HCl reacts with excess MnO_2, how many (a) moles of Cl_2 and (b) grams of Cl_2 form?

3.67 Bismuth oxide reacts with carbon to form bismuth metal:

$$Bi_2O_3(s) + 3C(s) \longrightarrow 2Bi(s) + 3CO(g)$$

When 283 g of Bi_2O_3 reacts with excess carbon, how many (a) moles of Bi_2O_3 react and (b) moles of Bi form?

3.68 Potassium nitrate decomposes on heating, producing potassium oxide and gaseous nitrogen and oxygen:

$$4KNO_3(s) \longrightarrow 2K_2O(s) + 2N_2(g) + 5O_2(g)$$

To produce 56.6 kg of oxygen, how many (a) moles of KNO_3 and (b) grams of KNO_3 must be heated?

3.69 Chromium(III) oxide reacts with hydrogen sulfide (H_2S) gas to form chromium(III) sulfide and water:

$$Cr_2O_3(s) + 3H_2S(g) \longrightarrow Cr_2S_3(s) + 3H_2O(l)$$

To produce 421 g of Cr_2S_3, how many (a) moles of Cr_2O_3 and (b) grams of Cr_2O_3 are required?

3.70 Calculate the mass (g) of each product formed when 43.82 g of diborane (B_2H_6) reacts with excess water:

$$B_2H_6(g) + H_2O(l) \longrightarrow H_3BO_3(s) + H_2(g) \text{ [unbalanced]}$$

3.71 Calculate the mass (g) of each product formed when 174 g of silver sulfide reacts with excess hydrochloric acid:

$$Ag_2S(s) + HCl(aq) \longrightarrow AgCl(s) + H_2S(g) \text{ [unbalanced]}$$

3.72 Elemental phosphorus occurs as tetratomic molecules, P_4. What mass (g) of chlorine gas is needed to react completely with 455 g of phosphorus to form phosphorus pentachloride?

3.73 Elemental sulfur occurs as octatomic molecules, S_8. What mass (g) of fluorine gas is needed to react completely with 17.8 g of sulfur to form sulfur hexafluoride?

3.74 Solid iodine trichloride is prepared in two steps: first, a reaction between solid iodine and gaseous chlorine to form solid iodine monochloride; then, treatment with more chlorine.
(a) Write a balanced equation for each step.
(b) Write a balanced equation for the overall reaction.
(c) How many grams of iodine are needed to prepare 2.45 kg of final product?

3.75 Lead can be prepared from galena [lead(II) sulfide] by first roasting the galena in oxygen gas to form lead(II) oxide and sulfur dioxide. Heating the metal oxide with more galena forms the molten metal and more sulfur dioxide.
(a) Write a balanced equation for each step.
(b) Write an overall balanced equation for the process.
(c) How many metric tons of sulfur dioxide form for every metric ton of lead obtained?

3.76 Many metals react with oxygen gas to form the metal oxide. For example, calcium reacts as follows:

$$2Ca(s) + O_2(g) \longrightarrow 2CaO(s)$$

You wish to calculate the mass (g) of calcium oxide that can be prepared from 4.20 g of Ca and 2.80 g of O_2.
(a) What amount (mol) of CaO can be produced from the given mass of Ca?
(b) What amount (mol) of CaO can be produced from the given mass of O_2?
(c) Which is the limiting reactant?
(d) How many grams of CaO can be produced?

3.77 Metal hydrides react with water to form hydrogen gas and the metal hydroxide. For example,

$$SrH_2(s) + 2H_2O(l) \longrightarrow Sr(OH)_2(s) + 2H_2(g)$$

You wish to calculate the mass (g) of hydrogen gas that can be prepared from 5.70 g of SrH_2 and 4.75 g of H_2O.
(a) What amount (mol) of H_2 can be produced from the given mass of SrH_2?
(b) What amount (mol) of H_2 can be produced from the given mass of H_2O?
(c) Which is the limiting reactant?
(d) How many grams of H_2 can be produced?

3.78 Calculate the maximum numbers of moles and grams of iodic acid (HIO_3) that can form when 635 g of iodine trichloride reacts with 118.5 g of water:

$$ICl_3 + H_2O \longrightarrow ICl + HIO_3 + HCl \text{ [unbalanced]}$$

How many grams of the excess reactant remains?

3.79 Calculate the maximum numbers of moles and grams of H_2S that can form when 158 g of aluminum sulfide reacts with 131 g of water:

$$Al_2S_3 + H_2O \longrightarrow Al(OH)_3 + H_2S \text{ [unbalanced]}$$

How many grams of the excess reactant remain?

3.80 When 0.100 mol of carbon is burned in a closed vessel with 8.00 g of oxygen, how many grams of carbon dioxide can form? Which reactant is in excess, and how many grams of it remain after the reaction?

3.81 A mixture of 0.0375 g of hydrogen and 0.0185 mol of oxygen in a closed container is sparked to initiate a reaction. How many grams of water can form? Which reactant is in excess, and how many grams of it remain after the reaction?

3.82 Aluminum nitrite and ammonium chloride react to form aluminum chloride, nitrogen, and water. How many grams of each substance are present after 72.5 g of aluminum nitrite and 58.6 g of ammonium chloride react completely?

3.83 Calcium nitrate and ammonium fluoride react to form calcium fluoride, dinitrogen monoxide, and water vapor. How many grams of each substance are present after 16.8 g of calcium nitrate and 17.50 g of ammonium fluoride react completely?

3.84 Two successive reactions, A $\longrightarrow$ B and B $\longrightarrow$ C, have yields of 73% and 68%, respectively. What is the overall percent yield for conversion of A to C?

3.85 Two successive reactions, D $\longrightarrow$ E and E $\longrightarrow$ F, have yields of 48% and 73%, respectively. What is the overall percent yield for conversion of D to F?

3.86 What is the percent yield of a reaction in which 45.5 g of tungsten(VI) oxide (WO_3) reacts with excess hydrogen gas to produce metallic tungsten and 9.60 mL of water (d = 1.00 g/mL)?

3.87 What is the percent yield of a reaction in which 200. g of phosphorus trichloride reacts with excess water to form 128 g of HCl and aqueous phosphorous acid (H_3PO_3)?

3.88 When 20.5 g of methane and 45.0 g of chlorine gas undergo a reaction that has a 75.0% yield, what mass (g) of chloromethane (CH_3Cl) forms? Hydrogen chloride also forms.

3.89 When 56.6 g of calcium and 30.5 g of nitrogen gas undergo a reaction that has a 93.0% yield, what mass (g) of calcium nitride forms?

Problems in Context

3.90 Cyanogen, $(CN)_2$, has been observed in the atmosphere of Titan, Saturn's largest moon, and in the gases of interstellar nebulas. On Earth, it is used as a welding gas and a fumigant. In its reaction with fluorine gas, carbon tetrafluoride and nitrogen trifluoride gases are produced. What mass (g) of carbon tetrafluoride forms when 60.0 g of each reactant is used?

3.91 Gaseous dichlorine monoxide decomposes readily to chlorine and oxygen gases. (a) Which of the following circles best depicts the product mixture after the decomposition?

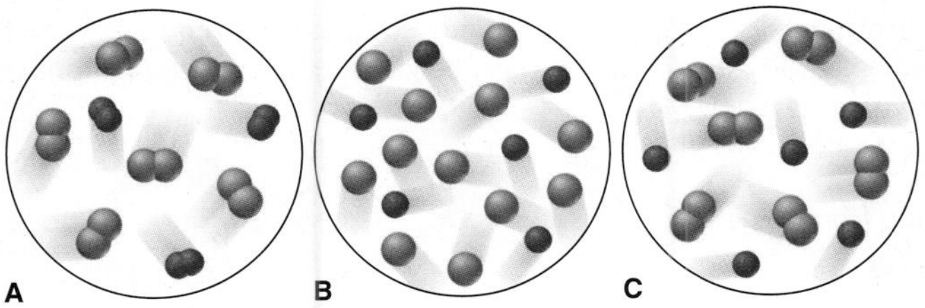

(b) Write the balanced equation for the decomposition.
(c) If each oxygen atom represents 0.050 mol, how many molecules of dichlorine monoxide were present before the decomposition?

3.92 An intermediate step in the production of nitric acid involves the reaction of ammonia with oxygen gas to form nitrogen monoxide and water. How many grams of nitrogen monoxide can form in the reaction of 485 g of ammonia with 792 g of oxygen?

3.93 Butane gas is compressed and used as a liquid fuel in disposable cigarette lighters and lightweight camping stoves. Suppose a lighter contains 5.50 mL of butane (d = 0.579 g/mL).
(a) How many grams of oxygen are needed to burn the butane completely?
(b) How many moles of H_2O form when all the butane burns?
(c) How many total molecules of gas form when the butane burns completely?

3.94 Sodium borohydride ($NaBH_4$) is used industrially in many organic syntheses. One way to prepare it is by reacting sodium hydride with gaseous diborane (B_2H_6). Assuming an 88.5% yield, how many grams of $NaBH_4$ can be prepared by reacting 7.98 g of sodium hydride and 8.16 g of diborane?

Fundamentals of Solution Stoichiometry

(Sample Problems 3.22 to 3.27)

Concept Review Questions

3.95 Box A represents a unit volume of a solution. Choose from boxes B and C the one representing the same unit volume of solution that has (a) more solute added; (b) more solvent added; (c) higher molarity; (d) lower concentration.

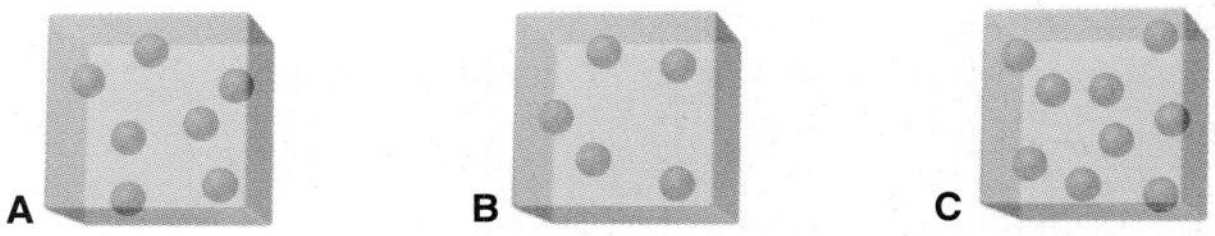

3.96 A mathematical equation useful for dilution calculations is $M_{dil} \times V_{dil} = M_{conc} \times V_{conc}$. (a) What does each symbol mean, and why does the equation work? (b) Given the volume and molarity of a $CaCl_2$ solution, how do you determine the amount (mol) and the mass (g) of solute?

3.97 Six different aqueous solutions (with solvent molecules omitted for clarity) are represented in the beakers below, and their total volumes are noted.

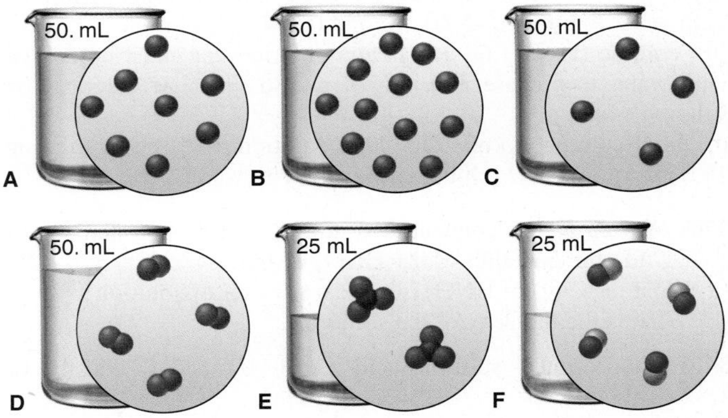

(a) Which solution has the highest molarity? (b) Which solutions have the same molarity? (c) If you mix solutions A and C, does the resulting solution have a higher, a lower, or the same molarity as solution B? (d) After 50. mL of water is added to solution D, is its molarity higher, lower, or the same as the molarity of solution F after 75 mL is added to it? (e) How much solvent must be evaporated from solution E for it to have the same molarity as solution A?

3.98 Are the following instructions for diluting a 10.0 M solution to a 1.00 M solution correct: "Take 100.0 mL of the 10.0 M solution and add 900.0 mL water"? Explain.

Skill-Building Exercises (grouped in similar pairs)

3.99 Calculate each of the following quantities:
(a) Mass (g) of solute in 185.8 mL of 0.267 M calcium acetate
(b) Molarity of 500. mL of solution containing 21.1 g of potassium iodide
(c) Amount (mol) of solute in 145.6 L of 0.850 M sodium cyanide

3.100 Calculate each of the following quantities:
(a) Volume (mL) of 2.26 M potassium hydroxide that contains 8.42 g of solute
(b) Number of Cu^{2+} ions in 52 L of 2.3 M copper(II) chloride
(c) Molarity of 275 mL of solution containing 135 mmol of glucose

3.101 Calculate each of the following quantities:
(a) Mass (g) of solute needed to make 475 mL of 5.62×10^{-2} *M* potassium sulfate
(b) Molarity of a solution that contains 7.25 mg of calcium chloride in each milliliter
(c) Number of Mg^{2+} ions in each milliliter of 0.184 *M* magnesium bromide

3.102 Calculate each of the following quantities:
(a) Molarity of the solution resulting from dissolving 46.0 g of silver nitrate in enough water to give a final volume of 335 mL
(b) Volume (L) of 0.385 *M* manganese(II) sulfate that contains 63.0 g of solute
(c) Volume (mL) of 6.44×10^{-2} *M* adenosine triphosphate (ATP) that contains 1.68 mmol of ATP

3.103 Calculate each of the following quantities:
(a) Molarity of a solution prepared by diluting 37.00 mL of 0.250 *M* potassium chloride to 150.00 mL
(b) Molarity of a solution prepared by diluting 25.71 mL of 0.0706 *M* ammonium sulfate to 500.00 mL
(c) Molarity of sodium ion in a solution made by mixing 3.58 mL of 0.348 *M* sodium chloride with 500. mL of 6.81×10^{-2} *M* sodium sulfate (assume volumes are additive)

3.104 Calculate each of the following quantities:
(a) Volume (L) of 2.050 *M* copper(II) nitrate that must be diluted with water to prepare 750.0 mL of a 0.8543 *M* solution
(b) Volume (L) of 1.63 *M* calcium chloride that must be diluted with water to prepare 350. mL of a 2.86×10^{-2} *M* chloride ion solution
(c) Final volume (L) of a 0.0700 *M* solution prepared by diluting 18.0 mL of 0.155 *M* lithium carbonate with water

3.105 A sample of concentrated nitric acid has a density of 1.41 g/mL and contains 70.0% HNO_3 by mass.
(a) What mass (g) of HNO_3 is present per liter of solution?
(b) What is the molarity of the solution?

3.106 Concentrated sulfuric acid (18.3 *M*) has a density of 1.84 g/mL.
(a) How many moles of H_2SO_4 are in each milliliter of solution?
(b) What is the mass % of H_2SO_4 in the solution?

3.107 How many milliliters of 0.383 *M* HCl are needed to react with 16.2 g of $CaCO_3$?

$$2HCl(aq) + CaCO_3(s) \longrightarrow CaCl_2(aq) + CO_2(g) + H_2O(l)$$

3.108 How many grams of NaH_2PO_4 are needed to react with 43.74 mL of 0.285 *M* NaOH?

$$NaH_2PO_4(s) + 2NaOH(aq) \longrightarrow Na_3PO_4(aq) + 2H_2O(l)$$

3.109 How many grams of solid barium sulfate form when 35.0 mL of 0.160 *M* barium chloride reacts with 58.0 mL of 0.065 *M* sodium sulfate? Aqueous sodium chloride forms also.

3.110 How many moles of excess reactant are present when 350. mL of 0.210 *M* sulfuric acid reacts with 0.500 L of 0.196 *M* sodium hydroxide to form water and aqueous sodium sulfate?

Problems in Context

3.111 Ordinary household bleach is an aqueous solution of sodium hypochlorite. What is the molarity of a bleach solution that contains 20.5 g of sodium hypochlorite in 375 mL?

3.112 Muriatic acid, an industrial grade of concentrated HCl, is used to clean masonry and cement. Its concentration is 11.7 *M*. (a) Write instructions for diluting the concentrated acid to make 3.0 gallons of 3.5 *M* acid for routine use (1 gal = 4 qt; 1 qt = 0.946 L). (b) How many milliliters of the muriatic acid solution contain 9.66 g of HCl?

3.113 A sample of impure magnesium was analyzed by allowing it to react with excess HCl solution:

$$Mg(s) + 2HCl(aq) \longrightarrow MgCl_2(aq) + H_2(g)$$

After 1.32 g of the impure metal was treated with 0.100 L of 0.750 *M* HCl, 0.0125 mol of HCl remained. Assuming the impurities do not react, what is the mass % of Mg in the sample?

Comprehensive Problems

3.114 The mole is defined in terms of the carbon-12 atom. Use the definition to find (a) the mass in grams equal to 1 atomic mass unit; (b) the ratio of the gram to the atomic mass unit.

3.115 The first sulfur-nitrogen compound was prepared in 1835 and has been used to synthesize many others. In the early 1980s, researchers made another such compound that conducts electricity like a metal. Mass spectrometry of the compound shows a molar mass of 184.27 g/mol, and analysis shows it to contain 2.288 g of S for every 1.000 g of N. What is its molecular formula?

3.116 Hydroxyapatite, $Ca_5(PO_4)_3(OH)$, is the main mineral component of dental enamel, dentin, and bone. Coating the compound on metallic implants (such as titanium alloys and stainless steels) helps the body accept the implant. When placed in bone voids, the powder encourages natural bone to grow into the void. Hydroxyapatite is prepared by adding aqueous phosphoric acid to a dilute slurry of calcium hydroxide. (a) Write a balanced equation for this preparation. (b) What mass (g) of hydroxyapatite could form from 100. g of 85% phosphoric acid and 100. g of calcium hydroxide?

3.117 Narceine is a narcotic in opium that crystallizes from solution as a hydrate that contains 10.8 mass % water and has a molar mass of 499.52 g/mol. Determine *x* in narceine·xH_2O.

3.118 Hydrogen-containing fuels have a "fuel value" based on their mass % H. Rank the following compounds from highest fuel value to lowest: ethane, propane, benzene, ethanol, cetyl palmitate (whale oil, $C_{32}H_{64}O_2$).

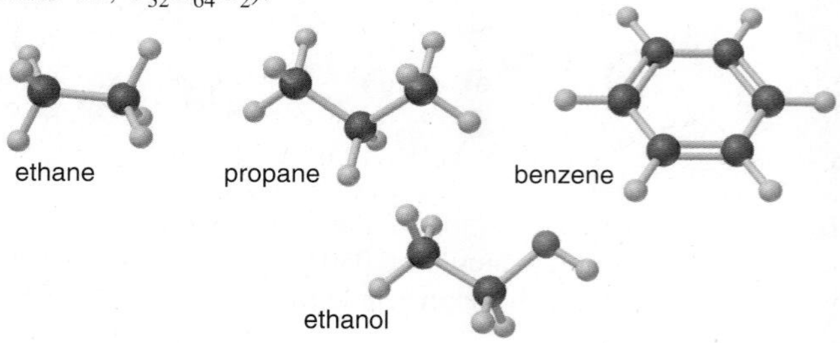

3.119 Serotonin ($\mathcal{M}$ = 176 g/mol) transmits nerve impulses between neurons. It contains 68.2% C, 6.86% H, 15.9% N, and 9.08% O by mass. What is its molecular formula?

3.120 In 1961, scientists agreed that the atomic mass unit (amu) would be defined as $\frac{1}{12}$ the mass of an atom of ^{12}C. Before then, it was defined as $\frac{1}{16}$ the *average* mass of an atom of naturally occurring oxygen (a mixture of ^{16}O, ^{17}O, and ^{18}O). The current atomic mass of oxygen is 15.9994 amu. (a) Did Avogadro's number change after the definition of an amu changed and, if so, in what direction? (b) Did the definition of the mole change? (c) Did the mass of a mole of a substance change? (d) Before 1961, was Avogadro's number 6.02×10^{23} (to three significant figures), as it is today?

3.121 Convert the following descriptions into balanced equations:
(a) In a gaseous reaction, hydrogen sulfide burns in oxygen to form sulfur dioxide and water vapor.
(b) When crystalline potassium chlorate is heated to just above its melting point, it reacts to form two different crystalline compounds, potassium chloride and potassium perchlorate.
(c) When hydrogen gas is passed over powdered iron(III) oxide, iron metal and water vapor form.
(d) The combustion of gaseous ethane in air forms carbon dioxide and water vapor.
(e) Iron(II) chloride is converted to iron(III) fluoride by treatment with chlorine trifluoride gas. Chlorine gas is also formed.

3.122 Isobutylene is a hydrocarbon used in the manufacture of synthetic rubber. When 0.847 g of isobutylene was subjected to combustion analysis, the gain in mass of the CO_2 absorber was 2.657 g and that of the H_2O absorber was 1.089 g. What is the empirical formula of isobutylene?

3.123 The multistep smelting of ferric oxide to form elemental iron occurs at high temperatures in a blast furnace. In the first step, ferric oxide reacts with carbon monoxide to form Fe_3O_4. This substance reacts with more carbon monoxide to form iron(II) oxide, which reacts with still more carbon monoxide to form molten iron. Carbon dioxide is also produced in each step. (a) Write an overall balanced equation for the iron-smelting process. (b) How many grams of carbon monoxide are required to form 45.0 metric tons of iron from ferric oxide?

3.124 One of the compounds used to increase the octane rating of gasoline is toluene (*right*). Suppose 20.0 mL of toluene (d = 0.867 g/mL) is consumed when a sample of gasoline burns in air.

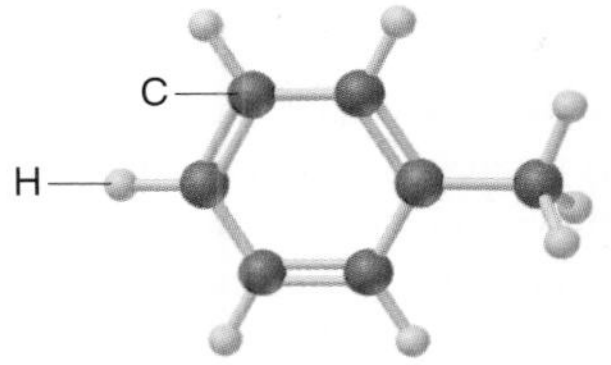

(a) How many grams of oxygen are needed for complete combustion of the toluene? (b) How many total moles of gaseous products form? (c) How many molecules of water vapor form?

3.125 During studies of the reaction in Sample Problem 3.20,

$$2N_2H_4(l) + N_2O_4(l) \longrightarrow 3N_2(g) + 4H_2O(g)$$

a chemical engineer measured a less-than-expected yield of N_2 and discovered that the following side reaction occurs:

$$N_2H_4(l) + 2N_2O_4(l) \longrightarrow 6NO(g) + 2H_2O(g)$$

In one experiment, 10.0 g of NO formed when 100.0 g of each reactant was used. What is the highest percent yield of N_2 that can be expected?

3.126 A 0.652-g sample of a pure strontium halide reacts with excess sulfuric acid. The solid strontium sulfate formed is separated, dried, and found to weigh 0.755 g. What is the formula of the original halide?

3.127 The following circles represent a chemical reaction between AB_2 and B_2:

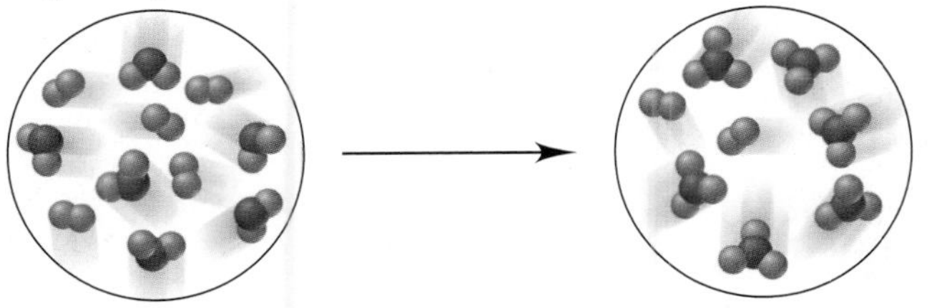

(a) Write a balanced equation for the reaction. (b) What is the limiting reactant? (c) How many moles of product can be made from 3.0 mol of B_2 and 5.0 mol of AB_2? (d) How many moles of excess reactant remain after the reaction in part (c)?

3.128 Calculate each of the following quantities:
(a) Volume (L) of 18.0 M sulfuric acid that must be added to water to prepare 2.00 L of a 0.429 M solution
(b) Molarity of the solution obtained by diluting 80.6 mL of 0.225 M ammonium chloride to 0.250 L
(c) Volume (L) of water added to 0.130 L of 0.0372 M sodium hydroxide to obtain a 0.0100 M solution (assume the volumes are additive at these low concentrations)
(d) Mass (g) of calcium nitrate in each milliliter of a solution prepared by diluting 64.0 mL of 0.745 M calcium nitrate to a final volume of 0.100 L

3.129 Which of the following models represent compounds having the same empirical formula? What is the molecular mass of this common empirical formula?

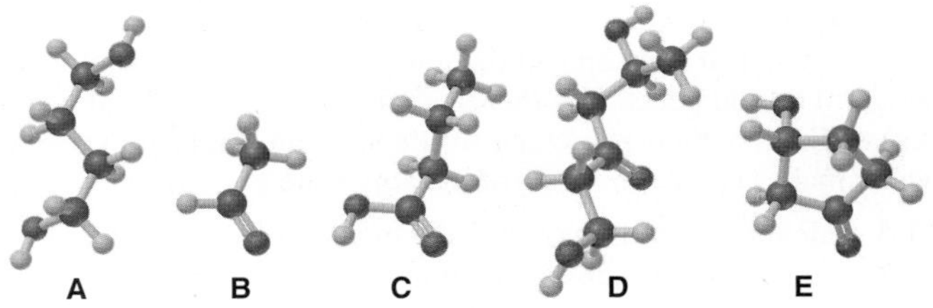

3.130 The zirconium oxalate $K_2Zr(C_2O_4)_3(H_2C_2O_4){\cdot}H_2O$ was synthesized by mixing 1.68 g of $ZrOCl_2{\cdot}8H_2O$ with 5.20 g of $H_2C_2O_4{\cdot}2H_2O$ and an excess of aqueous KOH. After 2 months, 1.25 g of crystalline product was obtained, along with aqueous KCl and water. Calculate the percent yield.

3.131 Seawater is approximately 4.0% by mass dissolved ions, 85% of which are from NaCl. (a) Find the mass % of NaCl in seawater. (b) Find the mass % of Na^+ ions and of Cl^- ions in seawater. (c) Find the molarity of NaCl in seawater at 15°C (d of seawater at 15°C = 1.025 g/mL).

3.132 Is each of the following statements true or false? Correct any that are false.
(a) A mole of one substance has the same number of atoms as a mole of any other substance.
(b) The theoretical yield for a reaction is based on the balanced chemical equation.
(c) A limiting-reactant problem is being stated when the available quantity of one of the reactants is given in moles.
(d) To prepare 1.00 L of 3.00 M NaCl, weigh 175.5 g of NaCl and dissolve it in 1.00 L of distilled water.
(e) The concentration of a solution is an intensive property, but the amount of solute in a solution is an extensive property.

3.133 Box A represents one unit volume of solution A. Which box—B, C, or D—represents one unit volume after adding enough solvent to solution A to (a) triple its volume; (b) double its volume; (c) quadruple its volume?

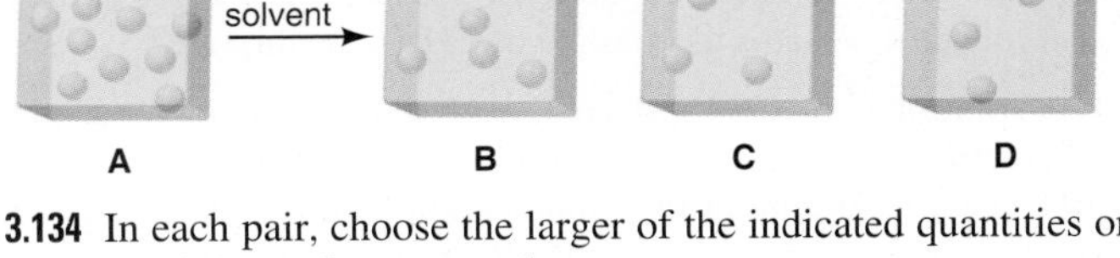

3.134 In each pair, choose the larger of the indicated quantities or state that the samples are equal:
(a) Entities: 0.4 mol of O_3 molecules or 0.4 mol of O atoms
(b) Grams: 0.4 mol of O_3 molecules or 0.4 mol of O atoms

(c) Moles: 4.0 g of N_2O_4 or 3.3 g of SO_2
(d) Grams: 0.6 mol of C_2H_4 or 0.6 mol of F_2
(e) Total ions: 2.3 mol of sodium chlorate or 2.2 mol of magnesium chloride
(f) Molecules: 1.0 g of H_2O or 1.0 g of H_2O_2
(g) Na^+ ions: 0.500 L of 0.500 *M* NaBr or 0.0146 kg of NaCl
(h) Grams: 6.02×10^{23} atoms of ^{235}U or 6.02×10^{23} atoms of ^{238}U

3.135 For the reaction between solid tetraphosphorus trisulfide and oxygen gas to form solid tetraphosphorus decaoxide and sulfur dioxide gas, write a balanced equation. Show the equation (see Table 3.4) in terms of (a) molecules, (b) moles, and (c) grams.

3.136 Hydrogen gas is considered a clean fuel because it produces only water vapor when it burns. If the reaction has a 98.8% yield, what mass (g) of hydrogen forms 105 kg of water?

3.137 Solar winds composed of free protons, electrons, and α particles bombard Earth constantly, knocking gas molecules out of the atmosphere. In this way, Earth loses about 3.0 kg of matter per second. It is estimated that the atmosphere will be gone in about 50 billion years. Use this estimate to calculate (a) the mass (kg) of Earth's atmosphere and (b) the amount (mol) of nitrogen, which makes up 75.5 mass % of the atmosphere.

3.138 Calculate each of the following quantities:
(a) Amount (mol) of 0.588 g of ammonium bromide
(b) Number of potassium ions in 88.5 g of potassium nitrate
(c) Mass (g) of 5.85 mol of glycerol ($C_3H_8O_3$)
(d) Volume (L) of 2.85 mol of chloroform ($CHCl_3$; $d = 1.48$ g/mL)
(e) Number of sodium ions in 2.11 mol of sodium carbonate
(f) Number of atoms in 25.0 μg of cadmium
(g) Number of atoms in 0.0015 mol of fluorine gas

3.139 Elements X (green) and Y (purple) react according to the following equation: $X_2 + 3Y_2 \longrightarrow 2XY_3$. Which molecular scene represents the product of the reaction?

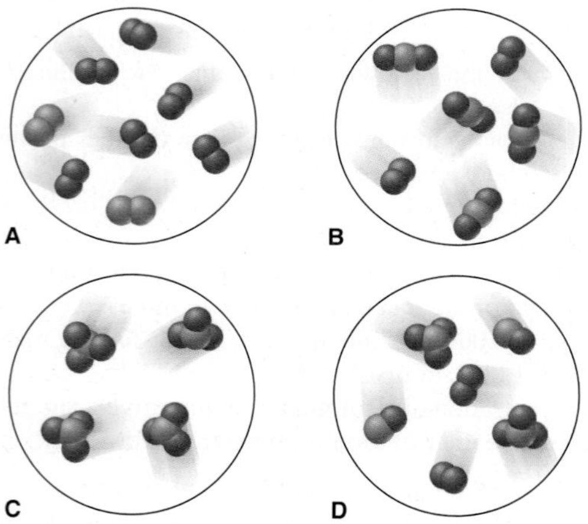

3.140 Hydrocarbon mixtures are used as fuels. (a) How many grams of $CO_2(g)$ are produced by the combustion of 200. g of a mixture that is 25.0% CH_4 and 75.0% C_3H_8 by mass? (b) A 252-g gaseous mixture of CH_4 and C_3H_8 burns in excess O_2, and 748 g of CO_2 gas is collected. What is the mass % of CH_4 in the mixture?

3.141 To 1.35 L of 0.325 *M* HCl, you add 3.57 L of a second HCl solution of unknown concentration. The resulting solution is 0.893 *M* HCl. Assuming the volumes are additive, calculate the molarity of the second HCl solution.

3.142 Nitrogen (N), phosphorus (P), and potassium (K) are the main nutrients in plant fertilizers. By industry convention, the numbers on a label refer to the mass percents of N, P_2O_5, and K_2O, in that order. Calculate the N/P/K ratio of a 30/10/10 fertilizer in terms of moles of each element, and express it as *x*/*y*/1.0.

3.143 What mass percents of ammonium sulfate, ammonium hydrogen phosphate, and potassium chloride would you use to prepare 10/10/10 plant fertilizer (see Problem 3.142)?

3.144 Ferrocene, synthesized in 1951, was the first organic iron compound with Fe—C bonds. An understanding of the structure of ferrocene gave rise to new ideas about chemical bonding and led to the preparation of many useful compounds. In the combustion analysis of ferrocene, which contains only Fe, C, and H, a 0.9437-g sample produced 2.233 g of CO_2 and 0.457 g of H_2O. What is the empirical formula of ferrocene?

3.145 When carbon-containing compounds are burned in a limited amount of air, some CO(*g*) as well as $CO_2(g)$ is produced. A gaseous product mixture is 35.0 mass % CO and 65.0 mass % CO_2. What is the mass % of C in the mixture?

3.146 Write a balanced equation for the reaction depicted below:

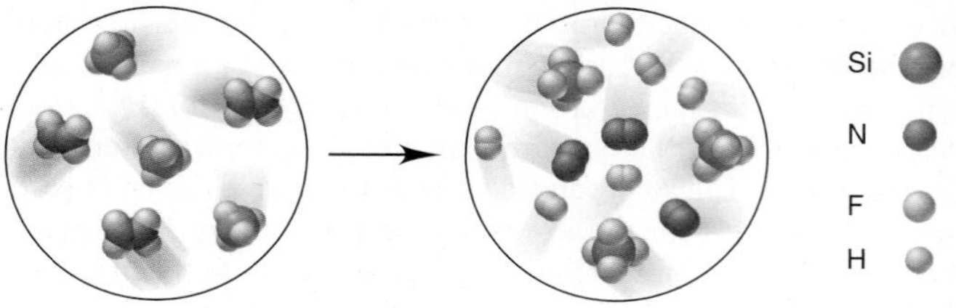

If each reactant molecule represents 1.25×10^{-2} mol and the reaction yield is 87%, how many grams of Si-containing product form?

3.147 Citric acid (*right*) is concentrated in citrus fruits and plays a central metabolic role in nearly every animal and plant cell. (a) What are the molar mass and formula of citric acid? (b) How many moles of citric acid are in 1.50 qt of lemon juice ($d = 1.09$ g/mL) that is 6.82% citric acid by mass?

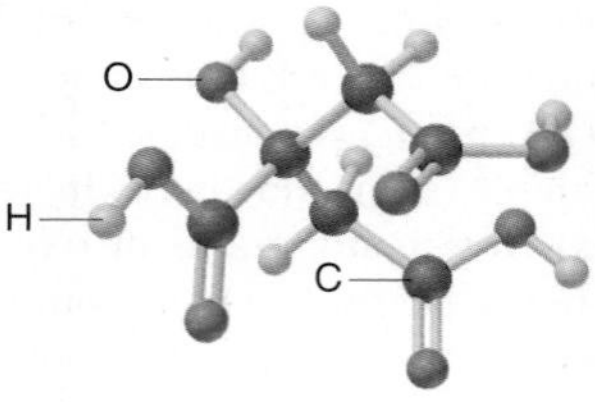

3.148 Various nitrogen oxides, as well as sulfur oxides, contribute to acidic rainfall through complex reaction sequences. Nitrogen and oxygen combine during high-temperature combustion of fuels in air to form nitrogen monoxide gas, which reacts with more oxygen to form nitrogen dioxide gas. In contact with water vapor, nitrogen dioxide forms aqueous nitric acid and more nitrogen monoxide. (a) Write balanced equations for these reactions. (b) Use the equations to write one overall balanced equation that does *not* include nitrogen monoxide and nitrogen dioxide. (c) How many metric tons (t) of nitric acid form when 1350 t of atmospheric nitrogen is consumed (1 t = 1000 kg)?

3.149 Nitrogen monoxide reacts with elemental oxygen to form nitrogen dioxide. The scene at right represents an initial mixture of reactants. If the reaction has a 66% yield, which of the scenes below (A, B, or C) best represents the final product mixture?

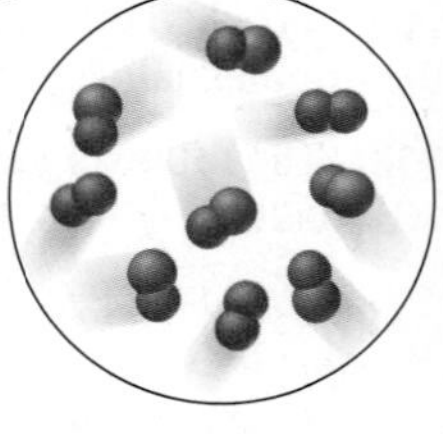

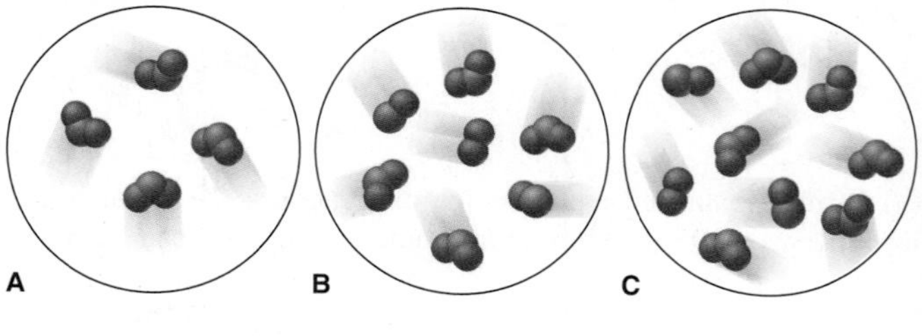

3.150 Fluorine is so reactive that it forms compounds with several of the noble gases.
(a) When 0.327 g of platinum is heated in fluorine, 0.519 g of a dark red, volatile solid forms. What is its empirical formula?
(b) When 0.265 g of this red solid reacts with excess xenon gas, 0.378 g of an orange-yellow solid forms. What is the empirical formula of this compound, the first to contain a noble gas?
(c) Fluorides of xenon can be formed by direct reaction of the elements at high pressure and temperature. Under conditions that produce only the tetra- and hexafluorides, 1.85×10^{-4} mol of xenon reacted with 5.00×10^{-4} mol of fluorine, and 9.00×10^{-6} mol of xenon was found in excess. What are the mass percents of each xenon fluoride in the product mixture?

3.151 Hemoglobin is 6.0% heme ($C_{34}H_{32}FeN_4O_4$) by mass. To remove the heme, hemoglobin is treated with acetic acid and NaCl, which forms hemin ($C_{34}H_{32}N_4O_4FeCl$). A blood sample from a crime scene contains 0.65 g of hemoglobin. (a) How many grams of heme are in the sample? (b) How many moles of heme? (c) How many grams of Fe? (d) How many grams of hemin could be formed for a forensic chemist to measure?

3.152 Manganese is a key component of extremely hard steel. The element occurs naturally in many oxides. A 542.3-g sample of a manganese oxide has an Mn/O ratio of 1.00/1.42 and consists of braunite (Mn_2O_3) and manganosite (MnO). (a) How many grams of braunite and of manganosite are in the ore? (b) What is the Mn^{3+}/Mn^{2+} ratio in the ore?

3.153 The human body excretes nitrogen in the form of urea, NH_2CONH_2. The key step in its biochemical formation is the reaction of water with arginine to produce urea and ornithine:

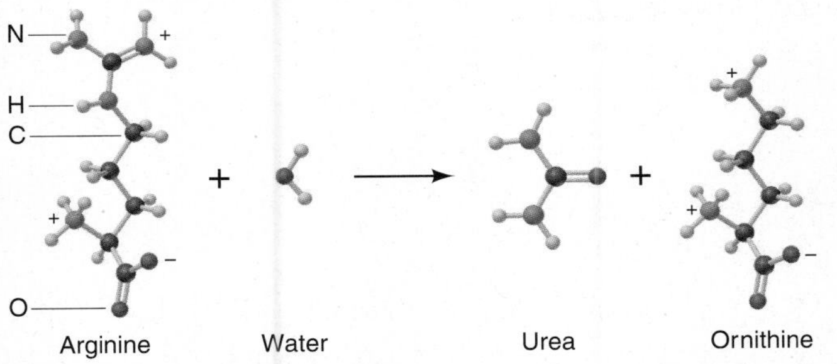

(a) What is the mass % of nitrogen in urea, in arginine, and in ornithine? (b) How many grams of nitrogen can be excreted as urea when 135.2 g of ornithine is produced?

3.154 Aspirin (acetylsalicylic acid, $C_9H_8O_4$) is made by reacting salicylic acid ($C_7H_6O_3$) with acetic anhydride [$(CH_3CO)_2O$]:

$$C_7H_6O_3(s) + (CH_3CO)_2O(l) \longrightarrow C_9H_8O_4(s) + CH_3COOH(l)$$

In one preparation, 3.077 g of salicylic acid and 5.50 mL of acetic anhydride react to form 3.281 g of aspirin. (a) Which is the limiting reactant (d of acetic anhydride = 1.080 g/mL)? (b) What is the percent yield of this reaction? (c) What is the percent atom economy of this reaction?

3.155 The rocket fuel hydrazine (N_2H_4) is made by the three-step Raschig process, which has the following overall equation:

$$NaOCl(aq) + 2NH_3(aq) \longrightarrow N_2H_4(aq) + NaCl(aq) + H_2O(l)$$

What is the percent atom economy of this process?

3.156 Lead(II) chromate ($PbCrO_4$) is used as the yellow pigment for marking traffic lanes but is banned from house paint because of the risk of lead poisoning. It is produced from chromite ($FeCr_2O_4$), an ore of chromium:

$$4FeCr_2O_4(s) + 8K_2CO_3(aq) + 7O_2(g) \longrightarrow 2Fe_2O_3(s) + 8K_2CrO_4(aq) + 8CO_2(g)$$

Lead(II) ion then replaces the K^+ ion. If a yellow paint is to have 0.511% $PbCrO_4$ by mass, how many grams of chromite are needed per kilogram of paint?

3.157 Ethanol (CH_3CH_2OH), the intoxicant in alcoholic beverages, is also used to make other organic compounds. In concentrated sulfuric acid, ethanol forms diethyl ether and water:

$$2CH_3CH_2OH(l) \longrightarrow CH_3CH_2OCH_2CH_3(l) + H_2O(g)$$

In a side reaction, some ethanol forms ethylene and water:

$$CH_3CH_2OH(l) \longrightarrow CH_2CH_2(g) + H_2O(g)$$

(a) If 50.0 g of ethanol yields 35.9 g of diethyl ether, what is the percent yield of diethyl ether? (b) If 45.0% of the ethanol that did not produce the ether reacts by the side reaction, what mass (g) of ethylene is produced?

3.158 When powdered zinc is heated with sulfur, a violent reaction occurs, and zinc sulfide forms:

$$Zn(s) + S_8(s) \longrightarrow ZnS(s) \text{ [unbalanced]}$$

Some of the reactants also combine with oxygen in air to form zinc oxide and sulfur dioxide. When 83.2 g of Zn reacts with 52.4 g of S_8, 104.4 g of ZnS forms.
(a) What is the percent yield of ZnS?
(b) If all the remaining reactants combine with oxygen, how many grams of each of the two oxides form?

3.159 Cocaine ($C_{17}H_{21}O_4N$) is a natural substance found in coca leaves, which have been used for centuries as a local anesthetic and stimulant. Illegal cocaine arrives in the United States either as the pure compound or as the hydrochloride salt ($C_{17}H_{21}O_4NHCl$). At 25°C, the salt is very soluble in water (2.50 kg/L), but cocaine is much less so (1.70 g/L).
(a) What is the maximum mass (g) of the salt that can dissolve in 50.0 mL of water?
(b) If this solution is treated with NaOH, the salt is converted to cocaine. How much more water (L) is needed to dissolve it?

3.160 High-temperature superconducting oxides hold great promise in the utility, transportation, and computer industries.
(a) One superconductor is $La_{2-x}Sr_xCuO_4$. Calculate the molar masses of this oxide when $x = 0$, $x = 1$, and $x = 0.163$.
(b) Another common superconducting oxide is made by heating a mixture of barium carbonate, copper(II) oxide, and yttrium(III) oxide, followed by further heating in O_2:

$$4BaCO_3(s) + 6CuO(s) + Y_2O_3(s) \longrightarrow$$
$$2YBa_2Cu_3O_{6.5}(s) + 4CO_2(g)2YBa_2Cu_3O_{6.5}(s) + \tfrac{1}{2}O_2(g) \longrightarrow 2YBa_2Cu_3O_7(s)$$

When equal masses of the three reactants are heated, which reactant is limiting?
(c) After the product in part (b) is removed, what is the mass % of each reactant in the remaining solid mixture?

Three Major Classes of Chemical Reactions

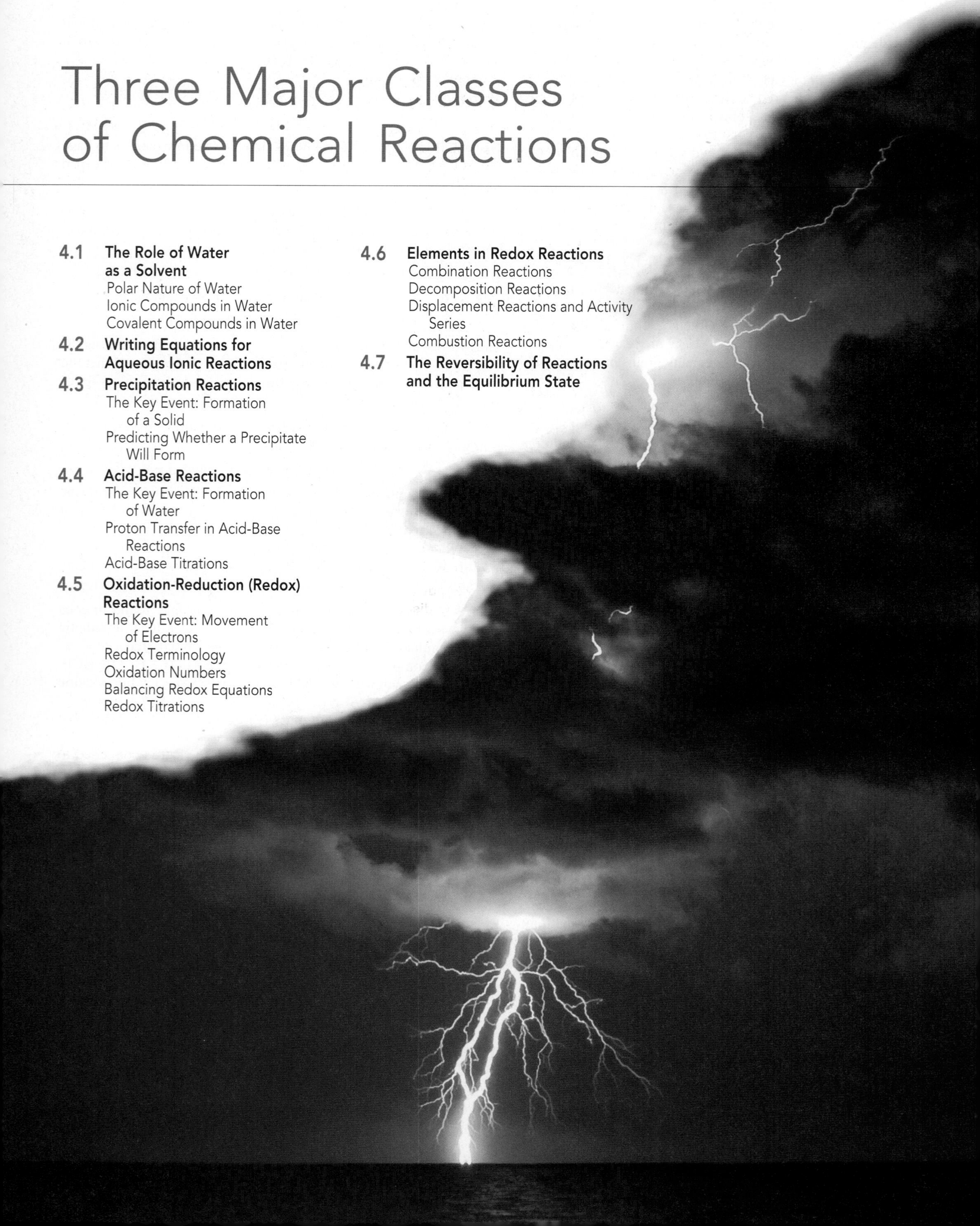

4

Concepts and skills to review before you study this chapter

- names and formulas of compounds (Section 2.8)
- nature of ionic and covalent bonding (Section 2.7)
- amount-mass-number conversions (Section 3.1)
- molarity and amount-mass-number conversions in solution (Section 3.5)
- balancing chemical equations (Section 3.3)
- calculating quantities of reactants and products (Section 3.4)

Rapid chemical changes occur among gas molecules as sunlight bathes the atmosphere or lightning rips through a stormy sky and strikes the sea. Aqueous reactions occur unceasingly in the gigantic containers we know as oceans. And, in every cell of your body, thousands of reactions taking place right now enable you to function. Indeed, the amazing variety in nature is largely a consequence of the amazing variety of chemical reactions. With millions of reactions occurring in and around you, it would be impossible to describe them all. Fortunately, it isn't necessary because, when we survey even a small percentage of reactions, especially those in aqueous solution, a few major classes emerge.

IN THIS CHAPTER . . . We examine the underlying nature of three classes of reactions and the complex part that water plays in aqueous chemistry.

- We visualize the molecular structure of water to learn its role as solvent, how it interacts with ionic and covalent compounds, and the nature of electrolytes.
- We write ionic equations that represent the species in solution and the actual change that occurs when ionic compounds dissolve and react in water.
- We describe precipitation reactions and learn how to predict when they will occur.
- We see how acids and bases act as electrolytes and how they neutralize each other. We view acid-base reactions as proton-transfer processes and discuss how to quantify these reactions through titration.
- We examine oxidation-reduction (redox) reactions in the formation of ionic and covalent substances. We learn how to determine oxidation numbers and use them to balance redox equations and how to quantify these reactions through titration. We describe several important types of redox reactions, one of which is used to predict the relative reactivity of metals.
- An introduction to the reversible nature of all chemical change and the nature of equilibrium previews coverage of this central topic in later chapters.

4.1 • THE ROLE OF WATER AS A SOLVENT

For any reaction in solution, the solvent plays a key role that depends on its chemical nature. Some solvents passively disperse the substances into individual molecules. But water is much more active, interacting strongly with the substances and even reacting with them in some cases. Let's focus on how the water molecule interacts with both ionic and covalent solutes.

The Polar Nature of Water

On the atomic scale, water's great solvent power arises from the *uneven distribution of electron charge* and its *bent molecular shape,* which create a *polar molecule:*

1. *Uneven charge distribution.* Recall from Section 2.7 that the electrons in a covalent bond are shared between the atoms. In a bond between identical atoms—as in H_2, Cl_2, O_2—the sharing is equal and electron charge is distributed evenly between the two nuclei (symmetrical shading in the space-filling model of Figure 4.1A on the next page). In covalent bonds between different atoms, the sharing is uneven because one atom attracts the electron pair more strongly than the other atom does.

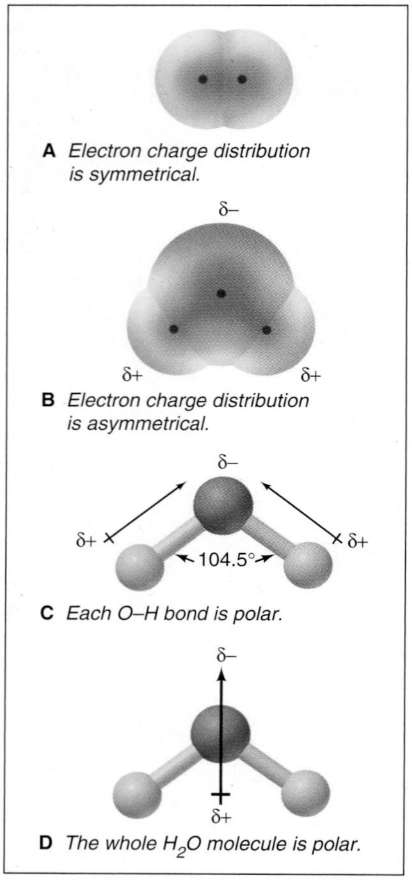

Figure 4.1 Electron distribution in molecules of H_2 and H_2O.

For example, in each O—H bond of water, the shared electrons are closer to the O atom because an O atom attracts electrons more strongly than an H atom does. (We'll discuss the reasons in Chapter 9.) This uneven charge distribution creates a *polar bond,* one with partially charged "poles." In Figure 4.1B, the asymmetrical shading shows this distribution, and the δ symbol indicates a partial charge. The O end is partially negative, represented by red shading and δ−, and the H end is partially positive, represented by blue shading and δ+. In the ball-and-stick model of Figure 4.1C, the *polar arrow* points to the negative pole, and the tail, shaped like a plus sign, marks the positive pole.

2. *Bent molecular shape.* The sequence of the H—O—H atoms in water is not linear: the water molecule is bent with a bond angle of 104.5° (Figure 4.1C).

3. *Molecular polarity.* The combination of polar bonds and bent shape makes water a **polar molecule:** the region near the O atom is partially negative, and the region between the H atoms is partially positive (Figure 4.1D).

Ionic Compounds in Water

In this subsection, we consider two closely related aspects of aqueous solutions of ionic compounds—how they occur and how they behave. We also use a compound's formula to calculate the amount (mol) of each ion in solution.

How Ionic Compounds Dissolve: Replacement of Charge Attractions In an ionic solid, oppositely charged ions are held together by electrostatic attractions (see Figure 1.3C and Section 2.7). Water separates the ions by *replacing these attractions with stronger ones between several water molecules and each ion.* Picture a granule of a soluble ionic compound in water: the negative ends of some water molecules are attracted to the cations, and the positive ends of other water molecules are attracted to the anions (Figure 4.2). Dissolution occurs because the *attractions between each type of ion and several water molecules outweigh the attractions between the ions.* Gradually, all the ions separate (dissociate), become **solvated**—surrounded closely by solvent molecules—and then move randomly in the solution.

For an ionic compound that doesn't dissolve in water, the attraction between ions is greater than the attraction between the ions and water. Actually, these so-called insoluble substances *do* dissolve to a very small extent, usually several orders of magnitude less than so-called soluble substances. For example, NaCl (a "soluble" compound) is over 4×10^4 times more soluble than AgCl (an "insoluble" compound):

$$\text{Solubility of NaCl in } H_2O \text{ at } 20°C = 365 \text{ g/L}$$
$$\text{Solubility of AgCl in } H_2O \text{ at } 20°C = 0.009 \text{ g/L}$$

Figure 4.2 An ionic compound dissolving in water. The inset shows the polar arrow and partial charges (not shown in the rest of the scene) of each water molecule.

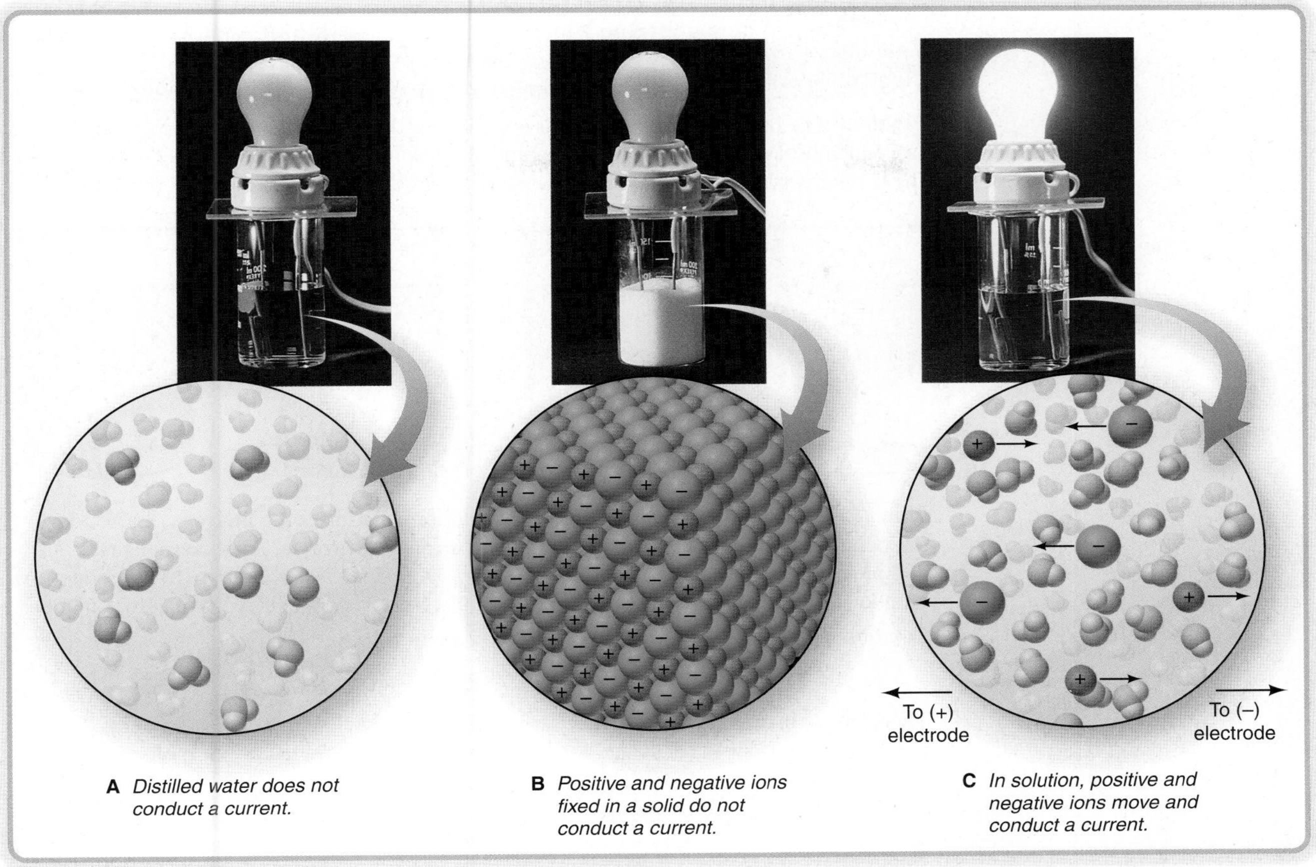

Figure 4.3 The electrical conductivity of ionic solutions.

In Chapter 13, you'll see that dissolving involves more than a contest between the relative attractions of ions for each other or for water. It also occurs because it frees ions from the solid to disperse randomly through the solution.

How Ionic Solutions Behave: Electrolytes and Electrical Conductivity When an ionic compound dissolves, the solution's *electrical conductivity,* the flow of electric current, increases dramatically. When electrodes are immersed in distilled water (Figure 4.3A) or pushed into an ionic solid (Figure 4.3B), no current flows, as shown by the unlit bulb. But in an aqueous solution of the compound, a large current flows, as shown by the lit bulb (Figure 4.3C). Current flow implies the *movement of charged particles:* when the ionic compound dissolves, the separate solvated ions move toward the electrode of opposite charge. A substance that conducts a current when dissolved in water is an **electrolyte.** Soluble ionic compounds are *strong* electrolytes because they dissociate completely and conduct a large current.

Calculating the Amount (mol) of Ions in Solution *The formula of the soluble ionic compound tells the number of moles of the component ions in solution.* For example, the equation for dissolving KBr in water to form solvated ions is

$$KBr(s) \xrightarrow{H_2O} K^+(aq) + Br^-(aq)$$

("H_2O" above the arrow means that water is the solvent, not a reactant.) Note that 1 mol of KBr dissociates into 2 mol of ions—1 mol of K^+ and 1 mol of Br^-. Sample Problems 4.1 and 4.2 apply these ideas, first with molecular scenes and then in calculations.

Sample Problem 4.1 Using Molecular Scenes to Depict an Ionic Compound in Aqueous Solution

Problem The beakers contain aqueous solutions of the strong electrolyte potassium sulfate. **(a)** Which beaker best represents the compound in solution (water molecules are not shown)? **(b)** If each particle represents 0.1 mol, what is the total number of particles in solution?

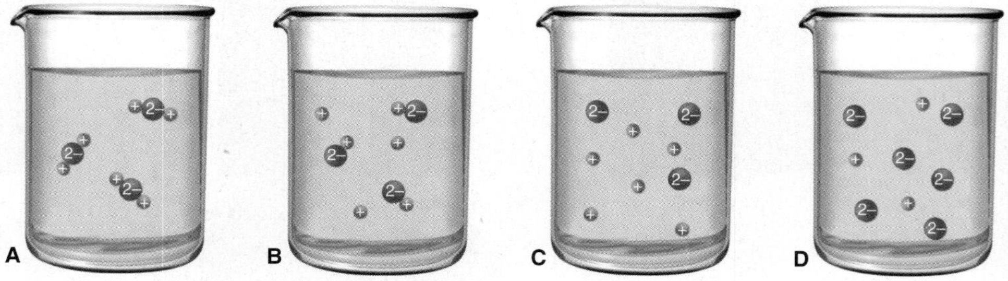

Plan (a) We determine the formula and write an equation for 1 mol of compound dissociating into ions. Potassium sulfate is a strong electrolyte, so it dissociates completely, but, in general, *polyatomic ions remain intact in solution.* **(b)** We count the number of separate particles, and then multiply by 0.1 mol and by Avogadro's number.

Solution (a) The formula is K_2SO_4, so the equation is

$$K_2SO_4(s) \xrightarrow{H_2O} 2K^+(aq) + SO_4^{2-}(aq)$$

There are two separate 1+ particles for every 2− particle, so beaker C is best.
(b) There are 9 particles, so the total amount (mol) of particles is 0.9 mol, and we have

$$\text{No. of particles} = 0.9\ \text{mol} \times \frac{6.022\times10^{23}\ \text{particles}}{1\ \text{mol}} = 5.420\times10^{23}\ \text{particles}$$

Check Rounding to check the math in (b) gives $0.9 \times 6 = 5.4$, so the answer seems correct. The number of particles is an exact number since we actually counted them; thus, the answer can have as many significant figures as in Avogadro's number.

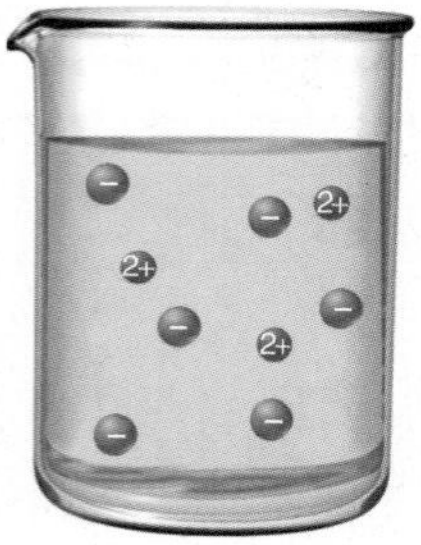

Follow-Up Problem 4.1 **(a)** Which strong electrolyte is dissolved in water (water molecules not shown) in the beaker at left: LiBr, Cs_2CO_3, or $BaCl_2$?
(b) If each particle represents 0.05 mol, what mass (g) of compound was dissolved?

Sample Problem 4.2 Determining Amount (mol) of Ions in Solution

Problem What amount (mol) of each ion is in each solution?
(a) 5.0 mol of ammonium sulfate dissolved in water
(b) 78.5 g of cesium bromide dissolved in water
(c) 7.42×10^{22} formula units of copper(II) nitrate dissolved in water
(d) 35 mL of 0.84 *M* zinc chloride

Plan We write an equation that shows 1 mol of compound dissociating into ions. **(a)** We multiply the number of moles of ions by 5.0. **(b)** We first convert grams to moles. **(c)** We first convert formula units to moles. **(d)** We first convert molarity and volume to moles.

Solution (a) $(NH_4)_2SO_4(s) \xrightarrow{H_2O} 2NH_4^+(aq) + SO_4^{2-}(aq)$

Calculating amount (mol) of NH_4^+ ions:

$$\text{Amount (mol) of } NH_4^+ = 5.0\ \text{mol}\ (NH_4)_2SO_4 \times \frac{2\ \text{mol}\ NH_4^+}{1\ \text{mol}\ (NH_4)_2SO_4} = 10.\ \text{mol}\ NH_4^+$$

The formula shows 1 mol of SO_4^{2-} per mole of $(NH_4)_2SO_4$, so 5.0 mol of SO_4^{2-} is also present.

(b) $CsBr(s) \xrightarrow{H_2O} Cs^+(aq) + Br^-(aq)$

Converting from mass (g) to amount (mol):

$$\text{Amount (mol) of CsBr} = 78.5\ \cancel{\text{g CsBr}} \times \frac{1\ \text{mol CsBr}}{212.8\ \cancel{\text{g CsBr}}} = 0.369\ \text{mol CsBr}$$

Thus, 0.369 mol of Cs^+ and 0.369 mol of Br^- are present.

(c) $Cu(NO_3)_2(s) \xrightarrow{H_2O} Cu^{2+}(aq) + 2NO_3^-(aq)$

Converting from formula units to amount (mol):

$$\text{Amount (mol) of } Cu(NO_3)_2 = 7.42\times10^{22}\ \cancel{\text{formula units } Cu(NO_3)_2} \times \frac{1\ \text{mol } Cu(NO_3)_2}{6.022\times10^{23}\ \cancel{\text{formula units } Cu(NO_3)_2}} = 0.123\ \text{mol } Cu(NO_3)_2$$

$$\text{Amount (mol) of } NO_3^- = 0.123\ \cancel{\text{mol } Cu(NO_3)_2} \times \frac{2\ \text{mol } NO_3^-}{1\ \cancel{\text{mol } Cu(NO_3)_2}} = 0.246\ \text{mol } NO_3^-$$

0.123 mol of Cu^{2+} is also present.

(d) $ZnCl_2(aq) \longrightarrow Zn^{2+}(aq) + 2Cl^-(aq)$

Converting from volume (mL) and molarity (mol/L) to amount (mol):

$$\text{Amount (mol) of } ZnCl_2 = 35\ \cancel{\text{mL}} \times \frac{1\ \cancel{\text{L}}}{10^3\ \cancel{\text{mL}}} \times \frac{0.84\ \text{mol } ZnCl_2}{1\ \cancel{\text{L}}} = 2.9\times10^{-2}\ \text{mol } ZnCl_2$$

$$\text{Amount (mol) of } Cl^- = 2.9\times10^{-2}\ \cancel{\text{mol } ZnCl_2} \times \frac{2\ \text{mol } Cl^-}{1\ \cancel{\text{mol } ZnCl_2}} = 5.8\times10^{-2}\ \text{mol } Cl^-$$

2.9×10^{-2} mol of Zn^{2+} is also present.

Check Round off to check the math and see if the relative numbers of moles of ions are consistent with the formula. For instance, in (a), 10 mol NH_4^+/5.0 mol SO_4^{2-} = 2 NH_4^+/1 SO_4^{2-}, or $(NH_4)_2SO_4$. In (d), 0.029 mol Zn^{2+}/0.058 mol Cl^- = 1 Zn^{2+}/2 Cl^-, or $ZnCl_2$.

Follow-Up Problem 4.2 What amount (mol) of each ion is in each solution?

(a) 2 mol of potassium perchlorate dissolved in water
(b) 354 g of magnesium acetate dissolved in water
(c) 1.88×10^{24} formula units of ammonium chromate dissolved in water
(d) 1.32 L of 0.55 *M* sodium bisulfate

Covalent Compounds in Water

Water dissolves many covalent (molecular) compounds also. Table sugar (sucrose, $C_{12}H_{22}O_{11}$), beverage (grain) alcohol (ethanol, CH_3CH_2OH), and automobile antifreeze (ethylene glycol, $HOCH_2CH_2OH$) are some familiar examples. All contain their own polar bonds, which interact with the bonds of water. However, most soluble covalent substances *do not* separate into ions, but remain intact molecules. For example,

$$HOCH_2CH_2OH(l) \xrightarrow{H_2O} HOCH_2CH_2OH(aq)$$

As a result, their aqueous solutions do not conduct an electric current, and these substances are **nonelectrolytes.** (As you'll see shortly, however, a small group of H-containing molecules that act as acids in aqueous solution *do* dissociate into ions.) Many other covalent substances, such as benzene (C_6H_6) and octane (C_8H_{18}), do not contain polar bonds, and these substances do not dissolve appreciably in water.

Summary of Section 4.1

- Because of polar bonds and a bent shape, the water molecule is polar, and water dissolves many ionic and covalent compounds.
- When an ionic compound dissolves, the attraction between each ion and water replaces the attraction between ions. Soluble ionic compounds are electrolytes because the ions are free to move and, thus, the solution conducts electricity.

- The formula of a soluble ionic compound shows the number of moles of each ion in solution per mole of compound dissolved.
- Water dissolves many covalent substances with polar bonds. These compounds are nonelectrolytes because the molecules remain intact and, thus, the solution does not conduct electricity.

4.2 • WRITING EQUATIONS FOR AQUEOUS IONIC REACTIONS

Chemists use three types of equations to represent aqueous ionic reactions. Let's examine a reaction to see what each type shows. When solutions of silver nitrate and sodium chromate are mixed, brick-red, solid silver chromate (Ag_2CrO_4) forms. Figure 4.4 depicts the reaction at the macroscopic level *(photos),* the atomic level *(blow-up circles),* and the symbolic level with the three types of equations (reacting ions are in red type):

- The **molecular equation** (*top*) reveals the least about the species that are actually in solution because *it shows all the reactants and products as if they were intact, undissociated compounds.* Only the designation for solid, (*s*), tells that a change has occurred:

$$2AgNO_3(aq) + Na_2CrO_4(aq) \longrightarrow Ag_2CrO_4(s) + 2NaNO_3(aq)$$

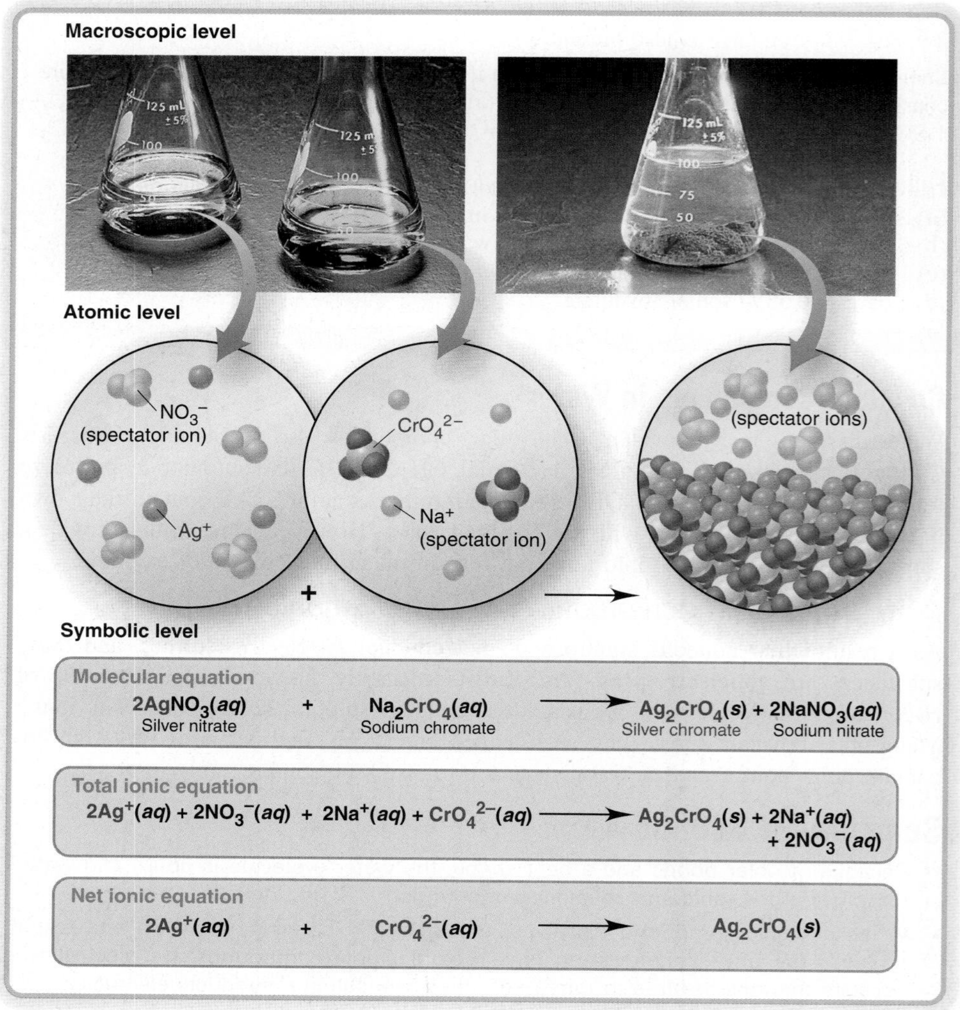

Figure 4.4 An aqueous ionic reaction and the three types of equations.

- The **total ionic equation** (*middle*) is much more accurate because *it shows all the soluble ionic substances dissociated into ions.* The $Ag_2CrO_4(s)$ stands out as the only undissociated substance:

$$2Ag^+(aq) + 2NO_3^-(aq) + 2Na^+(aq) + CrO_4^{2-}(aq) \longrightarrow Ag_2CrO_4(s) + 2Na^+(aq) + 2NO_3^-(aq)$$

  The charges also balance: four positive and four negative for a net zero charge on the left side, and two positive and two negative for a net zero charge on the right.

  Notice that $Na^+(aq)$ and $NO_3^-(aq)$ appear unchanged on both sides of the equation. These are called **spectator ions** (shown with pale colors in the atomic-level scenes). They are not involved in the actual chemical change but are present only as part of the reactants; that is, we can't add an Ag^+ ion without also adding an anion, in this case, the NO_3^- ion.

- The **net ionic equation** (*bottom*) is very useful because *it eliminates the spectator ions and shows only the actual chemical change:*

$$2Ag^+(aq) + CrO_4^{2-}(aq) \longrightarrow Ag_2CrO_4(s)$$

  The formation of solid silver chromate from silver ions and chromate ions *is* the only change. To make that point clearly, suppose we had mixed solutions of potassium chromate, $K_2CrO_4(aq)$, and silver acetate, $AgC_2H_3O_2(aq)$, instead of sodium chromate and silver nitrate. The three ionic equations would be

  Molecular: $2AgC_2H_3O_2(aq) + K_2CrO_4(aq) \longrightarrow Ag_2CrO_4(s) + 2KC_2H_3O_2(aq)$

  Total ionic: $2Ag^+(aq) + 2C_2H_3O_2^-(aq) + 2K^+(aq) + CrO_4^{2-}(aq) \longrightarrow Ag_2CrO_4(s) + 2K^+(aq) + 2C_2H_3O_2(aq)$

  Net ionic: $2Ag^+(aq) + CrO_4^{2-}(aq) \longrightarrow Ag_2CrO_4(s)$

  Thus, the same change would have occurred, and only the spectator ions would differ—$K^+(aq)$ and $C_2H_3O_2^-(aq)$ instead of $Na^+(aq)$ and $NO_3^-(aq)$.

Next, we'll apply these types of equations to three important classes of chemical reactions—precipitation, acid-base, and oxidation-reduction.

Summary of Section 4.2

- A molecular equation shows all substances intact and undissociated into ions.
- A total ionic equation shows all soluble ionic compounds as separate, solvated ions. Spectator ions appear unchanged on both sides of the equation.
- A net ionic equation eliminates the spectator ions and, thus, shows only the actual chemical change.

4.3 • PRECIPITATION REACTIONS

Precipitation reactions occur commonly in both nature and commerce. Coral reefs and some gems and minerals form, in part, through this process. And the chemical industry employs precipitation methods to make several important inorganic compounds.

The Key Event: Formation of a Solid from Dissolved Ions

In a **precipitation reaction,** two soluble ionic compounds react to form an insoluble product, a **precipitate.** The reaction you saw between silver nitrate and sodium chromate is one example. Precipitates form for the same reason that some ionic compounds don't dissolve: the electrostatic attraction between the ions outweighs the tendency of the ions to remain solvated and move throughout the solution. When the two solutions are mixed, the ions collide and stay together, and a solid product "comes out of solution." Thus, the key event in a precipitation reaction is *the formation of an insoluble product through the net removal of ions from solution.* Figure 4.5 (*on the next page*) shows the process for calcium fluoride.

Figure 4.5 The precipitation of calcium fluoride. When aqueous solutions of NaF (from pipet) and $CaCl_2$ (in test tube) react, solid CaF_2 forms (water molecules are omitted for clarity).

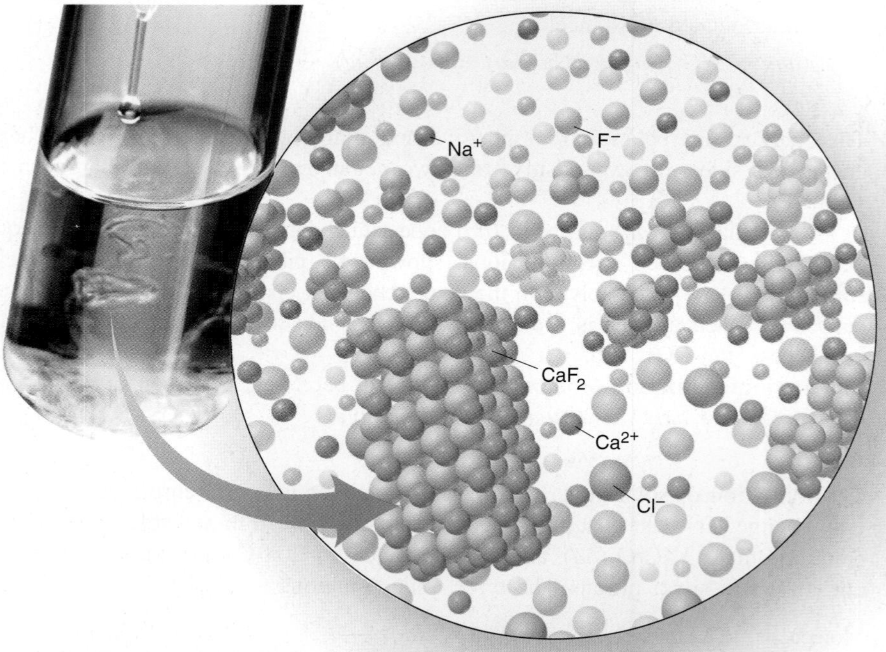

Molecular

$$CaCl_2(aq) + 2NaF(aq) \longrightarrow CaF_2(s) + 2NaCl(aq)$$

Total ionic

$$Ca^{2+}(aq) + 2Cl^-(aq) + 2Na^+(aq) + 2F^-(aq) \longrightarrow CaF_2(s) + 2Na^+(aq) + 2Cl^-(aq)$$

Net ionic

$$Ca^{2+}(aq) + 2F^-(aq) \longrightarrow CaF_2(s)$$

Predicting Whether a Precipitate Will Form

To predict whether a precipitate will form when you mix two aqueous ionic solutions, we refer to the short list of solubility rules in Table 4.1. Let's see how to apply these rules. When sodium iodide and potassium nitrate are each dissolved in water, their solutions consist of solvated, dispersed ions:

$$NaI(s) \xrightarrow{H_2O} Na^+(aq) + I^-(aq)$$
$$KNO_3(s) \xrightarrow{H_2O} K^+(aq) + NO_3^-(aq)$$

Three steps help us predict if a precipitate forms:

1. *Note the ions in the reactants.* The reactant ions are
$$Na^+(aq) + I^-(aq) + K^+(aq) + NO_3^-(aq) \longrightarrow ?$$
2. *Consider all possible cation-anion combinations.* In addition to NaI and KNO_3, which we know are soluble, the other cation-anion combinations are $NaNO_3$ and KI.
3. *Decide whether any combination is insoluble.* According to Table 4.1, no reaction occurs because all the combinations—NaI, KNO_3, $NaNO_3$, and KI—are soluble: Rules 1 and 2 say all compounds of Group 1A(1) ions and all nitrates are soluble.

Now, what happens if we substitute a solution of lead(II) nitrate, $Pb(NO_3)_2$, for the KNO_3 solution? The reactant ions are Na^+, I^-, Pb^{2+}, and NO_3^-. In addition to the two soluble reactants, NaI and $Pb(NO_3)_2$, the other two possible cation-anion combinations are $NaNO_3$ and PbI_2. According to Table 4.1, $NaNO_3$ is soluble

Table 4.1 Solubility Rules for Ionic Compounds in Water

Soluble Ionic Compounds	Insoluble Ionic Compounds
1. All common compounds of Group 1A(1) ions (Li^+, Na^+, K^+, etc.) and ammonium ion (NH_4^+) are soluble.	1. All common metal hydroxides are insoluble, *except* those of Group 1A(1) and the larger members of Group 2A(2) (beginning with Ca^{2+}).
2. All common nitrates (NO_3^-), acetates (CH_3COO^- or $C_2H_3O_2^-$), and most perchlorates (ClO_4^-) are soluble.	2. All common carbonates (CO_3^{2-}) and phosphates (PO_4^{3-}) are insoluble, *except* those of Group 1A(1) and NH_4^+.
3. All common chlorides (Cl^-), bromides (Br^-), and iodides (I^-) are soluble, *except* those of Ag^+, Pb^{2+}, Cu^+, and Hg_2^{2+}. All common fluorides (F^-) are soluble, *except* those of Pb^{2+} and Group 2A(2).	3. All common sulfides are insoluble except those of Group 1A(1), Group 2A(2), and NH_4^+.
4. All common sulfates (SO_4^{2-}) are soluble, except those of Ca^{2+}, Sr^{2+}, Ba^{2+}, Ag^+, and Pb^{2+}.	

(Rule 1), but PbI_2 is *not* (Rule 3). The total ionic equation shows the reaction that occurs as Pb^{2+} and I^- ions collide and form a precipitate:

$$2Na^+(aq) + 2I^-(aq) + Pb^{2+}(aq) + 2NO_3^-(aq) \longrightarrow 2Na^+(aq) + 2NO_3^-(aq) + PbI_2(s)$$

And the net ionic equation confirms it:

$$Pb^{2+}(aq) + 2I^-(aq) \longrightarrow PbI_2(s)$$

Metathesis Reactions The molecular equation for the reaction between $Pb(NO_3)_2$ and NaI shows *the ions exchanging partners* (Figure 4.6):

$$2NaI(aq) + Pb(NO_3)_2(aq) \longrightarrow PbI_2(s) + 2NaNO_3(aq)$$

Such reactions are called *double-displacement reactions,* or **metathesis** (pronounced *meh-TA-thuh-sis*) **reactions.** Several are important in industry, including the preparation of silver bromide for the manufacture of black-and-white film:

$$AgNO_3(aq) + KBr(aq) \longrightarrow AgBr(s) + KNO_3(aq)$$

The reactions that form Ag_2CrO_4 (Figure 4.4) and CaF_2 (Figure 4.5) are metathesis, too. Sample Problems 4.2 and 4.3 provide practice in predicting if a precipitate forms.

$2NaI(aq) + Pb(NO_3)_2(aq) \longrightarrow PbI_2(s) + 2NaNO_3(aq)$

Figure 4.6 The precipitation of PbI_2, a metathesis reaction.

Sample Problem 4.3 Predicting Whether a Precipitation Reaction Occurs; Writing Ionic Equations

Problem Does a reaction occur when each of these pairs of solutions is mixed? If so, write balanced molecular, total ionic, and net ionic equations, and identify the spectator ions.

(a) Potassium fluoride(aq) + strontium nitrate(aq) $\longrightarrow$

(b) Ammonium perchlorate(aq) + sodium bromide(aq) $\longrightarrow$

Plan We note the reactant ions, write the cation-anion combinations, and refer to Table 4.1 to see if any are insoluble. For the molecular equation, we predict the products and write them all as intact compounds. For the total ionic equation, we write the soluble compounds as separate ions. For the net ionic equation, we eliminate the spectator ions.

Solution (a) In addition to the reactants, the two other ion combinations are strontium fluoride and potassium nitrate. Table 4.1 shows that strontium fluoride is insoluble, so a reaction *does* occur. Writing the molecular equation:

$$2KF(aq) + Sr(NO_3)_2(aq) \longrightarrow SrF_2(s) + 2KNO_3(aq)$$

Writing the total ionic equation:

$$2K^+(aq) + 2F^-(aq) + Sr^{2+}(aq) + 2NO_3^-(aq) \longrightarrow SrF_2(s) + 2K^+(aq) + 2NO_3^-(aq)$$

Writing the net ionic equation:

$$Sr^{2+}(aq) + 2F^-(aq) \longrightarrow SrF_2(s)$$

The spectator ions are K^+ and NO_3^-.

(b) The other ion combinations are ammonium bromide and sodium perchlorate. Table 4.1 shows that all ammonium, sodium, and most perchlorate compounds are soluble, and all bromides are soluble except those of Ag^+, Pb^{2+}, Cu^+, and Hg_2^{2+}. Therefore, ***no*** reaction occurs. The compounds remain as solvated ions.

Follow-Up Problem 4.3 Predict whether a reaction occurs, and if so, write balanced total and net ionic equations:
(a) Iron(III) chloride(*aq*) + cesium phosphate(*aq*) ⟶
(b) Sodium hydroxide(*aq*) + cadmium nitrate(*aq*) ⟶
(c) Magnesium bromide(*aq*) + potassium acetate(*aq*) ⟶
(d) Silver nitrate(*aq*) + barium chloride(*aq*) ⟶

Sample Problem 4.4 Using Molecular Depictions in Precipitation Reactions

Problem The molecular views below show reactant solutions for a precipitation reaction (with ions shown as colored spheres and water omitted for clarity):

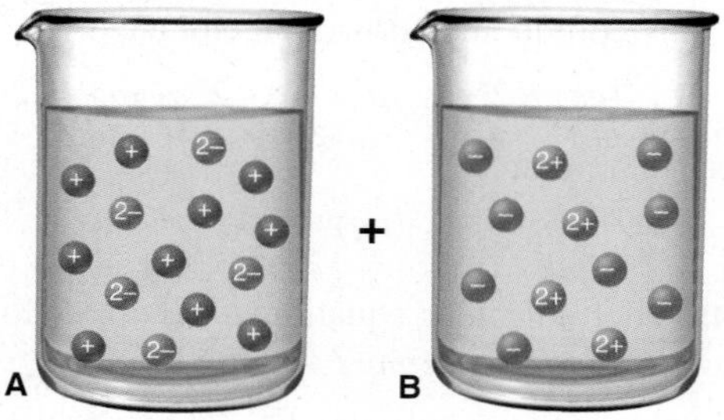

(a) Which compound is dissolved in beaker A: KCl, Na_2SO_4, $MgBr_2$, or Ag_2SO_4?
(b) Which compound is dissolved in beaker B: NH_4NO_3, $MgSO_4$, $Ba(NO_3)_2$, or CaF_2?
(c) Name the precipitate and the spectator ions when solutions A and B are mixed, and write balanced molecular, total ionic, and net ionic equations for any reaction.
(d) If each particle represents 0.010 mol of ions, what is the maximum mass (g) of precipitate that can form (assuming complete reaction)?

Plan (a) and **(b)** From the depictions, we note the charge and number of each kind of ion and use Table 4.1 to determine the ion combinations that are soluble. **(c)** Once we know the combinations, Table 4.1 tells which two ions form the solid, so the other two are spectator ions. **(d)** This part is a limiting-reactant problem because the amounts of two species are involved. We count the number of each kind of ion that formed the solid. We multiply the number of each reactant ion by 0.010 mol and calculate the amount (mol) of product formed from each. Whichever ion forms less is limiting, so we use the molar mass of the precipitate to find mass (g).

Solution (a) In solution A, there are two 1+ particles for each 2− particle. Therefore, the dissolved compound cannot be KCl or $MgBr_2$. Of the remaining two choices, Ag_2SO_4 is insoluble, so the dissolved compound must be Na_2SO_4.
(b) In solution B, there are two 1− particles for each 2+ particle. Therefore, the dissolved compound cannot be NH_4NO_3 or $MgSO_4$. Of the remaining two choices, CaF_2 is insoluble, so the dissolved compound must be $Ba(NO_3)_2$.
(c) Of the two possible ion combinations, $BaSO_4$ and $NaNO_3$, $BaSO_4$ is insoluble, so Na^+ and NO_3^- are spectator ions.

Molecular: $Ba(NO_3)_2(aq) + Na_2SO_4(aq) \longrightarrow BaSO_4(s) + 2NaNO_3(aq)$

Total ionic: $Ba^{2+}(aq) + 2NO_3^-(aq) + 2Na^+(aq) + SO_4^{2-}(aq) \longrightarrow BaSO_4(s) + 2NO_3^-(aq) + 2Na^+(aq)$

Net ionic: $Ba^{2+}(aq) + SO_4^{2-}(aq) \longrightarrow BaSO_4(s)$

(d) Finding the ion that is the limiting reactant:

For Ba^{2+}:

$$\text{Amount (mol) of } BaSO_4 = 4\ \cancel{Ba^{2+}\text{ particles}} \times \frac{0.010\ \cancel{\text{mol } Ba^{2+}\text{ ion}}}{1\ \cancel{\text{particle}}} \times \frac{1\text{ mol } BaSO_4}{1\ \cancel{\text{mol } Ba^{2+}\text{ ions}}}$$
$$= 0.040 \text{ mol } BaSO_4$$

For SO_4^{2-}:

$$\text{Amount (mol) of } BaSO_4 = 5\ \cancel{SO_4^{2-}\text{ particles}} \times \frac{0.010\ \cancel{\text{mol } SO_4^{2-}\text{ ions}}}{1\ \cancel{\text{particle}}} \times \frac{1\text{ mol } BaSO_4}{1\ \cancel{\text{mol } SO_4^{2-}\text{ ions}}}$$

$$= 0.050\text{ mol } BaSO_4$$

Therefore, Ba^{2+} ion is the limiting reactant.

Calculating the mass (g) of product ($\mathcal{M}$ of $BaSO_4$ = 233.4 g/mol):

$$\text{Mass (g) of } BaSO_4 = 0.040\ \cancel{\text{mol } BaSO_4} \times \frac{233.4\text{ g } BaSO_4}{1\ \cancel{\text{mol } BaSO_4}} = 9.3\text{ g } BaSO_4$$

Check Counting the number of Ba^{2+} ions allows a more direct calculation for a check: four Ba^{2+} particles means the maximum mass of $BaSO_4$ that can form is

$$\text{Mass (g) of } BaSO_4 = 4\ \cancel{Ba^{2+}\text{ particles}} \times \frac{0.010\ \cancel{\text{mol } Ba^{2+}\text{ ions}}}{1\ \cancel{\text{particle}}} \times \frac{1\ \cancel{\text{mol } BaSO_4}}{1\ \cancel{\text{mol } Ba^{2+}\text{ ions}}} \times \frac{233.4\text{ g } BaSO_4}{1\ \cancel{\text{mol}}} = 9.3\text{ g } BaSO_4$$

Follow-Up Problem 4.4 Molecular views of the reactant solutions for a precipitation reaction are shown below (with ions represented as spheres and water molecules omitted):

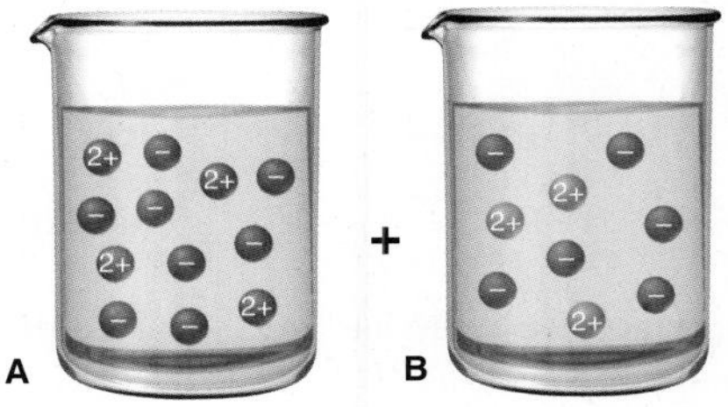

(a) Which compound is dissolved in beaker A: $Zn(NO_3)_2$, KCl, Na_2SO_4, or $PbCl_2$?
(b) Which compound is dissolved in beaker B: $(NH_4)_2SO_4$, $Cd(OH)_2$, $Ba(OH)_2$, or KNO_3?
(c) Name the precipitate and the spectator ions when solutions A and B are mixed, and write balanced molecular, total ionic, and net ionic equations for the reaction.
(d) If each particle represents 0.050 mol of ions, what is the maximum mass (g) of precipitate that can form (assuming complete reaction)?

Summary of Section 4.3

- In a precipitation reaction, an insoluble ionic compound forms when solutions of two soluble ones are mixed. The electrostatic attraction between certain pairs of solvated ions is strong enough to overcome the attraction of each ion for water.
- Based on a set of solubility rules, we can predict the formation of a precipitate by noting which of all possible cation-anion combinations is insoluble.

4.4 • ACID-BASE REACTIONS

Aqueous acid-base reactions occur in processes as diverse as the metabolic action of proteins, the industrial production of fertilizer, and the revitalization of lakes damaged by acid rain.

These reactions involve water as reactant or product, in addition to its common role as solvent. Of course, an **acid-base reaction** (also called a **neutralization reaction**) occurs when an acid reacts with a base, but the definitions of these terms and the scope of this reaction class have changed over the years. For our purposes at this point, we'll use definitions that apply to substances found commonly in the lab:

- *An* ***acid*** *is a substance that produces H^+ ions when dissolved in water.*

$$HX \xrightarrow{H_2O} H^+(aq) + X^-(aq)$$

- *A* ***base*** *is a substance that produces OH^- ions when dissolved in water.*

$$MOH \xrightarrow{H_2O} M^+(aq) + OH^-(aq)$$

(Other definitions are presented later in this section and in Chapter 18.)

Acids and the Solvated Proton *Acidic solutions arise when certain covalent H-containing molecules dissociate into ions in water.* In every case, these molecules contain a *polar bond to H* in which the other atom pulls much more strongly on the electron pair. A good example is HBr. The Br end of the H—Br bond is partially negative, and the H end is partially positive. When hydrogen bromide gas dissolves in water, the poles of H_2O molecules are attracted to the oppositely charged poles of the HBr. The bond breaks, with H becoming the solvated cation $H^+(aq)$ and Br becoming the solvated anion $Br^-(aq)$:

$$HBr(g) \xrightarrow{H_2O} H^+(aq) + Br^-(aq)$$

The solvated H^+ ion is a very unusual species. The H atom is a proton surrounded by an electron, so H^+ is just a proton. With a full positive charge concentrated in such a tiny volume, H^+ attracts the negative pole of water molecules so strongly that it forms a covalent bond to one of them. We can show this interaction by writing the solvated H^+ ion as an H_3O^+ ion (hydronium ion) that also is solvated:

$$HBr(g) + H_2O(l) \longrightarrow H_3O^+(aq) + Br^-(aq)$$

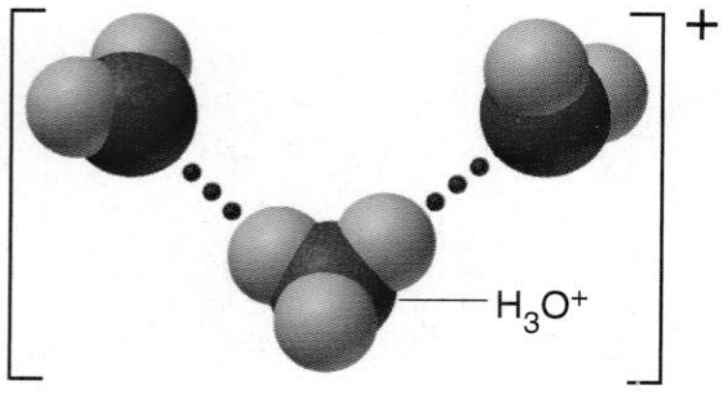

Figure 4.7 The H^+ ion as a solvated hydronium ion.

The hydronium ion, which we write as H_3O^+ [or $(H_2O)H^+$], associates with other water molecules to give species such as $H_5O_2^+$ [or $(H_2O)_2H^+$], $H_7O_3^+$ [or $(H_2O)_3H^+$], $H_9O_4^+$ [or $(H_2O)_4H^+$], and so forth. Figure 4.7 shows $H_7O_3^+$, an H_3O^+ ion associated *(dotted lines)* with two H_2O molecules. As a general notation for these various species, we write $H^+(aq)$, but later in this chapter and in much of the text, we'll use $H_3O^+(aq)$.

Table 4.2 Strong and Weak Acids and Bases

Acids

Strong
Hydrochloric acid, HCl
Hydrobromic acid, HBr
Hydriodic acid, HI
Nitric acid, HNO_3
Sulfuric acid, H_2SO_4
Perchloric acid, $HClO_4$

Weak (a few of many examples)
Hydrofluoric acid, HF
Phosphoric acid, H_3PO_4
Acetic acid, CH_3COOH (or $HC_2H_3O_2$)

Bases

Strong
Group 1A(1) hydroxides:
Lithium hydroxide, LiOH
Sodium hydroxide, NaOH
Potassium hydroxide, KOH
Rubidium hydroxide, RbOH
Cesium hydroxide, CsOH

Heavy Group 2A(2) hydroxides:
Calcium hydroxide, $Ca(OH)_2$
Strontium hydroxide, $Sr(OH)_2$
Barium hydroxide, $Ba(OH)_2$

Weak (one of many examples)
Ammonia, NH_3

Acids and Bases as Electrolytes Acids and bases are categorized in terms of their "strength," the degree to which they dissociate into ions in water (Table 4.2):

- *Strong acids and strong bases dissociate completely into ions.* Therefore, like soluble ionic compounds, they are *strong* electrolytes and conduct a large current, as shown by the brightly lit bulb (Figure 4.8A).
- *Weak acids and weak bases dissociate very little into ions.* Most of their molecules remain intact. Therefore, they are *weak* electrolytes, which means they conduct a small current (Figure 4.8B).

Because a strong acid (or strong base) dissociates completely, we can find the molarity of H^+ (or OH^-) and the amount (mol) or number of each ion in solution. (You'll see how to determine these quantities for weak acids in Chapter 18.)

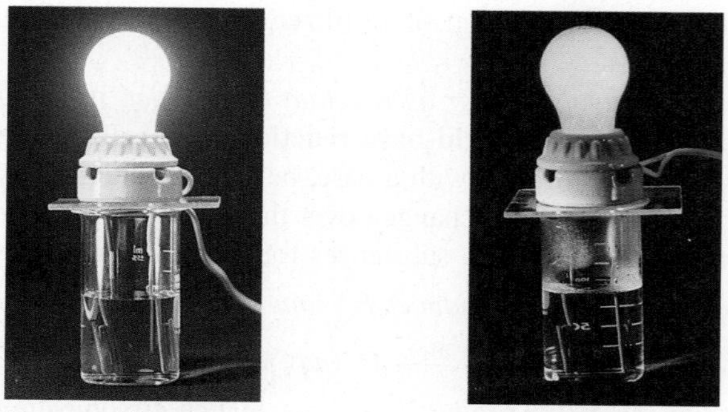

A Strong acid (or base) = strong electrolyte

B Weak acid (or base) = weak electrolyte

Figure 4.8 Acids and bases as electrolytes.

Sample Problem 4.5 Determining the Number of H^+ (or OH^-) Ions in Solution

Problem Nitric acid is a major chemical in the fertilizer and explosives industries. How many $H^+(aq)$ ions are in 25.3 mL of 1.4 *M* nitric acid?

Plan We know the volume (25.3 mL) and molarity (1.4 *M*) of nitric acid, and we need the number of $H^+(aq)$. We convert from mL to L and multiply by the molarity to find the amount (mol) of acid. Table 4.2 shows that nitric acid is a strong acid, so it dissociates completely. With the formula, we write a dissociation equation, which shows the amount (mol) of H^+ ions per mole of acid. We multiply that amount by Avogadro's number to find the number of $H^+(aq)$ ions (see the road map).

Road Map

Volume (mL) of HNO_3

↓ 10^3 mL = 1 L

Volume (L) of HNO_3

↓ multiply by *M* (mol/L)

Amount (mol) of HNO_3

↓ mol of H^+/mol of HNO_3

Amount (mol) of H^+ ions

↓ multiply by Avogadro's number

No. of H^+ ions

Solution Finding the amount (mol) of nitric acid:

$$\text{Amount (mol) of } HNO_3 = 25.3\ \cancel{\text{mL}} \times \frac{1\ \cancel{\text{L}}}{1000\ \cancel{\text{mL}}} \times \frac{1.4\ \text{mol}}{1\ \cancel{\text{L}}} = 0.035\ \text{mol}$$

Nitric acid is HNO_3, so we have:

$$HNO_3(l) \xrightarrow{H_2O} H^+(aq) + NO_3^-(aq)$$

Finding the number of H^+ ions:

$$\text{No. of } H^+ \text{ ions} = 0.035\ \cancel{\text{mol HNO}_3} \times \frac{1\ \cancel{\text{mol H}^+}}{1\ \cancel{\text{mol HNO}_3}} \times \frac{6.022\times10^{23}\ H^+\ \text{ions}}{1\ \cancel{\text{mol H}^+}}$$

$$= 2.1\times10^{22}\ H^+\ \text{ions}$$

Check The number of moles seems correct: 0.025 L × 1.4 mol/L = 0.035 mol, and multiplying by 6×10^{23} ions/mol gives 2×10^{22} ions.

Follow-Up Problem 4.5 How many moles of $OH^-(aq)$ are present in 451 mL of 1.20 *M* potassium hydroxide?

Structural Features of Acids and Bases A key structural feature appears in common laboratory acids and bases:

- *Acids.* Strong acids, such as HNO_3 and H_2SO_4, and weak acids, such as HF and H_3PO_4, have one or more H atoms as part of their structure, which are either completely released (strong) or partially released (weak) as protons in water.
- *Bases.* Strong bases have either OH^- (e.g., NaOH) or O^{2-} (e.g., K_2O) as part of their structure. The oxide ion is not stable in water and reacts to form OH^- ion:

$$O^{2-}(s) + H_2O(l) \longrightarrow 2OH^-(aq) \quad \text{so} \quad K_2O(s) + H_2O(l) \longrightarrow 2K^+(aq) + 2OH^-(aq)$$

Weak bases, such as ammonia, do not contain OH^- ions, but, as you'll see in later chapters, they all have an electron pair on N. Weak bases produce OH^- ions in a reaction that occurs to a small extent in water:

$$NH_3(g) + H_2O(l) \rightleftharpoons NH_4^+(aq) + OH^-(aq)$$

(The reaction arrow in the preceding equation indicates that the reaction proceeds in both directions; we'll discuss this important idea further in Section 4.7.)

The Key Event: Formation of H_2O from H^+ and OH^-

To see the key event in acid-base reactions, we'll write the three types of aqueous ionic equations (with color) and focus on the reaction between the strong acid HCl and the strong base $Ba(OH)_2$:

- The molecular equation is

$$2HCl(aq) + Ba(OH)_2(aq) \longrightarrow BaCl_2(aq) + 2H_2O(l)$$

- HCl and $Ba(OH)_2$ dissociate completely, so the total ionic equation is

$$2H^+(aq) + 2Cl^-(aq) + Ba^{2+}(aq) + 2OH^-(aq) \longrightarrow Ba^{2+}(aq) + 2Cl^-(aq) + 2H_2O(l)$$

- In the net ionic equation, we eliminate the spectator ions, $Ba^{2+}(aq)$ and $Cl^-(aq)$:

$$2H^+(aq) + 2OH^-(aq) \longrightarrow 2H_2O(l) \quad \text{or} \quad H^+(aq) + OH^-(aq) \longrightarrow H_2O(l)$$

Thus, *the key event in aqueous reactions between a strong acid and a strong base is that an H^+ ion from the acid and an OH^- ion from the base form a water molecule.* Only the spectator ions differ from one strong acid–strong base reaction to another.

Like precipitation reactions, acid-base reactions occur through *the electrostatic attraction of ions and their removal from solution as the product.* In this case, rather than an insoluble ionic solid, the product is H_2O, which consists almost entirely of undissociated molecules. Actually, water molecules dissociate *very* slightly (which, as you'll see in Chapter 18, is very important), but the formation of water in an acid-base reaction results in an enormous net removal of H^+ and OH^- ions.

The molecular and total ionic equations above show that if you evaporate the water, the spectator ions remain: the ionic compound that results from the reaction of an acid and a base is called a **salt,** which in this case is barium chloride. Thus, in an aqueous neutralization reaction, *an acid and a base form a salt solution and water:*

$$\underset{\text{acid}}{HX(aq)} + \underset{\text{base}}{MOH(aq)} \longrightarrow \underset{\text{salt}}{MX(aq)} + \underset{\text{water}}{H_2O(l)}$$

Note that *the cation of the salt comes from the base and the anion from the acid.*

Acid-base reactions, like precipitation reactions, are metathesis (double-displacement) reactions. The reaction of aluminum hydroxide, the active ingredient in some antacids, with HCl, the major component of stomach acid, is another example:

$$3HCl(aq) + Al(OH)_3(s) \longrightarrow AlCl_3(aq) + 3H_2O(l)$$

Sample Problem 4.6 Writing Ionic Equations for Acid-Base Reactions

Problem Write balanced molecular, total ionic, and net ionic equations for each of the following acid-base reactions and identify the spectator ions:

(a) Hydrochloric acid(aq) + potassium hydroxide(aq) $\longrightarrow$

(b) Strontium hydroxide(aq) + perchloric acid(aq) $\longrightarrow$

(c) Barium hydroxide(aq) + sulfuric acid(aq) $\longrightarrow$

Plan All are strong acids and bases (see Table 4.2), so the actual reaction is between H^+ and OH^-. The products are H_2O and a salt solution of spectator ions. In (c), we note that the salt ($BaSO_4$) is insoluble (see Table 4.1), so there are no spectator ions.

Solution (a) Writing the molecular equation:

$$HCl(aq) + KOH(aq) \longrightarrow KCl(aq) + H_2O(l)$$

Writing the total ionic equation:

$$H^+(aq) + Cl^-(aq) + K^+(aq) + OH^-(aq) \longrightarrow K^+(aq) + Cl^-(aq) + H_2O(l)$$

Writing the net ionic equation:

$$H^+(aq) + OH^-(aq) \longrightarrow H_2O(l)$$

$K^+(aq)$ and $Cl^-(aq)$ are the spectator ions.

(b) Writing the molecular equation:

$$Sr(OH)_2(aq) + 2HClO_4(aq) \longrightarrow Sr(ClO_4)_2(aq) + 2H_2O(l)$$

Writing the total ionic equation:

$$Sr^{2+}(aq) + 2OH^-(aq) + 2H^+(aq) + 2ClO_4^-(aq) \longrightarrow Sr^{2+}(aq) + 2ClO_4^-(aq) + 2H_2O(l)$$

Writing the net ionic equation:

$$2OH^-(aq) + 2H^+(aq) \longrightarrow 2H_2O(l) \quad \text{or} \quad OH^-(aq) + H^+(aq) \longrightarrow H_2O(l)$$

$Sr^{2+}(aq)$ and $ClO_4^-(aq)$ are the spectator ions.

(c) Writing the molecular equation:

$$Ba(OH)_2(aq) + H_2SO_4(aq) \longrightarrow BaSO_4(s) + 2H_2O(l)$$

Writing the total ionic equation:

$$Ba^{2+}(aq) + 2OH^-(aq) + 2H^+(aq) + SO_4^{2-}(aq) \longrightarrow BaSO_4(s) + 2H_2O(l)$$

This is a neutralization *and* a precipitation reaction, so the net ionic equation is the same as the total ionic. There are no spectator ions, because they appear in the solid.

Follow-Up Problem 4.6 Write balanced molecular, total ionic, and net ionic equations for the reaction between aqueous solutions of calcium hydroxide and nitric acid.

Proton Transfer in Acid-Base Reactions

When we take a closer look (with color) at the reaction between a strong acid and strong base, as well as several related reactions, a unifying pattern appears. Let's examine three types of reaction to gain insight about this pattern.

Reaction Between Strong Acid and Strong Base When HCl gas dissolves in water, the H^+ ion ends up bonded to a water molecule. Thus, hydrochloric acid actually consists of solvated H_3O^+ and Cl^- ions:

$$HCl(g) + H_2O(l) \longrightarrow H_3O^+(aq) + Cl^-(aq)$$

If we add NaOH solution, the total ionic equation shows that H_3O^+ *transfers a proton* to OH^- (leaving a water molecule written as H_2O, and forming a water molecule written as HOH):

$$[H_3O^+(aq) + Cl^-(aq)] + [Na^+(aq) + OH^-(aq)] \xrightarrow{\text{H}^+ \text{ transfer}} H_2O(l) + Cl^-(aq) + Na^+(aq) + HOH(l)$$

Without the spectator ions, the net ionic equation shows more clearly the *transfer of a proton* from H_3O^+ to OH^-:

$$H_3O^+(aq) + OH^-(aq) \xrightarrow{\text{H}^+ \text{ transfer}} H_2O(l) + HOH(l) \qquad [\text{or } 2H_2O(l)]$$

This equation is identical to the one we saw earlier (see p. 147),

$$H^+(aq) + OH^-(aq) \longrightarrow H_2O(l)$$

with the additional H_2O molecule left over from the H_3O^+. Figure 4.9 shows this process on the atomic level and also shows that, if the water is evaporated, the spectator ions, Cl^- and Na^+, crystallize as the salt NaCl.

Figure 4.9 An aqueous strong acid–strong base reaction as a proton-transfer process.

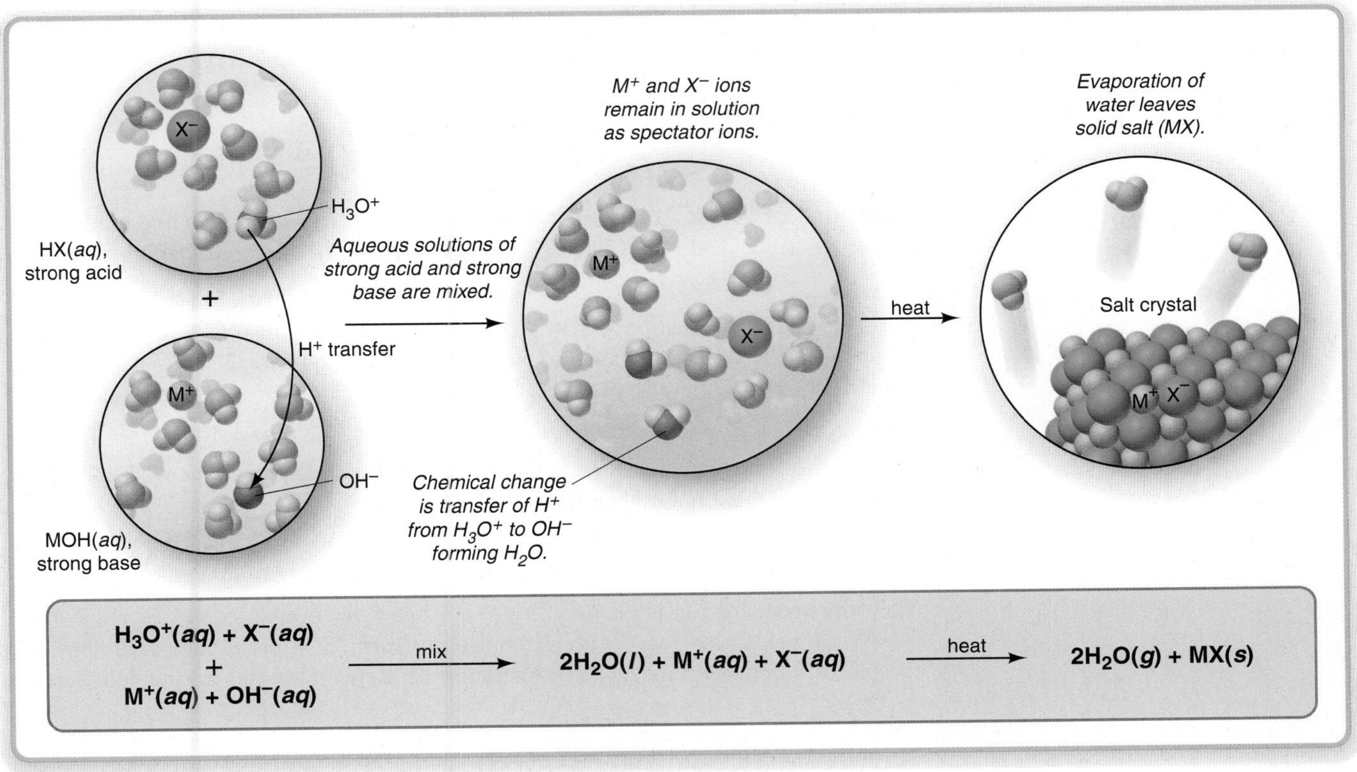

Thus, *an acid-base reaction is a proton-transfer process.* In the early 20th century, the chemists Johannes Brønsted and Thomas Lowry stated:

- *An acid is a molecule (or ion) that donates a proton.*
- *A base is a molecule (or ion) that accepts a proton.*

Therefore, in an aqueous reaction between strong acid and strong base, *H_3O^+ ion acts as the acid and donates a proton to OH^- ion, which acts as the base and accepts it.* (We discuss the Brønsted-Lowry concept thoroughly in Chapter 18.)

Gas-Forming Reactions: Acids with Carbonates (or Sulfites) When an ionic carbonate, such as K_2CO_3, is treated with an acid, such as HCl, one of the products is carbon dioxide, as the molecular equation shows:

$$2HCl(aq) + K_2CO_3(aq) \longrightarrow 2KCl(aq) + [H_2CO_3(aq)]$$
$$[H_2CO_3(aq)] \longrightarrow H_2O(l) + CO_2(g)$$

Square brackets around a species, in this case, H_2CO_3, mean it is very unstable: H_2CO_3 decomposes immediately into water and carbon dioxide. Combining these two equations (see Sample Problem 3.17, p. 106) cancels $[H_2CO_3]$ and gives the overall equation:

$$2HCl(aq) + K_2CO_3(aq) \longrightarrow 2KCl(aq) + H_2O(l) + CO_2(g)$$

Writing the total ionic equation with H_3O^+ ions from the HCl shows the actual species in solution and the key event in a gas-forming reaction, *removal of ions from solution through formation of both a gas* ***and*** *water:*

$$2H_3O^+(aq) + 2Cl^-(aq) + 2K^+(aq) + CO_3^{2-}(aq) \longrightarrow$$
$$2Cl^-(aq) + 2K^+(aq) + CO_2(g) + H_2O(l) + 2H_2O(l) \quad [\text{or } 3H_2O(l)]$$

Writing the net ionic equation, with the intermediate formation of H_2CO_3, eliminates the spectator ions, Cl^- and K^+, and makes it easier to see that *proton transfer* takes place as each of the two H_3O^+ ions transfers one proton to the carbonate ion:

$$\overset{\text{2H}^+ \text{ transfer}}{2H_3O^+(aq) + CO_3^{2-}(aq)} \longrightarrow [H_2CO_3(aq)] + 2H_2O(l) \longrightarrow$$
$$CO_2(g) + H_2O(l) + 2H_2O(l) \quad [\text{or } 3H_2O(l)]$$

In essence, this is an acid-base reaction with carbonate ion accepting the protons and, thus, acting as the base.

Ionic sulfites react similarly to form water and gaseous SO_2; the net ionic equation, in which SO_3^{2-} acts as the base and forms the unstable H_2SO_3, is

$$\overset{\text{2H}^+ \text{ transfer}}{2H_3O^+(aq) + SO_3^{2-}(aq)} \longrightarrow [H_2SO_3(aq)] + 2H_2O(l) \longrightarrow$$
$$SO_2(g) + H_2O(l) + 2H_2O(l) \quad [\text{or } 3H_2O(l)]$$

Reactions of Weak Acids with Bases When solutions of sodium hydroxide and the weak acid acetic acid (CH_3COOH, Table 4.2) are mixed, the molecular equation is

$$CH_3COOH(aq) + NaOH(aq) \longrightarrow CH_3COONa(aq) + H_2O(l)$$

The total ionic equation is written differently for the reaction of a weak acid. Because acetic acid is weak and, thus, dissociates very little, it appears as *undissociated, intact molecules:*

$$CH_3COOH(aq) + Na^+(aq) + OH^-(aq) \longrightarrow CH_3COO^-(aq) + Na^+(aq) + H_2O(l)$$

The net ionic equation reveals that proton transfer occurs here as well, but directly from the weak acid rather than from H_3O^+:

$$\overset{\text{H}^+ \text{ transfer}}{CH_3COOH(aq) + OH^-(aq)} \longrightarrow CH_3COO^-(aq) + H_2O(l)$$

The only spectator ion is $Na^+(aq)$.

Weak acids also react with carbonates to form CO_2, as Figure 4.10 shows for the reaction between vinegar (a 5% solution of acetic acid) and baking soda (sodium

Molecular equation

$$NaHCO_3(aq) + CH_3COOH(aq) \longrightarrow CH_3COONa(aq) + CO_2(g) + H_2O(l)$$

Total ionic equation

$$Na^+(aq) + HCO_3^-(aq) + CH_3COOH(aq) \longrightarrow CH_3COO^-(aq) + Na^+(aq) + CO_2(g) + H_2O(l)$$

Net ionic equation

$$HCO_3^-(aq) + CH_3COOH(aq) \longrightarrow CH_3COO^-(aq) + CO_2(g) + H_2O(l)$$

Figure 4.10 A gas-forming reaction with a weak acid. Note that the two ionic equations include acetic acid because it does *not* dissociate appreciably into ions.

hydrogen carbonate) solution. In fact, when stomach acid (mostly HCl) builds up, your duodenum releases the hormone secretin, which stimulates your pancreas to release HCO_3^- ions that react with the excess acid in an analogous reaction.

Sample Problem 4.7 Writing Proton-Transfer Equations for Acid-Base Reactions

Problem Write balanced total and net ionic equations for the following reactions and use curved arrows to show how the proton transfer occurs. For (a), give the name and formula of the salt present when the water evaporates. For (b), note that propionic acid (CH_3CH_2COOH) is a weak acid and identify the spectator ion(s).
(a) Hydriodic acid(*aq*) + calcium hydroxide(*aq*) ⟶
(b) Potassium hydroxide(*aq*) + propionic acid(*aq*) ⟶

Plan (a) The reactants are a strong acid and a strong base (Table 4.2), so the acidic species is H_3O^+, which transfers a proton to the OH^- from the base. The products are H_2O and a solution of spectator ions that becomes a solid salt when the water evaporates. **(b)** Since the acid is weak, it occurs as intact molecules in solution and transfers its proton to the OH^- from the base. The only spectator ion is the cation of the base.

Solution (a) Writing the total ionic equation:

$$2H_3O^+(aq) + 2I^-(aq) + Ca^{2+}(aq) + 2OH^-(aq) \longrightarrow 2I^-(aq) + Ca^{2+}(aq) + 4H_2O(l)$$

Writing the net ionic equation:

$$2H_3O^+(aq) + 2OH^-(aq) \longrightarrow 4H_2O(l) \quad \text{or} \quad H_3O^+(aq) + OH^-(aq) \longrightarrow 2H_2O(l)$$

$I^-(aq)$ and $Ca^{2+}(aq)$ are spectator ions, so the salt is calcium iodide, CaI_2.

(b) Writing the total ionic equation:

$$K^+(aq) + OH^-(aq) + CH_3CH_2COOH(aq) \longrightarrow K^+(aq) + H_2O(l) + CH_3CH_2COO^-(aq)$$

Writing the net ionic equation:

$$OH^-(aq) + CH_3CH_2COOH(aq) \longrightarrow H_2O(l) + CH_3CH_2COO^-(aq)$$

$K^+(aq)$ is the only spectator ion.

Follow-Up Problem 4.7 Write balanced total and net ionic equations for the reaction between aqueous solutions of calcium hydrogen carbonate and hydrobromic acid. Use a curved arrow in the net ionic equation to show the proton transfer. Give the name and formula of the salt that is present when the water evaporates.

Figure 4.11 An acid-base titration.

$$H^+(aq) + X^-(aq) + M^+(aq) + OH^-(aq) \longrightarrow H_2O(l) + M^+(aq) + X^-(aq)$$

Quantifying Acid-Base Reactions by Titration

In any **titration,** *the known concentration of one solution is used to determine the unknown concentration of another.* In a typical acid-base titration, a *standardized* solution of base, one whose concentration is *known,* is added to a solution of acid whose concentration is *unknown (or vice versa).*

Figure 4.11A shows the laboratory setup for an acid-base titration with a known volume of acid and a few drops of indicator in a flask. An *acid-base indicator* is a substance whose color is different in acid than in base; the indicator used in the figure is phenolphthalein, which is pink in base and colorless in acid. (We examine indicators in Chapters 18 and 19.) Base is added from a buret, and the OH^- ions react with the H^+ ions. As the titration nears its end (Figure 4.11B), the drop of added base creates a temporary excess of OH^-, causing some indicator molecules to change to the basic color; they return to the acidic color when the flask is swirled. There are two key stages in the titration:

- The **equivalence point** occurs when *the amount (mol) of H^+ ions in the original volume of acid has reacted with the same amount (mol) of OH^- ions from the buret:*

  Amount (mol) of H^+ (originally in flask) = amount (mol) of OH^- (added from buret)
- The **end point** occurs when a tiny excess of OH^- ions changes the indicator permanently to its basic color (Figure 4.11C).

In calculations, such as in Sample Problem 4.8, we assume that this tiny excess of OH^- ions is insignificant and that *the amount of base needed to reach the end point is the same as the amount needed to reach the equivalence point.*

Sample Problem 4.8 Finding the Concentration of an Acid from a Titration

Problem To standardize an HCl solution, you put 50.00 mL of it in a flask with a few drops of indicator and put 0.1524 *M* NaOH in a buret. The buret reads 0.55 mL at the start and 33.87 mL at the end point. Find the molarity of the HCl solution.

Plan We have to find the molarity of the acid from the volume of acid (50.00 mL), the initial (0.55 mL) and final (33.87 mL) volumes of base, and the molarity of the base (0.1524 *M*). First, we balance the equation. The volume of added base is the difference in buret readings, and we use the base's molarity to calculate the amount (mol) of base. Then, we use the molar ratio from the balanced equation to find the amount (mol) of acid originally present and divide by the acid's original volume to find the molarity (see the road map).

Solution Writing the balanced equation:

$$NaOH(aq) + HCl(aq) \longrightarrow NaCl(aq) + H_2O(l)$$

Finding the volume (L) of NaOH solution added:

$$\text{Volume (L) of solution} = (33.87\ \text{mL soln} - 0.55\ \text{mL soln}) \times \frac{1\ \text{L}}{1000\ \text{mL}}$$
$$= 0.03332\ \text{L soln}$$

Finding the amount (mol) of NaOH added:

$$\text{Amount (mol) of NaOH} = 0.03332\ \text{L soln} \times \frac{0.1524\ \text{mol NaOH}}{1\ \text{L soln}}$$
$$= 5.078\times10^{-3}\ \text{mol NaOH}$$

Finding the amount (mol) of HCl originally present: Since the molar ratio is 1/1,

$$\text{Amount (mol) of HCl} = 5.078\times10^{-3}\ \text{mol NaOH} \times \frac{1\ \text{mol HCl}}{1\ \text{mol NaOH}} = 5.078\times10^{-3}\ \text{mol HCl}$$

Calculating the molarity of HCl:

$$\text{Molarity of HCl} = \frac{5.078\times10^{-3}\ \text{mol HCl}}{50.00\ \text{mL}} \times \frac{1000\ \text{mL}}{1\ \text{L}} = 0.1016\ M\ \text{HCl}$$

Check The answer makes sense: a large volume of less concentrated acid neutralized a small volume of more concentrated base. With rounding, the numbers of moles of H^+ and OH^- are about equal: 50 mL × 0.1 M H^+ = 0.005 mol = 33 mL × 0.15 M OH^-.

Follow-Up Problem 4.8 What volume of 0.1292 M $Ba(OH)_2$ would neutralize 50.00 mL of the HCl solution standardized in Sample Problem 4.8?

Road Map

Volume (L) of base (difference in buret readings)

↓ multiply by M (mol/L) of base

Amount (mol) of base

↓ molar ratio

Amount (mol) of acid

↓ divide by volume (L) of acid

M (mol/L) of acid

Summary of Section 4.4

- In an acid-base (neutralization) reaction between an acid (an H^+-yielding substance) and a base (an OH^--yielding substance), H^+ and OH^- ions form H_2O.
- Strong acids and bases dissociate completely in water (strong electrolytes); weak acids and bases dissociate slightly (weak electrolytes).
- An acid-base reaction involves the transfer of a proton from an acid (a species that donates an H^+) to a base (a species that accepts an H^+).
- A gas-forming acid-base reaction occurs when an acid transfers a proton to a carbonate (or sulfite), forming water and a gas that leaves the reaction mixture.
- Since weak acids dissociate very little, ionic equations show a weak acid as an intact molecule transferring its proton to the base.
- In a titration, the known concentration of one solution is used to determine the concentration of the other.

4.5 • OXIDATION-REDUCTION (REDOX) REACTIONS

Oxidation-reduction (redox) reactions include the formation of a compound from its elements (and the reverse process), all combustion processes, the generation of electricity in batteries, the production of cellular energy, and many others. In fact, redox reactions are so widespread that many do not occur in aqueous solution. In this section, we examine the key event in the redox process, discuss important terminology, see one way to balance redox equations, and learn how to quantify them.

The Key Event: Movement of Electrons Between Reactants

The key chemical event in an **oxidation-reduction** (or **redox**) **reaction** is the *net movement of electrons from one reactant to another*. The movement occurs from the reactant (or atom in the reactant) with *less* attraction for electrons to the reactant (or atom) with *more* attraction for electrons.

Figure 4.12 The redox process in the formation of (A) ionic and (B) covalent compounds from their elements.

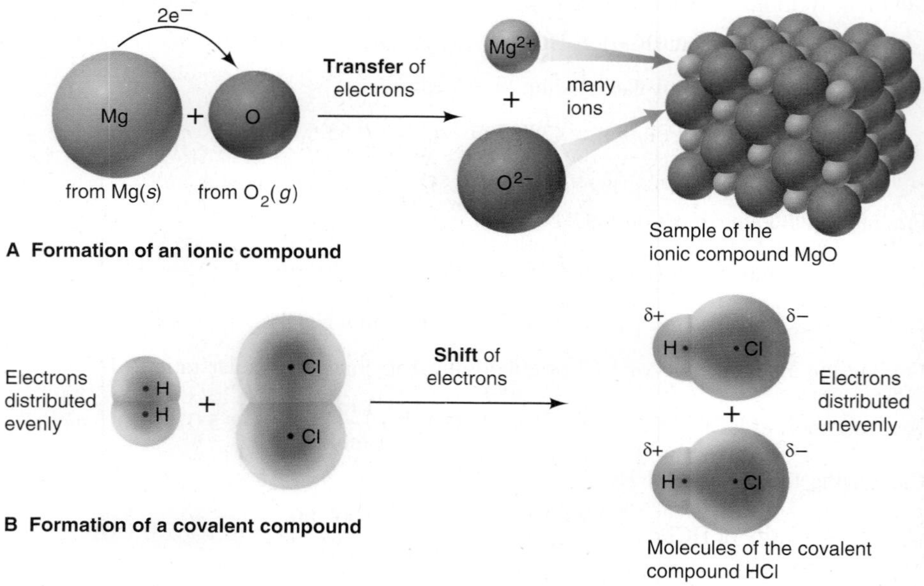

This process occurs in the formation of both ionic and covalent compounds:

- *Ionic compounds: transfer of electrons.* In the reaction that forms MgO from its elements (see Figure 3.7, p. 100), the balanced equation is

$$2Mg(s) + O_2(g) \longrightarrow 2MgO(s)$$

Figure 4.12A shows that each Mg atom loses two electrons and each O atom gains them. This loss and gain is a ***transfer*** *of electrons* away from each Mg atom to each O atom. The resulting Mg^{2+} and O^{2-} ions aggregate into an ionic solid.

- *Covalent compounds: shift of electrons.* During the formation of a covalent compound from its elements, there is more of a ***shift*** *of electrons* than a full transfer. Thus, *ions do not form.* Consider the formation of HCl gas:

$$H_2(g) + Cl_2(g) \longrightarrow 2HCl(g)$$

To see the electron movement, we'll compare the electron distribution in reactant and product. As Figure 4.12B shows, in H_2 and Cl_2, the electrons are shared equally between the atoms *(symmetrical shading).* Because the Cl atom attracts electrons more than the H atom, in HCl, the electrons are shared unequally *(asymmetrical shading).* Electrons shift away from H and toward Cl, so the Cl atom has more negative charge (*red* and $\delta-$) than it had in Cl_2, and the H atom has less negative charge (*blue* and $\delta+$) than it had in H_2.

Some Essential Redox Terminology

Certain key terms describe the process and explain the name of this reaction class:

- **Oxidation** is the *loss* of electrons.
- **Reduction** is the *gain* of electrons.

During the formation of MgO, Mg undergoes oxidation (loss of electrons), and O_2 undergoes reduction (gain of electrons). The loss and gain are simultaneous, but we can imagine them occurring separately:

Oxidation (electron loss by Mg): $Mg \longrightarrow Mg^{2+} + 2e^-$

Reduction (electron gain by O_2): $\frac{1}{2}O_2 + 2e^- \longrightarrow O^{2-}$

(Throughout the chapter, blue type indicates oxidation, and red type reduction.)

- The **oxidizing agent** is the species doing the oxidizing (causing the electron loss).
- The **reducing agent** is the species doing the reducing (causing the electron gain).

One reactant acts on the other. During the reaction that forms MgO, *O_2 oxidizes Mg,* so O_2 is the oxidizing agent, and *Mg reduces O_2,* so Mg is the reducing agent.

Note the give and take of electrons: O_2 takes the electrons that Mg gives up, or, put the other way around, Mg gives up the electrons that O_2 takes. This means that

- *The oxidizing agent is reduced:* it takes electrons (and, thus, gains them).
- *The reducing agent is oxidized:* it gives up electrons (and, thus, loses them).

In the formation of HCl, *Cl_2 oxidizes H_2* (H loses some electron charge and Cl gains it), which is the same as saying that *H_2 reduces Cl_2*. The reducing agent, H_2, is oxidized, and the oxidizing agent, Cl_2, is reduced.

Using Oxidation Numbers to Monitor Electron Charge

Chemists have devised a "bookkeeping" system to monitor which atom loses electron charge and which atom gains it: each atom in a molecule (or formula unit) is assigned an **oxidation number (O.N.),** or *oxidation state,* which is the charge the atom would have *if* electrons were transferred completely, not shared.

Each element in a binary *ionic* compound has a full charge because the atom transferred its electron(s), and so the atom's oxidation number equals the ionic charge. But, each element in a *covalent* compound (or in a polyatomic ion) has a partial charge because the electrons shifted away from one atom and toward the other. For these cases, we determine oxidation number by a set of rules (Table 4.3; you'll learn the atomic basis of the rules in Chapters 8 and 9).

An O.N. has the sign *before* the number (e.g., +2), whereas an ionic charge has the sign *after* the number (e.g., 2+). Also, unlike a unitary ionic charge, as in Na^+ or Cl^-, an O.N. of +1 or −1 retains the numeral. For example, we don't write the sodium ion as Na^{+1}, but the O.N. of the Na^+ ion is +1, not +.

Table 4.3 Rules for Assigning an Oxidation Number (O.N.)

General Rules

1. For an atom in its elemental form (Na, O_2, Cl_2, etc.): O.N. = 0
2. For a monatomic ion: O.N. = ion charge (with the sign *before* the numeral)
3. The sum of O.N. values for the atoms in a molecule or formula unit of a compound equals zero. The sum of O.N. values for the atoms in a polyatomic ion equals the ion's charge.

Rules for Specific Atoms or Periodic Table Groups

1. For Group 1A(1):	O.N. = +1 in all compounds
2. For Group 2A(2):	O.N. = +2 in all compounds
3. For hydrogen:	O.N. = +1 in combination with nonmetals
	O.N. = −1 in combination with metals and boron
4. For fluorine:	O.N. = −1 in all compounds
5. For oxygen:	O.N. = −1 in peroxides
	O.N. = −2 in all other compounds (except with F)
6. For Group 7A(17):	O.N. = −1 in combination with metals, nonmetals (except O), and other halogens lower in the group

Sample Problem 4.9 Determining the Oxidation Number of Each Element in a Compound (or Ion)

Problem Determine the oxidation number (O.N.) of each element in these species:
(a) Zinc chloride **(b)** Sulfur trioxide **(c)** Nitric acid **(d)** Dichromate ion

Plan We determine the formulas and consult Table 4.3, including the general rules that the O.N. values for a compound add up to zero and those for a polyatomic ion add up to the ion's charge.

Solution (a) $ZnCl_2$. The sum of O.N.s must equal zero. The O.N. of the Zn^{2+} ion is +2, so the O.N. of each Cl^- ion is −1, for a total of −2.
(b) SO_3. The O.N. of each oxygen is −2, for a total of −6. The O.N.s must add up to zero, so the O.N. of S is +6.

(c) HNO_3. The O.N. of H is +1, so the O.N.s of the atoms in NO_3^- must add up to −1 to equal the charge of the polyatomic ion and give zero for the compound. The O.N. of each O is −2, for a total of −6. Therefore, the O.N. of N is +5.
(d) $Cr_2O_7^{2-}$. The O.N. of each O is −2, so the total for seven O atoms is −14. Therefore, each Cr must have an O.N. of +6 in order for the sum of the O.N.s to equal the charge of the ion: +12 + (−14) = −2.

Follow-Up Problem 4.9 Determine the O.N. of each element in the following:
(a) Scandium oxide (Sc_2O_3) **(b)** Gallium chloride ($GaCl_3$)
(c) Hydrogen phosphate ion **(d)** Iodine trifluoride

Using O.N.s to Identify Redox Reactions A redox reaction is defined as one in which the oxidation numbers of the species change. Sample Problem 4.10 introduces the *tie-line,* a useful device for keeping track of these changes.

Sample Problem 4.10 Identifying Redox Reactions

Problem Use oxidation numbers to decide whether each of the following is a redox reaction:
(a) $CaO(s) + CO_2(g) \longrightarrow CaCO_3(s)$
(b) $4KNO_3(s) \longrightarrow 2K_2O(s) + 2N_2(g) + 5O_2(g)$
(c) $H_2SO_4(aq) + 2NaOH(aq) \longrightarrow Na_2SO_4(aq) + 2H_2O(l)$

Plan To determine whether a reaction is an oxidation-reduction process, we use Table 4.3 to assign an O.N. to each atom. If an O.N. changes during the reaction, we draw a tie-line from the atom on the left side to the one on the right and note the change.

Solution (a)

$$\overset{+2}{Ca}\overset{-2}{O}(s) + \overset{+4}{C}\overset{-2}{O_2}(g) \longrightarrow \overset{+2}{Ca}\overset{+4}{C}\overset{-2}{O_3}(s)$$

Because each atom in the product has the same O.N. that it had in the reactants, we conclude that this is *not* a redox reaction.

(b)

O.N. decreased: *reduction*

$$4\overset{+1}{K}\overset{+5}{N}\overset{-2}{O_3}(s) \longrightarrow 2\overset{+1}{K_2}\overset{-2}{O}(s) + 2\overset{0}{N_2}(g) + 5\overset{0}{O_2}(g)$$

O.N. increased: *oxidation*

In this case, the O.N. of N changes from +5 to 0, and the O.N. of O changes from −2 to 0, so this *is* a redox reaction.

(c)

$$\overset{+1}{H_2}\overset{+6}{S}\overset{-2}{O_4}(aq) + 2\overset{+1}{Na}\overset{-2}{O}\overset{+1}{H}(aq) \longrightarrow \overset{+1}{Na_2}\overset{+6}{S}\overset{-2}{O_4}(aq) + 2\overset{+1}{H_2}\overset{-2}{O}(l)$$

The O.N. values do not change, so this is *not* a redox reaction.

Comment The reaction in (c) is an acid-base reaction in which H_2SO_4 transfers two H^+ ions to two OH^- ions to form two H_2O molecules. In the net ionic equation,

$$\overset{+1}{H^+}(aq) + \overset{-2}{O}\overset{+1}{H^-}(aq) \longrightarrow \overset{+1}{H_2}\overset{-2}{O}(l)$$

we see that the O.N. values remain the same on both sides of the equation. Therefore, *an acid-base reaction is* ***not*** *a redox reaction.*

Follow-Up Problem 4.10 Use oxidation numbers to decide which, if any, of the following equations represents a redox reaction:
(a) $NCl_3(l) + 3H_2O(l) \longrightarrow NH_3(aq) + 3HOCl(aq)$
(b) $AgNO_3(aq) + NH_4I(aq) \longrightarrow AgI(s) + NH_4NO_3(aq)$
(c) $2H_2S(g) + 3O_2(g) \longrightarrow 2SO_2(g) + 2H_2O(g)$

Using O.N.s to Identify Oxidizing and Reducing Agents By assigning an oxidation number to each atom, we can see which species was oxidized and which reduced and, thus, which is the oxidizing agent and which the reducing agent:

- If an atom has a higher (more positive or less negative) O.N. in the product than it had in the reactant, the reactant that contains that atom was oxidized (lost electrons) and is the reducing agent. Thus, *oxidation is shown by an increase in O.N.*
- If an atom has a lower (more negative or less positive) O.N. in the product than it had in the reactant, the reactant that contains that atom was reduced (gained electrons) and is the oxidizing agent. Thus, *reduction is shown by a decrease in O.N.*

Sample Problem 4.11 Identifying Oxidizing and Reducing Agents

Problem Identify the oxidizing agent and the reducing agent in each of the following:
(a) $2Al(s) + 3H_2SO_4(aq) \longrightarrow Al_2(SO_4)_3(aq) + 3H_2(g)$
(b) $PbO(s) + CO(g) \longrightarrow Pb(s) + CO_2(g)$
(c) $2H_2(g) + O_2(g) \longrightarrow 2H_2O(g)$

Plan We assign an O.N. to each atom (or ion). The reducing agent contains an atom that is oxidized (O.N. *increased* from left to right in the equation). The oxidizing agent contains an atom that is reduced (O.N. *decreased*). We mark the changes with tie-lines.

Solution (a) Assigning oxidation numbers:

$$2\overset{0}{Al}(s) + 3\overset{+1}{H_2}\overset{+6}{S}\overset{-2}{O_4}(aq) \longrightarrow \overset{+3}{Al_2}(\overset{+6}{S}\overset{-2}{O_4})_3(aq) + 3\overset{0}{H_2}(g)$$

(oxidation: Al, 0 → +3; reduction: H, +1 → 0)

The O.N. of Al increased from 0 to +3 (Al lost electrons), so Al was oxidized; Al is the reducing agent.

The O.N. of H decreased from +1 to 0 (H gained electrons), so H^+ was reduced; H_2SO_4 is the oxidizing agent.

(b) Assigning oxidation numbers:

$$\overset{+2}{Pb}\overset{-2}{O}(s) + \overset{+2}{C}\overset{-2}{O}(g) \longrightarrow \overset{0}{Pb}(s) + \overset{+4}{C}\overset{-2}{O_2}(g)$$

(oxidation: C, +2 → +4; reduction: Pb, +2 → 0)

Pb decreased its O.N. from +2 to 0, so PbO was reduced; PbO is the oxidizing agent.
C increased its O.N. from +2 to +4, so CO was oxidized; CO is the reducing agent.
When a reactant (in this case, CO) becomes a product with more O atoms (CO_2), it is oxidized; when a reactant (PbO) becomes a product with fewer O atoms (Pb), it is reduced.

(c) Assigning oxidation numbers:

$$2\overset{0}{H_2}(g) + \overset{0}{O_2}(g) \longrightarrow 2\overset{+1}{H_2}\overset{-2}{O}(g)$$

(oxidation: H, 0 → +1; reduction: O, 0 → −2)

O_2 was reduced (O.N. of O decreased from 0 to −2); O_2 is the oxidizing agent.
H_2 was oxidized (O.N. of H increased from 0 to +1); H_2 is the reducing agent.
Oxygen is always the oxidizing agent in a combustion reaction.

Follow-Up Problem 4.11 Identify each oxidizing agent and each reducing agent:
(a) $2Fe(s) + 3Cl_2(g) \longrightarrow 2FeCl_3(s)$ **(b)** $2C_2H_6(g) + 7O_2(g) \longrightarrow 4CO_2(g) + 6H_2O(g)$
(c) $5CO(g) + I_2O_5(s) \longrightarrow I_2(s) + 5CO_2(g)$

Be sure to remember that *transferred electrons are never free because the reducing agent loses electrons and the oxidizing agent gains them* ***simultaneously.*** In other words, a complete reaction *cannot* be "an oxidation" *or* "a reduction"; it must be an oxidation-reduction. Figure 4.13 summarizes redox terminology.

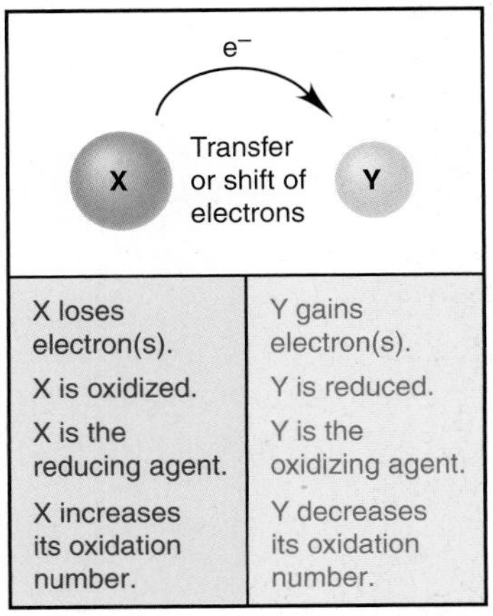

Figure 4.13 A summary of terminology for redox reactions.

Balancing Redox Equations

We balance a redox reaction by making sure that *the number of electrons lost by the reducing agent equals the number of electrons gained by the oxidizing agent.*

Two methods used to balance redox equations are the *oxidation number* method and the *half-reaction* method. This section describes the oxidation number method; the half-reaction method is covered in Chapter 21. (If your professor chooses to cover the half-reaction method here as well, it is easily transferable.)

The **oxidation number method** consists of five steps that use the changes in oxidation numbers to generate balancing coefficients. The first two steps are identical to those in Sample Problem 4.11:

Step 1. Assign O.N.s to all atoms.
Step 2. From the changes in O.N.s, identify the oxidized and reduced reactants.
Step 3. Compute the numbers of electrons lost in the oxidation and gained in the reduction, and draw tie-lines from the reactant atom to the product atom to show the change.
Step 4. Multiply the numbers of electrons by factor(s) that make the electrons lost equal the electrons gained, and use the factor(s) as balancing coefficients.
Step 5. Complete the balancing by inspection and add states of matter.

Sample Problem 4.12 Balancing Redox Equations by the Oxidation Number Method

Problem Use the oxidation number method to balance the following equations:
(a) $Cu(s) + HNO_3(aq) \longrightarrow Cu(NO_3)_2(aq) + NO_2(g) + H_2O(l)$
(b) $PbS(s) + O_2(g) \longrightarrow PbO(s) + SO_2(g)$

Copper in nitric acid.

(a) Reaction of copper and nitric acid

Solution *Step 1.* Assign oxidation numbers to all atoms:

$$\overset{0}{Cu} + \overset{+1}{H}\overset{+5}{N}\overset{-2}{O_3} \longrightarrow \overset{+2}{Cu}(\overset{+5}{N}\overset{-2}{O_3})_2 + \overset{+4}{N}\overset{-2}{O_2} + \overset{+1}{H_2}\overset{-2}{O}$$

Step 2. Identify oxidized and reduced reactants. The O.N. of Cu increased from 0 (in Cu metal) to +2 (in Cu^{2+}), so Cu was oxidized. The O.N. of N decreased from +5 (in HNO_3) to +4 (in NO_2), so HNO_3 was reduced. Note that some NO_3^- also acts as a spectator ion, appearing unchanged in $Cu(NO_3)_2$.

Step 3. Compute e^- lost and e^- gained and draw tie-lines. In the oxidation, $2e^-$ were lost from Cu. In the reduction, $1e^-$ was gained by N:

loses $2e^-$

$$Cu + HNO_3 \longrightarrow Cu(NO_3)_2 + NO_2 + H_2O$$

gains $1e^-$

Step 4. Multiply by factor(s) to make e^- lost equal e^- gained, and use the factor(s) as coefficients. Cu lost $2e^-$, so the $1e^-$ gained by N should be multiplied by 2. We put the coefficient 2 before *both* NO_2 and HNO_3:

$$Cu + 2HNO_3 \longrightarrow Cu(NO_3)_2 + 2NO_2 + H_2O$$

Step 5. Complete the balancing by inspection. Balancing N atoms requires a 4 in front of HNO_3 because two additional N atoms are in the NO_3^- ions in $Cu(NO_3)_2$:

$$Cu + 4HNO_3 \longrightarrow Cu(NO_3)_2 + 2NO_2 + H_2O$$

Then, balancing H atoms requires a 2 in front of H_2O, and we add states of matter:

$$Cu(s) + 4HNO_3(aq) \longrightarrow Cu(NO_3)_2(aq) + 2NO_2(g) + 2H_2O(l)$$

Check

Reactants (1 Cu, 4 H, 4 N, 12 O) $\longrightarrow$ products [1 Cu, 4 H, (2 + 2) N, (6 + 4 + 2) O]

Comment We often find that some of a species reacts and the rest doesn't. In this case, 2 mol of NO_3^- are reduced to NO_2, and 2 mol of NO_3^- are spectator ions.

(b) Reaction of lead(II) sulfide and oxygen

Solution *Step 1.* Assign oxidation numbers to all atoms:

$$\overset{+2\ -2}{PbS} + \overset{0}{O_2} \longrightarrow \overset{+2\ -2}{PbO} + \overset{+4\ -2}{SO_2}$$

Step 2. Identify oxidized and reduced reactants. The O.N. of S increased from -2 in PbS to $+4$ in SO_2, so PbS was oxidized. The O.N. of O decreased from 0 in O_2 to -2 in both PbO and SO_2, so O_2 was reduced.

Step 3. Compute e^- lost and e^- gained and draw tie-lines. In the oxidation, the S lost $6e^-$. In the reduction, each O gained $2e^-$:

loses $6e^-$

$$PbS + O_2 \longrightarrow PbO + SO_2$$

gains $2e^-$

gains $2e^-$

Step 4. Multiply by factor(s) to make e^- lost equal e^- gained. The S atom loses $6e^-$, and each O in O_2 gains $2e^-$, for a total gain of $4e^-$. Placing the coefficient $\frac{3}{2}$ before O_2 gives 3 O atoms that each gain $2e^-$, for a total gain of $6e^-$:

$$PbS + \tfrac{3}{2}O_2 \longrightarrow PbO + SO_2$$

Step 5. Complete the balancing by inspection. The atoms are balanced, but we multiply all coefficients by 2 to obtain integers and add states of matter:

$$2PbS(s) + 3O_2(g) \longrightarrow 2PbO(s) + 2SO_2(g)$$

Check Reactants (2 Pb, 2 S, 6 O) $\longrightarrow$ products [2 Pb, 2 S, (2 + 4) O]

Follow-Up Problem 4.12 Use the oxidation number method to balance the following equation: $K_2Cr_2O_7(aq) + HI(aq) \longrightarrow KI(aq) + CrI_3(aq) + I_2(s) + H_2O(l)$.

Quantifying Redox Reactions by Titration

In an acid-base titration, a known concentration of a base is used to find an unknown concentration of an acid (or vice versa). Similarly, in a redox titration, a known concentration of oxidizing agent is used to find an unknown concentration of reducing agent (or vice versa). This kind of titration has many applications, from measuring the iron content in drinking water to quantifying vitamin C in fruits and vegetables.

The permanganate ion, MnO_4^-, is a common oxidizing agent because it is deep purple, and so also serves as an indicator. In Figure 4.14, MnO_4^- is used to determine oxalate ion ($C_2O_4^{2-}$) concentration. As long as $C_2O_4^{2-}$ is present, it reduces the added MnO_4^- to faint pink (nearly colorless) Mn^{2+} (Figure 4.14, *left*). When all the $C_2O_4^{2-}$ has been oxidized, the next drop of MnO_4^- turns the solution light purple (Figure 4.14, *right*). This color change indicates the *end point,* which we assume is the same as the *equivalence point,* the point at which the electrons lost by the oxidized species ($C_2O_4^{2-}$) equal the electrons gained by the reduced species (MnO_4^-). We can calculate the $C_2O_4^{2-}$ concentration from the known volume of $Na_2C_2O_4$ solution and the known volume and concentration of $KMnO_4$ solution.

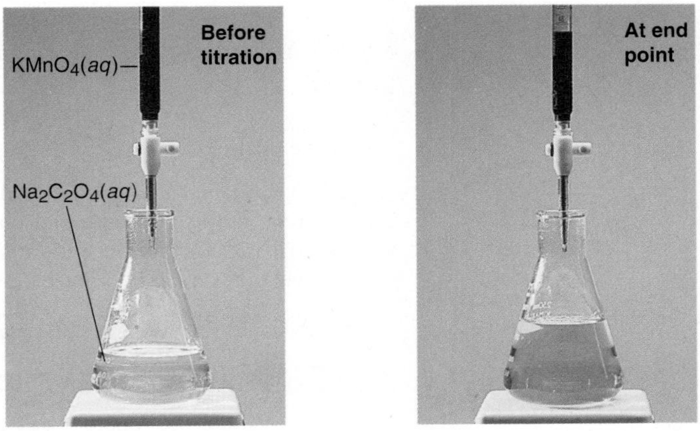

Net ionic equation:

$$2\overset{+7}{Mn}O_4^-(aq) + 5\overset{+3}{C_2}O_4^{2-}(aq) + 16H^+(aq) \longrightarrow 2\overset{+2}{Mn}{}^{2+}(aq) + 10\overset{+4}{C}O_2(g) + 8H_2O(l)$$

Figure 4.14 The redox titration of $C_2O_4^{2-}$ with MnO_4^-.

Sample Problem 4.13 Finding the Amount of Reducing Agent by Titration

Problem Calcium ion (Ca^{2+}) is necessary for the clotting of blood and many other physiological processes. To measure the Ca^{2+} concentration in 1.00 mL of human blood, $Na_2C_2O_4$ solution is added, which precipitates the Ca^{2+} as CaC_2O_4. This solid is dissolved in dilute H_2SO_4 to release $C_2O_4^{2-}$, and 2.05 mL of 4.88×10^{-4} *M* $KMnO_4$ is required to reach the end point. The balanced equation is

$$2KMnO_4(aq) + 5CaC_2O_4(s) + 8H_2SO_4(aq) \longrightarrow 2MnSO_4(aq) + K_2SO_4(aq) + 5CaSO_4(s) + 10CO_2(g) + 8H_2O(l)$$

Calculate the amount (mol) of Ca^{2+} in 1.00 mL of blood.

Plan We have to find the amount (mol) of Ca^{2+} from the volume (2.05 mL) and concentration (4.88×10^{-4} *M*) of $KMnO_4$ used to oxidize the CaC_2O_4 precipitated from 1.00 mL of blood. We find the amount (mol) of $KMnO_4$ needed to reach the end point and use the molar ratio to find the amount (mol) of CaC_2O_4. Then we use the chemical formula, which shows 1 mol of Ca^{2+} for every mol of CaC_2O_4.

Road Map

Volume (mL) of $KMnO_4$ solution

↓ 10^3 mL = 1 L

Volume (L) of $KMnO_4$ solution

↓ multiply by *M* (mol/L)

Amount (mol) of $KMnO_4$

↓ molar ratio

Amount (mol) of CaC_2O_4

↓ ratio of elements in chemical formula

Amount (mol) of Ca^{2+}

Solution Converting volume (mL) and concentration (*M*) to amount (mol) of $KMnO_4$:

$$\text{Amount (mol) of } KMnO_4 = 2.05\ \text{mL soln} \times \frac{1\ \text{L}}{1000\ \text{mL}} \times \frac{4.88\times10^{-4}\ \text{mol } KMnO_4}{1\ \text{L soln}}$$
$$= 1.00\times10^{-6}\ \text{mol } KMnO_4$$

Using the molar ratio to convert amount (mol) of $KMnO_4$ to amount (mol) of CaC_2O_4:

$$\text{Amount (mol) of } CaC_2O_4 = 1.00\times10^{-6}\ \text{mol } KMnO_4 \times \frac{5\ \text{mol } CaC_2O_4}{2\ \text{mol } KMnO_4}$$
$$= 2.50\times10^{-6}\ \text{mol } CaC_2O_4$$

Finding the amount (mol) of Ca^{2+}:

$$\text{Amount (mol) of } Ca^{2+} = 2.50\times10^{-6}\ \text{mol } CaC_2O_4 \times \frac{1\ \text{mol } Ca^{2+}}{1\ \text{mol } CaC_2O_4} = 2.50\times10^{-6}\ \text{mol } Ca^{+}$$

Check A very small volume of dilute $KMnO_4$ is needed, so 10^{-6} mol of $KMnO_4$ seems reasonable. The molar ratio of CaC_2O_4 to $KMnO_4$ is 5/2, which gives 2.5×10^{-6} mol of CaC_2O_4 and thus 2.5×10^{-6} mol of Ca^{2+}.

Comment 1. When blood is donated, the receiving bag contains $Na_2C_2O_4$ solution, which precipitates the Ca^{2+} ion to prevent clotting.
2. Normal Ca^{2+} concentration in human adult blood is 9.0 to 11.5 mg Ca^{2+}/100 mL. If we multiply the amount of Ca^{2+} in 1 mL by 100 and then multiply by the molar mass of Ca (40.08 g/mol), we get 1.0×10^{-2} g, or 10.0 mg Ca^{2+} in 100 mL:

$$\text{Mass (mg) of } Ca^{2+} = \frac{2.50\times10^{-6}\ \text{mol } Ca^{2+}}{1\ \text{mL}} \times 100\ \text{mL} \times \frac{40.08\ \text{g } Ca^{2+}}{1\ \text{mol } Ca^{2+}} \times \frac{1000\ \text{mg}}{1\ \text{g}}$$
$$= 10.0\ \text{mg } Ca^{2+}$$

Follow-Up Problem 4.13 When 2.50 mL of low-fat milk was treated with sodium oxalate and the precipitate dissolved in H_2SO_4, 6.53 mL of 4.56×10^{-3} *M* $KMnO_4$ was required to reach the end point. **(a)** Calculate the molarity of Ca^{2+} in the milk sample. **(b)** What is the concentration of Ca^{2+} in g/L? Is this value consistent with the typical value for milk of about 1.2 g Ca^{2+}/L?

Summary of Section 4.5

- When one reactant has a greater attraction for electrons than another, there is a net movement of electrons, and a redox reaction takes place. Electron gain (reduction) and electron loss (oxidation) occur simultaneously.
- Assigning oxidation numbers to all atoms in a reaction is a method for identifying a redox reaction. The species that is oxidized (contains an atom that increases in oxidation number) is the reducing agent; the species that is reduced (contains an atom that decreases in oxidation number) is the oxidizing agent.
- We balance redox reactions by keeping track of the changes in oxidation number.
- A redox titration determines the concentration of an oxidizing agent from the known concentration of the reducing agent (or vice versa).

4.6 • ELEMENTS IN REDOX REACTIONS

In many redox reactions, such as those in Sample Problems 4.11 and 4.12, *atoms occur as an element on one side of an equation and as part of a compound on the other.** One way to classify these is by comparing the *numbers* of reactants and products. With that approach, we have three types—*combination, decomposition,* and *displacement;* one other type involving elements is *combustion*. In this section, we survey each type with several examples.

Combination Redox Reactions

In a combination redox reaction, two or more reactants, at least one of which is an element, form a compound:

$$X + Y \longrightarrow Z$$

Combining Two Elements Two elements may react to form binary ionic or covalent compounds. Here are some important examples:

1. *Metal and nonmetal form an ionic compound.* Figure 4.15 shows a typical example, the reaction between the alkali metal potassium and the halogen chlorine, on the macroscopic, atomic, and symbolic levels. Note the change in oxidation numbers in the balanced equation: K is oxidized, so it is the reducing agent; Cl_2 is reduced, so it is the oxidizing agent. In fact, whenever a binary ionic compound forms from its elements, *the metal is the reducing agent and the nonmetal is the oxidizing agent.*

*Many other redox reactions, however, do *not* involve elements (see Sample Problem 4.13).

Figure 4.15 **Combining elements to form an ionic compound: potassium metal and chlorine gas form solid potassium chloride.** Darker atoms in the atomic view indicate the stoichiometry.

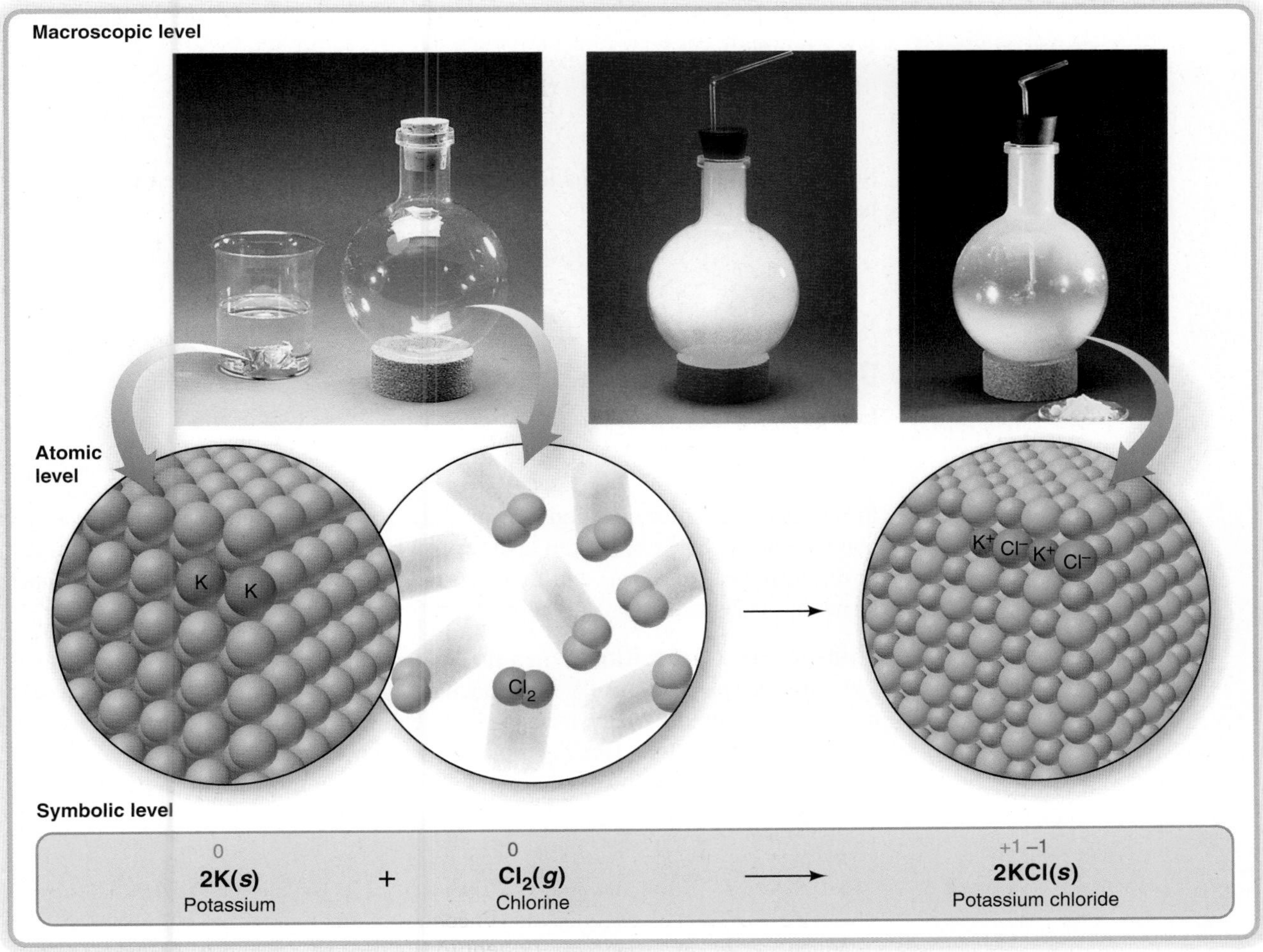

Aluminum reacts with O_2, as does nearly every metal, to form an ionic oxide:

$$4\overset{0}{\text{Al}}(s) + 3\overset{0}{\text{O}}_2(g) \longrightarrow 2\overset{+3}{\text{Al}}_2\overset{-2}{\text{O}}_3(s)$$

The Al_2O_3 layer on the surface of an aluminum pot prevents oxygen from reacting with the next layer of Al atoms, thus protecting the metal from further oxidation.

2. *Two nonmetals form a covalent compound.* In one of thousands of examples, ammonia forms from nitrogen and hydrogen in a reaction that occurs in industry on an enormous scale:

$$\overset{0}{\text{N}}_2(g) + 3\overset{0}{\text{H}}_2(g) \longrightarrow 2\overset{-3}{\text{N}}\overset{+1}{\text{H}}_3(g)$$

Halogens react with many other nonmetals, as in the formation of phosphorus trichloride, a reactant in the production of pesticides and other organic compounds:

$$\overset{0}{\text{P}}_4(s) + 6\overset{0}{\text{Cl}}_2(g) \longrightarrow 4\overset{+3}{\text{P}}\overset{-1}{\text{Cl}}_3(l)$$

Nearly every nonmetal reacts with O_2 to form a covalent oxide, as when nitrogen monoxide forms from the nitrogen and oxygen in air at the very high temperatures created by lightning and in a car's engine:

$$\overset{0}{\text{N}}_2(g) + \overset{0}{\text{O}}_2(g) \longrightarrow 2\overset{+2}{\text{N}}\overset{-2}{\text{O}}(g)$$

Combining Compound and Element Many binary covalent compounds react with nonmetals to form larger compounds. Many nonmetal oxides react with additional O_2 to form "higher" oxides (those with more O atoms in each molecule). For example,

$$2\overset{+2}{\text{N}}\overset{-2}{\text{O}}(g) + \overset{0}{\text{O}}_2(g) \longrightarrow 2\overset{+4}{\text{N}}\overset{-2}{\text{O}}_2(g)$$

Similarly, many nonmetal halides combine with additional halogen to form "higher" halides:

$$\overset{+3}{\text{P}}\overset{-1}{\text{Cl}}_3(l) + \overset{0}{\text{Cl}}_2(g) \longrightarrow \overset{+5}{\text{P}}\overset{-1}{\text{Cl}}_5(s)$$

Decomposition Redox Reactions

In a *decomposition redox reaction,* a compound forms two or more products, at least one of which is an element:

$$\text{Z} \longrightarrow \text{X} + \text{Y}$$

In any decomposition reaction, the reactant absorbs enough energy for one or more bonds to break. The energy can take several forms, but the most important are decomposition by heat (thermal) and by electricity (electrolytic). The products are either elements or elements and smaller compounds.

Thermal Decomposition When the energy absorbed is heat, the reaction is called a *thermal decomposition.* (A Greek delta, Δ, above the yield arrow indicates strong heating is required.) Many metal oxides, chlorates, and perchlorates release oxygen when strongly heated. Heating potassium chlorate is a method for forming small amounts of oxygen in the laboratory; the same reaction occurs in some explosives and fireworks:

$$2\overset{+1}{\text{K}}\overset{+5}{\text{Cl}}\overset{-2}{\text{O}}_3(s) \xrightarrow{\Delta} 2\overset{+1}{\text{K}}\overset{-1}{\text{Cl}}(s) + 3\overset{0}{\text{O}}_2(g)$$

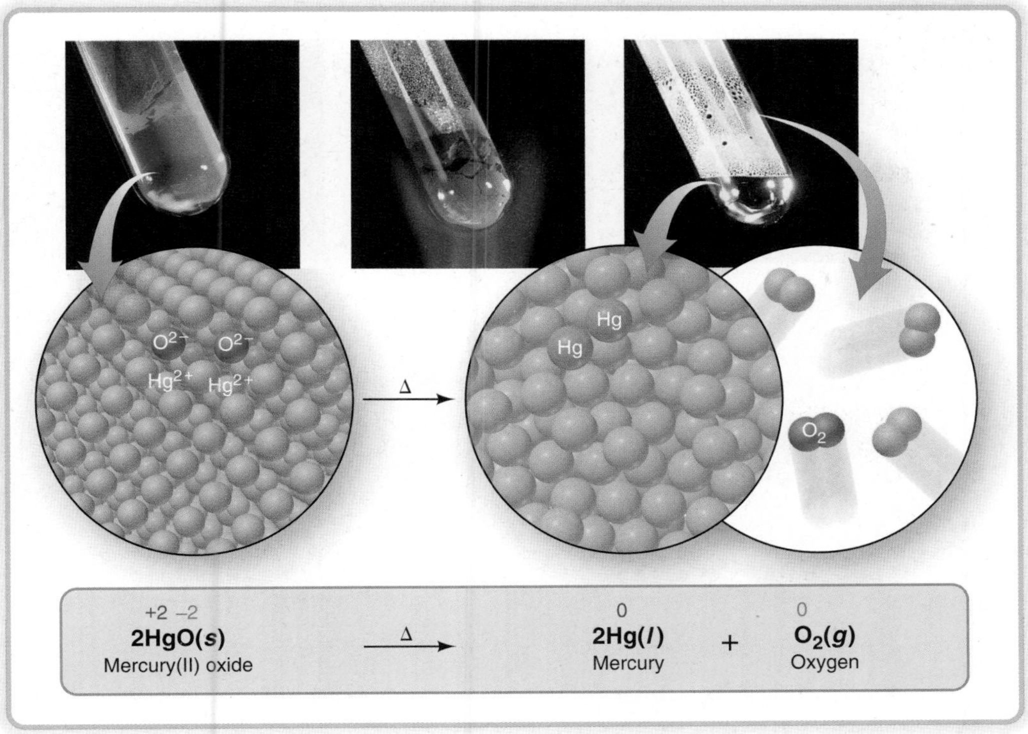

Figure 4.16 Decomposition of the compound mercury(II) oxide to its elements.

The decomposition of mercury(II) oxide, used by Lavoisier in his classic experiments, is shown in Figure 4.16. Notice that, in these cases, the lone reactant is the oxidizing *and* the reducing agent. For example, with the reactant HgO, the O^{2-} ion reduces the Hg^{2+} ion, and at the same time, Hg^{2+} oxidizes O^{2-}.

Electrolytic Decomposition In the process of electrolysis, a compound absorbs electrical energy and decomposes into its elements. In the early 19th century, the observation of the electrolysis of water was crucial for establishing atomic masses:

$$\overset{+1-2}{2H_2O(l)} \xrightarrow{\text{electricity}} \overset{0}{2H_2(g)} + \overset{0}{O_2(g)}$$

Many active metals, such as sodium, magnesium, and calcium, are produced industrially by electrolysis of their molten halides:

$$\overset{+2-1}{MgCl_2(l)} \xrightarrow{\text{electricity}} \overset{0}{Mg(l)} + \overset{0}{Cl_2(g)}$$

(We examine the details of electrolysis in Chapter 21 and its role in the industrial recovery of several elements in Chapter 22.)

Displacement Redox Reactions and Activity Series

In any *displacement reaction,* the number of substances on the two sides of the equation remains the same, but atoms (or ions) exchange places. There are two types:

1. In *double*-displacement (metathesis) reactions, such as precipitation and acid-base reactions (Sections 4.3 and 4.4), atoms (or ions) of two *compounds* exchange places; these reactions are *not* redox processes:

$$AB + CD \longrightarrow AC + BD$$

2. In *single*-displacement reactions, one of the substances is an *element;* therefore, *all single-displacement reactions **are** redox processes:*

$$X + YZ \longrightarrow XZ + Y$$

In solution, single-displacement reactions occur when an atom of one element displaces the ion of another: if the displacement involves metals, the atom *reduces* the

Figure 4.17 The active metal lithium displaces hydrogen from water. Only water molecules involved as products of the reaction are red and blue.

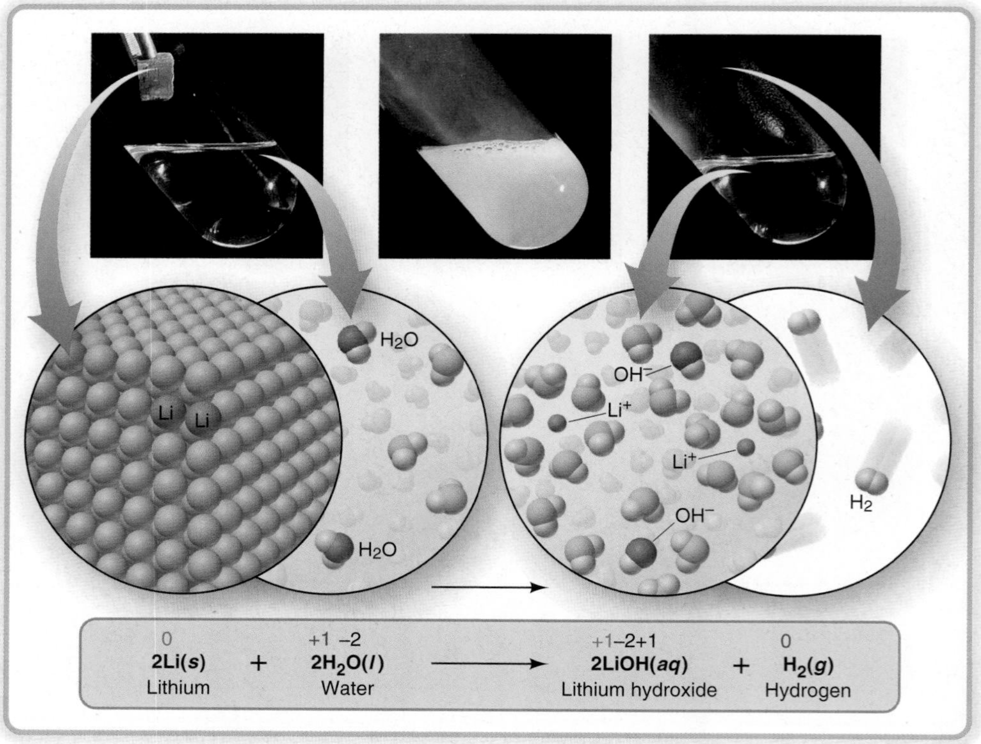

ion; if it involves nonmetals (specifically halogens), the atom *oxidizes* the ion. In two *activity series*—one for metals and one for halogens—the elements are ranked in order of their ability to displace hydrogen (for metals) and one another.

The Activity Series of the Metals Metals are ranked by their ability to displace H_2 from various sources and another metal from solution. In all displacements of H_2, the metal is the reducing agent (O.N. increases), and water or acid is the oxidizing agent (O.N. of H decreases). The activity series of the metals is based on these facts:

- *The most reactive metals displace H_2 from liquid water.* Group 1A(1) metals and Ca, Sr, and Ba from Group 2A(2) displace H_2 from water (Figure 4.17).
- *Slightly less reactive metals displace H_2 from steam.* Heat supplied by steam is needed for less reactive metals such as Al and Zn to displace H_2:

$$\overset{0}{2Al}(s) + 6\overset{+1}{H_2}\overset{-2}{O}(g) \xrightarrow{\Delta} 2\overset{+3}{Al}(\overset{-2}{O}\overset{+1}{H})_3(s) + 3\overset{0}{H_2}(g)$$

- *Still less reactive metals displace H_2 from acids.* The higher concentration of H^+ in acid solutions is needed for even less reactive metals such as Ni and Sn to displace H_2 (Figure 4.18). For nickel, the net ionic equation is

$$\overset{0}{Ni}(s) + 2\overset{+1}{H^+}(aq) \longrightarrow \overset{+2}{Ni^{2+}}(aq) + \overset{0}{H_2}(g)$$

- *The least reactive metals cannot displace H_2 from any source.* Fortunately, precious metals, such as silver, gold, and platinum, do *not* react with water or acid.
- *An atom of one metal displaces the ion of another.* Comparisons of metal reactivity show, for example, that Zn metal displaces Cu^{2+} ion from aqueous $CuSO_4$:

$$\overset{+2}{Cu^{2+}}(aq) + \overset{+6}{S}\overset{-2}{O_4}{}^{2-}(aq) + \overset{0}{Zn}(s) \longrightarrow \overset{0}{Cu}(s) + \overset{+2}{Zn^{2+}}(aq) + \overset{+6}{S}\overset{-2}{O_4}{}^{2-}(aq)$$

Figure 4.18 The displacement of H_2 from acid by nickel.

And Figure 4.19 shows that Cu metal displaces silver (Ag^+) ion from solution; therefore, zinc is more reactive than copper, which is more reactive than silver.

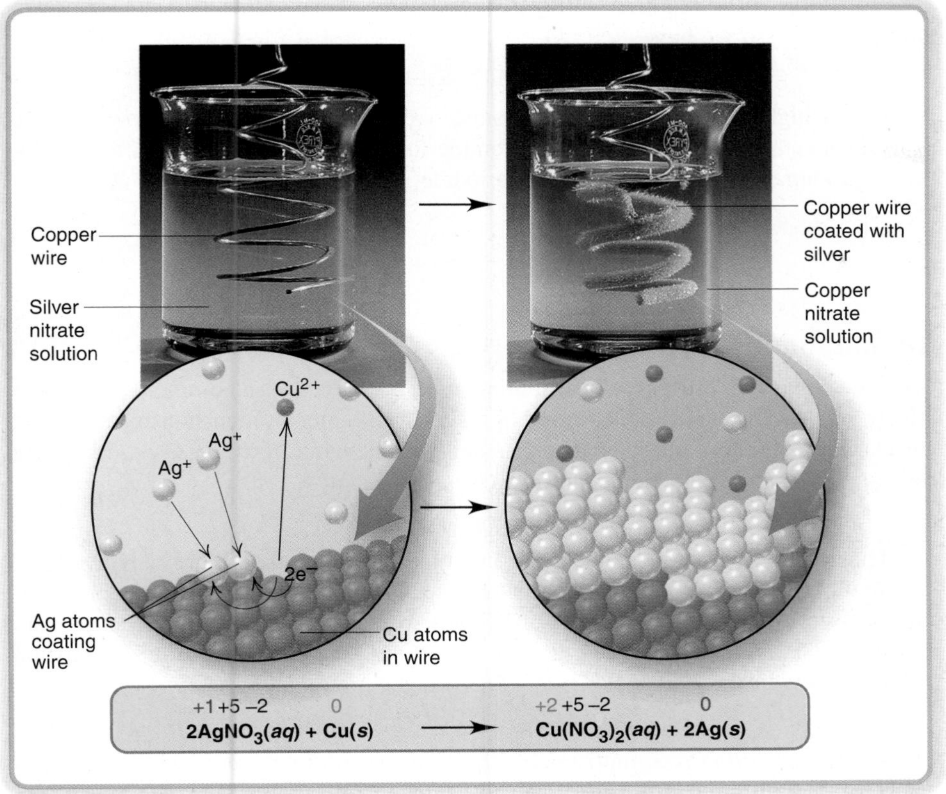

Figure 4.19 A more reactive metal (Cu) displacing the ion of a less reactive metal (Ag^+) from solution.

Many such reactions form the basis of the **activity series of the metals.** Note these two points from Figure 4.20:

- Elements higher on the list are stronger reducing agents than elements lower down; in other words, any metal can reduce the ions of metals below it.
- From higher to lower, a metal can displace H_2 (reduce H^+) from water, steam, acid, or not at all.

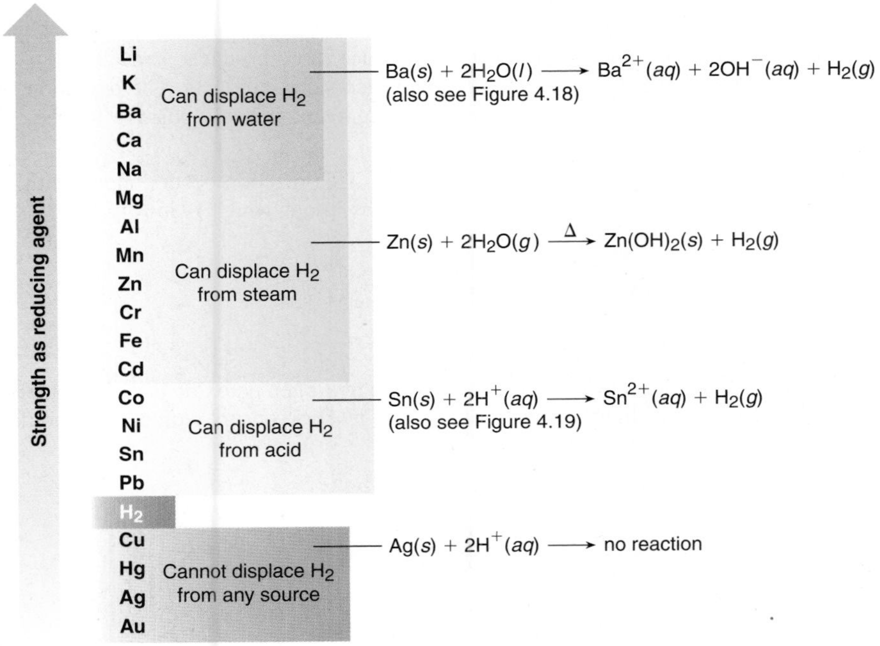

Figure 4.20 **The activity series of the metals.** The most active metal (strongest reducing agent) is at the top, and the least active metal (weakest reducing agent) is at the bottom.

The Activity Series of the Halogens Reactivity of the elements decreases down Group 7A(17), so we have

$$F_2 > Cl_2 > Br_2 > I_2$$

A halogen higher in the group is a stronger oxidizing agent than one lower down. Thus, elemental chlorine can oxidize bromide ions (*below*) or iodide ions from solution, and elemental bromine can oxidize iodide ions:

$$\overset{-1}{2Br^-}(aq) + \overset{0}{Cl_2}(aq) \longrightarrow \overset{0}{Br_2}(aq) + \overset{-1}{2Cl^-}(aq)$$

Combustion Reactions

Combustion is the process of combining with oxygen, most commonly with the release of heat and the production of light, as in a flame. Combustion reactions are not classified by the number of reactants and products, but *all of these reactions are redox processes* because elemental oxygen is a reactant:

$$2CO(g) + O_2(g) \longrightarrow 2CO_2(g)$$

The combustion reactions that we commonly use to produce energy involve coal, petroleum, gasoline, natural gas, or wood as a reactant. These mixtures consist of substances with many C—C and C—H bonds, which break during the reaction, and each C and H atom combines with oxygen to form CO_2 and H_2O. The combustion of butane is typical:

$$2C_4H_{10}(g) + 13O_2(g) \longrightarrow 8CO_2(g) + 10H_2O(g)$$

Biological *respiration* is a multistep combustion process that occurs within our cells when we "burn" foodstuffs, such as glucose, for energy:

$$C_6H_{12}O_6(s) + 6O_2(g) \longrightarrow 6CO_2(g) + 6H_2O(g) + \text{energy}$$

Sample Problem 4.14 Identifying the Type of Redox Reaction

Problem Classify each of the following redox reactions as a combination, decomposition, or displacement reaction, write a balanced molecular equation for each, as well as total and net ionic equations for part (c), and identify the oxidizing and reducing agents:
(a) Magnesium(s) + nitrogen(g) ⟶ magnesium nitride(s)
(b) Hydrogen peroxide(l) ⟶ water + oxygen gas
(c) Aluminum(s) + lead(II) nitrate(aq) ⟶ aluminum nitrate(aq) + lead(s)

Plan To decide on reaction type, recall that combination reactions produce fewer products than reactants, decomposition reactions produce more products, and displacement reactions have the same number of reactants and products. The oxidation number (O.N.) becomes more positive for the reducing agent and less positive for the oxidizing agent.

Solution (a) Combination: two substances form one. This reaction occurs, along with formation of magnesium oxide, when magnesium burns in air, which is mostly N_2:

$$3\overset{0}{Mg}(s) + \overset{0}{N_2}(g) \longrightarrow \overset{+2}{Mg_3}\overset{-3}{N_2}(s)$$

Mg is the reducing agent; N_2 is the oxidizing agent.

(b) Decomposition: one substance forms two. Because hydrogen peroxide is very unstable and breaks down from heat, light, or just shaking, this reaction occurs within every bottle of this common household antiseptic:

$$2\overset{+1}{H_2}\overset{-1}{O_2}(l) \longrightarrow 2\overset{+1}{H_2}\overset{-2}{O}(l) + \overset{0}{O_2}(g)$$

H_2O_2 is both the oxidizing *and* the reducing agent. The O.N. of O in peroxides is −1. It is shown in blue *and* red because it both increases to 0 in O_2 and decreases to −2 in H_2O.
(c) Displacement: two substances form two others. As Figure 4.20 shows, Al is more active than Pb and, thus, displaces it from aqueous solution:

$$\overset{0}{2Al(s)} + 3\overset{+2}{Pb}(\overset{+5}{N}\overset{-2}{O_3})_2(aq) \longrightarrow 2\overset{+3}{Al}(\overset{+5}{N}\overset{-2}{O_3})_3(aq) + 3\overset{0}{Pb}(s)$$

Al is the reducing agent; $Pb(NO_3)_2$ is the oxidizing agent.
The total ionic equation is

$$2Al(s) + 3Pb^{2+}(aq) + 6NO_3^-(aq) \longrightarrow 2Al^{3+}(aq) + 6NO_3^-(aq) + 3Pb(s)$$

The net ionic equation is

$$2Al(s) + 3Pb^{2+}(aq) \longrightarrow 2Al^{3+}(aq) + 3Pb(s)$$

Follow-Up Problem 4.14 Classify each of the following redox reactions as a combination, decomposition, or displacement reaction, write a balanced molecular equation for each, as well as total and net ionic equations for parts (b) and (c), and identify the oxidizing and reducing agents:
(a) $S_8(s) + F_2(g) \longrightarrow SF_4(g)$
(b) $CsI(aq) + Cl_2(aq) \longrightarrow CsCl(aq) + I_2(aq)$
(c) $Ni(NO_3)_2(aq) + Cr(s) \longrightarrow Ni(s) + Cr(NO_3)_3(aq)$

Summary of Section 4.6

- A reaction that has an element as reactant or product is a redox reaction.
- In combination redox reactions, elements combine to form a compound, or a compound and an element combine.
- In decomposition redox reactions, compounds break down by absorption of heat or electricity into elements or into a compound and an element.
- In displacement redox reactions, one element displaces the ion of another from solution.
- Activity series rank elements in order of ability to displace each other. A more reactive metal can displace (reduce) hydrogen ion or the ion of a less reactive metal from solution. A more reactive halogen can displace (oxidize) the ion of a less reactive halogen from solution.
- Combustion releases heat through a redox reaction of a substance with O_2.

4.7 • THE REVERSIBILITY OF REACTIONS AND THE EQUILIBRIUM STATE

So far, we have viewed reactions as transformations of reactants into products that proceed until they are complete, that is, until the limiting reactant is used up. However, many reactions stop before this happens because two opposing reactions are taking place simultaneously: the forward (left-to-right) reaction continues, but the reverse (right-to-left) reaction occurs just as fast (at the same rate). At this point, *no further changes appear in the amounts of reactants or products,* and the reaction mixture has reached **dynamic equilibrium.** On the macroscopic level, the reaction is *static,* but it is *dynamic* on the molecular level.

In principle, *every reaction is reversible and will reach dynamic equilibrium if all the reactants and products are present.* Consider the reversible breakdown and formation of calcium carbonate. When heated, it breaks down to calcium oxide and carbon dioxide:

$$CaCO_3(s) \xrightarrow{\Delta} CaO(s) + CO_2(g) \text{ [breakdown]}$$

And it forms when calcium oxide and carbon dioxide react:

$$CaO(s) + CO_2(g) \longrightarrow CaCO_3(s) \text{ [formation]}$$

Let's study this process with two experiments:

1. We place $CaCO_3$ in an *open* steel container and heat it to approximately 900°C (Figure 4.21A). The $CaCO_3$ starts breaking down to CaO and CO_2, and the CO_2 escapes from the open container. The reaction goes to completion because the reverse reaction (formation) cannot occur in the absence of CO_2.

2. We perform the same experiment in a *closed* container (Figure 4.21B). The breakdown (forward reaction) starts as before, but soon the CaO and CO_2 start reacting with each other (formation). Gradually, with time, as the amounts of CaO and CO_2 increase, the formation reaction speeds up. Eventually, the reverse reaction (formation) occurs as fast as the forward reaction (breakdown), and the amounts of $CaCO_3$, CaO, and CO_2 no longer change: the system has reached a state of equilibrium. We indicate this condition with a pair of arrows pointing in opposite directions:

$$CaCO_3(s) \rightleftharpoons CaO(s) + CO_2(g)$$

In contrast to the reaction in the open container, equilibrium *is* reached because *all the substances remain in contact with each other.*

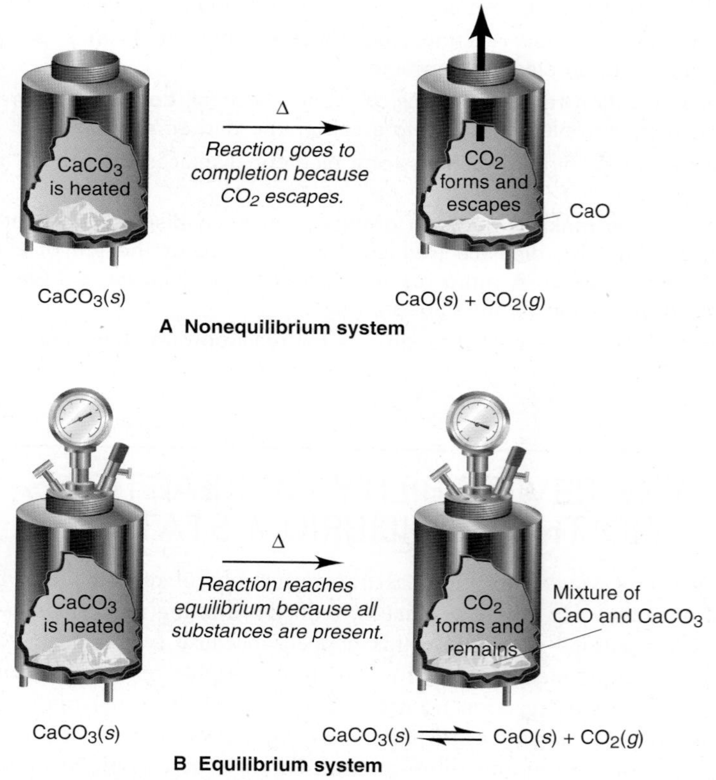

Figure 4.21 The equilibrium state. **A,** In an *open* container, $CaCO_3$ breaks down completely because CO_2 escapes. **B,** In a *closed* container, $CaCO_3$ breakdown and formation reach equilibrium.

Reaction reversibility applies to other systems as well:

1. *Weak acids in water.* Weak acids dissociate very little into ions in water because the dissociation becomes balanced by a reassociation of H_3O^+ with the anion to re-form the weak acid and water. For example, when acetic acid dissolves, some CH_3COOH molecules transfer a proton to H_2O and form H_3O^+ and CH_3COO^- ions. As more ions form, the ions react with each other more often to re-form acetic acid and water:

$$CH_3COOH(aq) + H_2O(l) \rightleftharpoons H_3O^+(aq) + CH_3COO^-(aq)$$

In fact, in 0.1 *M* CH_3COOH at 25°C, only about 1.3% of acid molecules are dissociated! Each weak acid dissociates to its own extent. For example, under the same conditions, propionic acid (CH_3CH_2COOH) is 1.1% dissociated, and hydrofluoric acid (HF) is 8.6% dissociated.

2. *Weak bases in water.* Similarly, the weak base ammonia reacts with water to form NH_4^+ and OH^- ions. As more ions form, they interact more often to re-form ammonia and water, and the rates of the forward and reverse reactions soon balance:

$$NH_3(aq) + H_2O(l) \rightleftharpoons NH_4^+(aq) + OH^-(aq)$$

The weak base methylamine (CH_3NH_2) reacts with water to a greater extent than ammonia does before reaching equilibrium, and the weak base aniline ($C_6H_5NH_2$) reacts to a lesser extent.

3. *Gas-forming reactions.* When an acid reacts with a carbonate, the reaction goes to completion in an open container because the CO_2 escapes. But, if the container is closed to keep the CO_2 present, the reverse reaction takes place and the mixture reaches equilibrium.

4. *Other acid-base and precipitation reactions.* These processes seem to "go to completion" because the ions become tied up in the product, either as water (acid-base) or as an insoluble solid (precipitation), and are not available to re-form reactants. In truth, though, water and ionic precipitates do dissociate to an extremely small extent, so these reactions also reach equilibrium, but the final reaction mixture consists of *almost* all product.

Thus, some reactions proceed very little before reaching equilibrium, others proceed almost to completion, and still others reach equilibrium with significant amounts of both reactants *and* products present. In Chapter 20, we'll examine the factors that determine to what extent a reaction proceeds.

Dynamic equilibrium occurs in many natural systems, from the cycling of water in the environment to the nuclear processes occurring in stars. We examine equilibrium in chemical and physical systems in Chapters 12, 13, and 17 through 21.

Summary of Section 4.7

- Every reaction is reversible if all the substances involved are present.
- As the amounts of products increase, the reactants begin to re-form. When the reverse reaction occurs as rapidly as the forward reaction, the amounts of the substances no longer change, and the reaction mixture has reached dynamic equilibrium.
- Weak acids and bases reach equilibrium in water with a very small proportion of their molecules dissociated.
- An aqueous ionic reaction "goes to completion" because a product is removed (gas) or products are formed that react very slightly in a reverse reaction (water or precipitate).

CHAPTER REVIEW GUIDE

Learning Objectives

Relevant section (§) and/or sample problem (SP) numbers appear in parentheses.

Understand These Concepts

1. Why water is a polar molecule and how it dissociates ionic compounds into ions (§4.1)
2. The differing nature of the species present when ionic and covalent compounds dissolve in water (§4.1)
3. The distinctions among strong electrolytes, weak electrolytes, and nonelectrolytes (§4.1, §4.4)
4. The three types of equations that specify the species and the chemical change in an aqueous ionic reaction (§4.2)
5. The key event in three classes of aqueous ionic reactions (§4.3–§4.5)
6. How to decide whether a precipitation reaction occurs (§4.3)
7. The distinction between strong and weak aqueous acids and bases (§4.4)
8. How acid-base reactions are proton transfers; how carbonates (and sulfites) act as bases in gas-forming reactions (§4.4)
9. The distinction between a transfer and a shift of electrons in the formation of ionic and covalent compounds (§4.5)
10. The relation between change in oxidation number and identity of oxidizing and reducing agents (§4.5)
11. The presence of elements in combination, decomposition, and displacement redox reactions; the meaning of an activity series (§4.6)
12. The balance between forward and reverse reactions in dynamic equilibrium; why some acids and bases are weak (§4.7)

Master These Skills

1. Using molecular scenes to depict a soluble ionic compound in water (SP 4.1)
2. Using the formula of a compound to find the number of moles of ions in solution (SP 4.2)
3. Predicting whether a precipitation reaction occurs (SP 4.3)
4. Using molecular depictions to understand a precipitation reaction (SP 4.4)
5. Determining the number of H^+ (or OH^-) ions in an aqueous acid (or base) solution (SP 4.5)
6. Writing ionic equations to describe precipitation and acid-base reactions (SPs 4.3, 4.4, 4.6)
7. Writing acid-base equations as proton transfers (SP 4.7)
8. Calculating an unknown concentration from an acid-base or redox titration (SPs 4.8, 4.13)
9. Determining the oxidation number of any element in a compound (SP 4.9)
10. Identifying redox reactions from changes in O.N.s (SP 4.10)
11. Identifying the oxidizing and reducing agents in a redox reaction (SP 4.11)
12. Balancing redox reactions by the oxidation number method (SP 4.12)
13. Distinguishing among combination, decomposition, and displacement redox reactions (SP 4.14)
14. Predicting the products of a single-dissociation reaction based on an activity series (§4.6)

Key Terms

Page numbers appear in parentheses.

Section 4.1
polar molecule (136)
solvated (136)
electrolyte (137)
nonelectrolyte (139)

Section 4.2
molecular equation (140)
total ionic equation (141)
spectator ion (141)
net ionic equation (141)

Section 4.3
precipitation reaction (141)
precipitate (141)
metathesis reaction (143)

Section 4.4
acid-base (neutralization) reaction (145)
acid (145)
base (145)
salt (148)
titration (152)
equivalence point (152)
end point (152)

Section 4.5
oxidation-reduction (redox) reaction (153)
oxidation (154)
reduction (154)
oxidizing agent (154)
reducing agent (154)
oxidation number (O.N.) (or oxidation state) (155)
oxidation number method (158)

Section 4.6
activity series of the metals (165)

Section 4.7
dynamic equilibrium (167)

Brief Solutions to Follow-Up Problems

4.1 The compound is $BaCl_2$.

$$\text{Mass (g) of } BaCl_2 = 9 \text{ \sout{particles}} \times \frac{0.05 \text{ \sout{mol particles}}}{1 \text{ \sout{particle}}} \times \frac{1 \text{ \sout{mol BaCl}}_2}{3 \text{ \sout{mol particles}}} \times \frac{208.2 \text{ g } BaCl_2}{1 \text{ \sout{mol BaCl}}_2} = 31.2 \text{ g } BaCl_2$$

4.2 (a) $KClO_4(s) \xrightarrow{H_2O} K^+(aq) + ClO_4^-(aq)$;
2 mol of K^+ and 2 mol of ClO_4^-

(b) $Mg(C_2H_3O_2)_2(s) \xrightarrow{H_2O} Mg^{2+}(aq) + 2C_2H_3O_2^-(aq)$;
2.49 mol of Mg^{2+} and 4.97 mol of $C_2H_3O_2^-$

(c) $(NH_4)_2CrO_4(s) \xrightarrow{H_2O} 2NH_4^+(aq) + CrO_4^{2-}(aq)$;
6.24 mol of NH_4^+ and 3.12 mol of CrO_4^{2-}

(d) $NaHSO_4(s) \xrightarrow{H_2O} Na^+(aq) + HSO_4^-(aq)$;
0.73 mol of Na^+ and 0.73 mol of HSO_4^-

4.3 (a) $Fe^{3+}(aq) + 3Cl^-(aq) + 3Cs^+(aq) + PO_4^{3-}(aq) \longrightarrow FePO_4(s) + 3Cl^-(aq) + 3Cs^+(aq)$

$Fe^{3+}(aq) + PO_4^{3-}(aq) \longrightarrow FePO_4(s)$

(b) $2Na^+(aq) + 2OH^-(aq) + Cd^{2+}(aq) + 2NO_3^-(aq) \longrightarrow 2Na^+(aq) + 2NO_3^-(aq) + Cd(OH)_2(s)$

$2OH^-(aq) + Cd^{2+}(aq) \longrightarrow Cd(OH)_2(s)$

(c) No reaction occurs

(d) $2Ag^+(aq) + 2NO_3^-(aq) + Ba^{2+}(aq) + 2Cl^-(aq) \longrightarrow 2AgCl(s) + 2NO_3^-(aq) + Ba^{2+}(aq)$

$Ag^+(aq) + Cl^-(aq) \longrightarrow AgCl(s)$

4.4 (a) Beaker A contains a solution of $Zn(NO_3)_2$.
(b) Beaker B contains a solution of $Ba(OH)_2$.
(c) The precipitate is zinc hydroxide, and the spectator ions are Ba^{2+} and NO_3^-.

Molecular: $Zn(NO_3)_2(aq) + Ba(OH)_2(aq) \longrightarrow Zn(OH)_2(s) + Ba(NO_3)_2(aq)$

Total ionic:
$Zn^{2+}(aq) + 2NO_3^-(aq) + Ba^{2+}(aq) + 2OH^-(aq) \longrightarrow Zn(OH)_2(s) + Ba^{2+}(aq) + 2NO_3^-(aq)$

Net ionic: $Zn^{2+}(aq) + 2OH^-(aq) \longrightarrow Zn(OH)_2(s)$

(d) The OH^- ion is limiting.

Mass (g) of $Zn(OH)_2$

$$= 6\ \cancel{OH^-\ particles} \times \frac{0.050\ \cancel{mol\ OH^-\ ions}}{1\ \cancel{OH^-\ particle}} \times \frac{1\ \cancel{mol\ Zn(OH)_2}}{2\ \cancel{mol\ OH^-\ ions}} \times \frac{99.43\ g\ Zn(OH)_2}{1\ \cancel{mol\ Zn(OH)_2}}$$
$$= 15\ g\ Zn(OH)_2$$

4.5 No. of OH^- ions $= 451\ \cancel{mL} \times \frac{1\ \cancel{L}}{10^3\ \cancel{mL}} \times \frac{1.20\ \cancel{mol\ KOH}}{1\ \cancel{L\ soln}} \times \frac{1\ \cancel{mol\ OH^-}}{1\ \cancel{mol\ KOH}} \times \frac{6.022\times10^{23}\ OH^-\ ions}{1\ \cancel{mol\ OH^-}}$
$= 3.26\times10^{23}\ OH^-$

4.6 $Ca(OH)_2(aq) + 2HNO_3(aq) \longrightarrow Ca(NO_3)_2(aq) + 2H_2O(l)$

$Ca^{2+}(aq) + 2OH^-(aq) + 2H^+(aq) + 2NO_3^-(aq) \longrightarrow Ca^{2+}(aq) + 2NO_3^-(aq) + 2H_2O(l)$

$H^+(aq) + OH^-(aq) \longrightarrow H_2O(l)$

4.7 $2H_3O^+(aq) + 2Br^-(aq) + Ca^{2+}(aq) + 2HCO_3^-(aq) \longrightarrow 2CO_2(g) + 4H_2O(l) + 2Br^-(aq) + Ca^{2+}(aq)$

or $H_3O^+(aq) + HCO_3^-(aq) \longrightarrow CO_2(g) + 2H_2O(l)$

The salt is calcium bromide, $CaBr_2$.

4.8 $Ba(OH)_2(aq) + 2HCl(aq) \longrightarrow BaCl_2(aq) + 2H_2O(l)$

Volume (L) of soln

$$= 50.00\ \cancel{mL\ HCl\ soln} \times \frac{1\ L}{10^3\ \cancel{mL}} \times \frac{0.1016\ \cancel{mol\ HCl}}{1\ \cancel{L\ soln}} \times \frac{1\ \cancel{mol\ Ba(OH)_2}}{2\ \cancel{mol\ HCl}} \times \frac{1\ \cancel{L\ soln}}{0.1292\ \cancel{mol\ Ba(OH)_2}}$$
$$= 0.01966\ L$$

4.9 (a) O.N. of Sc = +3; O.N. of O = −2
(b) O.N. of Ga = +3; O.N. of Cl = −1
(c) O.N. of H = +1; O.N. of P = +5; O.N. of O = −2
(d) O.N. of I = +3; O.N. of F = −1

4.10 O.N. decreased: *reduction*

(a) $\overset{+3\ -1}{NCl_3}(l) + 3\overset{+1\ -2}{H_2O}(l) \longrightarrow \overset{-3\ +1}{NH_3}(aq) + 3\overset{+1\ -2\ +1}{HOCl}(aq)$

O.N. increased: *oxidation*

Redox; O.N. of N decreases, and O.N. of Cl increases.

(b) $\overset{+1\ +5\ -2}{AgNO_3}(aq) + \overset{-3\ +1\ -1}{NH_4I}(aq) \longrightarrow \overset{+1\ -1}{AgI}(s) + \overset{-3\ +1\ +5\ -2}{NH_4NO_3}(aq)$

Not redox; no changes in O.N. values.

O.N. decreased: *reduction*

(c) $2\overset{+1\ -2}{H_2S}(g) + 3\overset{0}{O_2}(g) \longrightarrow 2\overset{+4\ -2}{SO_2}(g) + 2\overset{+1\ -2}{H_2O}(g)$

O.N. increased: *oxidation*

Redox; O.N. of S increases, and O.N. of O decreases.

4.11 (a) Fe is the reducing agent; Cl_2 is the oxidizing agent.
(b) C_2H_6 is the reducing agent; O_2 is the oxidizing agent.
(c) CO is the reducing agent; I_2O_5 is the oxidizing agent.

4.12 $K_2Cr_2O_7(aq) + 14HI(aq) \longrightarrow 2KI(aq) + 2CrI_3(aq) + 3I_2(s) + 7H_2O(l)$

4.13 (a) Amount (mol) of Ca^{2+}

$$= 6.53\ \cancel{mL\ soln} \times \frac{1\ \cancel{L}}{10^3\ \cancel{mL}} \times \frac{4.56\times10^{-3}\ \cancel{mol\ KMnO_4}}{1\ \cancel{L\ soln}} \times \frac{5\ \cancel{mol\ CaC_2O_4}}{2\ \cancel{mol\ KMnO_4}} \times \frac{1\ mol\ Ca^{2+}}{1\ \cancel{mol\ CaC_2O_4}}$$
$$= 7.44\times10^{-5}\ mol\ Ca^{2+}$$

$$\text{Molarity of } Ca^{2+} = \frac{7.44\times10^{-2}\ mol\ Ca^{2+}}{2.50\ \cancel{mL\ milk}} \times \frac{10^3\ \cancel{mL}}{1\ L} = 2.98\times10^{-2}\ M\ Ca^{2+}$$

(b) $$\text{Conc. of } Ca^{2+}\ (g/L) = \frac{2.98\times10^{-2}\ \cancel{mol\ Ca^{2+}}}{1\ L} \times \frac{40.08\ g\ Ca^{2+}}{1\ \cancel{mol\ Ca^{2+}}} = \frac{1.19\ g\ Ca^{2+}}{1\ L}$$

Yes, the calculated value is close to the typical value.

4.14 (a) Combination: $S_8(s) + 16F_2(g) \longrightarrow 8SF_4(g)$
S_8 is the reducing agent; F_2 is the oxidizing agent.

(b) Displacement:
$2CsI(aq) + Cl_2(aq) \longrightarrow 2CsCl(aq) + I_2(aq)$
$2Cs^+(aq) + 2I^-(aq) + Cl_2(aq) \longrightarrow 2Cs^+(aq) + 2Cl^-(aq) + I_2(aq)$
$2I^-(aq) + Cl_2(aq) \longrightarrow 2Cl^-(aq) + I_2(aq)$
Cl_2 is the oxidizing agent; CsI is the reducing agent.

(c) Displacement:
$3Ni(NO_3)_2(aq) + 2Cr(s) \longrightarrow 3Ni(s) + 2Cr(NO_3)_3(aq)$
$3Ni^{2+}(aq) + 6NO_3^-(aq) + 2Cr(s) \longrightarrow 3Ni(s) + 2Cr^{3+}(aq) + 6NO_3^-(aq)$
$3Ni^{2+}(aq) + 2Cr(s) \longrightarrow 3Ni(s) + 2Cr^{3+}(aq)$
Cr is the reducing agent; $Ni(NO_3)_2$ is the oxidizing agent.

PROBLEMS

Problems with **colored** numbers are answered in Appendix E and worked in detail in the Student Solutions Manual. Problem sections match those in the text and provide the numbers of relevant sample problems. Most offer Concept Review Questions, Skill-Building Exercises (grouped in pairs covering the same concept), and Problems in Context. The Comprehensive Problems are based on material from any section or previous chapter.

The Role of Water as a Solvent

(Sample Problems 4.1 and 4.2)

Concept Review Questions

4.1 What two factors cause water to be polar?

4.2 What types of substances are most likely to be soluble in water?

4.3 What must be present in an aqueous solution for it to conduct an electric current? What general classes of compounds form solutions that conduct?

4.4 What occurs on the molecular level when an ionic compound dissolves in water?

4.5 Which of the following scenes best represents how the ions occur in an aqueous solution of: (a) $CaCl_2$; (b) Li_2SO_4; (c) NH_4Br?

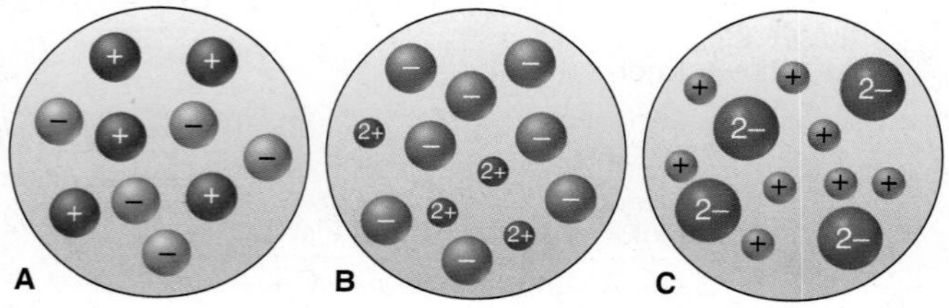

4.6 Which of the following scenes best represents a volume from a solution of magnesium nitrate?

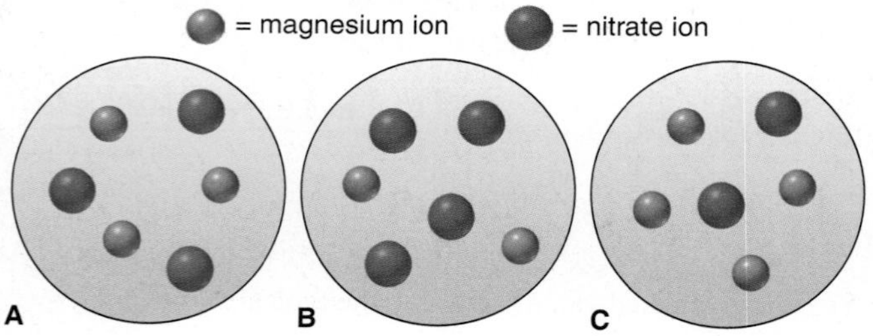

4.7 Why are some ionic compounds soluble in water and others are not?

4.8 Why are some covalent compounds soluble in water and others are not?

4.9 Some covalent compounds dissociate into ions in water. What atom do these compounds have in their structures? What type of solution do they form? Name three examples of such a solution.

Skill-Building Exercises (grouped in similar pairs)

4.10 Is each of the following very soluble in water? Explain.
(a) Benzene, C_6H_6 (b) Sodium hydroxide
(c) Ethanol, CH_3CH_2OH (d) Potassium acetate

4.11 Is each of the following very soluble in water? Explain.
(a) Lithium nitrate (b) Glycine, H_2NCH_2COOH
(c) Pentane (d) Ethylene glycol, $HOCH_2CH_2OH$

4.12 Does an aqueous solution of each of the following conduct an electric current? Explain.
(a) Cesium bromide (b) Hydrogen iodide

4.13 Does an aqueous solution of each of the following conduct an electric current? Explain.
(a) Potassium sulfate (b) Sucrose, $C_{12}H_{22}O_{11}$

4.14 How many total moles of ions are released when each of the following dissolves in water?
(a) 0.32 mol of NH_4Cl (b) 25.4 g of $Ba(OH)_2 \cdot 8H_2O$
(c) 3.55×10^{19} formula units of LiCl

4.15 How many total moles of ions are released when each of the following dissolves in water?
(a) 0.805 mol of Rb_2SO_4 (b) 3.85×10^{-3} g of $Ca(NO_3)_2$
(c) 4.03×10^{19} formula units of $Sr(HCO_3)_2$

4.16 How many total moles of ions are released when each of the following dissolves in water?
(a) 0.75 mol of K_3PO_4 (b) 6.88×10^{-3} g of $NiBr_2 \cdot 3H_2O$
(c) 2.23×10^{22} formula units of $FeCl_3$

4.17 How many total moles of ions are released when each of the following dissolves in water?
(a) 0.734 mol of Na_2HPO_4 (b) 3.86 g of $CuSO_4 \cdot 5H_2O$
(c) 8.66×10^{20} formula units of $NiCl_2$

4.18 How many moles and how many ions of each type are present in each of the following?
(a) 130. mL of 0.45 *M* aluminum chloride
(b) 9.80 mL of a solution containing 2.59 g lithium sulfate/L
(c) 245 mL of a solution containing 3.68×10^{22} formula units of potassium bromide per liter

4.19 How many moles and how many ions of each type are present in each of the following?
(a) 88 mL of 1.75 *M* magnesium chloride
(b) 321 mL of a solution containing 0.22 g aluminum sulfate/L
(c) 1.65 L of a solution containing 8.83×10^{21} formula units of cesium nitrate per liter

4.20 How many moles of H^+ ions are present in the following aqueous solutions?
(a) 1.40 L of 0.25 *M* perchloric acid
(b) 6.8 mL of 0.92 *M* nitric acid
(c) 2.6 L of 0.085 *M* hydrochloric acid

4.21 How many moles of H^+ ions are present in the following aqueous solutions?
(a) 1.4 mL of 0.75 *M* hydrobromic acid
(b) 2.47 mL of 1.98 *M* hydriodic acid
(c) 395 mL of 0.270 *M* nitric acid

Problems in Context

4.22 To study a marine organism, a biologist prepares a 1.00-kg sample to simulate the ion concentrations in seawater. She mixes 26.5 g of NaCl, 2.40 g of $MgCl_2$, 3.35 g of $MgSO_4$, 1.20 g of $CaCl_2$, 1.05 g of KCl, 0.315 g of $NaHCO_3$, and 0.098 g of NaBr in distilled water. (a) If the density of the solution is 1.025 g/cm^3, what is the molarity of each ion? (b) What is the total molarity of alkali metal ions? (c) What is the total molarity of alkaline earth metal ions? (d) What is the total molarity of anions?

4.23 Water "softeners" remove metal ions such as Ca^{2+} and Fe^{3+} by replacing them with enough Na^+ ions to maintain the same number of positive charges in the solution. If 1.0×10^3 L of "hard" water is 0.015 M Ca^{2+} and 0.0010 M Fe^{3+}, how many moles of Na^+ are needed to replace these ions?

Writing Equations for Aqueous Ionic Reactions

Concept Review Questions

4.24 Which ions do not appear in a net ionic equation? Why?

4.25 Write two sets of equations (both molecular and total ionic) with different reactants that have the same net ionic equation as the following equation:

$$Ba(NO_3)_2(aq) + Na_2CO_3(aq) \longrightarrow BaCO_3(s) + 2NaNO_3(aq)$$

Precipitation Reactions

(Sample Problems 4.3 and 4.4)

Concept Review Questions

4.26 Why do some pairs of ions precipitate and others do not?

4.27 Use Table 4.1 to determine which of the following combinations leads to a precipitation reaction. How can you identify the spectator ions in the reaction?
(a) Calcium nitrate(aq) + sodium chloride(aq) $\longrightarrow$
(b) Potassium chloride(aq) + lead(II) nitrate(aq) $\longrightarrow$

4.28 The beakers represent the aqueous reaction of $AgNO_3$ and NaCl. Silver ions are gray. What colors are used to represent NO_3^-, Na^+, and Cl^-? Write molecular, total ionic, and net ionic equations for the reaction.

Skill-Building Exercises (grouped in similar pairs)

4.29 Complete the following precipitation reactions with balanced molecular, total ionic, and net ionic equations:
(a) $Hg_2(NO_3)_2(aq) + KI(aq) \longrightarrow$
(b) $FeSO_4(aq) + Sr(OH)_2(aq) \longrightarrow$

4.30 Complete the following precipitation reactions with balanced molecular, total ionic, and net ionic equations:
(a) $CaCl_2(aq) + Cs_3PO_4(aq) \longrightarrow$
(b) $Na_2S(aq) + ZnSO_4(aq) \longrightarrow$

4.31 When each of the following pairs of aqueous solutions is mixed, does a precipitation reaction occur? If so, write balanced molecular, total ionic, and net ionic equations:
(a) Sodium nitrate + copper(II) sulfate
(b) Ammonium bromide + silver nitrate

4.32 When each of the following pairs of aqueous solutions is mixed, does a precipitation reaction occur? If so, write balanced molecular, total ionic, and net ionic equations:
(a) Potassium carbonate + barium hydroxide
(b) Aluminum nitrate + sodium phosphate

4.33 When each of the following pairs of aqueous solutions is mixed, does a precipitation reaction occur? If so, write balanced molecular, total ionic, and net ionic equations.
(a) Potassium chloride + iron(III) nitrate
(b) Ammonium sulfate + barium chloride

4.34 When each of the following pairs of aqueous solutions is mixed, does a precipitation reaction occur? If so, write balanced molecular, total ionic, and net ionic equations:
(a) Sodium sulfide + nickel(II) sulfate
(b) Lead(II) nitrate + potassium bromide

4.35 If 38.5 mL of lead(II) nitrate solution reacts completely with excess sodium iodide solution to yield 0.628 g of precipitate, what is the molarity of lead(II) ion in the original solution?

4.36 If 25.0 mL of silver nitrate solution reacts with excess potassium chloride solution to yield 0.842 g of precipitate, what is the molarity of silver ion in the original solution?

4.37 With ions shown as spheres and solvent molecules omitted for clarity, the circle (*right*) illustrates the solid formed when a solution containing K^+, Mg^{2+}, Ag^+, or Pb^{2+} (*blue*) is mixed with one containing ClO_4^-, NO_3^-, or SO_4^{2-} (*yellow*). (a) Identify the solid. (b) Write a balanced net ionic equation for the reaction. (c) If each sphere represents 5.0×10^{-4} mol of ion, what mass of product forms?

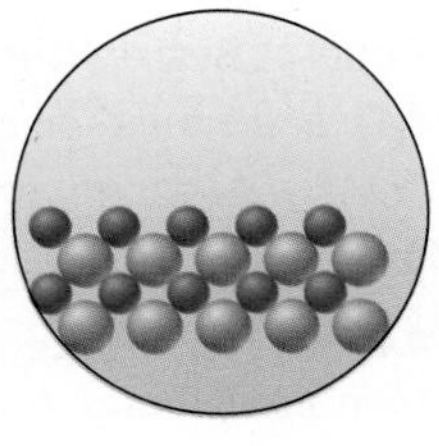

4.38 The precipitation reaction between 25.0 mL of a solution containing a cation (*purple*) and 35.0 mL of a solution containing an anion (*green*) is depicted below (with ions shown as spheres and solvent molecules omitted for clarity).

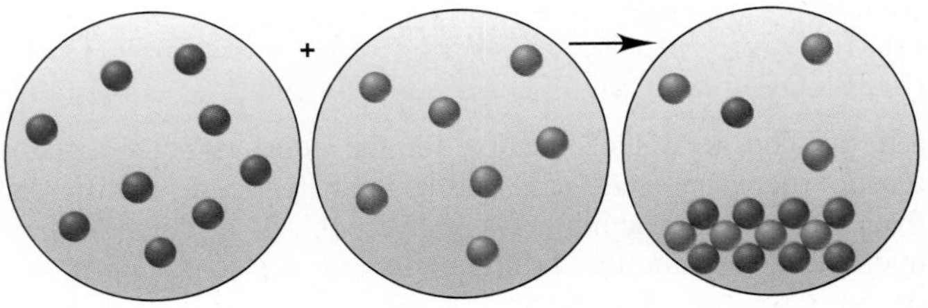

(a) Given the following choices of reactants, write balanced total ionic and net ionic equations that best represent the reaction:
(1) $KNO_3(aq) + CuCl_2(aq) \longrightarrow$
(2) $NaClO_4(aq) + CaCl_2(aq) \longrightarrow$
(3) $Li_2SO_4(aq) + AgNO_3(aq) \longrightarrow$
(4) $NH_4Br(aq) + Pb(CH_3COO)_2(aq) \longrightarrow$
(b) If each sphere represents 2.5×10^{-3} mol of ion, find the total number of ions present.
(c) What is the mass of solid formed?

4.39 A 1.50-g sample of an unknown alkali-metal carbonate was dissolved in water, and 31.10 mL of 0.350 M $CaCl_2$ was required to precipitate all the carbonate ions as $CaCO_3$. Give the name and formula of the unknown compound.

4.40 A 0.750-g sample of a compound that might be iron(II) chloride, nickel(II) chloride, or zinc chloride is dissolved in water, and 22.40 mL of 0.515 M $AgNO_3$ is required to completely precipitate all the chloride ion as AgCl. Name the compound, and write its formula.

Problems in Context

4.41 The mass percent of Cl^- in a seawater sample is determined by titrating 25.00 mL of seawater with $AgNO_3$ solution, causing a precipitation reaction. An indicator is used to detect the end point, which occurs when free Ag^+ ion is present in solution after all the Cl^- has reacted. If 53.63 mL of 0.2970 *M* $AgNO_3$ is required to reach the end point, what is the mass percent of Cl^- in the seawater (*d* of seawater = 1.024 g/mL)?

4.42 Aluminum sulfate, known as *cake alum,* has a wide range of uses, from dyeing leather and cloth to purifying sewage. In aqueous solution, it reacts with base to form a white precipitate. (a) Write balanced total and net ionic equations for its reaction with aqueous NaOH. (b) What mass of precipitate forms when 185.5 mL of 0.533 *M* NaOH is added to 627 mL of a solution that contains 15.8 g of aluminum sulfate per liter?

Acid-Base Reactions

(Sample Problems 4.5 to 4.8)

Concept Review Questions

4.43 Is the total ionic equation the same as the net ionic equation when $Sr(OH)_2(aq)$ and $H_2SO_4(aq)$ react? Explain.

4.44 State a general equation for a neutralization reaction.

4.45 (a) Name three common strong acids. (b) Name three common strong bases. (c) What is a characteristic behavior of a strong acid or a strong base?

4.46 (a) Name three common weak acids. (b) Name one common weak base. (c) What is the major difference between a weak acid and a strong acid or between a weak base and a strong base, and what experiment would you perform to observe it?

4.47 Do either of the following reactions go to completion? If so, what factor(s) cause(s) each to do so?

(a) $MgSO_3(s) + 2HCl(aq) \longrightarrow MgCl_2(aq) + SO_2(g) + H_2O(l)$

(b) $3Ba(OH)_2(aq) + 2H_3PO_4(aq) \longrightarrow Ba_3(PO_4)_2(s) + 6H_2O(l)$

4.48 (a) The net ionic equation for the aqueous neutralization reaction between acetic acid and sodium hydroxide is different from that for the reaction between hydrochloric acid and sodium hydroxide. Explain by writing balanced net ionic equations. (b) For a solution of acetic acid in water, list the major species in decreasing order of concentration.

Skill-Building Exercises (grouped in similar pairs)

4.49 Complete the following acid-base reactions with balanced molecular, total ionic, and net ionic equations:

(a) Potassium hydroxide(*aq*) + hydrobromic acid(*aq*) $\longrightarrow$

(b) Ammonia(*aq*) + hydrochloric acid(*aq*) $\longrightarrow$

4.50 Complete the following acid-base reactions with balanced molecular, total ionic, and net ionic equations:

(a) Cesium hydroxide(*aq*) + nitric acid(*aq*) $\longrightarrow$

(b) Calcium hydroxide(*aq*) + acetic acid(*aq*) $\longrightarrow$

4.51 Limestone (calcium carbonate) is insoluble in water but dissolves when a hydrochloric acid solution is added. Write balanced total ionic and net ionic equations, showing hydrochloric acid as it actually exists in water and the reaction as a proton-transfer process.

4.52 Zinc hydroxide is insoluble in water but dissolves when a nitric acid solution is added. Why? Write balanced total ionic and net ionic equations, showing nitric acid as it actually exists in water and the reaction as a proton-transfer process.

4.53 If 25.98 mL of 0.1180 *M* KOH solution reacts with 52.50 mL of CH_3COOH solution, what is the molarity of the acid solution?

4.54 If 26.25 mL of 0.1850 *M* NaOH solution reacts with 25.00 mL of H_2SO_4, what is the molarity of the acid solution?

Problems in Context

4.55 An auto mechanic spills 88 mL of 2.6 *M* H_2SO_4 solution from an auto battery. How many milliliters of 1.6 *M* $NaHCO_3$ must be poured on the spill to react completely with the sulfuric acid?

4.56 Sodium hydroxide is used extensively in acid-base titrations because it is a strong, inexpensive base. A sodium hydroxide solution was standardized by titrating 25.00 mL of 0.1528 *M* standard hydrochloric acid. The initial buret reading of the sodium hydroxide was 2.24 mL, and the final reading was 39.21 mL. What was the molarity of the base solution?

4.57 An unknown amount of acid can often be determined by adding an excess of base and then "back-titrating" the excess. A 0.3471-g sample of a mixture of oxalic acid, which has two ionizable protons, and benzoic acid, which has one, is treated with 100.0 mL of 0.1000 *M* NaOH. The excess NaOH is titrated with 20.00 mL of 0.2000 *M* HCl. Find the mass % of benzoic acid.

4.58 One of the first steps in the enrichment of uranium for use in nuclear power plants involves a displacement reaction between UO_2 and aqueous HF:

$$UO_2(s) + HF(aq) \longrightarrow UF_4(s) + H_2O(l) \text{ [unbalanced]}$$

How many liters of 2.40 *M* HF will react with 2.15 kg of UO_2?

4.59 A mixture of bases can sometimes be the active ingredient in antacid tablets. If 0.4826 g of a mixture of $Al(OH)_3$ and $Mg(OH)_2$ is neutralized with 17.30 mL of 1.000 *M* HNO_3, what is the mass % of $Al(OH)_3$ in the mixture?

Oxidation-Reduction (Redox) Reactions

(Sample Problems 4.9 to 4.13)

Concept Review Questions

4.60 Describe how to determine the oxidation number of sulfur in (a) H_2S and (b) SO_3^{2-}.

4.61 Is the following a redox reaction? Explain.

$$NH_3(aq) + HCl(aq) \longrightarrow NH_4Cl(aq)$$

4.62 Explain why an oxidizing agent undergoes reduction.

4.63 Why must every redox reaction involve an oxidizing agent and a reducing agent?

4.64 In which of the following equations does sulfuric acid act as an oxidizing agent? In which does it act as an acid? Explain.

(a) $4H^+(aq) + SO_4^{2-}(aq) + 2NaI(s) \longrightarrow 2Na^+(aq) + I_2(s) + SO_2(g) + 2H_2O(l)$

(b) $BaF_2(s) + 2H^+(aq) + SO_4^{2-}(aq) \longrightarrow 2HF(aq) + BaSO_4(s)$

4.65 Identify the oxidizing agent and the reducing agent in the following reaction, and explain your answer:

$$8NH_3(g) + 6NO_2(g) \longrightarrow 7N_2(g) + 12H_2O(l)$$

Skill-Building Exercises (grouped in similar pairs)

4.66 Give the oxidation number of carbon in the following:

(a) CF_2Cl_2 (b) $Na_2C_2O_4$ (c) HCO_3^- (d) C_2H_6

4.67 Give the oxidation number of bromine in the following:

(a) KBr (b) BrF_3 (c) $HBrO_3$ (d) CBr_4

4.68 Give the oxidation number of nitrogen in the following:

(a) NH_2OH (b) N_2F_4 (c) NH_4^+ (d) HNO_2

4.69 Give the oxidation number of sulfur in the following:
(a) $SOCl_2$ (b) H_2S_2 (c) H_2SO_3 (d) Na_2S

4.70 Give the oxidation number of arsenic in the following:
(a) AsH_3 (b) $H_2AsO_4^-$ (c) $AsCl_3$

4.71 Give the oxidation number of phosphorus in the following:
(a) $H_2P_2O_7^{2-}$ (b) PH_4^+ (c) PCl_5

4.72 Give the oxidation number of manganese in the following:
(a) MnO_4^{2-} (b) Mn_2O_3 (c) $KMnO_4$

4.73 Give the oxidation number of chromium in the following:
(a) CrO_3 (b) $Cr_2O_7^{2-}$ (c) $Cr_2(SO_4)_3$

4.74 Identify the oxidizing and reducing agents in the following:
(a) $5H_2C_2O_4(aq) + 2MnO_4^-(aq) + 6H^+(aq) \longrightarrow 2Mn^{2+}(aq) + 10CO_2(g) + 8H_2O(l)$
(b) $3Cu(s) + 8H^+(aq) + 2NO_3^-(aq) \longrightarrow 3Cu^{2+}(aq) + 2NO(g) + 4H_2O(l)$

4.75 Identify the oxidizing and reducing agents in the following:
(a) $Sn(s) + 2H^+(aq) \longrightarrow Sn^{2+}(aq) + H_2(g)$
(b) $2H^+(aq) + H_2O_2(aq) + 2Fe^{2+}(aq) \longrightarrow 2Fe^{3+}(aq) + 2H_2O(l)$

4.76 Identify the oxidizing and reducing agents in the following:
(a) $8H^+(aq) + 6Cl^-(aq) + Sn(s) + 4NO_3^-(aq) \longrightarrow SnCl_6^{2-}(aq) + 4NO_2(g) + 4H_2O(l)$
(b) $2MnO_4^-(aq) + 10Cl^-(aq) + 16H^+(aq) \longrightarrow 5Cl_2(g) + 2Mn^{2+}(aq) + 8H_2O(l)$

4.77 Identify the oxidizing and reducing agents in the following:
(a) $8H^+(aq) + Cr_2O_7^{2-}(aq) + 3SO_3^{2-}(aq) \longrightarrow 2Cr^{3+}(aq) + 3SO_4^{2-}(aq) + 4H_2O(l)$
(b) $NO_3^-(aq) + 4Zn(s) + 7OH^-(aq) + 6H_2O(l) \longrightarrow 4Zn(OH)_4^{2-}(aq) + NH_3(aq)$

4.78 Use the oxidation number method to balance the following equations. Identify the reducing and oxidizing agents:
(a) $HNO_3(aq) + K_2CrO_4(aq) + Fe(NO_3)_2(aq) \longrightarrow KNO_3(aq) + Fe(NO_3)_3(aq) + Cr(NO_3)_3(aq) + H_2O(l)$
(b) $HNO_3(aq) + C_2H_6O(l) + K_2Cr_2O_7(aq) \longrightarrow KNO_3(aq) + C_2H_4O(l) + H_2O(l) + Cr(NO_3)_3(aq)$
(c) $HCl(aq) + NH_4Cl(aq) + K_2Cr_2O_7(aq) \longrightarrow KCl(aq) + CrCl_3(aq) + N_2(g) + H_2O(l)$
(d) $KClO_3(aq) + HBr(aq) \longrightarrow Br_2(l) + H_2O(l) + KCl(aq)$

4.79 Use the oxidation number method to balance the following equations. Identify the reducing and oxidizing agents:
(a) $HCl(aq) + FeCl_2(aq) + H_2O_2(aq) \longrightarrow FeCl_3(aq) + H_2O(l)$
(b) $I_2(s) + Na_2S_2O_3(aq) \longrightarrow Na_2S_4O_6(aq) + NaI(aq)$
(c) $HNO_3(aq) + KI(aq) \longrightarrow NO(g) + I_2(s) + H_2O(l) + KNO_3(aq)$
(d) $PbO(s) + NH_3(aq) \longrightarrow N_2(g) + H_2O(l) + Pb(s)$

Problems in Context

4.80 The active agent in many hair bleaches is hydrogen peroxide. The amount of H_2O_2 in 14.8 g of hair bleach was determined by titration with a standard potassium permanganate solution:

$$2MnO_4^-(aq) + 5H_2O_2(aq) + 6H^+(aq) \longrightarrow 5O_2(g) + 2Mn^{2+}(aq) + 8H_2O(l)$$

(a) How many moles of MnO_4^- were required for the titration if 43.2 mL of 0.105 *M* $KMnO_4$ was needed to reach the end point?
(b) How many moles of H_2O_2 were present in the 14.8-g sample of bleach?
(c) How many grams of H_2O_2 were in the sample?
(d) What is the mass percent of H_2O_2 in the sample?
(e) What is the reducing agent in the redox reaction?

4.81 A person's blood alcohol (C_2H_5OH) level can be determined by titrating a sample of blood plasma with a potassium dichromate solution. The balanced equation is

$$16H^+(aq) + 2Cr_2O_7^{2-}(aq) + C_2H_5OH(aq) \longrightarrow 4Cr^{3+}(aq) + 2CO_2(g) + 11H_2O(l)$$

If 35.46 mL of 0.05961 *M* $Cr_2O_7^{2-}$ is required to titrate 28.00 g of plasma, what is the mass percent of alcohol in the blood?

Elements in Redox Reactions

(Sample Problem 4.14)

Concept Review Questions

4.82 Which type of redox reaction leads to each of the following?
(a) An increase in the number of substances
(b) A decrease in the number of substances
(c) No change in the number of substances

4.83 Why do decomposition redox reactions typically have compounds as reactants, whereas combination redox and displacement redox reactions have one or more elements?

4.84 Which of the types of reactions discussed in Section 4.6 commonly produce more than one compound?

4.85 Are all combustion reactions redox reactions? Explain.

4.86 Give one example of a combination reaction that is a redox reaction and another that is not a redox reaction.

Skill-Building Exercises (grouped in similar pairs)

4.87 Balance each of the following redox reactions and classify it as a combination, decomposition, or displacement reaction:
(a) $Ca(s) + H_2O(l) \longrightarrow Ca(OH)_2(aq) + H_2(g)$
(b) $NaNO_3(s) \longrightarrow NaNO_2(s) + O_2(g)$
(c) $C_2H_2(g) + H_2(g) \longrightarrow C_2H_6(g)$

4.88 Balance each of the following redox reactions and classify it as a combination, decomposition, or displacement reaction:
(a) $HI(g) \longrightarrow H_2(g) + I_2(g)$
(b) $Zn(s) + AgNO_3(aq) \longrightarrow Zn(NO_3)_2(aq) + Ag(s)$
(c) $NO(g) + O_2(g) \longrightarrow N_2O_4(l)$

4.89 Balance each of the following redox reactions and classify it as a combination, decomposition, or displacement reaction:
(a) $Sb(s) + Cl_2(g) \longrightarrow SbCl_3(s)$
(b) $AsH_3(g) \longrightarrow As(s) + H_2(g)$
(c) $Zn(s) + Fe(NO_3)_2(aq) \longrightarrow Zn(NO_3)_2(aq) + Fe(s)$

4.90 Balance each of the following redox reactions and classify it as a combination, decomposition, or displacement reaction:
(a) $Mg(s) + H_2O(g) \longrightarrow Mg(OH)_2(s) + H_2(g)$
(b) $Cr(NO_3)_3(aq) + Al(s) \longrightarrow Al(NO_3)_3(aq) + Cr(s)$
(c) $PF_3(g) + F_2(g) \longrightarrow PF_5(g)$

4.91 Predict the product(s) and write a balanced equation for each of the following redox reactions:
(a) $Sr(s) + Br_2(l) \longrightarrow$
(b) $Ag_2O(s) \xrightarrow{\Delta}$
(c) $Mn(s) + Cu(NO_3)_2(aq) \longrightarrow$

4.92 Predict the product(s) and write a balanced equation for each of the following redox reactions:

(a) $Mg(s) + HCl(aq) \longrightarrow$
(b) $LiCl(l) \xrightarrow{\text{electricity}}$
(c) $SnCl_2(aq) + Co(s) \longrightarrow$

4.93 Predict the product(s) and write a balanced equation for each of the following redox reactions:
(a) $N_2(g) + H_2(g) \longrightarrow$
(b) $NaClO_3(s) \xrightarrow{\Delta}$
(c) $Ba(s) + H_2O(l) \longrightarrow$

4.94 Predict the product(s) and write a balanced equation for each of the following redox reactions:
(a) $Fe(s) + HClO_4(aq) \longrightarrow$
(b) $S_8(s) + O_2(g) \longrightarrow$
(c) $BaCl_2(l) \xrightarrow{\text{electricity}}$

4.95 Predict the product(s) and write a balanced equation for each of the following redox reactions:
(a) Cesium + iodine $\longrightarrow$
(b) Aluminum + aqueous manganese(II) sulfate $\longrightarrow$
(c) Sulfur dioxide + oxygen $\longrightarrow$
(d) Butane and oxygen $\longrightarrow$
(e) Write a balanced net ionic equation for (b).

4.96 Predict the product(s) and write a balanced equation for each of the following redox reactions:
(a) Pentane (C_5H_{12}) + oxygen $\longrightarrow$
(b) Phosphorus trichloride + chlorine $\longrightarrow$
(c) Zinc + hydrobromic acid $\longrightarrow$
(d) Aqueous potassium iodide + bromine $\longrightarrow$
(e) Write a balanced net ionic equation for (d).

4.97 How many grams of O_2 can be prepared from the thermal decomposition of 4.27 kg of HgO? Name and calculate the mass (in kg) of the other product.

4.98 How many grams of chlorine gas can be produced from the electrolytic decomposition of 874 g of calcium chloride? Name and calculate the mass (in g) of the other product.

4.99 In a combination reaction, 1.62 g of lithium is mixed with 6.50 g of oxygen.
(a) Which reactant is present in excess?
(b) How many moles of product are formed?
(c) After reaction, how many grams of each reactant and product are present?

4.100 In a combination reaction, 2.22 g of magnesium is heated with 3.75 g of nitrogen.
(a) Which reactant is present in excess?
(b) How many moles of product are formed?
(c) After reaction, how many grams of each reactant and product are present?

4.101 A mixture of $KClO_3$ and KCl with a mass of 0.950 g was heated to produce O_2. After heating, the mass of residue was 0.700 g. Assuming all the $KClO_3$ decomposed to KCl and O_2, calculate the mass percent of $KClO_3$ in the original mixture.

4.102 A mixture of $CaCO_3$ and CaO weighing 0.693 g was heated to produce gaseous CO_2. After heating, the remaining solid weighed 0.508 g. Assuming all the $CaCO_3$ broke down to CaO and CO_2, calculate the mass percent of $CaCO_3$ in the original mixture.

Problems in Context

4.103 Before arc welding was developed, a displacement reaction involving aluminum and iron(III) oxide was commonly used to produce molten iron (the thermite process). This reaction was used, for example, to connect sections of iron rails for train tracks. Calculate the mass of molten iron produced when 1.50 kg of aluminum reacts with 25.0 mol of iron(III) oxide.

4.104 Iron reacts rapidly with chlorine gas to form a reddish brown, ionic compound (A), which contains iron in the higher of its two common oxidation states. Strong heating decomposes compound A to compound B, another ionic compound, which contains iron in the lower of its two oxidation states. When compound A is formed by the reaction of 50.6 g of Fe and 83.8 g of Cl_2 and then heated, how much compound B forms?

The Reversibility of Reactions and the Equilibrium State

Concept Review Questions

4.105 Why is the equilibrium state called "dynamic"?

4.106 In a decomposition reaction involving a gaseous product, what must be done for the reaction to reach equilibrium?

4.107 Describe what happens on the molecular level when acetic acid dissolves in water.

4.108 When either a mixture of NO and Br_2 or pure nitrosyl bromide (NOBr) is placed in a reaction vessel, the product mixture contains NO, Br_2, and NOBr. Explain.

Problem in Context

4.109 Ammonia is produced by the millions of tons annually for use as a fertilizer. It is commonly made from N_2 and H_2 by the Haber process. Because the reaction reaches equilibrium before going completely to product, the stoichiometric amount of ammonia is not obtained. At a particular temperature and pressure, 10.0 g of H_2 reacts with 20.0 g of N_2 to form ammonia. When equilibrium is reached, 15.0 g of NH_3 has formed. (a) Calculate the percent yield. (b) How many moles of N_2 and H_2 are present at equilibrium?

Comprehensive Problems

4.110 Nutritional biochemists have known for decades that acidic foods cooked in cast-iron cookware can supply significant amounts of dietary iron (ferrous ion). (a) Write a balanced net ionic equation, with oxidation numbers, that supports this fact. (b) Measurements show an increase from 3.3 mg of iron to 49 mg of iron per $\frac{1}{2}$-cup (125-g) serving during the slow preparation of tomato sauce in a cast-iron pot. How many ferrous ions are present in a 26-oz (737-g) jar of the tomato sauce?

4.111 Limestone ($CaCO_3$) is used to remove acidic pollutants from smokestack flue gases. It is heated to form lime (CaO), which reacts with sulfur dioxide to form calcium sulfite. Assuming a 70.% yield in the overall reaction, what mass of limestone is required to remove all the sulfur dioxide formed by the combustion of 8.5×10^4 kg of coal that is 0.33 mass % sulfur?

4.112 The brewing industry uses yeast to convert glucose to ethanol. The baking industry uses the carbon dioxide produced in the same reaction to make bread rise:

$$C_6H_{12}O_6(s) \xrightarrow{\text{yeast}} 2C_2H_5OH(l) + 2CO_2(g)$$

How many grams of ethanol can be produced from 100. g of glucose? What volume of CO_2 is produced? (Assume 1 mol of gas occupies 22.4 L at the conditions used.)

4.113 A chemical engineer determines the mass percent of iron in an ore sample by converting the Fe to Fe^{2+} in acid and then titrating the Fe^{2+} with MnO_4^-. A 1.1081-g sample was dissolved in acid and then titrated with 39.32 mL of 0.03190 *M* $KMnO_4$. The balanced equation is

$$8H^+(aq) + 5Fe^{2+}(aq) + MnO_4^-(aq) \longrightarrow 5Fe^{3+}(aq) + Mn^{2+}(aq) + 4H_2O(l)$$

Calculate the mass percent of iron in the ore.

4.114 Mixtures of $CaCl_2$ and NaCl are used to melt ice on roads. A dissolved 1.9348-g sample of such a mixture was analyzed by using excess $Na_2C_2O_4$ to precipitate the Ca^{2+} as CaC_2O_4. The CaC_2O_4 was dissolved in sulfuric acid, and the resulting $H_2C_2O_4$ was titrated with 37.68 mL of 0.1019 *M* $KMnO_4$ solution.
(a) Write the balanced net ionic equation for the precipitation reaction.
(b) Write the balanced net ionic equation for the titration reaction. (See Sample Problem 4.13.)
(c) What is the oxidizing agent?
(d) What is the reducing agent?
(e) Calculate the mass percent of $CaCl_2$ in the original sample.

4.115 You are given solutions of HCl and NaOH and must determine their concentrations. You use 27.5 mL of NaOH to titrate 100. mL of HCl and 18.4 mL of NaOH to titrate 50.0 mL of 0.0782 *M* H_2SO_4. Find the unknown concentrations.

4.116 The flask (*right*) represents the products of the titration of 25 mL of sulfuric acid with 25 mL of sodium hydroxide.

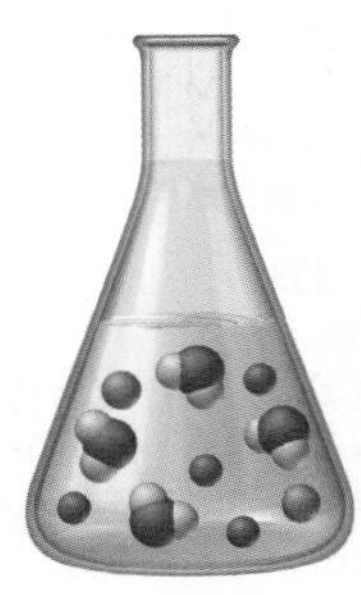

(a) Write balanced molecular, total ionic, and net ionic equations for the reaction.
(b) If each orange sphere represents 0.010 mol of sulfate ion, how many moles of acid and of base reacted?
(c) What are the molarities of the acid and the base?

4.117 To find the mass percent of dolomite $[CaMg(CO_3)_2]$ in a soil sample, a geochemist titrates 13.86 g of soil with 33.56 mL of 0.2516 *M* HCl. What is the mass percent of dolomite in the soil?

4.118 On a lab exam, you have to find the concentrations of the monoprotic (one proton per molecule) acids HA and HB. You are given 43.5 mL of HA solution in one flask. A second flask contains 37.2 mL of HA, and you add enough HB solution to it to reach a final volume of 50.0 mL. You titrate the first HA solution with 87.3 mL of 0.0906 *M* NaOH and the mixture of HA and HB in the second flask with 96.4 mL of the NaOH solution. Calculate the molarity of the HA and HB solutions.

4.119 Nitric acid, a major industrial and laboratory acid, is produced commercially by the multistep Ostwald process, which begins with the oxidation of ammonia:

Step 1. $4NH_3(g) + 5O_2(g) \longrightarrow 4NO(g) + 6H_2O(l)$
Step 2. $2NO(g) + O_2(g) \longrightarrow 2NO_2(g)$
Step 3. $3NO_2(g) + H_2O(l) \longrightarrow 2HNO_3(l) + NO(g)$

(a) What are the oxidizing and reducing agents in each step?
(b) Assuming 100% yield in each step, what mass (in kg) of ammonia must be used to produce 3.0×10^4 kg of HNO_3?

4.120 Various data can be used to find the composition of an alloy (a metallic mixture). Show that calculating the mass % of Mg in a magnesium-aluminum alloy (d = 2.40 g/cm^3) using each of the following pieces of data gives the same answer (within rounding): (a) a sample of the alloy has a mass of 0.263 g (d of Mg = 1.74 g/cm^3; d of Al = 2.70 g/cm^3); (b) an identical sample reacting with excess aqueous HCl forms 1.38×10^{-2} mol of H_2; (c) an identical sample reacting with excess O_2 forms 0.483 g of oxide.

4.121 Use the oxidation number method to balance the following equations by placing coefficients in the blanks. Identify the reducing and oxidizing agents:

(a) $\_KOH(aq) + \_H_2O_2(aq) + \_Cr(OH)_3(s) \longrightarrow \_K_2CrO_4(aq) + \_H_2O(l)$
(b) $\_MnO_4^-(aq) + \_ClO_2^-(aq) + \_H_2O(l) \longrightarrow \_MnO_2(s) + \_ClO_4^-(aq) + \_OH^-(aq)$
(c) $\_KMnO_4(aq) + \_Na_2SO_3(aq) + \_H_2O(l) \longrightarrow \_MnO_2(s) + \_Na_2SO_4(aq) + \_KOH(aq)$
(d) $\_CrO_4^{2-}(aq) + \_HSnO_2^-(aq) + \_H_2O(l) \longrightarrow \_CrO_2^-(aq) + \_HSnO_3^-(aq) + \_OH^-(aq)$
(e) $\_KMnO_4(aq) + \_NaNO_2(aq) + \_H_2O(l) \longrightarrow \_MnO_2(s) + \_NaNO_3(aq) + \_KOH(aq)$
(f) $\_I^-(aq) + \_O_2(g) + \_H_2O(l) \longrightarrow \_I_2(s) + \_OH^-(aq)$

4.122 In 1995, Mario Molina, Paul Crutzen, and F. Sherwood Rowland shared the Nobel Prize in chemistry for their work on atmospheric chemistry. One reaction sequence they proposed for the role of chlorine in the decomposition of stratospheric ozone (we'll see another sequence in Chapter 16) is

(1) $Cl(g) + O_3(g) \longrightarrow ClO(g) + O_2(g)$
(2) $ClO(g) + ClO(g) \longrightarrow Cl_2O_2(g)$
(3) $Cl_2O_2(g) \xrightarrow{\text{light}} 2Cl(g) + O_2(g)$

Over the tropics, O atoms are more common in the stratosphere:

(4) $ClO(g) + O(g) \longrightarrow Cl(g) + O_2(g)$

(a) Which, if any, of these are oxidation-reduction reactions?
(b) Write an overall equation combining reactions 1–3.

4.123 Sodium peroxide (Na_2O_2) is often used in self-contained breathing devices, such as those used in fire emergencies, because it reacts with exhaled CO_2 to form Na_2CO_3 and O_2. How many liters of respired air can react with 80.0 g of Na_2O_2 if each liter of respired air contains 0.0720 g of CO_2?

4.124 A student forgets to weigh a mixture of sodium bromide dihydrate and magnesium bromide hexahydrate. Upon strong heating, the sample loses 252.1 mg of water. The mixture of anhydrous salts reacts with excess $AgNO_3$ solution to form 6.00×10^{-3} mol of solid AgBr. Find the mass % of each compound in the original mixture.

4.125 A typical formulation for window glass is 75% SiO_2, 15% Na_2O, and 10.% CaO by mass. What masses of sand (SiO_2), sodium carbonate, and calcium carbonate must be combined to produce 1.00 kg of glass after carbon dioxide is driven off by thermal decomposition of the carbonates?

4.126 The quantity of dissolved oxygen (DO) in natural waters is an essential parameter for monitoring survival of most aquatic life. DO is affected by temperature and the amount of organic waste. An earlier method for determining DO involved a two-step process:

1. The water sample is treated with KI,

$$O_2(aq) + 4KI(aq) + 2H_2SO_4(aq) \longrightarrow 2I_2(aq) + 2H_2O(l) + 2K_2SO_4(aq)$$

2. The I_2 is titrated with sodium thiosulfate,

$$I_2(aq) + 2Na_2S_2O_3(aq) \longrightarrow Na_2S_4O_6(aq) + 2NaI(aq)$$

A 50.0-mL water sample is treated with KI, and then 15.75 mL of 0.0105 *M* $Na_2S_2O_3$ is required to reach the end point.
(a) Which substance is oxidized in step 1, and which is reduced in step 2?
(b) What mass (g) of O_2 is dissolved in the water sample?

4.127 Physicians who specialize in sports medicine routinely treat athletes and dancers. Ethyl chloride, a local anesthetic commonly used for simple injuries, is the product of the combination of ethylene with hydrogen chloride:

$$C_2H_4(g) + HCl(g) \longrightarrow C_2H_5Cl(g)$$

If 0.100 kg of C_2H_4 and 0.100 kg of HCl react: (a) How many molecules of gas (reactants plus products) are present when the reaction is complete? (b) How many moles of gas are present when half the product forms?

4.128 Thyroxine ($C_{15}H_{11}I_4NO_4$) is a hormone synthesized by the thyroid gland and used to control many metabolic functions in the body. A physiologist determines the mass percent of thyroxine in a thyroid extract by igniting 0.4332 g of extract with sodium carbonate, which converts the iodine to iodide. The iodide is dissolved in water, and bromine and hydrochloric acid are added, which convert the iodide to iodate.
(a) How many moles of iodate form per mole of thyroxine?
(b) Excess bromine is boiled off and more iodide is added, which reacts as shown in the following *unbalanced* equation:

$$IO_3^-(aq) + H^+(aq) + I^-(aq) \longrightarrow I_2(aq) + H_2O(l)$$

How many moles of iodine are produced per mole of thyroxine? (*Hint:* Be sure to balance the charges as well as the atoms.) What are the oxidizing and reducing agents in the reaction?
(c) The iodine reacts completely with 17.23 mL of 0.1000 *M* thiosulfate as shown in the following *unbalanced* equation:

$$I_2(aq) + S_2O_3^{2-}(aq) \longrightarrow I^-(aq) + S_4O_6^{2-}(aq)$$

What is the mass percent of thyroxine in the thyroid extract?

4.129 Over time, as their free fatty acid (FFA) content increases, edible fats and oils become rancid. To measure rancidity, the fat or oil is dissolved in ethanol, and any FFA present is titrated with KOH dissolved in ethanol. In a series of tests on olive oil, a stock solution of 0.050 *M* ethanolic KOH was prepared at 25°C, stored at 0°C, and then placed in a 100-mL buret to titrate oleic acid [an FFA with formula $CH_3(CH_2)_7CH{=}CH(CH_2)_7COOH$] in the oil. Each of four 10.00-g samples of oil took several minutes to titrate: the first required 19.60 mL, the second 19.80 mL, and the third and fourth 20.00 mL of the ethanolic KOH.
(a) What is the apparent acidity of each sample, in terms of mass % of oleic acid? (*Note:* As the ethanolic KOH warms in the buret, its volume increases by a factor of 0.00104/°C.)
(b) Is the variation in acidity a random or systematic error? Explain.
(c) What is the actual acidity? How would you demonstrate this?

4.130 A chemist mixes solid AgCl, $CuCl_2$, and $MgCl_2$ in enough water to give a final volume of 50.0 mL.
(a) With ions shown as spheres and solvent molecules omitted for clarity, which scene best represents the resulting mixture?

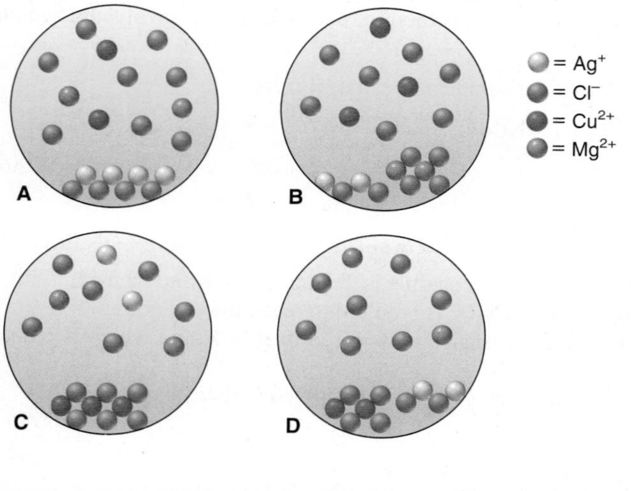

(b) If each sphere represents 5.0×10^{-3} mol of ions, what is the total concentration of *dissolved* (separated) ions?
(c) What is the total mass of solid?

4.131 Calcium dihydrogen phosphate, $Ca(H_2PO_4)_2$, and sodium hydrogen carbonate, $NaHCO_3$, are ingredients of baking powder that react to produce CO_2, which causes dough or batter to rise:

$$Ca(H_2PO_4)_2(s) + NaHCO_3(s) \longrightarrow CO_2(g) + H_2O(g) + CaHPO_4(s) + Na_2HPO_4(s)$$ [unbalanced]

If the baking powder contains 31% $NaHCO_3$ and 35% $Ca(H_2PO_4)_2$ by mass:
(a) How many moles of CO_2 are produced from 1.00 g of baking powder?
(b) If 1 mol of CO_2 occupies 37.0 L at 350°F (a typical baking temperature), what volume of CO_2 is produced from 1.00 g of baking powder?

4.132 In a titration of HNO_3, you add a few drops of phenolphthalein indicator to 50.00 mL of acid in a flask. You quickly add 20.00 mL of 0.0502 *M* NaOH but overshoot the end point, and the solution turns deep pink. Instead of starting over, you add 30.00 mL of the acid, and the solution turns colorless. Then, it takes 3.22 mL of the NaOH to reach the end point.
(a) What is the concentration of the HNO_3 solution?
(b) How many moles of NaOH were in excess after the first addition?

4.133 The active compound in Pepto-Bismol contains C, H, O, and Bi.
(a) When 0.22105 g of it was burned in excess O_2, 0.1422 g of bismuth(III) oxide, 0.1880 g of carbon dioxide, and 0.02750 g of water were formed. What is the empirical formula of this compound?
(b) Given a molar mass of 1086 g/mol, determine the molecular formula.
(c) Complete and balance the acid-base reaction between bismuth(III) hydroxide and salicylic acid ($HC_7H_5O_3$), which is used to form this compound.
(d) A dose of Pepto-Bismol contains 0.600 mg of active ingredient. If the yield of the reaction in part (c) is 88.0%, what mass (in mg) of bismuth(III) hydroxide is required to prepare one dose?

4.134 Two aqueous solutions contain the ions indicated below.

(a) Write balanced molecular, total ionic, and net ionic equations for the reaction that occurs when the solutions are mixed.
(b) If each sphere represents 0.050 mol of ion, what mass (in g) of precipitate forms, assuming 100% yield?
(c) What is the concentration of each ion in solution after reaction?

4.135 In 1997 and 2009, at United Nations conferences on climate change, many nations agreed to expand their research efforts to develop renewable sources of carbon-based fuels. For more than a quarter century, Brazil has been engaged in a program to replace gasoline with ethanol derived from the root crop manioc (cassava).

(a) Write separate balanced equations for the complete combustion of ethanol (C_2H_5OH) and of gasoline (represented by the formula C_8H_{18}).
(b) What mass of oxygen is required to burn completely 1.00 L of a mixture that is 90.0% gasoline (d = 0.742 g/mL) and 10.0% ethanol (d = 0.789 g/mL) by volume?
(c) If 1.00 mol of O_2 occupies 22.4 L, what volume of O_2 is needed to burn 1.00 L of the mixture?
(d) Air is 20.9% O_2 by volume. What volume of air is needed to burn 1.00 L of the mixture?

4.136 In a car engine, gasoline (represented by C_8H_{18}) does not burn completely, and some CO, a toxic pollutant, forms along with CO_2 and H_2O. If 5.0% of the gasoline forms CO:
(a) What is the ratio of CO_2 to CO molecules in the exhaust?
(b) What is the mass ratio of CO_2 to CO?
(c) What percentage of the gasoline must form CO for the mass ratio of CO_2 to CO to be exactly 1/1?

4.137 The amount of ascorbic acid (vitamin C; $C_6H_8O_6$) in tablets is determined by reaction with bromine and then titration of the hydrobromic acid with standard base:

$$C_6H_8O_6(aq) + Br_2(aq) \longrightarrow C_6H_6O_6(aq) + 2HBr(aq)$$
$$HBr(aq) + NaOH(aq) \longrightarrow NaBr(aq) + H_2O(l)$$

A certain tablet is advertised as containing 500 mg of vitamin C. One tablet was dissolved in water and reacted with Br_2. The solution was then titrated with 43.20 mL of 0.1350 M NaOH. Did the tablet contain the advertised quantity of vitamin C?

4.138 In the process of *salting-in,* protein solubility in a dilute salt solution is increased by adding more salt. Because the protein solubility depends on the total ion concentration as well as the ion charge, salts containing doubly charged ions are often more effective than those containing singly charged ions.
(a) How many grams of $MgCl_2$ must dissolve to equal the ion concentration of 12.4 g of NaCl?
(b) How many grams of CaS must dissolve?
(c) Which of the three salt solutions would dissolve the most protein?

4.139 At liftoff, a space shuttle uses a solid mixture of ammonium perchlorate and aluminum powder to obtain great thrust from the volume change of solid to gas. In the presence of a catalyst, the mixture forms solid aluminum oxide and aluminum trichloride and gaseous water and nitrogen monoxide.
(a) Write a balanced equation for the reaction, and identify the reducing and oxidizing agents.
(b) How many total moles of gas (water vapor and nitrogen monoxide) are produced when 50.0 kg of ammonium perchlorate reacts with a stoichiometric amount of Al?
(c) What is the change in volume from this reaction? (d of NH_4ClO_4 = 1.95 g/cc, Al = 2.70 g/cc, Al_2O_3 = 3.97 g/cc, and $AlCl_3$ = 2.44 g/cc; assume 1 mol of gas occupies 22.4 L.)

4.140 A *reaction cycle* for an element is a series of reactions beginning and ending with that element. In the following copper reaction cycle, copper has either a 0 or a +2 oxidation state. Write balanced molecular and net ionic equations for each step.
(1) Copper metal reacts with aqueous bromine to produce a green-blue solution.
(2) Adding aqueous sodium hydroxide forms a blue precipitate.
(3) The precipitate is heated and turns black (water is released).
(4) The black solid dissolves in nitric acid to give a blue solution.
(5) Adding aqueous sodium phosphate forms a green precipitate.
(6) The precipitate forms a blue solution in sulfuric acid.
(7) Copper metal is recovered from the blue solution when zinc metal is added.

4.141 Two 25.0-mL aqueous solutions, labeled A and B, contain the ions indicated:

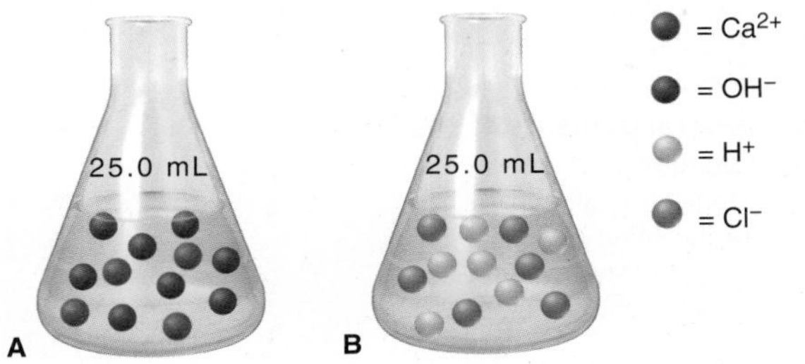

(a) If each sphere represents 1.0×10^{-3} mol of ion, will the equivalence point have been reached when all of B has been added to A?
(b) What is the molarity of B?
(c) What additional volume (mL) of B must be added to reach the equivalence point?

Gases and the Kinetic-Molecular Theory

5

Concepts and skills to review before you study this chapter

- physical states of matter (Section 1.1)
- SI unit conversions (Section 1.5)
- mole-mass-number conversions (Section 3.1)

Amazing as it may seem, what actually occurs when you drink through a straw is that you suck the air out of the straw and the weight of Earth's atmosphere pushes down on the liquid and forces it into your mouth! Other remarkable properties of gases are at work in the rising of a loaf of bread, the operation of a car engine, and, as we'll discuss later in the chapter, even in the act of breathing. People have been studying the behavior of gases and the other states of matter throughout history; in fact, three of the four "elements" of the ancient Greeks were air (gas), water (liquid), and earth (solid). Yet, despite millennia of observations, many questions remain. In this chapter and its companion, Chapter 12, we examine the physical states and their interrelations. Here, we highlight the gaseous state, the one we understand best.

Gases are everywhere. Our atmosphere is a colorless, odorless mixture of 18 gases, some of which—O_2, N_2, H_2O vapor, and CO_2—take part in life-sustaining cycles of redox reactions throughout the environment. And several other gases, such as chlorine and ammonia, have essential roles in industry. Yet, in this chapter, we put aside the *chemical* behavior unique to any particular gas and focus instead *on the* ***physical*** *behavior common to all gases.*

IN THIS CHAPTER . . . We explore the physical behavior of gases and the theory that explains it. In the process, we see how scientists use mathematics to model nature.

- We compare the behaviors of gases, liquids, and solids.
- We discuss laboratory methods for measuring gas pressure.
- We consider laws that describe the behavior of a gas in terms of how its volume changes with a change in (1) pressure, (2) temperature, or (3) amount. We focus on the ideal gas law, which encompasses these three laws, and apply it to solve gas law problems.
- We rearrange the ideal gas law to determine the density and molar mass of an unknown gas, the partial pressure of any gas in a mixture, and the amounts of gaseous reactants and products in a chemical change.
- We see how the kinetic-molecular theory explains the gas laws and accounts for other important behaviors of gas particles.
- We apply key ideas about gas behavior to Earth's atmosphere.
- We find that the behavior of real, not ideal, gases, especially under extreme conditions, requires refinements of the ideal gas law and the kinetic-molecular theory.

5.1 • AN OVERVIEW OF THE PHYSICAL STATES OF MATTER

Most substances can exist as a solid, a liquid, or a gas under appropriate conditions of pressure and temperature. In Chapter 1, we used the relative position and motion of the particles of a substance to distinguish how each state fills a container (see Figure 1.2, p. 6):

Figure 5.1 The three states of matter. Many pure substances, such as bromine (Br_2), can exist under appropriate conditions of pressure and temperature as a gas, liquid, or solid.

- A gas adopts the container shape and fills it, because its particles are far apart and move randomly.
- A liquid adopts the container shape to the extent of its volume, because its particles are close together but free to move around each other.
- A solid has a fixed shape regardless of the container shape, because its particles are close together and held rigidly in place.

Figure 5.1 focuses on the three states of bromine.

Several other aspects of their behaviors distinguish gases from liquids and solids:

1. *Gas volume changes significantly with pressure.* When a sample of gas is confined to a container of variable volume, such as a cylinder with a piston, *increasing* the force on the piston *decreases* the gas volume. Removing the external force allows the volume to increase again. Gases under pressure can do a lot of work: rapidly expanding compressed air in a jackhammer breaks rock and cement; compressed air in tires lifts the weight of a car. In contrast, the volume of a liquid or a solid does not change significantly under pressure.
2. *Gas volume changes significantly with temperature.* When a sample of gas is heated, it expands; when it is cooled, it shrinks. This volume change is 50 to 100 times greater for gases than for liquids or solids. The expansion that occurs when gases are rapidly heated can have dramatic effects, like lifting a rocket into space, and everyday ones, like popping corn.
3. *Gases flow very freely.* Gases flow much more freely than liquids and solids. This behavior allows gases to be transported more easily through pipes, but it also means they leak more rapidly out of small holes and cracks.
4. *Gases have relatively low densities.* Gas density is usually measured in units of grams per liter (g/L), whereas liquid and solid densities are in grams per milliliter (g/mL), about 1000 times as dense (see Table 1.5, p. 22). For example, at 20°C and normal atmospheric pressure, the density of $O_2(g)$ is 1.3 g/**L,** whereas the density of $H_2O(l)$ is 1.0 g/**mL** and the density of NaCl(s) is 2.2 g/**mL.** When a gas cools, its density *increases* because its volume *decreases:* on cooling from 20°C to 0°C, the density of $O_2(g)$ increases from 1.3 to 1.4 g/L.

5. *Gases form a solution in any proportions.* Air is a solution of 18 gases. Two liquids, however, may or may not form a solution: water and ethanol do, but water and gasoline do not. Two solids generally do not form a solution unless they are melted and mixed while liquids, then allowed to solidify (as is done to make the alloy bronze from copper and tin).

Like the way a gas completely fills a container, these macroscopic properties—changing volume with pressure or temperature, great ability to flow, low density, and ability to form solutions—arise because the particles in a gas are much farther apart than those in either a liquid or a solid.

Summary of Section 5.1

- The volume of a gas can be altered significantly by changing the applied force or the temperature. Corresponding changes for liquids and solids are *much* smaller.
- Gases flow more freely and have much lower densities than liquids and solids.
- Gases mix in any proportions to form solutions; liquids and solids generally do not.
- Differences in the physical states are due to the greater average distance between particles in a gas than in a liquid or a solid.

5.2 • GAS PRESSURE AND ITS MEASUREMENT

You can blow up a balloon or pump up a tire because *a gas exerts pressure on the walls of its container.* **Pressure (*P*)** is defined as the force exerted per unit of surface area:

$$\text{Pressure} = \frac{\text{force}}{\text{area}}$$

Earth's gravity attracts the atmospheric gases, and they exert a force uniformly on *all* surfaces. The force, or *weight,* of these gases creates a pressure of about 14.7 pounds per square inch (lb/in^2; psi) of surface. Thus, a pressure of 14.7 lb/in^2 exists on the outside of your room (or your body), and it equals the pressure on the inside. What would happen if the pressures were *not* equal? Consider the empty can attached to a vacuum pump in Figure 5.2. With the pump off (*left*) the can maintains its shape because the pressure on the outside is equal to the pressure on the inside. With the pump on (*right*), much of the air inside is removed, decreasing the internal pressure greatly, and the pressure of the atmosphere easily crushes the can. The vacuum-filtration flasks and tubing that you may have used in the lab have thick walls that withstand the relatively higher external pressure.

Laboratory Devices for Measuring Gas Pressure

The **barometer** is used to measure atmospheric pressure. The device is still essentially the same as it was when invented in 1643 by the Italian physicist Evangelista Torricelli:

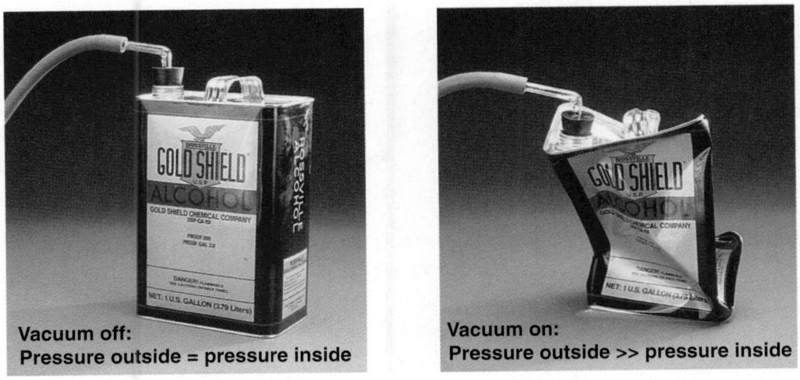

Figure 5.2 Effect of atmospheric pressure on a familiar object.

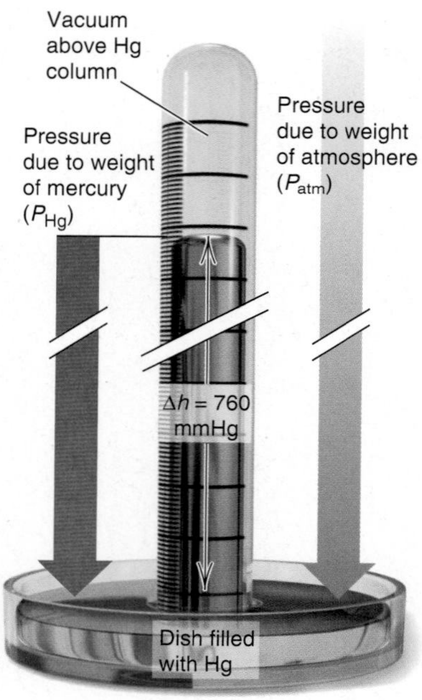

Figure 5.3 A mercury barometer. The pressure of the atmosphere, P_{atm}, balances the pressure of the mercury column, P_{Hg}.

a tube about 1 m long, closed at one end, filled with mercury (atomic symbol, Hg), and inverted into a dish containing more mercury. When the tube is inverted, some of the mercury flows out into the dish, and a vacuum forms above the mercury remaining in the tube (Figure 5.3). At sea level, under ordinary atmospheric conditions, the mercury stops flowing out when the surface of the mercury in the tube is about 760 mm above the surface of the mercury in the dish. At that height, the column of mercury exerts the same pressure (weight/area) on the mercury surface in the dish as the atmosphere does: $P_{Hg} = P_{atm}$. Likewise, if you evacuate a closed tube and invert it into a dish of mercury, the atmosphere pushes the mercury up to a height of about 760 mm.

Notice that we did not specify the diameter of the barometer tube. If the mercury in a 1-cm diameter tube rises to a height of 760 mm, the mercury in a 2-cm diameter tube will rise to that height also. The *weight* of mercury is greater in the wider tube, but so is the area; thus, the *pressure,* the *ratio* of weight to area, is the same.

Because the pressure of the mercury column is directly proportional to its height, a unit commonly used for pressure is millimeters of mercury (mmHg). We discuss other units of pressure shortly. *At sea level and 0°C, normal atmospheric pressure is 760 mmHg;* at the top of Mt. Everest (elevation 29,028 ft, or 8848 m), the atmospheric pressure is only about 270 mmHg. Thus, *pressure decreases with altitude:* the column of air above the sea is taller, so it weighs more than the column of air above Mt. Everest.

Laboratory barometers contain mercury because its high density allows a barometer to be a convenient size. If a barometer contained water instead, it would have to be more than 34 ft high, because the pressure of the atmosphere equals the pressure of a column of water about 10,300 mm (almost 34 ft) high. For a given pressure, the ratio of heights (h) of the liquid columns is inversely related to the ratio of the densities (d) of the liquids:

$$\frac{h_{H_2O}}{h_{Hg}} = \frac{d_{Hg}}{d_{H_2O}}$$

Interestingly, several centuries ago, people thought a vacuum had mysterious "suction" powers, and they didn't understand why a suction pump could remove water from a well only to a depth of 34 feet. We know now, as the great 17th-century scientist Galileo explained, that a vacuum does not suck mercury up into a barometer tube, a suction pump does not suck water up from a well, the vacuum pump in Figure 5.2 does not suck in the walls of the crushed can, and the vacuum you create in a straw does not suck the drink into your mouth. Only matter—in this case, the atmospheric gases—can exert a force.

Manometers are devices used to measure the pressure of a gas in an experiment. Figure 5.4 shows two types of manometer. In the *closed-end manometer (left side),* a

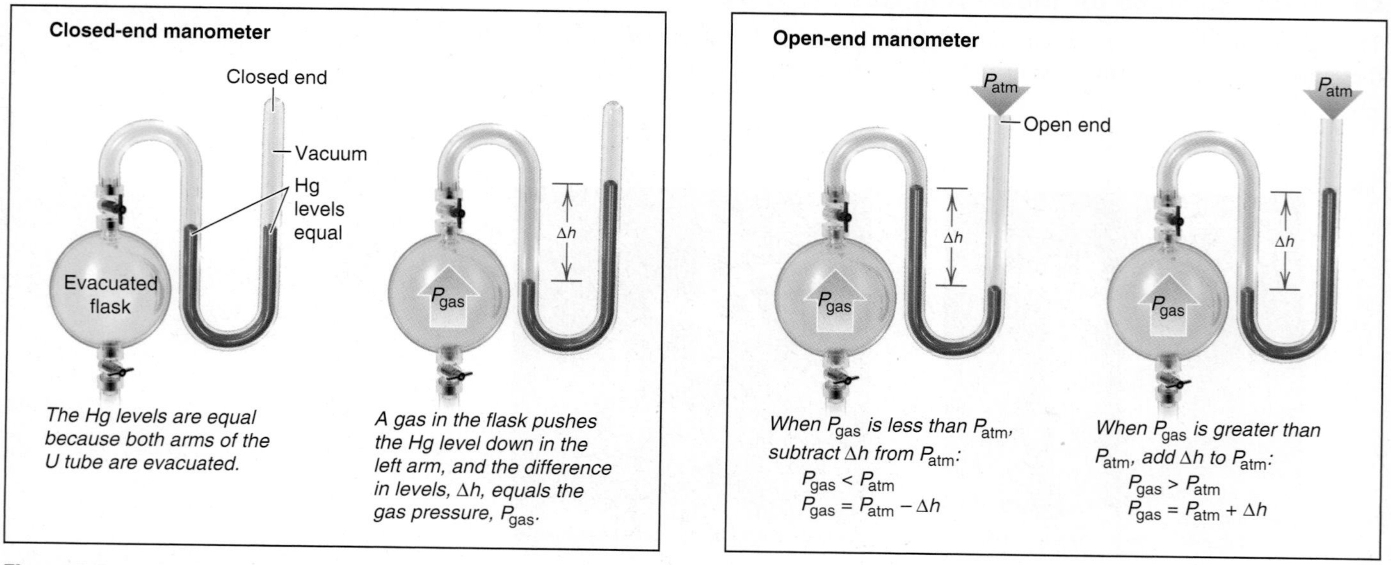

Figure 5.4 Two types of manometer.

mercury-filled, curved tube is *closed* at one end and attached to a flask at the other. When the flask is evacuated, the mercury levels in the two arms of the tube are the same because no gas exerts pressure on either mercury surface. When a gas is in the flask, it pushes down the mercury level in the near arm, causing the level to rise in the far arm. The *difference* in column heights (Δh) equals the gas pressure.

The *open-end manometer* (*right side* of Figure 5.4) also consists of a curved tube filled with mercury, but one end of the tube is *open* to the atmosphere and the other is connected to the gas sample. The atmosphere pushes on one mercury surface, and the gas pushes on the other. Again, Δh equals the difference between two pressures. But, when using this type of manometer, we must measure the atmospheric pressure with a barometer and either add or subtract Δh from that value.

Units of Pressure

Pressure results from a force exerted on an area. The SI unit of force is the newton (N): $1\ \text{N} = 1\ \text{kg}\cdot\text{m/s}^2$ (about the weight of an apple). The SI unit of pressure is the **pascal (Pa),** which equals a force of one newton exerted on an area of one square meter:

$$1\ \text{Pa} = 1\ \text{N/m}^2$$

A much larger unit is the **standard atmosphere (atm),** the average atmospheric pressure measured at sea level and 0°C. It is defined in terms of the pascal:

$$1\ \text{atm} = 101.325\ \text{kilopascals (kPa)} = 1.01325\times10^5\ \text{Pa}$$

Another common unit is the **millimeter of mercury (mmHg),** mentioned earlier; in honor of Torricelli, this unit has been renamed the **torr:**

$$1\ \text{torr} = 1\ \text{mmHg} = \frac{1}{760}\ \text{atm} = \frac{101.325}{760}\ \text{kPa} = 133.322\ \text{Pa}$$

The *bar* is coming into more common use in chemistry:

$$1\ \text{bar} = 1\times10^2\ \text{kPa} = 1\times10^5\ \text{Pa}$$

Despite a gradual change to SI units, many chemists still express pressure in torrs and atmospheres, so those units are used in this book, with reference to pascals and bars. Table 5.1 lists some important pressure units with the corresponding values for normal atmospheric pressure.

Table 5.1 Common Units of Pressure

Unit	Normal Atmospheric Pressure at Sea Level and 0°C
pascal (Pa); kilopascal (kPa)	1.01325×10^5 Pa; 101.325 kPa
atmosphere (atm)	1 atm*
millimeters of mercury (mmHg)	760 mmHg*
torr	760 torr*
pounds per square inch (lb/in^2 or psi)	14.7 lb/in^2
bar	1.01325 bar

*This is an exact quantity; in calculations, we use as many significant figures as necessary.

Sample Problem 5.1 Converting Units of Pressure

Problem A geochemist heats a limestone ($CaCO_3$) sample and collects the CO_2 released in an evacuated flask attached to a closed-end manometer. After the system comes to room temperature, $\Delta h = 291.4$ mmHg. Calculate the CO_2 pressure in torrs, atmospheres, and kilopascals.

Plan The CO_2 pressure is given in units of mmHg, so we construct conversion factors from Table 5.1 to find the pressure in the other units.

Solution Converting from mmHg to torr:

$$P_{CO_2}\text{ (torr)} = 291.4 \cancel{\text{mmHg}} \times \frac{1\text{ torr}}{1 \cancel{\text{mmHg}}} = 291.4\text{ torr}$$

Converting from torr to atm:

$$P_{CO_2}\text{ (atm)} = 291.4 \cancel{\text{torr}} \times \frac{1\text{ atm}}{760 \cancel{\text{torr}}} = 0.3834\text{ atm}$$

Converting from atm to kPa:

$$P_{CO_2}\text{ (kPa)} = 0.3834 \cancel{\text{atm}} \times \frac{101.325\text{ kPa}}{1 \cancel{\text{atm}}} = 38.85\text{ kPa}$$

Check There are 760 torr in 1 atm, so ~300 torr should be <0.5 atm. There are ~100 kPa in 1 atm, so <0.5 atm should be <50 kPa.

Comment 1. In the conversion from torr to atm, we retained four significant figures because this unit conversion factor involves *exact* numbers; that is, 760 torr has as many significant figures as the calculation requires (see the footnote on Table 5.1).
2. From here on, except in particularly complex situations, *unit canceling will no longer be shown.*

Follow-Up Problem 5.1 The CO_2 released from another mineral sample was collected in an evacuated flask connected to an open-end manometer. If the barometer reading is 753.6 mmHg and P_{gas} is less than P_{atm} to give a Δh of 174.0 mmHg, calculate P_{CO_2} in torrs, pascals, and lb/in^2.

Summary of Section 5.2

- Gases exert pressure (force/area) on all surfaces they contact.
- A barometer measures atmospheric pressure based on the height of a mercury column that the atmosphere can support (760 mmHg at sea level and 0°C).
- Closed-end and open-end manometers are used to measure the pressure of a gas sample.
- Pressure units include the atmosphere (atm), torr (identical to mmHg), and pascal (Pa, the SI unit).

5.3 • THE GAS LAWS AND THEIR EXPERIMENTAL FOUNDATIONS

The physical behavior of a sample of gas can be described completely by four variables: pressure (P), volume (V), temperature (T), and amount (number of moles, n). The variables are interdependent, which means that *any one of them can be determined by measuring the other three.* Three key relationships exist among the four gas variables—Boyle's, Charles's, and Avogadro's laws. Each of these *gas laws expresses the effect of one variable on another, with the remaining two variables held constant.* Because gas volume is so easy to measure, the laws are expressed as the effect on gas volume of a change in the pressure, temperature, or amount of the gas.

The individual gas laws are special cases of a unifying relationship called the *ideal gas law,* which quantitatively describes the behavior of an **ideal gas,** one that exhibits linear relationships among volume, pressure, temperature, and amount. Although *no ideal gas actually exists,* most simple gases, such as N_2, O_2, H_2, and the noble gases, behave nearly ideally at ordinary temperatures and pressures. We discuss the ideal gas law after the three individual laws.

The Relationship Between Volume and Pressure: Boyle's Law

Following Torricelli's invention of the barometer, the great 17th-century English chemist Robert Boyle studied the effect of pressure on the volume of a sample of gas.

1. *The experiment.* Figure 5.5 illustrates the setup Boyle might have used in his experiments (parts A and B), the data he might have collected (part C), and graphs of

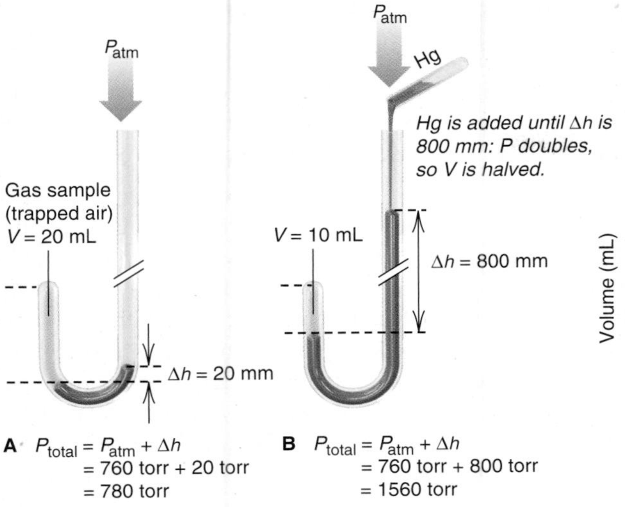

C

V (mL)	P (torr) Δh	+ P_{atm}	= P_{total}	$\frac{1}{P_{total}}$	PV (torr•mL)
20.0	20.0	760	780	0.00128	1.56×10^4
15.0	278	760	1038	0.000963	1.56×10^4
10.0	800	760	1560	0.000641	1.56×10^4
5.0	2352	760	3112	0.000321	1.56×10^4

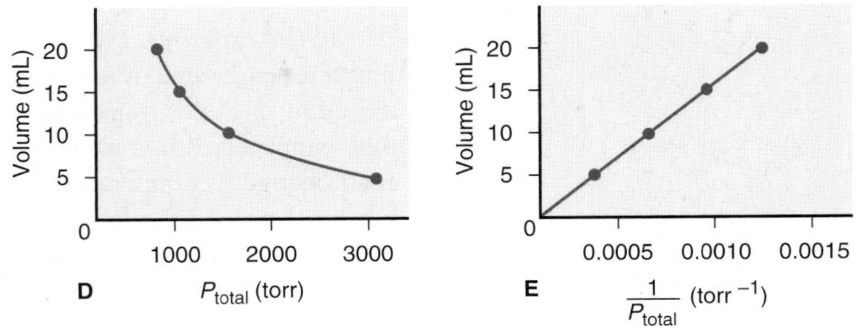

Figure 5.5 Boyle's law, the relationship between the volume and pressure of a gas.

the data (parts D and E). Boyle sealed the shorter leg of a J-shaped glass tube and poured mercury into the longer open leg, thereby trapping some air (the gas in the experiment) in the shorter leg. He calculated the gas volume (V_{gas}) from the height of the trapped air and the diameter of the tube. The total pressure, P_{total}, applied to the trapped gas is the pressure of the atmosphere, P_{atm} (760 mm, measured with a barometer), plus the difference in the heights of the mercury columns (Δh) in the two legs of the J tube, 20 mm (Figure 5.5A); thus, P_{total} is 780 torr. By adding mercury, Boyle increased P_{total}, and the gas volume decreased. In Figure 5.5B, more mercury has been added to the original Δh of 20 mm, so P_{total} doubles to 1560 torr; note that V_{gas} is halved from 20 mL to 10 mL. In this way, by keeping the temperature and amount of gas constant, Boyle was able to measure the effect of the applied pressure on gas volume.

Note the following results in Figure 5.5:

- The product of corresponding P and V values is a constant (part C, rightmost column).
- V is *inversely* proportional to P (part D).
- V is *directly* proportional to $1/P$ (part E), and a plot of V versus $1/P$ is linear. This *linear relationship between two gas variables* is a hallmark of ideal gas behavior.

2. *Conclusion and statement of the law.* The generalization of Boyle's observations is known as **Boyle's law:** *at constant temperature, the volume occupied by a fixed amount of gas is* ***inversely*** *proportional to the applied (external) pressure,* or

$$V \propto \frac{1}{P} \qquad [T \text{ and } n \text{ fixed}] \qquad (5.1)$$

This relationship can also be expressed as

$$PV = \text{constant} \quad \text{or} \quad V = \frac{\text{constant}}{P} \qquad [T \text{ and } n \text{ fixed}]$$

That is, at fixed T and n, $P\uparrow, V\downarrow$ and $P\downarrow, V\uparrow$

The constant is the same for most simple gases under ordinary conditions. Thus, tripling the external pressure reduces the volume of a gas to a third of its initial value; halving the pressure doubles the volume; and so forth.

The wording of Boyle's law focuses on *external* pressure. But, notice that the mercury level rises as mercury is added, until the pressure of the trapped gas *on* the mercury increases enough to stop its rise. At that point, the pressure exerted *on* the gas equals the pressure exerted *by* the gas (P_{gas}). Thus, in general, if V_{gas} increases, P_{gas} decreases, and vice versa.

The Relationship Between Volume and Temperature: Charles's Law

Boyle's work showed that the pressure-volume relationship holds only at constant temperature, but why should that be so? It would take more than a century, until the work of French scientists J. A. C. Charles and J. L. Gay-Lussac, for the relationship between gas volume and temperature to be understood.

1. *The experiment.* Let's examine this relationship by measuring the volume at different temperatures of a fixed amount of a gas under constant pressure. A straight tube, closed at one end, traps a fixed amount of gas (air) under a small mercury plug. The tube is immersed in a water bath that is warmed with a heater or cooled with ice. After each change of temperature, we measure the length of the gas column, which is proportional to its volume. The total pressure exerted on the gas is constant because the mercury plug and the atmospheric pressure do not change (Figure 5.6, parts A and B).

Figure 5.6C shows some typical data. Consider the red line, which shows how the volume of 0.04 mol of gas at 1 atm pressure changes with temperature. Extrapolating that line to lower temperatures (dashed portion) shows that, in theory, the gas occupies zero volume at −273.15°C (the intercept on the temperature axis). Plots for a different amount of gas (green) or a different gas pressure (blue) have different slopes, but they all converge at −273.15°C. William Thomson (Lord Kelvin) later used this linear relation between gas volume and temperature to devise the absolute temperature scale (Section 1.5).

2. *Conclusion and statement of the law.* Above all, note that *the volume-temperature relationship is linear,* but, unlike volume and pressure, volume and temperature are *directly* proportional. This behavior is incorporated into the modern statement of the volume-temperature relationship, which is known as **Charles's law:** *at constant pressure, the volume occupied by a fixed amount of gas is* ***directly*** *proportional to its absolute (Kelvin) temperature,* or

$$V \propto T \qquad [P \text{ and } n \text{ fixed}] \tag{5.2}$$

This relationship can also be expressed as

$$\frac{V}{T} = \text{constant} \quad \text{or} \quad V = \text{constant} \times T \qquad [P \text{ and } n \text{ fixed}]$$

That is, at fixed P and n, $T\uparrow, V\uparrow$ and $T\downarrow, V\downarrow$

If T increases, V increases, and vice versa. Once again, for any given P and n, the constant is the same for most simple gases under ordinary conditions.

Figure 5.6 Charles's law, the relationship between the volume and temperature of a gas.

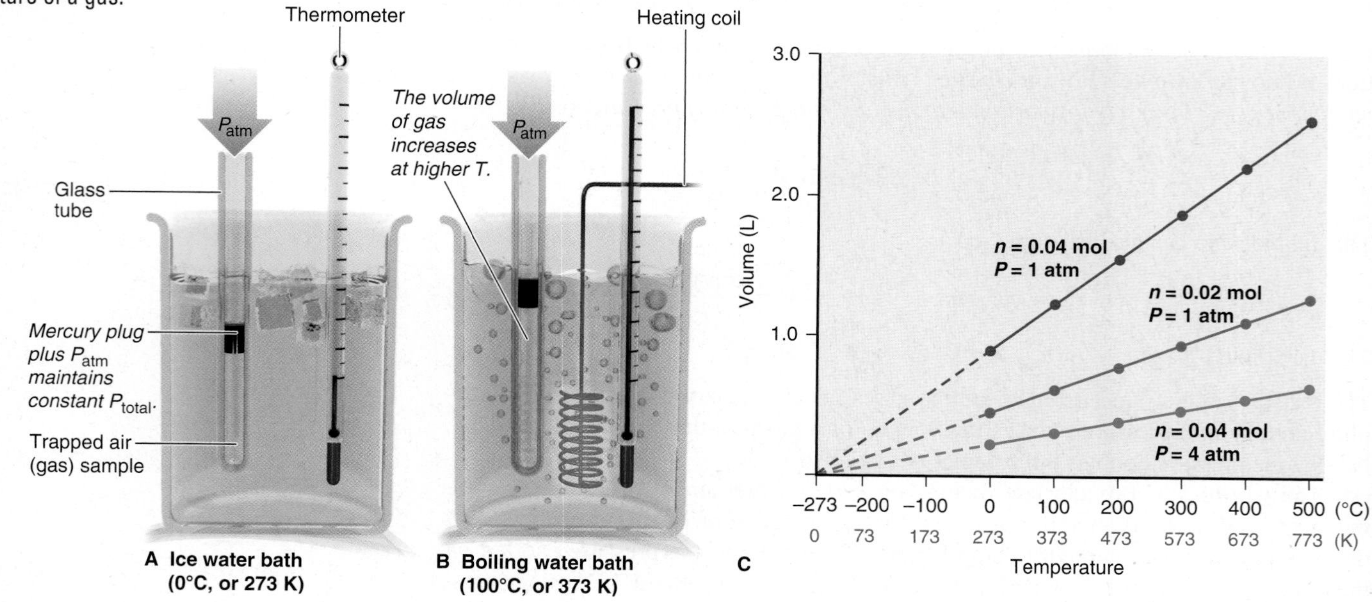

Absolute zero (0 K or −273.15°C) is the temperature at which an ideal gas would have zero volume. (Absolute zero has never been reached, but physicists have attained 10^{-9} K.) In reality, no sample of matter can have zero volume, and every real gas condenses to a liquid at some temperature higher than 0 K. Nevertheless, the linear dependence of volume on absolute temperature holds for most common gases over a wide temperature range. This dependence of gas volume on the *absolute* temperature adds a practical requirement for chemists (and chemistry students): *the Kelvin scale must be used in gas law calculations.* For instance, if the temperature changes from 200 K to 400 K, the volume of gas doubles. But, if the temperature changes from 200°C to 400°C, the volume increases by a factor of 1.42; that is,

$$\left(\frac{400°\text{C} + 273.15}{200°\text{C} + 273.15}\right) = \frac{673}{473} = 1.42$$

Other Relationships Based on Boyle's and Charles's Laws Two other important relationships arise from Boyle's and Charles's laws:

1. *The pressure-temperature relationship.* Charles's law is expressed as the effect of temperature on gas *volume* at constant pressure. But volume and pressure are interdependent, so a similar relationship can be expressed for the effect of temperature on pressure (sometimes referred to as *Amontons's law*). Measure the pressure in your car or bike tires before and after a long ride, and you'll find that it increases. Heating due to friction between the tires and the road increases the air temperature inside the tires, but since a tire's volume can't increase very much, the air pressure does. Thus, *at constant volume, the pressure exerted by a fixed amount of gas is directly proportional to the absolute temperature:*

$$P \propto T \qquad [V \text{ and } n \text{ fixed}] \qquad (5.3)$$

or

$$\frac{P}{T} = \text{constant} \qquad \text{or} \qquad P = \text{constant} \times T$$

That is, at fixed V and n, $T\uparrow, P\uparrow$ and $T\downarrow, P\downarrow$

2. *The combined gas law.* Combining Boyle's and Charles's laws gives the *combined gas law,* which applies to cases when changes in *two* of the three variables (V, P, T) affect the third:

$$V \propto \frac{T}{P} \qquad \text{or} \qquad V = \text{constant} \times \frac{T}{P} \qquad \text{or} \qquad \frac{PV}{T} = \text{constant}$$

The Relationship Between Volume and Amount: Avogadro's Law

Let's see why both Boyle's and Charles's laws specify a fixed amount of gas.

1. *The experiment.* Figure 5.7 shows an experiment that involves two small test tubes, each fitted to a much larger piston-cylinder assembly. We add 0.10 mol (4.4 g) of dry ice (solid CO_2) to the first tube (A) and 0.20 mol (8.8 g) to the second tube (B). As the solid CO_2 warms to room temperature, it changes to gaseous CO_2, and the volume increases until $P_{gas} = P_{atm}$. At constant temperature, when all the solid has changed to gas, cylinder B has twice the volume of cylinder A.

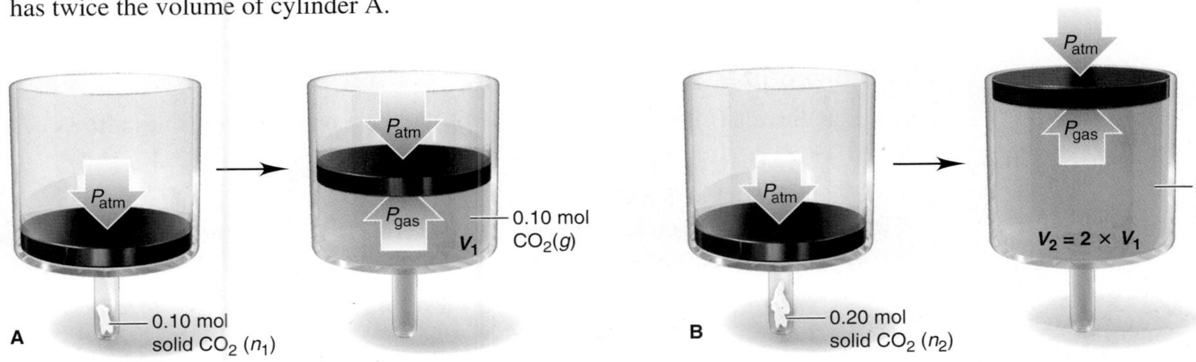

Figure 5.7 The relationship between the volume and amount of a gas.

2. *Conclusion and statement of the law.* Thus, *at fixed temperature and pressure, the volume occupied by a gas is directly proportional to the amount (mol) of gas:*

$$V \propto n \qquad [P \text{ and } T \text{ fixed}] \tag{5.4}$$

That is, as n increases, V increases, and vice versa. This relationship is also expressed as

$$\frac{V}{n} = \text{constant} \qquad \text{or} \qquad V = \text{constant} \times n$$

That is, at fixed P and T, $n\uparrow, V\uparrow$ and $n\downarrow, V\downarrow$

The constant is the same for all simple gases at ordinary temperature and pressure. This relationship is another way of expressing **Avogadro's law,** which states that *at fixed temperature and pressure, equal volumes of* ***any*** *ideal gas contain equal numbers of particles (or moles).*

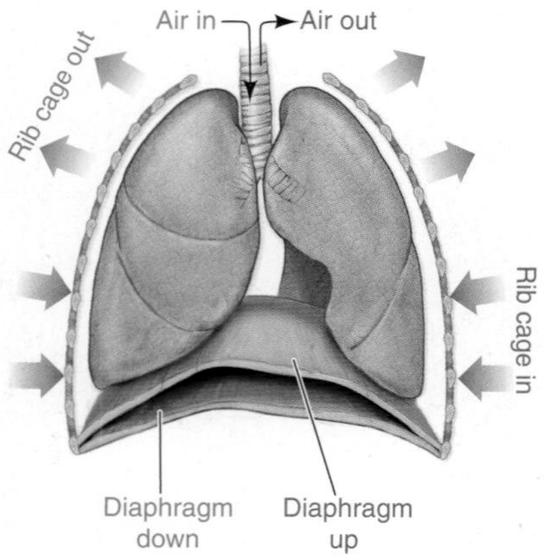

Figure 5.8 The process of breathing applies the gas laws.

Familiar Applications of the Gas Laws The gas laws apply to countless familiar phenomena. In a car engine, a reaction occurs in which fewer moles of gasoline and O_2 form more moles of CO_2 and H_2O vapor, and heat is released. The increase in n (Avogadro's law) and T (Charles's law) increases V, and the piston is pushed back. Dynamite is a solid that forms more moles of hot gases very rapidly when it reacts (Avogadro's and Charles's laws). Dough rises because yeast digests sugar, which creates bubbles of CO_2 (Avogadro's law); the dough expands more as the bread bakes in a hot oven (Charles's law).

No application of the gas laws can be more vital or familiar than breathing (Figure 5.8). When you inhale, muscles move your diaphragm down and your rib cage out (*blue*). This coordinated movement increases the volume of your lungs, which decreases the air pressure inside them (Boyle's law). The inside pressure is 1–3 torr *less* than atmospheric pressure, so air rushes in. The greater amount of air stretches the elastic tissue of the lungs and expands the volume further (Avogadro's law). The air also expands as it warms from the external temperature to your body temperature (Charles's law). When you exhale, the diaphragm moves up and the rib cage moves in, so your lung volume decreases (*red*). The inside pressure becomes 1–3 torr *more* than the outside pressure (Boyle's law), so air rushes out.

Gas Behavior at Standard Conditions

To better understand the factors that influence gas behavior, chemists have assigned a baseline set of *standard conditions* called **standard temperature and pressure (STP):**

$$\text{STP:} \quad 0°\text{C } (273.15 \text{ K}) \text{ and } 1 \text{ atm } (760 \text{ torr}) \tag{5.5}$$

Under these conditions, the volume of 1 mol of an ideal gas is called the **standard molar volume:**

$$\text{Standard molar volume} = 22.4141 \text{ L or } 22.4 \text{ L } [\text{to 3 sf}] \tag{5.6}$$

At STP, helium (He), nitrogen (N_2), oxygen (O_2), and other simple gases behave nearly ideally (Figure 5.9). Note that the mass, and thus the density (d), depend on the specific gas, but 1 mol of any of them occupies 22.4 L at STP. Figure 5.10 compares the volumes of some familiar objects with the standard molar volume of an ideal gas.

The Ideal Gas Law

Each of the three gas laws shows how one of the three other gas variables affects gas volume:

- Boyle's law focuses on pressure ($V \propto 1/P$).
- Charles's law focuses on temperature ($V \propto T$).
- Avogadro's law focuses on amount (mol) of gas ($V \propto n$).

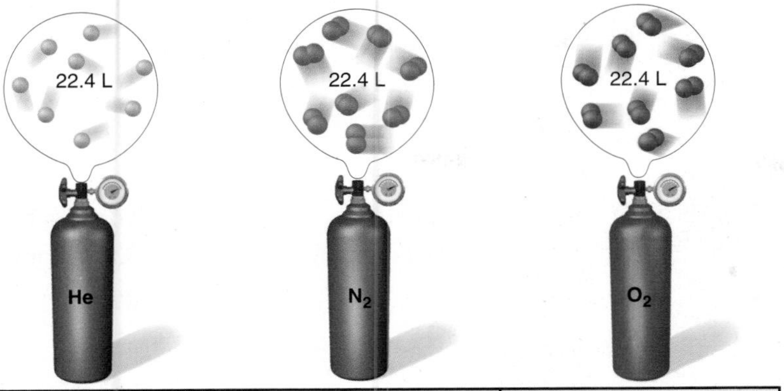

$n = 1$ mol	$n = 1$ mol	$n = 1$ mol
$P = 1$ atm (760 torr)	$P = 1$ atm (760 torr)	$P = 1$ atm (760 torr)
$T = 0°C$ (273 K)	$T = 0°C$ (273 K)	$T = 0°C$ (273 K)
$V = 22.4$ L	$V = 22.4$ L	$V = 22.4$ L
Number of gas particles $= 6.022 \times 10^{23}$	Number of gas particles $= 6.022 \times 10^{23}$	Number of gas particles $= 6.022 \times 10^{23}$
Mass = 4.003 g	Mass = 28.02 g	Mass = 32.00 g
$d = 0.179$ g/L	$d = 1.25$ g/L	$d = 1.43$ g/L

Figure 5.9 Standard molar volume. One mole of an ideal gas occupies 22.4 L at STP (0°C and 1 atm).

Figure 5.10 The volumes of 1 mol (22.4 L) of an ideal gas and of some familiar objects: 1 gal of milk (3.79 L), a basketball (7.50 L), and 2.00 L of a carbonated drink.

By combining these individual effects, we obtain the **ideal gas law** (or *ideal gas equation*):

$$V \propto \frac{nT}{P} \qquad \text{or} \qquad PV \propto nT \qquad \text{or} \qquad \frac{PV}{nT} = R$$

where R is a proportionality constant known as the **universal gas constant.** Rearranging gives the most common form of the ideal gas law:

$$PV = nRT \tag{5.7}$$

We obtain a value of R by measuring the volume, temperature, and pressure of a given amount of gas and substituting the values into the ideal gas law. For example, using standard conditions for the gas variables and 1 mol of gas, we have

$$R = \frac{PV}{nT} = \frac{1 \text{ atm} \times 22.4141 \text{ L}}{1 \text{ mol} \times 273.15 \text{ K}} = 0.082058 \frac{\text{atm·L}}{\text{mol·K}} = 0.0821 \frac{\text{atm·L}}{\text{mol·K}} \text{ [3 sf]} \tag{5.8}$$

This numerical value of R corresponds to P, V, and T expressed *in these units; R has a different numerical value when different units are used.* For example, on p. 209, R has the value 8.314 J/mol·K (J stands for joule, the SI unit of energy).

Figure 5.11 on the next page makes a central point: the ideal gas law *becomes* one of the individual gas laws when two of the four variables are kept constant. When initial conditions (subscript 1) change to final conditions (subscript 2), we have

$$P_1V_1 = n_1RT_1 \quad \text{and} \quad P_2V_2 = n_2RT_2$$

Thus, $$\frac{P_1V_1}{n_1T_1} = R \quad \text{and} \quad \frac{P_2V_2}{n_2T_2} = R, \quad \text{so} \quad \frac{P_1V_1}{n_1T_1} = \frac{P_2V_2}{n_2T_2}$$

Notice that if, for example, the two variables P and T remain constant, then $P_1 = P_2$ and $T_1 = T_2$, and we obtain an expression for Avogadro's law:

$$\frac{\cancel{P_1}V_1}{n_1\cancel{T_1}} = \frac{\cancel{P_2}V_2}{n_2\cancel{T_2}} \qquad \text{or} \qquad \frac{V_1}{n_1} = \frac{V_2}{n_2}$$

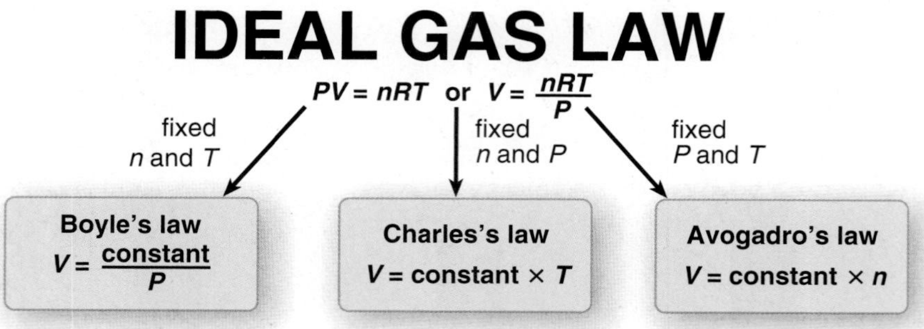

Figure 5.11 The individual gas laws as special cases of the ideal gas law.

As you'll see next, you can use a similar approach to solve gas law problems. Thus, by keeping track of the initial and final values of the gas variables, you avoid the need to memorize the three individual gas laws.

Solving Gas Law Problems

Gas law problems are phrased in many ways but can usually be grouped into two types:

1. *A change in one of the four variables causes a change in another, while the two other variables remain constant.* In this type, the ideal gas law reduces to one of the individual gas laws, and you solve for the new value of the affected variable. Units must be consistent and T must always be in kelvins, but R is not involved. Sample Problems 5.2 to 5.4 and 5.6 are of this type. [A variation on this type involves the combined gas law (p. 189) when simultaneous changes in two of the variables cause a change in a third.]

2. *One variable is unknown, but the other three are known and no change occurs.* In this type, exemplified by Sample Problem 5.5, you apply the ideal gas law directly to find the unknown, and the units must conform to those in R.

Solving these problems requires a systematic approach:

- Summarize the changing gas variables—knowns and unknown—and those held constant.
- Convert units, if necessary.
- Rearrange the ideal gas law to obtain the needed relationship of variables, and solve for the unknown.

Road Map

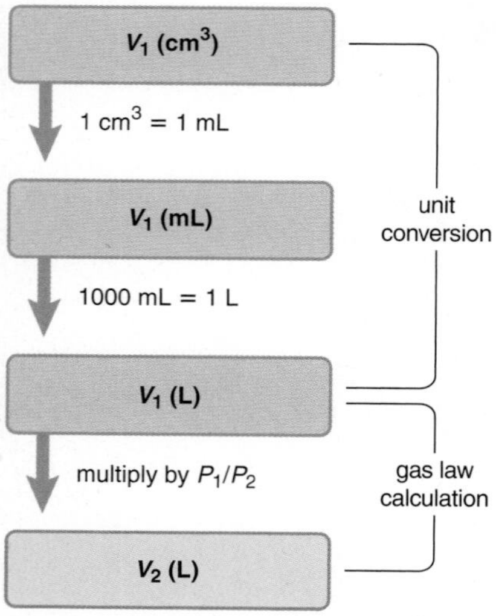

Sample Problem 5.2 Applying the Volume-Pressure Relationship

Problem Boyle's apprentice finds that the air trapped in a J tube occupies 24.8 cm^3 at 1.12 atm. By adding mercury to the tube, he increases the pressure on the trapped air to 2.64 atm. Assuming constant temperature, what is the new volume of air (in L)?

Plan We must find the final volume (V_2) in liters, given the initial volume (V_1), initial pressure (P_1), and final pressure (P_2). The temperature and amount of gas are fixed. We convert the units of V_1 from cm^3 to mL and then to L, rearrange the ideal gas law to the appropriate form, and solve for V_2. (Note that the road map has two parts.)

Solution Summarizing the gas variables:

$P_1 = 1.12$ atm $\qquad P_2 = 2.64$ atm

$V_1 = 24.8$ cm^3 (convert to L) $\qquad V_2 =$ unknown $\qquad$ T and n remain constant

Converting V_1 from cm^3 to L:

$$V_1 = 24.8\ \text{cm}^3 \times \frac{1\ \text{mL}}{1\ \text{cm}^3} \times \frac{1\ \text{L}}{1000\ \text{mL}} = 0.0248\ \text{L}$$

Rearranging the ideal gas law and solving for V_2: At fixed n and T, we have

$$\frac{P_1V_1}{\cancel{n_1}\cancel{T_1}} = \frac{P_2V_2}{\cancel{n_2}\cancel{T_2}} \quad \text{or} \quad P_1V_1 = P_2V_2$$

$$V_2 = V_1 \times \frac{P_1}{P_2} = 0.0248 \text{ L} \times \frac{1.12 \text{ atm}}{2.64 \text{ atm}} = 0.0105 \text{ L}$$

Check The relative values of P and V can help us check the math: P more than doubled, so V_2 should be less than $\frac{1}{2}V_1$ ($0.0105/0.0248 < \frac{1}{2}$).

Comment Predicting the direction of the change provides another check on the problem setup: Since P increases, V will decrease; thus, V_2 should be less than V_1. To make $V_2 < V_1$, we must multiply V_1 by a number *less than* 1. This means the ratio of pressures must be *less than* 1, so the larger pressure (P_2) must be in the denominator, or P_1/P_2.

Follow-Up Problem 5.2 A sample of argon gas occupies 105 mL at 0.871 atm. If the temperature remains constant, what is the volume (in L) at 26.3 kPa?

Sample Problem 5.3 Applying the Pressure-Temperature Relationship

Problem A steel tank used for fuel delivery is fitted with a safety valve that opens if the internal pressure exceeds 1.00×10^3 torr. It is filled with methane at 23°C and 0.991 atm and placed in boiling water 100.°C. Will the safety valve open?

Plan The question "Will the safety valve open?" translates to "Is P_2 greater than 1.00×10^3 torr at T_2?" Thus, P_2 is the unknown, and T_1, T_2, and P_1 are given, with V (steel tank) and n fixed. We convert both T values to kelvins and P_1 to torrs in order to compare P_2 with the safety-limit pressure. We rearrange the ideal gas law and solve for P_2.

Road Map

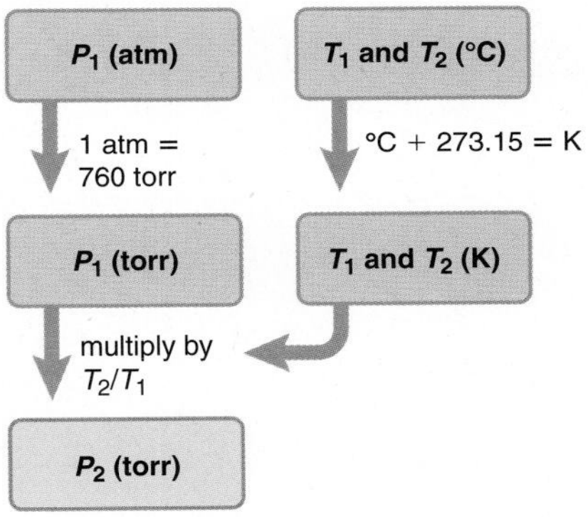

Solution Summarizing the gas variables:

$P_1 = 0.991$ atm (convert to torr) $\qquad P_2 =$ unknown

$T_1 = 23°\text{C}$ (convert to K) $\qquad T_2 = 100.°\text{C}$ (convert to K)

V and n remain constant

Converting T from °C to K:

$$T_1 \text{ (K)} = 23°\text{C} + 273.15 = 296 \text{ K} \qquad T_2 \text{ (K)} = 100.°\text{C} + 273.15 = 373 \text{ K}$$

Converting P from atm to torr:

$$P_1 \text{ (torr)} = 0.991 \text{ atm} \times \frac{760 \text{ torr}}{1 \text{ atm}} = 753 \text{ torr}$$

Rearranging the ideal gas law and solving for P_2: At fixed n and V, we have

$$\frac{P_1\cancel{V_1}}{\cancel{n_1}T_1} = \frac{P_2\cancel{V_2}}{\cancel{n_2}T_2} \quad \text{or} \quad \frac{P_1}{T_1} = \frac{P_2}{T_2}$$

$$P_2 = P_1 \times \frac{T_2}{T_1} = 753 \text{ torr} \times \frac{373 \text{ K}}{296 \text{ K}} = 949 \text{ torr}$$

P_2 is less than 1.00×10^3 torr, so the valve will *not* open.

Check Let's predict the change to check the math: Because $T_2 > T_1$, we expect $P_2 > P_1$. Thus, the temperature ratio should be >1 (T_2 in the numerator). The T ratio is about 1.25 (373/296), so the P ratio should also be about 1.25 ($950/750 \approx 1.25$).

Follow-Up Problem 5.3 An engineer pumps air at 0°C into a newly designed piston-cylinder assembly. The volume measures 6.83 cm^3. At what temperature (in K) will the volume be 9.75 cm^3?

Sample Problem 5.4 Applying the Volume-Amount Relationship

Problem A scale model of a blimp rises when it is filled with helium to a volume of 55.0 dm^3. When 1.10 mol of He is added to the blimp, the volume is 26.2 dm^3. How many more grams of He must be added to make it rise? Assume constant T and P.

Road Map

n_1 (mol) of He

↓ multiply by V_2/V_1

n_2 (mol) of He

↓ subtract n_1

$n_{add'l}$ (mol) of He

↓ multiply by $\mathcal{M}$ (g/mol)

Mass (g) of He

Plan We are given the initial amount of helium (n_1), the initial volume of the blimp (V_1), and the volume needed for it to rise (V_2), and we need the additional mass of helium to make it rise. So we first need to find n_2. We rearrange the ideal gas law to the appropriate form, solve for n_2, subtract n_1 to find the additional amount ($n_{add'l}$), and then convert moles to grams.

Solution Summarizing the gas variables:

$$n_1 = 1.10 \text{ mol} \qquad n_2 = \text{unknown (find, and then subtract } n_1)$$
$$V_1 = 26.2 \text{ dm}^3 \qquad V_2 = 55.0 \text{ dm}^3$$

P and T remain constant

Rearranging the ideal gas law and solving for n_2: At fixed P and T, we have

$$\frac{\cancel{P_1}V_1}{n_1\cancel{T_1}} = \frac{\cancel{P_2}V_2}{n_2\cancel{T_2}} \quad \text{or} \quad \frac{V_1}{n_1} = \frac{V_2}{n_2}$$

$$n_2 = n_1 \times \frac{V_2}{V_1} = 1.10 \text{ mol He} \times \frac{55.0 \text{ dm}^3}{26.2 \text{ dm}^3}$$
$$= 2.31 \text{ mol He}$$

Finding the additional amount of He:

$$n_{add'l} = n_2 - n_1 = 2.31 \text{ mol He} - 1.10 \text{ mol He}$$
$$= 1.21 \text{ mol He}$$

Converting amount (mol) of He to mass (g):

$$\text{Mass (g) of He} = 1.21 \text{ mol He} \times \frac{4.003 \text{ g He}}{1 \text{ mol He}}$$
$$= 4.84 \text{ g He}$$

Check We predict that $n_2 > n_1$ because $V_2 > V_1$: since V_2 is about twice V_1 ($55/26 \approx 2$), n_2 should be about twice n_1 ($2.3/1.1 \approx 2$). Since $n_2 > n_1$, we were right to multiply n_1 by a number >1 (that is, V_2/V_1). About 1.2 mol × 4 g/mol ≈ 4.8 g.

Comment 1. A different sequence of steps will give you the same answer: first find the additional volume ($V_{add'l} = V_2 - V_1$), and then solve directly for $n_{add'l}$. Try it for yourself.

2. You saw that Charles's law ($V \propto T$ at fixed P and n) becomes a similar relationship between P and T at fixed V and n. The follow-up problem demonstrates that Avogadro's law ($V \propto n$ at fixed P and T) becomes a similar relationship at fixed V and T.

Follow-Up Problem 5.4 A rigid plastic container holds 35.0 g of ethylene gas (C_2H_4) at a pressure of 793 torr. What is the pressure if 5.0 g of ethylene is removed at constant temperature?

Sample Problem 5.5 Solving for an Unknown Gas Variable at Fixed Conditions

Problem A steel tank has a volume of 438 L and is filled with 0.885 kg of O_2. Calculate the pressure of O_2 at 21°C.

Plan We are given V, T, and the mass of O_2, and we must find P. Since conditions are not changing, we apply the ideal gas law without rearranging it. We use the given V in liters, convert T to kelvins and mass (kg) of O_2 to amount (mol), and solve for P.

Solution Summarizing the gas variables:

$V = 438$ L $\quad$ $T = 21°C$ (convert to K)

$n = 0.885$ kg O_2 (convert to mol) $\quad$ $P =$ unknown

Converting T from °C to K:

$$T\text{ (K)} = 21°\text{C} + 273.15 = 294\text{ K}$$

Converting from mass (g) of O_2 to amount (mol):

$$n = \text{mol of } O_2 = 0.885\text{ kg } O_2 \times \frac{1000\text{ g}}{1\text{ kg}} \times \frac{1\text{ mol } O_2}{32.00\text{ g } O_2} = 27.7\text{ mol } O_2$$

Solving for P (note the unit canceling here):

$$P = \frac{nRT}{V} = \frac{27.7\ \cancel{\text{mol}} \times 0.0821\ \dfrac{\text{atm}\cdot\cancel{\text{L}}}{\cancel{\text{mol}}\cdot\cancel{\text{K}}} \times 294\ \cancel{\text{K}}}{438\ \cancel{\text{L}}}$$

$$= \boxed{1.53\text{ atm}}$$

Check The amount of O_2 seems correct: ~900 g/(30 g/mol) = 30 mol. To check the approximate size of the final calculation, round off the values, including that for R:

$$P = \frac{30\text{ mol } O_2 \times 0.1\ \dfrac{\text{atm}\cdot\text{L}}{\text{mol}\cdot\text{K}} \times 300\text{ K}}{450\text{ L}} = 2\text{ atm}$$

which is reasonably close to 1.53 atm.

Follow-Up Problem 5.5 The tank in the sample problem develops a slow leak that is discovered and sealed. The new pressure is 1.37 atm. How many grams of O_2 remain?

Finally, in a picture problem, we apply the gas laws to determine the balanced equation for a gaseous reaction.

Sample Problem 5.6 Using Gas Laws to Determine a Balanced Equation

Problem The piston-cylinder below is depicted before and after a gaseous reaction that is carried out in it at constant pressure: the temperature is 150 K before and 300 K after the reaction. (Assume the cylinder is insulated.)

Which of the following balanced equations describes the reaction?

(1) $A_2(g) + B_2(g) \longrightarrow 2AB(g)$ $\quad$ (2) $2AB(g) + B_2(g) \longrightarrow 2AB_2(g)$

(3) $A(g) + B_2(g) \longrightarrow AB_2(g)$ $\quad$ (4) $2AB_2(g) \longrightarrow A_2(g) + 2B_2(g)$

Plan We are shown a depiction of the volume and temperature of a gas mixture before and after a reaction and must deduce the balanced equation. The problem says that P is constant, and the picture shows that, when T doubles, V stays the same. If n were also constant, Charles's law tells us that V should double when T doubles. But, since V does not change, n cannot be constant. From Avogadro's law, the only way to maintain V constant, with P constant and T doubling, is for n to be halved. So we examine the four balanced equations and count the number of moles on each side to see in which equation n is halved.

Solution In equation (1), n does not change, so doubling T would double V.
In equation (2), n decreases from 3 mol to 2 mol, so doubling T would increase V by one-third.
In equation (3), n decreases from 2 mol to 1 mol. Doubling T would exactly balance the decrease from halving n, so V would stay the same.
In equation (4), n increases, so doubling T would more than double V.
Therefore, equation (3) is correct:

$$A(g) + B_2(g) \longrightarrow AB_2(g)$$

Follow-Up Problem 5.6 The piston-cylinder below shows the volumes of a gaseous reaction mixture before and after a reaction that takes place at constant pressure and an initial temperature of −73°C.

If the *unbalanced* equation is $CD(g) \longrightarrow C_2(g) + D_2(g)$, what is the final temperature (in °C)?

Summary of Section 5.3

- Four interdependent variables define the physical behavior of an ideal gas: volume (V), pressure (P), temperature (T), and amount (number of moles, n).
- Most simple gases display nearly ideal behavior at ordinary temperatures and pressures.
- Boyle's, Charles's, and Avogadro's laws refer to the linear relationships between the volume of a gas and the pressure, temperature, and amount of gas, respectively.
- At STP (0°C and 1 atm), 1 mol of an ideal gas occupies 22.4 L.
- The ideal gas law incorporates the individual gas laws into one equation: $PV = nRT$, where R is the universal gas constant.

5.4 • REARRANGEMENTS OF THE IDEAL GAS LAW

In this section, we mathematically rearrange the ideal gas law to find gas density, molar mass, the partial pressure of each gas in a mixture, and the amount of gaseous reactant or product in a reaction.

The Density of a Gas

One mole of any gas behaving ideally occupies the same volume at a given temperature and pressure, so differences in gas density ($d = m/V$) depend on differences in molar mass (see Figure 5.9, p. 191). For example, at STP, 1 mol of O_2 occupies the same volume as 1 mol of N_2; however, O_2 is denser because each O_2 molecule has a greater mass (32.00 amu) than each N_2 molecule (28.02 amu). Thus, d of O_2 is $\frac{32.00}{28.02} \times d$ of N_2.

We can rearrange the ideal gas law to calculate the density of a gas from its molar mass. Recall that the number of moles (n) is the mass (m) divided by the molar mass ($\mathcal{M}$), $n = m/\mathcal{M}$. Substituting for n in the ideal gas law gives

$$PV = \frac{m}{\mathcal{M}}RT$$

Rearranging to isolate m/V gives

$$\frac{m}{V} = d = \frac{\mathcal{M} \times P}{RT} \qquad (5.9)$$

Two important ideas are expressed by Equation 5.9:

- *The density of a gas is directly proportional to its molar mass.* The volume of a given amount of a heavier gas equals the volume of the same amount of a lighter gas (Avogadro's law), so the density of the heavier gas is higher (as you just saw for O_2 and N_2).
- *The density of a gas is inversely proportional to the temperature.* As the volume of a gas increases with temperature (Charles's law), the same mass occupies more space, so the density of the gas is lower.

We use Equation 5.9 to find the density of a gas at any temperature and pressure near standard conditions.

Sample Problem 5.7 Calculating Gas Density

Problem To apply a green chemistry approach, a chemical engineer uses waste CO_2 from a manufacturing process, instead of chlorofluorocarbons, as a "blowing agent" in the production of polystyrene. Find the density (in g/L) of CO_2 and the number of molecules per liter **(a)** at STP (0°C and 1 atm) and **(b)** at room conditions (20.°C and 1.00 atm).

Plan We must find the density (d) and the number of molecules of CO_2, given two sets of P and T data. We find $\mathcal{M}$, convert T to kelvins, and calculate d with Equation 5.9. Then we convert the mass per liter to molecules per liter with Avogadro's number.

Solution (a) Density and molecules per liter of CO_2 at STP. Summary of gas properties:

$$T = 0°\text{C} + 273.15 = 273\ \text{K} \qquad P = 1\ \text{atm} \qquad \mathcal{M}\text{ of } CO_2 = 44.01\ \text{g/mol}$$

Calculating density (note the unit canceling here):

$$d = \frac{\mathcal{M} \times P}{RT} = \frac{44.01\ \text{g/}\cancel{\text{mol}} \times 1.00\ \cancel{\text{atm}}}{0.0821\ \frac{\cancel{\text{atm}}\cdot\text{L}}{\cancel{\text{mol}}\cdot\cancel{\text{K}}} \times 273\ \cancel{\text{K}}} = 1.96\ \text{g/L}$$

Converting from mass/L to molecules/L:

$$\text{Molecules } CO_2/\text{L} = \frac{1.96\ \text{g } CO_2}{1\ \text{L}} \times \frac{1\ \text{mol } CO_2}{44.01\ \text{g } CO_2} \times \frac{6.022\times10^{23}\ \text{molecules } CO_2}{1\ \text{mol } CO_2}$$

$$= 2.68\times10^{22}\ \text{molecules } CO_2/\text{L}$$

(b) Density and molecules of CO_2 per liter at room conditions. Summary of gas properties:

$$T = 20.°\text{C} + 273.15 = 293\ \text{K} \qquad P = 1.00\ \text{atm} \qquad \mathcal{M}\text{ of } CO_2 = 44.01\ \text{g/mol}$$

Calculating density:

$$d = \frac{\mathcal{M} \times P}{RT} = \frac{44.01\ \text{g/mol} \times 1.00\ \text{atm}}{0.0821\ \frac{\text{atm}\cdot\text{L}}{\text{mol}\cdot\text{K}} \times 293\ \text{K}} = 1.83\ \text{g/L}$$

Converting from mass/L to molecules/L:

$$\text{Molecules } CO_2/\text{L} = \frac{1.83\ \text{g } CO_2}{1\ \text{L}} \times \frac{1\ \text{mol } CO_2}{44.01\ \text{g } CO_2} \times \frac{6.022\times10^{23}\ \text{molecules } CO_2}{1\ \text{mol } CO_2}$$

$$= 2.50\times10^{22}\ \text{molecules } CO_2/\text{L}$$

Check Round off to check the density values; for example, in (a), at STP:

$$\frac{50\ \text{g/mol} \times 1\ \text{atm}}{0.1\ \frac{\text{atm}\cdot\text{L}}{\text{mol}\cdot\text{K}} \times 250\ \text{K}} = 2\ \text{g/L} \approx 1.96\ \text{g/L}$$

At the higher temperature in (b), the density should decrease, which can happen only if there are fewer molecules per liter, so the answer is reasonable.

Comment 1. An *alternative approach* for finding the density of most simple gases, but *at STP only,* is to divide the molar mass by the standard molar volume, 22.4 L:

$$d = \frac{\mathcal{M}}{V} = \frac{44.01\ \text{g/mol}}{22.4\ \text{L/mol}} = 1.96\ \text{g/L}$$

Once you know the density at one temperature (0°C), you can find it at any other temperature with the following relationship: $d_1/d_2 = T_2/T_1$.
2. Note that we have different numbers of significant figures for the pressure values. In (a), "1 atm" is part of the definition of STP, so it is an exact number. In (b), we specified "1.00 atm" to allow three significant figures in the answer.

Follow-Up Problem 5.7 Compare the density of CO_2 at 0°C and 380. torr with its density at STP.

Gas Density and the Human Condition A few applications demonstrate the wide-ranging relevance of gas density:

- *Engineering.* Architectural designers and heating engineers place heating ducts near the floor so that the warmer, and thus less dense, air coming from the ducts will rise and mix with the cooler room air.
- *Safety and air pollution.* In the absence of mixing, a less dense gas will lie above a more dense one. Fire extinguishers that release CO_2 are effective because this gas is heavier than air: it sinks onto the fire and keeps more O_2 from reaching the fuel. The dense gases in smog that blankets urban centers, such as Mexico City, Los Angeles, and Beijing, contribute to respiratory illnesses.
- *Toxic releases.* During World War I, poisonous phosgene gas ($COCl_2$) was used against ground troops because it was dense enough to sink into their trenches. In 1984, the accidental release of poisonous methylisocyanate gas from a Union Carbide plant in India killed thousands of people as it blanketed nearby neighborhoods. In 1986, CO_2 released naturally from Lake Nyos in Cameroon suffocated thousands of people as it flowed down valleys into villages. Some paleontologists suggest that the release of CO_2 from volcanic lakes may have contributed to widespread dying off of dinosaurs.
- *Ballooning.* When the gas in a hot-air balloon is heated, its volume increases and the balloon inflates. Further heating causes some of the gas to escape. Thus, the gas density decreases and the balloon rises. In 1783, Jacques Charles (of Charles's law) made one of the first balloon flights, and 20 years later, Joseph Gay-Lussac (who studied the pressure-temperature relationship) set a solo altitude record that held for 50 years.

The Molar Mass of a Gas

Through another rearrangement of the ideal gas law, we can determine the molar mass of an unknown gas or a volatile liquid (one that is easily vaporized):

$$n = \frac{m}{\mathcal{M}} = \frac{PV}{RT} \quad \text{so} \quad \mathcal{M} = \frac{mRT}{PV} \tag{5.10}$$

Notice that this equation is just a rearrangement of Equation 5.9.

Sample Problem 5.8 Finding the Molar Mass of a Volatile Liquid

Problem An organic chemist isolates a colorless liquid from a petroleum sample. She places the liquid in a preweighed flask and puts the flask in boiling water, which vaporizes the liquid and fills the flask with gas. She closes the flask and reweighs it. She obtains the following data:

Volume (V) of flask = 213 mL T = 100.0°C P = 754 torr
Mass of flask + gas = 78.416 g   Mass of flask = 77.834 g

Calculate the molar mass of the liquid.

Plan We are given V, T, P, and mass data and must find the molar mass ($\mathcal{M}$) of the liquid. We convert V to liters, T to kelvins, and P to atmospheres, find the mass of gas by subtracting the mass of the flask from the mass of the flask plus gas, and use Equation 5.10 to calculate $\mathcal{M}$.

Solution Summarizing and converting the gas variables:

$$V\text{ (L)} = 213\text{ mL} \times \frac{1\text{ L}}{1000\text{ mL}} = 0.213\text{ L} \qquad T\text{ (K)} = 100.0°\text{C} + 273.15 = 373.2\text{ K}$$

$$P\text{ (atm)} = 754\text{ torr} \times \frac{1\text{ atm}}{760\text{ torr}} = 0.992\text{ atm} \qquad m = 78.416\text{ g} - 77.834\text{ g} = 0.582\text{ g}$$

Calculating $\mathcal{M}$:

$$\mathcal{M} = \frac{mRT}{PV} = \frac{0.582\text{ g} \times 0.0821\,\frac{\text{atm}\cdot\text{L}}{\text{mol}\cdot\text{K}} \times 373.2\text{ K}}{0.992\text{ atm} \times 0.213\text{ L}} = 84.4\text{ g/mol}$$

Check Rounding to check the arithmetic, we have

$$\frac{0.6\text{ g} \times 0.08\,\frac{\text{atm}\cdot\text{L}}{\text{mol}\cdot\text{K}} \times 375\text{ K}}{1\text{ atm} \times 0.2\text{ L}} = 90\text{ g/mol} \qquad \text{(which is close to 84.4 g/mol)}$$

Follow-Up Problem 5.8 An empty 149-mL flask weighs 68.322 g before a sample of volatile liquid is added. The flask is then placed in a hot (95.0°C) water bath; the barometric pressure is 740. torr. The liquid vaporizes and the gas fills the flask. After cooling, flask and condensed liquid together weigh 68.697 g. What is the molar mass of the liquid?

The Partial Pressure of Each Gas in a Mixture of Gases

The gas behaviors we've discussed so far were observed in experiments with air, which is a mixture of gases; thus, the ideal gas law holds for virtually any gas at ordinary conditions, whether pure or a mixture, because

- Gases mix homogeneously (form a solution) in any proportions.
- Each gas in a mixture behaves as if it were the only gas present (assuming no chemical interactions).

Dalton's Law of Partial Pressures The second point above was discovered by John Dalton during his lifelong study of humidity. He observed that when water vapor is added to dry air, the total air pressure increases by the pressure of the water vapor:

$$P_{\text{humid air}} = P_{\text{dry air}} + P_{\text{added water vapor}}$$

He concluded that each gas in the mixture exerts a **partial pressure** equal to the pressure it would exert *by itself.* Stated as **Dalton's law of partial pressures,** his discovery was that *in a mixture of unreacting gases, the total pressure is the sum of the partial pressures of the individual gases:*

$$P_{\text{total}} = P_1 + P_2 + P_3 + \cdots \qquad (5.11)$$

As an example, suppose we have a tank of fixed volume that contains nitrogen gas at a certain pressure, and we introduce a sample of hydrogen gas into the tank. Each gas behaves independently, so we can write an ideal gas law expression for each:

$$P_{N_2} = \frac{n_{N_2}RT}{V} \qquad \text{and} \qquad P_{H_2} = \frac{n_{H_2}RT}{V}$$

Because each gas occupies the same total volume and is at the same temperature, the pressure of each gas depends only on its amount, n. Thus, the total pressure is

$$P_{\text{total}} = P_{N_2} + P_{H_2} = \frac{n_{N_2}RT}{V} + \frac{n_{H_2}RT}{V} = \frac{(n_{N_2} + n_{H_2})RT}{V} = \frac{n_{\text{total}}RT}{V}$$

where $n_{\text{total}} = n_{N_2} + n_{H_2}$.

Each component in a mixture contributes a fraction of the total number of moles in the mixture; this portion is the **mole fraction** (*X*) of that component. Multiplying *X* by 100 gives the mole percent. The sum of the mole fractions of all components must be 1, and the sum of the mole percents must be 100%. For N_2 in our mixture, the mole fraction is

$$X_{N_2} = \frac{n_{N_2}}{n_{total}} = \frac{n_{N_2}}{n_{N_2} + n_{H_2}}$$

If the total pressure is due to the total number of moles, the partial pressure of gas A is the total pressure multiplied by the mole fraction of A, X_A:

$$P_A = X_A \times P_{total} \quad (5.12)$$

Equation 5.12 is a very useful result. To see that it is valid for the mixture of N_2 and H_2, we recall that $X_{N_2} + X_{H_2} = 1$; then we obtain

$$P_{total} = P_{N_2} + P_{H_2} = (X_{N_2} \times P_{total}) + (X_{H_2} \times P_{total}) = (X_{N_2} + X_{H_2})P_{total} = 1 \times P_{total}$$

Sample Problem 5.9 Applying Dalton's Law of Partial Pressures

Problem In a study of O_2 uptake by muscle at high altitude, a physiologist prepares an atmosphere consisting of 79 mole % N_2, 17 mole % $^{16}O_2$, and 4.0 mole % $^{18}O_2$. (The isotope ^{18}O will be measured to determine O_2 uptake.) The total pressure is 0.75 atm to simulate high altitude. Calculate the mole fraction and partial pressure of $^{18}O_2$ in the mixture.

Plan We must find $X_{^{18}O_2}$ and $P_{^{18}O_2}$ from P_{total} (0.75 atm) and the mole % of $^{18}O_2$ (4.0). Dividing the mole % by 100 gives the mole fraction, $X_{^{18}O_2}$. Then, using Equation 5.12, we multiply $X_{^{18}O_2}$ by P_{total} to find $P_{^{18}O_2}$.

Road Map

Mole % of $^{18}O_2$

↓ divide by 100

Mole fraction, $X_{^{18}O_2}$

↓ multiply by P_{total}

Partial pressure, $P_{^{18}O_2}$

Solution Calculating the mole fraction of $^{18}O_2$:

$$X_{^{18}O_2} = \frac{4.0 \text{ mol \% } ^{18}O_2}{100} = 0.040$$

Solving for the partial pressure of $^{18}O_2$:

$$P_{^{18}O_2} = X_{^{18}O_2} \times P_{total} = 0.040 \times 0.75 \text{ atm} = 0.030 \text{ atm}$$

Check $X_{^{18}O_2}$ is small because the mole % is small, so $P_{^{18}O_2}$ should be small also.

Comment At high altitudes, specialized brain cells that are sensitive to O_2 and CO_2 levels in the blood trigger an increase in rate and depth of breathing for several days, until a person becomes acclimated.

Follow-Up Problem 5.9 To prevent the presence of air, noble gases are placed over highly reactive chemicals to act as inert "blanketing" gases. A chemical engineer places a mixture of noble gases consisting of 5.50 g of He, 15.0 g of Ne, and 35.0 g of Kr in a piston-cylinder assembly at STP. Calculate the partial pressure of each gas.

Table 5.2 Vapor Pressure of Water (P_{H_2O}) at Different *T*

T (°C)	P_{H_2O} (torr)	*T* (°C)	P_{H_2O} (torr)
0	4.6	40	55.3
5	6.5	45	71.9
10	9.2	50	92.5
12	10.5	55	118.0
14	12.0	60	149.4
16	13.6	65	187.5
18	15.5	70	233.7
20	17.5	75	289.1
22	19.8	80	355.1
24	22.4	85	433.6
26	25.2	90	525.8
28	28.3	95	633.9
30	31.8	100	760.0
35	42.2		

Collecting a Gas over Water Whenever a gas is in contact with water, some of the water vaporizes into the gas. The water vapor that mixes with the gas contributes the *vapor pressure,* a portion of the total pressure that depends only on the water temperature (Table 5.2). A common use of the law of partial pressures is to determine the yield of a water-insoluble gas formed in a reaction: the gaseous product bubbles through water, some water vaporizes into the bubbles, and the mixture of product gas and water vapor is collected into an inverted container (Figure 5.12).

To determine the yield, we look up the vapor pressure (P_{H_2O}) at the temperature of the experiment in Table 5.2 and subtract it from the total gas pressure (P_{total}, corrected for barometric pressure) to get the partial pressure of the gaseous product (P_{gas}). With *V* and *T* known, we can calculate the amount of product.

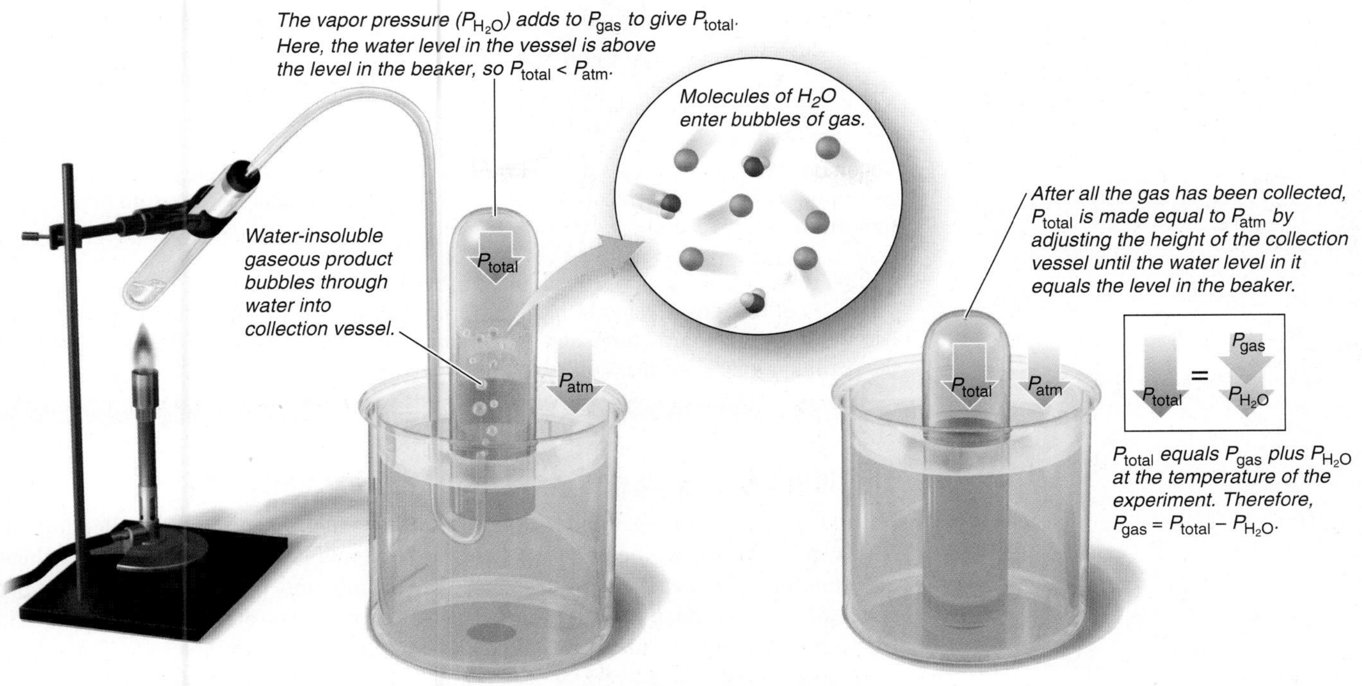

Figure 5.12 Collecting a water-insoluble gaseous product and determining its pressure.

Sample Problem 5.10 Calculating the Amount of Gas Collected over Water

Problem Acetylene (C_2H_2), an important fuel in welding, is produced in the laboratory when calcium carbide (CaC_2) reacts with water:

$$CaC_2(s) + 2H_2O(l) \longrightarrow C_2H_2(g) + Ca(OH)_2(aq)$$

For a sample of acetylene collected over water, total gas pressure (adjusted to barometric pressure) is 738 torr and the volume is 523 mL. At the temperature of the gas (23°C), the vapor pressure of water is 21 torr. How many grams of acetylene are collected?

Plan In order to find the mass of C_2H_2, we first need to find the number of moles of C_2H_2, $n_{C_2H_2}$, which we can obtain from the ideal gas law by calculating $P_{C_2H_2}$. The barometer reading gives us P_{total}, which is the sum of $P_{C_2H_2}$ and P_{H_2O}, and we are given P_{H_2O}, so we subtract to find $P_{C_2H_2}$. We are also given V and T, so we convert to consistent units, and find $n_{C_2H_2}$ from the ideal gas law. Then we convert moles to grams using the molar mass from the formula, as shown in the road map.

Road Map

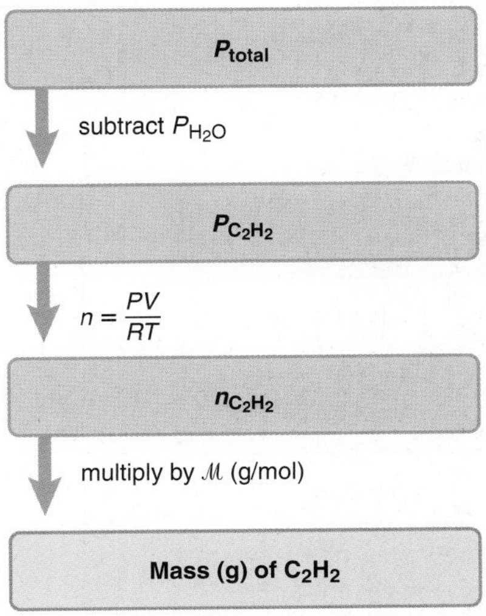

Solution Summarizing and converting the gas variables:

$$P_{C_2H_2}\text{ (torr)} = P_{total} - P_{H_2O} = 738\text{ torr} - 21\text{ torr} = 717\text{ torr}$$

$$P_{C_2H_2}\text{ (atm)} = 717\text{ torr} \times \frac{1\text{ atm}}{760\text{ torr}} = 0.943\text{ atm}$$

$$V\text{ (L)} = 523\text{ mL} \times \frac{1\text{ L}}{1000\text{ mL}} = 0.523\text{ L}$$

$$T\text{ (K)} = 23°\text{C} + 273.15 = 296\text{ K}$$

$$n_{C_2H_2} = \text{unknown}$$

Solving for $n_{C_2H_2}$:

$$n_{C_2H_2} = \frac{PV}{RT} = \frac{0.943\text{ atm} \times 0.523\text{ L}}{0.0821\,\frac{\text{atm}\cdot\text{L}}{\text{mol}\cdot\text{K}} \times 296\text{ K}} = 0.0203\text{ mol}$$

Converting $n_{C_2H_2}$ to mass (g):

$$\text{Mass (g) of } C_2H_2 = 0.0203\text{ mol } C_2H_2 \times \frac{26.04\text{ g } C_2H_2}{1\text{ mol } C_2H_2}$$

$$= 0.529\text{ g } C_2H_2$$

Check Rounding to one significant figure, a quick arithmetic check for n gives

$$n \approx \frac{1 \text{ atm} \times 0.5 \text{ L}}{0.08 \dfrac{\text{atm·L}}{\text{mol·K}} \times 300 \text{ K}} = 0.02 \text{ mol} \approx 0.0203 \text{ mol}$$

Comment The C_2^{2-} ion (called the *carbide,* or *acetylide, ion*) is an interesting anion. It is simply $^-C{\equiv}C^-$, which acts as a base in water, removing an H^+ ion from two H_2O molecules to form acetylene, $H{-}C{\equiv}C{-}H$.

Follow-Up Problem 5.10 A small piece of zinc reacts with dilute HCl to form H_2, which is collected over water at 16°C into a large flask. The total pressure is adjusted to barometric pressure (752 torr), and the volume is 1495 mL. Use Table 5.2 to help calculate the partial pressure and mass of H_2.

The Ideal Gas Law and Reaction Stoichiometry

As you saw in Chapters 3 and 4, and in the preceding discussion of collecting a gas over water, many reactions involve gases as reactants or products. From the balanced equation for such a reaction, you can calculate the amounts (mol) of reactants and products and convert these quantities into masses or numbers of molecules. Figure 5.13 shows how you use the ideal gas law to convert between gas variables (P, T, and V) and amounts (mol) of gaseous reactants and products. In effect, you combine a gas law problem with a stoichiometry problem, as you'll see in Sample Problems 5.11 and 5.12.

Figure 5.13 The relationships among the amount (mol, n) of gaseous reactant (or product) and the gas pressure (P), volume (V), and temperature (T).

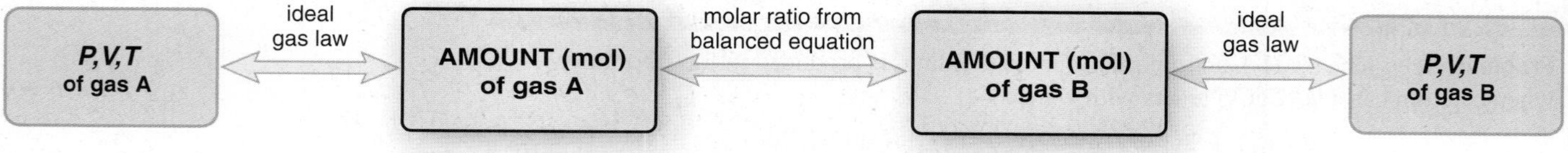

Sample Problem 5.11 Using Gas Variables to Find Amounts of Reactants or Products I

Problem Engineers use copper in absorbent beds to react with and remove oxygen impurities in ethylene used to make polyethylene. The beds are regenerated when hot H_2 reduces the copper(II) oxide, forming the pure metal and H_2O. On a laboratory scale, what volume of H_2 at 765 torr and 225°C is needed to reduce 35.5 g of copper(II) oxide?

Plan This is a stoichiometry *and* gas law problem. To find V_{H_2}, we first need n_{H_2}. We write and balance the equation. Next, we convert the given mass (35.5 g) of copper(II) oxide, CuO, to amount (mol) and use the molar ratio to find amount (mol) of H_2 needed (stoichiometry portion). Then, we use the ideal gas law to convert moles of H_2 to liters (gas law portion). A road map is shown, but you are familiar with all the steps.

Road Map

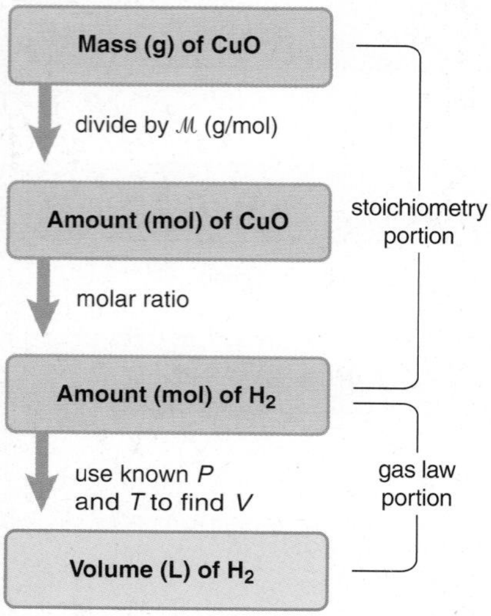

Solution Writing the balanced equation:

$$CuO(s) + H_2(g) \longrightarrow Cu(s) + H_2O(g)$$

Calculating n_{H_2}:

$$n_{H_2} = 35.5 \text{ g CuO} \times \frac{1 \text{ mol CuO}}{79.55 \text{ g CuO}} \times \frac{1 \text{ mol } H_2}{1 \text{ mol CuO}} = 0.446 \text{ mol } H_2$$

Summarizing and converting other gas variables:

$$V = \text{unknown} \qquad P\text{ (atm)} = 765 \text{ torr} \times \frac{1 \text{ atm}}{760 \text{ torr}} = 1.01 \text{ atm}$$

$$T\text{ (K)} = 225°\text{C} + 273.15 = 498 \text{ K}$$

Solving for V_{H_2}:

$$V = \frac{nRT}{P} = \frac{0.446\ \text{mol} \times 0.0821\ \frac{\text{atm}\cdot\text{L}}{\text{mol}\cdot\text{K}} \times 498\ \text{K}}{1.01\ \text{atm}} = 18.1\ \text{L}$$

Check One way to check the answer is to compare it with the molar volume of an ideal gas at STP (22.4 L at 273.15 K and 1 atm). One mole of H_2 at STP occupies about 22 L, so less than 0.5 mol occupies less than 11 L. *T* is less than twice 273 K, so *V* should be less than twice 11 L.

Comment The main point here is that the stoichiometry provides one gas variable (*n*), two more are given, and the ideal gas law is used to find the fourth.

Follow-Up Problem 5.11 Sulfuric acid reacts with sodium chloride to form aqueous sodium sulfate and hydrogen chloride gas. How many milliliters of gas form at STP when 0.117 kg of sodium chloride reacts with excess sulfuric acid?

Sample Problem 5.12 Using Gas Variables to Find Amounts of Reactants or Products II

Problem The alkali metals [Group 1A(1)] react with the halogens [Group 7A(17)] to form ionic metal halides. What mass of potassium chloride forms when 5.25 L of chlorine gas at 0.950 atm and 293 K reacts with 17.0 g of potassium (*see photo*)?

Plan The amounts of two reactants are given, so this is a limiting-reactant problem. The only difference between this and previous limiting-reactant problems (see Sample Problem 3.20, p. 111) is that here we use the ideal gas law to find the amount (*n*) of gaseous reactant from the known *V*, *P*, and *T*. We first write the balanced equation and then use it to find the limiting reactant and the amount and mass of product.

Solution Writing the balanced equation:

$$2\text{K}(s) + \text{Cl}_2(g) \longrightarrow 2\text{KCl}(s)$$

Summarizing the gas variables:

$$P = 0.950\ \text{atm} \qquad V = 5.25\ \text{L}$$
$$T = 293\ \text{K} \qquad n = \text{unknown}$$

Solving for n_{Cl_2}:

$$n_{Cl_2} = \frac{PV}{RT} = \frac{0.950\ \text{atm} \times 5.25\ \text{L}}{0.0821\ \frac{\text{atm}\cdot\text{L}}{\text{mol}\cdot\text{K}} \times 293\ \text{K}} = 0.207\ \text{mol}$$

Converting from mass (g) of potassium (K) to amount (mol):

$$\text{Amount (mol) of K} = 17.0\ \text{g K} \times \frac{1\ \text{mol K}}{39.10\ \text{g K}} = 0.435\ \text{mol K}$$

Determining the limiting reactant: If Cl_2 is limiting,

$$\text{Amount (mol) of KCl} = 0.207\ \text{mol Cl}_2 \times \frac{2\ \text{mol KCl}}{1\ \text{mol Cl}_2} = 0.414\ \text{mol KCl}$$

If K is limiting,

$$\text{Amount (mol) of KCl} = 0.435\ \text{mol K} \times \frac{2\ \text{mol KCl}}{2\ \text{mol K}} = 0.435\ \text{mol KCl}$$

Cl_2 is the limiting reactant because it forms less KCl.
Converting from amount (mol) of KCl to mass (g):

$$\text{Mass (g) of KCl} = 0.414\ \text{mol KCl} \times \frac{74.55\ \text{g KCl}}{1\ \text{mol KCl}} = 30.9\ \text{g KCl}$$

Chlorine gas reacting with potassium.

Check The gas law calculation seems correct. At STP, 22 L of Cl_2 gas contains about 1 mol, so a 5-L volume will contain a bit less than 0.25 mol of Cl_2. Moreover, since P (in numerator) is slightly lower than STP, and T (in denominator) is slightly higher than STP, these should lower the calculated n further below the ideal value. The mass of KCl seems correct: less than 0.5 mol of KCl gives $<0.5 \text{ mol} \times \mathcal{M}$ (~75 g/mol), and 30.9 g $<$ 0.5 mol $\times$ 75 g/mol.

Follow-Up Problem 5.12 Ammonia and hydrogen chloride gases react to form solid ammonium chloride. A 10.0-L reaction flask contains ammonia at 0.452 atm and 22°C, and 155 mL of hydrogen chloride gas at 7.50 atm and 271 K is introduced. After the reaction occurs and the temperature returns to 22°C, what is the pressure inside the flask? (Neglect the volume of the solid product.)

Summary of Section 5.4

- Gas density is inversely related to temperature: higher T causes lower d, and vice versa. At the same P and T, gases with larger $\mathcal{M}$ have higher d.
- In a mixture of gases, each component contributes its partial pressure to the total pressure (Dalton's law of partial pressures). The mole fraction of each component is the ratio of its partial pressure to the total pressure.
- When a gaseous reaction product is collected by bubbling it through water, the total pressure is the sum of the gas pressure and the vapor pressure of water at the given temperature.
- By converting the variables P, V, and T for a gaseous reactant (or product) to amount (n, mol), we can solve stoichiometry problems for gaseous reactions.

5.5 • THE KINETIC-MOLECULAR THEORY: A MODEL FOR GAS BEHAVIOR

The **kinetic-molecular theory** is the model that accounts for macroscopic gas behavior at the level of individual particles (atoms or molecules). Developed by some of the great scientists of the 19th century, most notably James Clerk Maxwell and Ludwig Boltzmann, the theory was able to explain the gas laws that some of the great scientists of the 18th century had arrived at empirically. The theory draws quantitative conclusions based on a few postulates (assumptions), but our discussion will be largely qualitative.

How the Kinetic-Molecular Theory Explains the Gas Laws

Let's address some questions the theory must answer, then state the postulates, and draw conclusions that explain the gas laws and related phenomena.

Questions Concerning Gas Behavior Observing gas behavior at the macroscopic level, we must derive a molecular model that explains it:

1. *Origin of pressure.* Pressure is a measure of the force a gas exerts on a surface. How do individual gas particles create this force?
2. *Boyle's law ($V \propto 1/P$).* A change in gas pressure in one direction causes a change in gas volume in the other. What happens to the particles when external pressure compresses the gas volume? And why aren't liquids and solids compressible?
3. *Dalton's law ($P_{total} = P_1 + P_2 + P_3 + \cdots$).* The pressure of a gas mixture is the sum of the pressures of the individual gases. Why does each gas contribute to the total pressure in proportion to its number of particles?
4. *Charles's law ($V \propto T$).* A change in temperature causes a corresponding change in volume. What effect does higher temperature have on gas particles that increases gas volume? This question raises a more fundamental one: what does temperature measure on the molecular scale?
5. *Avogadro's law ($V \propto n$).* Gas volume depends on the number of moles present, not on the chemical nature of the gas. But shouldn't 1 mol of heavier particles exert more pressure, and thus take up more space, than 1 mol of lighter ones?

Postulates of the Kinetic-Molecular Theory The theory is based on three postulates:

Postulate 1. *Particle volume.* A gas consists of a large collection of individual particles with empty space between them. The volume of each particle is so small compared with the volume of the whole sample that it is assumed to be zero; each particle is essentially a point of mass.

Postulate 2. *Particle motion.* The particles are in constant, random, straight-line motion, except when they collide with the container walls or with each other.

Postulate 3. *Particle collisions.* The collisions are *elastic,* which means that, like minute billiard balls, the colliding molecules exchange energy but do not lose any energy through friction. Thus, *their total kinetic energy (E_k) is constant.* Between collisions, the molecules do not influence each other by attractive or repulsive forces.

Imagine what a sample of gas in a container looks like. Countless minute particles move in every direction, smashing into the container walls and each other. Any given particle changes its speed often—at one moment standing still from a head-on collision and the next moment zooming away from a smash on the side.

In the sample as a whole, *each particle has a molecular speed* (u); *most are moving near the most probable speed, but some are much faster and others much slower.* Figure 5.14 depicts this distribution of molecular speeds for N_2 gas at three temperatures.

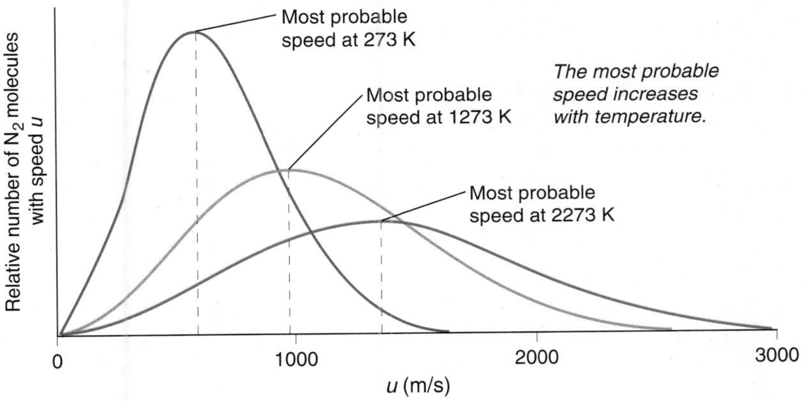

Figure 5.14 Distribution of molecular speeds for N_2 at three temperatures.

Note that the curves flatten and spread at higher temperatures and that the *most probable speed (the peak of each curve) increases as the temperature increases.* This increase occurs because the average kinetic energy of the molecules, which is related to the most probable speed, is proportional to the absolute temperature: $\overline{E_k} \propto T$, or $\overline{E_k} = c \times T$, where $\overline{E_k}$ is the average kinetic energy of the molecules (an overbar indicates the average value of a quantity) and c is a constant that is the same for any gas. (We'll return to this equation shortly.) Thus, a major conclusion based on the distribution of speeds, which arises directly from postulate 3, is that *at a given temperature, all gases have the same average kinetic energy.*

A Molecular View of the Gas Laws Let's keep visualizing gas particles in a container to see how the theory explains the macroscopic behavior of gases and answers the questions we posed above:

1. *Origin of pressure* (Figure 5.15). From postulates 1 and 2, each gas particle (point of mass) colliding with the container walls (and bottom of piston) exerts a force. Countless collisions over the inner surface of the container result in a pressure. The greater the number of particles, the more frequently they collide with the container, and so the greater the pressure.

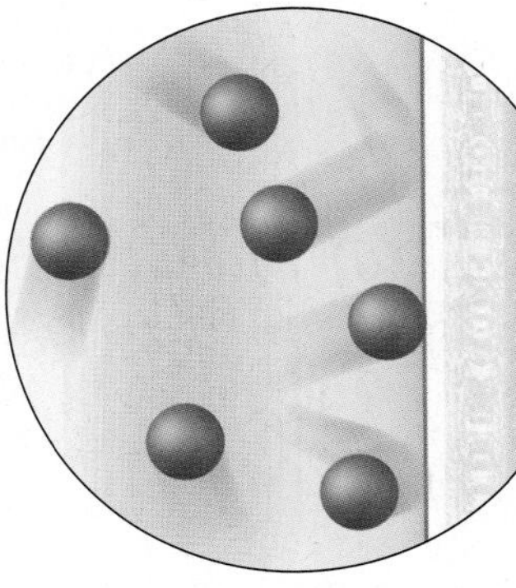

Figure 5.15 Pressure arises from countless collisions between gas particles and walls.

2. *Boyle's law* ($V \propto 1/P$) (Figure 5.16). The particles in a gas are points of mass with empty space between them (postulate 1). Before any change in pressure, the pressure exerted *by* the gas (P_{gas}) equals the pressure exerted *on* the gas (P_{ext}), and there is some average distance (d_1) between the particles and the container walls. As P_{ext} increases at constant temperature, the average distance (d_2) between the particles and the walls decreases (that is, $d_2 < d_1$), and so the sample volume decreases. Collisions of the particles with the walls become more frequent over the shorter average distance, which causes P_{gas} to increase until it again equals P_{ext}. The fact that liquids and solids cannot be compressed implies there is little, if any, free space between their particles.

Figure 5.16 A molecular view of Boyle's law.

3. *Dalton's law of partial pressures* ($P_{total} = P_A + P_B$) (Figure 5.17). Adding a given amount (mol) of gas A to a given amount of gas B causes an increase in the total number of particles, in proportion to the particles of A added. This increase causes a corresponding increase in the total number of collisions with the walls per second (postulate 2), which causes a corresponding increase in the total pressure of the gas mixture (P_{total}). Each gas exerts a fraction of P_{total} in proportion to its fraction of the total number of particles (or equivalently, its fraction of the total number of moles, that is, the mole fraction).

Figure 5.17 A molecular view of Dalton's law.

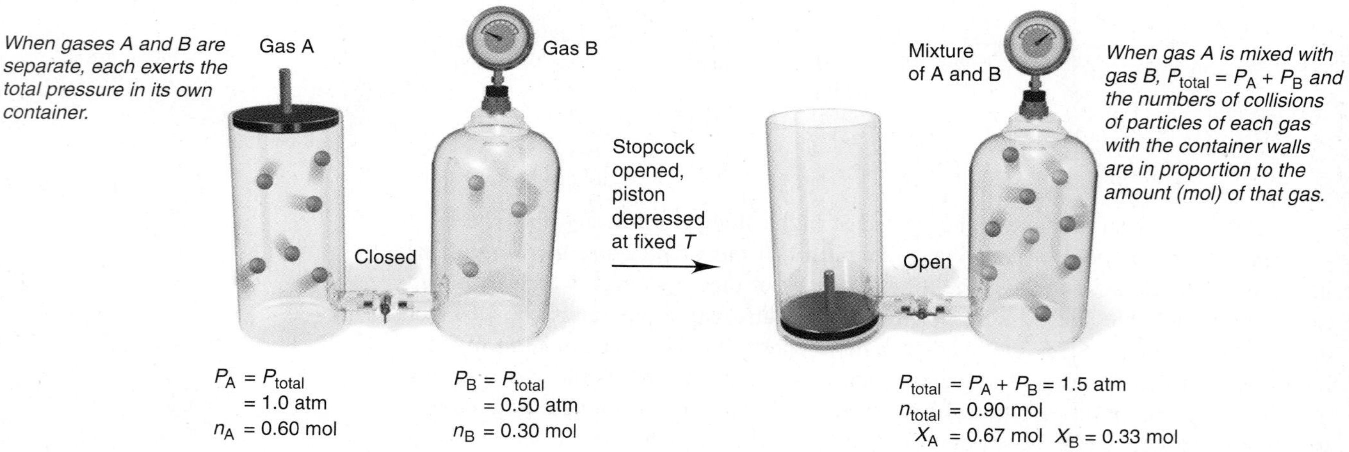

4. *Charles's law* ($V \propto T$) (Figure 5.18). At some starting temperature, T_1, the external (atmospheric) pressure (P_{atm}) equals the pressure of the gas (P_{gas}). When the gas is heated and the temperature increases to T_2, the most probable molecular speed and the average kinetic energy increase (postulate 3). Thus, the particles hit the walls more frequently *and* more energetically. This change temporarily increases P_{gas}. As a result, the piston moves up, which increases the volume and lowers the collision frequency until P_{atm} and P_{gas} are again equal.

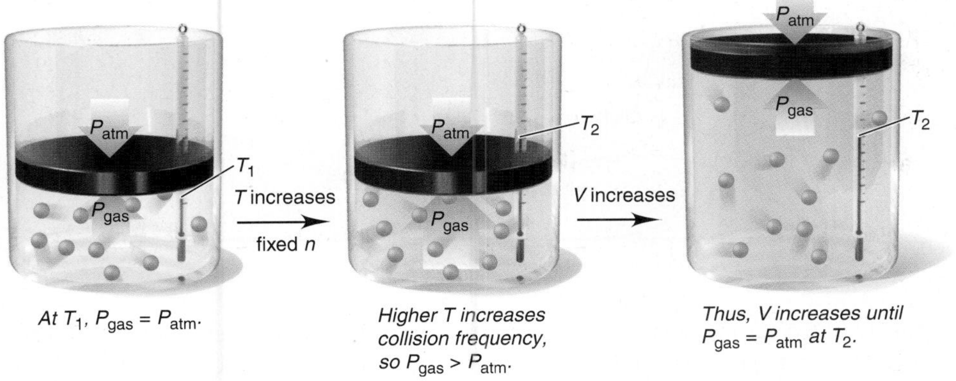

Figure 5.18 A molecular view of Charles's law.

5. *Avogadro's law* ($V \propto n$) (Figure 5.19). At some starting amount, n_1, of gas, P_{atm} equals P_{gas}. When more gas is added from the attached tank, the amount increases to n_2. Thus, more particles hit the walls more frequently, which temporarily increases P_{gas}. As a result, the piston moves up, which increases the volume and lowers the collision frequency until P_{atm} and P_{gas} are again equal.

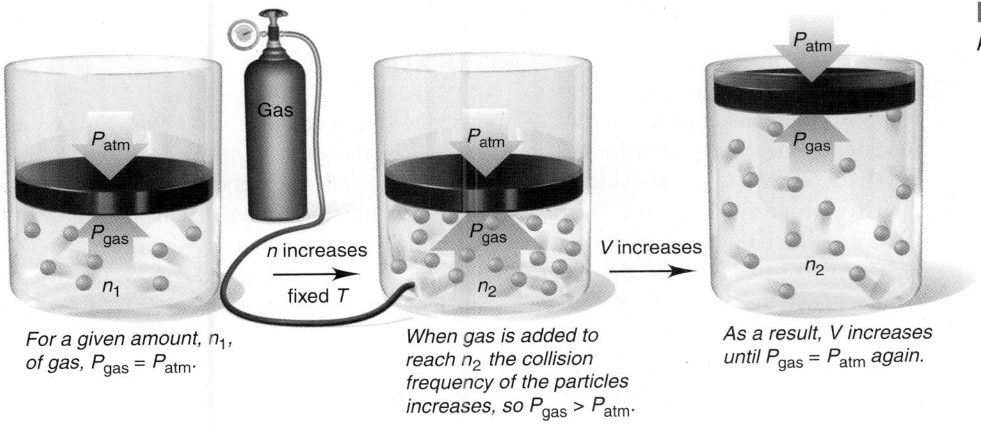

Figure 5.19 A molecular view of Avogadro's law.

The Central Importance of Kinetic Energy Recall from Chapter 1 that the kinetic energy of an object is the energy associated with its motion. It is key to explaining some implications of Avogadro's law and, most importantly, the meaning of temperature.

1. *Implications of Avogadro's law.* As we just saw, Avogadro's law says that, at any given T and P, the volume of a gas depends only on the number of moles—that is, number of particles—in the sample. The law doesn't mention the chemical nature of the gas, so equal numbers of particles of any two gases, say O_2 and H_2, should occupy the same volume. But, why don't the heavier O_2 molecules exert more pressure on the container walls, and thus take up more volume, than the lighter H_2 molecules? To answer this, we'll show one way to express kinetic energy mathematically:

$$E_k = \tfrac{1}{2}\text{mass} \times \text{speed}^2$$

This equation says that, for a given E_k, an object's mass and speed are inversely related, which means that *a heavier object moving slower can have the same kinetic energy as a lighter object moving faster.* Figure 5.20 on the next page shows that, for several gases, *the most probable speed (top of each curve) increases as the molar mass (number in parentheses) decreases.*

As we saw earlier, postulate 3 of the kinetic-molecular theory directly implies that, at a given T, all gases have the same average kinetic energy. From Figure 5.20, we see

Figure 5.20 The relationship between molar mass and molecular speed. At a given temperature, gases with lower molar masses (numbers in parentheses) have higher most probable speeds (peak of each curve).

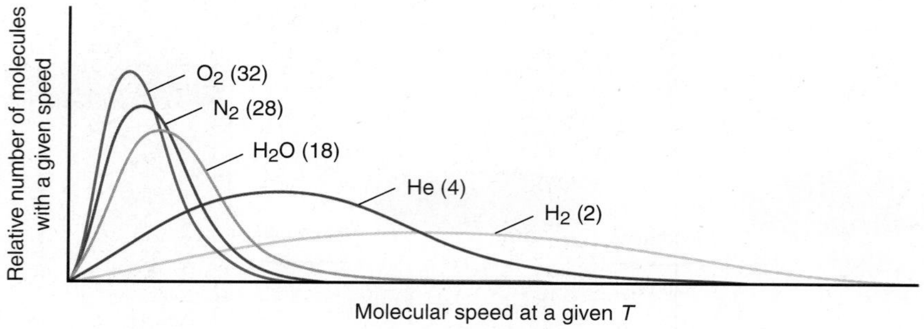

that O_2 molecules move more slowly, on average, than H_2 molecules. With their higher most probable speed, H_2 molecules collide with the walls of a container more often than O_2 molecules do, but their lower mass means that each collision has less force. Therefore, at a given T, equimolar samples of H_2 and O_2 (or any other gas) exert the same pressure and, thus, occupy the same volume because, on average, *their molecules hit the walls with the same kinetic energy.*

2. *The meaning of temperature.* Closely related to these ideas is the central relation between kinetic energy and temperature. Earlier we said that the average kinetic energy of the particles ($\overline{E_k}$) equals the absolute temperature times a constant; that is, $\overline{E_k} = c \times T$. Using definitions of velocity, momentum, force, and pressure, we can also express this relationship by the following equation:

$$\overline{E_k} = \tfrac{3}{2}\left(\frac{R}{N_A}\right)T$$

where R is the gas constant and N_A is the symbol for Avogadro's number. This equation makes the essential point that *temperature is a* ***measure*** *of the average kinetic energy of the particles:* as T increases, $\overline{E_k}$ increases, and vice versa. Temperature is an intensive property (Section 1.5), so it is not related to the *total* energy of motion of the particles, which depends on the size of the sample, but to the *average* energy.

Thus, for example, in the macroscopic world, we heat a beaker of water over a flame and see the mercury rise inside a thermometer we put in the beaker. We see this because, in the molecular world, kinetic energy transfers, in turn, from higher energy gas particles in the flame to lower energy particles in the beaker glass, the water molecules, the particles in the thermometer glass, and the atoms of mercury.

Root-Mean-Square Speed Finally, let's derive an expression for the speed of a gas particle that has the average kinetic energy of the particles in a sample. From the general expression for kinetic energy of an object,

$$E_k = \tfrac{1}{2}\text{mass} \times \text{speed}^2$$

the average kinetic energy of each particle in a large population is

$$\overline{E_k} = \tfrac{1}{2}m\overline{u^2}$$

where m is the particle's mass (atomic or molecular) and $\overline{u^2}$ is the average of the squares of the molecular speeds. Setting this expression for average kinetic energy equal to the earlier one gives

$$\tfrac{1}{2}m\overline{u^2} = \tfrac{3}{2}\left(\frac{R}{N_A}\right)T$$

Multiplying through by Avogadro's number, N_A, gives the average kinetic energy for a mole of gas particles:

$$\tfrac{1}{2}N_A\,m\overline{u^2} = \tfrac{3}{2}RT$$

Avogadro's number times the molecular mass, $N_A \times m$, is the molar mass, $\mathcal{M}$, and solving for $\overline{u^2}$, we have

$$\overline{u^2} = \frac{3RT}{\mathcal{M}}$$

The square root of $\overline{u^2}$ is the root-mean-square speed, or **rms speed (u_{rms})**: *a particle moving at this speed has the average kinetic energy.** That is, taking the square root of both sides of the previous equation gives

$$u_{rms} = \sqrt{\frac{3RT}{\mathcal{M}}} \quad (5.13)$$

where R is the gas constant, T is the absolute temperature, and $\mathcal{M}$ is the molar mass. (Because we want u in m/s and R includes the joule, which has units of kg·m²/s², we use the value 8.314 J/mol·K for R and express $\mathcal{M}$ in kg/mol.)

Thus, as an example, the root-mean-square speed of an O_2 molecule ($\mathcal{M}$ = 3.200×10^{-2} kg/mol) at room temperature (20°C, or 293 K) in the air you're breathing right now is

$$u_{rms} = \sqrt{\frac{3RT}{\mathcal{M}}} = \sqrt{\frac{3(8.314\ \text{J/mol·K})(293\ \text{K})}{3.200\times10^{-2}\ \text{kg/mol}}}$$

$$= \sqrt{\frac{3(8.314\ \cancel{\text{kg}}\text{·m}^2/\text{s}^2/\cancel{\text{mol}}\text{·}\cancel{\text{K}})(293\ \cancel{\text{K}})}{3.200\times10^{-2}\ \cancel{\text{kg}}/\cancel{\text{mol}}}}$$

$$= 478\ \text{m/s (about 1070 mi/hr)}$$

Effusion and Diffusion

The movement of a gas into a vacuum and the movement of gases through one another are phenomena with some vital applications.

The Process of Effusion One of the early triumphs of the kinetic-molecular theory was an explanation of **effusion,** the process by which a gas escapes through a tiny hole in its container into an evacuated space. In 1846, Thomas Graham studied the effusion rate of a gas, the number of molecules escaping per unit time, and found that it was inversely proportional to the square root of the gas density. But, density is directly related to molar mass, so **Graham's law of effusion** is stated as follows: *the rate of effusion of a gas is inversely proportional to the square root of its molar mass,* or

$$\text{Rate of effusion} \propto \frac{1}{\sqrt{\mathcal{M}}}$$

Argon (Ar) is lighter than krypton (Kr), so it effuses faster, assuming equal pressures of the two gases (Figure 5.21). Thus, the ratio of the rates is

$$\frac{\text{Rate}_{Ar}}{\text{Rate}_{Kr}} = \frac{\sqrt{\mathcal{M}_{Kr}}}{\sqrt{\mathcal{M}_{Ar}}} \quad \text{or, in general,} \quad \frac{\text{Rate}_A}{\text{Rate}_B} = \frac{\sqrt{\mathcal{M}_B}}{\sqrt{\mathcal{M}_A}} = \sqrt{\frac{\mathcal{M}_B}{\mathcal{M}_A}} \quad (5.14)$$

The kinetic-molecular theory explains that, at a given temperature and pressure, *the gas with the lower molar mass effuses faster because the rms speed of its molecules is higher; therefore, more molecules reach the hole and escape per unit time.*

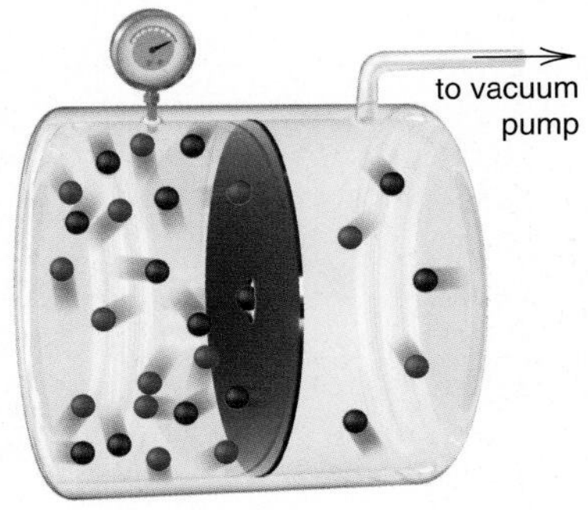

Figure 5.21 Effusion. Lighter (*black*) particles effuse faster than heavier (*red*) particles.

Sample Problem 5.13 Applying Graham's Law of Effusion

Problem A mixture of helium (He) and methane (CH_4) is placed in an effusion apparatus. Calculate the ratio of their effusion rates.

Plan The effusion rate is inversely proportional to $\sqrt{\mathcal{M}}$, so we find the molar mass of each substance from the formula and take its square root. The inverse of the ratio of the square roots is the ratio of the effusion rates.

Solution

$\mathcal{M}$ of CH_4 = 16.04 g/mol $\qquad$ $\mathcal{M}$ of He = 4.003 g/mol

*The rms speed, u_{rms}, is proportional to, but slightly higher than, the most probable speed; for an ideal gas, u_{rms} = 1.09 × average speed.

Calculating the ratio of the effusion rates:

$$\frac{\text{Rate}_{\text{He}}}{\text{Rate}_{\text{CH}_4}} = \sqrt{\frac{\mathcal{M}_{\text{CH}_4}}{\mathcal{M}_{\text{He}}}} = \sqrt{\frac{16.04\ \text{g/mol}}{4.003\ \text{g/mol}}} = \sqrt{4.007} = 2.002$$

Check A ratio >1 makes sense because the lighter He should effuse faster than the heavier CH_4. Because the molar mass of CH_4 is about four times the molar mass of He, He should effuse about twice as fast as CH_4 ($\sqrt{4}$).

Follow-Up Problem 5.13 If it takes 1.25 min for 0.010 mol of He to effuse, how long will it take for the same amount of ethane (C_2H_6) to effuse?

Applications of Effusion The process of effusion has two important uses.

1. *Determination of molar mass.* We can also use Graham's law to *determine the molar mass of an unknown gas.* By comparing the effusion rate of gas X with that of a known gas, such as He, we can solve for the molar mass of X:

$$\frac{\text{Rate}_{\text{X}}}{\text{Rate}_{\text{He}}} = \sqrt{\frac{\mathcal{M}_{\text{He}}}{\mathcal{M}_{\text{X}}}}$$

Squaring both sides and solving for the molar mass of X gives

$$\mathcal{M}_{\text{X}} = \mathcal{M}_{\text{He}} \times \left(\frac{\text{rate}_{\text{He}}}{\text{rate}_{\text{X}}}\right)^2$$

2. *Preparation of nuclear fuel.* By far the most important application of Graham's law is in the preparation of fuel for nuclear energy reactors. The process of *isotope enrichment* increases the proportion of fissionable, but rarer, ^{235}U (only 0.7% by mass of naturally occurring uranium) to the nonfissionable, more abundant ^{238}U (99.3% by mass). Because the two isotopes have identical chemical properties, they are extremely difficult to separate chemically. But, one way to separate them takes advantage of a difference in a physical property—the effusion rate of gaseous compounds. Uranium ore is treated with fluorine to yield a gaseous mixture of $^{238}UF_6$ and $^{235}UF_6$ that is pumped through a series of chambers separated by porous barriers. Molecules of $^{235}UF_6$ are slightly lighter ($\mathcal{M}$ = 349.03) than molecules of $^{238}UF_6$ ($\mathcal{M}$ = 352.04), so they move slightly faster and effuse through each barrier 1.0043 times faster. Many passes must be made, each one increasing the fraction of $^{235}UF_6$, until the mixture obtained is 3–5% by mass $^{235}UF_6$. This process was developed during the latter years of World War II and produced enough ^{235}U for two of the world's first atomic bombs. Today, a less expensive centrifuge process is used more often. The ability to enrich uranium has become a key international concern, as more countries aspire to develop nuclear energy and nuclear arms.

The Process of Diffusion Closely related to effusion is the process of gaseous **diffusion,** the movement of one gas through another. Diffusion rates are also described generally by Graham's law:

$$\text{Rate of diffusion} \propto \frac{1}{\sqrt{\mathcal{M}}}$$

For two gases at equal pressures, such as NH_3 and HCl, moving through another gas or a mixture of gases, such as air, we find

$$\frac{\text{Rate}_{\text{NH}_3}}{\text{Rate}_{\text{HCl}}} = \sqrt{\frac{\mathcal{M}_{\text{HCl}}}{\mathcal{M}_{\text{NH}_3}}}$$

The reason for this dependence on molar mass is the same as for effusion rates: *lighter molecules have higher average speeds than heavier molecules, so they move farther in a given time.*

If gas molecules move at hundreds of meters per second (see Figure 5.14), why does it take a second or two after you open a bottle of perfume to smell it? Although convection plays an important role in this process, another reason for the time lag is

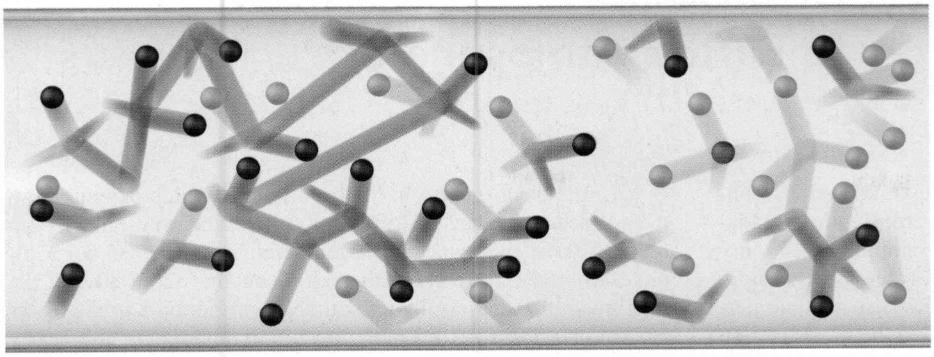

Figure 5.22 Diffusion of gases. When different gases (*black*, from the left, and *green*, from the right) move through each other, they mix. For simplicity, the complex path of only one black particle is shown (in *red*). In reality, all the particles have similar paths.

that a gas particle does not travel very far before it collides with another particle (Figure 5.22). Thus, a perfume molecule travels slowly because it collides with countless molecules in the air. The presence of so many other particles means that *diffusion rates are much lower than effusion rates.* Imagine how much quicker you can walk through an empty room than through a room crowded with other moving people.

Diffusion also occurs when a gas enters a liquid (and even to a small extent a solid). However, the average distances between molecules are so much shorter in a liquid that collisions are much more frequent; thus, diffusion of a gas through a liquid is *much* slower than through a gas. Nevertheless, this type of diffusion is a vital process in biological systems, for example, in the movement of O_2 from lungs to blood.

The Chaotic World of Gases: Mean Free Path and Collision Frequency

Refinements of the basic kinetic-molecular theory provide a view into the chaotic molecular world of gases. Try to visualize an "average" N_2 molecule in the room you are in now. It is continually changing speed as it collides with other molecules—at one instant, going 2500 mi/h, and at another, standing still. But these extreme speeds are *much* less likely than the most probable one and those near it (see Figure 5.14). At 20°C and 1 atm pressure, the N_2 molecule is hurtling at an average speed of 470 m/s (rms speed = 510 m/s), or nearly 1100 mi/h!

Mean Free Path From a particle's diameter, we can obtain the **mean free path,** the average distance it travels between collisions at a given temperature and pressure. An N_2 molecule (3.7×10^{-10} m in diameter) has a mean free path of 6.6×10^{-8} m, which means it travels an average of 180 molecular diameters before smashing into a fellow traveler. (An N_2 molecule the size of a billiard ball would travel an average of about 30 ft before hitting another.) Therefore, even though gas molecules are *not* points of mass, it is still valid to assume that a gas sample *is* nearly all empty space. Mean free path is a key factor in the rate of diffusion and the rate of heat flow through a gas.

Collision Frequency Divide the most probable speed (meters per second) by the mean free path (meters per collision) and you obtain the **collision frequency,** the average number of collisions per second that each particle undergoes. As you can see, the N_2 molecule experiences, on average, an enormous number of collisions every second: ●

$$\text{Collision frequency} = \frac{4.7\times10^{2}\ \text{m/s}}{6.6\times10^{-8}\ \text{m/collision}} = 7.0\times10^{9}\ \text{collision/s}$$

Distribution of speed (and kinetic energy) and collision frequency are essential ideas for understanding the speed of a reaction, as you'll see in Chapter 16. As the Chemical Connections essay shows, many of the concepts we've discussed so far apply directly to our planet's atmosphere.

● **Danger in a Molecular Amusement Park** To really appreciate the astounding events in the molecular world, let's use a two-dimensional analogy to compare the moving N_2 molecule with a bumper car you are driving in an enormous amusement park ride. To match the collision frequency of the N_2 molecule, you would need to be traveling 2.8 billion mi/s (4.5 billion km/s, much faster than the speed of light!) and would smash into another bumper car every 700 yd (640 m).

CHEMICAL CONNECTIONS TO ATMOSPHERIC SCIENCE | How Do the Gas Laws Apply to Earth's Atmosphere?

An **atmosphere** is the envelope of gases that extends continuously from a planet's surface outward, thinning gradually until it is identical with outer space. A sample of clean, dry air at sea level on Earth contains 18 gases (Table B5.1). Under standard conditions, they behave nearly ideally, so volume percent equals mole percent (Avogadro's law), and the mole fraction of a component relates directly to its partial pressure (Dalton's law). Let's see how the gas laws and kinetic-molecular theory apply to our atmosphere, first with regard to variations in pressure and temperature, and then as explanations of some very familiar phenomena.

Table B5.1 Composition of Clean, Dry Air at Sea Level

Component	Mole Fraction
Nitrogen (N_2)	0.78084
Oxygen (O_2)	0.20946
Argon (Ar)	0.00934
Carbon dioxide (CO_2)	0.00933
Neon (Ne)	1.818×10^{-5}
Helium (He)	5.24×10^{-6}
Methane (CH_4)	2×10^{-6}
Krypton (Kr)	1.14×10^{-6}
Hydrogen (H_2)	5×10^{-7}
Dinitrogen monoxide (N_2O)	5×10^{-7}
Carbon monoxide (CO)	1×10^{-7}
Xenon (Xe)	8×10^{-8}
Ozone (O_3)	2×10^{-8}
Ammonia (NH_3)	6×10^{-9}
Nitrogen dioxide (NO_2)	6×10^{-9}
Nitrogen monoxide (NO)	6×10^{-10}
Sulfur dioxide (SO_2)	2×10^{-10}
Hydrogen sulfide (H_2S)	2×10^{-10}

The Smooth Variation in Pressure with Altitude

Because gases are compressible (Boyle's law), the pressure of the atmosphere *increases* smoothly as we approach Earth's surface, with a more rapid increase at lower altitudes (Figure B5.1, *left*). No boundary delineates the beginning of the atmosphere from the end of outer space, but the densities and compositions are identical at an altitude of about 10,000 km (6000 mi). Yet, about 99% of the atmosphere's mass lies within 30 km (almost 19 mi) of the surface, and 75% lies within the lowest 11 km (almost 7 mi).

The Zig-Zag Variation in Temperature with Altitude

Unlike pressure, temperature does *not* change smoothly with altitude above Earth's surface. The atmosphere is classified into regions based on the direction of temperature change, and we'll start at the surface (Figure B5.1, *right*).

1. *The troposphere.* In the troposphere, which extends from the surface to between 7 km (23,000 ft) at the poles and 17 km (60,000 ft) at the equator, the temperature *drops* 7°C per kilometer to −55°C (218 K). This region contains about 80% of the total mass of the atmosphere, with 50% of the mass in the lower 5.6 km (18,500 ft). All weather occurs in this region, and nearly all, except supersonic, aircraft fly here.

2. *The stratosphere and the ozone layer.* In the stratosphere, the temperature *rises* from −55°C to about 7°C (280 K) at 50 km. This rise is due to a variety of complex reactions, mostly involving ozone, and is caused by the absorption of solar radiation. Most high-energy radiation is absorbed by upper levels of the atmosphere, but some that reaches the stratosphere breaks O_2 into O atoms. The energetic O atoms collide with more O_2 to form ozone (O_3), another molecular form of oxygen:

$$O_2(g) \xrightarrow{\text{high-energy radiation}} 2O(g)$$

$$M + O(g) + O_2(g) \longrightarrow O_3(g) + M + \textit{heat}$$

where M is any particle that can carry away excess energy. This reaction releases heat, which is why stratospheric temperatures increase with altitude. Over 90% of atmospheric ozone remains in a thin layer within the stratosphere, its thickness varying both geographically (greatest at the poles) and seasonally (greatest in spring in the Northern Hemisphere and in fall in the Southern). Stratospheric ozone is vital to life because it absorbs over 95% of the harmful ultraviolet (UV) solar radiation that would otherwise reach the surface. In Chapter 16, we'll discuss the destructive effect of certain industrial chemicals on the ozone layer.

3. *The mesosphere.* In the mesosphere, the temperature *drops* again to −93°C (180 K) at around 80 km.

4. *The outer atmosphere.* Within the *thermosphere,* which extends to around 500 km, the temperature *rises* again, but varies between 700 and 2000 K, depending on the intensity of solar radiation and sunspot activity. The *exosphere,* the outermost region, maintains these temperatures and merges with outer space.

What does it actually mean to have a temperature of 2000 K at 500 km (300 mi) above Earth's surface? Would a piece of iron (melting point = 1808 K) glow red-hot within a minute or so and melt in the thermosphere, as it does if heated to 2000 K in the troposphere? The answer involves the relation between temperature and the time it takes to transfer kinetic energy. Our use of the words "hot" and "cold" refers to measurements near the surface. There, the collision frequency of gas particles with a thermometer is enormous, and so the transfer of their kinetic energy is very fast. But, at an altitude of 500 km, where the density of gas particles is a million times *less,* collision frequency is extremely low, and a thermometer, or any object, experiences *very slow transfer of kinetic energy.* Thus, the object would not become "hot" in the usual sense in any reasonable time. But the high-energy solar radiation that *is* transferred to the few particles present in these regions makes their average kinetic energy extremely high, as indicated by the high absolute temperature.

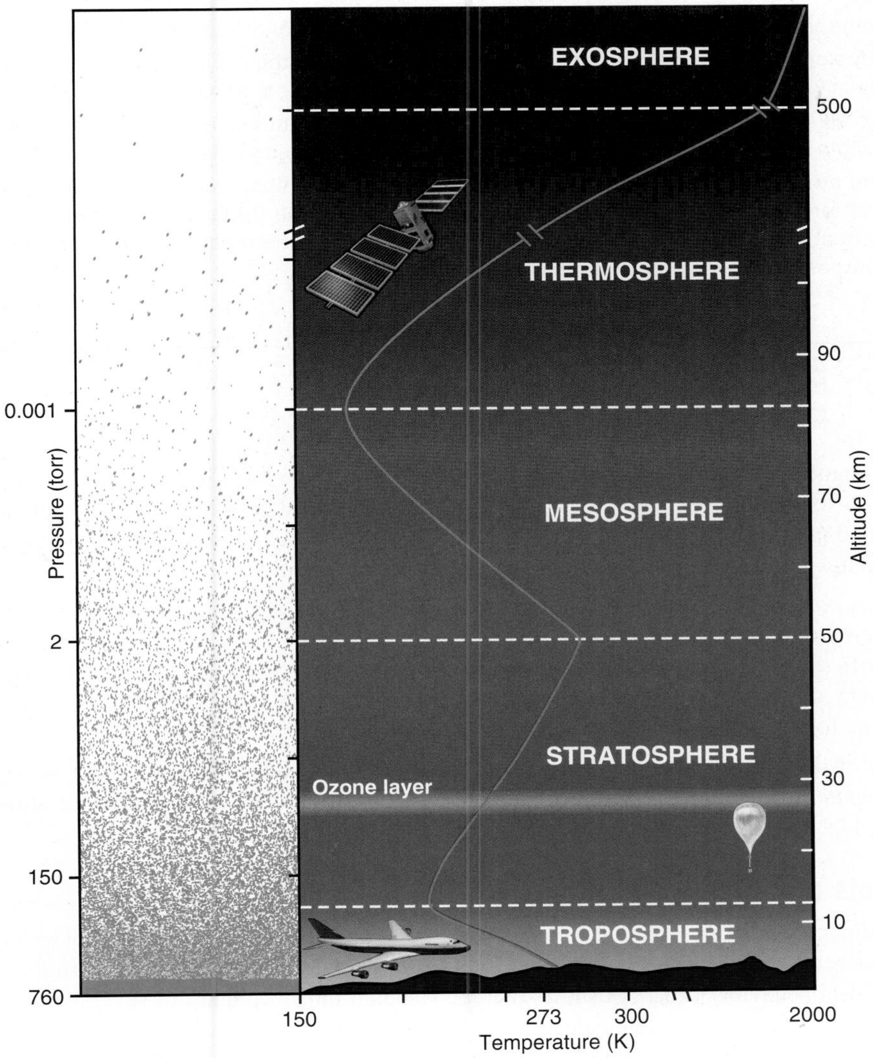

Figure B5.1 Variations in pressure and temperature with altitude in Earth's atmosphere.

Convection in the Lower Atmosphere

Why must you take more breaths per minute on a high mountaintop than at sea level? Because at the higher elevation, there is a smaller *amount* of O_2 in each breath. However, the *proportion* (mole percent) of O_2 throughout the lower atmosphere remains about 21%. This uniform composition arises from *vertical (convective) mixing,* and the gas laws explain how it occurs.

Let's follow an air mass from ground level, as solar heating of Earth's surface warms it. The warmer air mass expands (Charles's law), which makes it less dense, so it rises. As it does so, the pressure on it decreases, making it expand further (Boyle's law). Pushing against the surrounding air requires energy, so the temperature of the air mass decreases and thus the air mass shrinks slightly (Charles's law). But, as its temperature drops, its water vapor condenses (or solidifies), and these changes of state release heat; therefore, the air mass becomes warmer and rises further. Meanwhile, the cooler, and thus denser, air that was above it sinks, becomes warmer through contact with the surface, and goes through the same process as the first air mass. As a result of this vertical mixing, the composition of the lower atmosphere remains uniform.

Warm air rising from the ground, called a *thermal,* is used by soaring birds and glider pilots to stay aloft. Convection helps clean the air in urban areas, because the rising air carries up pollutants, which are dispersed by winds. Under certain conditions, however, a warm air mass remains stationary over a cool one. The resulting *temperature inversion* blocks normal convection, and harmful pollutants build up, causing severe health problems.

Problems

B5.1 Suggest a reason why supersonic aircraft are kept well below their maximum speeds until they reach their highest altitudes.

B5.2 Gases behave nearly ideally under Earth's conditions. Elsewhere in the Solar System, however, conditions are very different. On which would you expect atmospheric gases to deviate most from ideal behavior, Saturn (4×10^6 atm and 130 K) or Venus (90 atm and 730 K)? Explain.

B5.3 What is the volume percent and partial pressure (in torr) of argon in a sample of dry air at sea level?

B5.4 Earth's atmosphere is estimated to have a mass of 5.14×10^{15} t (1 t = 1000 kg).
(a) If the average molar mass of air is 28.8 g/mol, how many moles of gas are in the atmosphere?
(b) How many liters would the atmosphere occupy at 25°C and 1 atm?

Summary of Section 5.5

- The kinetic-molecular theory postulates that gas particles have no volume, move in straight-line paths between elastic (energy-conserving) collisions, and have average kinetic energies proportional to the absolute temperature of the gas.
- This theory explains the gas laws in terms of changes in distances between particles and the container walls, changes in molecular speed, and the energy of collisions.
- Temperature is a measure of the average kinetic energy of the particles.
- Effusion and diffusion rates are *inversely* proportional to the square root of the molar mass (Graham's law) because they are *directly* proportional to molecular speed.
- Molecular motion is characterized by a temperature-dependent, most probable speed (within a range of speeds), which affects mean free path and collision frequency.
- The atmosphere is a complex mixture of gases that exhibits variations in pressure and temperature with altitude. High temperatures in the upper atmosphere result from absorption of high-energy solar radiation. The lower atmosphere has a uniform composition as a result of convective mixing.

5.6 • REAL GASES: DEVIATIONS FROM IDEAL BEHAVIOR

A fundamental principle of science is that simpler models are more useful than complex ones, as long as they explain the data. With only a few postulates, the kinetic-molecular theory explains the behavior of most gases under ordinary conditions. But, two of the postulates are useful approximations that do not reflect reality:

1. *Gas particles are* **not** *points of mass* but have volumes determined by the sizes of their atoms and the lengths and directions of their bonds.
2. *Attractive and repulsive forces* **do** *exist among gas particles* because atoms contain charged subatomic particles and many bonds are polar. (As you'll see in Chapter 12, such forces lead to changes of physical state.)

These two features cause deviations from ideal behavior under *extreme conditions of low temperature and high pressure.* These deviations mean that we must alter the simple model and the ideal gas law to predict the behavior of real gases.

Effects of Extreme Conditions on Gas Behavior

At ordinary conditions—relatively high temperatures and low pressures—most real gases exhibit nearly ideal behavior. Yet, even at STP (0°C and 1 atm), gases deviate *slightly* from ideal behavior. Table 5.3 shows that the standard molar volumes of several gases, when measured to five significant figures, do not equal the ideal value. Note that the deviations increase as the boiling point rises.

Table 5.3 Molar Volume of Some Common Gases at STP (0°C and 1 atm)

Gas	Molar Volume (L/mol)	Boiling Point (°C)
He	22.435	−268.9
H_2	22.432	−252.8
Ne	22.422	−246.1
Ideal gas	**22.414**	—
Ar	22.397	−185.9
N_2	22.396	−195.8
O_2	22.390	−183.0
CO	22.388	−191.5
Cl_2	22.184	−34.0
NH_3	22.079	−33.4

The phenomena that cause slight deviations under standard conditions exert more influence as temperature decreases and pressure increases. Figure 5.23 shows a plot of PV/RT versus external pressure (P_{ext}) for 1 mol of several real gases and an ideal gas. The PV/RT values range from normal (at $P_{ext} = 1$ atm, $PV/RT = 1$) to very high (at $P_{ext} \approx 1000$ atm, $PV/RT \approx 1.6$ to 2.3). For the *ideal* gas, PV/RT is 1 at any P_{ext}.

The PV/RT curve for methane (CH_4) is typical of most gases: it decreases *below* the ideal value at moderately high P_{ext} and then rises *above* the ideal value as P_{ext} increases to very high values. This shape arises from two overlapping effects:

- At moderately high P_{ext}, PV/RT values are lower than ideal values (less than 1) because of *interparticle attractions.*
- At very high P_{ext}, PV/RT values are greater than ideal values (more than 1) because of *particle volume.*

Let's examine these effects on the molecular level:

1. *Effect of interparticle attractions.* Interparticle attractions occur between separate atoms or molecules and are caused by imbalances in electron distributions. They are important only over *very* short distances and are *much* weaker than the covalent bonding forces that hold a molecule together. At normal P_{ext}, the spaces between the particles are so large that attractions are negligible and the gas behaves nearly ideally.

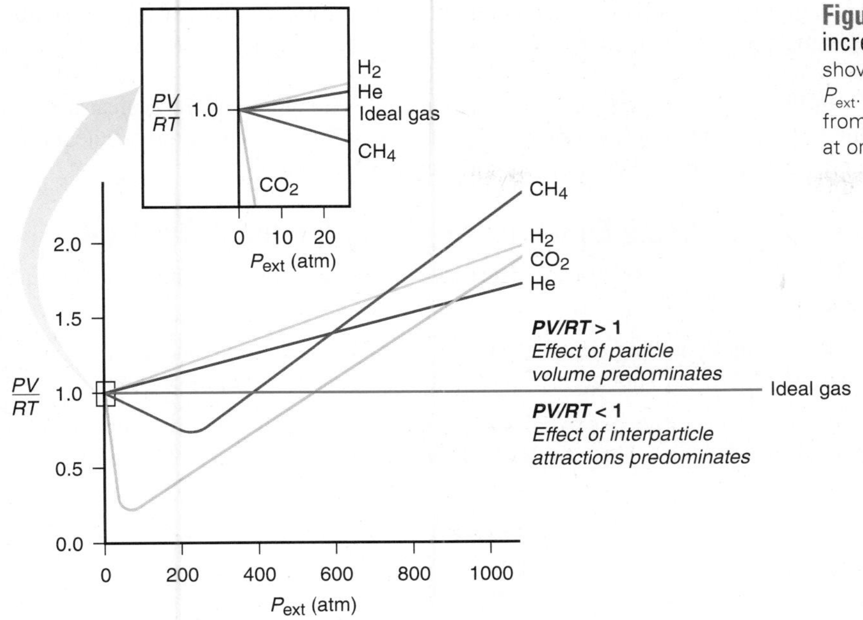

Figure 5.23 Deviations from ideal behavior with increasing external pressure. The horizontal line shows that, for 1 mol of ideal gas, $PV/RT = 1$ at all P_{ext}. At very high P_{ext}, real gases deviate significantly from ideal behavior, but small deviations appear even at ordinary pressures (expanded portion).

As P_{ext} rises, the volume of the sample decreases and the particles get closer together, so interparticle attractions have a greater effect. As a particle approaches the container wall under these higher pressures, nearby particles attract it, which lessens the force of its impact (Figure 5.24). *Repeated throughout the sample, this effect results in decreased gas pressure and, thus, a smaller numerator in PV/RT.* Similarly, lowering the temperature slows the particles, so they attract each other for a longer time.

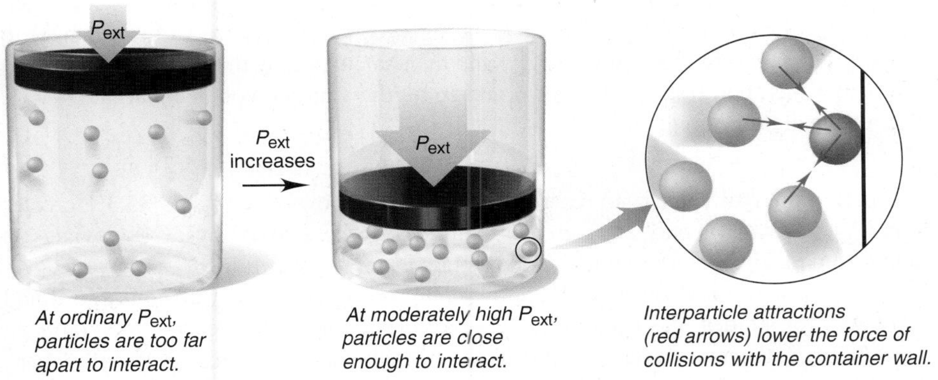

Figure 5.24 The effect of interparticle attractions on measured gas pressure.

2. *Effect of particle volume.* At normal P_{ext}, the space between particles (free volume) is enormous compared with the volume of the particles *themselves* (particle volume); thus, the free volume is essentially equal to V, the container volume in PV/RT. At *moderately* high P_{ext} and as free volume decreases, the particle volume makes up an increasing proportion of the container volume (Figure 5.25). At *extremely* high pressures, the space taken up by the particles themselves makes the free volume significantly *less* than the container volume. Nevertheless, we continue to use the container volume for V in PV/RT, which causes the numerator, and thus the ratio, to become

Figure 5.25 The effect of particle volume on measured gas volume.

artificially high. This particle volume effect increases as P_{ext} increases, eventually outweighing the effect of interparticle attractions and causing PV/RT to rise above the ideal value.

In Figure 5.23, note that the H_2 and He curves do not show the typical dip at moderate pressures. These gases consist of particles with such weak interparticle attractions that the particle volume effect predominates at all pressures.

The van der Waals Equation: Adjusting the Ideal Gas Law

To describe real gas behavior more accurately, we need to adjust the ideal gas equation in two ways:

1. Adjust P *up* by adding a factor that accounts for interparticle attractions.
2. Adjust V *down* by subtracting a factor that accounts for particle volume.

In 1873, Johannes van der Waals revised the ideal gas equation to account for the behavior of real gases. The **van der Waals equation** for n moles of a real gas is

$$\underbrace{\left(P + \frac{n^2a}{V^2}\right)}_{\text{adjusts } P \text{ up}}\underbrace{(V - nb)}_{\text{adjusts } V \text{ down}} = nRT \qquad (5.15)$$

where P is the measured pressure, V is the known container volume, n and T have their usual meanings, and a and b are **van der Waals constants,** experimentally determined and specific for a given gas (Table 5.4). The constant a depends on the number and distribution of electrons, which relates to the complexity of a particle and the strength of its interparticle attractions. The constant b relates to particle volume. For instance, CO_2 is both more complex and larger than H_2, and the values of their constants reflect this.

Table 5.4 Van der Waals Constants for Some Common Gases

Gas	$a\left(\frac{atm \cdot L^2}{mol^2}\right)$	$b\left(\frac{L}{mol}\right)$
He	0.034	0.0237
Ne	0.211	0.0171
Ar	1.35	0.0322
Kr	2.32	0.0398
Xe	4.19	0.0511
H_2	0.244	0.0266
N_2	1.39	0.0391
O_2	1.36	0.0318
Cl_2	6.49	0.0562
CH_4	2.25	0.0428
CO	1.45	0.0395
CO_2	3.59	0.0427
NH_3	4.17	0.0371
H_2O	5.46	0.0305

Here is a typical application of the van der Waals equation. A 1.98-L vessel contains 215 g (4.89 mol) of dry ice. After standing at 26°C (299 K), the $CO_2(s)$ changes to $CO_2(g)$. The pressure is measured (P_{real}) and then calculated by the ideal gas law (P_{IGL}) and, using the appropriate values of a and b, by the van der Waals equation (P_{VDW}). The results are revealing:

$$P_{real} = 44.8 \text{ atm} \qquad P_{IGL} = 60.6 \text{ atm} \qquad P_{VDW} = 45.9 \text{ atm}$$

Comparing the real value with each calculated value shows that P_{IGL} is 35.3% greater than P_{real}, but P_{VDW} is only 2.5% greater than P_{real}. At these conditions, CO_2 deviates so much from ideal behavior that the ideal gas law is not very useful.

A key point to realize: According to kinetic-molecular theory, the constants a and b are zero for an ideal gas because the gas particles do not attract each other and have no volume. Yet, even in a real gas at ordinary pressures, the particles are very far apart. This large average interparticle distance has two consequences:

- Attractive forces are miniscule, so $P + \frac{n^2a}{V^2} \approx P$.
- The particle volume is a minute fraction of the container volume, so $V - nb \approx V$.

Therefore, *at ordinary conditions, the van der Waals equation* ***becomes*** *the ideal gas equation.*

Summary of Section 5.6

- At very high P or low T, all gases deviate significantly from ideal behavior.
- As external pressure increases, most real gases exhibit first a lower and then a higher PV/RT; for 1 mol of an ideal gas, this ratio remains constant at 1.
- The deviations from ideal behavior are due to (1) attractions between particles, which lower the pressure (and decrease PV/RT), and (2) the volume of the particles themselves, which takes up an increasingly larger fraction of the container volume (and increases PV/RT).
- The van der Waals equation includes constants specific for a given gas to correct for deviations from ideal behavior. At ordinary P and T, the van der Waals equation reduces to the ideal gas equation.

CHAPTER REVIEW GUIDE

Learning Objectives

Relevant section (§) and/or sample problem (SP) numbers appear in parentheses.

Understand These Concepts

1. How gases differ in their macroscopic properties from liquids and solids (§5.1)
2. The meaning of pressure and the operation of a barometer and a manometer (§5.2)
3. The relations among gas variables expressed by Boyle's, Charles's, and Avogadro's laws (§5.3)
4. How the individual gas laws are incorporated into the ideal gas law (§5.3)
5. How the ideal gas law can be used to study gas density, molar mass, and amounts of gases in reactions (§5.4)
6. The relation between the density and the temperature of a gas (§5.4)
7. The meaning of Dalton's law and the relation between partial pressure and mole fraction of a gas; how Dalton's law applies to collecting a gas over water (§5.4)
8. How the postulates of the kinetic-molecular theory are applied to explain the origin of pressure and the gas laws (§5.5)
9. The relations among molecular speed, average kinetic energy, and temperature (§5.5)
10. The meanings of *effusion* and *diffusion* and how their rates are related to molar mass (§5.5)
11. The relations among mean free path, molecular speed, and collision frequency (§5.5)
12. Why intermolecular attractions and molecular volume cause gases to deviate from ideal behavior at low temperatures and high pressures (§5.6)
13. How the van der Waals equation corrects the ideal gas law for extreme conditions (§5.6)

Master These Skills

1. Interconverting among the units of pressure (atm, mmHg, torr, pascal, lb/in^2) (SP 5.1)
2. Reducing the ideal gas law to the individual gas laws (SPs 5.2–5.5)
3. Applying gas laws to choose the correct chemical equation (SP 5.6)
4. Rearranging the ideal gas law to calculate gas density (SP 5.7) and molar mass of a volatile liquid (SP 5.8)
5. Calculating the mole fraction and the partial pressure of a gas (SP 5.9)
6. Using the vapor pressure of water to correct for the amount of a gas collected over water (SP 5.10)
7. Applying stoichiometry and gas laws to calculate amounts of reactants and products (SPs 5.11, 5.12)
8. Using Graham's law to solve problems of gaseous effusion (SP 5.13)

Key Terms

Page numbers appear in parentheses.

Section 5.2
pressure (P) (183)
barometer (183)
manometer (184)
pascal (Pa) (185)
standard atmosphere (atm) (185)
millimeter of mercury (mmHg) (185)
torr (185)

Section 5.3
ideal gas (186)
Boyle's law (187)
Charles's law (188)
Avogadro's law (190)
standard temperature and pressure (STP) (190)
standard molar volume (190)
ideal gas law (191)
universal gas constant (R) (191)

Section 5.4
partial pressure (199)
Dalton's law of partial pressures (199)
mole fraction (X) (200)

Section 5.5
kinetic-molecular theory (204)
rms speed (u_{rms}) (209)
effusion (209)
Graham's law of effusion (209)
diffusion (210)
mean free path (211)
collision frequency (211)
atmosphere (212)

Section 5.6
van der Waals equation (216)
van der Waals constants (216)

Key Equations and Relationships

Page numbers appear in parentheses.

5.1 Expressing the volume-pressure relationship (Boyle's law) (187):

$$V \propto \frac{1}{P} \quad \text{or} \quad PV = \text{constant} \quad [T \text{ and } n \text{ fixed}]$$

5.2 Expressing the volume-temperature relationship (Charles's law) (188):

$$V \propto T \quad \text{or} \quad \frac{V}{T} = \text{constant} \quad [P \text{ and } n \text{ fixed}]$$

5.3 Expressing the pressure-temperature relationship (Amontons's law) (189):

$$P \propto T \quad \text{or} \quad \frac{P}{T} = \text{constant} \quad [V \text{ and } n \text{ fixed}]$$

5.4 Expressing the volume-amount relationship (Avogadro's law) (190):

$$V \propto n \quad \text{or} \quad \frac{V}{n} = \text{constant} \quad [P \text{ and } T \text{ fixed}]$$

5.5 Defining standard temperature and pressure (190):

STP: 0°C (273.15 K) and 1 atm (760 torr)

5.6 Defining the volume of 1 mol of an ideal gas at STP (190):

Standard molar volume = 22.4141 L = 22.4 L [3 sf]

5.7 Relating volume to pressure, temperature, and amount (ideal gas law) (191):

$$PV = nRT \quad \text{and} \quad \frac{P_1V_1}{n_1T_1} = \frac{P_2V_2}{n_2T_2}$$

5.8 Calculating the value of R (191):

$$R = \frac{PV}{nT} = \frac{1 \text{ atm} \times 22.4141 \text{ L}}{1 \text{ mol} \times 273.15 \text{ K}}$$

$$= 0.082058 \frac{\text{atm·L}}{\text{mol·K}} = 0.0821 \frac{\text{atm·L}}{\text{mol·K}} \quad [3 \text{ sf}]$$

5.9 Rearranging the ideal gas law to find gas density (196):

$$PV = \frac{m}{\mathcal{M}} RT$$

so

$$\frac{m}{V} = d = \frac{\mathcal{M} \times P}{RT}$$

5.10 Rearranging the ideal gas law to find molar mass (198):

$$n = \frac{m}{\mathcal{M}} = \frac{PV}{RT} \quad \text{so} \quad \mathcal{M} = \frac{mRT}{PV}$$

5.11 Relating the total pressure of a gas mixture to the partial pressures of the components (Dalton's law of partial pressures) (199):

$$P_{\text{total}} = P_1 + P_2 + P_3 + \cdots$$

5.12 Relating partial pressure to mole fraction (200):

$$P_A = X_A \times P_{\text{total}}$$

5.13 Defining rms speed as a function of molar mass and temperature (209):

$$u_{\text{rms}} = \sqrt{\frac{3RT}{\mathcal{M}}}$$

5.14 Applying Graham's law of effusion (209):

$$\frac{\text{Rate}_A}{\text{Rate}_B} = \frac{\sqrt{\mathcal{M}_B}}{\sqrt{\mathcal{M}_A}} = \sqrt{\frac{\mathcal{M}_B}{\mathcal{M}_A}}$$

5.15 Applying the van der Waals equation to find the pressure or volume of a gas under extreme conditions (216):

$$\left(P + \frac{n^2a}{V^2}\right)(V - nb) = nRT$$

Brief Solutions to Follow-Up Problems

5.1 $P_{CO_2}(\text{torr}) = (753.6 \text{ mmHg} - 174.0 \text{ mmHg}) \times \frac{1 \text{ torr}}{1 \text{ mmHg}}$

$= 579.6 \text{ torr}$

$P_{CO_2}(\text{Pa}) = 579.6 \text{ torr} \times \frac{1 \text{ atm}}{760 \text{ torr}} \times \frac{1.01325\times10^5 \text{ Pa}}{1 \text{ atm}}$

$= 7.727\times10^4 \text{ Pa}$

$P_{CO_2}(\text{lb/in}^2) = 579.6 \text{ torr} \times \frac{1 \text{ atm}}{760 \text{ torr}} \times \frac{14.7 \text{ lb/in}^2}{1 \text{ atm}}$

$= 11.2 \text{ lb/in}^2$

5.2 $P_2(\text{atm}) = 26.3 \text{ kPa} \times \frac{1 \text{ atm}}{101.325 \text{ kPa}} = 0.260 \text{ atm}$

$V_2(\text{L}) = 105 \text{ mL} \times \frac{1 \text{ L}}{1000 \text{ mL}} \times \frac{0.871 \text{ atm}}{0.260 \text{ atm}} = 0.352 \text{ L}$

5.3 $T_2(\text{K}) = 273 \text{ K} \times \frac{9.75 \text{ cm}^3}{6.83 \text{ cm}^3} = 390. \text{ K}$

5.4 $P_2(\text{torr}) = 793 \text{ torr} \times \frac{35.0 \text{ g} - 5.0 \text{ g}}{35.0 \text{ g}} = 680. \text{ torr}$

(There is no need to convert mass to moles because the ratio of masses equals the ratio of moles.)

5.5 $n = \frac{PV}{RT} = \frac{1.37 \text{ atm} \times 438 \text{ L}}{0.0821 \frac{\text{atm·L}}{\text{mol·K}} \times 294 \text{ K}} = 24.9 \text{ mol } O_2$

Mass (g) of O_2 = 24.9 mol $O_2 \times \frac{32.00 \text{ g } O_2}{1 \text{ mol } O_2} = 7.97\times10^2 \text{ g } O_2$

5.6 The balanced equation is $2CD(g) \longrightarrow C_2(g) + D_2(g)$, so n does not change. Therefore, given constant P, the temperature, T, must double: $T_1 = -73°C + 273.15 = 200$ K; so $T_2 = 400$ K, or 400 K − 273.15 = 127°C.

5.7 $d(\text{at } 0°C \text{ and } 380 \text{ torr}) = \frac{44.01 \text{ g/mol} \times \frac{380 \text{ torr}}{760 \text{ torr/atm}}}{0.0821 \frac{\text{atm·L}}{\text{mol·K}} \times 273 \text{ K}}$

$= 0.982 \text{ g/L}$

The density is lower at the smaller P because V is larger. In this case, d is lowered by one-half because P is one-half as much.

5.8

$$\mathcal{M} = \frac{(68.697 \text{ g} - 68.322 \text{ g}) \times 0.0821 \frac{\text{atm·L}}{\text{mol·K}} \times (273.15 + 95.0) \text{ K}}{\frac{740. \text{ torr}}{760 \text{ torr/atm}} \times \frac{149 \text{ mL}}{1000 \text{ mL/L}}}$$

$= 78.1 \text{ g/mol}$

5.9 $n_{total} = \left(5.50 \text{ g He} \times \frac{1 \text{ mol He}}{4.003 \text{ g He}}\right) + \left(15.0 \text{ g Ne} \times \frac{1 \text{ mol Ne}}{20.18 \text{ g Ne}}\right) + \left(35.0 \text{ g Kr} \times \frac{1 \text{ mol Kr}}{83.80 \text{ g Kr}}\right)$

$= 2.53 \text{ mol}$

$$P_{He} = \left(\frac{5.50 \text{ g He} \times \frac{1 \text{ mol He}}{4.003 \text{ g He}}}{2.53 \text{ mol}}\right) \times 1 \text{ atm} = 0.543 \text{ atm}$$

$P_{Ne} = 0.294 \text{ atm} \qquad P_{Kr} = 0.165 \text{ atm}$

5.10 $P_{H_2} = 752 \text{ torr} - 13.6 \text{ torr} = 738 \text{ torr}$

$$\text{Mass (g) of } H_2 = \left(\frac{\frac{738 \text{ torr}}{760 \text{ torr/atm}} \times 1.495 \text{ L}}{0.0821 \frac{\text{atm·L}}{\text{mol·K}} \times 289 \text{ K}}\right) \times \frac{2.016 \text{ g } H_2}{1 \text{ mol } H_2}$$

$= 0.123 \text{ g } H_2$

5.11 $H_2SO_4(aq) + 2NaCl(s) \longrightarrow Na_2SO_4(aq) + 2HCl(g)$

$$n_{HCl} = 0.117 \text{ kg NaCl} \times \frac{10^3 \text{ g}}{1 \text{ kg}} \times \frac{1 \text{ mol NaCl}}{58.44 \text{ g NaCl}} \times \frac{2 \text{ mol HCl}}{2 \text{ mol NaCl}}$$

$= 2.00 \text{ mol HCl}$

$$\text{At STP, } V(\text{mL}) = 2.00 \text{ mol} \times \frac{22.4 \text{ L}}{1 \text{ mol}} \times \frac{10^3 \text{ mL}}{1 \text{ L}}$$

$= 4.48 \times 10^4 \text{ mL}$

5.12 $NH_3(g) + HCl(g) \longrightarrow NH_4Cl(s)$

$n_{NH_3} = 0.187$ mol and $n_{HCl} = 0.0522$ mol; thus, HCl is the limiting reactant.

n_{NH_3} after reaction

$$= 0.187 \text{ mol } NH_3 - \left(0.0522 \text{ mol HCl} \times \frac{1 \text{ mol } NH_3}{1 \text{ mol HCl}}\right)$$

$= 0.135 \text{ mol } NH_3$

$$P = \frac{0.135 \text{ mol} \times 0.0821 \frac{\text{atm·L}}{\text{mol·K}} \times 295 \text{ K}}{10.0 \text{ L}} = 0.327 \text{ atm}$$

5.13 $$\frac{\text{Rate of He}}{\text{Rate of } C_2H_6} = \sqrt{\frac{30.07 \text{ g/mol}}{4.003 \text{ g/mol}}} = 2.741$$

Time for C_2H_6 to effuse $= 1.25 \text{ min} \times 2.741 = 3.43 \text{ min}$

PROBLEMS

Problems with **colored** numbers are answered in Appendix E and worked in detail in the Student Solutions Manual. Problem sections match those in the text and provide the numbers of relevant sample problems. Most offer Concept Review Questions, Skill-Building Exercises (grouped in pairs covering the same concept), and Problems in Context. The Comprehensive Problems are based on material from any section or previous chapter.

An Overview of the Physical States of Matter

Concept Review Questions

5.1 How does a sample of gas differ in its behavior from a sample of liquid in each of the following situations?
(a) The sample is transferred from one container to a larger one.
(b) The sample is heated in an expandable container, but no change of state occurs.
(c) The sample is placed in a cylinder with a piston, and an external force is applied.

5.2 Are the particles in a gas farther apart or closer together than the particles in a liquid? Use your answer to explain each of the following general observations:
(a) Gases are more compressible than liquids.
(b) Gases have lower viscosities than liquids.
(c) After thorough stirring, all gas mixtures are solutions.
(d) The density of a substance in the gas state is lower than in the liquid state.

Gas Pressure and Its Measurement

(Sample Problem 5.1)

Concept Review Questions

5.3 How does a barometer work? Is the column of mercury in a barometer shorter when it is on a mountaintop or at sea level? Explain.

5.4 How can a unit of length such as millimeter of mercury (mmHg) be used as a unit of pressure, which has the dimensions of force per unit area?

5.5 In a closed-end manometer, the mercury level in the arm attached to the flask can never be higher than the mercury level in the other arm, whereas in an open-end manometer, it *can* be higher. Explain.

Skill-Building Exercises (grouped in similar pairs)

5.6 On a cool, rainy day, the barometric pressure is 730 mmHg. Calculate the barometric pressure in centimeters of water (cmH_2O) (d of Hg = 13.5 g/mL; d of H_2O = 1.00 g/mL).

5.7 A long glass tube, sealed at one end, has an inner diameter of 10.0 mm. The tube is filled with water and inverted into a pail of water. If the atmospheric pressure is 755 mmHg, how high (in mmH_2O) is the column of water in the tube (d of Hg = 13.5 g/mL; d of H_2O = 1.00 g/mL)?

5.8 Convert the following:
(a) 0.745 atm to mmHg (b) 992 torr to bar
(c) 365 kPa to atm (d) 804 mmHg to kPa

5.9 Convert the following:
(a) 76.8 cmHg to atm (b) 27.5 atm to kPa
(c) 6.50 atm to bar (d) 0.937 kPa to torr

5.10 In Figure P5.10, what is the pressure of the gas in the flask (in atm) if the barometer reads 738.5 torr?

5.11 In Figure P5.11, what is the pressure of the gas in the flask (in kPa) if the barometer reads 765.2 mmHg?

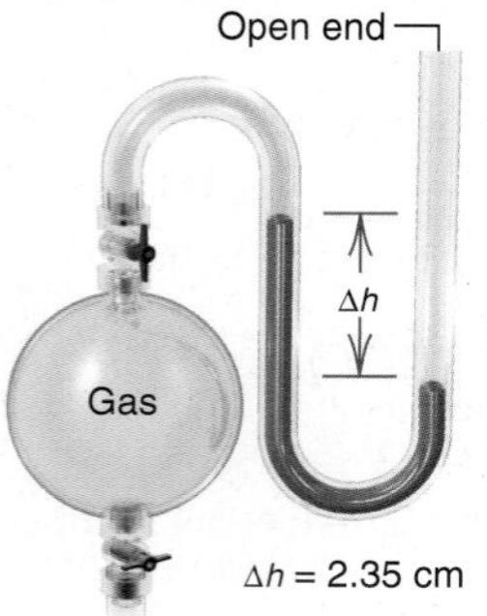

Figure P5.10

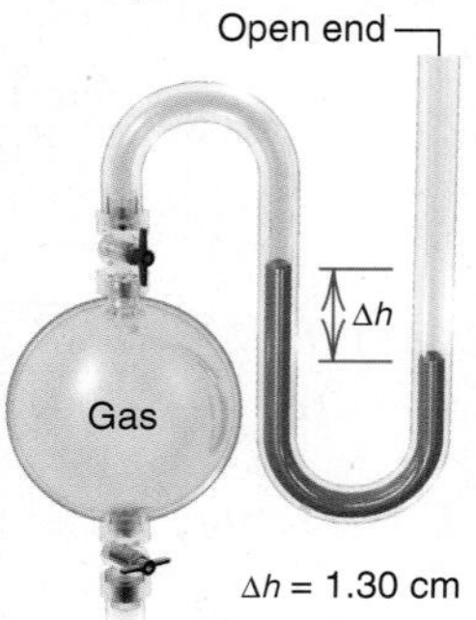

Figure P5.11

5.12 If the sample flask in Figure P5.12 is open to the air, what is the atmospheric pressure (in atm)?

5.13 What is the pressure (in Pa) of the gas in the flask in Figure P5.13?

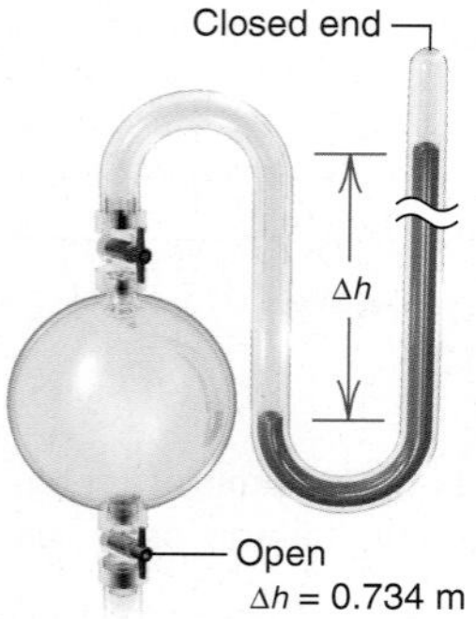

Figure P5.12

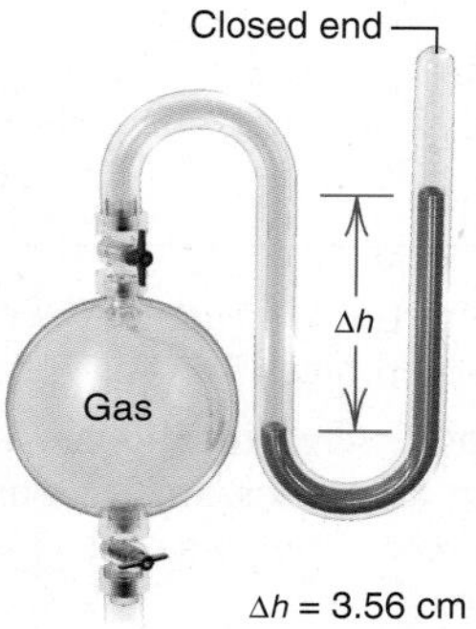

Figure P5.13

Problems in Context

5.14 Convert each of the pressures described below to atm:
(a) At the peak of Mt. Everest, atmospheric pressure is only 2.75×10^2 mmHg.
(b) A cyclist fills her bike tires to 86 psi.
(c) The surface of Venus has an atmospheric pressure of 9.15×10^6 Pa.
(d) At 100 ft below sea level, a scuba diver experiences a pressure of 2.54×10^4 torr.

5.15 The gravitational force exerted by an object is given by $F = mg$, where F is the force in newtons, m is the mass in kilograms, and g is the acceleration due to gravity (9.81 m/s^2).
(a) Use the definition of the pascal to calculate the mass (in kg) of the atmosphere above 1 m^2 of ocean.
(b) Osmium ($Z = 76$) is a transition metal in Group 8B(8) and has the highest density of any element (22.6 g/mL). If an osmium column is 1 m^2 in area, how high must it be for its pressure to equal atmospheric pressure? [Use the answer from part (a) in your calculation.]

The Gas Laws and Their Experimental Foundations

(Sample Problems 5.2 to 5.6)

Concept Review Questions

5.16 A student states Boyle's law as follows: "The volume of a gas is inversely proportional to its pressure." How is this statement incomplete? Give a correct statement of Boyle's law.

5.17 In the following relationships, which quantities are variables and which are fixed: (a) Charles's law; (b) Avogadro's law; (c) Amontons's law?

5.18 Boyle's law relates gas volume to pressure, and Avogadro's law relates gas volume to amount (mol). State a relationship between gas pressure and amount (mol).

5.19 Each of the following processes caused the gas volume to double, as shown. For each process, tell how the remaining gas variable changed or state that it remained fixed:
(a) T doubles at fixed P.
(b) T and n are fixed.
(c) At fixed T, the reaction is $CD_2(g) \longrightarrow C(g) + D_2(g)$.
(d) At fixed P, the reaction is $A_2(g) + B_2(g) \longrightarrow 2AB(g)$.

Skill-Building Exercises (grouped in similar pairs)

5.20 What is the effect of the following on the volume of 1 mol of an ideal gas?
(a) The pressure is tripled (at constant T).
(b) The absolute temperature is increased by a factor of 3.0 (at constant P).
(c) Three more moles of the gas are added (at constant P and T).

5.21 What is the effect of the following on the volume of 1 mol of an ideal gas?
(a) The pressure is reduced by a factor of 4 (at constant T).
(b) The pressure changes from 760 torr to 202 kPa, and the temperature changes from 37°C to 155 K.
(c) The temperature changes from 305 K to 32°C, and the pressure changes from 2 atm to 101 kPa.

5.22 What is the effect of the following on the volume of 1 mol of an ideal gas?
(a) Temperature decreases from 800 K to 400 K (at constant P).
(b) Temperature increases from 250°C to 500°C (at constant P).
(c) Pressure increases from 2 atm to 6 atm (at constant T).

5.23 What is the effect of the following on the volume of 1 mol of an ideal gas?
(a) Half the gas escapes (at constant P and T).
(b) The initial pressure is 722 torr, and the final pressure is 0.950 atm; the initial temperature is 32°F, and the final temperature is 273 K.
(c) Both the pressure and temperature decrease to one-fourth of their initial values.

5.24 A sample of sulfur hexafluoride gas occupies 9.10 L at 198°C. Assuming that the pressure remains constant, what temperature (in °C) is needed to reduce the volume to 2.50 L?

5.25 A 93-L sample of dry air cools from 145°C to −22°C while the pressure is maintained at 2.85 atm. What is the final volume?

5.26 A sample of Freon-12 (CF_2Cl_2) occupies 25.5 L at 298 K and 153.3 kPa. Find its volume at STP.

5.27 A sample of carbon monoxide occupies 3.65 L at 298 K and 745 torr. Find its volume at −14°C and 367 torr.

5.28 A sample of chlorine gas is confined in a 5.0-L container at 328 torr and 37°C. How many moles of gas are in the sample?

5.29 If 1.47×10^{-3} mol of argon occupies a 75.0-mL container at 26°C, what is the pressure (in torr)?

5.30 You have 357 mL of chlorine trifluoride gas at 699 mmHg and 45°C. What is the mass (in g) of the sample?

5.31 A 75.0-g sample of dinitrogen monoxide is confined in a 3.1-L vessel. What is the pressure (in atm) at 115°C?

Problems in Context

5.32 In preparation for a demonstration, your professor brings a 1.5-L bottle of sulfur dioxide into the lecture hall before class to allow the gas to reach room temperature. If the pressure gauge reads 85 psi and the temperature in the hall is 23°C, how many moles of sulfur dioxide are in the bottle? (*Hint:* The gauge reads zero when 14.7 psi of gas remains.)

5.33 A gas-filled weather balloon with a volume of 65.0 L is released at sea-level conditions of 745 torr and 25°C. The balloon can expand to a maximum volume of 835 L. When the balloon rises to an altitude at which the temperature is −5°C and the pressure is 0.066 atm, will it reach its maximum volume?

Rearrangements of the Ideal Gas Law

(Sample Problems 5.7 to 5.12)

Concept Review Questions

5.34 Why is moist air less dense than dry air?

5.35 To collect a beaker of H_2 gas by displacing the air already in the beaker, would you hold the beaker upright or inverted? Why? How would you hold the beaker to collect CO_2?

5.36 Why can we use a gas mixture, such as air, to study the general behavior of an ideal gas under ordinary conditions?

5.37 How does the partial pressure of gas A in a mixture compare to its mole fraction in the mixture? Explain.

5.38 The scene at right represents a portion of a mixture of four gases A (*purple*), B (*black*), C (*green*), and D_2 (*orange*). (a) Which has the highest partial pressure? (b) Which has the lowest partial pressure? (c) If the total pressure is 0.75 atm, what is the partial pressure of D_2?

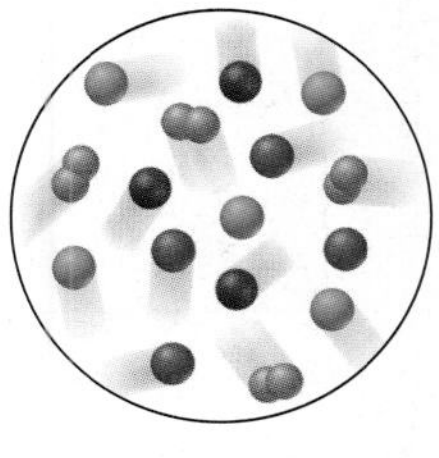

Skill-Building Exercises (grouped in similar pairs)

5.39 What is the density of Xe gas at STP?

5.40 Find the density of Freon-11 ($CFCl_3$) at 120°C and 1.5 atm.

5.41 How many moles of gaseous arsine (AsH_3) occupy 0.0400 L at STP? What is the density of gaseous arsine?

5.42 The density of a noble gas is 2.71 g/L at 3.00 atm and 0°C. Identify the gas.

5.43 Calculate the molar mass of a gas at 388 torr and 45°C if 206 ng occupies 0.206 μL.

5.44 When an evacuated 63.8-mL glass bulb is filled with a gas at 22°C and 747 mmHg, the bulb gains 0.103 g in mass. Is the gas N_2, Ne, or Ar?

5.45 After 0.600 L of Ar at 1.20 atm and 227°C is mixed with 0.200 L of O_2 at 501 torr and 127°C in a 400-mL flask at 27°C, what is the pressure in the flask?

5.46 A 355-mL container holds 0.146 g of Ne and an unknown amount of Ar at 35°C and a total pressure of 626 mmHg. Calculate the number of moles of Ar present.

5.47 How many grams of phosphorus react with 35.5 L of O_2 at STP to form tetraphosphorus decaoxide?

$$P_4(s) + 5O_2(g) \longrightarrow P_4O_{10}(s)$$

5.48 How many grams of potassium chlorate decompose to potassium chloride and 638 mL of O_2 at 128°C and 752 torr?

$$2KClO_3(s) \longrightarrow 2KCl(s) + 3O_2(g)$$

5.49 How many grams of phosphine (PH_3) can form when 37.5 g of phosphorus and 83.0 L of hydrogen gas react at STP?

$$P_4(s) + H_2(g) \longrightarrow PH_3(g) \quad \text{[unbalanced]}$$

5.50 When 35.6 L of ammonia and 40.5 L of oxygen gas at STP burn, nitrogen monoxide and water form. After the products return to STP, how many grams of nitrogen monoxide are present?

$$NH_3(g) + O_2(g) \longrightarrow NO(g) + H_2O(l) \quad \text{[unbalanced]}$$

5.51 Aluminum reacts with excess hydrochloric acid to form aqueous aluminum chloride and 35.8 mL of hydrogen gas over water at 27°C and 751 mmHg. How many grams of aluminum reacted?

5.52 How many liters of hydrogen gas are collected over water at 18°C and 725 mmHg when 0.84 g of lithium reacts with water? Aqueous lithium hydroxide also forms.

Problems in Context

5.53 The air in a hot-air balloon at 744 torr is heated from 17°C to 60.0°C. Assuming that the amount (mol) of air and the pressure remain constant, what is the density of the air at each temperature? (The average molar mass of air is 28.8 g/mol.)

5.54 On a certain winter day in Utah, the average atmospheric pressure is 650. torr. What is the molar density (in mol/L) of the air if the temperature is −25°C?

5.55 A sample of a liquid hydrocarbon known to consist of molecules with five carbon atoms is vaporized in a 0.204-L flask by immersion in a water bath at 101°C. The barometric pressure is 767 torr, and the remaining gas weighs 0.482 g. What is the molecular formula of the hydrocarbon?

5.56 A sample of air contains 78.08% nitrogen, 20.94% oxygen, 0.05% carbon dioxide, and 0.93% argon, by volume. How many molecules of each gas are present in 1.00 L of the sample at 25°C and 1.00 atm?

5.57 An environmental chemist sampling industrial exhaust gases from a coal-burning plant collects a CO_2-SO_2-H_2O mixture in a 21-L steel tank until the pressure reaches 850. torr at 45°C.
(a) How many moles of gas are collected?

(b) If the SO_2 concentration in the mixture is 7.95×10^3 parts per million by volume (ppmv), what is its partial pressure? [*Hint:* ppmv = (volume of component/volume of mixture) $\times$ 10^6.]

5.58 "Strike anywhere" matches contain the compound tetraphosphorus trisulfide, which burns to form tetraphosphorus decaoxide and sulfur dioxide gas. How many milliliters of sulfur dioxide, measured at 725 torr and 32°C, can be produced from burning 0.800 g of tetraphosphorus trisulfide?

5.59 Freon-12 (CF_2Cl_2), widely used as a refrigerant and aerosol propellant, is a dangerous air pollutant. In the troposphere, it traps heat 25 times as effectively as CO_2, and in the stratosphere, it participates in the breakdown of ozone. Freon-12 is prepared industrially by reaction of gaseous carbon tetrachloride with hydrogen fluoride. Hydrogen chloride gas also forms. How many grams of carbon tetrachloride are required for the production of 16.0 dm^3 of Freon-12 at 27°C and 1.20 atm?

5.60 Xenon hexafluoride was one of the first noble gas compounds synthesized. The solid reacts rapidly with the silicon dioxide in glass or quartz containers to form liquid $XeOF_4$ and gaseous silicon tetrafluoride. What is the pressure in a 1.00-L container at 25°C after 2.00 g of xenon hexafluoride reacts? (Assume that silicon tetrafluoride is the only gas present and that it occupies the entire volume.)

5.61 In the four cylinder-piston assemblies below, the reactant in the left cylinder is about to undergo a reaction at constant T and P:

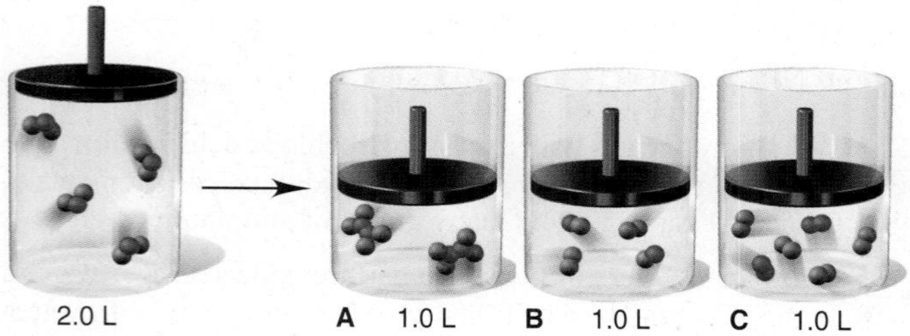

Which of the other three depictions best represents the products of the reaction?

5.62 Roasting galena [lead(II) sulfide] is a step in the industrial isolation of lead. How many liters of sulfur dioxide, measured at STP, are produced by the reaction of 3.75 kg of galena with 228 L of oxygen gas at 220°C and 2.0 atm? Lead(II) oxide also forms.

5.63 In one of his most critical studies into the nature of combustion, Lavoisier heated mercury(II) oxide and isolated elemental mercury and oxygen gas. If 40.0 g of mercury(II) oxide is heated in a 502-mL vessel and 20.0% (by mass) decomposes, what is the pressure (in atm) of the oxygen that forms at 25.0°C? (Assume that the gas occupies the entire volume.)

The Kinetic-Molecular Theory: A Model for Gas Behavior

(Sample Problem 5.13)

Concept Review Questions

5.64 Use the kinetic-molecular theory to explain the change in gas pressure that results from warming a sample of gas.

5.65 How does the kinetic-molecular theory explain why 1 mol of krypton and 1 mol of helium have the same volume at STP?

5.66 Is the rate of effusion of a gas higher than, lower than, or equal to its rate of diffusion? Explain. For two gases with molecules of approximately the same size, is the ratio of their effusion rates higher than, lower than, or equal to the ratio of their diffusion rates? Explain.

5.67 Consider two 1-L samples of gas: one is H_2 and the other is O_2. Both are at 1 atm and 25°C. How do the samples compare in terms of (a) mass, (b) density, (c) mean free path, (d) average molecular kinetic energy, (e) average molecular speed, and (f) time for a given fraction of molecules to effuse?

5.68 Three 5-L flasks, fixed with pressure gauges and small valves, each contain 4 g of gas at 273 K. Flask A contains H_2, flask B contains He, and flask C contains CH_4. Rank the flask contents in terms of (a) pressure, (b) average molecular kinetic energy, (c) diffusion rate after the valve is opened, (d) total kinetic energy of the molecules, (e) density, and (f) collision frequency.

Skill-Building Exercises (grouped in similar pairs)

5.69 What is the ratio of effusion rates for the lightest gas, H_2, and the heaviest known gas, UF_6?

5.70 What is the ratio of effusion rates for O_2 and Kr?

5.71 The graph below shows the distribution of molecular speeds for argon and helium at the same temperature.

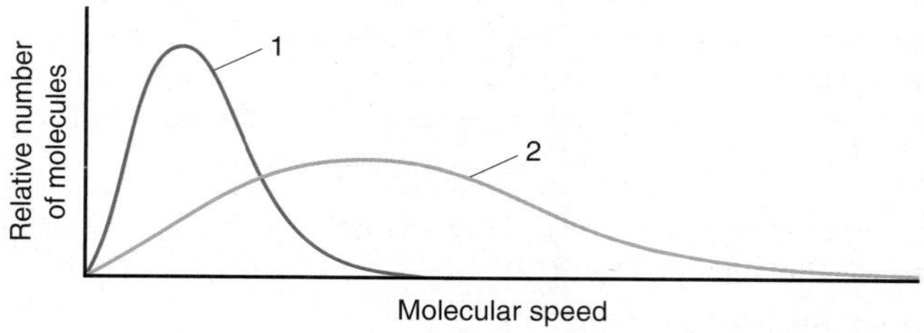

(a) Does curve 1 or 2 better represent the behavior of argon?
(b) Which curve represents the gas that effuses more slowly?
(c) Which curve more closely represents the behavior of fluorine gas? Explain.

5.72 The graph below shows the distribution of molecular speeds for a gas at two different temperatures.

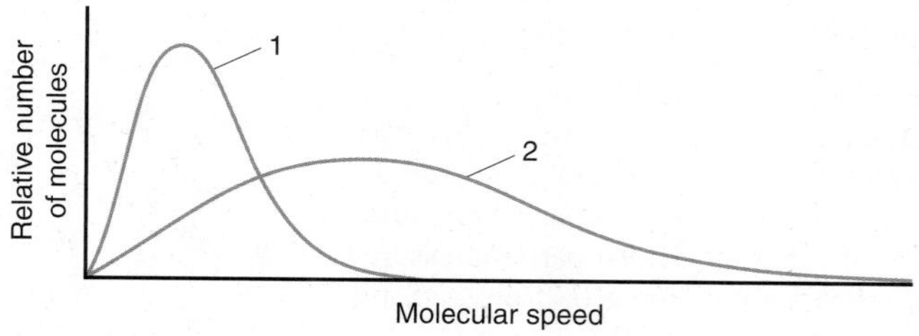

(a) Does curve 1 or 2 better represent the behavior of the gas at the lower temperature?
(b) Which curve represents the gas when it has a higher $\overline{E_k}$?
(c) Which curve is consistent with a higher diffusion rate?

5.73 At a given pressure and temperature, it takes 4.85 min for a 1.5-L sample of He to effuse through a membrane. How long does it take for 1.5 L of F_2 to effuse under the same conditions?

5.74 A sample of an unknown gas effuses in 11.1 min. An equal volume of H_2 in the same apparatus under the same conditions effuses in 2.42 min. What is the molar mass of the unknown gas?

Problems in Context

5.75 White phosphorus melts and then vaporizes at high temperature. The gas effuses at a rate that is 0.404 times that of neon in the same apparatus under the same conditions. How many atoms are in a molecule of gaseous white phosphorus?

5.76 Helium (He) is the lightest noble gas component of air, and xenon (Xe) is the heaviest. [For this problem, use $R = 8.314$ J/(mol·K) and $\mathcal{M}$ in kg/mol.] (a) Find the rms speed of He in winter (0.°C) and in summer (30.°C). (b) Compare the rms speed of He with that of Xe at 30.°C. (c) Find the average kinetic energy per mole of He and of Xe at 30.°C. (d) Find the average kinetic energy per molecule of He at 30.°C.

5.77 A mixture of gaseous disulfur difluoride, dinitrogen tetrafluoride, and sulfur tetrafluoride is placed in an effusion apparatus. (a) Rank the gases in order of increasing effusion rate. (b) Find the ratio of effusion rates of disulfur difluoride and dinitrogen tetrafluoride. (c) If gas X is added, and it effuses at 0.935 times the rate of sulfur tetrafluoride, find the molar mass of X.

Real Gases: Deviations from Ideal Behavior

Skill-Building Exercises (grouped in similar pairs)

5.78 Do interparticle attractions cause negative or positive deviations from the *PV/RT* ratio of an ideal gas? Use Table 5.3 to rank Kr, CO_2, and N_2 in order of increasing magnitude of these deviations.

5.79 Does particle volume cause negative or positive deviations from the *PV/RT* ratio of an ideal gas? Use Table 5.3 to rank Cl_2, H_2, and O_2 in order of increasing magnitude of these deviations.

5.80 Does N_2 behave more ideally at 1 atm or at 500 atm? Explain.

5.81 Does SF_6 (boiling point = 16°C at 1 atm) behave more ideally at 150°C or at 20°C? Explain.

Comprehensive Problems

5.82 An "empty" gasoline can with dimensions 15.0 cm by 40.0 cm by 12.5 cm is attached to a vacuum pump and evacuated. If the atmospheric pressure is 14.7 lb/in^2, what is the total force (in pounds) on the outside of the can?

5.83 Hemoglobin is the protein that transports O_2 through the blood from the lungs to the rest of the body. In doing so, each molecule of hemoglobin combines with four molecules of O_2. If 1.00 g of hemoglobin combines with 1.53 mL of O_2 at 37°C and 743 torr, what is the molar mass of hemoglobin?

5.84 A baker uses sodium hydrogen carbonate (baking soda) as the leavening agent in a banana-nut quickbread. The baking soda decomposes in either of two possible reactions:

(1) $2NaHCO_3(s) \longrightarrow Na_2CO_3(s) + H_2O(l) + CO_2(g)$

(2) $NaHCO_3(s) + H^+(aq) \longrightarrow H_2O(l) + CO_2(g) + Na^+(aq)$

Calculate the volume (in mL) of CO_2 that forms at 200.°C and 0.975 atm per gram of $NaHCO_3$ by each of the reaction processes.

5.85 A weather balloon containing 600. L of He is released near the equator at 1.01 atm and 305 K. It rises to a point where conditions are 0.489 atm and 218 K and eventually lands in the northern hemisphere under conditions of 1.01 atm and 250 K. If one-fourth of the helium leaked out during this journey, what is the volume (in L) of the balloon at landing?

5.86 Chlorine is produced from sodium chloride by the electrochemical chlor-alkali process. During the process, the chlorine is collected in a container that is isolated from the other products to prevent unwanted (and explosive) reactions. If a 15.50-L container holds 0.5950 kg of Cl_2 gas at 225°C, calculate:

(a) P_{IGL} (b) P_{VDW} $\left(\text{use } R = 0.08206 \dfrac{\text{atm·L}}{\text{mol·K}}\right)$

5.87 In a certain experiment, magnesium boride (Mg_3B_2) reacted with acid to form a mixture of four boron hydrides (B_xH_y), three as liquids (labeled I, II, and III) and one as a gas (IV).
(a) When a 0.1000-g sample of each liquid was transferred to an evacuated 750.0-mL container and volatilized at 70.00°C, sample I had a pressure of 0.05951 atm; sample II, 0.07045 atm; and sample III, 0.05767 atm. What is the molar mass of each liquid?
(b) Boron is 85.63% by mass in sample I, 81.10% in II, and 82.98% in III. What is the molecular formula of each sample?
(c) Sample IV was found to be 78.14% boron. Its rate of effusion was compared to that of sulfur dioxide; under identical conditions, 350.0 mL of sample IV effused in 12.00 min and 250.0 mL of sulfur dioxide effused in 13.04 min. What is the molecular formula of sample IV?

5.88 Three equal volumes of gas mixtures, all at the same *T*, are depicted below (with gas A *red,* gas B *green,* and gas C *blue*):

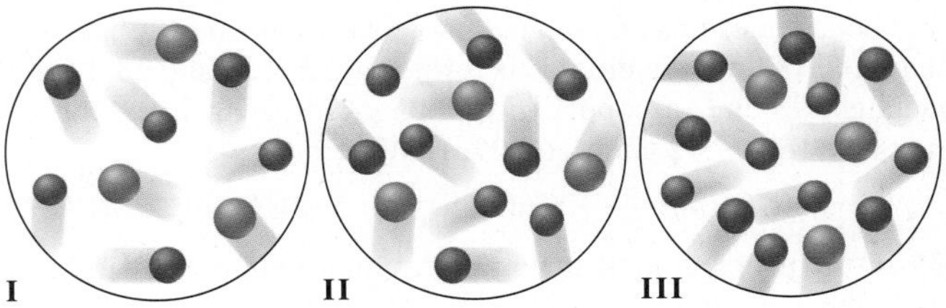

(a) Which sample, if any, has the highest partial pressure of A?
(b) Which sample, if any, has the lowest partial pressure of B?
(c) In which sample, if any, do the gas particles have the highest average kinetic energy?

5.89 Will the volume of a gas increase, decrease, or remain unchanged for each of the following sets of changes?
(a) The pressure is decreased from 2 atm to 1 atm, while the temperature is decreased from 200°C to 100°C.
(b) The pressure is increased from 1 atm to 3 atm, while the temperature is increased from 100°C to 300°C.
(c) The pressure is increased from 3 atm to 6 atm, while the temperature is increased from −73°C to 127°C.
(d) The pressure is increased from 0.2 atm to 0.4 atm, while the temperature is decreased from 300°C to 150°C.

5.90 When air is inhaled, it enters the alveoli of the lungs, and varying amounts of the component gases exchange with dissolved gases in the blood. The resulting alveolar gas mixture is quite different from the atmospheric mixture. The following table presents selected data on the composition and partial pressure of four gases in the atmosphere and in the alveoli:

	Atmosphere (sea level)		Alveoli	
Gas	Mole %	Partial Pressure (torr)	Mole %	Partial Pressure (torr)
N_2	78.6	—	—	569
O_2	20.9	—	—	104
CO_2	00.04	—	—	40
H_2O	00.46	—	—	47

If the total pressure of each gas mixture is 1.00 atm, calculate:
(a) The partial pressure (in torr) of each gas in the atmosphere
(b) The mole % of each gas in the alveoli
(c) The number of O_2 molecules in 0.50 L of alveolar air (volume of an average breath of a person at rest) at 37°C

5.91 Radon (Rn) is the heaviest, and only radioactive, member of Group 8A(18) (noble gases). It is a product of the disintegration of heavier radioactive nuclei found in minute concentrations in many common rocks used for building and construction. In recent years, health concerns about the cancers caused from inhaled residential radon have grown. If 1.0×10^{15} atoms of radium (Ra) produce an average of 1.373×10^{4} atoms of Rn per second, how many liters of Rn, measured at STP, are produced per day by 1.0 g of Ra?

5.92 At 1450. mmHg and 286 K, a skin diver exhales a 208-mL bubble of air that is 77% N_2, 17% O_2, and 6.0% CO_2 by volume.
(a) How many milliliters would the volume of the bubble be if it were exhaled at the surface at 1 atm and 298 K?
(b) How many moles of N_2 are in the bubble?

5.93 Nitrogen dioxide is used industrially to produce nitric acid, but it contributes to acid rain and photochemical smog. What volume (in L) of nitrogen dioxide is formed at 735 torr and 28.2°C by reacting 4.95 cm³ of copper (d = 8.95 g/cm³) with 230.0 mL of nitric acid (d = 1.42 g/cm³, 68.0% HNO_3 by mass)?

$$Cu(s) + 4HNO_3(aq) \longrightarrow Cu(NO_3)_2(aq) + 2NO_2(g) + 2H_2O(l)$$

5.94 In the average adult male, the residual volume (RV) of the lungs, the volume of air remaining after a forced exhalation, is 1200 mL. (a) How many moles of air are present in the RV at 1.0 atm and 37°C? (b) How many molecules of gas are present under these conditions?

5.95 In a bromine-producing plant, how many liters of gaseous elemental bromine at 300°C and 0.855 atm are formed by the reaction of 275 g of sodium bromide and 175.6 g of sodium bromate in aqueous acid solution? (Assume no Br_2 dissolves.)

$$5NaBr(aq) + NaBrO_3(aq) + 3H_2SO_4(aq) \longrightarrow 3Br_2(g) + 3Na_2SO_4(aq) + 3H_2O(g)$$

5.96 In a collision of sufficient force, automobile air bags respond by electrically triggering the explosive decomposition of sodium azide (NaN_3) to its elements. A 50.0-g sample of sodium azide was decomposed, and the nitrogen gas generated was collected over water at 26°C. The total pressure was 745.5 mmHg. How many liters of dry N_2 were generated?

5.97 An anesthetic gas contains 64.81% carbon, 13.60% hydrogen, and 21.59% oxygen, by mass. If 2.00 L of the gas at 25°C and 0.420 atm weighs 2.57 g, what is the molecular formula of the anesthetic?

5.98 Aluminum chloride is easily vaporized above 180°C. The gas escapes through a pinhole 0.122 times as fast as helium at the same conditions of temperature and pressure in the same apparatus. What is the molecular formula of aluminum chloride gas?

5.99 (a) What is the total volume (in L) of gaseous *products,* measured at 350°C and 735 torr, when an automobile engine burns 100. g of C_8H_{18} (a typical component of gasoline)?
(b) For part (a), the source of O_2 is air, which is 78% N_2, 21% O_2, and 1.0% Ar by volume. Assuming all the O_2 reacts, but no N_2 or Ar does, what is the total volume (in L) of gaseous *exhaust?*

5.100 An atmospheric chemist studying the pollutant SO_2 places a mixture of SO_2 and O_2 in a 2.00-L container at 800. K and 1.90 atm. When the reaction occurs, gaseous SO_3 forms, and the pressure falls to 1.65 atm. How many moles of SO_3 form?

5.101 The thermal decomposition of ethylene occurs during the compound's transit in pipelines and during the formation of polyethylene. The decomposition reaction is

$$CH_2{=}CH_2(g) \longrightarrow CH_4(g) + C(graphite)$$

If the decomposition begins at 10°C and 50.0 atm with a gas density of 0.215 g/mL and the temperature increases by 950 K,
(a) What is the final pressure of the confined gas (ignore the volume of graphite and use the van der Waals equation)?
(b) How does the PV/RT value of CH_4 compare to that in Figure 5.23? Explain.

5.102 Ammonium nitrate, a common fertilizer, was used by terrorists in the tragic explosion in Oklahoma City in 1995. How many liters of gas at 307°C and 1.00 atm are formed by the explosive decomposition of 15.0 kg of ammonium nitrate to nitrogen, oxygen, and water vapor?

5.103 An environmental engineer analyzes a sample of air contaminated with sulfur dioxide. To a 500.-mL sample at 700. torr and 38°C, she adds 20.00 mL of 0.01017 M aqueous iodine, which reacts as follows:

$$SO_2(g) + I_2(aq) + H_2O(l) \longrightarrow HSO_4^-(aq) + I^-(aq) + H^+(aq) \quad [\text{unbalanced}]$$

Excess I_2 reacts with 11.37 mL of 0.0105 M sodium thiosulfate:

$$I_2(aq) + S_2O_3^{2-}(aq) \longrightarrow I^-(aq) + S_4O_6^{2-}(aq) \quad [\text{unbalanced}]$$

What is the volume % of SO_2 in the air sample?

5.104 Canadian chemists have developed a modern variation of the 1899 Mond process for preparing extremely pure metallic nickel. A sample of impure nickel reacts with carbon monoxide at 50°C to form gaseous nickel carbonyl, $Ni(CO)_4$.
(a) How many grams of nickel can be converted to the carbonyl with 3.55 m³ of CO at 100.7 kPa?
(b) The carbonyl is then decomposed at 21 atm and 155°C to pure (>99.95%) nickel. How many grams of nickel are obtained per cubic meter of the carbonyl?
(c) The released carbon monoxide is cooled and collected for reuse by passing it through water at 35°C. If the barometric pressure is 769 torr, what volume (in m³) of CO is formed per cubic meter of carbonyl?

5.105 Analysis of a newly discovered gaseous silicon-fluorine compound shows that it contains 33.01 mass % silicon. At 27°C, 2.60 g of the compound exerts a pressure of 1.50 atm in a 0.250-L vessel. What is the molecular formula of the compound?

5.106 A gaseous organic compound containing only carbon, hydrogen, and nitrogen is burned in oxygen gas, and the volume of each reactant and product is measured under the same conditions of temperature and pressure. Reaction of four volumes of the compound produces four volumes of CO_2, two volumes of N_2, and ten volumes of water vapor. (a) How many volumes of O_2 were required? (b) What is the empirical formula of the compound?

5.107 Containers A, B, and C are attached by closed stopcocks of negligible volume.

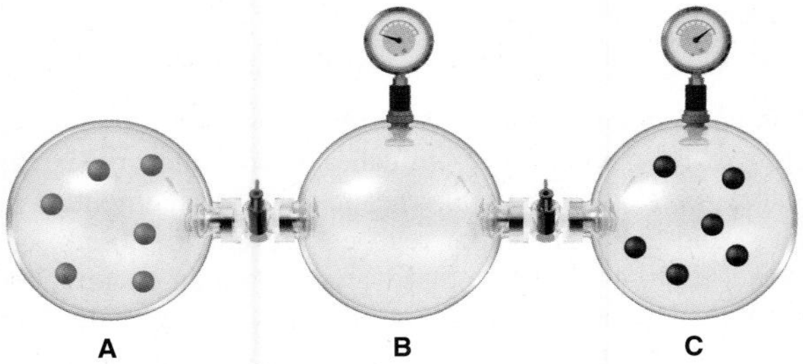

If each particle shown in the picture represents 10^6 particles,
(a) How many blue particles and black particles are in B after the stopcocks are opened and the system reaches equilibrium?
(b) How many blue particles and black particles are in A after the stopcocks are opened and the system reaches equilibrium?
(c) If the pressure in C, P_C, is 750 torr before the stopcocks are opened, what is P_C afterward? (d) What is P_B afterward?

5.108 Combustible vapor-air mixtures are flammable over a limited range of concentrations. The minimum volume % of vapor that gives a combustible mixture is called the *lower flammable limit* (LFL). Generally, the LFL is about half the stoichiometric mixture, the concentration required for complete combustion of the vapor in air. (a) If oxygen is 20.9 vol % of air, estimate the LFL for *n*-hexane, C_6H_{14}. (b) What volume (in mL) of *n*-hexane (d = 0.660 g/cm^3) is required to produce a flammable mixture of hexane in 1.000 m^3 of air at STP?

5.109 By what factor would a scuba diver's lungs expand if she ascended rapidly to the surface from a depth of 125 ft without inhaling or exhaling? If an expansion factor greater than 1.5 causes lung rupture, how far could she safely ascend from 125 ft without breathing? Assume constant temperature (d of seawater = 1.04 g/mL; d of Hg = 13.5 g/mL).

5.110 When 15.0 g of fluorite (CaF_2) reacts with excess sulfuric acid, hydrogen fluoride gas is collected at 744 torr and 25.5°C. Solid calcium sulfate is the other product. What gas temperature is required to store the gas in an 8.63-L container at 875 torr?

5.111 Dilute aqueous hydrogen peroxide is used as a bleaching agent and for disinfecting surfaces and small cuts. Its concentration is sometimes given as a certain number of "volumes hydrogen peroxide," which refers to the number of volumes of O_2 gas, measured at STP, that a given volume of hydrogen peroxide solution will release when it decomposes to O_2 and liquid H_2O. How many grams of hydrogen peroxide are in 0.100 L of "20 volumes hydrogen peroxide" solution?

5.112 At a height of 300 km above Earth's surface, an astronaut finds that the atmospheric pressure is about 10^{-8} mmHg and the temperature is 500 K. How many molecules of gas are there per milliliter at this altitude?

5.113 (a) What is the rms speed of O_2 at STP? (b) If the mean free path of O_2 molecules at STP is 6.33×10^{-8} m, what is their collision frequency? [Use R = 8.314 J/(mol·K) and $\mathcal{M}$ in kg/mol.]

5.114 Acrylic acid ($CH_2{=}CHCOOH$) is used to prepare polymers, adhesives, and paints. The first step in making acrylic acid involves the vapor-phase oxidation of propylene ($CH_2{=}CHCH_3$) to acrolein ($CH_2{=}CHCHO$). This step is carried out at 330°C and 2.5 atm in a large bundle of tubes around which circulates a heat-transfer agent. The reactants spend an average of 1.8 s in the tubes, which have a void space of 100 ft^3. How many pounds of propylene must be added per hour in a mixture whose mole fractions are 0.07 propylene, 0.35 steam, and 0.58 air?

5.115 Standard conditions are based on relevant environmental conditions. If normal average surface temperature and pressure on Venus are 730. K and 90 atm, respectively, what is the standard molar volume of an ideal gas on Venus?

5.116 A barometer tube is 1.00×10^2 cm long and has a cross-sectional area of 1.20 cm^2. The height of the mercury column is 74.0 cm, and the temperature is 24°C. A small amount of N_2 is introduced into the evacuated space above the mercury, which causes the mercury level to drop to a height of 64.0 cm. How many grams of N_2 were introduced?

5.117 What is the molarity of the cleaning solution formed when 10.0 L of ammonia gas at 33°C and 735 torr dissolves in enough water to give a final volume of 0.750 L?

5.118 The Hawaiian volcano Kilauea emits an average of 1.5×10^3 m^3 of gas each day, when corrected to 298 K and 1.00 atm. The mixture contains gases that contribute to global warming and acid rain, and some are toxic. An atmospheric chemist analyzes a sample and finds the following mole fractions: 0.4896 CO_2, 0.0146 CO, 0.3710 H_2O, 0.1185 SO_2, 0.0003 S_2, 0.0047 H_2, 0.0008 HCl, and 0.0003 H_2S. How many metric tons (t) of each gas are emitted per year (1 t = 1000 kg)?

5.119 To study a key fuel-cell reaction, a chemical engineer has 20.0-L tanks of H_2 and of O_2 and wants to use up both tanks to form 28.0 mol of water at 23.8°C. (a) Use the ideal gas law to find the pressure needed in each tank. (b) Use the van der Waals equation to find the pressure needed in each tank. (c) Compare the results from the two equations.

5.120 For each of the following, which shows the greater deviation from ideal behavior at the same set of conditions? Explain.
(a) Argon or xenon (b) Water vapor or neon
(c) Mercury vapor or radon (d) Water vapor or methane

5.121 How many liters of gaseous hydrogen bromide at 29°C and 0.965 atm will a chemist need if she wishes to prepare 3.50 L of 1.20 *M* hydrobromic acid?

5.122 A mixture consisting of 7.0 g of CO and 10.0 g of SO_2, two atmospheric pollutants, has a pressure of 0.33 atm when placed in a sealed container. What is the partial pressure of CO?

5.123 Sulfur dioxide is used to make sulfuric acid. One method of producing it is by roasting mineral sulfides, for example,

$$FeS_2(s) + O_2(g) \xrightarrow{\Delta} SO_2(g) + Fe_2O_3(s) \quad [\text{unbalanced}]$$

A production error leads to the sulfide being placed in a 950-L vessel with insufficient oxygen. Initially, the partial pressure of O_2 is 0.64 atm, and the total pressure is 1.05 atm, with the balance due to N_2. The reaction is run until 85% of the O_2 is consumed, and the vessel is then cooled to its initial temperature. What is the total pressure and the partial pressure of each gas in the vessel?

5.124 A mixture of CO_2 and Kr weighs 35.0 g and exerts a pressure of 0.708 atm in its container. Since Kr is expensive, you wish to recover it from the mixture. After the CO_2 is completely removed by absorption with NaOH(*s*), the pressure in the container is 0.250 atm. How many grams of CO_2 were originally present? How many grams of Kr can you recover?

5.125 When a car accelerates quickly, the passengers feel a force that presses them back into their seats, but a balloon filled with helium floats forward. Why?

5.126 Gases such as CO are gradually oxidized in the atmosphere, not by O_2 but by the hydroxyl radical, •OH, a species with one fewer electron than a hydroxide ion. At night, the •OH concentration is nearly zero, but it increases to 2.5×10^{12} molecules/m^3 in polluted air during the day. At daytime conditions of 1.00 atm and 22°C, what is the partial pressure and mole percent of •OH in air?

5.127 Aqueous sulfurous acid (H_2SO_3) was made by dissolving 0.200 L of sulfur dioxide gas at 19°C and 745 mmHg in water to yield 500.0 mL of solution. The acid solution required 10.0 mL of sodium hydroxide solution to reach the titration end point. What was the molarity of the sodium hydroxide solution?

5.128 In the 19th century, J. B. A. Dumas devised a method for finding the molar mass of a volatile liquid from the volume, temperature, pressure, and mass of its vapor. He placed a sample of such a liquid in a flask that was closed with a stopper fitted with a narrow tube, immersed the flask in a hot water bath to vaporize the liquid, and then cooled the flask. Find the molar mass of a volatile liquid from the following:
Mass of empty flask = 65.347 g
Mass of flask filled with water at 25°C = 327.4 g
Density of water at 25°C = 0.997 g/mL
Mass of flask plus condensed unknown liquid = 65.739 g
Barometric pressure = 101.2 kPa
Temperature of water bath = 99.8°C

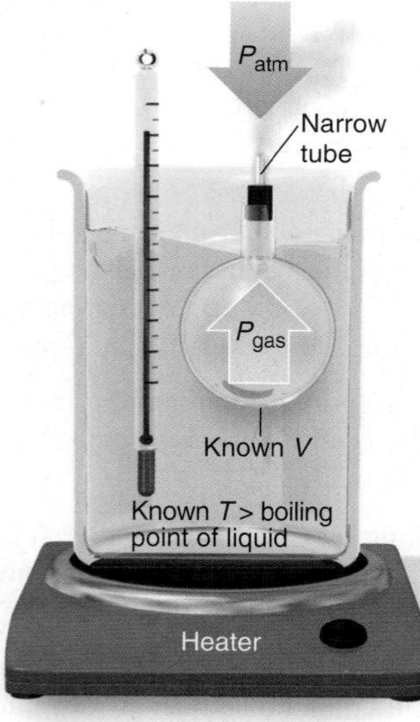

5.129 During World War II, a portable source of hydrogen gas was needed for weather balloons, and solid metal hydrides were the most convenient form. Many metal hydrides react with water to generate the metal hydroxide and hydrogen. Two candidates were lithium hydride and magnesium hydride. What volume (in L) of gas is formed from 1.00 lb of each hydride reacting with excess water at 750. torr and 27°C?

5.130 The lunar surface reaches 370 K at midday. The atmosphere consists of neon, argon, and helium at a total pressure of only 2×10^{-14} atm. Calculate the rms speed of each component in the lunar atmosphere. [Use $R = 8.314$ J/(mol·K) and $\mathcal{M}$ in kg/mol.]

5.131 A person inhales air richer in O_2 and exhales air richer in CO_2 and water vapor. During each hour of sleep, a person exhales a total of about 300 L of this CO_2-enriched and H_2O-enriched air. (a) If the partial pressures of CO_2 and H_2O in exhaled air are each 30.0 torr at 37.0°C, calculate the mass (g) of CO_2 and of H_2O exhaled in 1 h of sleep. (b) How many grams of body mass does the person lose in an 8-h sleep if all the CO_2 and H_2O exhaled come from the metabolism of glucose?

$$C_6H_{12}O_6(s) + 6O_2(g) \longrightarrow 6CO_2(g) + 6H_2O(g)$$

5.132 Popcorn pops because the horny endosperm, a tough, elastic material, resists gas pressure within the heated kernel until it reaches explosive force. A 0.25-mL kernel has a water content of 1.6% by mass, and the water vapor reaches 170°C and 9.0 atm before the kernel ruptures. Assume that water vapor can occupy 75% of the kernel's volume. (a) What is the mass (in g) of the kernel? (b) How many milliliters would this amount of water vapor occupy at 25°C and 1.00 atm?

5.133 Sulfur dioxide emissions from coal-burning power plants are removed by *flue-gas desulfurization.* The flue gas passes through a scrubber, and a slurry of wet calcium carbonate reacts with it to form carbon dioxide and calcium sulfite. The calcium sulfite then reacts with oxygen to form calcium sulfate, which is sold as gypsum. (a) If the sulfur dioxide concentration is 1000 times higher than its mole fraction in clean dry air (2×10^{-10}), how much calcium sulfate (kg) can be made from scrubbing 4 GL of flue gas (1 GL = 1×10^9 L)? A state-of-the-art scrubber removes at least 95% of the sulfur dioxide. (b) If the mole fraction of oxygen in air is 0.209, what volume (L) of air at 1.00 atm and 25°C is needed to react with all the calcium sulfite?

5.134 Many water treatment plants use chlorine gas to kill microorganisms before the water is released for residential use. A plant engineer has to maintain the chlorine pressure in a tank below the 85.0-atm rating and, to be safe, decides to fill the tank to 80.0% of this maximum pressure. (a) How many moles of Cl_2 gas can be kept in an 850.-L tank at 298 K if she uses the ideal gas law in the calculation? (b) What is the tank pressure if she uses the van der Waals equation for this amount of gas? (c) Did the engineer fill the tank to the desired pressure?

5.135 At 10.0°C and 102.5 kPa, the density of dry air is 1.26 g/L. What is the average "molar mass" of dry air at these conditions?

5.136 In A, the picture shows a cylinder with 0.1 mol of a gas that behaves ideally. Choose the cylinder (B, C, or D) that correctly represents the volume of the gas after each of the following changes. If none of the cylinders is correct, specify "none."
(a) P is doubled at fixed n and T.
(b) T is reduced from 400 K to 200 K at fixed n and P.
(c) T is increased from 100°C to 200°C at fixed n and P.
(d) 0.1 mol of gas is added at fixed P and T.
(e) 0.1 mol of gas is added and P is doubled at fixed T.

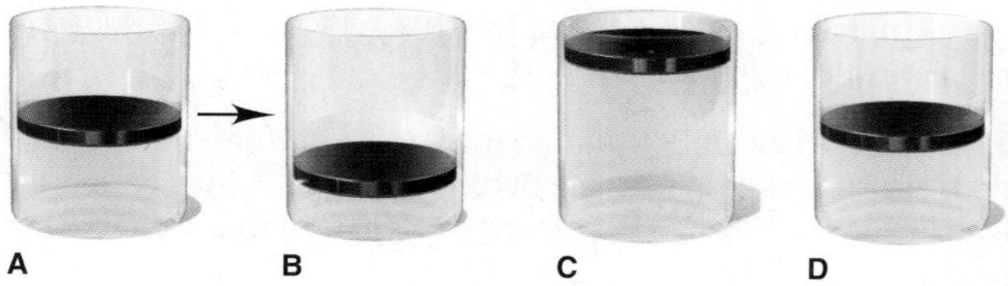

5.137 Ammonia is essential to so many industries that, on a molar basis, it is the most heavily produced substance in the world. Calculate P_{IGL} and P_{VDW} (in atm) of 51.1 g of ammonia in a 3.000-L container at 0°C and 400.°C, the industrial temperature. (See Table 5.4 for the values of the van der Waals constants.)

5.138 A 6.0-L flask contains a mixture of methane (CH_4), argon, and helium at 45°C and 1.75 atm. If the mole fractions of helium and argon are 0.25 and 0.35, respectively, how many molecules of methane are present?

5.139 A large portion of metabolic energy arises from the biological combustion of glucose:

$$C_6H_{12}O_6(s) + 6O_2(g) \longrightarrow 6CO_2(g) + 6H_2O(g)$$

(a) If this reaction is carried out in an expandable container at 37°C and 780. torr, what volume of CO_2 is produced from 20.0 g of glucose and excess O_2? (b) If the reaction is carried out at the same conditions with the stoichiometric amount of O_2, what is the partial pressure of each gas when the reaction is 50% complete (10.0 g of glucose remains)?

5.140 What is the average kinetic energy and rms speed of N_2 molecules at STP? Compare these values with those of H_2 molecules at STP. [Use $R = 8.314$ J/(mol·K) and $\mathcal{M}$ in kg/mol.]

5.141 According to government standards, the *8-h threshold limit value* is 5000 ppmv for CO_2 and 0.1 ppmv for Br_2 (1 ppmv is 1 part by volume in 10^6 parts by volume). Exposure to either gas for 8 h above these limits is unsafe. At STP, which of the following would be unsafe for 8 h of exposure?
(a) Air with a partial pressure of 0.2 torr of Br_2
(b) Air with a partial pressure of 0.2 torr of CO_2
(c) 1000 L of air containing 0.0004 g of Br_2 gas
(d) 1000 L of air containing 2.8×10^{22} molecules of CO_2

5.142 One way to prevent emission of the pollutant NO from industrial plants is by a catalyzed reaction with NH_3:

$$4NH_3(g) + 4NO(g) + O_2(g) \xrightarrow{\text{catalyst}} 4N_2(g) + 6H_2O(g)$$

(a) If the NO has a partial pressure of 4.5×10^{-5} atm in the flue gas, how many liters of NH_3 are needed per liter of flue gas at 1.00 atm? (b) If the reaction takes place at 1.00 atm and 365°C, how many grams of NH_3 are needed per kL of flue gas?

5.143 An equimolar mixture of Ne and Xe is accidentally placed in a container that has a tiny leak. After a short while, a very small proportion of the mixture has escaped. What is the mole fraction of Ne in the effusing gas?

5.144 From the relative rates of effusion of $^{235}UF_6$ and $^{238}UF_6$, find the number of steps needed to produce a sample of the enriched fuel used in many nuclear reactors, which is 3.0 mole % ^{235}U. The natural abundance of ^{235}U is 0.72%.

5.145 A slight deviation from ideal behavior exists even at normal conditions. If it behaved ideally, 1 mol of CO would occupy 22.414 L and exert 1 atm pressure at 273.15 K. Calculate P_{VDW} for 1.000 mol of CO at 273.15 K. $\left(\text{Use } R = 0.08206 \dfrac{\text{atm}\cdot\text{L}}{\text{mol}\cdot\text{K}}.\right)$

5.146 In preparation for a combustion demonstration, a professor fills a balloon with equal molar amounts of H_2 and O_2, but the demonstration has to be postponed until the next day. During the night, both gases leak through pores in the balloon. If 35% of the H_2 leaks, what is the O_2/H_2 ratio in the balloon the next day?

5.147 Phosphorus trichloride is important in the manufacture of insecticides, fuel additives, and flame retardants. Phosphorus has only one naturally occurring isotope, ^{31}P, whereas chlorine has two, ^{35}Cl (75%) and ^{37}Cl (25%). (a) What different molecular masses (in amu) can be found for PCl_3? (b) Which is the most abundant? (c) What is the ratio of the effusion rates of the heaviest and the lightest PCl_3 molecules?

5.148 A truck tire has a volume of 218 L and is filled with air to 35.0 psi at 295 K. After a drive, the air heats up to 318 K. (a) If the tire volume is constant, what is the pressure (in psi)? (b) If the tire volume increases 2.0%, what is the pressure (in psi)? (c) If the tire leaks 1.5 g of air per minute and the temperature is constant, how many minutes will it take for the tire to reach the original pressure of 35.0 psi ($\mathcal{M}$ of air = 28.8 g/mol)?

5.149 Allotropes are different molecular forms of an element, such as dioxygen (O_2) and ozone (O_3). (a) What is the density of each oxygen allotrope at 0°C and 760 torr? (b) Calculate the ratio of densities, d_{O_3}/d_{O_2}, and explain the significance of this number.

5.150 When gaseous F_2 and solid I_2 are heated to high temperatures, the I_2 sublimes and gaseous iodine heptafluoride forms. If 350. torr of F_2 and 2.50 g of solid I_2 are put into a 2.50-L container at 250. K and the container is heated to 550. K, what is the final pressure (in torr)? What is the partial pressure of I_2 gas?

Thermochemistry: Energy Flow and Chemical Change

6

Concepts and skills to review before you study this chapter

- energy and its interconversion (Section 1.1)
- distinction between heat and temperature (Section 1.5)
- nature of chemical bonding (Section 2.7)
- calculations of reaction stoichiometry (Section 3.4)
- properties of the gaseous state (Section 5.1)
- relation between kinetic energy and temperature (Section 5.5)

All matter contains energy, so *whenever matter undergoes a change, the quantity of energy that the matter contains also changes.* When a burning candle melts a piece of ice, both chemical and physical changes occur. In the chemical change, the higher energy reactants (wax and O_2) form lower energy products (CO_2 and H_2O), and the difference in energy is *released* as heat and light. Then, during the physical change, some of that heat is *absorbed* when lower energy ice becomes higher energy water. In a thunderstorm, the changes in energy are reversed: lower energy N_2 and O_2 *absorb* energy from lightning to form higher energy NO, and higher energy water vapor *releases* energy as it condenses to lower energy liquid water that falls as rain.

This interplay of matter and energy is profoundly important and has an enormous impact on society. On an everyday level, many familiar materials release, absorb, or alter the flow of energy. Fuels such as oil and wood release energy to warm our homes or power our vehicles. Fertilizers help crops convert solar energy into food. Metal wires increase the flow of electrical energy, and polymer fibers in winter clothing limit the flow of thermal energy away from our bodies.

Thermodynamics is the study of energy and its transformations, and two chapters in this text address this central topic. Our focus here is on **thermochemistry,** the branch of thermodynamics that deals with heat in chemical and physical change. In Chapter 20, we consider the fundamental question of *why* reactions occur.

IN THIS CHAPTER . . . We see how heat, or thermal energy, flows when matter changes, how to measure the quantity of heat for a given change, and how to determine the heat flow accompanying any reaction.

- We see that energy always flows between a system and its surroundings in the form of heat or work, so the total energy is conserved.
- We discuss the units of energy and show that the total size of an energy change does not depend on how the change occurs.
- We identify the heat of a reaction in an open container as a change in enthalpy, which can be negative (exothermic reaction) or positive (endothermic reaction).
- We describe how a calorimeter measures heat and how the quantity of heat in a reaction is proportional to the amounts of substances.
- We define standard conditions to compare enthalpies of reactions and see how to obtain the change in enthalpy for any reaction.
- We discuss some current and future energy sources and describe the critical relation between energy demand and climate change.

6.1 • FORMS OF ENERGY AND THEIR INTERCONVERSION

In Chapter 1, we saw that all energy is either potential or kinetic, and that these forms are interconvertible. An object has potential energy by virtue of its position and kinetic energy by virtue of its motion. Let's re-examine these ideas by considering a weight raised above the ground. As your muscles or a motor raise the weight, its potential energy increases; this energy is converted to kinetic energy as the weight falls (see Figure 1.3, p. 9). When it hits the ground, some of that kinetic energy appears as *work* done when the weight moves the soil and pebbles slightly, and some appears as *heat* when it warms them slightly. Thus, in this situation, *potential energy is converted to kinetic energy, which appears as work and heat.*

Several other forms of energy—solar, electrical, nuclear, and chemical—are examples of potential and kinetic energy on the atomic scale. No matter what the form of energy or the situation, *when energy is transferred from one object to another, it appears as work and/or heat.* In this section, we examine this idea in terms of the release or absorption of energy during a chemical or physical change.

Figure 6.1 A chemical system and its surroundings.

Defining the System and Its Surroundings

In any thermodynamic study, including measuring a change in energy, the first step is to define the **system**—the part of the universe we are focusing on. And the moment we define the system, everything else is defined as the **surroundings.**

Figure 6.1 shows a typical chemical system—the contents of a flask; the flask itself, other equipment, and perhaps the rest of the laboratory are the surroundings. In principle, the rest of the universe is the surroundings, but in practice, we consider only the parts that are relevant to the system: it's not likely that a thunderstorm in central Asia or a methane blizzard on Neptune will affect the contents of the flask, but the temperature and pressure of the lab might. Thus, the experimenter defines the system and the relevant surroundings. An astronomer defines a galaxy as the system and nearby galaxies as the surroundings; a microbiologist defines a given cell as the system and neighboring cells and the extracellular fluid as the surroundings; and so forth.

Energy Transfer to and from a System

Each particle in a system has potential energy and kinetic energy, and the sum of all these energies is the **internal energy, E,** of the system (some texts use the symbol U). When the reactants in a chemical system change to products, the system's internal energy has changed. This change, ΔE, is the difference between the internal energy *after* the change (E_{final}) and *before* the change ($E_{initial}$):

$$\Delta E = E_{final} - E_{initial} = E_{products} - E_{reactants} \quad (6.1)$$

where Δ (Greek *delta*) means "change (or difference) in" and refers to the *final state **minus** the initial state.* Thus, ΔE is the final quantity of energy of the system **minus** the initial quantity.

Because the universe consists of only system and surroundings, *a change in the energy of the system must be accompanied by an **equal** and **opposite** change in the energy of the surroundings.* In an *energy diagram,* the final and initial states are horizontal lines along a vertical energy axis, with ΔE the difference in the heights of the lines. A system can change its internal energy in one of two ways:

- By releasing some energy in a transfer *to* the surroundings (Figure 6.2A):

$$E_{final} < E_{initial} \quad \text{so} \quad \Delta E < 0$$

- By absorbing some energy in a transfer *from* the surroundings (Figure 6.2B):

$$E_{final} > E_{initial} \quad \text{so} \quad \Delta E > 0$$

Thus, ΔE is a *transfer* of energy from system to surroundings, or vice versa.

Heat and Work: Two Forms of Energy Transfer

Energy transferred from system to surroundings or vice versa appears in two forms:

1. *Heat.* **Heat** or *thermal energy* (symbolized by q) is the energy transferred as a result of a difference in temperature between the system and the surroundings. For example, energy in the form of heat is transferred from hot soup (system) to the bowl, air, and table (surroundings) because they are at a lower temperature.

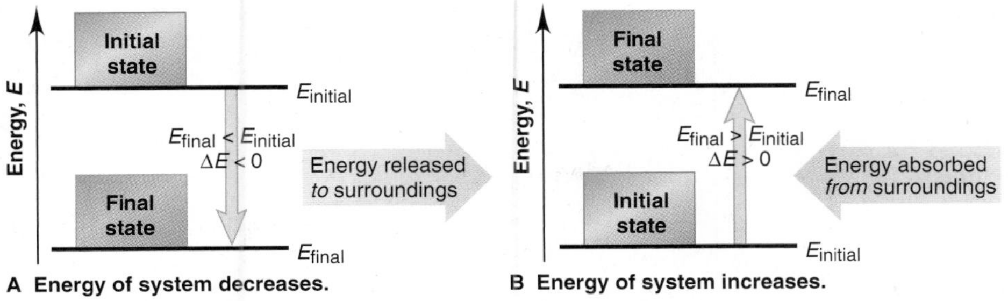

Figure 6.2 Energy diagrams for the transfer of internal energy (E) between a system and its surroundings. **A,** When the system releases energy, ΔE ($E_{final} - E_{initial}$) is negative. **B,** When the system absorbs energy, ΔE ($E_{final} - E_{initial}$) is positive. (The vertical yellow arrow always has its tail at the initial state.)

2. *Work.* All other forms of energy transfer involve some type of **work (w),** the energy transferred when an object is moved by a force. When you (system) kick a football, energy is transferred as work because the force of the kick moves the ball and air (surroundings). When you pump up a ball, energy is transferred as work because the added air (system) exerts a force on the inner wall of the ball (surroundings) and moves it outward.

The total change in a system's internal energy is the sum of the energy transferred as heat and/or work:

$$\Delta E = q + w \qquad (6.2)$$

The values of q and w (and, therefore, of ΔE) can have either a positive or negative sign. *We define the sign of the energy change from the* ***system's*** *perspective:*

- Energy transferred *into* the system is *positive* because the *system ends up with more* energy.
- Energy transferred *out from* the system is *negative,* because the *system ends up with less* energy.

Innumerable combinations of heat and/or work can change a system's internal energy. In the rest of this subsection, we'll examine the four simplest cases—two that involve only heat and two that involve only work.

Energy Transferred as Heat Only For a system that transfers energy only as heat (q) and does no work ($w = 0$), we have, from Equation 6.2, $\Delta E = q + 0 = q$. There are two ways this transfer can happen:

1. *Heat flowing* ***out*** *from a system.* Suppose hot water is the system, and the beaker holding it and the rest of the lab are the surroundings. The water transfers energy as heat outward until the temperature of the water and the surroundings are equal. Since heat flows *out* from the system, the final energy of the system is less than the initial energy. Heat was released, so *q is negative,* and therefore *ΔE is negative* (Figure 6.3A).

2. *Heat flowing* ***into*** *a system.* If the system consists of ice water, the surroundings transfer energy as heat *into* the system, once again until the ice melts and the temperature of the water and the surroundings become equal. In this case, heat flows *in,* so the final energy of the system is higher than its initial energy. Heat was absorbed, so *q is positive,* and therefore *ΔE is positive* (Figure 6.3B). ●

● **Thermodynamics in the Kitchen** A new view of two familiar kitchen appliances can clarify the sign of q. The air in a refrigerator (surroundings) has a lower temperature than a newly added piece of food (system), so the food releases energy as heat to the refrigerator air, $q < 0$. The air in a hot oven (surroundings) has a higher temperature than a newly added piece of food (system), so the food absorbs energy as heat from the oven air, $q > 0$.

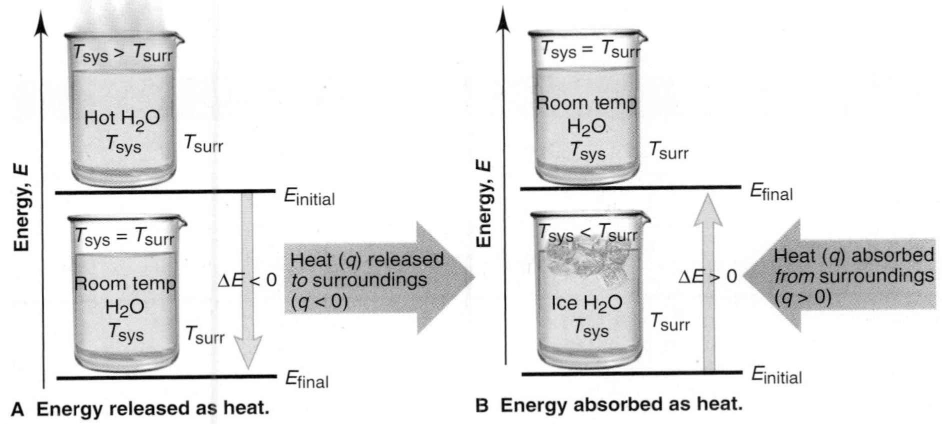

Figure 6.3 The two cases where energy is transferred as heat only. **A,** The system releases heat. **B,** The system absorbs heat.

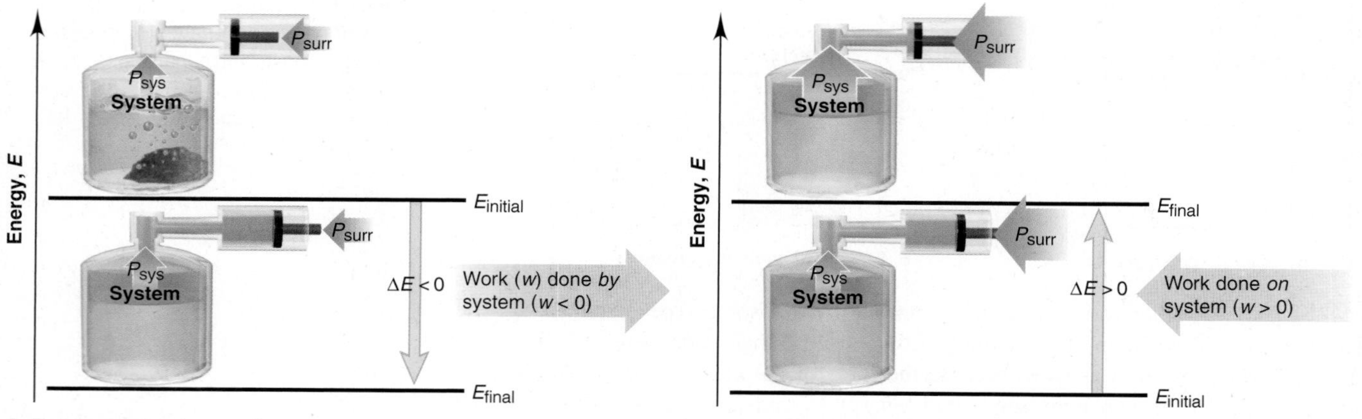

Figure 6.4 The two cases where energy is transferred as work only. **A,** The system does work *on* the surroundings. **B,** The system has work done on it *by* the surroundings.

Energy Transferred as Work Only For a system that transfers energy only as work, $q = 0$; therefore, $\Delta E = 0 + w = w$. There are two ways this transfer can happen:

1. *Work done* ***by*** *a system* (Figure 6.4A). Consider an aqueous reaction of a gray metal (for example, Zn) and a strong acid (for example, HCl) that takes place in a nearly evacuated (narrow P_{sys} arrow), insulated container attached to a piston-cylinder assembly and that has a gas (e.g., H_2) as one of the products. (The container is insulated so that heat does not flow.) We define the system as the reaction mixture, and the container, piston-cylinder, outside air, and so forth as the surroundings. In the initial state, the internal energy is the energy of the reactants, and in the final state, it is the energy of the products. As the gas forms, it pushes back the piston. Thus, energy is transferred as work done *by* the system *on* the surroundings. Since the system releases energy as work, *w is negative;* the final energy of the system is less than the intital energy, so *ΔE is negative.**

2. *Work done* ***on*** *a system* (Figure 6.4B). Suppose that, after the reaction is over, we increase the pressure of the surroundings (wider P_{surr} arrow) so that the piston moves in. Energy is transferred as work done *by* the surroundings *on* the system, so *w is positive.* The final energy of the system is greater than the intitial energy, so *ΔE is positive.*

Table 6.1 summarizes the sign conventions for q and w and their effect on the sign of ΔE.

*The system shown in Figure 6.4A is not doing very useful work because it just pushes back the piston and outside air. But, if the reaction mixture is gasoline and oxygen and the surroundings are an automobile engine, much of the internal energy is transferred as the work done to move a car.

Table 6.1 The Sign Conventions* for q, w, and ΔE

q	+	w	=	ΔE
+		+		+
+		−		Depends on the sizes of q and w
−		+		Depends on the sizes of q and w
−		−		−

*For q: + means system *absorbs* heat; − means system *releases* heat.
*For w: + means work done *on* system; − means work done *by* system.

The Law of Energy Conservation

As you've seen, when a system absorbs energy, the surroundings release it, and when a system releases energy, the surroundings absorb it. Energy transferred between system and surroundings can be in the form of heat and/or various types of work—mechanical, electrical, radiant, chemical, and so forth.

Indeed, energy is often converted from one form to another during transfers. For example, when gasoline burns in a car engine, the reaction releases energy that is transferred as heat and work. The heat warms the car parts, passenger compartment, and surrounding air. The work is done when mechanical energy turns the car's wheels and belts. That energy is converted into the electrical energy of the sound system, the radiant energy of the headlights, the chemical energy of the battery, and so forth. The sum of all these forms equals the change in energy between reactants and products as the gasoline is burned.

Complex biological processes exhibit the same general pattern. During photosynthesis, green plants convert solar energy into the chemical energy of the bonds in starch and O_2; when you digest starch, the bonds in the compound are converted into the muscular (mechanical) energy needed to run a marathon.

The most important point to realize in these, and all other situations, is that the energy changes form but does not simply appear or disappear—energy cannot be created or destroyed. Put another way, *energy is conserved: the total energy of the system plus the surroundings remains constant.* The **law of conservation of energy,** also known as the **first law of thermodynamics,** restates this basic observation: *the total energy of the universe is constant.* It is expressed mathematically as

$$\Delta E_{\text{universe}} = \Delta E_{\text{system}} + \Delta E_{\text{surroundings}} = 0 \quad (6.3)$$

This law applies, as far as we know, to all systems, from a burning match to continental drift, from the pumping of your heart to the formation of the Solar System.

Units of Energy

The SI unit of energy is the **joule (J),** a derived unit composed of three base units:

$$1\ \text{J} = 1\ \text{kg·m}^2/\text{s}^2$$

Both heat and work are expressed in joules. Let's see why the joule is the unit for work. The work (w) done on a mass is the force (F) times the distance (d) that the mass moves: $w = F \times d$. A *force* changes the velocity of a mass over time; that is, a force *accelerates* a mass. Velocity has units of meters per second (m/s), so acceleration (a) has units of meters per second per second (m/s^2). Force, therefore, has units of mass (m, in kilograms) times acceleration:

$$F = m \times a \quad \text{has units of} \quad \text{kg·m/s}^2$$

Therefore, $$w = F \times d \quad \text{has units of} \quad (\text{kg·m/s}^2) \times \text{m} = \text{kg·m}^2/\text{s}^2 = \text{J}$$

The **calorie (cal)** is an older unit defined originally as the quantity of energy needed to raise the temperature of 1 g of water by 1°C (from 14.5°C to 15.5°C). The calorie is now defined in terms of the joule:

$$1\ \text{cal} \equiv 4.184\ \text{J} \quad \text{or} \quad 1\ \text{J} = \frac{1}{4.184}\ \text{cal} = 0.2390\ \text{cal}$$

Since the quantities of energy involved in chemical reactions are usually quite large, chemists use the kilojoule (kJ), or, in earlier sources, the kilocalorie (kcal):

$$1\ \text{kJ} = 1000\ \text{J} = 0.2390\ \text{kcal} = 239.0\ \text{cal}$$

The nutritional Calorie (note the capital C), the unit that shows the energy available from food, is actually a kilocalorie.

The *British thermal unit (Btu),* a unit that you may have seen used for the energy output of appliances, is the quantity of energy required to raise the temperature of 1 lb of water by 1°F; *1 Btu is equivalent to 1055 J.* In general, the SI unit (J or kJ) is used in this text. Some interesting quantities of energy appear in Figure 6.5.

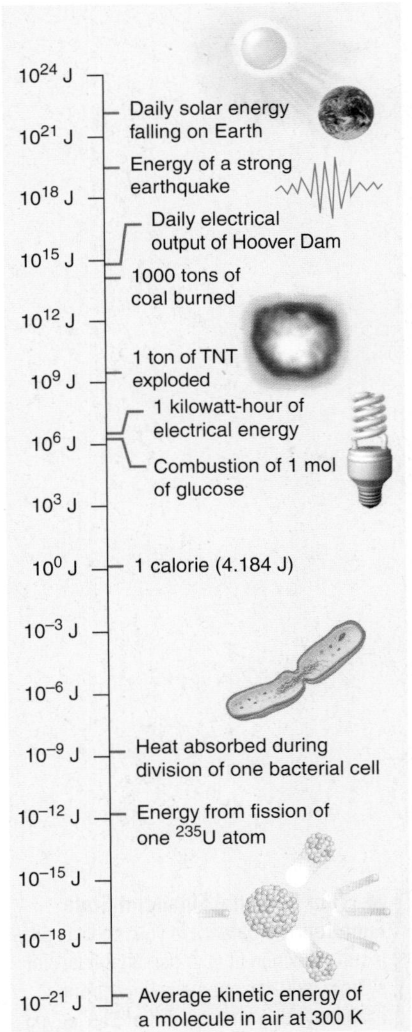

Figure 6.5 Some quantities of energy. The vertical scale is exponential.

Sample Problem 6.1 Determining the Change in Internal Energy of a System

Problem When gasoline burns in a car engine, the heat released causes the products CO_2 and H_2O to expand, which pushes the pistons outward. Excess heat is removed by the car's radiator. If the expanding gases do 451 J of work on the pistons and the system releases 325 J to the surroundings as heat, calculate the change in energy (ΔE) in J, kJ, and kcal.

Plan We must define system and surroundings to choose signs for q and w, and then we calculate ΔE with Equation 6.2. The system is the reactants and products, and the surroundings are the pistons, the radiator, and the rest of the car. Heat is released by the system, so q is negative. Work is done by the system to push the pistons outward, so w is also negative. We obtain the answer in J and then convert it to kJ and kcal.

Solution Calculating ΔE (from Equation 6.2) in J:

$$q = -325 \text{ J}$$
$$w = -451 \text{ J}$$
$$\Delta E = q + w = -325 \text{ J} + (-451 \text{ J}) = -776 \text{ J}$$

Converting from J to kJ:

$$\Delta E = -776 \text{ J} \times \frac{1 \text{ kJ}}{1000 \text{ J}} = -0.776 \text{ kJ}$$

Converting from kJ to kcal:

$$\Delta E = -0.776 \text{ kJ} \times \frac{1 \text{ kcal}}{4.184 \text{ kJ}} = -0.185 \text{ kcal}$$

Check The answer is reasonable: combustion of gasoline releases energy from the system, so $E_{final} < E_{initial}$ and ΔE should be negative. Rounding shows that, since $4 \text{ kJ} \approx 1 \text{ kcal}$, nearly 0.8 kJ should be nearly 0.2 kcal.

Follow-Up Problem 6.1 In a reaction, gaseous reactants form a liquid product. The heat absorbed by the surroundings is 26.0 kcal, and the work done on the system is 15.0 Btu. Calculate ΔE (in kJ).

State Functions and the Path Independence of the Energy Change

The internal energy (E) of a system is called a **state function,** a property dependent only on the *current* state of the system (its composition, volume, pressure, and temperature), *not* on the path the system takes to reach that state. The energy change of a system can occur by countless combinations of heat (q) and/or work (w). However, because E is a state function, the overall ΔE is the same no matter what the specific combination may be. That is, *ΔE does **not** depend on how the change takes place, but only on the **difference** between the final and initial states.*

As an example, let's define a system in its initial state as 1 mol of octane (a component of gasoline) together with enough O_2 to burn it. In its final state, the system is the CO_2 and H_2O that form:

$$\underset{\text{initial state } (E_{\text{initial}})}{C_8H_{18}(l) + \tfrac{25}{2}O_2(g)} \longrightarrow \underset{\text{final state } (E_{\text{final}})}{8CO_2(g) + 9H_2O(g)}$$

Energy is transferred *out* from the system as heat and/or work, so ΔE is negative. Figure 6.6 shows just two of the many ways the change can occur. If we burn the octane in an open container (*left*), ΔE is transferred almost completely as heat (with a small amount of work done to push back the atmosphere). If we burn it in a car engine (*right*), a much larger portion ($\sim$30%) of ΔE is transferred as work that moves the car, with the rest released as heat that warms the car, exhaust gases, and surrounding air. If we burn the octane in a lawn mower or a plane, ΔE appears as other combinations of work and heat. Thus, q and w are *not* state functions because their values *do* depend on the path the system takes, but ΔE (the *sum* of q and w) *does not.*

Your Personal Financial State Function The *balance* in your checkbook is a state function of your personal financial system. You can open a new checking account with a birthday gift of $50, or you can open one with a deposit of a $100 paycheck and then write two $25 checks. The two paths to the balance are different, but the balance (current state) is the same.

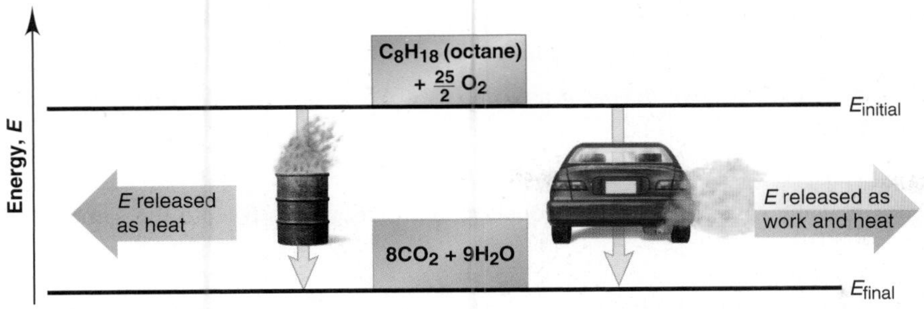

Figure 6.6 Two different paths for the energy change of a system. Even though q and w for the two paths are different, ΔE is the same.

Pressure (P), volume (V), and temperature (T) are some other state functions. Path independence means that *changes in state functions—ΔE, ΔP, ΔV, and ΔT—depend only on the initial and final states.*

Summary of Section 6.1

- Internal energy (E) is transferred as heat (q) when system and surroundings are at different temperatures or as work (w) when an object is moved by a force.
- Heat or work absorbed by a system ($q > 0$; $w > 0$) increases its E; heat or work released by the system ($q < 0$; $w < 0$) decreases its E. The change in the internal energy is the sum of the heat and work: $\Delta E = q + w$. Heat and work are measured in joules (J).
- Energy is always conserved: it can change from one form to another and move into or out of the system, but the total quantity of energy in the universe (system *plus* surroundings) is constant.
- The internal energy of a system is a state function and, thus, is independent of how the system attained that energy; therefore, the same overall ΔE can occur through any combination of q and w.

6.2 • ENTHALPY: CHEMICAL CHANGE AT CONSTANT PRESSURE

Most physical and chemical changes occur at nearly constant atmospheric pressure—a reaction in an open flask, the freezing of a lake, a biochemical process in an organism. In this section, we discuss *enthalpy,* a thermodynamic variable that relates directly to energy changes at constant pressure.

The Meaning of Enthalpy

To determine ΔE, we must measure both heat and work. The two most important types of chemical work are electrical work, done by moving charged particles (Chapter 21), and **pressure-volume work (*PV* work),** the mechanical work done when the volume of the system changes in the presence of an external pressure (P). The quantity of PV work equals P times the change in volume (ΔV, or $V_{final} - V_{initial}$). In an open flask (or in a cylinder with a weightless, frictionless piston) (Figure 6.7), a system of an expanding gas does PV work *on* the surroundings, so it has a negative sign:

$$w = -P\Delta V \qquad (6.4)$$

For reactions *at constant pressure,* a thermodynamic variable called **enthalpy (H)** eliminates the need to measure PV work. The enthalpy of a system is defined as the internal energy *plus* the product of the pressure and volume:

$$H = E + PV$$

The **change in enthalpy (ΔH)** is the change in internal energy *plus* the product of the pressure, which is constant, and the change in volume (ΔV):

$$\Delta H = \Delta E + P\Delta V \qquad (6.5)$$

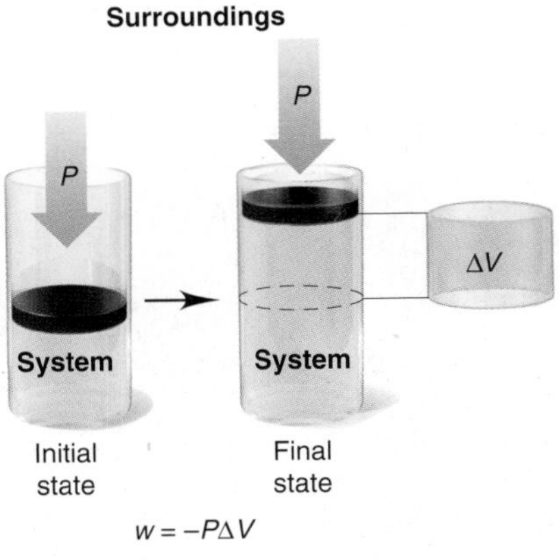

Figure 6.7 Pressure-volume work. An expanding gas pushing back the atmosphere does PV work ($w = -P\Delta V$).

Combining Equations 6.2 ($\Delta E = q + w$) and 6.4 ($w = -P\Delta V$) gives

$$\Delta E = q + w = q + (-P\Delta V) = q - P\Delta V$$

At constant pressure, we denote q as q_P, giving $\Delta E = q_P - P\Delta V$, which we can use to solve for q_P:

$$q_P = \Delta E + P\Delta V$$

Notice that the right sides of this equation and of Equation 6.5 are the same:

$$q_P = \Delta E + P\Delta V = \Delta H \quad (6.6)$$

Thus, *the change in enthalpy equals the heat absorbed or released at* ***constant*** *pressure.* For most changes occurring at constant pressure, ΔH is more relevant than ΔE *and* easier to obtain: *to find* ΔH, *measure* q_P. We discuss the laboratory method in Section 6.3.

Comparing ΔE and ΔH

Knowing the *enthalpy* change of a system tells us a lot about its *energy* change as well. In fact, because many reactions involve little (if any) *PV* work, most (or all) of the energy change occurs as a transfer of heat. Here are three cases:

1. *Reactions that do not involve gases.* Gases do not appear in precipitation, many acid-base, many redox reactions, and so forth. For example,

   $$2KOH(aq) + H_2SO_4(aq) \longrightarrow K_2SO_4(aq) + 2H_2O(l)$$

   Because liquids and solids undergo *very* small volume changes, $\Delta V \approx 0$; thus $P\Delta V \approx 0$ and $\Delta H \approx \Delta E$.
2. *Reactions in which the amount (mol) of gas does* ***not*** *change.* When the total amount of gaseous reactants equals the total amount of gaseous products, the volume is constant, $\Delta V = 0$, so $P\Delta V = 0$ and $\Delta H = \Delta E$. For example,

   $$N_2(g) + O_2(g) \longrightarrow 2NO(g)$$
3. *Reactions in which the amount (mol) of gas* ***does*** *change.* In these cases, $P\Delta V \neq 0$. However, q_P is usually *much* larger than $P\Delta V$, so ΔH is still very close to ΔE. For instance, in the combustion of H_2, 3 mol of gas yields 2 mol of gas:

   $$2H_2(g) + O_2(g) \longrightarrow 2H_2O(g)$$

   In this reaction, $\Delta H = -483.6$ kJ and $P\Delta V = -2.5$ kJ, so (from Equation 6.5),

   $$\Delta H = \Delta E + P\Delta V \quad \text{and} \quad \Delta E = \Delta H - P\Delta V = -483.6\ \text{kJ} - (-2.5\ \text{kJ}) = -481.1\ \text{kJ}$$

   Since most of ΔE occurs as energy transferred as heat, $\Delta H \approx \Delta E$.

Thus, *for most reactions,* ΔH *equals, or is very close to,* ΔE.

Exothermic and Endothermic Processes

Because H is a combination of the three state functions E, P, and V, it is also a state function. Therefore, ΔH equals H_{final} ***minus*** $H_{initial}$. For a reaction, H_{final} is $H_{products}$ and $H_{initial}$ is $H_{reactants}$, so the enthalpy change of a reaction is

$$\Delta H = H_{final} - H_{initial} = H_{products} - H_{reactants}$$

Since $H_{products}$ can be either more or less than $H_{reactants}$, the *sign* of ΔH indicates whether heat is absorbed or released during the reaction. We determine the sign of ΔH *by imagining the heat as "reactant" or "product."* The two possibilities are

1. *Exothermic process.* An **exothermic** ("heat out") **process** *releases* heat and results in a *decrease* in the enthalpy of the system:

$$\text{Exothermic:} \quad H_{products} < H_{reactants} \quad \text{so} \quad \Delta H < 0$$

For example, when methane burns in air, heat flows *out of* the system into the surroundings, so we show it as a product:

$$CH_4(g) + 2O_2(g) \longrightarrow CO_2(g) + 2H_2O(g) + heat$$

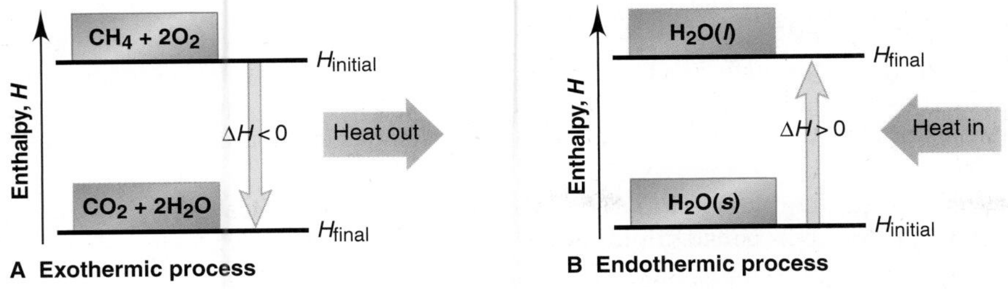

Figure 6.8 Enthalpy diagrams for exothermic and endothermic processes. **A,** The combustion of methane is exothermic: $\Delta H < 0$. **B,** The melting of ice is endothermic: $\Delta H > 0$.

The reactants (1 mol of CH_4 and 2 mol of O_2) release heat during the reaction, so they originally had more enthalpy than the products (1 mol of CO_2 and 2 mol of H_2O):

$$H_{\text{reactants}} > H_{\text{products}} \quad \text{so} \quad \Delta H\ (H_{\text{products}} - H_{\text{reactants}}) < 0$$

This exothermic change is shown in the **enthalpy diagram** in Figure 6.8A.

2. *Endothermic process.* An **endothermic** ("heat in") **process** *absorbs* heat and results in an *increase* in the enthalpy of the system:

$$\text{Endothermic:} \qquad H_{\text{products}} > H_{\text{reactants}} \quad \text{so} \quad \Delta H > 0$$

When ice melts, for instance, heat flows *into* the ice from the surroundings, so we show the heat as a reactant:

$$\textit{heat} + H_2O(s) \longrightarrow H_2O(l)$$

Because heat is absorbed, the enthalpy of the product (water) must be higher than that of the reactant (ice):

$$H_{\text{water}} > H_{\text{ice}} \quad \text{so} \quad \Delta H\ (H_{\text{water}} - H_{\text{ice}}) > 0$$

This endothermic change is shown in Figure 6.8B. (In general, the value of an enthalpy change is determined with reactants and products at the same temperature.)

Sample Problem 6.2 Drawing Enthalpy Diagrams and Determining the Sign of ΔH

Problem In each of the following cases, determine the sign of ΔH, state whether the reaction is exothermic or endothermic, and draw an enthalpy diagram:

(a) $H_2(g) + \frac{1}{2}O_2(g) \longrightarrow H_2O(l) + 285.8\text{ kJ}$
(b) $40.7\text{ kJ} + H_2O(l) \longrightarrow H_2O(g)$

Plan From each equation, we note whether heat is a "product" (exothermic; $\Delta H < 0$) or a "reactant" (endothermic; $\Delta H > 0$). For exothermic reactions, reactants are above products on the enthalpy diagram; for endothermic reactions, reactants are below products. The ΔH arrow *always* points from reactants to products.

Solution (a) Heat is a product (on the right), so $\Delta H < 0$ and the reaction is exothermic. The enthalpy diagram appears in the margin (*top*).
(b) Heat is a reactant (on the left), so $\Delta H > 0$ and the reaction is endothermic. The enthalpy diagram appears in the margin (*bottom*).

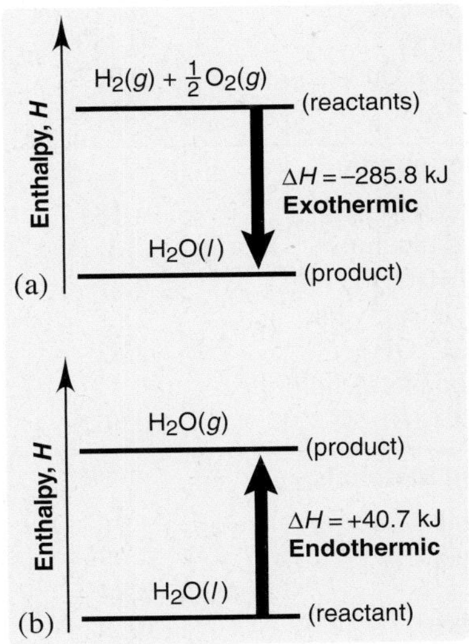

Check Substances that are on the same side of the equation as the heat have less enthalpy than substances on the other side, so make sure those substances are placed on the lower line of the diagram.

Follow-Up Problem 6.2 When nitroglycerine decomposes, the reaction creates a violent explosion and releases 5.72×10^3 kJ of heat per mole:

$$C_3H_5(NO_3)_3(l) \longrightarrow 3CO_2(g) + \tfrac{5}{2}H_2O(g) + \tfrac{1}{4}O_2(g) + \tfrac{3}{2}N_2(g)$$

Is the decomposition of nitroglycerine exothermic or endothermic? Draw an enthalpy diagram for the process.

Summary of Section 6.2

- Enthalpy (H) is a state function, so any change in enthalpy (ΔH) is independent of how the change occurred. At constant P, the value of ΔH equals $\Delta E + PV$ work, which occurs when the volume of the system changes in the presence of an external pressure.
- ΔH equals q_P, the heat released or absorbed during a chemical or physical change that takes place at constant pressure.
- In most cases, ΔH is equal, or very close, to ΔE.
- A change that releases heat is exothermic ($\Delta H < 0$); a change that absorbs heat is endothermic ($\Delta H > 0$).

6.3 • CALORIMETRY: MEASURING THE HEAT OF A CHEMICAL OR PHYSICAL CHANGE

Data about energy content and usage are everywhere—the caloric value of a slice of bread, the energy efficiency of a dishwasher, the gas mileage of a new car. In this section, we'll see how these values are determined.

Specific Heat Capacity

To find the energy change during a process, we measure the quantity of heat released or absorbed by relating it to the change in temperature. You know from everyday experience that the more you heat an object, the higher its temperature, and the more you cool it, the lower its temperature; in other words, the quantity of heat (q) absorbed or released by an object is proportional to its temperature change:

$$q \propto \Delta T \qquad \text{or} \qquad q = \text{constant} \times \Delta T \qquad \text{or} \qquad \frac{q}{\Delta T} = \text{constant}$$

What you might not know is that the temperature change depends on the object. Every object has its own **heat capacity,** the quantity of heat required to change its temperature by 1 K. Heat capacity is the proportionality constant in the preceding equation:

$$\text{Heat capacity} = \frac{q}{\Delta T} \quad [\text{in units of J/K}]$$

A related property is **specific heat capacity (c),** the quantity of heat required to change the temperature of 1 *gram* of an object by 1 K:

$$\text{Specific heat capacity } (c) = \frac{q}{\text{mass} \times \Delta T} \quad [\text{in units of J/g·K}]$$

If we know c of the object being heated (or cooled), we can measure the mass and the temperature change and calculate the heat absorbed (or released):

$$q = c \times \text{mass} \times \Delta T \tag{6.7}$$

Equation 6.7 says that when an object gets hotter, that is, when ΔT ($T_{\text{final}} - T_{\text{initial}}$) is positive, $q > 0$ (the sample absorbs heat). And when an object gets cooler, that is, when ΔT is negative, $q < 0$ (the sample releases heat). Table 6.2 lists the specific heat capacities of some representative substances and materials. Notice that metals have relatively low values of c and water has a very high value: for instance, it takes over 30 times as much energy to increase the temperature of a gram of water by 1 K as it does a gram of gold!

Closely related to the specific heat capacity (but reserved for substances) is the **molar heat capacity** (*C;* note the capital letter), the quantity of heat required to change the temperature of 1 *mole* of a substance by 1 K:

$$\text{Molar heat capacity } (C) = \frac{q}{\text{amount (mol)} \times \Delta T} \quad [\text{in units of J/mol·K}]$$

Table 6.2 Specific Heat Capacities (c) of Some Elements, Compounds, and Materials

Substance	c (J/g·K)*
Elements	
Aluminum, Al	0.900
Graphite, C	0.711
Iron, Fe	0.450
Copper, Cu	0.387
Gold, Au	0.129
Compounds	
Water, $H_2O(l)$	4.184
Ethyl alcohol, $C_2H_5OH(l)$	2.46
Ethylene glycol, $(CH_2OH)_2(l)$	2.42
Carbon tetracholoride, $CCl_4(l)$	0.862
Solid Materials	
Wood	1.76
Cement	0.88
Glass	0.84
Granite	0.79
Steel	0.45

*At 298 K (25°C)

To find C of liquid H_2O, we multiply c of liquid H_2O (4.184 J/g·K) by the molar mass of H_2O (18.02 g/mol):

$$C \text{ of } H_2O(l) = 4.184\,\frac{\text{J}}{\text{g·K}} \times \frac{18.02\text{ g}}{1\text{ mol}} = 75.40\,\frac{\text{J}}{\text{mol·K}}$$

Liquid water has a *very* high specific heat capacity (~4.2 J/g·K), about six times that of rock (~0.7 J/g·K). If Earth had no oceans (*see margin*), it would take one-sixth as much energy for the Sun to heat the rocky surface, and the surface would give off six times as much heat after sundown. Days would be scorching and nights frigid.

What if Earth had no oceans?

Sample Problem 6.3 **Finding the Quantity of Heat from a Temperature Change**

Problem A layer of copper welded to the bottom of a skillet weighs 125 g. How much heat is needed to raise the temperature of the copper layer from 25°C to 300.°C? The specific heat capacity (c) of Cu is given in Table 6.2.

Plan We know the mass (125 g) and c (0.387 J/g·K) of Cu and can find ΔT in °C, which equals ΔT in K. We then use Equation 6.7 to calculate the heat.

Solution Calculating ΔT and then q:

$$\Delta T = T_{\text{final}} - T_{\text{initial}} = 300.°\text{C} - 25°\text{C} = 275°\text{C} = 275\text{ K}$$

$$q = c \times \text{mass (g)} \times \Delta T = 0.387\text{ J/g·K} \times 125\text{ g} \times 275\text{ K} = 1.33\times10^4\text{ J}$$

Check Heat is absorbed by the copper bottom (system), so q is positive. Rounding shows the arithmetic is reasonable: $q \approx 0.4$ J/g·K $\times$ 100 g $\times$ 300 K = 1.2×10^4 J.

Follow-Up Problem 6.3 Find the heat released (in kJ) when 5.50 L of ethylene glycol (d = 1.11 g/mL; see Table 6.2) in a car radiator cools from 37.0°C to 25.0°C.

The Two Major Types of Calorimetry

How do we know the heat of an acid-base reaction or the Calories in a teaspoon of sugar? We construct "surroundings" that retain the heat as reactants change to products, and then note the temperature change. In the laboratory, these "surroundings" take the form of a **calorimeter,** a device used to measure the heat released (or absorbed) by a physical or chemical process. Let's look at two types of calorimeter—one designed to measure the heat at constant pressure and the other at constant volume.

Constant-Pressure Calorimetry For processes that take place at constant pressure, the heat transferred (q_P) is often measured in a *coffee-cup calorimeter* (Figure 6.9). This simple apparatus is often used to find the heat of an aqueous reaction or the heat accompanying the dissolving of a salt.

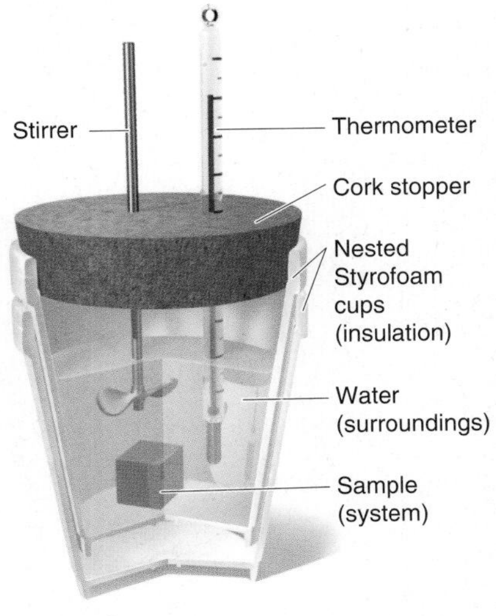

Figure 6.9 Coffee-cup calorimeter. This device measures the heat transferred at constant pressure (q_P).

A coffee-cup calorimeter can also be used to find the specific heat capacity of a solid, as long as it does not react with or dissolve in water. The solid (the system) is weighed, heated to some known temperature, and added to a known mass and temperature of water (surroundings) in the calorimeter. After stirring, the final water temperature is measured, which is also the final temperature of the solid. Assuming no heat escapes the calorimeter, the heat released by the system ($-q_{\text{sys}}$, or $-q_{\text{solid}}$) is equal in magnitude but opposite in sign to the heat absorbed by the surroundings ($+q_{\text{surr}}$, or $+q_{H_2O}$):

$$-q_{\text{solid}} = q_{H_2O}$$

Substituting from Equation 6.7 on each side of this equation gives

$$-(c_{\text{solid}} \times \text{mass}_{\text{solid}} \times \Delta T_{\text{solid}}) = c_{H_2O} \times \text{mass}_{H_2O} \times \Delta T_{H_2O}$$

All the quantities are known or measured except c_{solid}:

$$c_{\text{solid}} = -\frac{c_{H_2O} \times \text{mass}_{H_2O} \times \Delta T_{H_2O}}{\text{mass}_{\text{solid}} \times \Delta T_{\text{solid}}}$$

Sample Problem 6.4 Determining the Specific Heat Capacity of a Solid

Problem You heat 22.05 g of a solid in a test tube to 100.00°C and add it to 50.00 g of water in a coffee-cup calorimeter. The water temperature changes from 25.10°C to 28.49°C. Find the specific heat capacity of the solid.

Plan We are given the masses of the solid (22.05 g) and of H_2O (50.00 g), and we can find the temperature changes of the water and of the solid by subtracting the given values, always using $T_{final} - T_{initial}$. Using Equation 6.7, we set the heat released by the solid ($-q_{solid}$) equal to the heat absorbed by the water (q_{water}). The specific heat of water is known, and we solve for c_{solid}.

Solution Finding ΔT_{solid} and ΔT_{water}:

$$\Delta T_{water} = T_{final} - T_{initial} = (28.49°C - 25.10°C) = 3.39°C = 3.39\ K$$

$$\Delta T_{solid} = T_{final} - T_{initial} = (28.49°C - 100.00°C) = -71.51°C = -71.51\ K$$

Solving for c_{solid}:

$$c_{solid} = -\frac{c_{H_2O} \times mass_{H_2O} \times \Delta T_{H_2O}}{mass_{solid} \times \Delta T_{solid}} = -\frac{4.184\ J/g{\cdot}K \times 50.00\ g \times 3.39\ K}{22.05\ g \times (-71.51\ K)} = 0.450\ J/g{\cdot}K$$

Check Rounding gives -4 J/g·K × 50 g × 3 K/[20 g × (−70°C)] = 0.4 J/g·K, so the answer seems correct.

Follow-Up Problem 6.4 A 12.18-g sample of a shiny, orange-brown metal is heated to 65.00°C in a controlled water bath. The metal is then added to 25.00 g of water in a coffee-cup calorimeter, and the water temperature changes from 25.55°C to 27.25°C. What is the unknown metal (see Table 6.2)?

In the next sample problem, the calorimeter is used to study the change in heat during an aqueous acid-base reaction. Recall that, if a reaction takes place at constant pressure, the heat of the reaction (q_{rxn}) is equal to its enthalpy change (ΔH).

Sample Problem 6.5 Determining the Enthalpy Change of an Aqueous Reaction

Problem You place 50.0 mL of 0.500 *M* NaOH in a coffee-cup calorimeter at 25.00°C and add 25.0 mL of 0.500 *M* HCl, also at 25.00°C. After stirring, the final temperature is 27.21°C. [Assume that the total volume is the sum of the individual volumes and that the final solution has the same density (1.00 g/mL) and specific heat capacity (Table 6.2) as water.] **(a)** Calculate q_{soln} (in J). **(b)** Calculate the change in enthalpy, ΔH, of the reaction (in kJ/mol of H_2O formed).

(a) Calculate q_{soln}

Plan The solution is the surroundings, and as the reaction takes place, heat flows into the solution. To find q_{soln}, we use Equation 6.7, so we need the mass of solution, the change in temperature, and the specific heat capacity. We know the solutions' volumes (25.0 mL and 50.0 mL), so we find their masses with the given density (1.00 g/mL). Then, to find q_{soln}, we multiply the total mass by the given c (4.184 J/g·K) and the change in T, which we find from $T_{final} - T_{initial}$.

Solution Finding $mass_{soln}$ and ΔT_{soln}:

$$\text{Total mass (g) of solution} = (25.0\ mL + 50.0\ mL) \times 1.00\ g/mL = 75.0\ g$$

$$\Delta T = 27.21°C - 25.00°C = 2.21°C = 2.21\ K$$

Finding q_{soln}:

$$q_{soln} = c_{soln} \times mass_{soln} \times \Delta T_{soln} = (4.184\ J/g{\cdot}K)(75.0\ g)(2.21\ K) = 693\ J$$

Check Rounding to check q_{soln} gives 4 J/g·K × 75 g × 2 K = 600 J, which is close to the answer.

(b) Calculate the change in enthalpy (ΔH)

Plan To find ΔH, we write the balanced equation for the acid-base reaction and use the volumes and the concentrations (0.500 *M*) to find amount (mol) of each reactant (H^+ and OH^-). Since the amounts of two reactants are given, we determine which is limiting, that is, which gives less product (H_2O). The heat of the surroundings is q_{soln}, and it is the negative of the heat of the reaction (q_{rxn}), which equals ΔH. And dividing q_{rxn} by the amount (mol) of water formed gives ΔH in kJ/mol of water formed.

Solution Writing the balanced equation:

$$HCl(aq) + NaOH(aq) \longrightarrow H_2O(l) + NaCl(aq)$$

Finding amount (mol) of reactants:

$$\text{Amount (mol) of HCl} = 0.500 \text{ mol HCl/L} \times 0.0250 \text{ L} = 0.0125 \text{ mol HCl}$$

$$\text{Amount (mol) of NaOH} = 0.500 \text{ mol NaOH/L} \times 0.0500 \text{ L} = 0.0250 \text{ mol NaOH}$$

Finding the amount (mol) of product: All the coefficients in the equation are 1, which means that the amount (mol) of reactant yields that amount of product. Therefore, HCl is limiting because it yields less product: 0.0125 mol of H_2O.

Finding ΔH: Heat absorbed by the solution was released by the reaction; that is,

$$q_{soln} = -q_{rxn} = 693 \text{ J} \quad \text{so} \quad q_{rxn} = -693 \text{ J}$$

$$\Delta H \text{(kJ/mol)} = \frac{q_{rxn}}{\text{mol } H_2O} \times \frac{1 \text{ kJ}}{1000 \text{ J}} = \frac{-693 \text{ J}}{0.0125 \text{ mol } H_2O} \times \frac{1 \text{ kJ}}{1000 \text{ J}} = -55.4 \text{ kJ/mol } H_2O$$

Check We check for the limiting reactant: The volume of H^+ is half the volume of OH^-, but they have the same concentration and a 1:1 stoichiometric ratio. Therefore, the amount (mol) of H^+ determines the amount of product. Rounding and taking the negative of q_{soln} to find ΔH gives -600 J/0.012 mol $= -5\times10^4$ J/mol, or -50 kJ/mol, so the answer seems correct.

Follow-Up Problem 6.5 After 50.0 mL of 0.500*M* $Ba(OH)_2$ and the same volume and concentration of HCl react in a coffee-cup calorimeter, you find q_{soln} to be 1.386 kJ. Calculate ΔH of the reaction in kJ/mol of H_2O formed.

Constant-Volume Calorimetry Constant-volume calorimetry is often carried out in a *bomb calorimeter,* a device commonly used to measure the heat of combustion reactions, such as for fuels and foods. In the coffee-cup calorimeter, we assume all the heat is absorbed by the water, but in reality, some must be absorbed by the stirrer, thermometer, and so forth. With the much more precise bomb calorimeter, the *heat capacity of the entire calorimeter* is known (or can be determined).

Figure 6.10 depicts the preweighed combustible sample in a metal-walled chamber (the bomb), which is filled with oxygen gas and immersed in an insulated water bath fitted with motorized stirrer and thermometer. A heating coil connected to an electrical source ignites the sample, and the heat released raises the temperature of the bomb, water, and other calorimeter parts. Because we know the mass of the sample and the heat capacity of the entire calorimeter, we can use the measured ΔT to calculate the heat released.

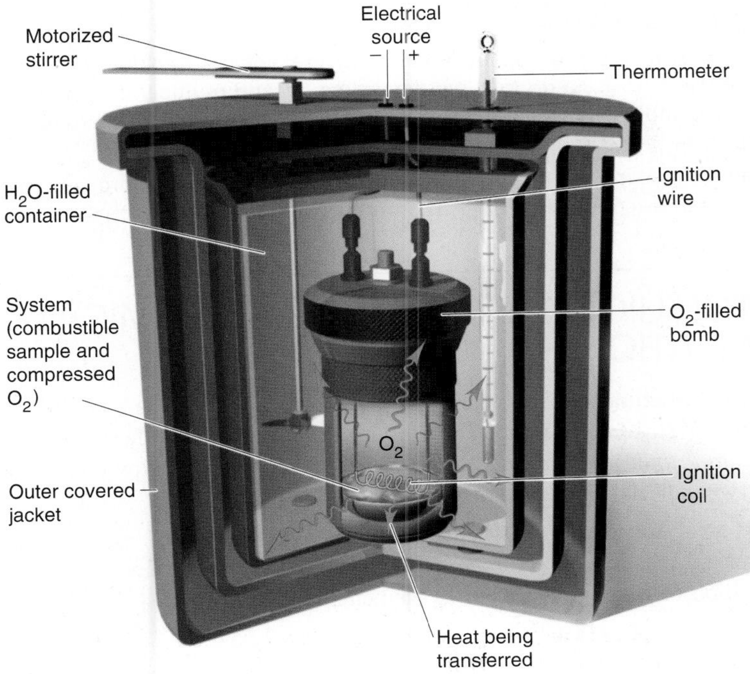

Figure 6.10 A bomb calorimeter. This device measures the heat released at constant volume (q_V). It is often used to study combustion reactions.

Note that the steel bomb is tightly sealed, not open to the atmosphere as is the coffee cup, so the pressure is *not* constant. And the volume of the bomb is fixed, so $\Delta V = 0$, and thus $P\Delta V = 0$. Thus, the energy change measured is the *heat released at constant volume* (q_V), which equals ΔE, not ΔH:

$$\Delta E = q + w = q_V + 0 = q_V$$

Recall from Section 6.2, however, that even though the number of moles of gas may change, $P\Delta V$ is usually *much* less than ΔE, so ΔH is very close to ΔE. For example, ΔH is only 0.5% larger than ΔE for the combustion of H_2 and only 0.2% smaller than ΔE for the combustion of octane.

Sample Problem 6.6 Calculating the Heat of a Combustion Reaction

Problem A manufacturer claims that its new dietetic dessert has "fewer than 10 Calories per serving." To test the claim, a chemist at the Department of Consumer Affairs places one serving in a bomb calorimeter and burns it in O_2. The initial temperature is 21.862°C and the temperature rises to 26.799°C. If the heat capacity of the calorimeter is 8.151 kJ/K, is the manufacturer's claim correct?

Plan When the dessert (system) burns, the heat released is absorbed by the calorimeter:

$$-q_{\text{system}} = q_{\text{calorimeter}}$$

The claim is correct if the heat of the system is less than 10 Calories. To find the heat, we multiply the given heat capacity of the calorimeter (8.151 kJ/K) by ΔT and then convert to Calories.

Solution Finding ΔT:

$$\Delta T = T_{\text{final}} - T_{\text{initial}} = 26.799°\text{C} - 21.862°\text{C} = 4.937°\text{C} = 4.937 \text{ K}$$

Calculating the heat absorbed by the calorimeter:

$$q_{\text{calorimeter}} = \text{heat capacity} \times \Delta T = 8.151 \text{ kJ/K} \times 4.937 \text{ K} = 40.24 \text{ kJ}$$

Recall that 1 Calorie = 1 kcal = 4.184 kJ. Therefore, 10 Calories = 41.84 kJ, so the claim is correct.

Check A quick math check shows that the answer is reasonable: 8 kJ/K × 5 K = 40 kJ.

Follow-Up Problem 6.6 A chemist burns 0.8650 g of graphite (a form of carbon) in a new bomb calorimeter, and CO_2 forms. If 393.5 kJ of heat is released per mole of graphite and ΔT is 2.613 K, what is the heat capacity of the bomb calorimeter?

Summary of Section 6.3

- We calculate ΔH of a process by measuring the energy transferred as heat at constant pressure (q_P). To do this, we determine ΔT and multiply it by the mass of the substance and by its specific heat capacity (c), which is the quantity of energy needed to raise the temperature of 1 g of the substance by 1 K.
- Calorimeters measure the heat released (or absorbed) during a process either at constant pressure (coffee cup; $q_P = \Delta H$) or at constant volume (bomb; $q_V = \Delta E$).

6.4 • STOICHIOMETRY OF THERMOCHEMICAL EQUATIONS

A **thermochemical equation** is a balanced equation that includes the enthalpy change of the reaction (ΔH). Keep in mind that a given ΔH refers only to the *amounts (mol) of substances* ***and*** *their states of matter in that equation.* The enthalpy change of any process has two aspects:

- *Sign.* The sign of ΔH depends on whether the reaction is exothermic (−) or endothermic (+). A forward reaction has the *opposite* sign of the reverse reaction.
  Decomposition of 2 mol of water to its elements (endothermic):

$$2H_2O(l) \longrightarrow 2H_2(g) + O_2(g) \qquad \Delta H = 572 \text{ kJ}$$

Formation of 2 mol of water from its elements (exothermic):

$$2H_2(g) + O_2(g) \longrightarrow 2H_2O(l) \quad \Delta H = -572 \text{ kJ}$$

- *Magnitude.* The magnitude of ΔH is *proportional to the amount of substance.* Formation of 1 mol of water from its elements (half the preceding amount):

$$H_2(g) + \tfrac{1}{2}O_2(g) \longrightarrow H_2O(l) \quad \Delta H = -286 \text{ kJ}$$

Two key points to understand about thermochemical equations are as follows:

1. *Balancing coefficients.* When necessary, we use fractional coefficients to balance an equation, because we are specifying the magnitude of ΔH for a *particular amount,* often 1 mol, *of substance:*

$$\tfrac{1}{8}S_8(s) + O_2(g) \longrightarrow SO_2(g) \quad \Delta H = -296.8 \text{ kJ}$$

2. *Thermochemical equivalence.* For a *particular reaction,* a certain amount of substance is thermochemically equivalent to a certain quantity of energy. For example, in the preceding reaction,

296.8 kJ is thermochemically equivalent to $\tfrac{1}{8}$ mol of $S_8(s)$
286 kJ is thermochemically equivalent to $\tfrac{1}{2}$ mol of $O_2(g)$
286 kJ is thermochemically equivalent to 1 mol of $H_2O(l)$

Just as we use stoichiometrically equivalent molar ratios to find amounts of substances, we use thermochemically equivalent quantities to find the ΔH of a reaction for a given amount of substance. Also, just as we use molar mass (in g/mol) to convert an amount (mol) of a substance to mass (g), we use the ΔH (in kJ/mol) to convert an amount of a substance to an equivalent quantity of heat (in kJ). Figure 6.11 shows this new relationship, and Sample Problem 6.7 applies it.

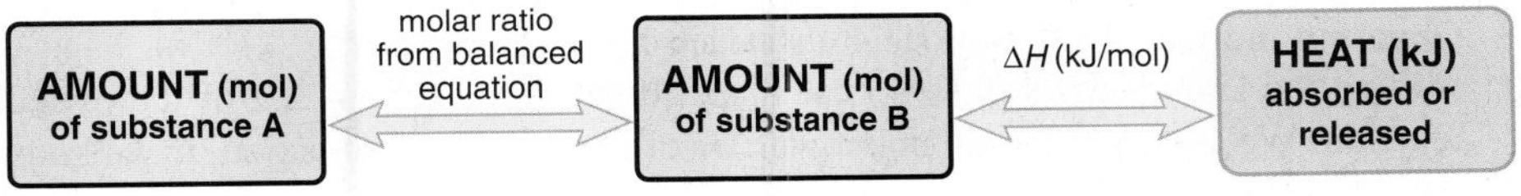

Figure 6.11 The relationship between amount (mol) of substance and the energy (kJ) transferred as heat during a reaction.

Sample Problem 6.7 Using the Enthalpy Change of a Reaction (ΔH) to Find Amounts of Substance

Problem The major source of aluminum in the world is bauxite (mostly aluminum oxide). Its thermal decomposition can be written as

$$Al_2O_3(s) \xrightarrow{\Delta} 2Al(s) + \tfrac{3}{2}O_2(g) \quad \Delta H = 1676 \text{ kJ}$$

If aluminum is produced this way (see Comment), how many grams of aluminum can form when 1.000×10^3 kJ of heat is transferred?

Plan From the balanced equation and the enthalpy change, we see that 2 mol of Al forms when 1676 kJ of heat is absorbed. With this equivalent quantity, we convert the given number of kJ to amount (mol) formed and then convert amount to mass (g).

Solution Combining steps to convert from heat transferred to mass of Al:

$$\text{Mass (g) of Al} = (1.000\times10^3 \text{ kJ}) \times \frac{2 \text{ mol Al}}{1676 \text{ kJ}} \times \frac{26.98 \text{ g Al}}{1 \text{ mol Al}} = 32.20 \text{ g Al}$$

Check The mass of aluminum seems correct: ~1700 kJ forms about 2 mol of Al (54 g), so 1000 kJ should form a bit more than half that amount (27 g).

Comment In practice, aluminum is not obtained by heating bauxite but by supplying electrical energy (as you'll see in Chapter 22). Because H is a state function, however, the total energy required for the change, ΔH, is the same no matter how it occurs.

Road Map

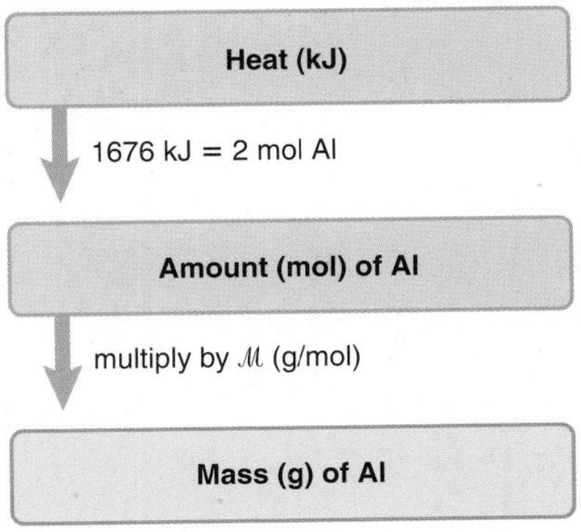

Follow-Up Problem 6.7 Hydrogenation reactions, in which H_2 and an "unsaturated" organic compound combine, are used in the food, fuel, and polymer industries. In the simplest case, ethene (C_2H_4) and H_2 form ethane (C_2H_6). If 137 kJ is given off per mole of C_2H_4 reacting, how much heat is released when 15.0 kg of C_2H_6 forms?

Summary of Section 6.4

- A thermochemical equation shows a balanced reaction *and* its ΔH value. The sign of ΔH for a forward reaction is opposite that for the reverse reaction. The magnitude of ΔH is specific for the given equation.
- The amount of a substance and the quantity of heat specified by the balanced equation are thermochemically equivalent and act as conversion factors to find the quantity of heat transferred when any amount of the substance reacts.

6.5 • HESS'S LAW: FINDING ΔH OF ANY REACTION

In some cases, a reaction is difficult, even impossible, to carry out individually: it may be part of a complex biochemical process, or take place under extreme conditions, or require a change in conditions to occur. Even if we can't run a reaction in the lab, we can still find its enthalpy change. In fact, the state-function property of enthalpy (H) allows us to find ΔH of *any* reaction for which we can write an equation.

This application is based on **Hess's law:** *the enthalpy change of an overall process is the sum of the enthalpy changes of its individual steps:*

$$\Delta H_{\text{overall}} = \Delta H_1 + \Delta H_2 + \cdots + \Delta H_n \tag{6.8}$$

This law follows from the fact that ΔH for a process depends only on the difference between the final and initial states. We apply Hess's law by

- Imagining that an overall reaction occurs through a series of individual reaction steps, whether or not it actually does. Adding the steps must give the overall reaction.
- Choosing individual reaction steps that each has a known ΔH.
- Adding the known ΔH values for the steps to get the unknown ΔH of the overall reaction. We can also find an unknown ΔH of any step by subtraction, if we know the ΔH values for the overall reaction and all the other steps.

Let's apply Hess's law to the oxidation of sulfur to sulfur trioxide, the key change in the industrial production of sulfuric acid and in the formation of acid rain. (To introduce this approach, we'll use S as the formula for sulfur, rather than the more correct S_8.) When we burn S in an excess of O_2, sulfur dioxide (SO_2) forms, *not* sulfur trioxide (SO_3) (Equation 1). After a change in conditions, we add more O_2 and oxidize SO_2 to SO_3 (Equation 2). Thus, we cannot put S and O_2 in a calorimeter and find ΔH for the overall reaction of S to SO_3 (Equation 3). But, we *can* find it with Hess's law. The three equations are

Equation 1: $S(s) + O_2(g) \longrightarrow SO_2(g) \quad \Delta H_1 = -296.8\ \text{kJ}$

Equation 2: $2SO_2(g) + O_2(g) \longrightarrow 2SO_3(g) \quad \Delta H_2 = -198.4\ \text{kJ}$

Equation 3: $S(s) + \frac{3}{2}O_2(g) \longrightarrow SO_3(g) \quad \Delta H_3 = ?$

If we can manipulate Equation 1 and/or Equation 2, *along with their ΔH value(s),* so the equations add up to Equation 3, their ΔH values will add up to the unknown ΔH_3.

First, we identify our "target" equation, the one whose ΔH we want to find, and note the amount (mol) of each reactant and product; our "target" is Equation 3. Then, we manipulate Equations 1 and/or 2 to make them add up to Equation 3:

- Equations 3 and 1 have the same amount of S, so we don't change Equation 1.
- Equation 3 has half as much SO_3 as Equation 2, so we multiply Equation 2, ***and* ΔH_2**, by $\frac{1}{2}$; that is, we always treat the equation and its ΔH value the same.
- With the targeted amounts of reactants and products present, we add Equation 1 to the halved Equation 2 and cancel terms that appear on both sides:

Equation 1: $S(s) + O_2(g) \longrightarrow SO_2(g) \quad \Delta H_1 = -296.8\ \text{kJ}$

$\frac{1}{2}$(Equation 2): $SO_2(g) + \frac{1}{2}O_2(g) \longrightarrow SO_3(g) \quad \frac{1}{2}(\Delta H_2) = -99.2\ \text{kJ}$

Equation 3: $S(s) + O_2(g) + \cancel{SO_2(g)} + \frac{1}{2}O_2(g) \longrightarrow \cancel{SO_2(g)} + SO_3(g)$

or, $S(s) + \frac{3}{2}O_2(g) \longrightarrow SO_3(g) \quad \Delta H_3 = -396.0\ \text{kJ}$

Because ΔH depends only on the difference between H_{final} and $H_{initial}$, Hess's law tells us that the difference between the enthalpies of the reactants (1 mol of S and $\frac{3}{2}$ mol of O_2) and the product (1 mol of SO_3) is the same, whether S is oxidized directly to SO_3 (impossible) or through the intermediate formation of SO_2 (actual).

To summarize, calculating an unknown ΔH involves three steps:

1. Identify the target equation, the step whose ΔH is unknown, and note the amount (mol) of each reactant and product.
2. Manipulate each equation with known ΔH values so that the target amount (mol) of each substance is on the correct side of the equation. Remember to:
   - Change the sign of ΔH when you reverse an equation.
   - Multiply amount (mol) and ΔH by the same factor.
3. Add the manipulated equations and their resulting ΔH values to get the target equation and its ΔH. All substances except those in the target equation must cancel.

Sample Problem 6.8 Using Hess's Law to Calculate an Unknown ΔH

Problem Two pollutants that form in auto exhaust are CO and NO. An environmental chemist must convert these pollutants to less harmful gases through the following:

$$CO(g) + NO(g) \longrightarrow CO_2(g) + \tfrac{1}{2}N_2(g) \qquad \Delta H = ?$$

Given the following information, calculate the unknown ΔH:

Equation A: $CO(g) + \tfrac{1}{2}O_2(g) \longrightarrow CO_2(g) \qquad \Delta H = -283.0\text{ kJ}$

Equation B: $N_2(g) + O_2(g) \longrightarrow 2NO(g) \qquad \Delta H = 180.6\text{ kJ}$

Plan We note the amount (mol) of each substance and on which side each appears in the target equation. We manipulate Equations A and/or B *and* their ΔH values as needed and add them together to obtain the target equation and the unknown ΔH.

Solution Noting substances in the target equation: For reactants, there are 1 mol of CO and of NO; for products, there are 1 mol of CO_2 and $\frac{1}{2}$ mol of N_2.

Manipulating the given equations:

- Equation A has the same amounts of CO and CO_2 on the same sides of the arrow as in the target, so we leave it as written.
- Equation B has twice as much N_2 and NO as the target, and they are on the opposite sides in the target. Thus, we reverse Equation B, change the sign of its ΔH, and multiply both by $\frac{1}{2}$:

$$\tfrac{1}{2}[2NO(g) \longrightarrow N_2(g) + O_2(g)] \qquad \Delta H = -\tfrac{1}{2}(\Delta H) = -\tfrac{1}{2}(180.6\text{ kJ})$$

or

$$NO(g) \longrightarrow \tfrac{1}{2}N_2(g) + \tfrac{1}{2}O_2(g) \qquad \Delta H = -90.3\text{ kJ}$$

Adding the manipulated equations to obtain the target equation:

Equation A:	$CO(g) + \cancel{\tfrac{1}{2}O_2(g)} \longrightarrow CO_2(g)$	$\Delta H = -283.0\text{ kJ}$
$\frac{1}{2}$(Equation B reversed)	$NO(g) \longrightarrow \tfrac{1}{2}N_2(g) + \cancel{\tfrac{1}{2}O_2(g)}$	$\Delta H = -90.3\text{ kJ}$
Target equation:	$CO(g) + NO(g) \longrightarrow CO_2(g) + \tfrac{1}{2}N_2(g)$	$\Delta H = -373.3\text{ kJ}$

Check Obtaining the desired target equation is a sufficient check. Be sure to remember to change the *sign* of ΔH for any equation you reverse.

Follow-Up Problem 6.8 Nitrogen oxides undergo many reactions in the environment and in industry. Given the following information, calculate ΔH for the overall equation, $2NO_2(g) + \frac{1}{2}O_2(g) \longrightarrow N_2O_5(s)$:

$$N_2O_5(s) \longrightarrow 2NO(g) + \tfrac{3}{2}O_2(g) \qquad \Delta H = 223.7\text{ kJ}$$

$$NO(g) + \tfrac{1}{2}O_2(g) \longrightarrow NO_2(g) \qquad \Delta H = -57.1\text{ kJ}$$

Summary of Section 6.5

- Because H is a state function, we can use Hess's law to determine ΔH of any reaction by assuming that it is the sum of other reactions.
- After manipulating the equations of those reactions and their ΔH values to match the substances in the target equation, we add the manipulated ΔH values to find the unknown ΔH.

Table 6.3 Selected Standard Enthalpies of Formation at 25°C (298 K)

Formula	ΔH°_f (kJ/mol)
Calcium	
$Ca(s)$	0
$CaO(s)$	−635.1
$CaCO_3(s)$	−1206.9
Carbon	
C(graphite)	0
C(diamond)	1.9
$CO(g)$	−110.5
$CO_2(g)$	−393.5
$CH_4(g)$	−74.9
$CH_3OH(l)$	−238.6
$HCN(g)$	135
$CS_2(l)$	87.9
Chlorine	
$Cl(g)$	121.0
$Cl_2(g)$	0
$HCl(g)$	−92.3
Hydrogen	
$H(g)$	218.0
$H_2(g)$	0
Nitrogen	
$N_2(g)$	0
$NH_3(g)$	−45.9
$NO(g)$	90.3
Oxygen	
$O_2(g)$	0
$O_3(g)$	143
$H_2O(g)$	−241.8
$H_2O(l)$	−285.8
Silver	
$Ag(s)$	0
$AgCl(s)$	−127.0
Sodium	
$Na(s)$	0
$Na(g)$	107.8
$NaCl(s)$	−411.1
Sulfur	
S_8(rhombic)	0
S_8(monoclinic)	0.3
$SO_2(g)$	−296.8
$SO_3(g)$	−396.0

6.6 • STANDARD ENTHALPIES OF REACTION (ΔH°_{rxn})

In this section, we see how Hess's law is used to determine the ΔH values of an enormous number of reactions. Thermodynamic variables, such as ΔH, vary somewhat with conditions. Therefore, in order to study and compare reactions, chemists have established a set of specific conditions called **standard states:**

- For a *gas,* the standard state is 1 atm* and ideal behavior.
- For a substance in *aqueous solution,* the standard state is 1 *M* concentration.
- For a *pure substance* (element or compound), the standard state is usually the most stable form of the substance at 1 atm and the temperature of interest. In this text (and in most thermodynamic tables), that temperature is usually 25°C (298 K).

The standard-state symbol (shown as a degree sign) indicates that the variable has been measured with *all the substances in their standard states.* For example, when the enthalpy change of a reaction is measured at the standard state, it is the **standard enthalpy of reaction, ΔH°_{rxn}** (also called *standard heat of reaction;* "rxn" stands for reaction).

Formation Equations and Their Standard Enthalpy Changes

In a **formation equation,** 1 mol of a compound forms from its elements. The **standard enthalpy of formation (ΔH°_f;** or *standard heat of formation*) is the enthalpy change for the formation equation when all the substances are in their standard states. For instance, the formation equation for methane (CH_4) is

$$C(graphite) + 2H_2(g) \longrightarrow CH_4(g) \quad \Delta H^\circ_f = -74.9 \text{ kJ}$$

Fractional coefficients are often used with reactants to obtain 1 mol of the product:

$$Na(s) + \tfrac{1}{2}Cl_2(g) \longrightarrow NaCl(s) \quad \Delta H^\circ_f = -411.1 \text{ kJ}$$

$$2C(graphite) + 3H_2(g) + \tfrac{1}{2}O_2(g) \longrightarrow C_2H_5OH(l) \quad \Delta H^\circ_f = -277.6 \text{ kJ}$$

Standard enthalpies of formation have been tabulated for many substances. Table 6.3 shows several, and a much more extensive table appears in Appendix B. The values in Table 6.3 make two points:

1. *For an element in its standard state, $\Delta H^\circ_f = 0$.*
   - The standard state for metals, like sodium, is the solid ($\Delta H^\circ_f = 0$); it takes 107.8 kJ of heat to form 1 mol of gaseous Na ($\Delta H^\circ_f = 107.8$ kJ/mol).
   - The standard state for molecular elements, such as the halogens, is the molecular form, not separate atoms: for Cl_2, $\Delta H^\circ_f = 0$, but for Cl, $\Delta H^\circ_f = 121.0$ kJ/mol.
   - Some elements exist in different forms (called *allotropes;* Chapter 14), but only one is the standard state. The standard state of carbon is graphite ($\Delta H^\circ_f = 0$), not diamond ($\Delta H^\circ_f = 1.9$ kJ/mol), the standard state of oxygen is O_2 ($\Delta H^\circ_f = 0$), not ozone (O_3; $\Delta H^\circ_f = 143$ kJ/mol), and the standard state of sulfur is S_8 in its rhombic crystal form ($\Delta H^\circ_f = 0$), not in its monoclinic form ($\Delta H^\circ_f = 0.3$ kJ/mol).
2. *Most compounds have a negative ΔH°_f.* That is, most compounds have exothermic formation reactions: *under standard conditions, heat is released when most compounds form from their elements.*

Sample Problem 6.9 Writing Formation Equations

Problem Write a balanced formation equation for each of the following and include the value of ΔH°_f:
(a) $AgCl(s)$ **(b)** $CaCO_3(s)$ **(c)** $HCN(g)$

Plan We write the elements as the reactants and 1 mol of the compound as the product, being sure all substances are in their standard states. Then, we balance the equations and find the ΔH°_f values in Table 6.3 or Appendix B.

*The definition of the standard state for gases has been changed to 1 bar, a slightly lower pressure than the 1 atm standard on which the data in this book are based (1 atm = 101.3 kPa = 1.013 bar). For most purposes, this makes very little difference in the standard enthalpy values.

Solution (a) $Ag(s) + \frac{1}{2}Cl_2(g) \longrightarrow AgCl(s) \quad \Delta H^\circ_f = -127.0\ kJ$

(b) $Ca(s) + C(graphite) + \frac{3}{2}O_2(g) \longrightarrow CaCO_3(s) \quad \Delta H^\circ_f = -1206.9\ kJ$

(c) $\frac{1}{2}H_2(g) + C(graphite) + \frac{1}{2}N_2(g) \longrightarrow HCN(g) \quad \Delta H^\circ_f = 135\ kJ$

Follow-Up Problem 6.9 Write a balanced formation equation for each of the following and include its ΔH°_f: **(a)** $CH_3OH(l)$, **(b)** $CaO(s)$, **(c)** $CS_2(l)$.

Determining ΔH°_{rxn} from ΔH°_f Values for Reactants and Products

We can use ΔH°_f values to determine ΔH°_{rxn} for any reaction. By applying Hess's law, we can imagine the reaction occurring in two steps (Figure 6.12):

Step 1. Each reactant decomposes to its elements. This is the *reverse* of the formation reaction for the *reactant,* so the standard enthalpy change is $-\Delta H^\circ_f$.

Step 2. Each product forms from its elements. This step *is* the formation reaction for the *product,* so the standard enthalpy change is ΔH°_f.

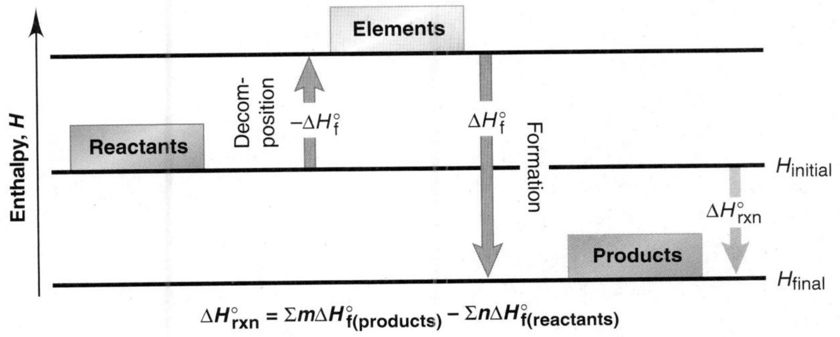

Figure 6.12 The two-step process for determining ΔH°_{rxn} from ΔH°_f values.

According to Hess's law, we add the enthalpy changes for these steps to obtain the overall enthalpy change for the reaction (ΔH°_{rxn}). Suppose we want ΔH°_{rxn} for

$$TiCl_4(l) + 2H_2O(g) \longrightarrow TiO_2(s) + 4HCl(g)$$

We write this equation as though it were the sum of four individual equations, one for each compound. The first two show step 1, the decomposition of the reactants to their elements (*reverse* of their formation); the second two show step 2, the formation of the products from their elements:

$$\begin{aligned} TiCl_4(l) &\longrightarrow Ti(s) + 2Cl_2(g) && -\Delta H^\circ_f[TiCl_4(l)] \\ 2H_2O(g) &\longrightarrow 2H_2(g) + O_2(g) && -2\Delta H^\circ_f[H_2O(g)] \\ Ti(s) + O_2(g) &\longrightarrow TiO_2(s) && \Delta H^\circ_f[TiO_2(s)] \\ 2H_2(g) + 2Cl_2(g) &\longrightarrow 4HCl(g) && 4\Delta H^\circ_f[HCl(g)] \end{aligned}$$

$$TiCl_4(l) + 2H_2O(g) + \cancel{Ti(s)} + \cancel{O_2(g)} + \cancel{2H_2(g)} + \cancel{2Cl_2(g)} \longrightarrow \cancel{Ti(s)} + \cancel{2Cl_2(g)} + \cancel{2H_2(g)} + \cancel{O_2(g)} + TiO_2(s) + 4HCl(g)$$

or

$$TiCl_4(l) + 2H_2O(g) \longrightarrow TiO_2(s) + 4HCl(g)$$

It's important to realize that when titanium(IV) chloride and water react, the reactants don't *actually* decompose to their elements, which then recombine to form the products. But the great usefulness of Hess's law and the state-function concept is that ΔH°_{rxn} is the difference between two state functions, $H^\circ_{products}$ minus $H^\circ_{reactants}$, so it doesn't matter how the reaction *actually* occurs. We add the individual enthalpy changes to find ΔH°_{rxn}:

$$\begin{aligned} \Delta H^\circ_{rxn} &= \Delta H^\circ_f[TiO_2(s)] + 4\Delta H^\circ_f[HCl(g)] + \{-\Delta H^\circ_f[TiCl_4(l)]\} + \{-2\Delta H^\circ_f[H_2O(g)]\} \\ &= \underbrace{\{\Delta H^\circ_f[TiO_2(s)] + 4\Delta H^\circ_f[HCl(g)]\}}_{\text{Products}} - \underbrace{\{\Delta H^\circ_f[TiCl_4(l)] + 2\Delta H^\circ_f[H_2O(g)]\}}_{\text{Reactants}} \end{aligned}$$

The arithmetic in this case gives $\Delta H^\circ_{rxn} = -25.39$ kJ, but more importantly, when we generalize the pattern, we see that *the standard enthalpy of reaction is the sum of the standard enthalpies of formation of the* ***products*** *minus the sum of the standard enthalpies of formation of the* ***reactants*** (see Figure 6.12):

$$\Delta H^\circ_{rxn} = \Sigma m\Delta H^\circ_{f\,(products)} - \Sigma n\Delta H^\circ_{f\,(reactants)} \quad (6.9)$$

where Σ means "sum of," and m and n are the amounts (mol) of the products and reactants given by the coefficients in the balanced equation.

Sample Problem 6.10 Calculating ΔH°_{rxn} from ΔH°_f Values

Problem Nitric acid is used to make many products, including fertilizers, dyes, and explosives. The first step in its production is the oxidation of ammonia:

$$4NH_3(g) + 5O_2(g) \longrightarrow 4NO(g) + 6H_2O(g)$$

Calculate ΔH°_{rxn} from ΔH°_f values.

Plan We use values from Table 6.3 (or Appendix B) and apply Equation 6.9.

Solution Calculating ΔH°_{rxn}:

$$\begin{aligned}\Delta H^\circ_{rxn} &= \Sigma m\Delta H^\circ_{f\,(products)} - \Sigma n\Delta H^\circ_{f\,(reactants)}\\ &= \{4\Delta H^\circ_f[NO(g)] + 6\Delta H^\circ_f[H_2O(g)]\} - \{4\Delta H^\circ_f[NH_3(g)] + 5\Delta H^\circ_f[O_2(g)]\}\\ &= (4\text{ mol})(90.3\text{ kJ/mol}) + (6\text{ mol})(-241.8\text{ kJ/mol})\\ &\quad -[(4\text{ mol})(-45.9\text{ kJ/mol}) + (5\text{ mol})(0\text{ kJ/mol})]\\ &= 361\text{ kJ} - 1451\text{ kJ} + 184\text{ kJ} - 0\text{ kJ} = -906\text{ kJ}\end{aligned}$$

Check We write formation equations, with ΔH°_f values for the amounts of each compound, in the correct direction (forward for products and reverse for reactants) and find the sum:

$$\begin{array}{lll} 4NH_3(g) \longrightarrow \cancel{2N_2(g)} + \cancel{6H_2(g)} & -4\Delta H^\circ_f = -4(-45.9\text{ kJ}) = & 184\text{ kJ}\\ \cancel{2N_2(g)} + 2O_2(g) \longrightarrow 4NO(g) & 4\Delta H^\circ_f = 4(90.3\text{ kJ}) = & 361\text{ kJ}\\ \cancel{6H_2(g)} + 3O_2(g) \longrightarrow 6H_2O(g) & 6\Delta H^\circ_f = 6(-241.8\text{ kJ}) = & -1451\text{ kJ}\\ \hline 4NH_3(g) + 5O_2(g) \longrightarrow 4NO(g) + 6H_2O(g) & \Delta H^\circ_{rxn} = & -906\text{ kJ}\end{array}$$

Comment In this problem, we know the individual ΔH°_f values and find the sum, ΔH°_{rxn}. In the follow-up problem, we know the sum and want to find one of the ΔH°_f values.

Follow-Up Problem 6.10 Use the following to find ΔH°_f of methanol [$CH_3OH(l)$]:

$$CH_3OH(l) + \tfrac{3}{2}O_2(g) \longrightarrow CO_2(g) + 2H_2O(g) \quad \Delta H^\circ_{rxn} = -638.5\text{ kJ}$$

$$\Delta H^\circ_f \text{ of } CO_2(g) = -393.5\text{ kJ/mol}$$

$$\Delta H^\circ_f \text{ of } H_2O(g) = -241.8\text{ kJ/mol}$$

The Chemical Connections essay applies ideas from this chapter to new approaches for energy utilization.

Summary of Section 6.6

- Standard states are a set of specific conditions used for determining thermodynamic variables for all substances.
- When 1 mol of a compound forms from its elements with all substances in their standard states, the enthalpy change is the standard enthalpy of formation, ΔH°_f.
- Hess's law allows us to picture a reaction as the decomposition of the reactants to their elements followed by the formation of the products from their elements.
- We use tabulated ΔH°_f values to find ΔH°_{rxn} or use known ΔH°_{rxn} and ΔH°_f values to find an unknown ΔH°_f.
- Because of major concerns about climate change, chemists are developing energy alternatives, including coal and biomass conversion, hydrogen fuel, and noncombustible energy sources.

CHEMICAL CONNECTIONS TO ENVIRONMENTAL SCIENCE | The Future of Energy Use

Out of necessity, we must rethink our global use of energy. The dwindling supplies of our most common fuels and the environmental impact of their combustion products threaten human well-being and the survival of many other species. Energy production presents scientists, engineers, and political leaders with some of the greatest challenges of our time.

A changeover in energy sources from wood to coal and then petroleum took place over the past century. The **fossil fuels**—coal, petroleum, and natural gas—remain our major sources, but they are *nonrenewable* because natural processes form them many orders of magnitude slower than we consume them. In the United States, ongoing research seeks new approaches to using coal and nuclear energy, and utilizing *renewable* sources—biomass, hydrogen, sunlight, wind, geothermal heat, and tides—is the subject of intensive efforts as well.

In this discussion, we focus on converting coal and biomass to cleaner fuels, understanding the effect of carbon-based fuels on climate, developing hydrogen as a fuel, utilizing solar energy, and conserving energy.

Converting Coal to Cleaner Fuels U.S. reserves of coal are enormous, but the burning of coal, in addition to forming CO_2, produces SO_2 and particulates, and releases mercury. Exposure to SO_2 and particulates causes respiratory disease, and SO_2 can be oxidized to H_2SO_4, the key component of acid rain (Chapter 19). The trace amounts of Hg, a neurotoxin, spread as Hg vapor and bioaccumulate in fish.

Two processes reduce the amounts of SO_2:

Desulfurization. The removal of sulfur dioxide from flue gases is done with devices called *scrubbers* that heat powdered limestone ($CaCO_3$) or spray lime-water slurries [$Ca(OH)_2$]:

$$CaCO_3(s) + SO_2(g) \xrightarrow{\Delta} CaSO_3(s) + CO_2(g)$$
$$2CaSO_3(s) + O_2(g) + 4H_2O(l) \longrightarrow 2CaSO_4\cdot 2H_2O(s; \text{gypsum})$$
$$2Ca(OH)_2(aq) + 2SO_2(g) + O_2(g) + 2H_2O(l) \longrightarrow 2CaSO_4\cdot 2H_2O(s)$$

A wallboard (drywall) plant built next to the power plant sells the gypsum (1 ton per customer each year); about 20% of the drywall produced each year is made with synthetic gypsum.

Gasification. In **coal gasification,** solid coal is converted to sulfur-free gaseous fuels. In this process, the sulfur in the coal is reduced to H_2S, which is removed through an acid-base reaction with a base, such as ethanolamine ($HOCH_2CH_2NH_2$). The resulting salt is heated to release H_2S, which is converted to elemental sulfur by the Claus process (Chapter 22) and sold. Several reactions yield mixtures with increasing fuel value, that is, with a lower C/H ratio:

- Pulverized coal reacts with limited O_2 and water at 800–1500°C to form approximately a 2/1 mixture of CO/H_2.
- Alternatively, in the *water-gas reaction* (or *steam-carbon reaction*), an exothermic oxidation of C to CO is followed by the endothermic reaction of C with steam to form a nearly 1/1 mixture of CO/H_2 called *water gas:*

$$C(s) + \tfrac{1}{2}O_2(g) \longrightarrow CO(g) \qquad \Delta H^\circ_{rxn} = -110\text{ kJ}$$
$$C(s) + H_2O(g) \longrightarrow CO(g) + H_2(g) \qquad \Delta H^\circ_{rxn} = 131\text{ kJ}$$

However, water gas has a much lower fuel value than methane (CH_4). For example, a mixture of 0.5 mol of CO and 0.5 mol of H_2 releases about one-third as much energy as 1.0 mol of methane ($\Delta H = -802$ kJ/mol):

$$\tfrac{1}{2}H_2(g) + \tfrac{1}{4}O_2(g) \longrightarrow \tfrac{1}{2}H_2O(g) \qquad \Delta H^\circ_{rxn} = -121\text{ kJ}$$
$$\tfrac{1}{2}CO(g) + \tfrac{1}{4}O_2(g) \longrightarrow \tfrac{1}{2}CO_2(g) \qquad \Delta H^\circ_{rxn} = -142\text{ kJ}$$
$$\tfrac{1}{2}H_2(g) + \tfrac{1}{2}CO(g) + \tfrac{1}{2}O_2(g) \longrightarrow \tfrac{1}{2}H_2O(g) + \tfrac{1}{2}CO_2(g) \qquad \Delta H^\circ_{rxn} = -263\text{ kJ}$$

- In the *CO-shift* (or *water-gas shift*) reaction, the H_2 content of water gas is increased to produce synthesis gas (*syngas*):

$$CO(g) + H_2O(g) \longrightarrow CO_2(g) + H_2(g) \qquad \Delta H^\circ_{rxn} = -41\text{ kJ}$$

- To produce CH_4, a syngas that is a 3/1 mixture of H_2/CO from which the CO_2 has been removed, is employed:

$$CO(g) + 3H_2(g) \longrightarrow CH_4(g) + H_2O(g) \qquad \Delta H^\circ_{rxn} = -206\text{ kJ}$$

Drying the product gives **synthetic natural gas (SNG).**

Syngas is used is some newer methods as well. In *integrated gasification combined cycle (IGCC),* electricity is produced in two ways—when syngas is burned in a combustion turbine and when the hot product gases generate steam to power a steam turbine. In the *Fischer-Tropsch process,* syngas is used to form liquid hydrocarbon fuels that have higher molar masses than methane:

$$nCO(g) + (2n + 1)H_2(g) \longrightarrow C_nH_{2n+2}(l) + nH_2O(g)$$

Converting Biomass to Fuels Nearly half the world's people rely on wood for energy. In principle, wood is renewable, but widespread deforestation has resulted from its use for fuel, lumber, and paper. Therefore, great emphasis has been placed on **biomass conversion** of vegetable and animal waste. In one process, chemical and/or microbial methods convert vegetable (sugarcane, corn, switchgrass) and tree waste into fuel, mainly ethanol (C_2H_5OH). In the United States, ethanol is mixed with gasoline to form *gasohol;* in Brazil, it substitutes directly for gasoline.

Methanogenesis forms methane by anaerobic (oxygen-free) biodegradation of organic sources such as manure and vegetable waste or wastewater. China's biogas-generating facilities apply this technique, and similar ones in the U.S. use garbage and sewage. In addition to producing methane, the process yields residues that improve soil; it also prevents the wastes from polluting natural waters.

Another biomass conversion process changes vegetable oils (soybean, cottonseed, sunflower, canola, and even used cooking oil) into a mixture called *biodiesel,* whose combustion produces less CO, SO_2, and particulate matter than fossil-fuel-based diesel. The CO_2 produced in combustion of biodiesel has minimal impact on the net atmospheric amount because the carbon is taken up by the plants grown as sources of the vegetable oils.

The Greenhouse Effect and Global Warming Combustion of all carbon-based fuels releases CO_2, and over the past two decades, it has become clear that the atmospheric buildup of this gas from our increased use of these fuels is changing the climate. Throughout Earth's history, CO_2 has played a key

(continued)

temperature-regulating role in the atmosphere. Much of the sunlight that shines on Earth is absorbed by the land and oceans and converted to heat (IR radiation; Figure B6.1). Like the glass of a greenhouse, CO_2 does not absorb visible light from the Sun, but it absorbs and re-emits some of the heat radiating from Earth's surface and, thus, helps warm the atmosphere. This process is called the *natural greenhouse effect* (Figure B6.1, *left*).

Over several billion years, due to the spread of plant life, which uses CO_2 in photosynthesis, the amount of CO_2 originally present (from volcanic activity) decreased to 0.028% by volume. With this amount, Earth's average temperature was about 14°C (57°F); without CO_2, it would be −17°C (2°F)! However, as a result of intensive use of fossil fuels for the past 150 years, this amount increased to 0.039%. Thus, although the same quantity of solar energy passes through the atmosphere, more is being trapped as heat, which has created an *enhanced greenhouse effect* that is changing the climate through *global warming* (Figure B6.1, *right*). Based on current trends, CO_2 amounts will increase to between 0.049% and 0.126% by 2100 (Figure B6.2).

If this projected increase in CO_2 occurs, two closely related questions arise: (1) How much will the temperature rise? (2) How will this rise affect life on Earth? Despite constantly improving models, answers are difficult to obtain. Natural fluctuations in temperature must be taken into account, as well as cyclic changes in solar activity. Moreover, as the amount of CO_2 increases from fossil-fuel burning, so do the amounts of particulate matter and SO_2, which may block sunlight and have a cooling effect. Water vapor also traps heat, and as temperatures rise, more water evaporates. The increased amounts of water vapor may thicken the cloud cover and lead to cooling as well.

Despite such opposing factors, all of the best models predict net warming, and scientists are observing the effects. The average temperature has increased by 0.6±0.2°C since the late 19th century and 0.2–0.3°C over the past 25 years. Globally, the decade from 2001 to 2010 was the warmest on record. Snow cover and glacial size in the northern hemisphere and floating ice in the Arctic Ocean have decreased dramatically. Antarctica is also experiencing widespread breakup of icebound regions. Globally, sea level has risen an average of 17 cm (6.7 in) over the past century, and flooding and other extreme weather events have increased.

Fifteen years ago, the best models predicted a temperature rise of 1.0–3.5°C; today, their predictions are more than 50% higher. Such increases would alter rainfall patterns and crop yields throughout the world and increase sea level as much as 1 meter, thus flooding regions such as the Netherlands, half of Florida, much of southern Asia, coastal New England and New York, and many Pacific island nations. To make matters worse, as we burn fossil fuels that *release* CO_2, we cut down forests that *absorb* it.

In addition to ways to reduce fossil-fuel consumption, researchers are studying methods of *carbon capture and storage (CCS)*, including *CO_2 sequestration,* both naturally by maintaining forests and jungles and industrially by liquefying CO_2 formed and either burying it underground or using it to produce mineral carbonates.

The 1997 United Nations Conference on Climate Change in Kyoto, Japan, created a treaty with legally binding targets to limit greenhouse gases. It was ratified by 189 countries, but not by the United States, the largest emitter. The 2009 conference in Copenhagen, Denmark, was attended by representatives from 192 countries (including the U.S.), but did not result in legally binding emission targets or financial commitments.

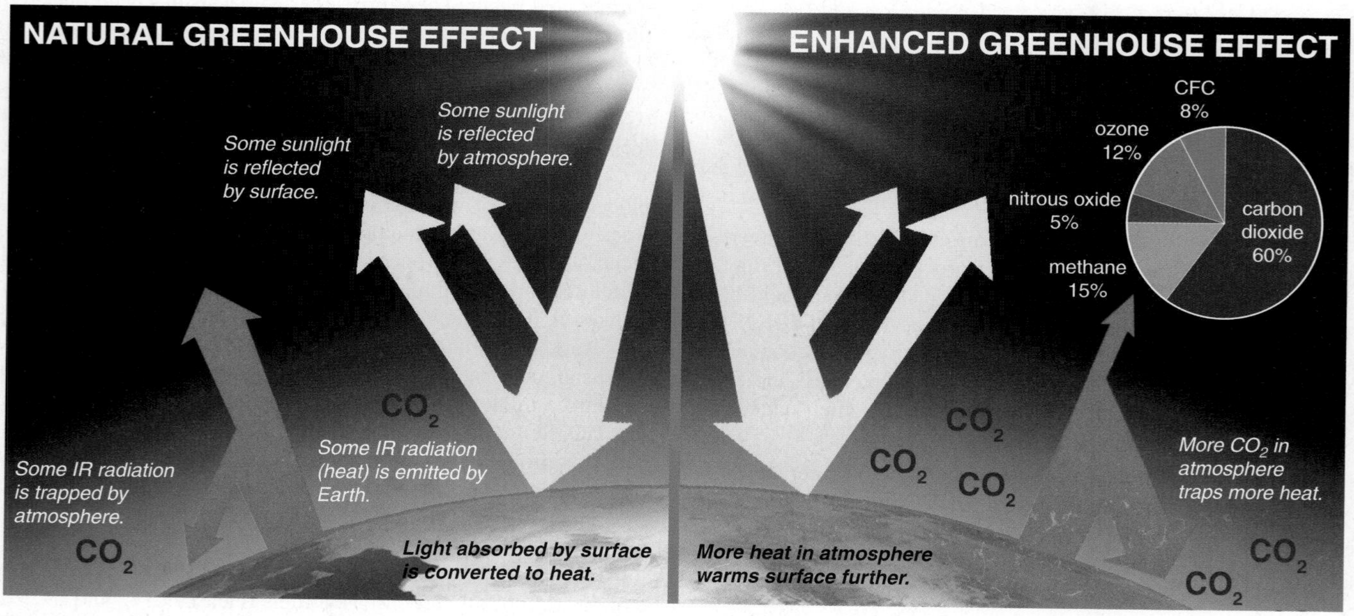

Figure B6.1 The trapping of heat by the atmosphere. Of the total sunlight reaching Earth, some is reflected and some is absorbed and converted to IR radiation (heat). Some heat emitted by the surface is trapped by atmospheric CO_2, creating a *natural* greenhouse effect (*left*) that has been essential to life. But, largely as a result of human activity in the past 150 years, and especially the past several decades, the buildup of CO_2 and several other greenhouse gases (*pie chart*) has created an *enhanced* greenhouse effect (*right*).

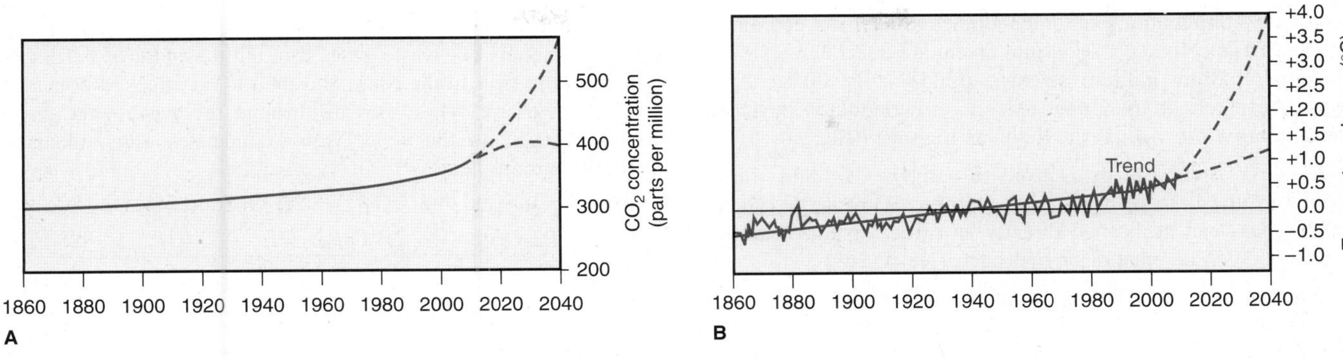

Figure B6.2 **Evidence for the enhanced greenhouse effect.** **A,** Since the mid-19th century, atmospheric CO_2 has increased. **B,** Since the mid-19th century, average global temperature has risen 0.6°C. (Zero is the average from 1957 to 1970.) The projections in the graphs (*dashed lines*) assume that current fossil fuel consumption and deforestation continue (*upper line*) or slow (*lower line*).

Hydrogen The use of H_2 as an energy source holds great promise but presents several problems. The simplest element and most plentiful gas in the universe always occurs on Earth in compounds, most importantly with oxygen in water and carbon in hydrocarbons. Once freed, however, H_2 is an excellent energy source because of several properties:

- It has the highest energy content per *mass* unit of any fuel—nearly three times as much as gasoline.
- Its energy content per *volume* unit is low at STP but increases greatly when the H_2 is liquefied under extremely high P and low T.
- Its combustion does not produce CO_2, particulates, or sulfur oxides. It is such a clean energy source that H_2-fuel cells operate electrical systems aboard the space shuttles, and the crews drink the pure water product.

A hydrogen-based economy is the dream of many because, even though combustion of H_2 ($\Delta H^\circ_{rxn} = -242$ kJ/mol) produces less than one-third as much energy per mole as combustion of CH_4 ($\Delta H^\circ_{rxn} = -802$ kJ/mol), it yields nonpolluting water vapor. The keys to realizing the dream, however, involve major improvements in both production of H_2 and its transportation and storage.

Production of H_2. Hydrogen is produced by a number of methods, some more widely used than others.

- *Fossil-fuel byproduct.* In the United States today, almost all H_2 is produced by the *steam-reforming process,* in which methane or natural gas is treated with steam in high-temperature reactions (Chapter 22).
- *Electrolysis of liquid water.* Formation of H_2 from the decomposition of liquid water is endothermic ($\Delta H^\circ_{rxn} = 286$ kJ/mol), and most direct methods that utilize electricity are costly. However, energy from flowing water, wind, and geothermal sources can provide the needed electricity. An exciting new *photoelectrochemical approach* uses a photovoltaic panel coupled to an electrolysis unit: the energy of sunlight powers the decomposition of water.
- *Biological methods.* Green algae and cyanobacteria store the energy of sunlight in the form of starch or glycogen for their own metabolism. Under certain conditions, however, these microbes can be made to produce H_2 gas instead of these large organic molecules. For example, eliminating sulfur from the diet of green algae activates a long dormant gene and the cells produce H_2. But, major improvements in yields are needed to make this method cost-effective.

Transportation and storage of H_2. The absence of an infrastructure for transporting and storing large quantities of hydrogen is still a roadblock to realizing a hydrogen-based economy. Currently, the cost of energy to cool and compress the gas to liquefy it is very high. Hydrogen is carried in pipelines, but its ability to escape through metals and make them brittle requires more expensive piping. Storage in the form of solid metal hydrides has been explored, but heating the hydrides to release the stored hydrogen requires energy. Use of H_2 in fuel cells is a major area of electrochemical research (Chapter 21). Tests are underway to commercialize fuel-cell technology using the hydrogen that is a byproduct of the petrochemical and coal industries.

Solar Energy The Sun's energy drives global winds and ocean currents, the cycle of evaporation and condensation, and many biological processes, especially photosynthesis. More energy falls on Earth's surface as sunlight in 1 h [1.2×10^5 TW (terawatts); 1 TW = 1×10^{12} W] than is used in all human activity in 1 year. Solar energy is, however, a dilute source (only 1 kW/m^2 at noon); in 1 h, about 600–1000 TW strikes land at sites suitable for collecting. Nevertheless, covering 0.16% of that land with today's photovoltaic systems would provide 20 TW/h, equivalent to the output of 20,000 nuclear power plants producing 1 GW (gigawatt) each. Clearly, solar energy is the largest carbon-free option among renewable sources.

Three important ways to utilize solar energy are with electronic materials, biomass, and thermal systems:

Electronic materials. A **photovoltaic cell** converts sunlight directly into electricity by employing certain combinations of elements (usually metalloids; we discuss the behavior of elements with *semiconductor* properties in Chapter 12). Early cells relied primarily on crystalline silicon, but their *yield,* the proportion of electrical energy produced relative to the radiant energy supplied, was only about 10%. More recent devices have achieved much higher yields by using thin films of polycrystalline materials that

(continued)

incorporate combinations of other elements, such as cadmium telluride (CdTe cells, 16%), gallium arsenide (GaAs cells, 18%), and copper indium gallium selenide (CIGS cells, 20%). And ongoing research on nanometer-sized semiconductor devices, called *quantum dots,* suggests yields as high as 70%.

Biomass. Solar energy is used to convert CO_2 and water via photosynthesis to plant material (carbohydrate) and oxygen. Plant biomass can be burned directly as a fuel or converted to other fuels, such as ethanol or hydrogen (see p. 249).

Thermal systems. The operation of a photovoltaic cell creates a buildup of heat, which lowers its efficiency. A *photovoltaic thermal (PVT) hybrid cell* thus combines such a cell with conductive metal piping (filled with water or antifreeze) that transfers the heat from the cell to a domestic hot-water system.

Because sunlight is typically available only 6 to 8 hours a day and is greatly reduced in cloudy weather, another thermal system focuses on storing solar energy during the day and releasing it at night. When an ionic hydrate, such as $Na_2SO_4 \cdot 10H_2O$, is warmed by sunlight to over 32°C, the 3 mol of ions dissolve in the 10 mol of water in an endothermic process:

$$Na_2SO_4(aq) \cdot 10H_2O(s) \xrightarrow{>32°C} Na_2SO_4(aq) \qquad \Delta H^\circ_{rxn} = 354 \text{ kJ}$$

When cooled below 32°C after sunset, the solution recrystallizes, releasing the absorbed energy for heating:

$$Na_2SO_4(aq) \xrightarrow{<32°C} Na_2SO_4(aq) \cdot 10H_2O(s) \qquad \Delta H^\circ_{rxn} = -354 \text{ kJ}$$

Unfortunately, as of the end of the first decade of the 21st century, solar energy is not yet competitive with highly subsidized fossil fuels. Nevertheless, changes in economic policy as well as improvements in photovoltaic technology and biomass processing should greatly increase solar energy's contribution to a carbon-free energy future.

Nuclear Energy Despite ongoing problems with disposal of radioactive waste, energy from nuclear *fission*—the splitting of large, unstable atomic nuclei—is used extensively, especially in France and other parts of northern Europe. Nuclear *fusion*—the combining of small atomic nuclei—avoids the problems of fission but has been achieved so far only with a net consumption of power. (We'll discuss these processes in detail in Chapter 24.)

Energy Conservation: More from Less All systems, whether organisms or factories, waste energy, which is, in effect, a waste of fuel. For example, the production of one aluminum beverage can requires energy equivalent to burning 0.25 L of gasoline. Energy conservation lowers costs, extends our fuel supply, and reduces the effects of climate change. Following are three examples of conservation.

Passive solar design. Heating and cooling costs can be reduced by as much as 50% when buildings are constructed with large windows and materials that absorb the Sun's heat in the day and release it slowly at night.

Residential heating systems. A high-efficiency gas-burning furnace channels hot waste gases through a system of baffles to transfer more heat to the room and then to an attached domestic hot-water system. While moving through the system, the gases cool to 100°C, so the water vapor condenses, thus releasing about 10% more heat:

$$CH_4(g) + 2O_2(g) \longrightarrow CO_2(g) + 2H_2O(g) \qquad \Delta H^\circ_{rxn} = -802 \text{ kJ}$$
$$2H_2O(g) \longrightarrow 2H_2O(l) \qquad \Delta H^\circ_{rxn} = -88 \text{ kJ}$$
$$CH_4(g) + 2O_2(g) \longrightarrow CO_2(g) + 2H_2O(l) \qquad \Delta H^\circ_{rxn} = -890 \text{ kJ}$$

Modern lighting. Incandescent bulbs give off light when the material in their filament reaches a high temperature. They are very inefficient because less than 7% of the electrical energy is converted to light, the rest being wasted as heat. *Compact fluorescent lamps (CFLs)* have an efficiency of about 18% and are having a major economic impact: in many parts of Europe, incandescent bulbs are no longer sold. *Light-emitting diodes (LEDs)* are even more efficient (about 30%) and are already being used in car indicator lamps and tail lights. Light-emitting devices based on organic semiconductors (OLEDs) are used in flat-panel displays, and recent use of Al-In-Ga-P materials and Ga and In nitrides in LEDs has increased brightness and improved color richness. Over 20% of electricity generated in the U.S. is used for lighting, and burning of fossil fuels in power plants creates smog, particulates, and CO_2. By 2020, use of these devices for lighting can cut electricity usage by 50%, eliminating the emission of 2.8×10^7 metric tons of carbon per year.

Engineers and chemists will continue to explore alternatives for energy production and use, but a more hopeful energy future ultimately depends on our dedication to conserving planetary resources.

Problems

B6.1 To make use of an ionic hydrate for storing solar energy, you place 500.0 kg of sodium sulfate decahydrate on your house roof. Assuming complete reaction and 100% efficiency of heat transfer, how much heat (in kJ) is released to your house at night?

B6.2 In one step of coal gasification, coal reacts with superheated steam:

$$C(coal) + H_2O(g) \longrightarrow CO(g) + H_2(g) \qquad \Delta H^\circ_{rxn} = 129.7 \text{ kJ}$$

(a) Use this reaction and the following two to write an overall reaction for the production of methane:

$$CO(g) + H_2O(g) \longrightarrow CO_2(g) + H_2(g) \qquad \Delta H^\circ_{rxn} = -41 \text{ kJ}$$
$$CO(g) + 3H_2(g) \longrightarrow CH_4(g) + H_2O(g) \qquad \Delta H^\circ_{rxn} = -206 \text{ kJ}$$

(b) Calculate ΔH°_{rxn} for this overall change.

(c) Using the value from part (b) and a calculated value of ΔH°_{rxn} for the combustion of methane, find the total ΔH for gasifying 1.00 kg of coal and burning the methane formed (assume water forms as a gas and $\mathcal{M}$ of coal = 12.00 g/mol).

CHAPTER REVIEW GUIDE

Learning Objectives

Relevant section (§) and/or sample problem (SP) numbers appear in parentheses.

Understand These Concepts

1. The distinction between a system and its surroundings (§6.1)
2. The transfer of energy to or from a system as heat and/or work (§6.1)
3. The relation of internal energy change, heat, and work (§6.1)
4. The meaning of energy conservation (§6.1)
5. The meaning of a state function and why ΔE is constant even though q and w vary (§6.1)
6. The meaning of enthalpy and the relation between ΔE and ΔH (§6.2)
7. The meaning of ΔH and the distinction between exothermic and endothermic reactions (§6.2)
8. The relation between specific heat capacity and heat (§6.3)
9. How constant-pressure (coffee-cup) and constant-volume (bomb) calorimeters work (§6.3)
10. The relation between ΔH and amount of substance (§6.4)
11. The calculation of ΔH values with Hess's law (§6.5)
12. The meaning of a formation equation and the standard enthalpy of formation (§6.6)
13. How a reaction can be viewed as the decomposition of reactants followed by the formation of products (§6.6)

Master These Skills

1. Determining the change in a system's internal energy in different units (SP 6.1)
2. Drawing enthalpy diagrams for chemical and physical changes (SP 6.2)
3. Solving problems involving specific heat capacity and heat transferred in a reaction (SPs 6.3–6.6)
4. Relating the heat transferred in a reaction to the amounts of substances changing (SP 6.7)
5. Using Hess's law to find an unknown ΔH (SP 6.8)
6. Writing formation equations and using ΔH°_f values to find ΔH°_{rxn} (SPs 6.9, 6.10)

Key Terms

Page numbers appear in parentheses.

thermodynamics (229)
thermochemistry (229)

Section 6.1
system (230)
surroundings (230)
internal energy (E) (230)
heat (q) (230)
work (w) (231)
law of conservation of energy (first law of thermodynamics) (233)
joule (J) (233)
calorie (cal) (233)
state function (234)

Section 6.2
pressure-volume work (PV work) (235)
enthalpy (H) (235)
change in enthalpy (ΔH) (235)
exothermic process (236)
enthalpy diagram (237)
endothermic process (237)

Section 6.3
heat capacity (238)
specific heat capacity (c) (238)
molar heat capacity (C) (238)
calorimeter (239)

Section 6.4
thermochemical equation (242)

Section 6.5
Hess's law (244)

Section 6.6
standard state (246)
standard enthalpy of reaction (ΔH°_{rxn}) (246)
formation equation (246)
standard enthalpy of formation (ΔH°_f) (246)
fossil fuel (249)
coal gasification (249)
synthetic natural gas (SNG) (249)
biomass conversion (249)
methanogenesis (249)
photovoltaic cell (251)

Key Equations and Relationships

Page numbers appear in parentheses.

6.1 Defining the change in internal energy (230):

$$\Delta E = E_{final} - E_{initial} = E_{products} - E_{reactants}$$

6.2 Expressing the change in internal energy in terms of heat and work (231):

$$\Delta E = q + w$$

6.3 Stating the first law of thermodynamics (law of conservation of energy) (233):

$$\Delta E_{universe} = \Delta E_{system} + \Delta E_{surroundings} = 0$$

6.4 Determining the work due to a change in volume at constant pressure (PV work) (235):

$$w = -P\Delta V$$

6.5 Relating the enthalpy change to the internal energy change at constant pressure (235):

$$\Delta H = \Delta E + P\Delta V$$

6.6 Identifying the enthalpy change with the heat absorbed or released at constant pressure (236):

$$q_P = \Delta E + P\Delta V = \Delta H$$

6.7 Calculating the heat absorbed or released when a substance undergoes a temperature change or a reaction occurs (238):

$$q = c \times \text{mass} \times \Delta T$$

6.8 Calculating the overall enthalpy change of a reaction (Hess's law) (244):

$$\Delta H_{overall} = \Delta H_1 + \Delta H_2 + \cdots + \Delta H_n$$

6.9 Calculating the standard enthalpy of reaction (248):

$$\Delta H^\circ_{rxn} = \Sigma m\Delta H^\circ_{f\,(products)} - \Sigma n\Delta H^\circ_{f\,(reactants)}$$

Brief Solutions to Follow-Up Problems

6.1 $\Delta E = q + w$

$$= \left(-26.0\text{ kcal} \times \frac{4.184\text{ kJ}}{1\text{ kcal}}\right) + \left(15.0\text{ Btu} \times \frac{1.055\text{ kJ}}{1\text{ Btu}}\right)$$

$$= -93\text{ kJ}$$

6.2 The reaction is exothermic.

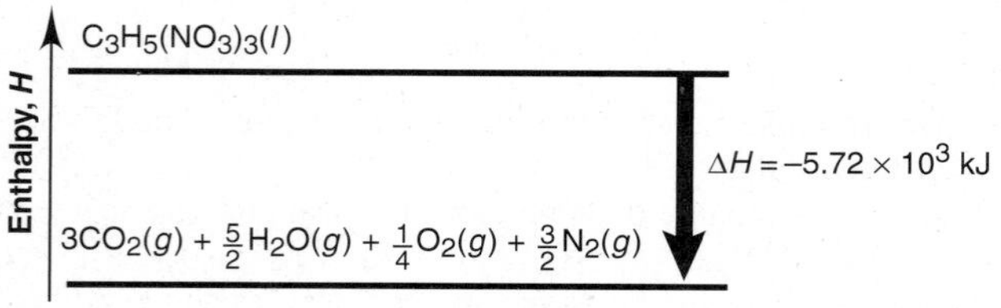

6.3 $\Delta T = 25.0°\text{C} - 37.0°\text{C} = -12.0°\text{C} = -12.0\text{ K}$

$$\text{Mass (g)} = 1.11\text{ g/mL} \times \frac{1000\text{ mL}}{1\text{ L}} \times 5.50\text{ L} = 6.10\times10^3\text{ g}$$

$$q = c \times \text{mass} \times \Delta T$$

$$= (2.42\text{ J/g·K})\left(\frac{1\text{ kJ}}{1000\text{ J}}\right)(6.10\times10^3\text{ g})(-12.0\text{ K}) = -177\text{ kJ}$$

6.4 $$c_{\text{solid}} = -\frac{4.184\text{ J/g·K} \times 25.00\text{ g} \times 1.70\text{ K}}{12.18\text{ g} \times (-37.75\text{ K})} = 0.387\text{ J/g·K}$$

From Table 6.2, the metal is copper.

6.5 $2HCl(aq) + Ba(OH)_2(aq) \longrightarrow 2H_2O(l) + BaCl_2(aq)$

Amount (mol) of HCl = 0.500 mol HCl/L × 0.0500 L = 0.0250 mol HCl

Similarly, we have 0.0250 mol $BaCl_2$.

Finding the limiting reactant from the balanced equation:

$$\text{Amount (mol) of } H_2O = 0.0250\text{ mol HCl} \times \frac{2\text{ mol } H_2O}{2\text{ mol HCl}}$$

$$= 0.0250\text{ mol } H_2O$$

$$\text{Amount (mol) of } H_2O = 0.0250\text{ mol } Ba(OH)_2 \times \frac{2\text{ mol } H_2O}{1\text{ mol } Ba(OH)_2}$$

$$= 0.0500\text{ mol } H_2O$$

Thus, HCl is limiting.

$$\Delta H\text{ (kJ/mol } H_2O) = \frac{q_{\text{rxn}}}{\text{mol } H_2O} = \frac{-1.386\text{ kJ}}{0.0250\text{ mol } H_2O}$$

$$= -55.4\text{ kJ/mol } H_2O$$

6.6

$$-q_{\text{sample}} = q_{\text{calorimeter}}$$

$$-(0.8650\text{ g C})\left(\frac{1\text{ mol C}}{12.01\text{ g C}}\right)(-393.5\text{ kJ/mol C}) = (2.613\text{ K})x$$

$$x = 10.85\text{ kJ/K}$$

6.7 $C_2H_4(g) + H_2(g) \longrightarrow C_2H_6(g) + 137\text{ kJ}$

$$\text{Heat (kJ)} = 15.0\text{ kg} \times \frac{1000\text{ g}}{1\text{ kg}} \times \frac{1\text{ mol } C_2H_6}{30.07\text{ g } C_2H_6} \times \frac{137\text{ kJ}}{1\text{ mol}}$$

$$= 6.83\times10^4\text{ kJ}$$

6.8

$$2NO(g) + \tfrac{3}{2}O_2(g) \longrightarrow N_2O_5(s) \qquad \Delta H = -223.7\text{ kJ}$$

$$2NO_2(g) \longrightarrow 2NO(g) + O_2(g) \qquad \Delta H = 114.2\text{ kJ}$$

$$\cancel{2NO(g)} + \tfrac{1}{2}\cancel{\tfrac{3}{2}}O_2(g) + 2NO_2(g) \longrightarrow N_2O_5(s) + \cancel{2NO(g)} + \cancel{O_2(g)}$$

$$2NO_2(g) + \tfrac{1}{2}O_2(g) \longrightarrow N_2O_5(s) \qquad \Delta H = -109.5\text{ kJ}$$

6.9 (a) $C(\text{graphite}) + 2H_2(g) + \tfrac{1}{2}O_2(g) \longrightarrow CH_3OH(l)$ $\quad \Delta H_f^\circ = -238.6\text{ kJ}$

(b) $Ca(s) + \tfrac{1}{2}O_2(g) \longrightarrow CaO(s) \quad \Delta H_f^\circ = -635.1\text{ kJ}$

(c) $C(\text{graphite}) + \tfrac{1}{4}S_8(\text{rhombic}) \longrightarrow CS_2(l) \quad \Delta H_f^\circ = 87.9\text{ kJ}$

6.10 ΔH_f° of $CH_3OH(l)$

$$= -\Delta H_{\text{rxn}}^\circ + 2\Delta H_f^\circ[H_2O(g)] + \Delta H_f^\circ[CO_2(g)]$$

$$= 638.5\text{ kJ} + (2\text{ mol})(-241.8\text{ kJ/mol}) + (1\text{ mol})(-393.5\text{ kJ/mol})$$

$$= -238.6\text{ kJ}$$

PROBLEMS

Problems with **colored** numbers are answered in Appendix E and worked in detail in the Student Solutions Manual. Problem sections match those in the text and provide the numbers of relevant sample problems. Most offer Concept Review Questions, Skill-Building Exercises (grouped in pairs covering the same concept), and Problems in Context. The Comprehensive Problems are based on material from any section or previous chapter.

Forms of Energy and Their Interconversion

(Sample Problem 6.1)

Concept Review Questions

6.1 Why do heat (q) and work (w) have positive values when entering a system and negative values when leaving?

6.2 If you feel warm after exercising, have you increased the internal energy of your body? Explain.

6.3 An *adiabatic* process is one that involves no heat transfer. What is the relationship between work and the change in internal energy in an adiabatic process?

6.4 State two ways that you increase the internal energy of your body and two ways that you decrease it.

6.5 Name a common device used to accomplish each change:
(a) Electrical energy to thermal energy
(b) Electrical energy to sound energy
(c) Electrical energy to light energy
(d) Mechanical energy to electrical energy
(e) Chemical energy to electrical energy

6.6 In winter, an electric heater uses a certain amount of electrical energy to heat a room to 20°C. In summer, an air conditioner uses the same amount of electrical energy to cool the room to 20°C. Is the change in internal energy of the heater larger, smaller, or the same as that of the air conditioner? Explain.

6.7 You lift your textbook and drop it onto a desk. Describe the energy transformations (from one form to another) that occur, moving backward in time from a moment after impact.

Skill-Building Exercises (grouped in similar pairs)

6.8 A system receives 425 J of heat from and delivers 425 J of work to its surroundings. What is the change in internal energy of the system (in J)?

6.9 A system conducts 255 cal of heat to the surroundings and delivers 428 cal of work. What is the change in internal energy of the system (in cal)?

6.10 What is the change in internal energy (in J) of a system that releases 675 J of thermal energy to its surroundings and has 530 cal of work done on it?

6.11 What is the change in internal energy (in J) of a system that absorbs 0.615 kJ of heat from its surroundings and has 0.247 kcal of work done on it?

6.12 Complete combustion of 2.0 metric tons of coal to gaseous carbon dioxide releases 6.6×10^{10} J of heat. Convert this energy to (a) kilojoules; (b) kilocalories; (c) British thermal units.

6.13 Thermal decomposition of 5.0 metric tons of limestone to lime and carbon dioxide absorbs 9.0×10^{6} kJ of heat. Convert this energy to (a) joules; (b) calories; (c) British thermal units.

Problems in Context

6.14 The nutritional calorie (Calorie) is equivalent to 1 kcal. One pound of body fat is equivalent to about 4.1×10^{3} Calories. Express this quantity of energy in joules and kilojoules.

6.15 If an athlete expends 1950 kJ/h, how long does it take her to work off 1.0 lb of body fat? (See Problem 6.14.)

Enthalpy: Chemical Change at Constant Pressure

(Sample Problem 6.2)

Concept Review Questions

6.16 Why is the work done when a system expands against a constant external pressure assigned a negative sign?

6.17 Why is it often more convenient to measure ΔH than ΔE?

6.18 "Hot packs" used by skiers use the crystallization of sodium acetate from a concentrated solution. What is the sign of ΔH for this crystallization? Is the reaction exothermic or endothermic?

6.19 Classify the following processes as exothermic or endothermic: (a) freezing of water; (b) boiling of water; (c) digestion of food; (d) a person running; (e) a person growing; (f) wood being chopped; (g) heating with a furnace.

6.20 What are the two main components of the internal energy of a substance? On what are they based?

6.21 For each process, state whether ΔH is less than (more negative), equal to, or greater than ΔE of the system. Explain.
(a) An ideal gas is cooled at constant pressure.
(b) A gas mixture reacts exothermically at fixed volume.
(c) A solid reacts exothermically to yield a mixture of gases in a container of variable volume.

Skill-Building Exercises (grouped in similar pairs)

6.22 Draw an enthalpy diagram for a general exothermic reaction; label the axis, reactants, products, and ΔH with its sign.

6.23 Draw an enthalpy diagram for a general endothermic reaction; label the axis, reactants, products, and ΔH with its sign.

6.24 Write a balanced equation and draw an approximate enthalpy diagram for: (a) combustion of 1 mol of ethane; (b) freezing of liquid water.

6.25 Write a balanced equation and draw an approximate enthalpy diagram for (a) formation of 1 mol of sodium chloride from its elements (heat is released); (b) vaporization of liquid benzene.

6.26 Write a balanced equation and draw an approximate enthalpy diagram for (a) combustion of 1 mol of liquid methanol (CH_3OH); (b) formation of 1 mol of NO_2 from its elements (heat is absorbed).

6.27 Write a balanced equation and draw an approximate enthalpy diagram for (a) sublimation of dry ice [conversion of $CO_2(s)$ directly to $CO_2(g)$]; (b) reaction of 1 mol of SO_2 with O_2.

6.28 The circles represent a phase change at constant temperature:

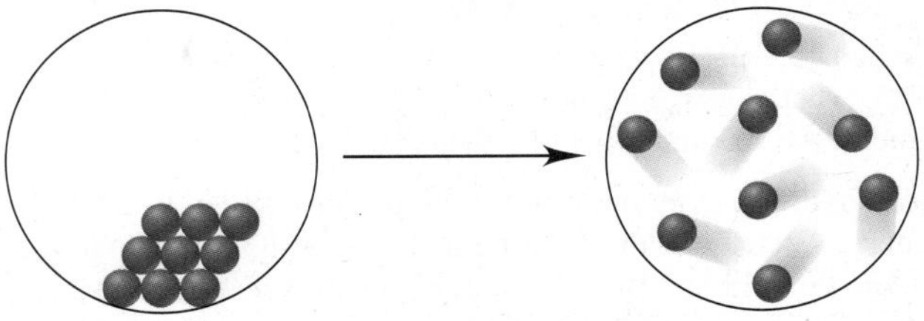

Is the value of each of the following positive (+), negative (−), or zero: (a) q_{sys}; (b) ΔE_{sys}; (c) ΔE_{univ}?

6.29 The scenes below represent a physical change taking place in a piston-cylinder assembly:

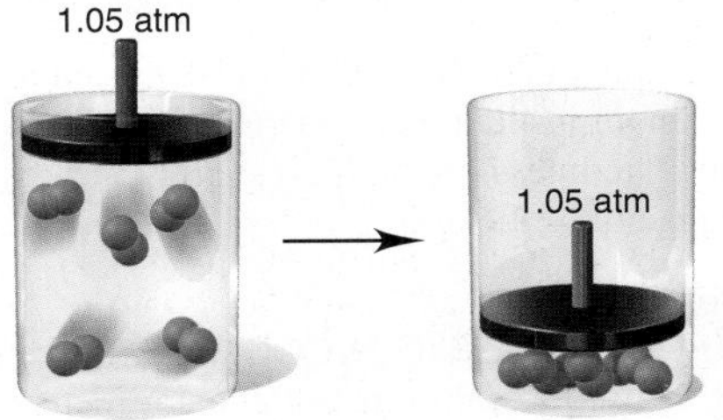

(a) Is w_{sys} +, −, or 0? (b) Is ΔH_{sys} +, −, or 0? (c) Can you determine whether ΔE_{surr} is +, −, or 0? Explain.

Calorimetry: Measuring the Heat of a Chemical or Physical Change

(Sample Problems 6.3 to 6.6)

Concept Review Questions

6.30 Which is larger, the specific heat capacity or the molar heat capacity of a substance? Explain.

6.31 What data do you need to determine the specific heat capacity of a substance?

6.32 Is the specific heat capacity of a substance an intensive or extensive property? Explain.

6.33 Distinguish between specific heat capacity, molar heat capacity, and heat capacity.

6.34 Both a coffee-cup calorimeter and a bomb calorimeter can be used to measure the heat transferred in a reaction. Which measures ΔE and which measures ΔH? Explain.

Skill-Building Exercises (grouped in similar pairs)

6.35 Find q when 22.0 g of water is heated from 25.0°C to 100.°C.

6.36 Calculate q when 0.10 g of ice is cooled from 10.°C to −75°C (c_{ice} = 2.087 J/g·K).

6.37 A 295-g aluminum engine part at an initial temperature of 13.00°C absorbs 75.0 kJ of heat. What is the final temperature of the part (c of Al = 0.900 J/g·K)?

6.38 A 27.7-g sample of the radiator coolant ethylene glycol releases 688 J of heat. What was the initial temperature of the sample if the final temperature is 32.5°C (c of ethylene glycol = 2.42 J/g·K)?

6.39 Two iron bolts of equal mass—one at 100.°C, the other at 55°C—are placed in an insulated container. Assuming the heat capacity of the container is negligible, what is the final temperature inside the container (c of iron = 0.450 J/g·K)?

6.40 One piece of copper jewelry at 105°C has twice the mass of another piece at 45°C. Both are placed in a calorimeter of negligible heat capacity. What is the final temperature inside the calorimeter (c of copper = 0.387 J/g·K)?

6.41 When 155 mL of water at 26°C is mixed with 75 mL of water at 85°C, what is the final temperature? (Assume that no heat is released to the surroundings; d of water is 1.00 g/mL.)

6.42 An unknown volume of water at 18.2°C is added to 24.4 mL of water at 35.0°C. If the final temperature is 23.5°C, what was the unknown volume? (Assume that no heat is released to the surroundings; d of water is 1.00 g/mL.)

6.43 A 455-g piece of copper tubing is heated to 89.5°C and placed in an insulated vessel containing 159 g of water at 22.8°C. Assuming no loss of water and a heat capacity of 10.0 J/K for the vessel, what is the final temperature (c of copper = 0.387 J/g·K)?

6.44 A 30.5-g sample of an alloy at 93.0°C is placed into 50.0 g of water at 22.0°C in an insulated coffee cup with a heat capacity of 9.2 J/K. If the final temperature of the system is 31.1°C, what is the specific heat capacity of the alloy?

Problems in Context

6.45 High-purity benzoic acid (C_6H_5COOH; ΔH for combustion = −3227 kJ/mol) is used to calibrate bomb calorimeters. A 1.221-g sample burns in a calorimeter (heat capacity = 1365 J/°C) that contains 1.200 kg of water. What is the temperature change?

6.46 Two aircraft rivets, one iron and the other copper, are placed in a calorimeter that has an initial temperature of 20.°C. The data for the rivets are as follows:

	Iron	Copper
Mass (g)	30.0	20.0
Initial T (°C)	0.0	100.0
c (J/g·K)	0.450	0.387

(a) Will heat flow from Fe to Cu or from Cu to Fe?
(b) What other information is needed to correct any measurements in an actual experiment?
(c) What is the maximum final temperature of the system (assuming the heat capacity of the calorimeter is negligible)?

6.47 A chemical engineer placed 1.520 g of a hydrocarbon in the bomb of a calorimeter (see Figure 6.10, p. 241). The bomb was immersed in 2.550 L of water and the sample was burned. The water temperature rose from 20.00°C to 23.55°C. If the calorimeter (excluding the water) had a heat capacity of 403 J/K, what was the heat released (q_V) per gram of hydrocarbon?

6.48 When 25.0 mL of 0.500 M H_2SO_4 is added to 25.0 mL of 1.00 M KOH in a coffee-cup calorimeter at 23.50°C, the temperature rises to 30.17°C. Calculate ΔH of this reaction. (Assume the total volume is the sum of the volumes and the density and specific heat capacity of the solution are the same as for water.)

Stoichiometry of Thermochemical Equations

(Sample Problem 6.7)

Concept Review Questions

6.49 Does a negative ΔH mean that the heat should be treated as a reactant or as a product?

6.50 Would you expect $O_2(g) \longrightarrow 2O(g)$ to have a positive or a negative ΔH? Explain.

6.51 Is ΔH positive or negative when 1 mol of water vapor condenses to liquid water? Why? How does this value compare with ΔH for the vaporization of 2 mol of liquid water to water vapor?

Skill-Building Exercises (grouped in similar pairs)

6.52 Consider the following balanced thermochemical equation for a reaction sometimes used for H_2S production:

$$\tfrac{1}{8}S_8(s) + H_2(g) \longrightarrow H_2S(g) \quad \Delta H = -20.2 \text{ kJ}$$

(a) Is this an exothermic or endothermic reaction?
(b) What is ΔH for the reverse reaction?
(c) What is ΔH when 2.6 mol of S_8 reacts?
(d) What is ΔH when 25.0 g of S_8 reacts?

6.53 Consider the following balanced thermochemical equation for the decomposition of the mineral magnesite:

$$MgCO_3(s) \longrightarrow MgO(s) + CO_2(g) \quad \Delta H = 117.3 \text{ kJ}$$

(a) Is heat absorbed or released in the reaction?
(b) What is ΔH for the reverse reaction?
(c) What is ΔH when 5.35 mol of CO_2 reacts with excess MgO?
(d) What is ΔH when 35.5 g of CO_2 reacts with excess MgO?

6.54 When 1 mol of NO(g) forms from its elements, 90.29 kJ of heat is absorbed. (a) Write a balanced thermochemical equation. (b) What is ΔH when 3.50 g of NO decomposes to its elements?

6.55 When 1 mol of KBr(s) decomposes to its elements, 394 kJ of heat is absorbed. (a) Write a balanced thermochemical equation. (b) What is ΔH when 10.0 kg of KBr forms from its elements?

Problems in Context

6.56 Liquid hydrogen peroxide, an oxidizing agent in many rocket fuel mixtures, releases oxygen gas on decomposition:

$$2H_2O_2(l) \longrightarrow 2H_2O(l) + O_2(g) \quad \Delta H = -196.1 \text{ kJ}$$

How much heat is released when 652 kg of H_2O_2 decomposes?

6.57 Compounds of boron and hydrogen are remarkable for their unusual bonding (described in Section 14.5) and also for their reactivity. With the more reactive halogens, for example, diborane (B_2H_6) forms trihalides even at low temperatures:

$$B_2H_6(g) + 6Cl_2(g) \longrightarrow 2BCl_3(g) + 6HCl(g) \quad \Delta H = -755.4 \text{ kJ}$$

What is ΔH per kilogram of diborane that reacts?

6.58 Deterioration of buildings, bridges, and other structures through the rusting of iron costs millions of dollars a day. The actual process requires water, but a simplified equation is

$$4Fe(s) + 3O_2(g) \longrightarrow 2Fe_2O_3(s) \quad \Delta H = -1.65\times10^3 \text{ kJ}$$

(a) How much heat is released when 0.250 kg of iron rusts?
(b) How much rust forms when 4.85×10^3 kJ of heat is released?

6.59 A mercury mirror forms inside a test tube as a result of the thermal decomposition of mercury(II) oxide:

$$2HgO(s) \longrightarrow 2Hg(l) + O_2(g) \quad \Delta H = 181.6 \text{ kJ}$$

(a) How much heat is absorbed to decompose 555 g of the oxide?
(b) If 275 kJ of heat is absorbed, how many grams of Hg form?

6.60 Most ethylene (C_2H_4), the starting material for producing polyethylene, comes from petroleum processing. It also occurs naturally as a fruit-ripening hormone and as a component of natural gas. (a) The heat transferred during combustion of C_2H_4 is −1411 kJ/mol. Write a balanced thermochemical equation. (b) How many grams of C_2H_4 must burn to give 70.0 kJ of heat?

6.61 Sucrose ($C_{12}H_{22}O_{11}$, table sugar) is oxidized in the body by O_2 via a complex set of reactions that produces $CO_2(g)$ and $H_2O(g)$ and releases 5.64×10^3 kJ/mol of sucrose. (a) Write a balanced thermochemical equation for the overall process. (b) How much heat is released per gram of sucrose oxidized?

Hess's Law: Finding ΔH of Any Reaction

(Sample Problem 6.8)

Concept Review Questions

6.62 Express Hess's law in your own words.

6.63 What is the main application of Hess's law?

6.64 When carbon burns in a deficiency of O_2, a mixture of CO and CO_2 forms. Carbon burns in excess O_2 to form only CO_2, and CO burns in excess O_2 to form only CO_2. Use ΔH values of the latter two reactions (from Appendix B) to calculate ΔH for

$$\text{C(graphite)} + \tfrac{1}{2}O_2(g) \longrightarrow CO(g)$$

Skill-Building Exercises (grouped in similar pairs)

6.65 Calculate ΔH for

$$Ca(s) + \tfrac{1}{2}O_2(g) + CO_2(g) \longrightarrow CaCO_3(s)$$

given the following reactions:

$$Ca(s) + \tfrac{1}{2}O_2(g) \longrightarrow CaO(s) \qquad \Delta H = -635.1\text{ kJ}$$
$$CaCO_3(s) \longrightarrow CaO(s) + CO_2(g) \qquad \Delta H = 178.3\text{ kJ}$$

6.66 Calculate ΔH for

$$2NOCl(g) \longrightarrow N_2(g) + O_2(g) + Cl_2(g)$$

given the following reactions:

$$\tfrac{1}{2}N_2(g) + \tfrac{1}{2}O_2(g) \longrightarrow NO(g) \qquad \Delta H = 90.3\text{ kJ}$$
$$NO(g) + \tfrac{1}{2}Cl_2(g) \longrightarrow NOCl(g) \qquad \Delta H = -38.6\text{ kJ}$$

6.67 Write the balanced overall equation (equation 3) for the following process, calculate $\Delta H_{\text{overall}}$, and match the number of each equation with the letter of the appropriate arrow in Figure P6.67:

(1) $N_2(g) + O_2(g) \longrightarrow 2NO(g)$ $\qquad \Delta H = 180.6$ kJ

(2) $2NO(g) + O_2(g) \longrightarrow 2NO_2(g)$ $\qquad \Delta H = -114.2$ kJ

(3) $\qquad \Delta H_{\text{overall}} = ?$

6.68 Write the balanced overall equation (equation 3) for the following process, calculate $\Delta H_{\text{overall}}$, and match the number of each equation with the letter of the appropriate arrow in Figure P6.68:

(1) $P_4(s) + 6Cl_2(g) \longrightarrow 4PCl_3(g)$ $\qquad \Delta H = -1148$ kJ

(2) $4PCl_3(g) + 4Cl_2(g) \longrightarrow 4PCl_5(g)$ $\qquad \Delta H = -460$ kJ

(3) $\qquad \Delta H_{\text{overall}} = ?$

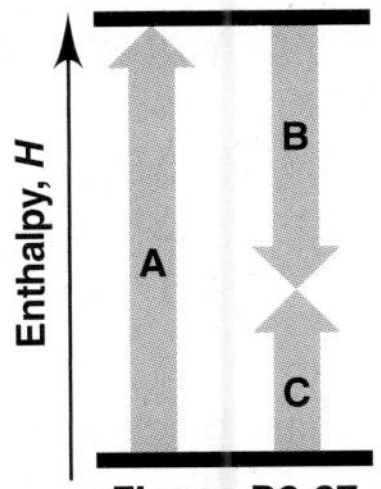

Figure P6.67

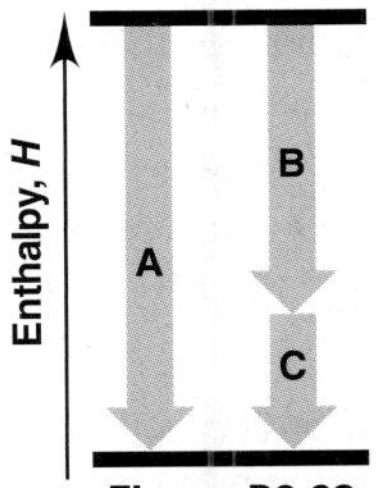

Figure P6.68

6.69 At a given set of conditions, 241.8 kJ of heat is given off when 1 mol of $H_2O(g)$ forms from its elements. Under the same conditions, 285.8 kJ is given off when 1 mol of $H_2O(l)$ forms from its elements. Find ΔH for the vaporization of water at these conditions.

6.70 When 1 mol of $CS_2(l)$ forms from its elements at 1 atm and 25°C, 89.7 kJ of heat is absorbed, and it takes 27.7 kJ to vaporize 1 mol of the liquid. How much heat is absorbed when 1 mol of $CS_2(g)$ forms from its elements at these conditions?

Problems in Context

6.71 Diamond and graphite are two crystalline forms of carbon. At 1 atm and 25°C, diamond changes to graphite so slowly that the enthalpy change of the process must be obtained indirectly. Using equations from the numbered list below, determine ΔH for

$$\text{C(diamond)} \longrightarrow \text{C(graphite)}$$

(1) $\text{C(diamond)} + O_2(g) \longrightarrow CO_2(g)$ $\qquad \Delta H = -395.4$ kJ

(2) $2CO_2(g) \longrightarrow 2CO(g) + O_2(g)$ $\qquad \Delta H = 566.0$ kJ

(3) $\text{C(graphite)} + O_2(g) \longrightarrow CO_2(g)$ $\qquad \Delta H = -393.5$ kJ

(4) $2CO(g) \longrightarrow \text{C(graphite)} + CO_2(g)$ $\qquad \Delta H = -172.5$ kJ

Standard Enthalpies of Reaction ($\Delta H^\circ_{\text{rxn}}$)

(Sample Problems 6.9 and 6.10)

Concept Review Questions

6.72 What is the difference between the standard enthalpy of formation and the standard enthalpy of reaction?

6.73 How are ΔH°_f values used to calculate $\Delta H^\circ_{\text{rxn}}$?

6.74 Make any changes needed in each of the following equations to make the enthalpy change equal to ΔH°_f for the compound:

(a) $Cl(g) + Na(s) \longrightarrow NaCl(s)$

(b) $H_2O(g) \longrightarrow 2H(g) + \tfrac{1}{2}O_2(g)$

(c) $\tfrac{1}{2}N_2(g) + \tfrac{3}{2}H_2(g) \longrightarrow NH_3(g)$

Skill-Building Exercises (grouped in similar pairs)

6.75 Use Table 6.3 or Appendix B to write a balanced formation equation at standard conditions for each of the following compounds: (a) $CaCl_2$; (b) $NaHCO_3$; (c) CCl_4; (d) HNO_3.

6.76 Use Table 6.3 or Appendix B to write a balanced formation equation at standard conditions for each of the following compounds: (a) HI; (b) SiF_4; (c) O_3; (d) $Ca_3(PO_4)_2$.

6.77 Calculate $\Delta H^\circ_{\text{rxn}}$ for each of the following:

(a) $2H_2S(g) + 3O_2(g) \longrightarrow 2SO_2(g) + 2H_2O(g)$

(b) $CH_4(g) + Cl_2(g) \longrightarrow CCl_4(l) + HCl(g)$ [unbalanced]

6.78 Calculate $\Delta H^\circ_{\text{rxn}}$ for each of the following:

(a) $SiO_2(s) + 4HF(g) \longrightarrow SiF_4(g) + 2H_2O(l)$

(b) $C_2H_6(g) + O_2(g) \longrightarrow CO_2(g) + H_2O(g)$ [unbalanced]

6.79 Copper(I) oxide can be oxidized to copper(II) oxide:

$$Cu_2O(s) + \tfrac{1}{2}O_2(g) \longrightarrow 2CuO(s) \qquad \Delta H^\circ_{\text{rxn}} = -146.0\text{ kJ}$$

Given ΔH°_f of $Cu_2O(s) = -168.6$ kJ/mol, find ΔH°_f of $CuO(s)$.

6.80 Acetylene burns in air by the following equation:

$$C_2H_2(g) + \tfrac{5}{2}O_2(g) \longrightarrow 2CO_2(g) + H_2O(g)$$
$$\Delta H^\circ_{\text{rxn}} = -1255.8\text{ kJ}$$

Given ΔH°_f of $CO_2(g) = -393.5$ kJ/mol and ΔH°_f of $H_2O(g) = -241.8$ kJ/mol, find ΔH°_f of $C_2H_2(g)$.

Problems in Context

6.81 The common lead-acid car battery produces a large burst of current, even at low temperatures, and is rechargeable. The reaction that occurs while recharging a "dead" battery is

$$2PbSO_4(s) + 2H_2O(l) \longrightarrow Pb(s) + PbO_2(s) + 2H_2SO_4(l)$$

(a) Use ΔH°_f values from Appendix B to calculate $\Delta H^\circ_{\text{rxn}}$.

(b) Use the following equations to check your answer to part (a):

(1) $Pb(s) + PbO_2(s) + 2SO_3(g) \longrightarrow 2PbSO_4(s)$ $\Delta H^\circ_{rxn} = -768$ kJ

(2) $SO_3(g) + H_2O(l) \longrightarrow H_2SO_4(l)$ $\Delta H^\circ_{rxn} = -132$ kJ

Comprehensive Problems

6.82 Stearic acid ($C_{18}H_{36}O_2$) is a fatty acid, a molecule with a long hydrocarbon chain and an organic acid group (COOH) at the end. It is used to make cosmetics, ointments, soaps, and candles and is found in animal tissue as part of many saturated fats. In fact, when you eat meat, you are ingesting some fats containing stearic acid. (a) Write a balanced equation for the combustion of stearic acid to gaseous products. (b) Calculate ΔH°_{rxn} for this combustion (ΔH°_f of $C_{18}H_{36}O_2 = -948$ kJ/mol). (c) Calculate the heat (q) released in kJ and kcal when 1.00 g of stearic acid is burned completely. (d) A candy bar contains 11.0 g of fat and 100. Cal from fat; is this consistent with your answer for part (c)?

6.83 Diluting sulfuric acid with water is highly exothermic:

$$H_2SO_4(l) \xrightarrow{H_2O} H_2SO_4(aq) + \textit{heat}$$

(a) Use Appendix B to find ΔH°_{rxn} for diluting 1.00 mol of $H_2SO_4(l)$ ($d = 1.83$ g/mL) to 1 L of 1.00 M $H_2SO_4(aq)$ ($d = 1.060$ g/mL).
(b) Suppose you carry out the dilution in a calorimeter. The initial T is 25.0°C, and the specific heat capacity of the final solution is 3.50 J/g·K. What is the final T?
(c) Use the ideas of density and heat capacity to explain why you should add acid to water rather than water to acid.

6.84 A balloonist begins a trip in a helium-filled balloon in early morning when the temperature is 15°C. By mid-afternoon, the temperature is 30.°C. Assuming the pressure remains at 1.00 atm, for each mole of helium, calculate the following:
(a) The initial and final volumes
(b) The change in internal energy, ΔE (*Hint:* Helium behaves like an ideal gas, so $E = \frac{3}{2}nRT$. Be sure the units of R are consistent with those of E.)
(c) The work (w) done by the helium (in J)
(d) The heat (q) transferred (in J)
(e) ΔH for the process (in J)
(f) Explain the relationship between the answers to parts (d) and (e).

6.85 In winemaking, the sugars in grapes undergo *fermentation* by yeast to yield CH_3CH_2OH and CO_2. During cellular *respiration* (combustion), sugar and ethanol yield water vapor and CO_2.
(a) Using $C_6H_{12}O_6$ for sugar, calculate ΔH°_{rxn} of fermentation and of respiration.
(b) Write a combustion reaction for ethanol. Which has a higher ΔH°_{rxn} for combustion per mole of C, sugar or ethanol?

6.86 Three of the reactions that occur when the paraffin of a candle (typical formula $C_{21}H_{44}$) burns are as follows:
(1) Complete combustion forms CO_2 and water vapor.
(2) Incomplete combustion forms CO and water vapor.
(3) Some wax is oxidized to elemental C (soot) and water vapor.
(a) Find ΔH°_{rxn} of each reaction (ΔH°_f of $C_{21}H_{44} = -476$ kJ/mol; use graphite for elemental carbon).
(b) Find q (in kJ) when a 254-g candle burns completely.
(c) Find q (in kJ) when 8.00% by mass of the candle burns incompletely and 5.00% by mass of it undergoes soot formation.

6.87 Ethylene oxide (EO) is prepared by the vapor-phase oxidation of ethylene. Its main uses are in the preparation of the antifreeze ethylene glycol and in the production of poly(ethylene terephthalate), which is used to make beverage bottles and fibers. Pure EO vapor can decompose explosively:

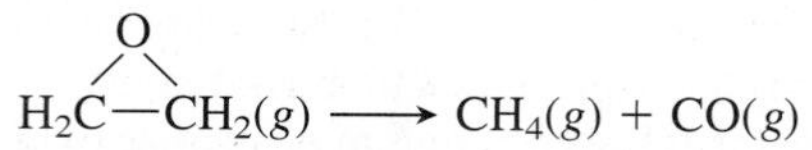

Liquid EO has $\Delta H^\circ_f = -77.4$ kJ/mol and ΔH° for its vaporization = 569.4 J/g. (a) Calculate ΔH°_{rxn} for the gas-phase reaction. (b) External heating causes the vapor to decompose at 10 bar and 93°C in a distillation column. What is the final temperature if the average specific heat capacity of the products is 2.5 J/g·°C?

6.88 The following scenes represent a gaseous reaction between compounds of nitrogen (blue) and oxygen (red) at 298 K:

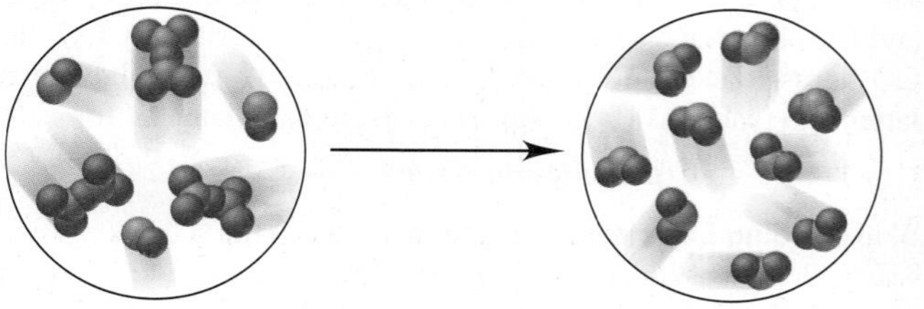

(a) Write a balanced equation and use Appendix B to calculate ΔH°_{rxn}.
(b) If each molecule of product represents 1.50×10^{-2} mol, what quantity of heat (in J) is released or absorbed?

6.89 Isooctane (C_8H_{18}; $d = 0.692$ g/mL) is used as the fuel in a test of a new automobile drive train.
(a) How much energy (in kJ) is released by combustion of 20.4 gal of isooctane to gases ($\Delta H^\circ_{rxn} = -5.44 \times 10^3$ kJ/mol)?
(b) The energy delivered to the wheels at 65 mph is 5.5×10^4 kJ/h. Assuming *all* the energy is transferred as work to the wheels, how far (in km) can the car travel on the 20.4 gal of fuel?
(c) If the actual range is 455 miles, explain your answer to (b).

6.90 Four 50.-g samples of different colorless liquids are placed in beakers at $T_{initial} = 25.00$°C. Each liquid is heated until 450. J of heat has been absorbed; T_{final} is shown on each beaker below. Rank the liquids in order of increasing specific heat capacity.

6.91 Reaction of gaseous ClF with F_2 yields liquid ClF_3, an important fluorinating agent. Use the following thermochemical equations to calculate ΔH°_{rxn} for this reaction:

(1) $2ClF(g) + O_2(g) \longrightarrow Cl_2O(g) + OF_2(g)$ $\Delta H^\circ_{rxn} = 167.5$ kJ
(2) $2F_2(g) + O_2(g) \longrightarrow 2OF_2(g)$ $\Delta H^\circ_{rxn} = -43.5$ kJ
(3) $2ClF_3(l) + 2O_2(g) \longrightarrow Cl_2O(g) + 3OF_2(g)$ $\Delta H^\circ_{rxn} = 394.1$ kJ

6.92 Silver bromide is used to coat ordinary black-and-white photographic film, while high-speed film uses silver iodide.
(a) When 50.0 mL of 5.0 g/L $AgNO_3$ is added to a coffee-cup calorimeter containing 50.0 mL of 5.0 g/L NaI, with both solutions at 25°C, what mass of AgI forms?
(b) Use Appendix B to find ΔH°_{rxn}.
(c) What is ΔT_{soln} (assuming the volumes are additive and the solution has the density and specific heat capacity of water)?

6.93 The calorie (4.184 J) is defined as the quantity of energy needed to raise the temperature of 1.00 g of liquid water 1.00°C. The British thermal unit (Btu) is defined as the quantity of energy needed to raise the temperature of 1.00 lb of liquid water 1.00°F.
(a) How many joules are in 1.00 Btu (1 lb = 453.6 g; 1.0°C = 1.8°F)?
(b) The *therm* is a unit of energy consumption and is defined as 100,000 Btu. How many joules are in 1.00 therm?
(c) How many moles of methane must be burned to give 1.00 therm of energy? (Assume water forms as a gas.)
(d) If natural gas costs \$0.66 per therm, what is the cost per mole of methane? (Assume natural gas is pure methane.)
(e) How much would it cost to warm 318 gal of water in a hot tub from 15.0°C to 42.0°C by burning methane (1 gal = 3.78 L)?

6.94 When organic matter decomposes under oxygen-free (anaerobic) conditions, methane is one of the products. Thus, enormous deposits of natural gas, which is almost entirely methane, serve as a major source of fuel for home and industry.
(a) Known deposits of natural gas can produce 5600 EJ of energy (1 EJ = 10^{18} J). Current total global energy usage is 4.0×10^2 EJ per year. Find the mass (in kg) of known deposits of natural gas (ΔH°_{rxn} for the combustion of CH_4 = −802 kJ/mol).
(b) At current rates of usage, for how many years could these deposits supply the world's total energy needs?
(c) What volume (in ft^3) of natural gas, measured at STP, is required to heat 1.00 qt of water from 25.0°C to 100.0°C (*d* of H_2O = 1.00 g/mL; *d* of CH_4 at STP = 0.72 g/L)?
(d) The fission of 1 mol of uranium (about 4×10^{-4} ft^3) in a nuclear reactor produces 2×10^{13} J. What volume (in ft^3) of natural gas would produce the same amount of energy?

6.95 A reaction takes place in a steel vessel within a chamber filled with argon gas. Shown below are molecular views of the argon adjacent to the surface of the reaction vessel before and after the reaction. Was the reaction exothermic or endothermic? Explain.

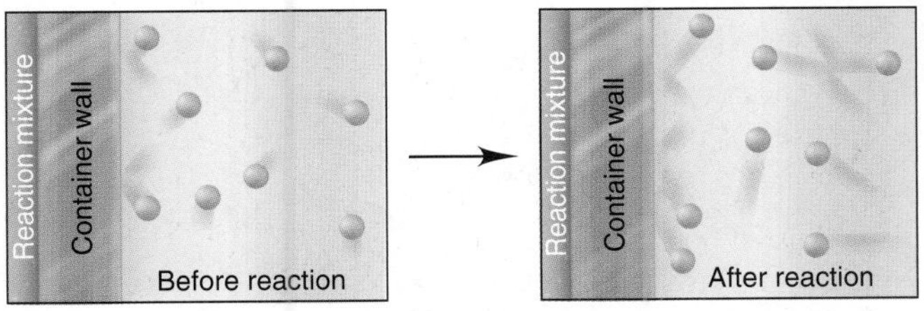

6.96 An aqueous waste stream with a maximum concentration of 0.50 *M* H_2SO_4 (*d* = 1.030 g/mL at 25°C) is neutralized by controlled addition of 40% NaOH (*d* = 1.430 g/L) before it goes to the process sewer and then to the chemical plant waste treatment facility. A safety review finds that the waste stream could meet a small stream of an immiscible organic compound, which could form a flammable vapor in air at 40.°C. The maximum temperature reached by the NaOH solution and the waste stream is 31°C. Could the temperature increase due to the heat transferred by the neutralization cause the organic vapor to explode? Assume the specific heat capacity of each solution is 4.184 J/g·K.

6.97 Kerosene, a common space-heater fuel, is a mixture of hydrocarbons whose "average" formula is $C_{12}H_{26}$.
(a) Write a balanced equation, using the simplest whole-number coefficients, for the complete combustion of kerosene to gases.
(b) If $\Delta H^\circ_{rxn} = -1.50\times10^4$ kJ for the combustion equation as written in part (a), determine ΔH°_f of kerosene.
(c) Calculate the heat released by combustion of 0.50 gal of kerosene (*d* of kerosene = 0.749 g/mL).
(d) How many gallons of kerosene must be burned for a kerosene furnace to produce 1250. Btu (1 Btu = 1.055 kJ)?

6.98 Silicon tetrachloride is produced annually on the multikiloton scale and used in making transistor-grade silicon. It can be produced directly from the elements (reaction 1) or, more cheaply, by heating sand and graphite with chlorine gas (reaction 2). If water is present in reaction 2, some tetrachloride may be lost in an unwanted side reaction (reaction 3):

$$(1)\ Si(s) + 2Cl_2(g) \longrightarrow SiCl_4(g)$$
$$(2)\ SiO_2(s) + 2C(\text{graphite}) + 2Cl_2(g) \longrightarrow SiCl_4(g) + 2CO(g)$$
$$(3)\ SiCl_4(g) + 2H_2O(g) \longrightarrow SiO_2(s) + 4HCl(g) \qquad \Delta H^\circ_{rxn} = -139.5\ \text{kJ}$$

(a) Use reaction 3 to calculate the standard enthalpies of reaction of reactions 1 and 2. (b) What is the standard enthalpy of reaction for a fourth reaction that is the sum of reactions 2 and 3?

6.99 One mole of nitrogen gas confined within a cylinder by a piston is heated from 0°C to 819°C at 1.00 atm.
(a) Calculate the work done by the expanding gas in joules (1 J = 9.87×10^{-3} atm·L). Assume all the energy is used to do work.
(b) What would be the temperature change if the gas were heated using the same amount of energy in a container of fixed volume? (Assume the specific heat capacity of N_2 is 1.00 J/g·K.)

6.100 The chemistry of nitrogen oxides is very versatile. Given the following reactions and their standard enthalpy changes,

$$(1)\ NO(g) + NO_2(g) \longrightarrow N_2O_3(g) \qquad \Delta H^\circ_{rxn} = -39.8\ \text{kJ}$$
$$(2)\ NO(g) + NO_2(g) + O_2(g) \longrightarrow N_2O_5(g) \qquad \Delta H^\circ_{rxn} = -112.5\ \text{kJ}$$
$$(3)\ 2NO_2(g) \longrightarrow N_2O_4(g) \qquad \Delta H^\circ_{rxn} = -57.2\ \text{kJ}$$
$$(4)\ 2NO(g) + O_2(g) \longrightarrow 2NO_2(g) \qquad \Delta H^\circ_{rxn} = -114.2\ \text{kJ}$$
$$(5)\ N_2O_5(s) \longrightarrow N_2O_5(g) \qquad \Delta H^\circ_{rxn} = 54.1\ \text{kJ}$$

calculate the standard enthalpy of reaction for

$$N_2O_3(g) + N_2O_5(s) \longrightarrow 2N_2O_4(g)$$

6.101 Electric generating plants transport large amounts of hot water through metal pipes, and oxygen dissolved in the water can cause a major corrosion problem. Hydrazine (N_2H_4) added to the water avoids the problem by reacting with the oxygen:

$$N_2H_4(aq) + O_2(g) \longrightarrow N_2(g) + 2H_2O(l)$$

About 4×10^7 kg of hydrazine is produced every year by reacting ammonia with sodium hypochlorite in the *Raschig process:*

$$2NH_3(aq) + NaOCl(aq) \longrightarrow N_2H_4(aq) + NaCl(aq) + H_2O(l) \qquad \Delta H^\circ_{rxn} = -151\ \text{kJ}$$

(a) If ΔH°_f of NaOCl(*aq*) = −346 kJ/mol, find ΔH°_f of $N_2H_4(aq)$.
(b) What is the heat released when aqueous N_2H_4 is added to 5.00×10^3 L of water that is 2.50×10^{-4} *M* O_2?

6.102 Liquid methanol (CH_3OH) can be used as an alternative fuel in pickup and SUV engines. An industrial method for preparing it involves the catalytic hydrogenation of carbon monoxide:

$$CO(g) + 2H_2(g) \xrightarrow{\text{catalyst}} CH_3OH(l)$$

How much heat (in kJ) is released when 15.0 L of CO at 85°C and 112 kPa reacts with 18.5 L of H_2 at 75°C and 744 torr?

6.103 (a) How much heat is released when 25.0 g of methane burns in excess O_2 to form gaseous CO_2 and H_2O?
(b) Calculate the temperature of the product mixture if the methane and air are both at an initial temperature of 0.0°C. Assume a stoichiometric ratio of methane to oxygen from the air, with air being 21% O_2 by volume (*c* of CO_2 = 57.2 J/mol·K; *c* of $H_2O(g)$ = 36.0 J/mol·K; *c* of N_2 = 30.5 J/mol·K).

Quantum Theory and Atomic Structure

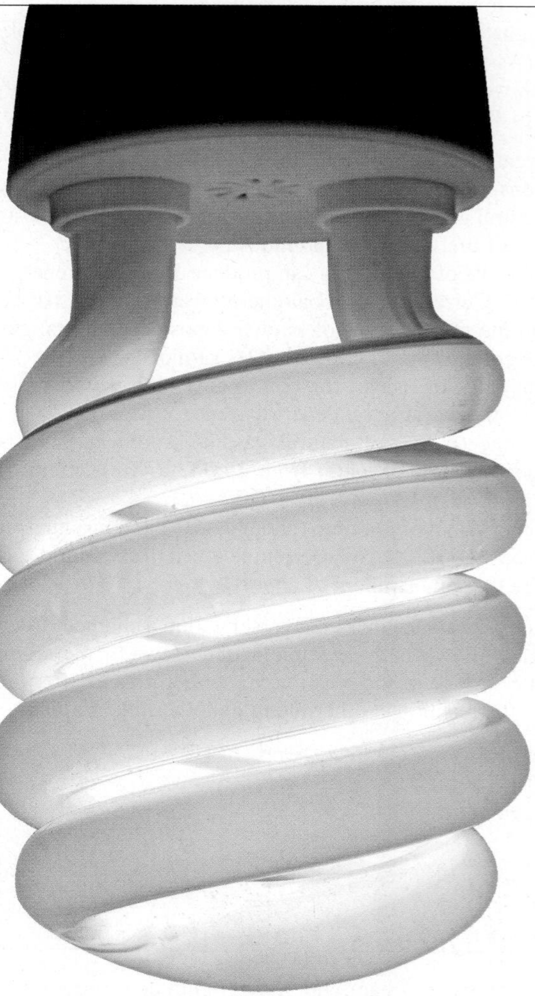

7

Concepts and skills to review before you study this chapter

- discovery of the electron and atomic nucleus (Section 2.4)
- major features of atomic structure (Section 2.5)
- changes in the energy state of a system (Section 6.1)

Over a few remarkable decades—from around 1890 to 1930—a number of revolutions took place in Western science and culture. ● One concerned our view of matter and energy, and you demonstrate it with every flick of a light switch (*photo*). That new view is essential for understanding TV screens, fireworks, and neon signs, not to mention the structure of the atom! But revolutions in science are not the violent upheavals of political overthrow. Flaws appear in a model due to conflicting evidence, a startling discovery widens the flaws into cracks, and the theoretical structure crumbles. Then, new insight, verified by experiment, builds a model more consistent with reality. So it was when Lavoisier's theory of combustion overthrew the phlogiston model, when Dalton's atomic theory established the idea of individual units of matter, and when Rutherford's model substituted nuclear atoms for "billiard balls" or "plum puddings." You will see this process unfold again as we discuss the development of modern atomic theory.

● **A Time of Revolution** Here are some of the revolutionary discoveries and events witnessed by the Western world during those decades:

1895 Röntgen: discovery of x-rays
1896 Becquerel: discovery of radioactivity
1897 Thomson: discovery of the electron
1900 Freud: theory of the unconscious
1900 Planck: quantum theory
1901 Marconi: invention of the radio
1903 Wright brothers: flight of a plane
1905 Ford: assembly line to build cars
1905 Rutherford: radioactivity explained
1905 Einstein: relativity/photon theories
1906 St. Denis: modern dance
1908 Matisse/Picasso: modern art
1909 Schoenberg/Berg: modern music
1911 Rutherford: nuclear model
1913 Bohr: atomic spectra and new model
1914–1918: World War I
1923 Compton: photon momentum
1924 De Broglie: wave theory of matter
1926 Schrödinger: wave equation
1927 Heisenberg: uncertainty principle

IN THIS CHAPTER . . . We discuss quantum mechanics, the theory that explains the fundamental nature of energy and matter and accounts for atomic structure.

- We consider the classical distinction between the wave properties of energy and the particle properties of matter.
- We then examine two observations—blackbody radiation and the photoelectric effect—whose explanations led to a *quantized*, or particulate, model of light.
- We see that light emitted by excited atoms—an *atomic spectrum*—suggests an atom with distinct energy levels, and we apply spectra to chemical analysis.
- We see how wave-particle duality, which shows that matter and energy have similar properties, and the uncertainty principle, which proposes that electron behavior can never be known exactly, led to the current model of the H atom.
- We present quantum numbers, which specify the size, shape, and orientation of atomic orbitals, the regions an electron occupies in the H atom. (In Chapter 8, we'll examine quantum numbers for atoms with more than one electron.)

7.1 • THE NATURE OF LIGHT

Visible light, x-rays, and microwaves are some of the types of **electromagnetic radiation** (also called *electromagnetic energy* or *radiant energy*). All electromagnetic radiation consists of energy propagated by electric and magnetic fields that increase and decrease in intensity as they move through space. This *classical wave model* explains why rainbows form, how magnifying glasses work, and many other familiar observations. But, it cannot explain observations on the very *un*familiar atomic scale. In this section, we describe some properties of electromagnetic radiation and note how they are distinguished from the properties of matter. But, then, we see that some other properties blur that distinction and require a new model to explain them.

The Wave Nature of Light

The wave properties of electromagnetic radiation are described by three variables and one constant (Figure 7.1, *next page*):

1. *Frequency* (ν, Greek *nu*). The **frequency** of a wave is the number of cycles it undergoes per second, expressed by the unit 1/second [s^{-1}; also called a *hertz* (Hz)].

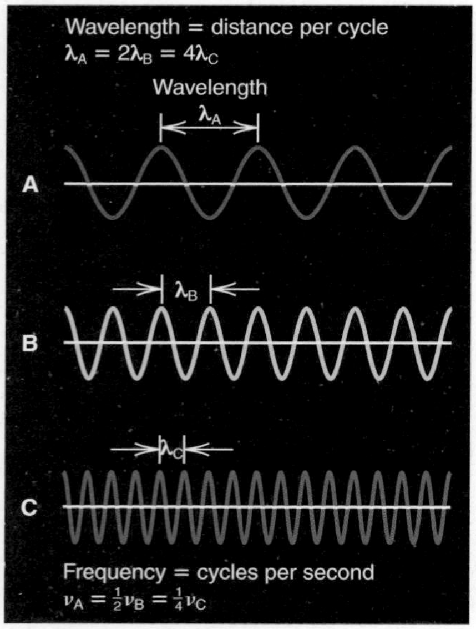

Figure 7.1 The reciprocal relationship of frequency and wavelength.

2. *Wavelength* (λ, Greek *lambda*). The **wavelength** is the distance between any point on a wave and the corresponding point on the next crest (or trough) of the wave, that is, the distance the wave travels during one cycle. Wavelength has units of meters or, for very short wavelengths, nanometers (nm, 10^{-9} m), picometers (pm, 10^{-12} m), or the non-SI unit angstroms (Å, 10^{-10} m).
3. *Speed.* The speed of a wave is the distance it moves per unit time (meters per second), the product of its frequency (cycles per second) and wavelength (meters per cycle):

$$\text{Units for speed of wave:} \quad \frac{\cancel{\text{cycles}}}{\text{s}} \times \frac{\text{m}}{\cancel{\text{cycle}}} = \frac{\text{m}}{\text{s}}$$

In a vacuum, electromagnetic radiation moves at 2.99792458×10^8 m/s (3.00×10^8 m/s to three significant figures), a *physical constant* called the **speed of light (*c*):**

$$c = \nu \times \lambda \tag{7.1}$$

Since the product of ν and λ is a constant, they have a reciprocal relationship—*radiation with a high frequency has a short wavelength, and vice versa*:

$$\nu\uparrow\lambda\downarrow \quad \text{and} \quad \nu\downarrow\lambda\uparrow$$

4. *Amplitude.* The **amplitude** of a wave is the height of the crest (or depth of the trough). For an electromagnetic wave, the amplitude is related to the *intensity* of the radiation, or its brightness in the case of visible light. Light of a particular color has a specific frequency (and thus, wavelength) but, as Figure 7.2 shows, it can be dimmer (lower amplitude, less intense) or brighter (higher amplitude, more intense).

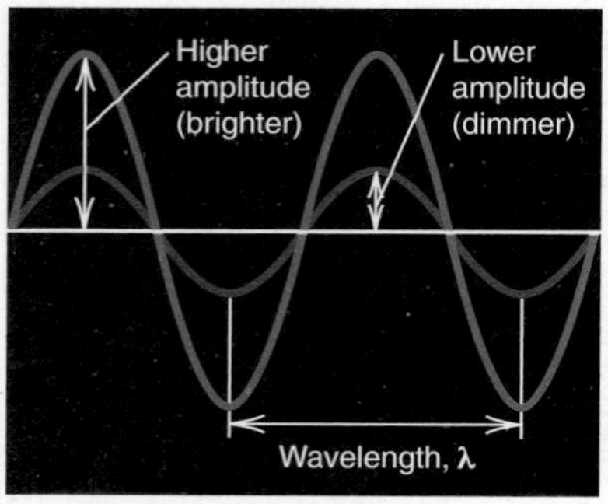

Figure 7.2 Differing amplitude (brightness, or intensity) of a wave.

The Electromagnetic Spectrum Visible light represents a small region of the **electromagnetic spectrum** (Figure 7.3). *All waves in the spectrum travel at the same speed through a vacuum but differ in frequency and, therefore, wavelength.*

The spectrum is a *continuum of radiant energy,* so each region meets the next. For instance, the **infrared (IR)** region meets the *microwave* region on one end and the *visible* region on the other. We perceive different wavelengths (or frequencies) of visible light as colors, from red (λ ≈ 750 nm) to violet (λ ≈ 400 nm). Light of a single wavelength is called *monochromatic* (Greek, "one color"), whereas light of many wavelengths is *polychromatic.* White light is polychromatic. The region adjacent to visible light on the short-wavelength end consists of **ultraviolet (UV)** radiation (also called *ultraviolet light*). Still shorter wavelengths (higher frequencies) make up the x-ray and gamma (γ) ray regions.

Some types of electromagnetic radiation are utilized by familiar devices; for example, long-wavelength, low-frequency radiation is used by microwave ovens, radios, and cell phones. But electromagnetic emissions are everywhere: coming from

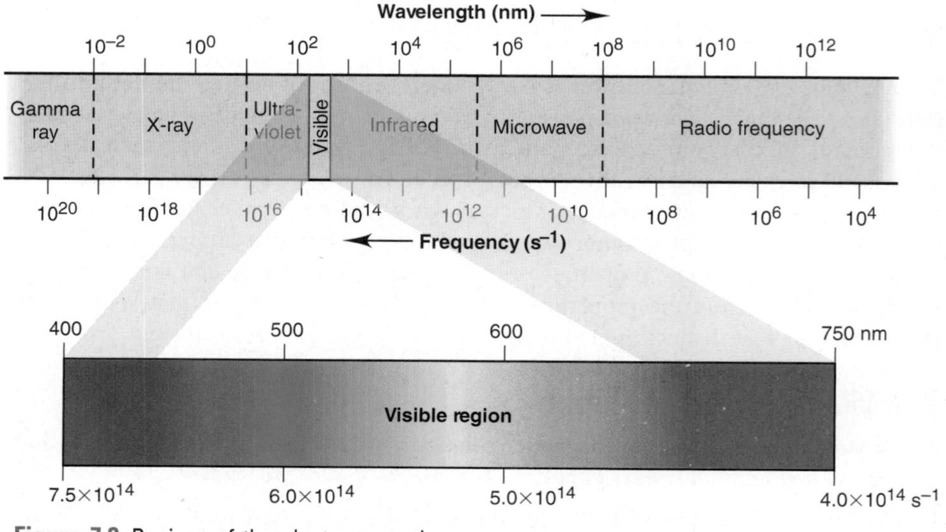

Figure 7.3 Regions of the electromagnetic spectrum. The visible region is expanded (and the scale made linear) to show the component colors.

human artifacts such as lightbulbs, x-ray equipment, and car motors, and from natural sources such as the Sun, lightning, radioactivity, and even the glow of fireflies! Our knowledge of the universe comes from radiation entering our eyes and our light, x-ray, and radio telescopes.

Sample Problem 7.1 Interconverting Wavelength and Frequency

Problem A dental hygienist uses x-rays (λ = 1.00 Å) to take a series of dental radiographs while the patient listens to a radio station (λ = 325 cm) and looks out the window at the blue sky (λ = 473 nm). What is the frequency (in s^{-1}) of the electromagnetic radiation from each source? (Assume that the radiation travels at the speed of light, 3.00×10^8 m/s.)

Plan We are given the wavelengths, so we use Equation 7.1 to find the frequencies. However, we must first convert the wavelengths to meters because c has units of m/s.

Solution For the x-rays: Converting from angstroms to meters,

$$\lambda = 1.00\ \text{Å} \times \frac{10^{-10}\ \text{m}}{1\ \text{Å}} = 1.00\times10^{-10}\ \text{m}$$

Calculating the frequency:

$$\nu = \frac{c}{\lambda} = \frac{3.00\times10^{8}\ \text{m/s}}{1.00\times10^{-10}\ \text{m}} = 3.00\times10^{18}\ \text{s}^{-1}$$

For the radio signal: Combining steps to calculate the frequency,

$$\nu = \frac{c}{\lambda} = \frac{3.00\times10^{8}\ \text{m/s}}{325\ \text{cm} \times \dfrac{10^{-2}\ \text{m}}{1\ \text{cm}}} = 9.23\times10^{7}\ \text{s}^{-1}$$

For the blue sky: Combining steps to calculate the frequency,

$$\nu = \frac{c}{\lambda} = \frac{3.00\times10^{8}\ \text{m/s}}{473\ \text{nm} \times \dfrac{10^{-9}\ \text{m}}{1\ \text{nm}}} = 6.34\times10^{14}\ \text{s}^{-1}$$

Check The orders of magnitude are correct for the regions of the electromagnetic spectrum (see Figure 7.3): x-rays (10^{19} to 10^{16} s^{-1}), radio waves (10^9 to 10^4 s^{-1}), and visible light (7.5×10^{14} to 4.0×10^{14} s^{-1}).

Comment The radio station here is broadcasting at 92.3×10^6 s^{-1}, or 92.3 million Hz (92.3 MHz), about midway in the FM range.

Follow-Up Problem 7.1 Some diamonds appear yellow because they contain nitrogen compounds that absorb purple light of frequency 7.23×10^{14} Hz. Calculate the wavelength (in nm and Å) of the absorbed light.

Road Map

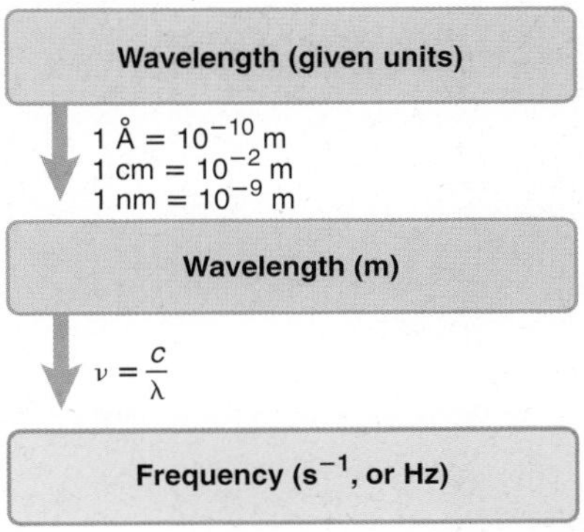

The Classical Distinction Between Energy and Matter In our everyday world, matter comes in chunks you can hold and weigh, and you can change the quantity of matter piece by piece. In contrast, energy is "massless," and its quantity can change continuously. Matter moves in specific paths, whereas radiant energy (light) travels in diffuse waves. Let's examine some distinctions between the behavior of waves of energy and particles of matter.

1. *Refraction and dispersion.* Light of a given wavelength travels at different speeds through various transparent media—vacuum, air, water, quartz, and so forth. Therefore, when a light wave passes from one medium into another, the speed of the wave changes. Figure 7.4A on the next page shows the phenomenon known as **refraction.** If the wave strikes the boundary between media, say, between air and water, at an angle other than 90°, the change in speed causes a change in direction, and the wave continues at a different angle. The angle of refraction depends on the two media and the wavelength of the light. In the related process of *dispersion,* white light separates (disperses) into its component colors when it passes through a prism (or other refracting object) because each incoming wave is refracted at a slightly different angle.

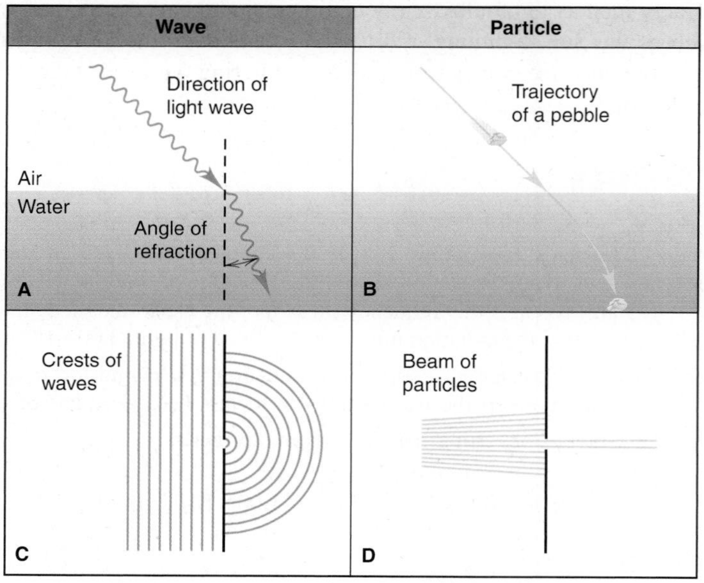

Figure 7.4 **Different behaviors of waves and particles.** **A,** Refraction: The speed of a light wave passing between media changes immediately, which bends its path. **B,** The speed of a particle continues changing gradually. **C,** Diffraction: A wave bends around both edges of a small opening, forming a semicircular wave. **D,** Particles either enter a small opening or not.

In contrast to a wave of light, a particle of matter, like a pebble, does not undergo refraction. If you throw a pebble through the air into a pond, it continues to slow down gradually along a curved path after entering the water (Figure 7.4B).

Two of many familiar applications of refraction and dispersion involve rainbows and diamonds. You see a rainbow when sunlight entering the near surface of a droplet is dispersed and reflected off the far surface. Red light is bent least, so it appears higher in the sky and violet lower *(see photo)*. A diamond's color sparkles because its facets disperse and reflect the incoming light.

How does wave theory explain rainbows?

2. *Diffraction and interference*. When a wave strikes the edge of an object, it bends around it in a phenomenon called **diffraction.** If the wave passes through a slit about as wide as its wavelength, it bends around both edges of the slit and forms a semicircular wave on the other side of the opening (Figure 7.4C).

In contrast, when you throw a collection of particles, like a handful of sand, at a small opening, some particles hit the edge, while others go through the opening and continue in a narrower group (Figure 7.4D).

When waves of light pass through two adjacent slits, the nearby emerging circular waves interact through the process of *interference*. If the crests of the waves coincide *(in phase),* they interfere *constructively*—the amplitudes add together to form a brighter region. If crests coincide with troughs *(out of phase),* they interfere *destructively*—the amplitudes cancel to form a darker region. The result is a *diffraction pattern* (Figure 7.5).

In contrast, particles passing through adjacent openings continue in straight paths, some colliding and moving at different angles.

The Particle Nature of Light

Three observations involving matter and light confounded physicists at the turn of the 20th century: blackbody radiation, the photoelectric effect, and atomic spectra. Explaining these phenomena required a radically new picture of energy. We discuss the first two of them here and the third in Section 7.2.

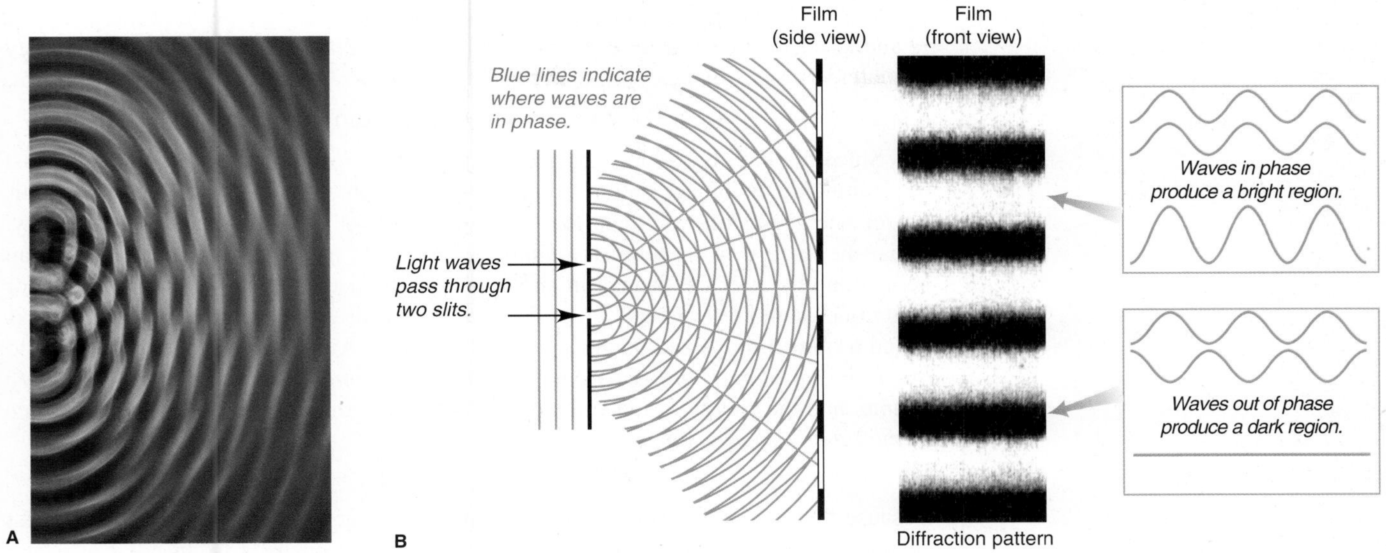

Figure 7.5 Formation of a diffraction pattern. **A,** Constructive interference and destructive interference occur as water waves pass through two adjacent slits. **B,** Light waves passing through two slits also emerge as circular waves and create a diffraction pattern.

Blackbody Radiation and the Quantum Theory of Energy The first of the puzzling observations involved the light given off by an object being heated.

- *Observation: blackbody radiation.* When a solid object is heated to about 1000 K, it begins to emit visible light, as you can see in the red glow of smoldering coal (Figure 7.6A). At about 1500 K, the light is brighter and more orange, like that from an electric heating coil (Figure 7.6B). At temperatures greater than 2000 K, the light is still brighter and whiter, like that emitted by the filament of a lightbulb (Figure 7.6C). These changes in intensity and wavelength of emitted light as an object is heated are characteristic of *blackbody radiation,* light given off by a hot *blackbody.** All attempts to account for these changes by applying classical electromagnetic theory failed.
- *Explanation: the quantum theory.* In 1900, the German physicist Max Planck (1858–1947) developed a formula that fit the data perfectly. To find a physical explanation for his formula, Planck assumed, in a self-proclaimed "act of despair," that the hot, glowing object could emit (or absorb) only *certain* quantities of energy:

$$E = nh\nu$$

*A blackbody is an idealized object that absorbs all the radiation incident on it. A hollow cube with a small hole in one wall approximates a blackbody.

A Smoldering coal **B Electric heating element** **C Lightbulb filament**

Figure 7.6 Familiar examples of light emission related to blackbody radiation.

where E is the energy of the radiation, ν is its frequency, n is a positive integer (1, 2, 3, and so on) called a **quantum number,** and h is **Planck's constant.** With energy in joules (J) and frequency in s^{-1}, h has units of J·s:

$$h = 6.62606876\times10^{-34}\ \text{J·s} = 6.626\times10^{-34}\ \text{J·s} \quad (4\ \text{sf})$$

Since the hot object emits only certain quantities of energy, and the energy must be emitted by the object's atoms, this means that each atom *emits* only certain quantities of energy. It follows, then, that each atom *has* only certain quantities of energy. Thus, the energy of an atom is *quantized:* it occurs in fixed quantities, rather than being continuous. Each change in an atom's energy occurs when the atom absorbs or emits one or more "packets," or definite amounts, of energy. Each energy packet is called a **quantum** ("fixed quantity"; plural, *quanta*). A quantum of energy is equal to $h\nu$. Thus, *an atom changes its energy state by emitting (or absorbing) one or more quanta,* and the energy of the emitted (or absorbed) radiation is equal to the *difference in the atom's energy states:*

$$\Delta E_{\text{atom}} = E_{\text{emitted (or absorbed) radiation}} = \Delta nh\nu$$

Because the atom can change its energy only by integer multiples of $h\nu$, the smallest change occurs when an atom in a given energy state changes to an adjacent state, that is, when $\Delta n = 1$:

$$\Delta E = h\nu \qquad (7.2)$$

The Photoelectric Effect and the Photon Theory of Light Despite the idea of quantization, physicists still pictured energy as traveling in waves. But, the wave model could not explain the second confusing observation, the flow of current when light strikes a metal.

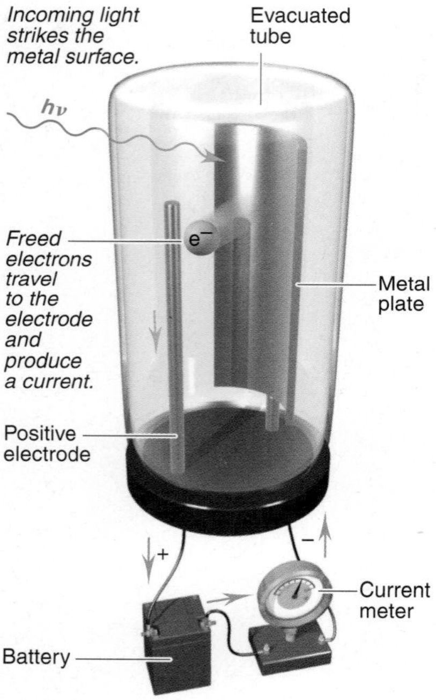

Figure 7.7 The photoelectric effect.

- *Observation: the **photoelectric effect.*** When monochromatic light of sufficient frequency shines on a metal plate, a current flows (Figure 7.7). It was thought that the current arises because light transfers energy that frees electrons from the metal surface. However, the effect had two confusing features, the presence of a threshold frequency and the absence of a time lag:
  1. *Presence of a threshold frequency.* For current to flow, the light shining on the metal must have a minimum, or threshold, *frequency,* and different metals have different minimum frequencies. But, the wave theory associates the energy of light with its *amplitude* (intensity), not its frequency (color). Thus, the theory predicts that an electron would break free when it absorbed enough energy from light of *any* color.
  2. *Absence of a time lag.* Current flows the moment light of the minimum frequency shines on the metal, regardless of the light's intensity. But the wave theory predicts that with dim light there would be a time lag before the current flows, because the electrons would have to absorb enough energy to break free.
- *Explanation: the photon theory.* Building on Planck's ideas, Einstein proposed that light itself is particulate, quantized into tiny "bundles" of energy, later called **photons.** Each atom changes its energy, ΔE_{atom}, when it absorbs or emits one photon, one "particle" of light, whose energy is related to its *frequency,* not its amplitude:

  $$E_{\text{photon}} = h\nu = \Delta E_{\text{atom}}$$

  Let's see how the photon theory explains the two features of the photoelectric effect:
  1. *Why there is a threshold frequency.* A beam of light consists of an enormous number of photons. The intensity (brightness) is related to the *number* of photons, but *not* to the energy of each. Therefore, a photon of a certain *minimum* energy must be absorbed to free an electron from the surface (see Figure 7.7). Since energy depends on frequency ($h\nu$), the theory predicts a threshold frequency.
  2. *Why there is no time lag.* An electron breaks free when it absorbs a photon of *enough* energy; it cannot break free by "saving up" energy from several photons, each having less than the minimum energy. The current is weak in dim light because fewer photons of enough energy can free fewer electrons per unit time, but some current flows *as soon as* light of sufficient energy (frequency) strikes the metal.

Ping-Pong Photons This analogy helps explain why light of *insufficient* energy *cannot* free an electron from the metal surface. If one Ping-Pong ball doesn't have enough energy to knock a book off a shelf, neither does a series of Ping-Pong balls, because the book can't save up the energy from the individual impacts. But one baseball traveling at the same speed does have enough energy.

Sample Problem 7.2 Calculating the Energy of Radiation from Its Wavelength

Problem A student uses a microwave oven to heat a meal. The wavelength of the radiation is 1.20 cm. What is the energy of one photon of this microwave radiation?

Plan We know λ in centimeters (1.20 cm) so we convert to meters, find the frequency with Equation 7.1, and then find the energy of one photon with Equation 7.2.

Solution Combining steps to find the energy of a photon:

$$E = h\nu = \frac{hc}{\lambda} = \frac{(6.626\times10^{-34}\ \text{J}\cdot\text{s})(3.00\times10^{8}\ \text{m/s})}{(1.20\ \text{cm})\left(\dfrac{10^{-2}\ \text{m}}{1\ \text{cm}}\right)} = 1.66\times10^{-23}\ \text{J}$$

Check Checking the order of magnitude gives

$$\frac{10^{-33}\ \text{J}\cdot\text{s}\times10^{8}\ \text{m/s}}{10^{-2}\ \text{m}} = 10^{-23}\ \text{J}$$

Follow-Up Problem 7.2 Calculate the energy of one photon of **(a)** ultraviolet light ($\lambda = 1\times10^{-8}$ m); **(b)** visible light ($\lambda = 5\times10^{-7}$ m); and **(c)** infrared light ($\lambda = 1\times10^{-4}$ m). What do the answers indicate about the relationship between the wavelength and energy of light?

Summary of Section 7.1

- Electromagnetic radiation travels in waves characterized by a given wavelength (λ) and frequency (ν).
- Electromagnetic waves travel through a vacuum at the speed of light, c (3.00×10^8 m/s), which equals $\nu \times \lambda$. Therefore, wavelength and frequency have a reciprocal relationship.
- The intensity (brightness) of light is related to the amplitude of its waves.
- The electromagnetic spectrum ranges from very long radio waves to very short gamma rays and includes the visible region between wavelengths 750 nm (red) and 400 nm (violet).
- Refraction (change in a wave's speed when entering a different medium) and diffraction (bend of a wave around an edge of an object) indicate that energy is wavelike, with properties distinct from those of particles of mass.
- Blackbody radiation and the photoelectric effect, however, are consistent with energy occurring in discrete packets, like particles.
- Light exists as photons (quanta) whose energy is proportional to the frequency.
- According to quantum theory, an atom has only certain quantities of energy ($E = nh\nu$), and it can change its energy only by absorbing or emitting a photon whose energy equals the change in the atom's energy.

7.2 • ATOMIC SPECTRA

The third confusing observation about matter and energy involved the light emitted when an element is vaporized and then excited electrically. In this section, we discuss the nature of that light and see why it created a problem for the existing atomic model and how a new model solved the problem.

Line Spectra and the Rydberg Equation

When light from electrically excited gaseous atoms passes through a slit and is refracted by a prism, it does not create a *continuous spectrum,* or rainbow, as sunlight does. Instead, it creates a **line spectrum,** a series of fine lines at specific frequencies separated by black spaces. Figure 7.8A on the next page shows the apparatus and the line spectrum of atomic hydrogen. Figure 7.8B shows that each spectrum is *characteristic* of the element producing it.

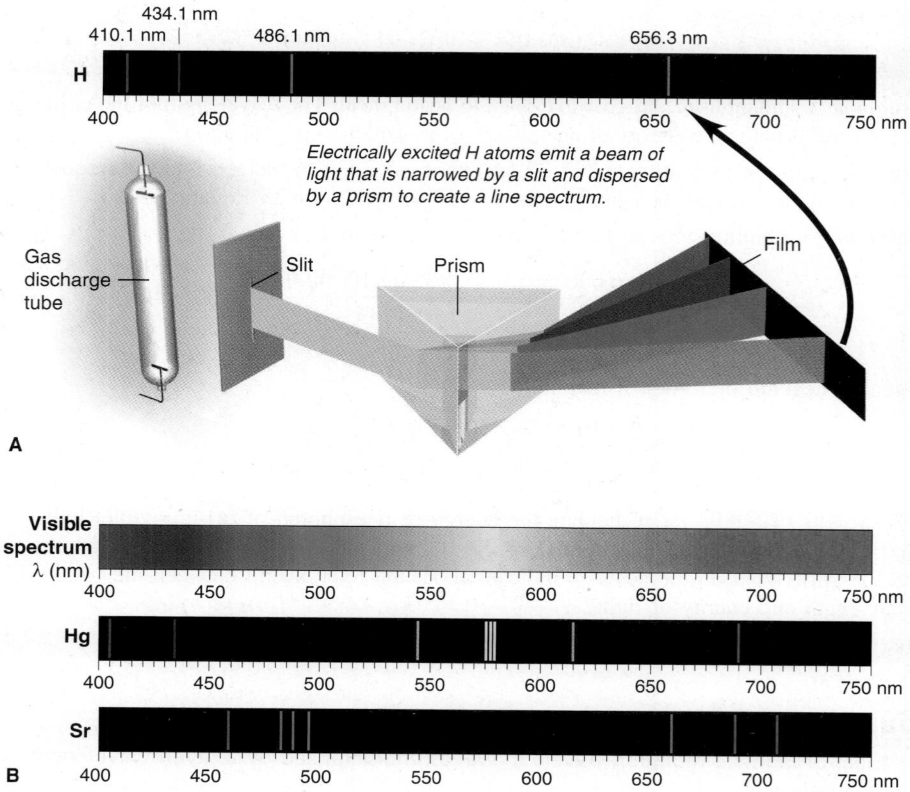

Figure 7.8 The line spectra of several elements. **A,** The line spectrum of atomic hydrogen. **B,** Unlike the continuous spectrum of white light, emission spectra of elements, such as mercury and strontium, appear as characteristic series of colored lines.

Features of the Rydberg Equation Spectroscopists studying atomic hydrogen identified several series of spectral lines in different regions of the electromagnetic spectrum. Figure 7.9 shows three of them. Using data, not theory, the Swedish physicist Johannes Rydberg developed a relationship, called the *Rydberg equation,* that predicted the position and wavelength of any line in a given series:

$$\frac{1}{\lambda} = R\left(\frac{1}{n_1^2} - \frac{1}{n_2^2}\right) \tag{7.3}$$

where λ is the wavelength of the line, n_1 and n_2 are positive integers with $n_2 > n_1$, and R is the Rydberg constant ($1.096776\times10^7\ \text{m}^{-1}$). For the visible series, $n_1 = 2$:

$$\frac{1}{\lambda} = R\left(\frac{1}{2^2} - \frac{1}{n_2^2}\right), \quad \text{with } n_2 = 3, 4, 5, \ldots$$

(Problems 7.23 and 7.24 are two of several that apply the Rydberg equation.)

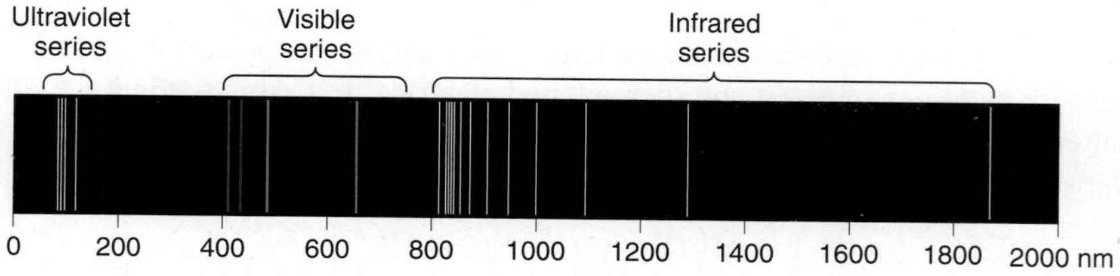

Figure 7.9 Three series of spectral lines of atomic hydrogen.

Problems with Rutherford's Nuclear Model Almost as soon as Rutherford proposed his nuclear model (described in Chapter 2), a major problem arose. A positive nucleus and a negative electron attract each other, and for them to stay apart, the kinetic energy of the electron's motion must counterbalance the potential energy of attraction. However, the laws of classical physics say that a negative particle moving in a curved path around a positive particle *must* emit radiation and thus lose energy. If the orbiting electrons behaved in that way, they would spiral into the nucleus, and all atoms would collapse! The laws of classical physics also say that the frequency of the emitted radiation should change smoothly as the negative particle spirals inward and, thus, create a continuous spectrum, not a line spectrum. The behavior of subatomic particles seemed to violate real-world experience and accepted principles.

The Bohr Model of the Hydrogen Atom

Two years after the nuclear model was proposed, Niels Bohr (1885–1962), a young Danish physicist working in Rutherford's laboratory, suggested a model for the H atom that *did* predict the existence of line spectra.

Postulates of the Model In his model, Bohr used Planck's and Einstein's ideas about quantized energy and proposed three postulates:

1. *The H atom has only certain energy levels,* which Bohr called **stationary states.** Each state is associated with a fixed circular orbit of the electron around the nucleus. The higher the energy level, the farther the orbit is from the nucleus.
2. *The atom does* **not** *radiate energy while in one of its stationary states.* Even though it violates principles of classical physics, the atom does not change energy while the electron moves *within* an orbit.
3. *The atom changes to another stationary state* (the electron moves to another orbit) *only by absorbing or emitting a photon. The energy of the photon ($h\nu$) equals the difference in the energies of the two states:*

$$E_{\text{photon}} = \Delta E_{\text{atom}} = E_{\text{final}} - E_{\text{initial}} = h\nu$$

Features of the Model The model has several key features:

- *Quantum numbers and electron orbit.* The quantum number n is a positive integer (1, 2, 3, . . .) associated with the radius of an electron orbit, which is directly related to the electron's energy: *the lower the n value, the smaller the radius of the orbit, and the lower the energy level.*
- *Ground state.* When the electron is in the first orbit ($n = 1$), it is closest to the nucleus, and the H atom is in its lowest (first) energy level, called the **ground state.**
- *Excited states.* If the electron is in any orbit farther from the nucleus, the atom is in an **excited state.** With the electron in the second orbit ($n = 2$), the atom is in the first excited state; when it's in the third orbit ($n = 3$), the atom is in the second excited state, and so forth.
- *Absorption.* If an H atom *absorbs* a photon whose energy equals the *difference* between lower and higher energy levels, the electron moves to the outer (higher energy) orbit.
- *Emission.* If an H atom in a higher energy level (electron in farther orbit) returns to a lower energy level (electron in closer orbit), the atom *emits* a photon whose energy equals the difference between the two levels. Figure 7.10 shows an analogy that illustrates absorption and emission.

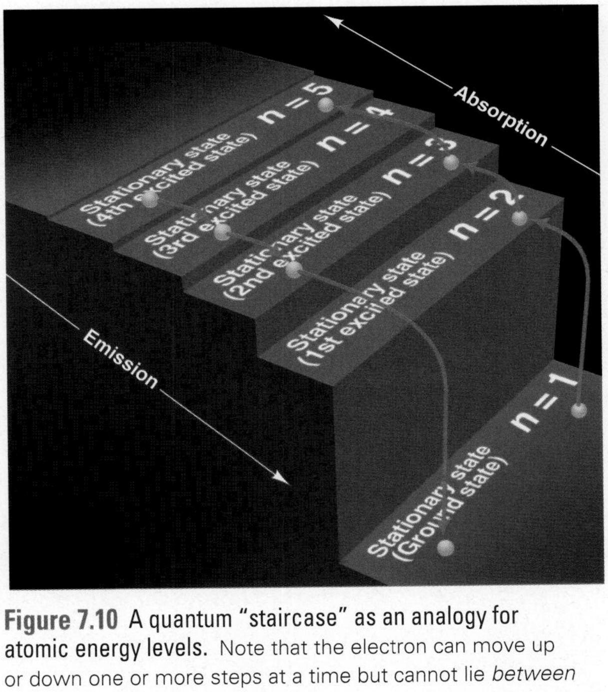

Figure 7.10 A quantum "staircase" as an analogy for atomic energy levels. Note that the electron can move up or down one or more steps at a time but cannot lie *between* steps.

How the Model Explains Line Spectra A spectral line results because a photon of specific energy (and thus frequency) is *emitted.* The emission occurs when the electron moves to an orbit closer to the nucleus as the atom's energy changes from a higher state to a lower one. Therefore, *an atomic spectrum is not continuous because the atom's energy is not continuous, but rather has only certain states.*

Figure 7.11A shows how Bohr's model accounts for three series of spectral lines of hydrogen. When a sample of gaseous H atoms is excited, the atoms absorb different quantities of energy. Each atom has one electron, but there are so many atoms in the whole sample that all the energy levels (orbits) have electrons. When electrons drop from outer orbits to the $n = 3$ orbit (second excited state), the emitted photons create the *infrared* series of lines. The *visible* series arises when electrons drop to the $n = 2$ orbit (first excited state), and the *ultraviolet* series arises when electrons drop to the $n = 1$ orbit (ground state). Figure 7.11B shows how the specific lines in the ultraviolet series appear.

Limitations of the Model Despite its great success in accounting for the spectral lines of the H atom, the Bohr model failed to predict the spectrum of any other atom. The reason is that it is a *one-electron model:* it works beautifully for the H atom and for other one-electron species, such as He^+ ($Z = 2$), Li^{2+} ($Z = 3$), and Be^{3+} ($Z = 4$). It fails completely for atoms with more than one electron because the electron-electron repulsions and additional nucleus-electron attractions that are present create much more complex interactions. But, even more fundamentally, as we'll see in Section 7.4, *electrons do not move in fixed, defined orbits.* Even though, as a picture of the atom, the Bohr model is incorrect, we still use the terms "ground state" and "excited state" and retain the central idea that *the energy of an atom occurs in discrete levels and it changes energy by absorbing or emitting a photon of specific energy.*

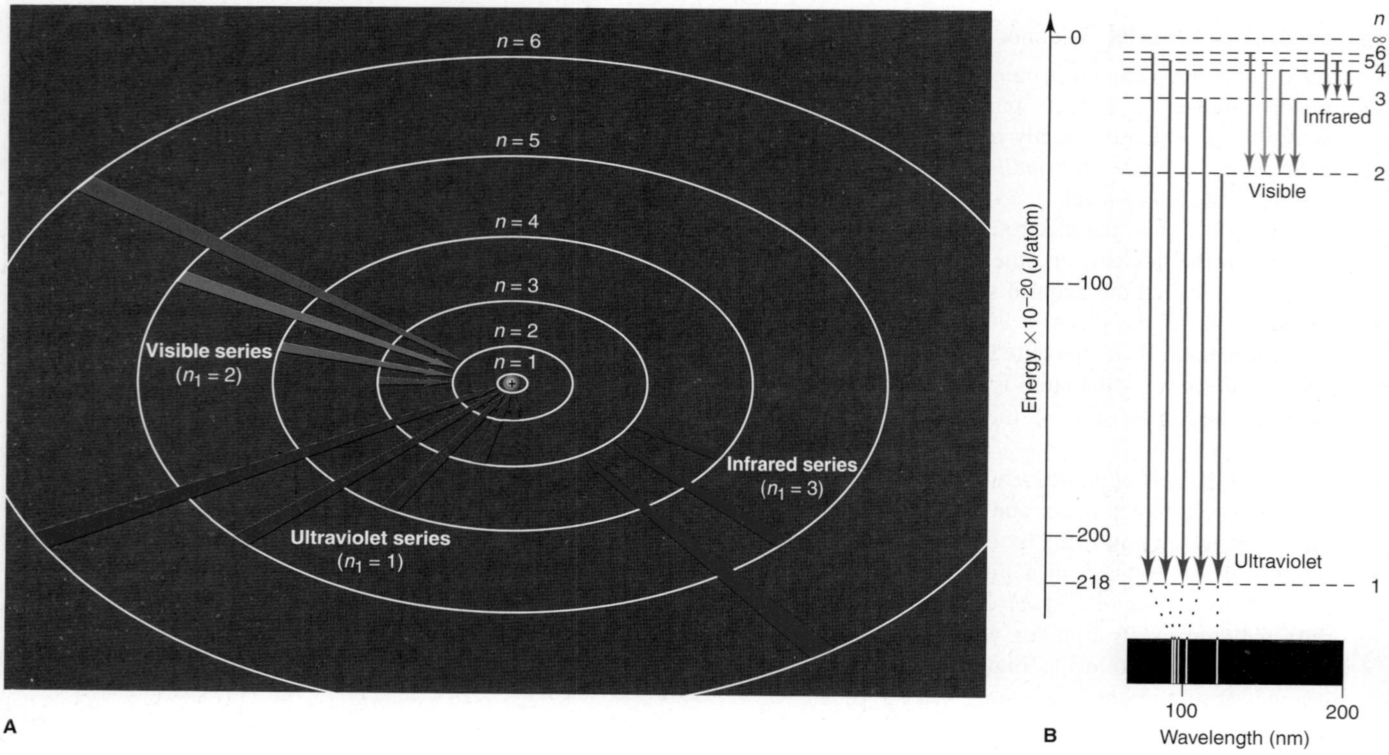

Figure 7.11 The Bohr explanation of three series of spectral lines emitted by the H atom. **A,** In a given series, the outer electron drops to the same inner orbit (the same value of n_1 in the Rydberg equation). **B,** An energy diagram shows how the ultraviolet series arises.

The Energy Levels of the Hydrogen Atom

Bohr's work leads to an equation for calculating the energy levels of an atom:

$$E = -2.18\times10^{-18}\ \text{J}\left(\frac{Z^2}{n^2}\right)$$

where Z is the charge of the nucleus. For the H atom, $Z = 1$, so we have

$$E = -2.18\times10^{-18}\ \text{J}\left(\frac{1^2}{n^2}\right) = -2.18\times10^{-18}\ \text{J}\left(\frac{1}{n^2}\right)$$

Therefore, the energy of the ground state ($n = 1$) of the H atom is

$$E = -2.18\times10^{-18}\ \text{J}\left(\frac{1}{1^2}\right) = -2.18\times10^{-18}\ \text{J}$$

The negative sign for the energy (also used on the axis in Figure 7.11B) appears because we *define* the zero point of the atom's energy when *the electron is completely removed from the nucleus.* Thus, $E = 0$ when $n = \infty$, so $E < 0$ for any smaller n.

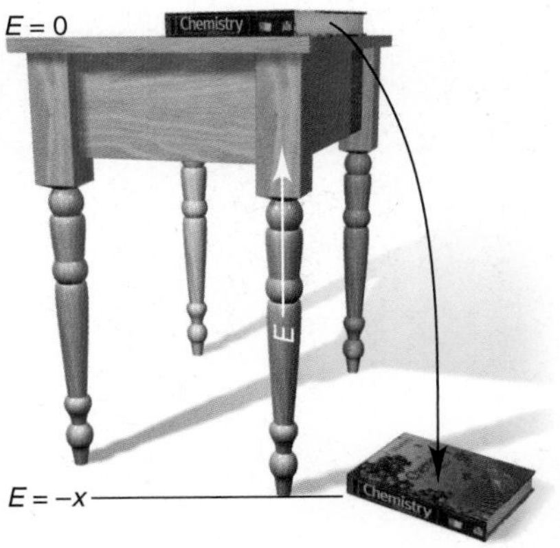

A tabletop analogy for defining the energy of a system. If you define the zero point of your textbook's potential energy when the book is on a table, the energy is negative when it's on the floor.

Applying Bohr's Equation for the Energy Levels of an Atom We can use the equation for the energy levels in several ways:

1. *Finding the difference in energy between two levels.* By subtracting the initial energy level of the atom from its final energy level, we find the change in energy when the electron moves between the two levels:

$$\Delta E = E_{\text{final}} - E_{\text{initial}} = -2.18\times10^{-18}\ \text{J}\left(\frac{1}{n^2_{\text{final}}} - \frac{1}{n^2_{\text{initial}}}\right) \qquad (7.4)$$

Note that, since n is in the denominator,

- *When the atom emits energy,* the electron moves closer to the nucleus ($n_{\text{final}} < n_{\text{initial}}$), so the atom's final energy is a *larger* negative number and ΔE is negative.
- *When the atom absorbs energy,* the electron moves away from the nucleus ($n_{\text{final}} > n_{\text{initial}}$), so the atom's final energy is a *smaller* negative number and ΔE is positive. (Analogously, in Chapter 6, you saw that, when the system releases heat, ΔH is negative, and when it absorbs heat, ΔH is positive.)

2. *Finding the energy needed to ionize the H atom.* We can also find the energy needed to remove the electron completely, that is, find ΔE for the following change:

$$H(g) \longrightarrow H^+(g) + e^-$$

We substitute $n_{\text{final}} = \infty$ and $n_{\text{initial}} = 1$ into Equation 7.4 and obtain

$$\Delta E = E_{\text{final}} - E_{\text{initial}} = -2.18\times10^{-18}\ \text{J}\left(\frac{1}{\infty^2} - \frac{1}{1^2}\right)$$

$$= -2.18\times10^{-18}\ \text{J}\,(0 - 1) = 2.18\times10^{-18}\ \text{J}$$

Energy must be *absorbed* to remove the electron from the nucleus, so ΔE is positive.

The *ionization energy* of hydrogen is the energy required to form 1 mol of gaseous H^+ ions from 1 mol of gaseous H atoms. Thus, for 1 mol of H atoms,

$$\Delta E = \left(2.18\times10^{-18}\ \frac{\text{J}}{\text{atom}}\right)\left(6.022\times10^{23}\ \frac{\text{atoms}}{\text{mol}}\right)\left(\frac{1\ \text{kJ}}{10^3\ \text{J}}\right) = 1.31\times10^3\ \text{kJ/mol}$$

Ionization energy is a key atomic property, and we'll return to it in Chapter 8.

3. *Finding the wavelength of a spectral line.* Once we know ΔE from Equation 7.4, we find the wavelengths of the spectral lines of the H atom by combining the relation between frequency and wavelength (Equation 7.1) with Planck's expression for the change in energy of an atom (Equation 7.2) and solving for λ:

$$\Delta E = h\nu = \frac{hc}{\lambda} \quad \text{or} \quad \lambda = \frac{hc}{\Delta E}$$

In Sample Problem 7.3, we find the energy change when an H atom absorbs a photon.

Sample Problem 7.3 Determining ΔE and λ of an Electron Transition

Problem A hydrogen atom absorbs a photon of UV light (see Figure 7.11), and its electron enters the $n = 4$ energy level. Calculate **(a)** the change in energy of the atom and **(b)** the wavelength (in nm) of the photon.

Plan **(a)** The H atom absorbs energy, so $E_{final} > E_{initial}$. We are given $n_{final} = 4$, and Figure 7.11 shows that $n_{initial} = 1$ because a UV photon is absorbed. We apply Equation 7.4 to find ΔE. **(b)** Once we know ΔE, we find the frequency with Equation 7.2 and the wavelength (in m) with Equation 7.1. Then we convert from meters to nanometers.

Solution **(a)** Substituting the known values into Equation 7.4:

$$\Delta E = -2.18\times10^{-18}\text{ J}\left(\frac{1}{n_{final}^2} - \frac{1}{n_{initial}^2}\right)$$

$$= -2.18\times10^{-18}\text{ J}\left(\frac{1}{4^2} - \frac{1}{1^2}\right) = -2.18\times10^{-18}\text{ J}\left(\frac{1}{16} - \frac{1}{1}\right)$$

$$= 2.04\times10^{-18}\text{ J}$$

(b) Using Equations 7.2 and 7.1 to solve for λ:

$$\Delta E = h\nu = \frac{hc}{\lambda}$$

therefore,

$$\lambda = \frac{hc}{\Delta E} = \frac{(6.626\times10^{-34}\text{ J·s})(3.00\times10^{8}\text{ m/s})}{2.04\times10^{-18}\text{ J}} = 9.74\times10^{-8}\text{ m}$$

Converting m to nm:

$$\lambda = 9.74\times10^{-8}\text{ m} \times \frac{1\text{ nm}}{10^{-9}\text{ m}} = 97.4\text{ nm}$$

Check **(a)** The energy change is positive, which is consistent with absorption. **(b)** The wavelength is within the UV region (about 10–380 nm).

Comment In the follow-up problem, note that if ΔE is negative (the atom loses energy), we use its absolute value, $|\Delta E|$, because λ must have a positive value.

Follow-Up Problem 7.3 A hydrogen atom with its electron in the $n = 6$ energy level emits a photon of IR light. Calculate **(a)** the change in energy of the atom and **(b)** the wavelength (in Å) of the photon.

Spectrometric analysis of the H atom led to the Bohr model, the first step toward our current model of the atom. From its use by 19th-century chemists as a means of identifying elements and compounds, spectrometry has developed into a major tool of modern chemistry (see Tools of the Laboratory).

Summary of Section 7.2

- Unlike sunlight, light emitted by electrically excited atoms of elements appears as separate spectral lines.
- Spectroscopists use an empirical formula (the Rydberg equation) to determine the wavelength of a spectral line. Atomic hydrogen displays several series of spectral lines.
- To explain the existence of line spectra, Bohr proposed that an electron moves in fixed orbits. It moves from one orbit to another when the atom absorbs or emits a photon whose energy equals the difference in energy levels (orbits).
- Bohr's model predicts only the spectrum of the H atom and other one-electron species. Despite this, Bohr was correct that an atom's energy is quantized.
- Spectrometry is an instrumental technique that uses emission and absorption spectra to identify substances and measure their concentrations.

TOOLS OF THE LABORATORY | Spectrometry in Chemical Analysis

The use of spectral data to identify and quantify substances is essential to modern chemical analysis. The terms *spectroscopy* and **spectrometry** refer to a large group of instrumental techniques that obtain spectra to gather data on a substance's atomic and molecular energy levels.

Types of Spectra

Emission and absorption spectra are two important types:

1. An **emission spectrum,** such as the H atom line spectrum, occurs when atoms in an excited state *emit* photons as they return to a lower energy state. Some elements produce an intense spectral line (or several closely spaced ones) that is evidence of their presence. **Flame tests,** performed by placing a granule of an ionic compound or a drop of its solution in a flame, rely on these intense emissions (Figure B7.1, part A), and some colors of fireworks are due to the same elements (Figure B7.1, part B). The colors of sodium-vapor and mercury-vapor streetlamps are due to intense emissions lines in these elements' spectra.

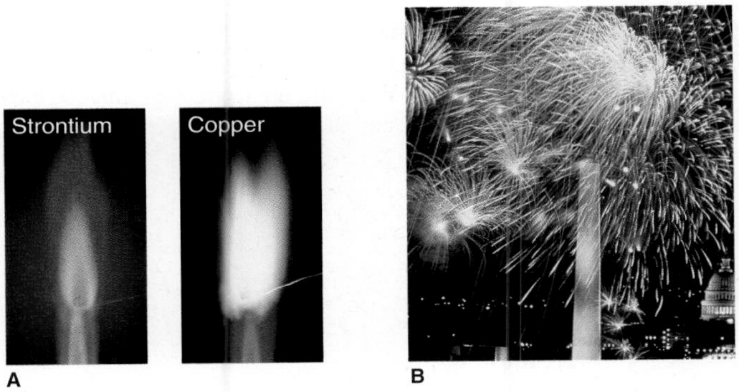

Figure B7.1 Flame tests and fireworks. **A,** The flame's color is due to intense emission by the element of light of a particular wavelength. **B,** Fireworks display emissions similar to those seen in flame tests.

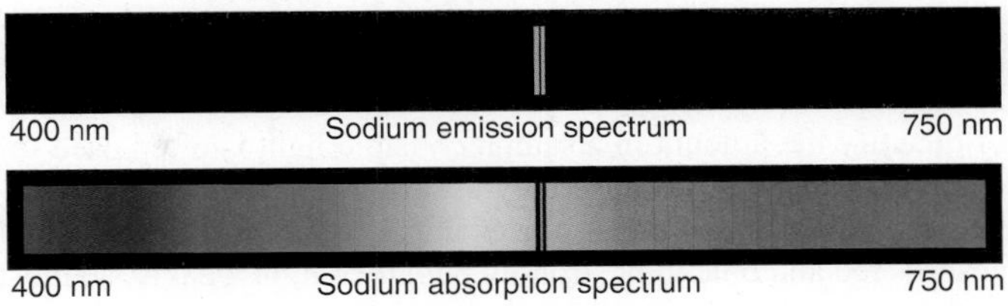

Figure B7.2 Emission and absorption spectra of sodium atoms. The wavelengths of the bright emission lines correspond to those of the dark absorption lines because both are created by the same energy change: $\Delta E_{\text{emission}} = -\Delta E_{\text{absorption}}$. (Only the two most intense lines in the Na spectra are shown.)

2. An **absorption spectrum** is produced when atoms *absorb* photons of certain wavelengths and become excited. When white light passes through sodium vapor, for example, the absorption spectrum shows dark lines at the same wavelengths as the yellow-orange lines in sodium's emission spectrum (Figure B7.2).

Basic Instrumentation

Instruments based on absorption spectra are much more common than those based on emission spectra because many substances absorb relatively few wavelengths so their spectra are more characteristic, and absorption is less destructive of fragile molecules.

Design differences depend on the region of the electromagnetic spectrum used to irradiate the sample, but all modern spectrometers have components that perform the same basic functions (Figure B7.3). (We discuss infrared spectroscopy and nuclear magnetic resonance spectroscopy in later chapters.)

(continued)

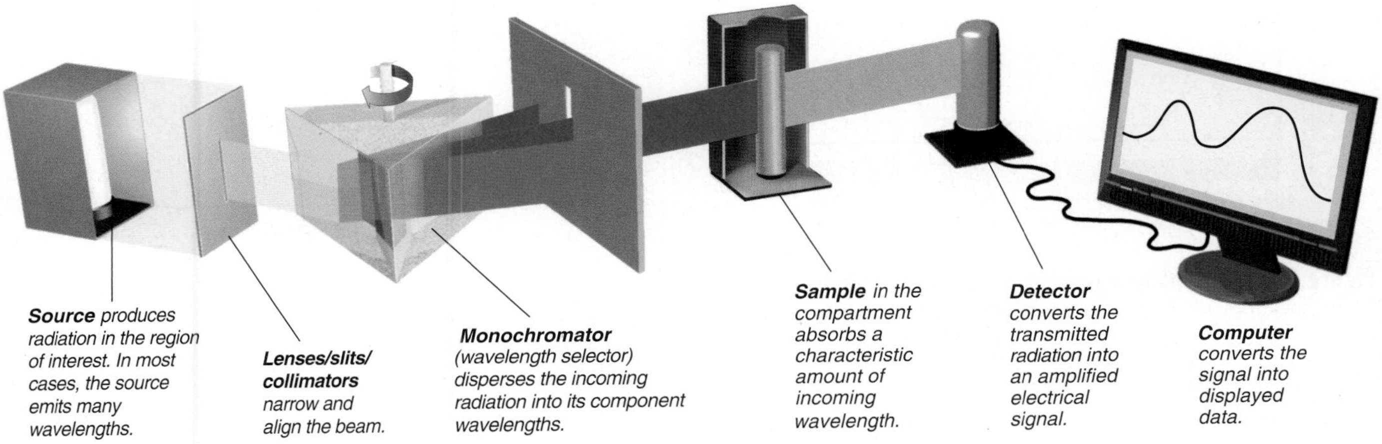

Figure B7.3 Components of a typical spectrometer.

Identifying and Quantifying a Substance

In chemical analysis, spectra are used to identify a substance and/or quantify the amount in a sample. Visible light is often used for colored substances, because they absorb only some of the wavelengths. A leaf looks green, for example, because its chlorophyll absorbs red and blue light strongly but green light weakly, so most of the green light is reflected.

Figure B7.4 shows the visible absorption spectrum of chlorophyll *a* in ether solution. The shape of the curve and the wavelengths of the major peaks are characteristic of chlorophyll *a*. The curve varies in height because chlorophyll *a* absorbs light of different wavelengths to different extents. The absorptions appear as broad bands, rather than as the distinct lines seen on absorption spectra of elements, because there are greater numbers and types of energy levels within a molecule and between molecules and solvent.

In addition to identifying a substance, a spectrometer can be used to measure its concentration because *absorbance,* the quantity of light of a given wavelength absorbed by a substance, is *proportional to the number of molecules.* Suppose you want to determine the concentration of chlorophyll *a* in a leaf extract. You select a strongly absorbed wavelength from the compound's spectrum (such as 663 nm in Figure B7.4, part A), measure the absorbance of the *unknown* solution, and compare it with the absorbances of a series of solutions of *known* concentration (Figure B7.4, part B).

Problems

B7.1 The sodium salt of 2-quinizarinsulfonic acid forms a complex with Al^{3+} that absorbs strongly at 560 nm. (a) Use the data below to draw a plot of absorbance vs. concentration of the complex in solution and find the slope and *y*-intercept:

Concentration (*M*)	Absorbance (560 nm)
1.0×10^{-5}	0.131
1.5×10^{-5}	0.201
2.0×10^{-5}	0.265
2.5×10^{-5}	0.329
3.0×10^{-5}	0.396

(b) When 20.0 mL of a solution of this complex is diluted with water to 150. mL, its absorbance is 0.236. Find the concentrations of the diluted solution and of the original solution.

B7.2 In fireworks displays, flame tests, and other emission events, light of a given wavelength often indicates the presence of a particular element or ion. What are the frequency and color of the light associated with each of the following?
(a) Li, $\lambda = 671$ nm
(b) Cs^+, $\lambda = 453$ nm
(c) Na, $\lambda = 589$ nm

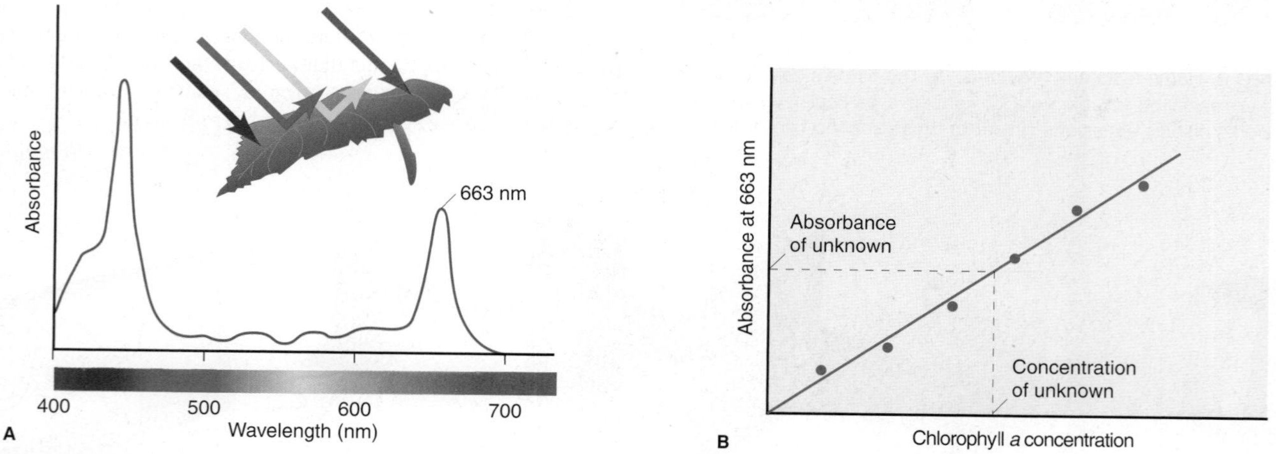

Figure B7.4 Measuring chlorophyll *a* concentration in leaf extract. **A,** The spectrometer is set to measure the strong absorption at 663 nm in the chlorophyll *a* spectrum. **B,** The absorbance from the leaf extract is compared to a series of known standards.

7.3 • THE WAVE-PARTICLE DUALITY OF MATTER AND ENERGY

The year 1905 was a busy one for Albert Einstein. He had just presented the photon theory and explained the photoelectric effect. A friend remembered him in his small apartment, rocking his baby in its carriage with one hand, while scribbling with the other ideas for a new branch of physics—the theory of relativity. One of its revelations was that *matter and energy are alternate forms of the same entity*. This idea is embodied in his famous equation $E = mc^2$, relating the quantity of energy equivalent to a given mass. Some results that showed energy to be particle-like had to coexist with others that showed matter to be wavelike. These remarkable ideas are the key to understanding our modern atomic model.

The Wave Nature of Electrons and the Particle Nature of Photons

Bohr's model was a perfect case of fitting theory to data: he *assumed* that an atom has only certain energy levels in order to *explain* line spectra. However, Bohr had no theoretical basis for the assumption. Several breakthroughs in the early 1920s provided that basis and blurred the distinction between matter (chunky and massive) and energy (diffuse and massless).

The Wave Nature of Electrons Attempting to explain why an atom has fixed energy levels, a French physics student, Louis de Broglie, considered other systems that display only certain allowed motions, such as the vibrations of a plucked guitar string. Figure 7.12 shows that, because the end of the string is fixed, only certain vibrational frequencies (and wavelengths) are allowable to create a note. De Broglie proposed that *if energy is particle-like, perhaps matter is wavelike.* He reasoned that *if electrons have wavelike motion* in orbits of fixed radii, they would have only certain allowable frequencies and energies.

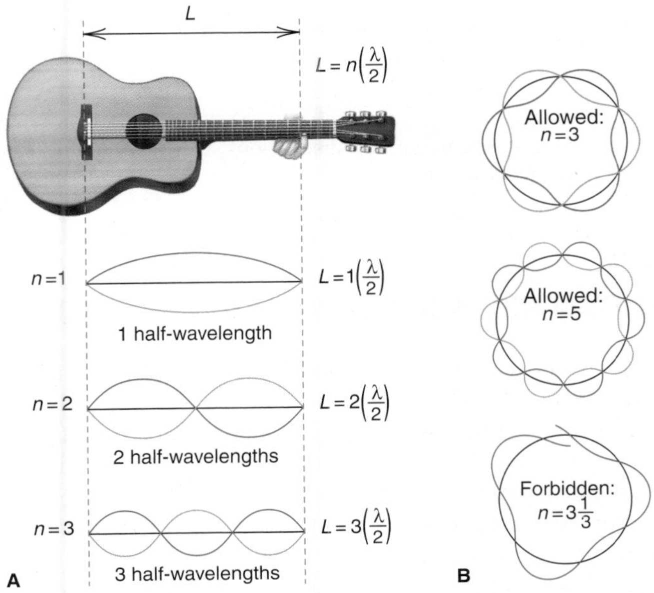

Figure 7.12 Wave motion in restricted systems. **A,** One half-wavelength (λ/2) is the "quantum" of the guitar string's vibration. With string length L fixed by a finger on the fret, allowed vibrations occur when L is a whole-number multiple (n) of λ/2. **B,** In a circular electron orbit, only whole numbers of wavelengths are allowed ($n = 3$ and $n = 5$ are shown). A wave with a fractional number of wavelengths (such as $n = 3\frac{1}{3}$) is "forbidden" because it dies out through overlap of crests and troughs.

Combining the equations for mass-energy equivalence ($E = mc^2$) and energy of a photon ($E = h\nu = hc/\lambda$), de Broglie derived an equation for the wavelength of any particle of mass m—whether planet, baseball, or electron—moving at speed u:

$$\lambda = \frac{h}{mu} \quad (7.5)$$

According to this equation for the **de Broglie wavelength,** *matter behaves as though it moves in a wave.* An object's wavelength is *inversely* proportional to its mass, so heavy objects such as planets and baseballs have wavelengths *many* orders of magnitude smaller than the object itself (Table 7.1).

Table 7.1 The de Broglie Wavelengths of Several Objects

Substance	Mass (g)	Speed (m/s)	λ (m)
Slow electron	9×10^{-28}	1.0	7×10^{-4}
Fast electron	9×10^{-28}	5.9×10^{6}	1×10^{-10}
Alpha particle	6.6×10^{-24}	1.5×10^{7}	7×10^{-15}
1-gram mass	1.0	0.01	7×10^{-29}
Baseball	142	40.0	1×10^{-34}
Earth	6.0×10^{27}	3.0×10^{4}	4×10^{-63}

Sample Problem 7.4 Calculating the de Broglie Wavelength of an Electron

Problem Find the de Broglie wavelength of an electron with a speed of 1.00×10^{6} m/s (electron mass = 9.11×10^{-31} kg; $h = 6.626\times10^{-34}$ kg·m²/s).

Plan We know the speed (1.00×10^{6} m/s) and mass (9.11×10^{-31} kg) of the electron, so we substitute these into Equation 7.5 to find λ.

Solution

$$\lambda = \frac{h}{mu} = \frac{6.626\times10^{-34}\ \text{kg·m}^2\text{/s}}{(9.11\times10^{-31}\ \text{kg})(1.00\times10^{6}\ \text{m/s})} = 7.27\times10^{-10}\ \text{m}$$

Check The order of magnitude and units seem correct:

$$\lambda \approx \frac{10^{-33}\ \text{kg·m}^2\text{/s}}{(10^{-30}\ \text{kg})(10^{6}\ \text{m/s})} = 10^{-9}\ \text{m}$$

Comment As you'll see in the upcoming discussion, such fast-moving electrons, with wavelengths in the range of atomic sizes, exhibit remarkable properties.

Follow-Up Problem 7.4 What is the speed of an electron that has a de Broglie wavelength of 100. nm?

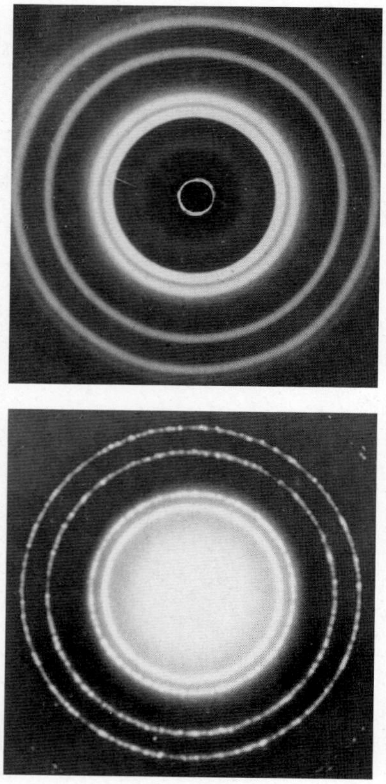

Figure 7.13 Diffraction patterns of aluminum with x-rays (*top*) and electrons (*bottom*).

If electrons travel in waves, they should exhibit diffraction and interference. A fast-moving electron has a wavelength of about 10^{-10} m, so a beam of such electrons should be diffracted by the spaces between atoms in a crystal—about 10^{-10} m. In 1927, C. Davisson and L. Germer guided a beam of x-rays and then a beam of electrons at a nickel crystal and obtained two diffraction patterns; Figure 7.13 shows these patterns for aluminum. Thus, electrons—particles with mass and charge—create diffraction patterns, just as electromagnetic waves do.

A major application of electrons traveling in waves is the *electron microscope.* Its great advantage over light microscopes is that high-speed electrons have much smaller wavelengths than visible light, which allow much higher resolution. A transmission electron microscope focuses a beam of electrons through a lens, and the beam then passes through a thin section of the specimen to a second and then third lens. In this instrument, these "lenses" are electromagnetic fields, which can result in up to 200,000-fold magnification. In a scanning electron microscope, the beam scans the specimen, knocking electrons from it that create a current, which generates an image that looks like the object's surface (Figure 7.14).

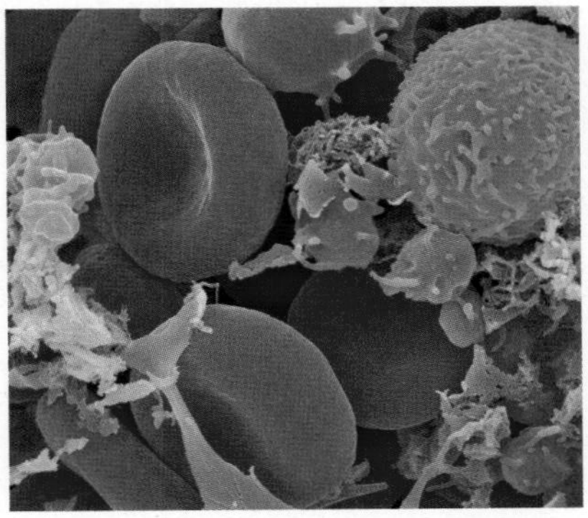

Figure 7.14 False-color scanning electron micrograph of blood cells (x1200).

The Particle Nature of Photons If electrons have properties of energy, do photons have properties of matter? The de Broglie equation suggests that we can calculate the momentum (p), the product of mass and speed, for a photon. Substituting the speed of light (c) for speed u in Equation 7.5 and solving for p gives

$$\lambda = \frac{h}{mc} = \frac{h}{p} \qquad \text{and} \qquad p = \frac{h}{\lambda}$$

The inverse relationship between p and λ in this equation means that shorter wavelength (higher energy) photons have greater momentum. Thus, a decrease in a photon's momentum should appear as an increase in its wavelength. In 1923, Arthur Compton directed a beam of x-ray photons at graphite and observed an increase in the wavelength of the reflected photons. Thus, just as billiard balls transfer momentum when they collide, the photons transferred momentum to the electrons in the carbon atoms of the graphite. In this experiment, photons behaved as particles.

Wave-Particle Duality Classical experiments had shown matter to be particle-like and energy to be wavelike. But, results on the atomic scale show electrons moving in waves and photons having momentum. Thus, every property of matter was also a property of energy. The truth is that *both* matter and energy show *both* behaviors: each possesses both "faces." In some experiments, we observe one face; in other experiments, we observe the other face. Our everyday distinction between matter and energy is meaningful in the macroscopic world, *not* in the atomic world. The distinction is in our minds and the limited definitions we have created, not inherent in nature. This dual character of matter and energy is known as the **wave-particle duality.** Figure 7.15 summarizes the theories and observations that led to this new understanding.

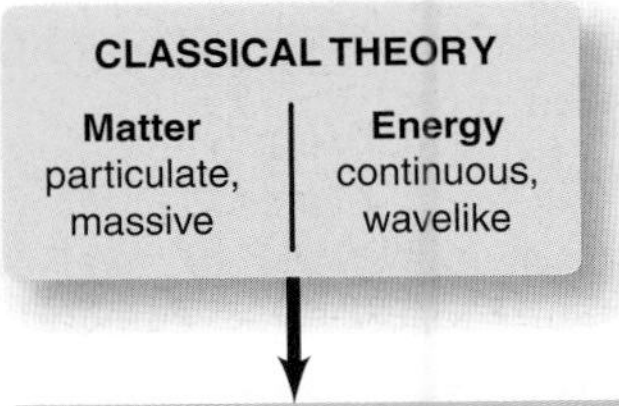

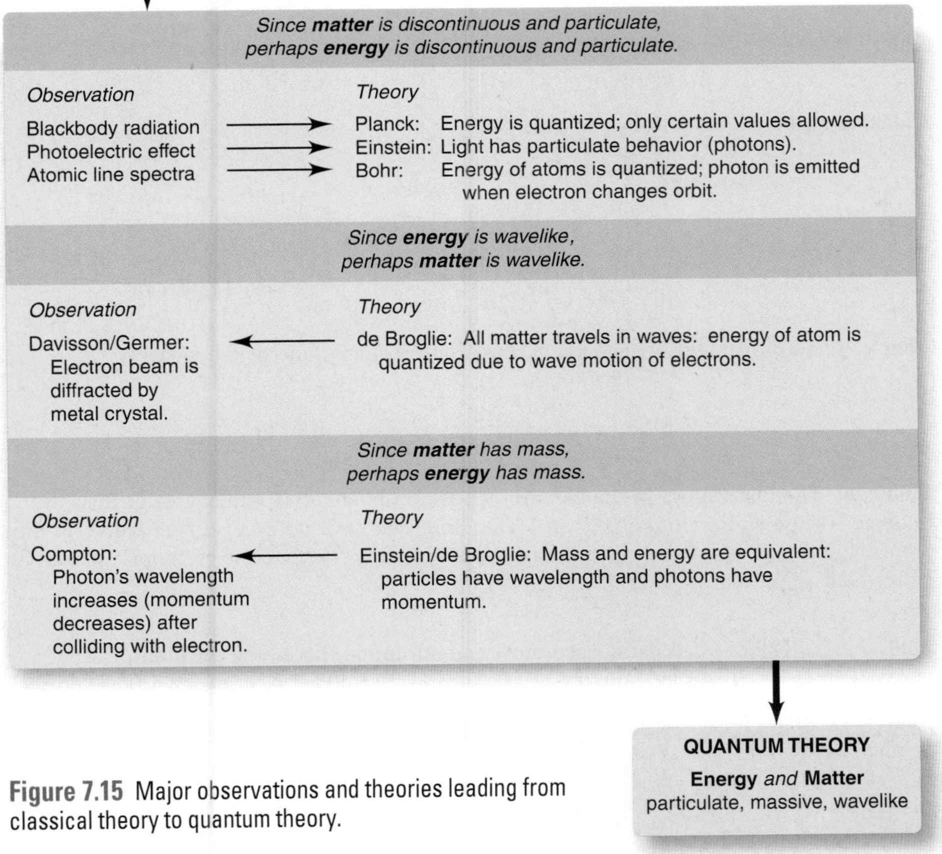

Figure 7.15 Major observations and theories leading from classical theory to quantum theory.

Heisenberg's Uncertainty Principle

In classical physics, a moving particle has a definite location at any instant, whereas a wave is spread out in space. If an electron has the properties of *both* a particle and a wave, can we determine its position in the atom? In 1927, the German physicist Werner Heisenberg postulated the **uncertainty principle,** which states that it is impossible to know simultaneously the position *and* momentum (mass times speed) of a particle. For a particle with constant mass m, the principle is expressed mathematically as

$$\Delta x \cdot m\Delta u \geq \frac{h}{4\pi} \tag{7.6}$$

where Δx is the uncertainty in position, Δu is the uncertainty in speed, and h is Planck's constant. The more accurately we know the position of the particle (smaller Δx), the less accurately we know its speed (larger Δu), and vice versa. The best-case scenario is that we know the product of these uncertainties, which is equal to $h/4\pi$.

For a macroscopic object like a baseball, Δx and Δu are insignificant because the mass is enormous compared with $h/4\pi$. Thus, by knowing the position and speed of a pitched baseball, we can use the laws of motion to predict its trajectory and whether it will be a ball or a strike. However, using the position and speed of an electron to find its trajectory is a very different proposition, as Sample Problem 7.5 demonstrates.

Sample Problem 7.5 Applying the Uncertainty Principle

Problem An electron moving near an atomic nucleus has a speed of 6×10^6 m/s $\pm$ 1%. What is the uncertainty in its position (Δx)?

Plan The uncertainty in the speed (Δu) is given as 1%, so we multiply u (6×10^6 m/s) by 0.01 to calculate the value of Δu, substitute it into Equation 7.6, and solve for the uncertainty in position (Δx).

Solution Finding the uncertainty in speed, Δu:

$$\Delta u = 1\% \text{ of } u = 0.01(6\times10^6 \text{ m/s}) = 6\times10^4 \text{ m/s}$$

Calculating the uncertainty in position, Δx:

$$\Delta x \cdot m\Delta u \geq \frac{h}{4\pi}$$

Thus,

$$\Delta x \geq \frac{h}{4\pi m\Delta u} \geq \frac{6.626\times10^{-34}\ \text{kg}\cdot\text{m}^2/\text{s}}{4\pi(9.11\times10^{-31}\ \text{kg})(6\times10^4\ \text{m/s})} \geq 1\times10^{-9}\ \text{m}$$

Check Be sure to round off and check the order of magnitude of the answer:

$$\Delta x \geq \frac{10^{-33}\ \text{kg}\cdot\text{m}^2/\text{s}}{(10^1)(10^{-30}\ \text{kg})(10^5\ \text{m/s})} = 10^{-9}\ \text{m}$$

Comment The uncertainty in the electron's position is about 10 times greater than the diameter of the entire atom (10^{-10} m)! Therefore, we have no precise idea where in the atom the electron is located. In the follow-up problem, you'll see if an umpire has any better idea about the position of a baseball.

Follow-Up Problem 7.5 How accurately can an umpire know the position of a baseball (mass = 0.142 kg) moving at 100.0 mi/h $\pm$ 1.00% (44.7 m/s $\pm$ 1.00%)?

Summary of Section 7.3

- As a result of Planck's quantum theory and Einstein's theory of relativity, we no longer view matter and energy as distinct entities.
- The de Broglie wavelength is based on the idea that an electron (or any object) has wavelike motion. Allowed atomic energy levels are related to allowed wavelengths of the electron's motion.
- Electrons exhibit diffraction, just as light waves do, and photons exhibit transfer of momentum, just as objects do. This wave-particle duality of matter and energy is observable only on the atomic scale.
- According to the uncertainty principle, we can never know the position and speed of an electron simultaneously.

7.4 • THE QUANTUM-MECHANICAL MODEL OF THE ATOM

Acceptance of the dual nature of matter and energy and of the uncertainty principle culminated in the field of **quantum mechanics,** which examines the wave nature of objects on the atomic scale. In 1926, Erwin Schrödinger derived an equation that is the basis for the *quantum-mechanical model* of the H atom. The model describes an atom with specific quantities of energy that result from allowed frequencies of its electron's wavelike motion. The electron's position can only be known within a certain probability. Key features of the model are described in the following subsections.

The Atomic Orbital and the Probable Location of the Electron

Two central aspects of the quantum-mechanical model concern the atomic orbital and the electron's probable location.

The Schrödinger Equation and the Atomic Orbital The electron's matter-wave occupies the space near the nucleus and is continuously influenced by it. The **Schrödinger equation** is quite complex but can be represented in simpler form as

$$\mathcal{H}\psi = E\psi$$

where E is the energy of the atom. The symbol ψ (Greek *psi,* pronounced "sigh") is called a **wave function (or atomic orbital),** a mathematical description of the electron's matter-wave in three dimensions. The symbol $\mathcal{H}$, called the Hamiltonian operator, represents a set of mathematical operations that, when carried out with a particular ψ, yields one of the allowed energy states of the atom.* Thus, *each solution of the equation gives an energy state associated with a given atomic orbital.*

An important point to keep in mind throughout this discussion is that an "orbital" in the quantum-mechanical model *bears no resemblance* to an "orbit" in the Bohr model: an *orbit* is an electron's actual path around the nucleus, whereas an *orbital* is a mathematical function that describes the electron's matter-wave but has no physical meaning.

The Probable Location of the Electron While we cannot know *exactly* where the electron is at any moment, we can know where it *probably* is, that is, where it spends most of its time. We get this information by squaring the wave function. Thus, even

*The complete form of the Schrödinger equation in terms of the three linear axes is

$$\left[-\frac{h^2}{8\pi^2 m_e}\left(\frac{d^2}{dx^2}+\frac{d^2}{dy^2}+\frac{d^2}{dz^2}\right)+V(x, y, z)\right]\psi(x, y, z) = E\psi(x, y, z)$$

where ψ is the wave function; m_e is the electron's mass; E is the total quantized energy of the atomic system; and V is the potential energy at point (x, y, z).

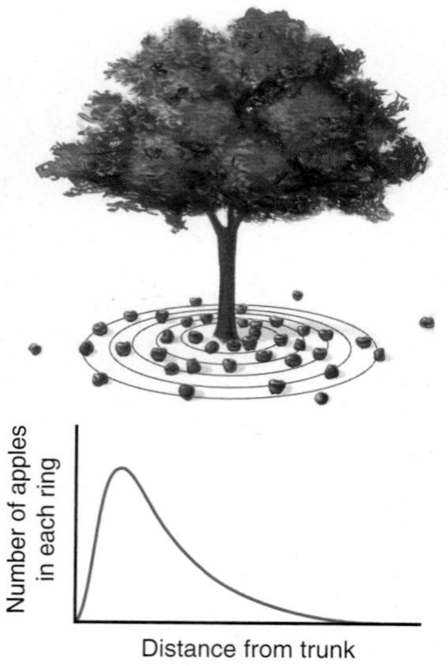

A Radial Probability Distribution of Apples An analogy might clarify why the curve in the radial probability distribution plot peaks and then falls off. Picture fallen apples around the base of an apple tree: the density of apples is greatest near the trunk and decreases with distance. Divide the ground under the tree into foot-wide concentric rings and collect the apples within each ring. Apple density is greatest in the first ring, but the area of the second ring is larger, and so it contains a greater *total* number of apples. Farther out near the edge of the tree, rings have more area but lower apple "density," so the total number of apples decreases. A plot of "number of apples in each ring" vs. "distance from trunk" shows a peak at some distance close to the trunk, as in Figure 7.16D.

though ψ has no physical meaning, ψ^2 does and is called the *probability density,* a measure of the probability of finding the electron in some tiny volume of the atom. We depict the electron's probable location in several ways, which we'll look at first for the H atom's *ground state:*

1. *Probability of the electron being in some tiny volume of the atom.* For each energy level, we can create an *electron probability density diagram,* or more simply, an **electron density diagram.** The value of ψ^2 for a given volume is shown with dots: the greater the density of dots, the higher the probability of finding the electron in that volume. Note, that for the ground state of the H atom, *the electron probability density decreases with distance from the nucleus* along a line, *r* (Figure 7.16A).

These diagrams are also called **electron cloud depictions** because, if we *could* take a time-exposure photograph of the electron in wavelike motion around the nucleus, it would appear as a "cloud" of positions. The electron cloud is an *imaginary* picture of the electron changing its position rapidly over time; it does *not* mean that an electron is a diffuse cloud of charge.

Figure 7.16B shows a plot of ψ^2 vs. *r*. Due to the thickness of the printed line, the curve appears to touch the axis; however, in the blow-up circle, we see that *the probability of the electron being far from the nucleus is very small, but not zero.*

2. *Total probability density at some distance from the nucleus.* To find *radial probability distribution,* that is, the *total* probability of finding the electron at some distance *r* from the nucleus, we first mentally divide the volume around the nucleus into thin, concentric, spherical layers, like the layers of an onion (shown in cross section in Figure 7.16C). Then, we find the *sum of ψ^2 values* in each layer to see which is most likely to contain the electron.

The falloff in probability density with distance has an important effect. Near the nucleus, *the volume of each layer increases faster than its density of dots decreases.* The result of these opposing effects is that the *total* probability peaks in a layer *near,* but not *at,* the nucleus. For example, the total probability in the second layer is higher than in the first, but this result disappears with greater distance. Figure 7.16D shows this result as a **radial probability distribution plot.**

3. *Probability contour and the size of the atom.* How far away from the nucleus can we find the electron? This is the same as asking "How big is the H atom?" Recall from Figure 7.16B that the probability of finding the electron far from the nucleus

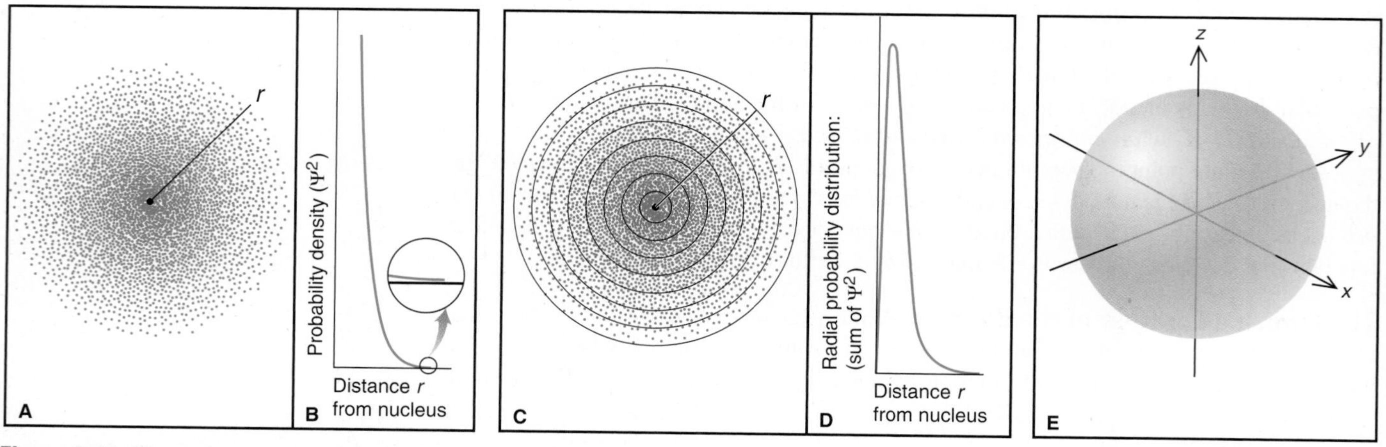

Figure 7.16 Electron probability density in the ground-state H atom. **A,** In the electron density diagram, the density of dots represents the probability of the electron within a tiny volume and decreases with distance, *r*, from the nucleus. **B,** The probability density (ψ^2) decreases with *r* but does not reach zero (*blow-up circle*). **C,** Counting dots within each layer gives the total probability of the electron being in that layer. **D,** A radial probability distribution plot shows that total electron density peaks *near,* but not *at,* the nucleus. **E,** A 90% probability contour for the ground state of the H atom.

is not zero. Therefore, we *cannot* assign a definite volume to an atom. However, we can visualize an atom with a 90% **probability contour:** the electron is somewhere within that volume 90% of the time (Figure 7.16E).

As you'll see later in this section, each atomic orbital has a distinctive radial probability distribution and 90% probability contour.

Quantum Numbers of an Atomic Orbital

An atomic orbital is specified by three quantum numbers (Table 7.2) that are part of the solution of the Schrödinger equation and indicate the size, shape, and orientation in space of the orbital.*

1. The **principal quantum number (n)** *is a positive integer* (1, 2, 3, and so forth). It indicates the relative *size* of the orbital and therefore the relative *distance from the nucleus* of the peak in the radial probability distribution plot. The principal quantum number specifies the *energy level* of the H atom: *the higher the n value, the higher the energy level.* When the electron occupies an orbital with $n = 1$, the H atom is in its ground state and has its lowest energy. When the electron occupies an orbital with $n = 2$ (first excited state), the atom has more energy.

2. The **angular momentum quantum number (l)** *is an integer from 0 to* $n - 1$. It is related to the *shape* of the orbital. Note that the principal quantum number sets a limit on the angular momentum quantum number: n limits l. For an orbital with $n = 1$, l can have only one value, 0. For orbitals with $n = 2$, l can have two values, 0 or 1. For orbitals with $n = 3$, l can have three values, 0, 1, or 2; and so forth. Thus, the number of possible l values equals the value of n.

3. The **magnetic quantum number (m_l)** *is an integer from* $-l$ *through 0 to* $+l$. It prescribes the three-dimensional *orientation* of the orbital in the space around the nucleus. The angular momentum quantum number sets a limit on the magnetic quantum number: l limits m_l. An orbital with $l = 0$ can have only $m_l = 0$. However, an orbital with $l = 1$ can have one of three m_l values, -1, 0, or $+1$; that is, there are three possible orbitals with $l = 1$, each with its own orientation. Note that the number of m_l values *equals* $2l + 1$, which is the number of orbitals for a given l. The total number of m_l values, that is, the total number of orbitals, for a given n value is n^2.

*For ease in discussion, chemists often refer to the size, shape, and orientation of an "atomic orbital," although we really mean the size, shape, and orientation of an "atomic orbital's radial probability distribution."

Table 7.2 The Hierarchy of Quantum Numbers for Atomic Orbitals

Name, Symbol (Property)	Allowed Values	Quantum Numbers							
Principal, n (size, energy)	Positive integer (1, 2, 3, ...)	1	2		3		
Angular momentum, l (shape)	0 to $n - 1$	0	0	1	0	1	2
Magnetic, m_l (orientation)	$-l, \ldots, 0, \ldots, +l$	0	0	-1 0 $+1$	0	-1 0 $+1$	-2 -1 0 $+1$ $+2$

Sample Problem 7.6 Determining Quantum Numbers for an Energy Level

Problem What values of the angular momentum (l) and magnetic (m_l) quantum numbers are allowed for a principal quantum number (n) of 3? How many orbitals are allowed?

Plan We determine allowable quantum numbers with the rules from the text: l values are integers from 0 to $n - 1$, and m_l values are integers from $-l$ to 0 to $+l$. One m_l value is assigned to each orbital, so the number of m_l values gives the number of orbitals.

Solution Determining l values: for $n = 3$, $l = 0, 1, 2$.

Determining m_l for each l value:

$$\text{For } l = 0, \quad m_l = 0$$
$$\text{For } l = 1, \quad m_l = -1, 0, +1$$
$$\text{For } l = 2, \quad m_l = -2, -1, 0, +1, +2$$

There are nine m_l values, so there are nine orbitals with $n = 3$.

Check Table 7.2 shows that we are correct. As we saw, the total number of orbitals for a given n value is n^2, and for $n = 3$, $n^2 = 9$.

Follow-Up Problem 7.6 What are the possible l and m_l values for $n = 4$?

Quantum Numbers and Energy Levels

The energy states and orbitals of the atom are described with specific terms and are associated with one or more quantum numbers:

1. *Level.* The atom's energy **levels,** or *shells,* are given by the n value: the smaller the n value, the lower the energy level and the greater the probability that the electron is closer to the nucleus.

2. *Sublevel.* The atom's levels are divided into **sublevels,** or *subshells,* that are given by the l value. Each designates the orbital shape with a letter:

$l = 0$ is an *s* sublevel.
$l = 1$ is a *p* sublevel.
$l = 2$ is a *d* sublevel.
$l = 3$ is an *f* sublevel.

(The letters derive from names of spectroscopic lines: *s*harp, *p*rincipal, *d*iffuse, and *f*undamental.) Sublevels with l values greater than 3 are designated by consecutive letters after *f*: *g* sublevel, *h* sublevel, and so on. A sublevel is named with its n value and letter designation; for example, the sublevel (subshell) with $n = 2$ and $l = 0$ is called the 2*s* sublevel. We discuss orbital shapes below.

3. *Orbital.* Each combination of n, l, and m_l specifies the size (energy), shape, and spatial orientation of one of the atom's orbitals. We know the quantum numbers of the orbitals in a sublevel from the sublevel name and the quantum-number hierarchy. For example, any orbital in the 2*s* sublevel has $n = 2$ and $l = 0$, and given that l value, it can have only $m_l = 0$; thus, the 2*s* sublevel has only one orbital. Any orbital in the 3*p* sublevel has $n = 3$ and $l = 1$, and given that l value, one orbital has $m_l = -1$, another has $m_l = 0$, and a third has $m_l = +1$; thus, the 3*p* sublevel has three orbitals.

Sample Problem 7.7 Determining Sublevel Names and Orbital Quantum Numbers

Problem Give the name, magnetic quantum numbers, and number of orbitals for each sublevel with the given n and l quantum numbers:
(a) $n = 3$, $l = 2$
(b) $n = 2$, $l = 0$
(c) $n = 5$, $l = 1$
(d) $n = 4$, $l = 3$

Plan We name the sublevel (subshell) with the n value and the letter designation of the l value. From the l value, we find the number of possible m_l values, which equals the number of orbitals in that sublevel.

Solution

n	l	Sublevel Name	Possible m_l Values	No. of Orbitals
(a) 3	2	3*d*	−2, −1, 0, +1, +2	5
(b) 2	0	2*s*	0	1
(c) 5	1	5*p*	−1, 0, +1	3
(d) 4	3	4*f*	−3, −2, −1, 0, +1, +2, +3	7

Check Check the number of orbitals in each sublevel using

$$\text{No. of orbitals} = \text{no. of } m_l \text{ values} = 2l + 1$$

Follow-Up Problem 7.7 What are the n, l, and possible m_l values for the 2*p* and 5*f* sublevels?

Sample Problem 7.8 Identifying Incorrect Quantum Numbers

Problem What is wrong with each of the following quantum number designations and/or sublevel names?

n	l	m_l	Name
(a) 1	1	0	1*p*
(b) 4	3	+1	4*d*
(c) 3	1	−2	3*p*

Solution (a) A sublevel with $n = 1$ can have only $l = 0$, not $l = 1$. The only possible sublevel name is 1*s*.
(b) A sublevel with $l = 3$ is an *f* sublevel, not a *d* sublevel. The name should be 4*f*.
(c) A sublevel with $l = 1$ can have only −1, 0, or +1 for m_l, not −2.

Check Check that l is always less than n, and m_l is always $\geq -l$ and $\leq +l$.

Follow-Up Problem 7.8 Supply the missing quantum numbers and sublevel names.

n	l	m_l	Name
(a) ?	?	0	4*p*
(b) 2	1	0	?
(c) 3	2	−2	?
(d) ?	?	?	2*s*

Shapes of Atomic Orbitals

Each sublevel of the H atom consists of a set of orbitals with characteristic shapes. As you'll see in Chapter 8, orbitals for the other atoms have similar shapes.

The *s* Orbital An orbital with $l = 0$ has a *spherical* shape with the nucleus at its center and is called an ***s* orbital.** Because a sphere has only one orientation, an *s* orbital has only one m_l value: for any *s* orbital, $m_l = 0$.

1. *The 1s orbital* holds the electron in the H atom's ground state. *The electron probability density is highest at the nucleus.* Figure 7.17A shows this graphically (*top*), and an electron density *relief map (inset)* depicts the graph's curve in three dimensions. Note the quarter-section of a three-dimensional electron cloud depiction (*middle*) has the darkest shading at the nucleus. For reasons discussed earlier (see Figure 7.16D and the margin note, p. 280), the radial probability distribution plot

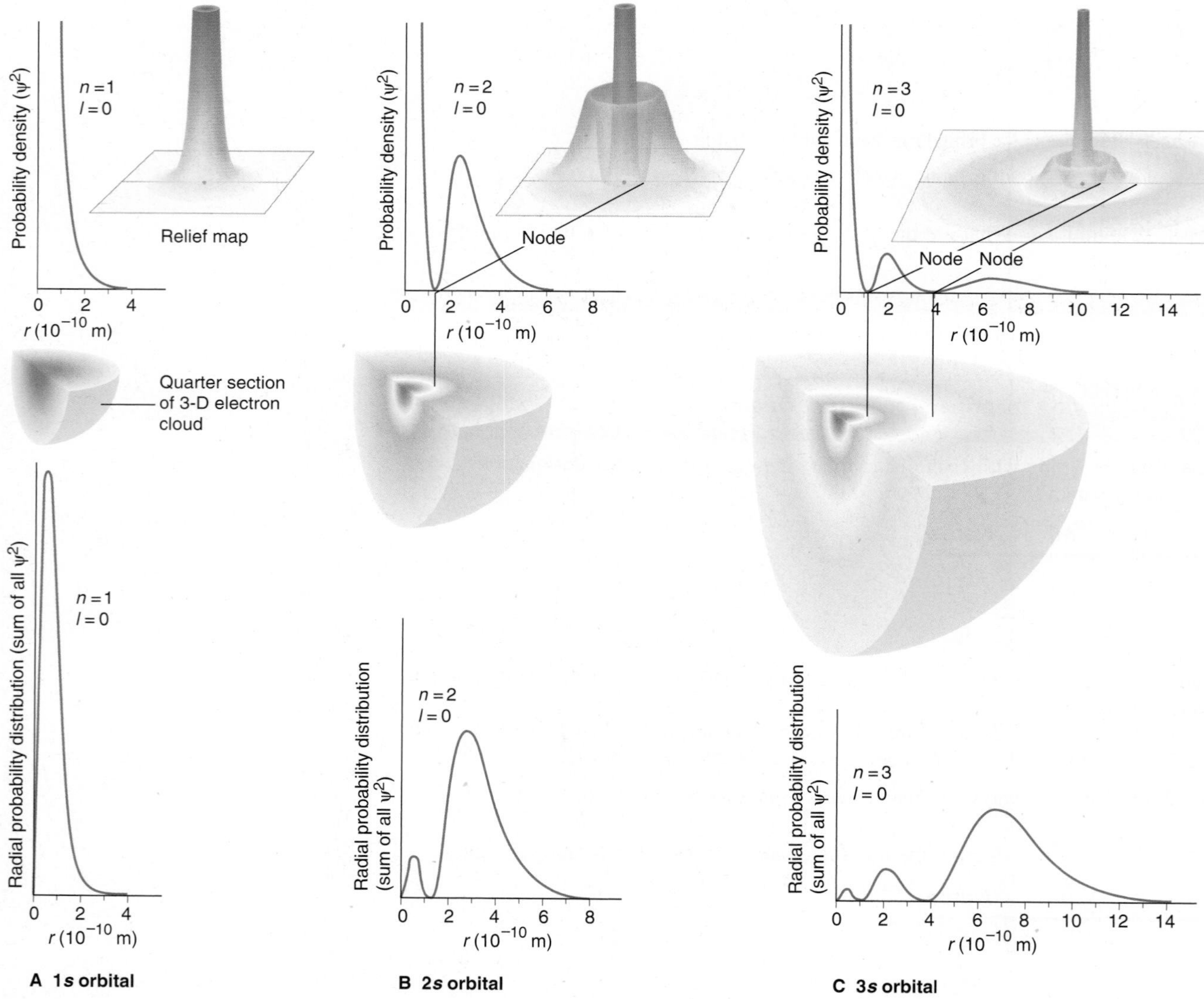

Figure 7.17 The 1*s*, 2*s*, and 3*s* orbitals. For each of the *s* orbitals, a plot of probability density vs. distance (*top*, with the relief map, *inset*, showing the plot in three dimensions) lies above a quarter section of an electron cloud depiction of the 90% probability contour (*middle*), which lies above a radial probability distribution plot (*bottom*). **A,** The 1*s* orbital. **B,** The 2*s* orbital. **C,** The 3*s* orbital.

(*bottom*) is highest slightly out from the nucleus. Both plots fall off smoothly with distance.

2. *The 2s orbital* (Figure 7.17B) has two regions of higher electron density. The radial probability distribution (Figure 7.17B, *bottom*) of the more distant region is *higher* than that of the closer one because the sum of ψ^2 for it is taken over a much larger volume. Between the two regions is a spherical **node,** where the probability of finding the electron drops to zero ($\psi^2 = 0$ at the node, analogous to zero amplitude of a wave exactly between the peak and trough). Because the 2*s* orbital is larger than the 1*s*, an electron in the 2*s* spends more time farther from the nucleus (in the larger of the two regions) than it does when it occupies the 1*s*.

3. *The 3s orbital* (Figure 7.17C) has three regions of high electron density and two nodes. Here again, the highest radial probability is at the greatest distance from the nucleus. This pattern of more nodes and higher probability with distance from the nucleus continues with the 4*s*, 5*s*, and so forth.

The *p* Orbital An orbital with $l = 1$ is called a ***p* orbital** and has two regions (lobes) of high probability, one on *either side* of the nucleus (Figure 7.18). The *nucleus lies at the nodal plane* of this dumbbell-shaped orbital. Since the maximum value of l is $n - 1$, only levels with $n = 2$ or higher have a *p* orbital: the lowest energy *p* orbital (the one closest to the nucleus) is the 2*p*. *One p* orbital consists of *two* lobes, and the electron spends *equal* time in both. Similar to the pattern for *s* orbitals, a 3*p* orbital is larger than a 2*p*, a 4*p* is larger than a 3*p*, and so forth.

Unlike *s* orbitals, *p* orbitals *have* different spatial orientations. The three possible m_l values of -1, 0, and $+1$ refer to three *mutually perpendicular* orientations; that is, while identical in size, shape, and energy, the three *p* orbitals differ in orientation. We associate *p* orbitals with the *x*, *y*, and *z* axes: the p_x orbital lies along the *x* axis, the p_y along the *y* axis, and the p_z along the *z* axis. (There is no relationship between a particular axis and a given m_l value.)

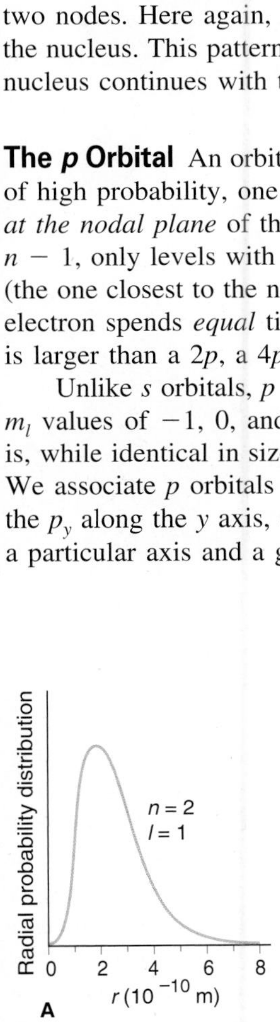

A

Figure 7.18 The 2*p* orbitals. **A,** A radial probability distribution plot of the 2*p* orbital shows a peak much farther from the nucleus than for the 1*s*. **B,** Cross section of an electron cloud depiction of the 90% probability contour of the $2p_z$ orbital shows a nodal plane. **C,** An accurate representation of the $2p_z$ probability contour. **D,** The stylized depiction of the 2*p* probability contour used in the text. **E,** The three (stylized) 2*p* orbitals occupy mutually perpendicular regions of space, contributing to the atom's overall spherical shape.

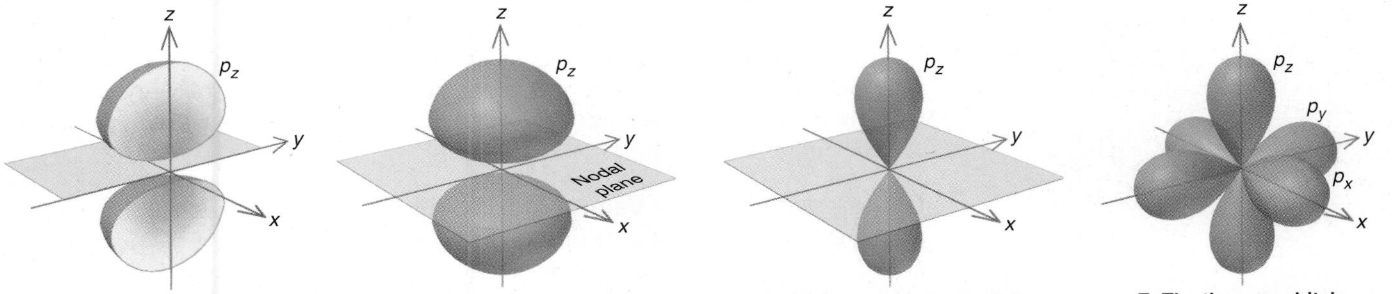

B Cross section of electron cloud depiction **C Accurate probability contour** **D Stylized probability contour** **E The three *p* orbitals**

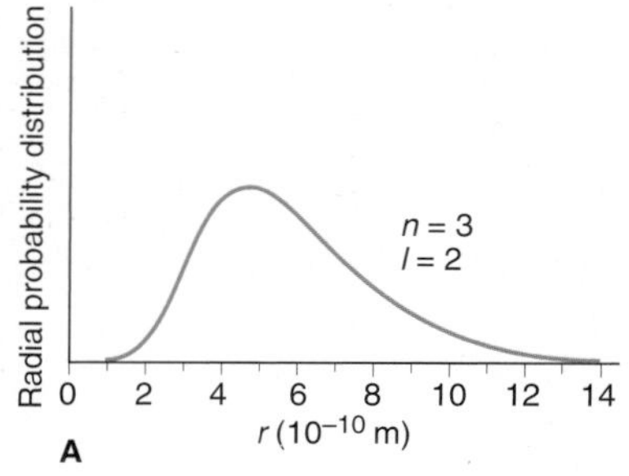

Figure 7.19 The 3*d* orbitals. **A,** A radial probability distribution plot. **B,** Cross section of an electron cloud depiction of the $3d_{yz}$ orbital probability contour shows two mutually perpendicular nodal planes and lobes lying *between* the axes. **C,** An accurate representation of the $3d_{yz}$ orbital probability contour. **D,** The stylized depiction of the $3d_{yz}$ orbital used in the text. **E,** The $3d_{xz}$ orbital. **F,** The $3d_{xy}$ orbital. **G,** The lobes of the $d_{x^2-y^2}$ orbital lie *along* the *x* and *y* axes. **H,** The d_{z^2} orbital has two lobes and a central, donut-shaped region. **I,** A composite of the five 3*d* (stylized) orbitals shows how they contribute to the atom's spherical shape.

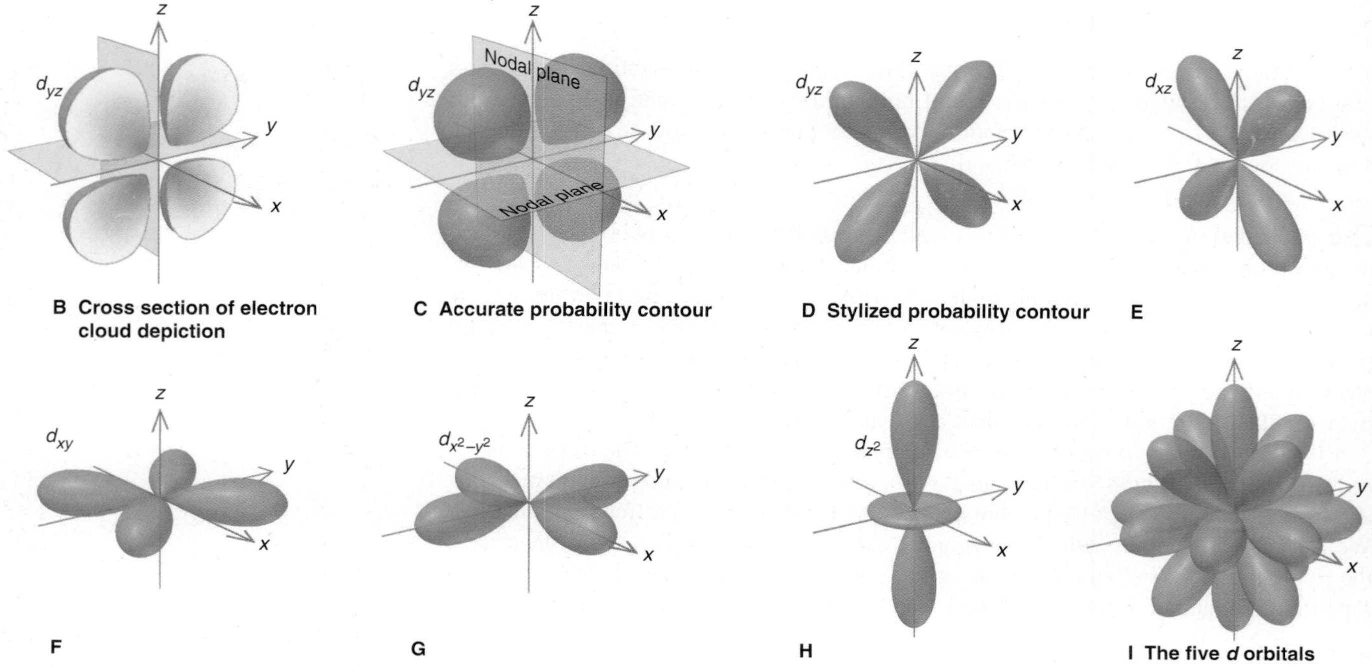

The *d* Orbital

An orbital with $l = 2$ is called a ***d* orbital.** There are five possible m_l values for $l = 2$: -2, -1, 0, $+1$, and $+2$. Thus, a *d* orbital has any one of five orientations (Figure 7.19). Four of the five *d* orbitals have four lobes (a cloverleaf shape) with two mutually perpendicular nodal planes between them and the nucleus at the junction of the lobes (Figure 7.19C). (The orientation of the nodal planes always lies between the orbital lobes.) Three of these orbitals lie in the *xy, xz,* and *yz* planes, with their lobes *between* the axes, and are called the d_{xy}, d_{xz}, and d_{yz} orbitals. A fourth, the $d_{x^2-y^2}$ orbital, also lies in the *xy* plane, but its lobes are *along* the axes. The fifth *d* orbital, the d_{z^2}, has two major lobes *along* the *z* axis, and a donut-shaped region girdles the center. An electron in a *d* orbital spends equal time in all of its lobes.

In keeping with the quantum-number hierarchy, a *d* orbital ($l = 2$) must have a principal quantum number of $n = 3$ or higher, so 3*d* is the lowest energy *d* sublevel. Orbitals in the 4*d* sublevel are larger (extend farther from the nucleus) than the 3*d*, and the 5*d* are larger still.

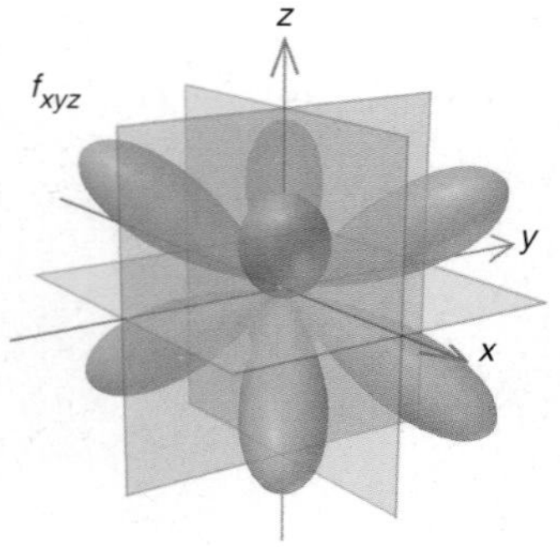

Figure 7.20 The $4f_{xyz}$ orbital, one of the seven 4*f* orbitals.

Orbitals with Higher *l* Values

Orbitals with $l = 3$ are *f* orbitals and have a principal quantum number of at least $n = 4$. Figure 7.20 shows one of the seven *f* orbitals ($2l + 1 = 7$); each *f* orbital has a complex, multilobed shape with several nodal planes. Orbitals with $l = 4$ are *g* orbitals, but they play no known role in chemical bonding.

The Special Case of Energy Levels in the H Atom

With regard to energy levels and sublevels, the H atom is a special case. When an H atom gains energy, its electron occupies an orbital of higher n value, which is (on average) farther from the nucleus. But, because it has just one electron, *hydrogen is the only atom whose energy state depends completely on the principal quantum number, n.* As you'll see in Chapter 8, because of additional nucleus-electron attractions and electron-electron repulsions, the energy states of all other atoms depend on the *n and l* values of the occupied orbitals. Thus, *for the H atom only,* all four $n = 2$ orbitals (one 2*s* and three 2*p*) have the same energy, all nine $n = 3$ orbitals (one 3*s*, three 3*p*, and five 3*d*) have the same energy (Figure 7.21), and so forth.

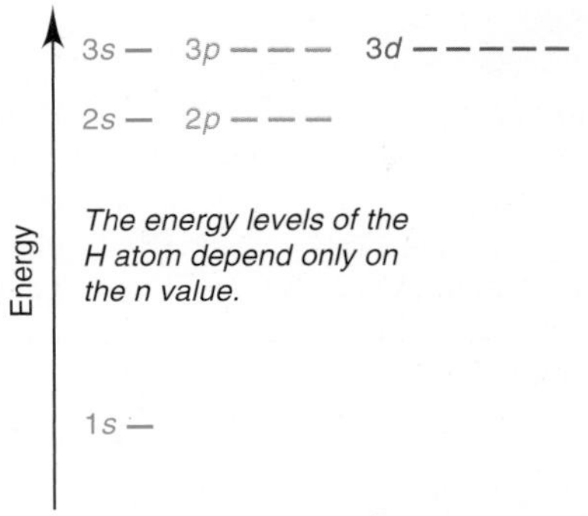

Figure 7.21 Energy levels of the H atom.

Summary of Section 7.4

- The atomic orbital (ψ, wave function) is a mathematical description of the electron's wavelike behavior in an atom. The Schrödinger equation converts each allowed wave function to one of the atom's energy states.
- The probability density of finding the electron at a particular location is represented by ψ^2. For a given energy level, an electron density diagram and a radial probability distribution plot show how the electron occupies the space near the nucleus.
- An atomic orbital is described by three quantum numbers: size (n), shape (l), and orientation (m_l): n limits l to $n - 1$ values, and l limits m_l to $2l + 1$ values.
- An energy level has sublevels with the same n value; a sublevel has orbitals with the same n and l values but differing m_l values.
- A sublevel with $l = 0$ has a spherical (*s*) orbital; a sublevel with $l = 1$ has three, two-lobed (*p*) orbitals; and a sublevel with $l = 2$ has five multilobed (*d*) orbitals.
- In the special case of the H atom, the energy levels depend only on the n value.

CHAPTER REVIEW GUIDE

Learning Objectives

Relevant section (§) and/or sample problem (SP) numbers appear in parentheses.

Understand These Concepts

1. The wave characteristics of light (the interrelations of frequency, wavelength, and speed; the meaning of amplitude) and the general regions of the electromagnetic spectrum (§7.1)
2. How particles and waves differ in terms of the phenomena of refraction, diffraction, and interference (§7.1)
3. The quantization of energy and how an atom changes its energy by emitting or absorbing quanta of radiation (§7.1)
4. How the photon theory explains the photoelectric effect (§7.1)
5. How Bohr's theory explained the line spectra of the H atom; why the theory is wrong and which ideas we retain (§7.2)
6. The wave-particle duality of matter and energy and the relevant theories and experiments that led to it (de Broglie wavelength, electron diffraction, and photon momentum) (§7.3)
7. The meaning of the uncertainty principle and how uncertainty limits our knowledge of electron properties (§7.3)
8. The distinction between ψ (wave function, or atomic orbital) and ψ^2 (probability density) (§7.4)
9. How electron density diagrams and radial probability distribution plots depict the electron's location within the atom (§7.4)
10. The hierarchy of the quantum numbers that describe the size (n, energy), shape (l), and orientation (m_l) of an orbital (§7.4)
11. The distinction between energy level (shell), sublevel (subshell), and orbital (§7.4)
12. The shapes of *s*, *p*, and *d* orbitals (§7.4)

Master These Skills

1. Interconverting wavelength and frequency (SP 7.1)
2. Calculating the energy of a photon from its wavelength (SP 7.2)
3. Finding the energy change and wavelength of the photon absorbed or emitted when an H atom changes its energy level (SP 7.3)
4. Applying de Broglie's equation to find the wavelength of an electron (SP 7.4)
5. Applying the uncertainty principle to see that the location and speed of a particle cannot be determined simultaneously (SP 7.5)
6. Determining quantum numbers and sublevel designations (SPs 7.6–7.8)

Key Terms

Page numbers appear in parentheses.

Key Equations and Relationships

Page numbers appear in parentheses.

7.1 Relating the speed of light to its frequency and wavelength (262):

$$c = \nu \times \lambda$$

7.2 Determining the smallest change in an atom's energy (266):

$$\Delta E = h\nu$$

7.3 Calculating the wavelength of any line in the H atom spectrum (Rydberg equation) (268):

$$\frac{1}{\lambda} = R\left(\frac{1}{n_1^2} - \frac{1}{n_2^2}\right)$$

where n_1 and n_2 are positive integers and $n_2 > n_1$

7.4 Finding the difference between two energy levels in the H atom (271):

$$\Delta E = E_{\text{final}} - E_{\text{initial}} = -2.18\times10^{-18}\ \text{J}\left(\frac{1}{n_{\text{final}}^2} - \frac{1}{n_{\text{initial}}^2}\right)$$

7.5 Calculating the wavelength of any moving particle (de Broglie wavelength) (276):

$$\lambda = \frac{h}{mu}$$

7.6 Finding the uncertainty in position or speed of a particle (Heisenberg's uncertainty principle) (278):

$$\Delta x \cdot m\Delta u \geq \frac{h}{4\pi}$$

Brief Solutions to Follow-Up Problems

7.1 $\lambda\ (\text{nm}) = \dfrac{3.00\times10^8\ \text{m/s}}{7.23\times10^{14}\ \text{s}^{-1}} \times \dfrac{10^9\ \text{nm}}{1\ \text{m}} = 415\ \text{nm}$

$\lambda\ (\text{Å}) = 415\ \text{nm} \times \dfrac{10\ \text{Å}}{1\ \text{nm}} = 4150\ \text{Å}$

7.2 (a) UV: $E = hc/\lambda$

$$= \frac{(6.626\times10^{-34}\ \text{J}\cdot\text{s})(3.00\times10^8\ \text{m/s})}{1\times10^{-8}\ \text{m}} = 2\times10^{-17}\ \text{J}$$

(b) Visible: $E = 4\times10^{-19}$ J; (c) IR: $E = 2\times10^{-21}$ J

As λ increases, E decreases.

7.3 (a) With $n_{\text{final}} = 3$ for an IR photon:

$$\Delta E = -2.18\times10^{-18}\ \text{J}\left(\frac{1}{n_{\text{final}}^2} - \frac{1}{n_{\text{initial}}^2}\right)$$

$$= -2.18\times10^{-18}\ \text{J}\left(\frac{1}{3^2} - \frac{1}{6^2}\right)$$

$$= -2.18\times10^{-18}\ \text{J}\left(\frac{1}{9} - \frac{1}{36}\right) = -1.82\times10^{-19}\ \text{J}$$

(b) $\lambda = \dfrac{hc}{|\Delta E|} = \dfrac{(6.626\times10^{-34}\ \text{J}\cdot\text{s})(3.00\times10^8\ \text{m/s})}{1.82\times10^{-19}\ \text{J}} \times \dfrac{1\ \text{Å}}{10^{-10}\ \text{m}}$

$= 1.09\times10^4\ \text{Å}$

7.4 $u = \dfrac{h}{m\lambda} = \dfrac{6.626\times10^{-34}\ \text{kg}\cdot\text{m}^2/\text{s}}{(9.11\times10^{-31}\ \text{kg})\left(100\ \text{nm} \times \dfrac{1\ \text{m}}{10^9\ \text{nm}}\right)}$

$= 7.27\times10^3\ \text{m/s}$

7.5 $\Delta x \geq \dfrac{6.626\times10^{-34}\ \text{kg}\cdot\text{m}^2/\text{s}}{4\pi(0.142\ \text{kg})(0.447\ \text{m/s})} \geq 8.31\times10^{-34}\ \text{m}$

7.6 $n = 4$, so $l = 0, 1, 2, 3$. In addition to the nine m_l values in Sample Problem 7.6 there are those for $l = 3$:

$$m_l = -3, -2, -1, 0, +1, +2, +3$$

7.7 For $2p$: $n = 2$, $l = 1$, $m_l = -1, 0, +1$

For $5f$: $n = 5$, $l = 3$, $m_l = -3, -2, -1, 0, +1, +2, +3$

7.8 (a) $n = 4$, $l = 1$; (b) name is $2p$; (c) name is $3d$; (d) $n = 2$, $l = 0$, $m_l = 0$

PROBLEMS

Problems with **colored** numbers are answered in Appendix E and worked in detail in the Student Solutions Manual. Problem sections match those in the text and provide numbers of relevant sample problems. Most offer Concept Review Questions, Skill-Building Exercises (grouped in pairs covering the same concept), and Problems in Context. Comprehensive Problems are based on material from any section or previous chapter.

The Nature of Light

(Sample Problems 7.1 and 7.2)

Concept Review Questions

7.1 In what ways are microwave and ultraviolet radiation the same? In what ways are they different?

7.2 Consider the following types of electromagnetic radiation:
(1) Microwave (2) Ultraviolet (3) Radio waves
(4) Infrared (5) X-ray (6) Visible
(a) Arrange them in order of increasing wavelength.
(b) Arrange them in order of increasing frequency.
(c) Arrange them in order of increasing energy.

7.3 Define each of the following wave phenomena, and give an example of where each occurs: (a) refraction; (b) diffraction; (c) dispersion; (d) interference.

7.4 In the 17th century, Newton proposed that light was a stream of particles. The wave-particle debate continued for over 250 years until Planck and Einstein presented their ideas. Give two pieces of evidence for the wave model and two for the particle model.

7.5 Portions of electromagnetic waves A, B, and C are represented below (not drawn to scale):

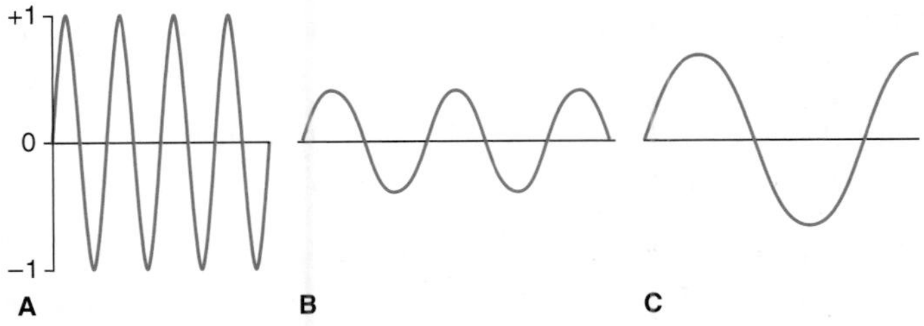

Rank them in order of (a) increasing frequency; (b) increasing energy; (c) increasing amplitude. (d) If wave B just barely fails to cause a current when shining on a metal, is wave A or C more likely to do so? (e) If wave B represents visible radiation, is wave A or C more likely to be IR radiation?

7.6 What new idea about light did Einstein use to explain the photoelectric effect? Why does the photoelectric effect exhibit a threshold frequency but not a time lag?

Skill-Building Exercises (grouped in similar pairs)

7.7 An AM station broadcasts rock music at "950 on your radio dial." Units for AM frequencies are given in kilohertz (kHz). Find the wavelength of the station's radio waves in meters (m), nanometers (nm), and angstroms (Å).

7.8 An FM station broadcasts music at 93.5 MHz (megahertz, or 10^6 Hz). Find the wavelength (in m, nm, and Å) of these waves.

7.9 A radio wave has a frequency of 3.8×10^{10} Hz. What is the energy (in J) of one photon of this radiation?

7.10 An x-ray has a wavelength of 1.3 Å. Calculate the energy (in J) of one photon of this radiation.

7.11 Rank these photons in terms of increasing energy: (a) blue (λ = 453 nm); (b) red (λ = 660 nm); (c) yellow (λ = 595 nm).

7.12 Rank these photons in terms of decreasing energy: (a) IR ($\nu = 6.5\times10^{13}\ s^{-1}$); (b) microwave ($\nu = 9.8\times10^{11}\ s^{-1}$); (c) UV ($\nu = 8.0\times10^{15}\ s^{-1}$).

Problems in Context

7.13 Police often monitor traffic with "K-band" radar guns, which operate in the microwave region at 22.235 GHz (1 GHz = 10^9 Hz). Find the wavelength (in nm and Å) of this radiation.

7.14 Covalent bonds in a molecule absorb radiation in the IR region and vibrate at characteristic frequencies.
(a) The C—O bond absorbs radiation of wavelength 9.6 μm. What frequency (in s^{-1}) corresponds to that wavelength?
(b) The H—Cl bond has a frequency of vibration of 8.652×10^{13} Hz. What wavelength (in μm) corresponds to that frequency?

7.15 Cobalt-60 is a radioactive isotope used to treat cancers. A gamma ray emitted by this isotope has an energy of 1.33 MeV (million electron volts; 1 eV = 1.602×10^{-19} J). What is the frequency (in Hz) and the wavelength (in m) of this gamma ray?

7.16 (a) Ozone formation in the upper atmosphere starts when oxygen molecules absorb UV radiation of wavelengths ≤ 242 nm. Find the frequency and energy of the least energetic of these photons. (b) Ozone absorbs radiation of wavelengths 2200–2900 Å, thus protecting organisms from this radiation. Find the frequency and energy of the most energetic of these photons.

Atomic Spectra

(Sample Problem 7.3)

Concept Review Questions

7.17 How is n_1 in the Rydberg equation (Equation 7.3) related to the quantum number n in the Bohr model?

7.18 What key assumption of Bohr's model would a "Solar System" model of the atom violate? What was the theoretical basis for this assumption?

7.19 Distinguish between an absorption spectrum and an emission spectrum. With which did Bohr work?

7.20 Which of these electron transitions correspond to absorption of energy and which to emission?
(a) $n = 2$ to $n = 4$ (b) $n = 3$ to $n = 1$
(c) $n = 5$ to $n = 2$ (d) $n = 3$ to $n = 4$

7.21 Why couldn't the Bohr model predict spectra for atoms other than hydrogen?

7.22 The H atom and the Be^{3+} ion each have one electron. Would you expect the Bohr model to predict their spectra accurately? Would you expect their spectra to be identical? Explain.

Skill-Building Exercises (grouped in similar pairs)

7.23 Use the Rydberg equation to find the wavelength (in nm) of the photon emitted when an H atom undergoes a transition from $n = 5$ to $n = 2$.

7.24 Use the Rydberg equation to find the wavelength (in Å) of the photon absorbed when an H atom undergoes a transition from $n = 1$ to $n = 3$.

7.25 What is the wavelength (in nm) of the least energetic spectral line in the infrared series of the H atom?

7.26 What is the wavelength (in nm) of the least energetic spectral line in the visible series of the H atom?

7.27 Calculate the energy difference (ΔE) for the transition in Problem 7.23 for 1 mol of H atoms.

7.28 Calculate the energy difference (ΔE) for the transition in Problem 7.24 for 1 mol of H atoms.

7.29 Arrange the following H atom electron transitions in order of *increasing* frequency of the photon absorbed or emitted:
(a) $n = 2$ to $n = 4$ (b) $n = 2$ to $n = 1$
(c) $n = 2$ to $n = 5$ (d) $n = 4$ to $n = 3$

7.30 Arrange the following H atom electron transitions in order of *decreasing* wavelength of the photon absorbed or emitted:
(a) $n = 2$ to $n = \infty$ (b) $n = 4$ to $n = 20$
(c) $n = 3$ to $n = 10$ (d) $n = 2$ to $n = 1$

7.31 The electron in a ground-state H atom absorbs a photon of wavelength 97.20 nm. To what energy level does it move?

7.32 An electron in the $n = 5$ level of an H atom emits a photon of wavelength 1281 nm. To what energy level does it move?

Problems in Context

7.33 In addition to continuous radiation, fluorescent lamps emit some visible lines from mercury. A prominent line has a wavelength of 436 nm. What is the energy (in J) of one photon of it?

7.34 A Bohr-model representation of the H atom is shown below with several electron transitions depicted by arrows:

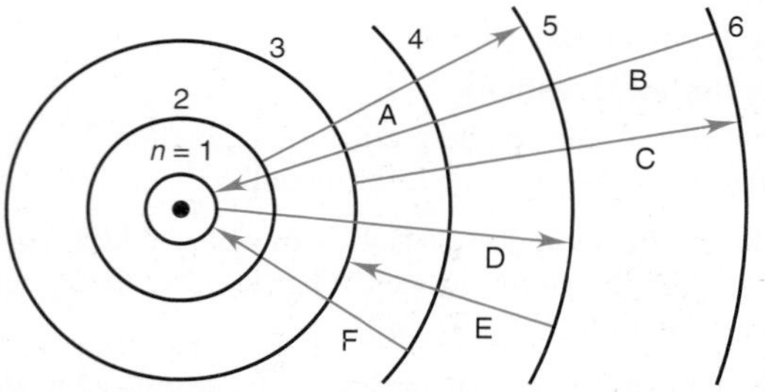

(a) Which transitions are absorptions and which are emissions? (b) Rank the emissions in terms of increasing energy. (c) Rank the absorptions in terms of increasing wavelength of light emitted.

The Wave-Particle Duality of Matter and Energy

(Sample Problems 7.4 and 7.5)

Concept Review Questions

7.35 In what sense is the wave motion of a guitar string analogous to the motion of an electron in an atom?

7.36 What experimental support did de Broglie's concept receive?

7.37 If particles have wavelike motion, why don't we observe that motion in the macroscopic world?

7.38 Why can't we overcome the uncertainty predicted by Heisenberg's principle by building more precise instruments to reduce the error in measurements below the $h/4\pi$ limit?

Skill-Building Exercises (grouped in similar pairs)

7.39 A 232-lb fullback runs 40 yd at 19.8 ± 0.1 mi/h.
(a) What is his de Broglie wavelength (in meters)?
(b) What is the uncertainty in his position?

7.40 An alpha particle (mass $= 6.6\times10^{-24}$ g) emitted by a radium isotope travels at $3.4\times10^7 \pm 0.1\times10^7$ mi/h.
(a) What is its de Broglie wavelength (in meters)?
(b) What is the uncertainty in its position?

7.41 How fast must a 56.5-g tennis ball travel to have a de Broglie wavelength equal to that of a photon of green light (5400 Å)?

7.42 How fast must a 142-g baseball travel to have a de Broglie wavelength equal to that of an x-ray photon with $\lambda = 100.$ pm?

7.43 A sodium flame has a characteristic yellow color due to emissions of wavelength 589 nm. What is the mass equivalence of one photon of this wavelength ($1\ J = 1\ kg{\cdot}m^2/s^2$)?

7.44 A lithium flame has a characteristic red color due to emissions of wavelength 671 nm. What is the mass equivalence of 1 mol of photons of this wavelength ($1\ J = 1\ kg{\cdot}m^2/s^2$)?

The Quantum-Mechanical Model of the Atom

(Sample Problems 7.6 to 7.8)

Concept Review Questions

7.45 What physical meaning is attributed to ψ^2?

7.46 What does "electron density in a tiny volume of space" mean?

7.47 Explain what it means for the peak in the radial probability distribution plot for the $n = 1$ level of an H atom to be at 0.529 Å. Is the probability of finding an electron at 0.529 Å from the nucleus greater for the 1*s* or the 2*s* orbital?

7.48 What feature of an orbital is related to each of the following?
(a) Principal quantum number (n)
(b) Angular momentum quantum number (l)
(c) Magnetic quantum number (m_l)

Skill-Building Exercises (grouped in similar pairs)

7.49 How many orbitals in an atom can have each of the following designations: (a) 1*s*; (b) 4*d*; (c) 3*p*; (d) $n = 3$?

7.50 How many orbitals in an atom can have each of the following designations: (a) 5*f*; (b) 4*p*; (c) 5*d*; (d) $n = 2$?

7.51 Give all possible m_l values for orbitals that have each of the following: (a) $l = 2$; (b) $n = 1$; (c) $n = 4$, $l = 3$.

7.52 Give all possible m_l values for orbitals that have each of the following: (a) $l = 3$; (b) $n = 2$; (c) $n = 6$, $l = 1$.

7.53 Draw 90% probability contours (with axes) for each of the following orbitals: (a) *s*; (b) p_x.

7.54 Draw 90% probability contours (with axes) for each of the following orbitals: (a) p_z; (b) d_{xy}.

7.55 For each of the following, give the sublevel designation, the allowable m_l values, and the number of orbitals:
(a) $n = 4$, $l = 2$ (b) $n = 5$, $l = 1$ (c) $n = 6$, $l = 3$

7.56 For each of the following, give the sublevel designation, the allowable m_l values, and the number of orbitals:
(a) $n = 2$, $l = 0$ (b) $n = 3$, $l = 2$ (c) $n = 5$, $l = 1$

7.57 For each of the following sublevels, give the n and l values and the number of orbitals: (a) 5*s*; (b) 3*p*; (c) 4*f*.

7.58 For each of the following sublevels, give the n and l values and the number of orbitals: (a) 6*g*; (b) 4*s*; (c) 3*d*.

7.59 Are the following combinations allowed? If not, show two ways to correct them:
(a) $n = 2; l = 0; m_l = -1$ (b) $n = 4; l = 3; m_l = -1$
(c) $n = 3; l = 1; m_l = 0$ (d) $n = 5; l = 2; m_l = +3$

7.60 Are the following combinations allowed? If not, show two ways to correct them:
(a) $n = 1; l = 0; m_l = 0$ (b) $n = 2; l = 2; m_l = +1$
(c) $n = 7; l = 1; m_l = +2$ (d) $n = 3; l = 1; m_l = -2$

Comprehensive Problems

7.61 The orange color of carrots and orange peel is due mostly to β-carotene, an organic compound insoluble in water but soluble in benzene and chloroform. Describe an experiment to determine the concentration of β-carotene in the oil from orange peel.

7.62 The quantum-mechanical treatment of the H atom gives the energy, E, of the electron as a function of n:

$$E = -\frac{h^2}{8\pi^2 m_e a_0^2 n^2} \qquad (n = 1, 2, 3, \ldots)$$

where h is Planck's constant, m_e is the electron mass, and a_0 is 52.92×10^{-12} m.
(a) Write the expression in the form $E = -(\text{constant})(1/n^2)$, evaluate the constant (in J), and compare it with the corresponding expression from Bohr's theory.
(b) Use the expression to find ΔE between $n = 2$ and $n = 3$.
(c) Calculate the wavelength of the photon that corresponds to this energy change.

7.63 The photoelectric effect is illustrated in a plot of the kinetic energies of electrons ejected from the surface of potassium metal or silver metal at different frequencies of incident light.

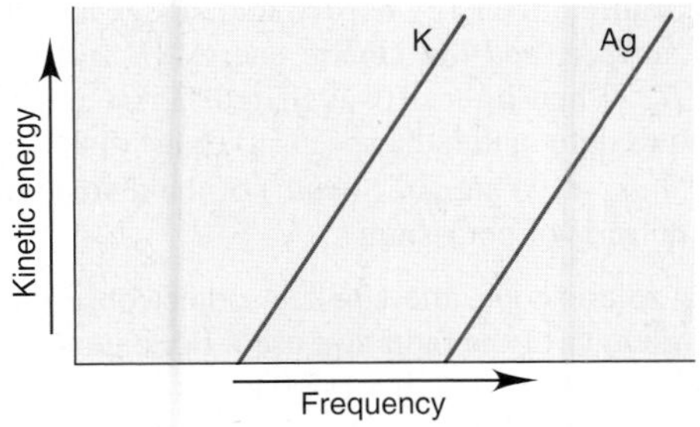

(a) Why don't the lines begin at the origin? (b) Why don't the lines begin at the same point? (c) From which metal will light of shorter wavelength eject an electron? (d) Why are the slopes equal?

7.64 The optic nerve needs a minimum of 2.0×10^{-17} J of energy to trigger a series of impulses that eventually reach the brain. (a) How many photons of red light (700. nm) are needed? (b) How many photons of blue light (475 nm)?

7.65 One reason carbon monoxide (CO) is toxic is that it binds to the blood protein hemoglobin more strongly than oxygen does. The bond between hemoglobin and CO absorbs radiation of 1953 cm^{-1}. (The units are the reciprocal of the wavelength in centimeters.) Calculate the wavelength (in nm and Å) and the frequency (in Hz) of the absorbed radiation.

7.66 A metal ion M^{n+} has a single electron. The highest energy line in its emission spectrum has a frequency of 2.961×10^{16} Hz. Identify the ion.

7.67 Compare the wavelengths of an electron (mass = 9.11×10^{-31} kg) and a proton (mass = 1.67×10^{-27} kg), each having (a) a speed of 3.4×10^6 m/s; (b) a kinetic energy of 2.7×10^{-15} J.

7.68 Five lines in the H atom spectrum have these wavelengths (in Å): (a) 1212.7; (b) 4340.5; (c) 4861.3; (d) 6562.8; (e) 10,938. Three lines result from transitions to $n_{\text{final}} = 2$ (visible series). The other two result from transitions in different series, one with $n_{\text{final}} = 1$ and the other with $n_{\text{final}} = 3$. Identify n_{initial} for each line.

7.69 In his explanation of the threshold frequency in the photoelectric effect, Einstein reasoned that the absorbed photon must have a minimum energy to dislodge an electron from the metal surface. This energy is called the *work function* (ϕ) of that metal. What is the longest wavelength of radiation (in nm) that could cause the photoelectric effect in each of these metals: (a) calcium, $\phi = 4.60\times10^{-19}$ J; (b) titanium, $\phi = 6.94\times10^{-19}$ J; (c) sodium, $\phi = 4.41\times10^{-19}$ J?

7.70 Refractometry is based on the difference in the speed of light through a substance (v) and through a vacuum (c). In the procedure, light of known wavelength passes through a fixed thickness of the substance at a known temperature. The index of refraction equals c/v. Using yellow light (λ = 589 nm) at 20°C, for example, the index of refraction of water is 1.33 and that of diamond is 2.42. Calculate the speed of light in (a) water and (b) diamond.

7.71 A laser (*l*ight *a*mplification by *s*timulated *e*mission of *r*adiation) provides nearly monochromatic high-intensity light. Lasers are used in eye surgery, CD/DVD players, basic research, and many other areas. Some dye lasers can be "tuned" to emit a desired wavelength. Fill in the blanks in the following table of the properties of some common lasers:

Type	λ (nm)	ν (s^{-1})	E (J)	Color
He-Ne	632.8	?	?	?
Ar	?	6.148×10^{14}	?	?
Ar-Kr	?	?	3.499×10^{-19}	?
Dye	663.7	?	?	?

7.72 The following combinations are not allowed. If n and m_l are correct, change the l value to create an allowable combination:
(a) $n = 3; l = 0; m_l = -1$ (b) $n = 3; l = 3; m_l = +1$
(c) $n = 7; l = 2; m_l = +3$ (d) $n = 4; l = 1; m_l = -2$

7.73 A ground-state H atom absorbs a photon of wavelength 94.91 nm, and its electron attains a higher energy level. The atom then emits two photons: one of wavelength 1281 nm to reach an intermediate energy level, and a second to return to the ground state.
(a) What higher level did the electron reach?
(b) What intermediate level did the electron reach?
(c) What was the wavelength of the second photon emitted?

7.74 Ground-state ionization energies of some one-electron species are

$H = 1.31\times10^3$ kJ/mol $\qquad He^{+} = 5.24\times10^3$ kJ/mol
$Li^{2+} = 1.18\times10^4$ kJ/mol

(a) Write a general expression for the ionization energy of any one-electron species. (b) Use your expression to calculate the ionization energy of B^{4+}. (c) What is the minimum wavelength required to remove the electron from the $n = 3$ level of He^+? (d) What is the minimum wavelength required to remove the electron from the $n = 2$ level of Be^{3+}?

7.75 Use the relative size of the 3*s* orbital below to answer the following questions about orbitals A–D.

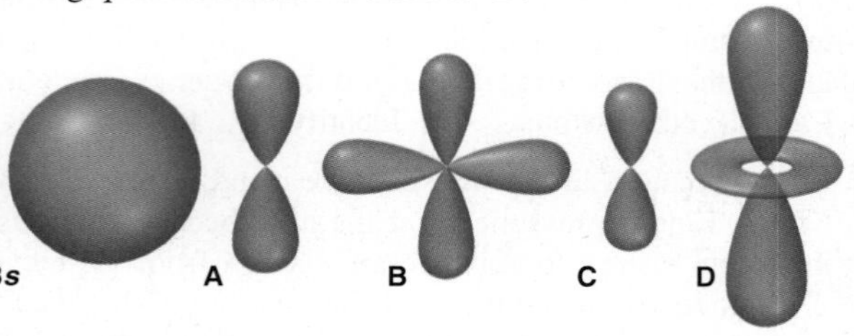

(a) Which orbital has the highest value of *n*? (b) Which orbital(s) have a value of $l = 1$? $l = 2$? (c) How many other orbitals with the same value of *n* have the same shape as orbital B? Orbital C? (d) Which orbital has the highest energy? Lowest energy?

7.76 In the course of developing his model, Bohr arrived at the following formula for the radius of the electron's orbit: $r_n = n^2h^2\epsilon_0/\pi m_e e^2$, where m_e is the electron mass, *e* is its charge, and ϵ_0 is a constant related to charge attraction in a vacuum. Given that $m_e = 9.109\times10^{-31}$ kg, $e = 1.602\times10^{-19}$ C, and $\epsilon_0 = 8.854\times10^{-12}$ C²/J·m, calculate the following:
(a) The radius of the first ($n = 1$) orbit in the H atom
(b) The radius of the tenth ($n = 10$) orbit in the H atom

7.77 (a) Find the Bohr radius of an electron in the $n = 3$ orbit of an H atom (see Problem 7.76). (b) What is the energy (in J) of the atom in part (a)? (c) What is the energy of an Li^{2+} ion with its electron in the $n = 3$ orbit? (d) Why are the answers to (b) and (c) different?

7.78 Enormous numbers of microwave photons are needed to warm macroscopic samples of matter. A portion of soup containing 252 g of water is heated in a microwave oven from 20.°C to 98°C, with radiation of wavelength 1.55×10^{-2} m. How many photons are absorbed by the water in the soup?

7.79 The quantum-mechanical treatment of the hydrogen atom gives this expression for the wave function, ψ, of the 1*s* orbital:

$$\psi = \frac{1}{\sqrt{\pi}}\left(\frac{1}{a_0}\right)^{3/2} e^{-r/a_0}$$

where *r* is the distance from the nucleus and a_0 is 52.92 pm. The probability of finding the electron in a tiny volume at distance *r* from the nucleus is proportional to ψ^2. The total probability of finding the electron at all points at distance *r* from the nucleus is proportional to $4\pi r^2\psi^2$. Calculate the values (to three significant figures) of ψ, ψ^2, and $4\pi r^2\psi^2$ to fill in the following table and sketch a plot of each set of values versus *r*. Compare the latter two plots with those in Figure 7.17A, p. 284:

r (pm)	ψ (pm$^{-3/2}$)	ψ^2 (pm^{-3})	$4\pi r^2\psi^2$ (pm^{-1})
0			
50			
100			
200			

7.80 Lines in one spectral series can overlap lines in another. (a) Does the range of wavelengths in the $n_1 = 1$ series for the H atom overlap the range in the $n_1 = 2$ series? (b) Does the range in the $n_1 = 3$ series overlap the range in the $n_1 = 4$ series? (c) How many lines in the $n_1 = 4$ series lie in the range of the $n_1 = 5$ series? (d) What does this overlap imply about the H atom line spectrum at longer wavelengths?

7.81 The following values are the only energy levels of a hypothetical one-electron atom:

$E_6 = -2\times10^{-19}$ J $E_5 = -7\times10^{-19}$ J
$E_4 = -11\times10^{-19}$ J $E_3 = -15\times10^{-19}$ J
$E_2 = -17\times10^{-19}$ J $E_1 = -20\times10^{-19}$ J

(a) If the electron were in the $n = 3$ level, what would be the highest frequency (and minimum wavelength) of radiation that could be emitted? (b) What is the ionization energy (in kJ/mol) of the atom in its ground state? (c) If the electron were in the $n = 4$ level, what would be the shortest wavelength (in nm) of radiation that could be absorbed without causing ionization?

7.82 Photoelectron spectroscopy applies the principle of the photoelectric effect to study orbital energies of atoms and molecules. High-energy radiation (usually UV or x-ray) is absorbed by a sample and an electron is ejected. The orbital energy can be calculated from the known energy of the radiation and the measured energy of the electron lost. The following energy differences were determined for several electron transitions:

$\Delta E_{2\longrightarrow1} = 4.098\times10^{-17}$ J $\Delta E_{3\longrightarrow1} = 4.854\times10^{-17}$ J
$\Delta E_{5\longrightarrow1} = 5.242\times10^{-17}$ J $\Delta E_{4\longrightarrow2} = 1.024\times10^{-17}$ J

Calculate ΔE and λ of a photon emitted in the following transitions: (a) level 3 $\longrightarrow$ 2; (b) level 4 $\longrightarrow$ 1; (c) level 5 $\longrightarrow$ 4.

7.83 Horticulturists know that, for many plants, dark green leaves are associated with low light levels and pale green with high levels. (a) Use the photon theory to explain this behavior. (b) What change in leaf composition might account for this difference?

7.84 In order to comply with the requirement that energy be conserved, Einstein showed in the photoelectric effect that the energy of a photon ($h\nu$) absorbed by a metal is the sum of the work function (ϕ), the minimum energy needed to dislodge an electron from the metal's surface, and the kinetic energy (E_k) of the electron: $h\nu = \phi + E_k$. When light of wavelength 358.1 nm falls on the surface of potassium metal, the speed (*u*) of the dislodged electron is 6.40×10^5 m/s. (a) What is E_k ($\frac{1}{2}mu^2$) of the dislodged electron? (b) What is ϕ (in J) of potassium?

7.85 For any microscope, the smallest object observable is one-half the wavelength of the radiation used. For example, the smallest object observable with light of 400 nm is 2×10^{-7} m. (a) What is the smallest object observable with an electron microscope using electrons moving at 5.5×10^4 m/s? (b) At 3.0×10^7 m/s?

7.86 In fireworks, the heat of the reaction of an oxidizing agent, such as $KClO_4$, with an organic compound excites certain salts, which emit specific colors. Strontium salts have an intense emission at 641 nm, and barium salts have one at 493 nm. (a) What colors do these emissions produce? (b) What is the energy (in kJ) of these emissions for 5.00 g each of the chloride salts of Sr and Ba? (Assume that all the heat produced is converted to emitted light.)

7.87 Atomic hydrogen produces several series of spectral lines. Each series fits the Rydberg equation with its own particular n_1 value. Calculate the value of n_1 (by trial and error if necessary) that would produce a series of lines in which:
(a) The *highest* energy line has a wavelength of 3282 nm.
(b) The *lowest* energy line has a wavelength of 7460 nm.

7.88 Fish-liver oil is a good source of vitamin A, whose concentration is measured spectrometrically at a wavelength of 329 nm.
(a) Suggest a reason for using this wavelength.
(b) In what region of the spectrum does this wavelength lie?
(c) When 0.1232 g of fish-liver oil is dissolved in 500. mL of solvent, the absorbance is 0.724 units. When 1.67×10^{-3} g of vitamin A is dissolved in 250. mL of solvent, the absorbance is 1.018 units. Calculate the vitamin A concentration in the fish-liver oil.

7.89 Many calculators use photocells as their energy source. Find the maximum wavelength needed to remove an electron from silver ($\phi = 7.59\times10^{-19}$ J). Is silver a good choice for a photocell that uses visible light? [The concept of the work function (ϕ) is explained in Problem 7.69.]

7.90 In a game of "Clue," Ms. White is killed in the conservatory. A spectrometer in each room records who is present to help find the murderer. For example, if someone wearing yellow is in a room, light at 580 nm is reflected. The suspects are Col. Mustard, Prof. Plum, Mr. Green, Ms. Peacock (blue), and Ms. Scarlet. At the time of the murder, the spectrometer in the dining room shows a reflection at 520 nm, those in the lounge and study record lower frequencies, and the one in the library records the shortest possible wavelength. Who killed Ms. White? Explain.

7.91 Technetium (Tc; $Z = 43$) is a synthetic element used as a radioactive tracer in medical studies. A Tc atom emits a beta particle (electron) with a kinetic energy (E_k) of 4.71×10^{-15} J. What is the de Broglie wavelength of this electron ($E_k = \frac{1}{2}mv^2$)?

7.92 Electric power is measured in watts (1 W = 1 J/s). About 95% of the power output of an incandescent bulb is converted to heat and 5% to light. If 10% of that light shines on your chemistry text, how many photons per second shine on the book from a 75-W bulb? (Assume the photons have a wavelength of 550 nm.)

7.93 The flame tests for sodium and potassium are based on the emissions at 589 nm and 404 nm, respectively. When both elements are present, the Na^+ emission is so strong that the K^+ emission can only be seen by looking through a cobalt-glass filter. (a) What are the colors of these Na^+ and K^+ emissions? (b) What does the cobalt-glass filter do? (c) Why is $KClO_4$ used as an oxidizing agent in fireworks rather than $NaClO_4$?

7.94 The net change during photosynthesis involves CO_2 and H_2O forming glucose ($C_6H_{12}O_6$) and O_2. Chlorophyll absorbs light in the 600–700 nm region.
(a) Write a balanced thermochemical equation for formation of 1.00 mol of glucose.
(b) What is the minimum number of photons with $\lambda = 680.$ nm needed to form 1.00 mol of glucose?

7.95 Only certain transitions are allowed from one energy level to another. In one-electron species, the change in l of an allowed transition is ±1. For example, a $3p$ electron can move to a $2s$ orbital but not to a $2p$. Thus, in the UV series, where $n_{final} = 1$, allowed transitions can start in a p orbital ($l = 1$) of $n = 2$ or higher, not in an s ($l = 0$) or d ($l = 2$) orbital of $n = 2$ or higher. From what orbital do each of the allowed transitions start for the first four emission lines in the visible series ($n_{final} = 2$)?

7.96 The discharge of phosphate in detergents to the environment has led to imbalances in the life cycle of freshwater lakes. A chemist uses a spectrometric method to measure total phosphate and obtains the following data for known standards:

Absorbance (880 nm)	Concentration (mol/L)
0	0.0×10^{-5}
0.10	2.5×10^{-5}
0.16	3.2×10^{-5}
0.20	4.4×10^{-5}
0.25	5.6×10^{-5}
0.38	8.4×10^{-5}
0.48	10.5×10^{-5}
0.62	13.8×10^{-5}
0.76	17.0×10^{-5}
0.88	19.4×10^{-5}

(a) Draw a curve of absorbance vs. phosphate concentration.
(b) If a sample of lake water has an absorbance of 0.55, what is its phosphate concentration?

Electron Configuration and Chemical Periodicity

8

Concepts and skills to review before you study this chapter

- format of the periodic table (Section 2.6)
- characteristics of metals and nonmetals (Section 2.6)
- attractions, repulsions, and Coulomb's law (Section 2.7)
- characteristics of acids and bases (Section 4.4)
- rules for assigning quantum numbers (Section 7.4)

We have become expert at measuring recurring patterns in nature—day and night, the seasons, solar and lunar eclipses, even the swirl in a shell or the rhythm of a heartbeat. Elements exhibit recurring patterns in properties because their atoms do, and we can measure these patterns, too.

The outpouring of scientific creativity by early 20th-century physicists that led to the new quantum-mechanical model of the atom was preceded by countless hours of laboratory work by 19th-century chemists who were exploring the nature of electrolytes, the kinetic-molecular theory, and chemical thermodynamics. The fields of organic chemistry and biochemistry were born in the 19th century, as were the fertilizer, explosives, glassmaking, soapmaking, bleaching, and dyestuff industries. And, for the first time, chemistry became a subject in universities in Europe and America.

Condensed from all these efforts, an enormous body of facts emerged about the elements, which became organized into the periodic table:

- *The original periodic table*. In 1870, the Russian chemist Dmitri Mendeleev arranged the 65 elements known at the time into a table and summarized their behavior in the **periodic law:** when arranged by *atomic mass,* the elements exhibit a periodic recurrence of similar properties. Mendeleev left blank spaces in his table and was even able to *predict* the properties of several elements, for example, germanium, that were not discovered until later.
- *The modern periodic table*. Today's table *(inside front cover)* includes 52 elements not known in 1870 and, most importantly, arranges the elements by *atomic number* (number of protons) *not* atomic mass. This change is based on the work of the British physicist Henry G. J. Moseley, who obtained x-ray spectra of various metals by bombarding the metals with electrons. Moseley found that the largest x-ray peak for each metal was related to the nuclear charge, which increased by 1 for each successive element.

The great test for the new atomic model was to answer one of the central questions in chemistry: *why* do the elements behave as they do? Or, rephrasing to fit the main topic of this chapter, how does the **electron configuration** of an element—*the distribution of electrons within the levels and sublevels of its atoms*—relate to its chemical and physical properties?

IN THIS CHAPTER . . . We explore recurring patterns of electron distributions in atoms to see how they account for the recurring behavior of the elements.

- We describe a new quantum number and a restriction on the number of electrons in an orbital, which allows us to define a unique set of quantum numbers for each electron in an atom of any element.
- We explore electrostatic effects that lead to splitting of atomic energy levels into sublevels and give rise to the order in which orbitals fill with electrons. This filling order correlates with the order of elements in the periodic table.
- We examine the reasons for periodic trends in three atomic properties.
- We see how these trends account for chemical reactivity with regard to metallic and redox behavior, oxide acidity, ion formation, and magnetic behavior.

8.1 • CHARACTERISTICS OF MANY-ELECTRON ATOMS

The Schrödinger equation (introduced in Chapter 7) does not give *exact* solutions for the energy levels of *many-electron atoms,* those with more than one electron—that is, all atoms except hydrogen. However, unlike the Bohr model, it gives excellent *approximate* solutions. Three additional features become important in many-electron atoms: (1) a fourth quantum number, (2) a limit on the number of electrons in an orbital, and (3) a splitting of energy levels into sublevels.

The Electron-Spin Quantum Number

The three quantum numbers n, l, and m_l describe the size (energy), shape, and orientation, respectively, of an atomic orbital. An additional quantum number describes a property called *spin,* which is a property of the electron and not the orbital.

When a beam of atoms that have one or more lone electrons passes through a nonuniform magnetic field (created by magnet faces with different shapes), it splits into two beams; Figure 8.1 shows this for a beam of H atoms. Each electron behaves like a spinning charge and generates a tiny magnetic field, which can have one of two values of *spin*. The two electron fields have opposing directions, so half of the electrons are *attracted* by the large external magnetic field while the other half are *repelled* by it.

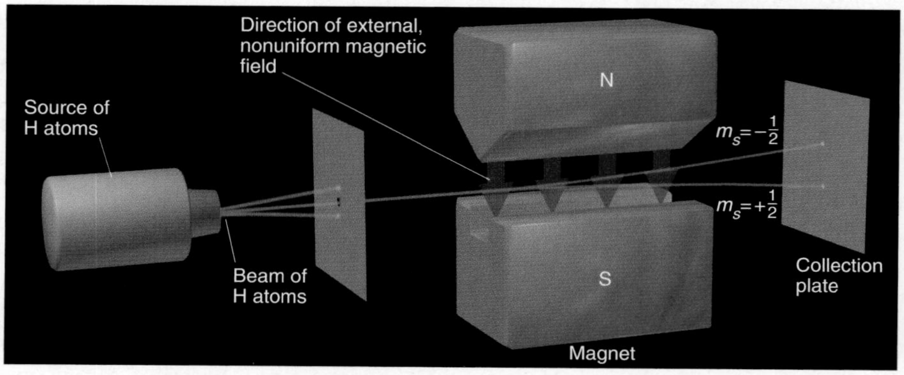

Figure 8.1 The effect of electron spin. A beam of H atoms splits because each atom's electron has one of the two possible values of spin.

Corresponding to the two directions of the electron's field, the **spin quantum number (m_s)** has two possible values, $+\frac{1}{2}$ or $-\frac{1}{2}$. Thus, *each electron in an atom is described completely by a set of* ***four*** *quantum numbers: the first three describe its orbital, and the fourth describes its spin.* The quantum numbers are summarized in Table 8.1.

Now we can write a set of four quantum numbers for any electron in the ground state of any atom. For example, the set of quantum numbers for the lone electron in hydrogen (H; $Z = 1$) is $n = 1$, $l = 0$, $m_l = 0$, and $m_s = +\frac{1}{2}$. (The spin quantum number could just as well have been $-\frac{1}{2}$, but by convention, we assign $+\frac{1}{2}$ to the first electron in an orbital.)

Table 8.1 Summary of Quantum Numbers of Electrons in Atoms

Name	Symbol	Permitted Values	Property
Principal	n	Positive integers (1, 2, 3, . . .)	Orbital energy (size)
Angular momentum	l	Integers from 0 to $n - 1$	Orbital shape (the l values 0, 1, 2, and 3 correspond to *s, p, d,* and *f* orbitals, respectively.)
Magnetic	m_l	Integers from $-l$ to 0 to $+l$	Orbital orientation
Spin	m_s	$+\frac{1}{2}$ or $-\frac{1}{2}$	Direction of e^- spin

The Exclusion Principle

The element after hydrogen is helium (He; Z = 2), the first with atoms having more than one electron. The first electron in the He ground state has the same set of quantum numbers as the electron in the H atom, but the second He electron does not. Based on observations of excited states, the Austrian physicist Wolfgang Pauli formulated the **exclusion principle:** *no two electrons in the same atom can have the same four quantum numbers.* Therefore, the second He electron occupies the same orbital as the first but has an opposite spin: $n = 1$, $l = 0$, $m_l = 0$, and $m_s = -\frac{1}{2}$.

The major consequence of the exclusion principle is that *an atomic orbital can hold a maximum of two electrons and they must have opposing spins.* We say that the 1*s* orbital in He is *filled* and that the electrons have *paired spins.* Thus, a beam of He atoms is not split in an experiment like that in Figure 8.1.

Baseball Quantum Numbers
The unique set of quantum numbers that describes an electron is analogous to the unique location of a box seat at a baseball game. The stadium (atom) is divided into section (*n*, level), box (*l*, sublevel), row (m_l, orbital), and seat (m_s, spin). Only one person (electron) can have this particular set of stadium "quantum numbers."

Electrostatic Effects and Energy-Level Splitting

Electrostatic effects—attraction of opposite charges and repulsion of like charges—play a major role in determining the energy states of many-electron atoms. Unlike the H atom, in which there is only the attraction between nucleus and electron and the energy state is determined *only* by the *n* value, the energy states of many-electron atoms are also affected by electron-electron repulsions. You'll see shortly how these additional interactions give rise to *the splitting of energy levels into sublevels of differing energies: the energy of an orbital in a many-electron atom depends mostly on its n value (size) and to a lesser extent on its l value (shape).*

Our first encounter with energy-level splitting occurs with lithium (Li; Z = 3). The first two electrons of Li fill its 1*s* orbital, so the third Li electron must go into the $n = 2$ level. But, this level has 2*s and* 2*p* sublevels: which does the third electron enter? For reasons we discuss below, the 2*s* is lower in energy than the 2*p*, so the ground state of Li has its third electron in the 2*s*.

This energy difference arises from three factors—*nuclear attraction, electron repulsions,* and *orbital shape* (i.e., radial probability distribution). Their interplay leads to two phenomena—*shielding* and *penetration*—that occur in all atoms *except* hydrogen. [In the following discussion, keep in mind that more energy is needed to remove an electron from a more stable (lower energy) sublevel than from a less stable (higher energy) sublevel.]

The Effect of Nuclear Charge (*Z*) on Sublevel Energy Higher charges interact more strongly than lower charges (Coulomb's law, Section 2.7). Therefore, *a higher nuclear charge increases nucleus-electron attractions and, thus, lowers sublevel energy (stabilizes the atom).* We see this effect by comparing the 1*s* sublevel energies of three species with one electron—H atom (Z = 1), He^+ ion (Z = 2), and Li^{2+} ion (Z = 3). Figure 8.2 shows that the 1*s* sublevel in H is the least stable (highest energy), so the least energy is needed to remove its electron; and the 1*s* sublevel in Li^{2+} is the most stable, so the most energy is needed to remove its electron.

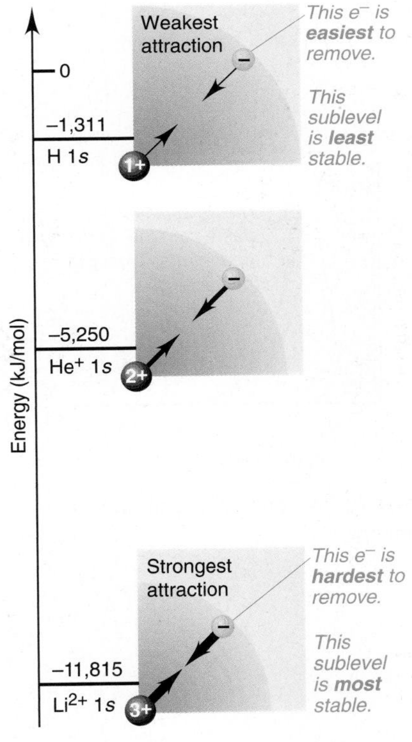

Figure 8.2 The effect of nuclear charge on sublevel energy. Greater nuclear charge lowers sublevel energy (to a more negative number), which makes the electron harder to remove. (The strength of attraction is indicated by the thickness of the black arrows.)

Shielding: The Effect of Electron Repulsions on Sublevel Energy In many-electron atoms, each electron "feels" not only the attraction to the nucleus but also repulsions from other electrons. Repulsions counteract the nuclear attraction somewhat, making each electron easier to remove by, in effect, helping to push it away. We speak of each electron "shielding" the other electrons to some extent from the nuclear charge. **Shielding** (also called *screening*) reduces the full nuclear charge to an **effective nuclear charge (Z_{eff})**, the nuclear charge an electron *actually experiences, and this lower nuclear charge makes the electron easier to remove.*

1. *Shielding by other electrons in a given energy level.* Electrons in the *same* energy level shield each other somewhat. Compare the He atom and He^+ ion: both have a 2+ nuclear charge, but He has two electrons in the 1*s* sublevel and He^+ has

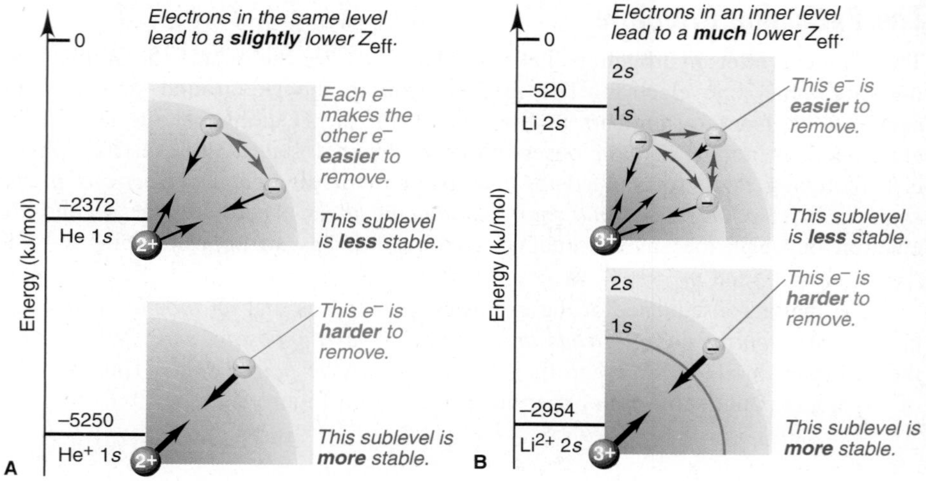

Figure 8.3 Shielding and energy levels. **A,** Within an energy level, each electron shields *(red arrows)* other electrons from the full nuclear charge *(black arrows)*, so they experience a lower Z_{eff}. **B,** Inner electrons shield outer electrons *much* more effectively than electrons in the same energy level.

only one (Figure 8.3A). It takes less than half as much energy to remove an electron from He (2372 kJ/mol) than from He^+ (5250 kJ/mol) because the second electron in He repels the first, in effect causing a lower Z_{eff}.

2. *Shielding by electrons in inner energy levels.* Because inner electrons spend nearly all their time *between* the outer electrons and the nucleus, they cause a *much* lower Z_{eff} than do electrons in the same level. We can see this by comparing two atomic systems with the same nucleus, one *with* inner electrons and the other *without.* The ground-state Li atom has two inner (1*s*) electrons and one outer (2*s*) electron, while the Li^{2+} ion has only one electron, which occupies the 2*s* orbital in the first excited state (Figure 8.3B). It takes about one-sixth as much energy to remove the 2*s* electron from the Li atom (520 kJ/mol) as it takes to remove it from the Li^{2+} ion (2954 kJ/mol), because the *inner electrons shield very effectively.*

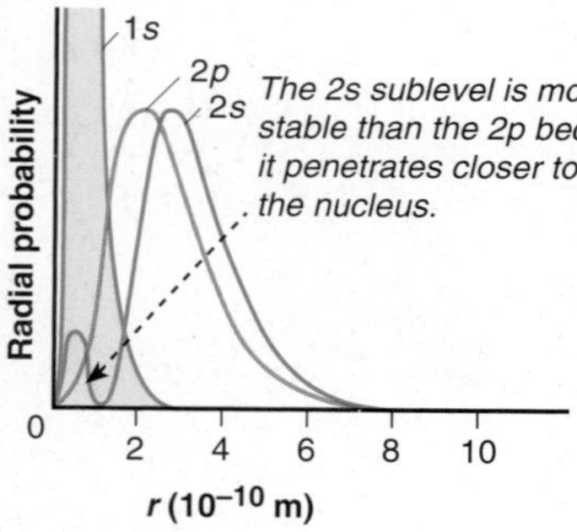

Figure 8.4 Penetration and sublevel energy.

Penetration: The Effect of Orbital Shape on Sublevel Energy To see why the third Li electron occupies the 2*s* sublevel rather than the 2*p*, we have to consider orbital shapes, that is, radial probability distributions (Figure 8.4). A 2*p* orbital *(orange curve)* is slightly closer to the nucleus, on average, than the major portion of the 2*s* orbital *(blue curve).* But a small portion of the 2*s* radial probability distribution peaks within the 1*s* region. Thus, an electron in the 2*s* orbital spends part of its time "penetrating" very close to the nucleus. **Penetration** has two effects:

- It *increases the nuclear attraction* for a 2*s* electron over that for a 2*p* electron.
- It *decreases the shielding* of a 2*s* electron by the 1*s* electrons.

Thus, since it takes more energy to remove a 2*s* electron (520 kJ/mol) than a 2*p* (341 kJ/mol), the 2*s* sublevel is lower in energy than the 2*p*.

Splitting of Levels into Sublevels In general, *penetration and the resulting effects on shielding cause an energy level to split into sublevels of differing energy.* The lower the *l* value of a sublevel, the more its electrons penetrate, and so the greater their attraction to the nucleus. Therefore, *for a given n value, a lower l value indicates a more stable (lower energy) sublevel:*

$$\text{Order of sublevel energies: } s < p < d < f \qquad (8.1)$$

Thus, the 2*s* ($l = 0$) is lower in energy than the 2*p* ($l = 1$), the 3*p* ($l = 1$) is lower than the 3*d* ($l = 2$), and so forth.

Figure 8.5 shows the general energy order of levels (*n* value) and how they are split into sublevels (*l* values) of differing energies. (Compare this with the H atom energy levels in Figure 7.21, p. 287.) Next, we'll use this energy order to construct a periodic table of ground-state atoms.

Summary of Section 8.1

- Identifying electrons in many-electron atoms requires four quantum numbers: three (n, l, m_l) describe the orbital, and a fourth (m_s) describes electron spin.
- The exclusion principle requires each electron to have a unique set of four quantum numbers; therefore, an orbital can hold no more than two electrons, and their spins must be paired (opposite).
- Electrostatic interactions determine sublevel energies as follows:
  1. Greater nuclear charge lowers sublevel energy, making electrons harder to remove.
  2. Electron-electron repulsions raise sublevel energy, making electrons easier to remove. Repulsions shield electrons from the full nuclear charge, reducing it to an effective nuclear charge, Z_{eff}. Inner electrons shield outer electrons very effectively.
  3. Penetration makes an electron harder to remove because nuclear attraction increases and shielding decreases. As a result, an energy level is split into sublevels with the energy order $s < p < d < f$.

8.2 • THE QUANTUM-MECHANICAL MODEL AND THE PERIODIC TABLE

Quantum mechanics provides the theoretical foundation for the experimentally based periodic table. In this section, we fill the table by determining the ground-state electron configuration of each element—*the lowest-energy distribution of electrons in the sublevels of its atoms*. Note especially the *recurring pattern in electron configurations, which is the basis for recurring patterns in chemical behavior.*

A useful way to determine electron configurations is based on the **aufbau principle** (German *aufbauen,* "to build up"). We start at the beginning of the periodic table and add one proton to the nucleus and one electron to the *lowest energy sublevel available.* (Of course, one or more neutrons are also added to the nucleus.)

There are two common ways to indicate the distribution of electrons:

- *The electron configuration.* This shorthand notation consists of the principal energy level (n value), the letter designation of the sublevel (l value), and the number of electrons (#) in the sublevel, written as a superscript: $nl^{\#}$.
- *The orbital diagram.* An **orbital diagram** consists of a box (or circle, or just a line) for each orbital in a given energy level, grouped by sublevel (with nl designation shown beneath), with an arrow representing an electron *and* its spin: ↑ is $+\frac{1}{2}$ and ↓ is $-\frac{1}{2}$. (Throughout the text, orbital occupancy is also indicated by color intensity: no color is empty, pale color is half-filled, and full color is filled.)

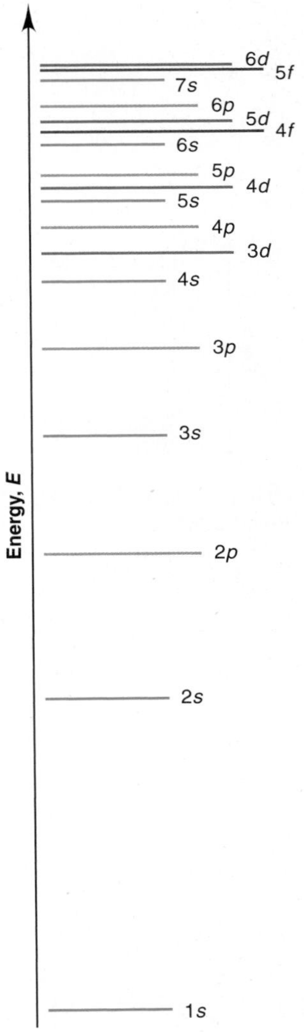

Figure 8.5 Order for filling energy sublevels with electrons. In general, energies of sublevels increase with the principal quantum number n ($1 < 2 < 3$, etc.) and the angular momentum quantum number l ($s < p < d < f$). As n increases, some sublevels overlap; for example, the 4s sublevel is lower in energy than the 3d. (Line color indicates sublevel type.)

Building Up Period 1

Let's begin by applying the aufbau principle to Period 1, whose ground-state elements have only the $n = 1$ level and, thus, only the 1s sublevel, which consists of only the 1s orbital. We'll also assign a set of four quantum numbers to each element's *last added* electron.

1. *Hydrogen.* For the electron in H, as you've seen, the set of quantum numbers is H ($Z = 1$): $n = 1, l = 0, m_l = 0, m_s = +\frac{1}{2}$. The electron configuration (spoken "one-ess-one") and orbital diagram are

H ($Z = 1$) $1s^1$ [↑]
1s

2. *Helium.* Recall that the first electron in He has the same quantum numbers as the electron in H, but the second He electron has opposing spin (exclusion principle) He ($Z = 2$): $n = 1, l = 0, m_l = 0, m_s = -\frac{1}{2}$. The electron configuration (spoken "one-ess-two," *not* "one-ess-squared") and orbital diagram are

He ($Z = 2$) $1s^2$ [↑↓]
1s

Building Up Period 2

The exclusion principle says an orbital can hold no more than two electrons. Therefore, with He, the 1*s* orbital, the 1*s* sublevel, the $n = 1$ level, and Period 1 are filled. Filling the $n = 2$ level builds up Period 2 and begins with the 2*s* sublevel, which is the next lowest in energy (see Figure 8.4) and consists of only the 2*s* orbital. When the 2*s* sublevel is filled, we proceed to fill the 2*p*.

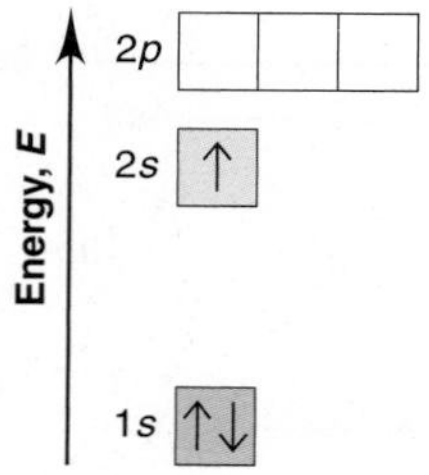

Figure 8.6 A vertical orbital diagram for the Li ground state.

1. *Lithium.* The first two electrons in Li fill the 1*s* sublevel, and the last added Li electron has quantum numbers $n = 2$, $l = 0$, $m_l = 0$, $m_s = +\frac{1}{2}$. The electron configuration and orbital diagram are

Energy, *E* →

Li (Z = 3) $1s^22s^1$ [↑↓] [↑] [| |]
1*s* 2*s* 2*p*

(Note that a complete orbital diagram shows all the orbitals for the given *n* value, whether or not they are occupied.) To save space on a page, orbital diagrams are written horizontally, with *the sublevel energy increasing left to right.* But Figure 8.6 highlights the energy increase with a vertical orbital diagram for lithium.

2. *Beryllium.* The 2*s* orbital is only half-filled in Li, and the fourth electron of beryllium fills it with the electron's spin paired: $n = 2$, $l = 0$, $m_l = 0$, $m_s = -\frac{1}{2}$.

Be (Z = 4) $1s^22s^2$ [↑↓] [↑↓] [| |]
1*s* 2*s* 2*p*

3. *Boron.* The next lowest energy sublevel is the 2*p*. A *p* sublevel has $l = 1$, so the m_l (orientation) values can be −1, 0, or +1. The three orbitals in the 2*p* sublevel have *equal energy* (same *n* and *l* values), which means that the fifth electron of boron can go into *any one of the 2p orbitals.* For convenience, let's label the boxes from left to right: −1, 0, +1. By convention, we start on the left and place the fifth electron in the $m_l = -1$ orbital: $n = 2$, $l = 1$, $m_l = -1$, $m_s = +\frac{1}{2}$.

−1 0 +1

B (Z = 5) $1s^22s^22p^1$ [↑↓] [↑↓] [↑ | |]
1*s* 2*s* 2*p*

4. *Carbon.* To minimize electron-electron repulsions, the sixth electron of carbon enters one of the *unoccupied* 2*p* orbitals; by convention, we place it in the $m_l = 0$ orbital. Experiment shows that the spin of this electron is *parallel* to (the same as) the spin of the other 2*p* electron. This result exemplifies **Hund's rule:** *when orbitals of equal energy are available, the electron configuration of lowest energy has the maximum number of unpaired electrons with parallel spins.* Thus, the sixth electron has $n = 2$, $l = 1$, $m_l = 0$, and $m_s = +\frac{1}{2}$.

C (Z = 6) $1s^22s^22p^2$ [↑↓] [↑↓] [↑ | ↑ |]
1*s* 2*s* 2*p*

5. *Nitrogen.* Based on Hund's rule, nitrogen's seventh electron enters the last empty 2*p* orbital, with its spin parallel to the other two: $n = 2$, $l = 1$, $m_l = +1$, $m_s = +\frac{1}{2}$.

N (Z = 7) $1s^22s^22p^3$ [↑↓] [↑↓] [↑ | ↑ | ↑]
1*s* 2*s* 2*p*

6. *Oxygen.* The eighth electron in oxygen must enter one of the three half-filled 2*p* orbitals and "pair up" with (oppose the spin of) the electron present. We place the electron in a half-filled 2*p* orbital: $n = 2$, $l = 1$, $m_l = -1$, $m_s = -\frac{1}{2}$.

O (Z = 8) $1s^22s^22p^4$ [↑↓] [↑↓] [↑↓ | ↑ | ↑]
1*s* 2*s* 2*p*

7. *Fluorine.* Fluorine's ninth electron enters the next of the two remaining half-filled 2*p* orbitals: $n = 2$, $l = 1$, $m_l = 0$, $m_s = -\frac{1}{2}$.

F (Z = 9) $1s^22s^22p^5$ [↑↓] [↑↓] [↑↓|↑↓|↑]
1*s* 2*s* 2*p*

8. *Neon.* Only one unfilled 2*p* orbital remains, so the tenth electron of neon occupies it: $n = 2$, $l = 1$, $m_l = +1$, $m_s = -\frac{1}{2}$. With neon, the $n = 2$ level is filled.

Ne (Z = 10) $1s^22s^22p^6$ [↑↓] [↑↓] [↑↓|↑↓|↑↓]
1*s* 2*s* 2*p*

Sample Problem 8.1 Determining Quantum Numbers from Orbital Diagrams

Problem Use the orbital diagram shown above to write the set of quantum numbers for the third electron and the set for the eighth electron of the F atom.

Plan Referring to the orbital diagram, we identify the electron of interest and note its level (n), sublevel (l), orbital (m_l), and spin (m_s).

Solution The third electron is in the 2*s* orbital. The upward arrow indicates a spin of $+\frac{1}{2}$:

$$n = 2, l = 0, m_l = 0, m_s = +\tfrac{1}{2}$$

The eighth electron is in the first 2*p* orbital, which is designated $m_l = -1$, and has a downward arrow:

$$n = 2, l = 1, m_l = -1, m_s = -\tfrac{1}{2}$$

Follow-Up Problem 8.1 Use the periodic table to identify the element with the electron configuration $1s^22s^22p^4$. Write its orbital diagram and the set of quantum numbers for its sixth electron.

With our attention on these notations, it's easy to forget that atoms are real objects and electrons occupy volumes with specific shapes and orientations. Figure 8.7 shows orbital contours for the first 10 elements arranged in periodic table format.

Even now, we can make an important correlation: *elements in the same group have similar outer electron configurations and similar patterns of reactivity.* As an example, helium (He) and neon (Ne) in Group 8A(18) both have filled outer sublevels—$1s^2$ for helium and $2s^22p^6$ for neon—and neither element forms compounds. Filled outer sublevels make elements much more stable and unreactive.

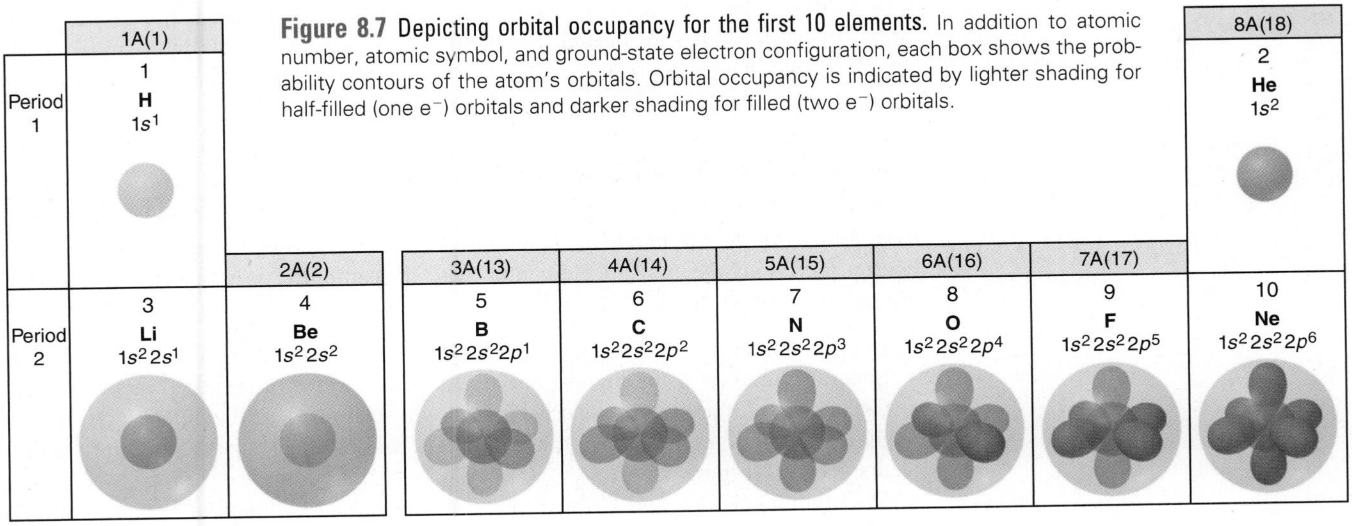

Figure 8.7 Depicting orbital occupancy for the first 10 elements. In addition to atomic number, atomic symbol, and ground-state electron configuration, each box shows the probability contours of the atom's orbitals. Orbital occupancy is indicated by lighter shading for half-filled (one e^-) orbitals and darker shading for filled (two e^-) orbitals.

Table 8.2 Partial Orbital Diagrams and Electron Configurations* for the Elements in Period 3

Atomic Number	Element	Partial Orbital Diagram (3s and 3p Sublevels Only): 3s	3p	Full Electron Configuration†	Condensed Electron Configuration
11	Na	↑					$[1s^2 2s^2 2p^6]\ 3s^1$	$[Ne]\ 3s^1$
12	Mg	↑↓					$[1s^2 2s^2 2p^6]\ 3s^2$	$[Ne]\ 3s^2$
13	Al	↑↓	↑			$[1s^2 2s^2 2p^6]\ 3s^2 3p^1$	$[Ne]\ 3s^2 3p^1$
14	Si	↑↓	↑	↑		$[1s^2 2s^2 2p^6]\ 3s^2 3p^2$	$[Ne]\ 3s^2 3p^2$
15	P	↑↓	↑	↑	↑	$[1s^2 2s^2 2p^6]\ 3s^2 3p^3$	$[Ne]\ 3s^2 3p^3$
16	S	↑↓	↑↓	↑	↑	$[1s^2 2s^2 2p^6]\ 3s^2 3p^4$	$[Ne]\ 3s^2 3p^4$
17	Cl	↑↓	↑↓	↑↓	↑	$[1s^2 2s^2 2p^6]\ 3s^2 3p^5$	$[Ne]\ 3s^2 3p^5$
18	Ar	↑↓	↑↓	↑↓	↑↓	$[1s^2 2s^2 2p^6]\ 3s^2 3p^6$	$[Ne]\ 3s^2 3p^6$

*Colored type indicates the sublevel to which the last electron is added.

†The full configuration is not usually written with square brackets; they are included here to show how the [Ne] designation arises.

Building Up Period 3

The Period 3 elements, Na through Ar, lie directly under the Period 2 elements, Li through Ne. That is, even though the $n = 3$ level splits into 3*s*, 3*p*, and 3*d* sublevels, Period 3 fills only 3*s* and 3*p*; as you'll see shortly, the 3*d* is filled in Period 4. Table 8.2 introduces two ways to present electron distributions more concisely:

- *Partial orbital diagrams* show only the sublevels being filled, here the 3*s* and 3*p*.
- *Condensed electron configurations (rightmost column)* have the element symbol of the previous noble gas in brackets, to stand for its configuration, followed by the electron configuration of filled inner sublevels and the energy level being filled. For example, the condensed electron configuration of sulfur is [Ne] $3s^2 3p^4$, where [Ne] stands for $1s^2 2s^2 2p^6$.

In Na (the second alkali metal) and Mg (the second alkaline earth metal), electrons are added to the 3*s* sublevel, which contains only the 3*s* orbital; this is directly comparable to the filling of the 2*s* sublevel in Li and Be in Period 2. Then, in the same way as the 2*p* orbitals of B, C, and N in Period 2 are half-filled, the last electrons added to Al, Si, and P in Period 3 half-fill successive 3*p* orbitals with spins parallel (Hund's rule). The last electrons added to S, Cl, and Ar then successively pair up to fill those 3*p* orbitals, which fills the 3*p* sublevel.

Similar Electron Configurations Within Groups

One of the central points in chemistry is that *similar outer electron configurations correlate with similar chemical behavior.* Figure 8.8 shows the condensed electron configurations of the first 18 elements. Note the similarity within each group. Here are examples from three of the groups:

- In Group 1A(1), Li and Na have the outer electron configuration ns^1 (where *n* is the quantum number of the highest energy level), as do the other alkali metals (K, Rb, Cs, and Fr). All are highly reactive metals whose atoms lose the outer electron when they form ionic compounds with nonmetals, and all react vigorously with water to displace H_2 (Figure 8.9A).
- In Group 7A(17), F and Cl have the outer electron configuration ns^2np^5, as do the other halogens (Br, I, and At). All are reactive nonmetals that occur as diatomic

Period	1A (1)	2A (2)	3A (13)	4A (14)	5A (15)	6A (16)	7A (17)	8A (18)
1	1 **H** $1s^1$							2 **He** $1s^2$
2	3 **Li** [He] $2s^1$	4 **Be** [He] $2s^2$	5 **B** [He] $2s^22p^1$	6 **C** [He] $2s^22p^2$	7 **N** [He] $2s^22p^3$	8 **O** [He] $2s^22p^4$	9 **F** [He] $2s^22p^5$	10 **Ne** [He] $2s^22p^6$
3	11 **Na** [Ne] $3s^1$	12 **Mg** [Ne] $3s^2$	13 **Al** [Ne] $3s^23p^1$	14 **Si** [Ne] $3s^23p^2$	15 **P** [Ne] $3s^23p^3$	16 **S** [Ne] $3s^23p^4$	17 **Cl** [Ne] $3s^23p^5$	18 **Ar** [Ne] $3s^23p^6$

Figure 8.8 Condensed electron configurations in the first three periods. Elements in a group have similar outer electron configurations (*color*).

molecules (X_2), and all form ionic compounds with metals (KX, MgX_2) in which the ion charge is 1− (Figure 8.9B), covalent compounds with hydrogen (HX) that yield acidic solutions in water, and covalent compounds with carbon (CX_4).

- In Group 8A(18), He has the electron configuration ns^2, and all the other elements in the group have the outer configuration ns^2np^6. Consistent with their *filled* energy levels, all the members are very unreactive monatomic gases.

To summarize the major connection between quantum mechanics and chemical periodicity: *sublevels are filled in order of increasing energy, which leads to outer electron configurations that recur periodically, which leads to chemical properties that recur periodically.*

A

B

Figure 8.9 Similar reactivities in a group. A, Potassium reacting with water. **B,** Chlorine reacting with potassium.

Building Up Period 4: The First Transition Series

Period 4 contains the first series of **transition elements,** those in which *d* orbitals are being filled. Let's examine three factors that affect the filling pattern in a period with a transition series.

1. *Effects of shielding and penetration on sublevel energy.* The 3*d* sublevel is filled in Period 4, but *the 4s sublevel is filled first.* This switch in filling order is due to shielding and penetration effects. Based on the 3*d* radial probability distribution (see Figure 7.19, p. 286), a 3*d* electron spends most of the time outside the filled inner $n = 1$ and $n = 2$ levels, so it is shielded very effectively from the nuclear charge. However, the outermost 4*s* electron penetrates close to the nucleus part of the time, so it is subject to a greater attraction. As a result, the 4*s* orbital is slightly *lower* in energy than the 3*d* and fills first. In any period, *the ns sublevel fills before the*

$(n - 1)d$ *sublevel.* Other variations in the filling pattern occur at higher values of n because sublevel energies become very close together (see Figure 8.5).

2. *Filling the 4s and 3d sublevels.* Table 8.3 shows the partial orbital diagrams and full and condensed electron configurations for the 18 elements in Period 4. The first two elements, K and Ca, are the next alkali and alkaline earth metals, respectively; the last electron of K half-fills and that of Ca fills the $4s$ sublevel. The last electron of scandium (Sc; $Z = 21$), the first transition element, occupies any one of the five $3d$ orbitals because they are equal in energy; Sc has the electron configuration [Ar] $4s^23d^1$. Filling of the $3d$ orbitals proceeds one electron at a time, as with the p orbitals, except in two cases, chromium (Cr; $Z = 24$) and copper (Cu; $Z = 29$), discussed next.

3. *Stability of half-filled and filled sublevels.* Vanadium (V; $Z = 23$) has three half-filled d orbitals ([Ar] $4s^23d^3$). However, the last electron of the next element, Cr, does not enter a fourth empty d orbital to give [Ar] $4s^23d^4$; instead, Cr has one electron in the $4s$ sublevel and five in the $3d$ sublevel, making both sublevels half filled: [Ar] $4s^13d^5$ *(see margin).* In the next element, manganese (Mn; $Z = 25$), the $4s$ sublevel is filled again ([Ar] $4s^23d^5$).

Cr ($Z = 24$) [Ar] $4s^13d^5$

4s	3d	4p
[↑]	[↑][↑][↑][↑][↑]	[ ][ ][ ]

Table 8.3 Partial Orbital Diagrams and Electron Configurations* for the Elements in Period 4

Atomic Number	Element	Partial Orbital Diagram (4s, 3d, and 4p Sublevels Only): 4s	3d	4p	Full Electron Configuration	Condensed Electron Configuration
19	K	[↑]	[ ][ ][ ][ ][ ]	[ ][ ][ ]	$1s^22s^22p^63s^23p^64s^1$	[Ar] $4s^1$
20	Ca	[↑↓]	[ ][ ][ ][ ][ ]	[ ][ ][ ]	$1s^22s^22p^63s^23p^64s^2$	[Ar] $4s^2$
21	Sc	[↑↓]	[↑][ ][ ][ ][ ]	[ ][ ][ ]	$1s^22s^22p^63s^23p^64s^23d^1$	[Ar] $4s^23d^1$
22	Ti	[↑↓]	[↑][↑][ ][ ][ ]	[ ][ ][ ]	$1s^22s^22p^63s^23p^64s^23d^2$	[Ar] $4s^23d^2$
23	V	[↑↓]	[↑][↑][↑][ ][ ]	[ ][ ][ ]	$1s^22s^22p^63s^23p^64s^23d^3$	[Ar] $4s^23d^3$
24	Cr	[↑]	[↑][↑][↑][↑][↑]	[ ][ ][ ]	$1s^22s^22p^63s^23p^64s^13d^5$	[Ar] $4s^13d^5$
25	Mn	[↑↓]	[↑][↑][↑][↑][↑]	[ ][ ][ ]	$1s^22s^22p^63s^23p^64s^23d^5$	[Ar] $4s^23d^5$
26	Fe	[↑↓]	[↑↓][↑][↑][↑][↑]	[ ][ ][ ]	$1s^22s^22p^63s^23p^64s^23d^6$	[Ar] $4s^23d^6$
27	Co	[↑↓]	[↑↓][↑↓][↑][↑][↑]	[ ][ ][ ]	$1s^22s^22p^63s^23p^64s^23d^7$	[Ar] $4s^23d^7$
28	Ni	[↑↓]	[↑↓][↑↓][↑↓][↑][↑]	[ ][ ][ ]	$1s^22s^22p^63s^23p^64s^23d^8$	[Ar] $4s^23d^8$
29	Cu	[↑]	[↑↓][↑↓][↑↓][↑↓][↑↓]	[ ][ ][ ]	$1s^22s^22p^63s^23p^64s^13d^{10}$	[Ar] $4s^13d^{10}$
30	Zn	[↑↓]	[↑↓][↑↓][↑↓][↑↓][↑↓]	[ ][ ][ ]	$1s^22s^22p^63s^23p^64s^23d^{10}$	[Ar] $4s^23d^{10}$
31	Ga	[↑↓]	[↑↓][↑↓][↑↓][↑↓][↑↓]	[↑][ ][ ]	$1s^22s^22p^63s^23p^64s^23d^{10}4p^1$	[Ar] $4s^23d^{10}4p^1$
32	Ge	[↑↓]	[↑↓][↑↓][↑↓][↑↓][↑↓]	[↑][↑][ ]	$1s^22s^22p^63s^23p^64s^23d^{10}4p^2$	[Ar] $4s^23d^{10}4p^2$
33	As	[↑↓]	[↑↓][↑↓][↑↓][↑↓][↑↓]	[↑][↑][↑]	$1s^22s^22p^63s^23p^64s^23d^{10}4p^3$	[Ar] $4s^23d^{10}4p^3$
34	Se	[↑↓]	[↑↓][↑↓][↑↓][↑↓][↑↓]	[↑↓][↑][↑]	$1s^22s^22p^63s^23p^64s^23d^{10}4p^4$	[Ar] $4s^23d^{10}4p^4$
35	Br	[↑↓]	[↑↓][↑↓][↑↓][↑↓][↑↓]	[↑↓][↑↓][↑]	$1s^22s^22p^63s^23p^64s^23d^{10}4p^5$	[Ar] $4s^23d^{10}4p^5$
36	Kr	[↑↓]	[↑↓][↑↓][↑↓][↑↓][↑↓]	[↑↓][↑↓][↑↓]	$1s^22s^22p^63s^23p^64s^23d^{10}4p^6$	[Ar] $4s^23d^{10}4p^6$

*Colored type indicates sublevel(s) whose occupancy changes when the last electron is added.

Because it follows nickel (Ni; [Ar] $4s^2 3d^8$), copper would be expected to have the configuration [Ar] $4s^2 3d^9$. Instead, the 4*s* sublevel of Cu is *half-filled* with 1 electron, and the 3*d* sublevel is *filled* with 10 *(see margin)*. From these two exceptions, Cr and Cu, we conclude that *half-filled and filled sublevels are unexpectedly stable (low in energy);* we see this pattern with many other elements.

Cu (Z = 29) [Ar] $4s^1 3d^{10}$

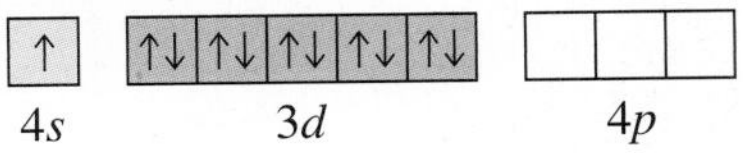

With zinc (Zn; Z = 30), the 4*s* sublevel is filled ([Ar] $4s^2 3d^{10}$), and the first transition series ends. The 4*p* sublevel is filled by the next six elements, and Period 4 ends with the noble gas krypton (Kr; Z = 36).

General Principles of Electron Configurations

Figure 8.10 shows the partial (highest energy sublevels being filled) ground-state electron configurations of the 117 known elements. Let's highlight some key relationships among them.

Similar Outer Electron Configurations Within a Group Among the main-group elements (A groups)—the *s*-block and *p*-block elements—outer electron configurations within a group are identical. Some variations in the transition elements (B groups, *d* block) and inner transition elements (*f* block) occur, as we'll see.

Orbital Filling Order When the elements are "built up" by filling levels and sublevels in order of increasing energy, we obtain the sequence in the periodic table. Reading the table from left to right, like words on a page, gives the energy order

Figure 8.10 A periodic table of partial ground-state electron configurations.

Main-Group Elements (*s* block) | Transition Elements (*d* block) | Main-Group Elements (*p* block)

Period number: highest occupied energy level

Period	1A (1) ns^1	2A (2) ns^2	3B (3)	4B (4)	5B (5)	6B (6)	7B (7)	8B (8)	8B (9)	8B (10)	1B (11)	2B (12)	3A (13) ns^2np^1	4A (14) ns^2np^2	5A (15) ns^2np^3	6A (16) ns^2np^4	7A (17) ns^2np^5	8A (18) ns^2np^6
1	1 H $1s^1$																	2 He $1s^2$
2	3 Li $2s^1$	4 Be $2s^2$											5 B $2s^22p^1$	6 C $2s^22p^2$	7 N $2s^22p^3$	8 O $2s^22p^4$	9 F $2s^22p^5$	10 Ne $2s^22p^6$
3	11 Na $3s^1$	12 Mg $3s^2$											13 Al $3s^23p^1$	14 Si $3s^23p^2$	15 P $3s^23p^3$	16 S $3s^23p^4$	17 Cl $3s^23p^5$	18 Ar $3s^23p^6$
4	19 K $4s^1$	20 Ca $4s^2$	21 Sc $4s^23d^1$	22 Ti $4s^23d^2$	23 V $4s^23d^3$	24 Cr $4s^13d^5$	25 Mn $4s^23d^5$	26 Fe $4s^23d^6$	27 Co $4s^23d^7$	28 Ni $4s^23d^8$	29 Cu $4s^13d^{10}$	30 Zn $4s^23d^{10}$	31 Ga $4s^24p^1$	32 Ge $4s^24p^2$	33 As $4s^24p^3$	34 Se $4s^24p^4$	35 Br $4s^24p^5$	36 Kr $4s^24p^6$
5	37 Rb $5s^1$	38 Sr $5s^2$	39 Y $5s^24d^1$	40 Zr $5s^24d^2$	41 Nb $5s^14d^4$	42 Mo $5s^14d^5$	43 Tc $5s^24d^5$	44 Ru $5s^14d^7$	45 Rh $5s^14d^8$	46 Pd $4d^{10}$	47 Ag $5s^14d^{10}$	48 Cd $5s^24d^{10}$	49 In $5s^25p^1$	50 Sn $5s^25p^2$	51 Sb $5s^25p^3$	52 Te $5s^25p^4$	53 I $5s^25p^5$	54 Xe $5s^25p^6$
6	55 Cs $6s^1$	56 Ba $6s^2$	57 La* $6s^25d^1$	72 Hf $6s^25d^2$	73 Ta $6s^25d^3$	74 W $6s^25d^4$	75 Re $6s^25d^5$	76 Os $6s^25d^6$	77 Ir $6s^25d^7$	78 Pt $6s^15d^9$	79 Au $6s^15d^{10}$	80 Hg $6s^25d^{10}$	81 Tl $6s^26p^1$	82 Pb $6s^26p^2$	83 Bi $6s^26p^3$	84 Po $6s^26p^4$	85 At $6s^26p^5$	86 Rn $6s^26p^6$
7	87 Fr $7s^1$	88 Ra $7s^2$	89 Ac** $7s^26d^1$	104 Rf $7s^26d^2$	105 Db $7s^26d^3$	106 Sg $7s^26d^4$	107 Bh $7s^26d^5$	108 Hs $7s^26d^6$	109 Mt $7s^26d^7$	110 Ds $7s^26d^8$	111 Rg $7s^26d^9$	112 Cn $7s^26d^{10}$	113 $7s^27p^1$	114 $7s^27p^2$	115 $7s^27p^3$	116 $7s^27p^4$		118 $7s^27p^6$

Inner Transition Elements (*f* block)

Period															
6	*Lanthanides	58 Ce $6s^24f^15d^1$	59 Pr $6s^24f^3$	60 Nd $6s^24f^4$	61 Pm $6s^24f^5$	62 Sm $6s^24f^6$	63 Eu $6s^24f^7$	64 Gd $6s^24f^75d^1$	65 Tb $6s^24f^9$	66 Dy $6s^24f^{10}$	67 Ho $6s^24f^{11}$	68 Er $6s^24f^{12}$	69 Tm $6s^24f^{13}$	70 Yb $6s^24f^{14}$	71 Lu $6s^24f^{14}5d^1$
7	**Actinides	90 Th $7s^26d^2$	91 Pa $7s^25f^26d^1$	92 U $7s^25f^36d^1$	93 Np $7s^25f^46d^1$	94 Pu $7s^25f^6$	95 Am $7s^25f^7$	96 Cm $7s^25f^76d^1$	97 Bk $7s^25f^9$	98 Cf $7s^25f^{10}$	99 Es $7s^25f^{11}$	100 Fm $7s^25f^{12}$	101 Md $7s^25f^{13}$	102 No $7s^25f^{14}$	103 Lr $7s^25f^{14}6d^1$

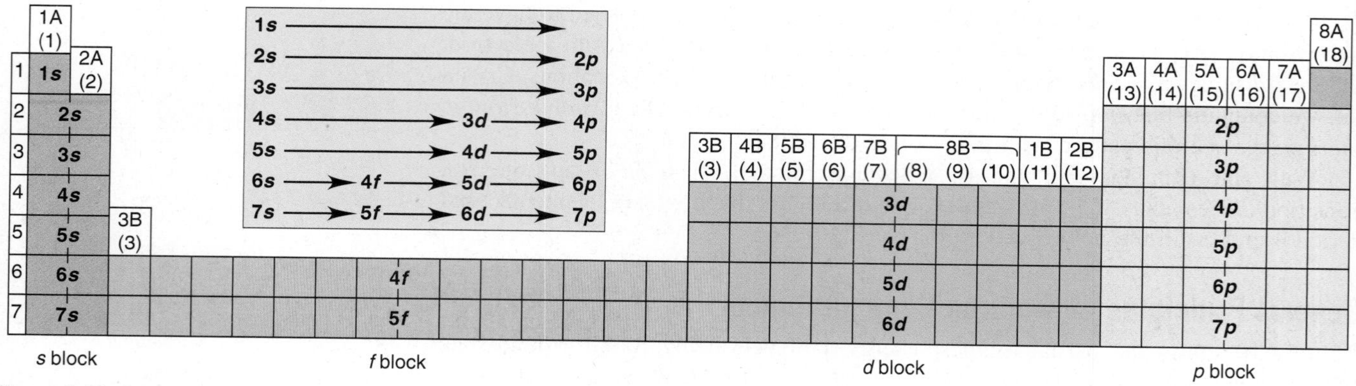

Figure 8.11 Orbital filling and the periodic table. This form of the periodic table shows the sublevel blocks. *Pale green inset:* A summary of the sublevel filling order.

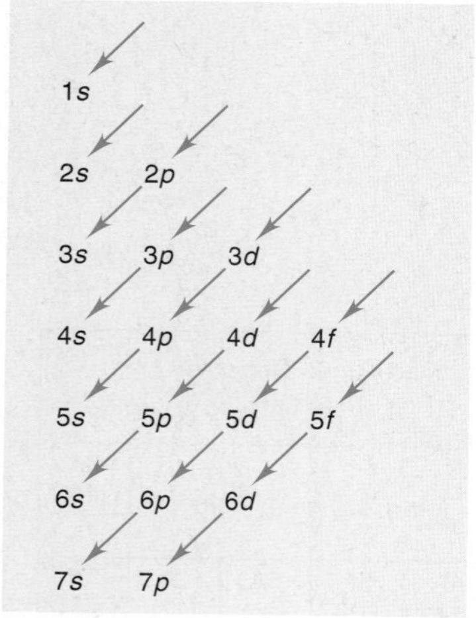

Aid to memorizing sublevel filling order. List the sublevels as shown, and read from 1*s*, following the direction of the arrows. Note that the
- *n* value is constant horizontally
- *l* value is constant vertically
- *n* + *l* is constant diagonally

of levels and sublevels (Figure 8.11); the margin note is a memory aid for sublevel filling order when a periodic table is not available.

Categories of Electrons Atoms have three categories of electrons:

1. **Inner (core) electrons** are those an atom has in common with the previous noble gas and any *completed* transition series. They fill all the *lower energy levels* of an atom.
2. **Outer electrons** are those in the *highest energy level* (highest *n* value). They spend most of their time farthest from the nucleus.
3. **Valence electrons** are those involved in forming compounds:
   - For main-group elements, the *valence electrons* ***are*** *the outer electrons.*
   - For transition elements, in addition to the outer *ns* electrons, the $(n - 1)d$ electrons are also valence electrons, though the metals Fe ($Z = 26$) through Zn ($Z = 30$) may use only a few, if any, of their *d* electrons in bonding.

Group and Period Numbers Key information is embedded in the periodic table:

- Among the main-group elements (A groups), *the A number equals the number of outer electrons* (those with the highest *n*); thus, chlorine (Cl; Group **7A**) has 7 outer electrons, and so forth.
- *The period number is the n value of the highest energy level.*
- For an energy level, the *n* value squared (n^2) is the number of *orbitals,* and $2n^2$ is the maximum number of *electrons* (or elements). For example, consider the $n = 3$ level. The number of orbitals is $n^2 = 9$: one 3*s*, three 3*p*, and five 3*d*. The number of electrons is $2n^2 = 18$: two 3*s* and six 3*p* electrons for the eight elements of Period 3, and ten 3*d* electrons for the ten transition elements of Period 4.

Intervening Series: Transition and Inner Transition Elements

As Figure 8.11 shows, the *d* block and *f* block occur between the main-group *s* and *p* blocks.

1. *Transition series.* Periods 4, 5, 6, and 7 incorporate the 3*d,* 4*d,* 5*d,* and 6*d* sublevels, respectively. As you've seen, the general pattern is that the $(n - 1)d$ sublevel is filled between the *ns* and *np* sublevels. Thus, in Period 5, the filling order is 5*s,* then 4*d,* and then 5*p.*

2. *Inner transition series.* In Period 6, the first of two series of **inner transition elements,** those in which *f* orbitals are being filled, appears (Figure 8.11). The *f* orbitals have $l = 3$, so the possible m_l values are $-3, -2, -1, 0, +1, +2,$ and $+3$; that is, there are seven *f* orbitals, for a total of 14 elements in *each* of the two inner transition series:

- The Period 6 inner transition series, called the **lanthanides** (or **rare earths**), occurs after lanthanum (La; $Z = 57$), and the 4*f* orbitals are filled.
- The Period 7 inner transition series, called the **actinides,** occurs after actinium (Ac; $Z = 89$), and the 5*f* orbitals are filled.

Thus, in Periods 6 and 7, the filling sequence is

ns, first of the $(n - 1)d$, all $(n - 2)f$, remainder of the $(n - 1)d$, and np

Period 6 ends with the $6p$ sublevel. Period 7 is incomplete because only five elements with $7p$ electrons are known at this time; element 117 has not yet been synthesized.

3. *Irregular filling patterns.* Irregularities in the filling pattern, such as those for Cr and Cu in Period 4, occur in the d and f blocks because the sublevel energies in these larger atoms differ very little. Even though occasional deviations occur in the d block, the sum of ns electrons and $(n - 1)d$ electrons always equals the new group number (in parentheses). For instance, despite variations in Group 6B(**6**)—Cr, Mo, W, and Sg—the sum of ns and $(n - 1)d$ electrons is 6; for Group 8B(**10**)—Ni, Pd, Pt, and Ds—the sum is 10.

Sample Problem 8.2 Determining Electron Configurations

Problem Using the periodic table (not Figure 8.10 or Table 8.3) and assuming a regular filling pattern, give the full and condensed electron configurations, partial orbital diagrams showing valence electrons only, and number of inner electrons for the following elements:
(a) Potassium (K; Z = 19) **(b)** Technetium (Tc; Z = 43) **(c)** Lead (Pb; Z = 82)

Plan The atomic number tells us the number of electrons, and the periodic table shows the order for filling sublevels. In the partial orbital diagrams, we include all electrons added after the previous noble gas *except* those in *filled* inner sublevels. The number of inner electrons is the sum of those in the previous noble gas and in filled d and f sublevels.

Solution (a) For K (Z = 19), the full electron configuration is $1s^22s^22p^63s^23p^64s^1$.
The condensed configuration is [Ar] $4s^1$.
The partial orbital diagram showing valence electrons is

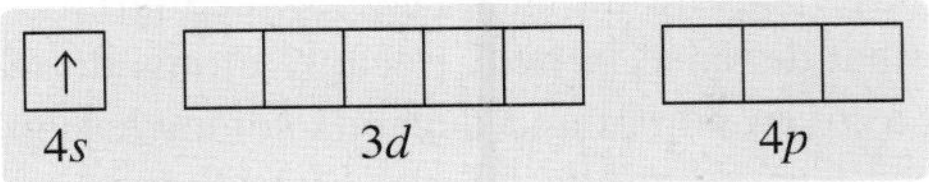

K is a main-group element in Group 1A(1) and Period 4, so there are 18 inner electrons.
(b) For Tc (Z = 43), assuming the expected pattern, the full electron configuration is $1s^22s^22p^63s^23p^64s^23d^{10}4p^65s^24d^5$.
The condensed electron configuration is [Kr] $5s^24d^5$.
The partial orbital diagram showing valence electrons is

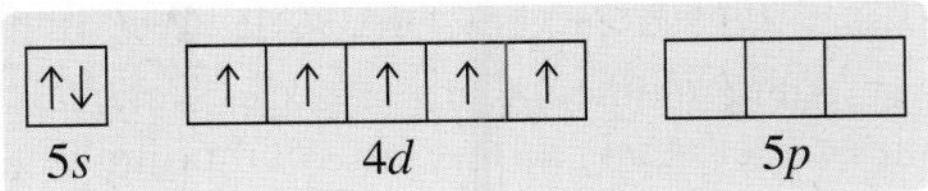

Tc is a transition element in Group 7B(7) and Period 5, so there are 36 inner electrons.
(c) For Pb (Z = 82), the full electron configuration is
$1s^22s^22p^63s^23p^64s^23d^{10}4p^65s^24d^{10}5p^66s^24f^{14}5d^{10}6p^2$.
The condensed electron configuration is [Xe] $6s^24f^{14}5d^{10}6p^2$.
The partial orbital diagram showing valence electrons (no filled inner sublevels) is

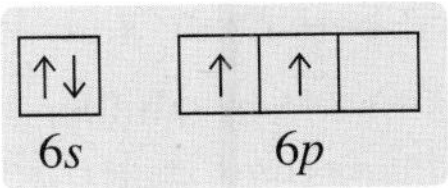

Pb is a main-group element in Group 4A(14) and Period 6, so there are 54 (in Xe) + 14 (in the $4f$ sublevel) + 10 (in the $5d$ sublevel) = 78 inner electrons.

Check Be sure that the sum of the superscripts (numbers of electrons) in the full electron configuration equals the atomic number and that the number of *valence* electrons in the condensed configuration equals the number of electrons in the partial orbital diagram.

Follow-Up Problem 8.2 Without referring to Table 8.3 or Figure 8.10, give full and condensed electron configurations, partial orbital diagrams showing valence electrons only, and the number of inner electrons for the following elements:
(a) Ni (Z = 28) **(b)** Sr (Z = 38) **(c)** Po (Z = 84)

Summary of Section 8.2

- By the aufbau principle, one electron is added to an atom of each successive element in accord with the exclusion principle (no two electrons can have the same set of quantum numbers) and Hund's rule (orbitals of equal energy become half-filled, with electron spins parallel, before any pairing of spins occurs).
- The elements of a group have similar outer electron configurations and similar chemical behavior.
- For the main-group elements, valence electrons (those involved in reactions) are in the outer (highest energy) level only. For transition elements, $(n-1)d$ electrons are also considered valence electrons.
- Because of shielding of d electrons by electrons in inner sublevels and penetration by the ns electron, the $(n-1)d$ sublevel fills after the ns and before the np sublevels.
- In Periods 6 and 7, $(n-2)f$ orbitals fill between the first and second $(n-1)d$ orbitals.

8.3 • TRENDS IN THREE ATOMIC PROPERTIES

In this section, we focus on three atomic properties directly influenced by electron configuration and effective nuclear charge: atomic size, ionization energy, and electron affinity. Most importantly, these properties are *periodic,* which means they generally exhibit consistent changes, or *trends,* within a group or period.

Trends in Atomic Size

Recall from Chapter 7 that we often represent atoms with spherical contours in which the electrons spend 90% of their time. We *define* atomic size (the extent of the contour) in terms of how closely one atom lies next to another. But, in practice, as we discuss in Chapter 12, we measure the distance between atomic nuclei in a sample of an element and divide that distance in half. Because atoms do not have hard surfaces, the size of an atom in a given compound depends somewhat on the atoms near it. In other words, *atomic size varies slightly from substance to substance.*

Figure 8.12 shows two common definitions of atomic size:

1. **Metallic radius.** Used mostly for *metals,* it is one-half the shortest distance between nuclei of adjacent, individual atoms in a crystal of the element (Figure 8.12A).
2. **Covalent radius.** Used for elements occurring as molecules, mostly *nonmetals,* it is one-half the shortest distance between nuclei of bonded atoms (Figure 8.12B).

Radii measured for some elements are used to determine the radii of other elements from distances between atoms in compounds. For instance, in a carbon-chlorine compound, the distance between nuclei in a C—Cl bond is 177 pm. Using the known covalent radius of Cl (100 pm), we find the covalent radius of C (177 pm − 100 pm = 77 pm) (Figure 8.12C).

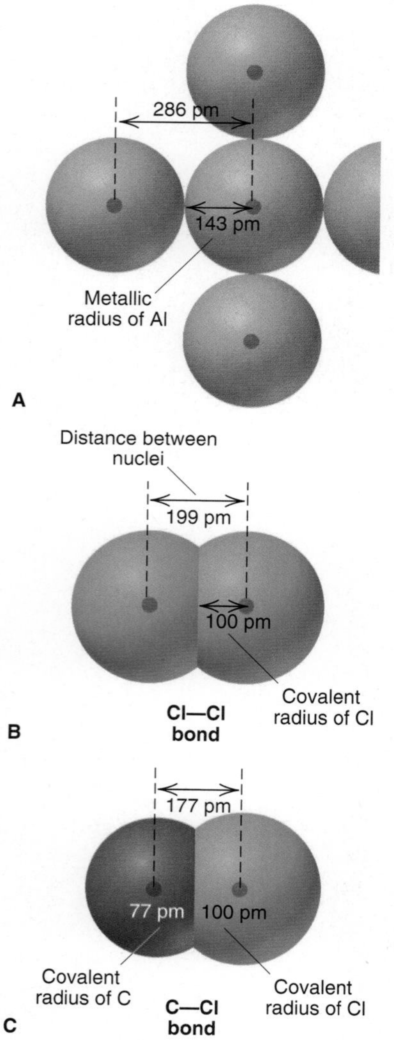

Figure 8.12 Defining atomic size. **A,** The metallic radius of aluminum. **B,** The covalent radius of chlorine. **C,** Known covalent radii and distances between nuclei can be used to find unknown radii.

Main-Group Elements Figure 8.13 shows the atomic radii of the main-group elements and most of the transition elements. Among the main-group elements, atomic size varies within both groups and periods as a result of two opposing influences:

1. *Changes in n.* As the principal quantum number (n) increases, the probability that outer electrons spend most of their time farther from the nucleus increases as well; thus, atomic size increases.
2. *Changes in* Z_{eff}. As the effective nuclear charge (Z_{eff}) increases, outer electrons are pulled closer to the nucleus; thus, atomic size decreases.

The net effect of these influences depends on how effectively the inner electrons shield the increasing nuclear charge:

1. *Down a group, n dominates.* As we move down a main group, each member has *one more level of inner electrons that shield the outer electrons very effectively.* Even though additional protons do moderately increase Z_{eff} for the outer electrons, the atoms get larger as a result of the increasing n value:

Atomic radius generally ***increases*** *down a group.*

2. *Across a period,* Z_{eff} *dominates.* Across a period from left to right, electrons are added to the *same* outer level, so the shielding by inner electrons does not change. Despite greater electron repulsions, outer electrons shield each other only slightly, so Z_{eff} rises significantly, and the outer electrons are pulled closer to the nucleus:

Atomic radius generally ***decreases*** *across a period.*

Transition Elements As Figure 8.13 shows, size trends are *not* as consistent for the transition elements:

1. *Down a transition group, n* increases, but shielding by an additional level of inner electrons results in only a small size increase from Period 4 to 5 and none from 5 to 6.

2. *Across a transition series*, atomic size shrinks through the first two or three elements because of the increasing nuclear charge. But, from then on, *size remains relatively constant* because shielding by the inner *d* electrons counteracts the increase in Z_{eff}. Thus, for example, in Period 4, the third transition element, vanadium (V; $Z = 23$), has the same radius as the last, zinc (Zn; $Z = 30$). This pattern also appears in Periods 5 and 6 in the transition and both inner transition series.

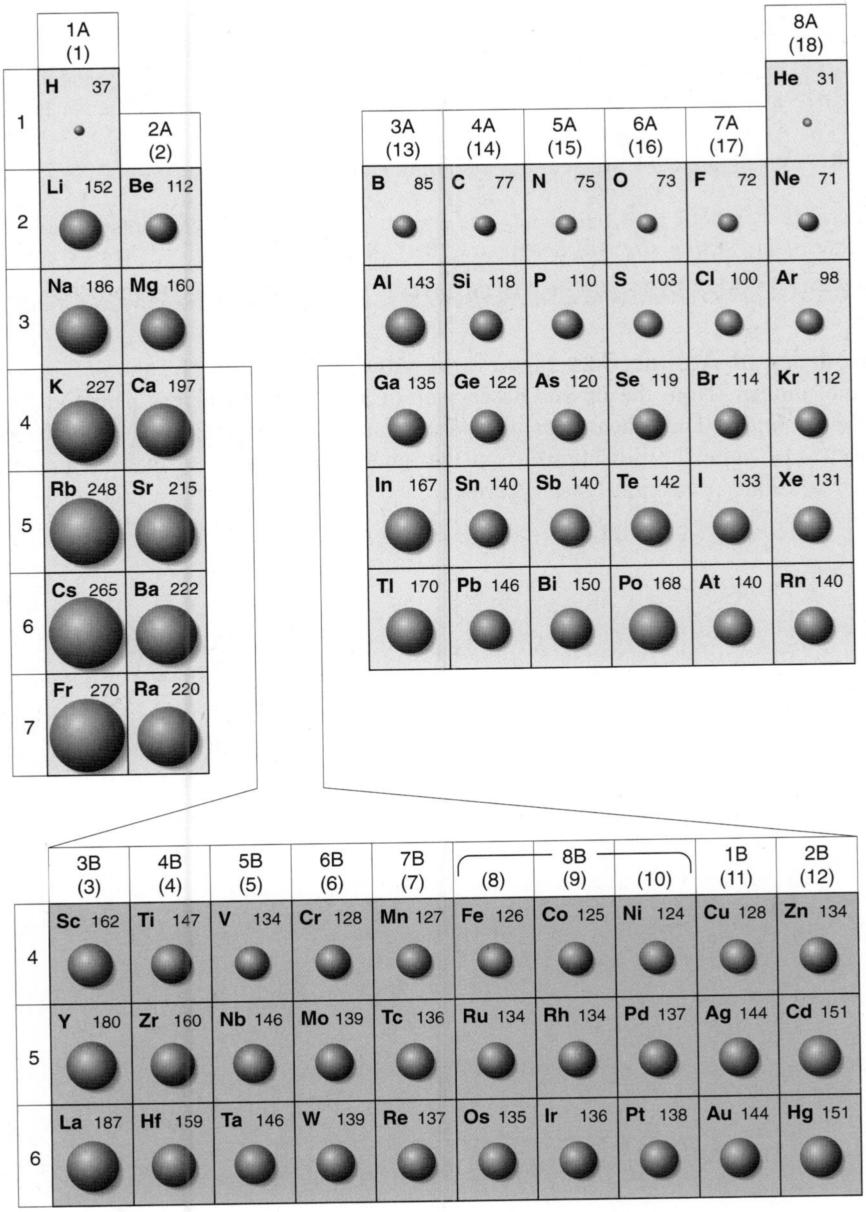

Figure 8.13 Atomic radii of the main-group and transition elements. Atomic radii (in picometers) are shown for the main-group elements (*tan*) and the transition elements (*blue*). (Values for the noble gases are calculated.)

3. *A transition series affects atomic size in neighboring main groups.* Shielding by *d* electrons causes a *major size decrease from Group 2A(2) to Group 3A(13)* in Periods 4 through 6. Because the *np* sublevel has more penetration than the $(n - 1)d$, the first *np* electron [added in Group 3A(13)] "feels" a much greater Z_{eff}, due to all the protons added in the intervening transition elements. The greatest decrease occurs in Period 4: calcium (Ca; $Z = 20$) in Group 2A(2) is nearly 50% larger than gallium (Ga; $Z = 31$) in 3A(13). In fact, *d*-orbital shielding causes gallium to be slightly *smaller* than aluminum (Al; $Z = 13$), the element above it!

Sample Problem 8.3 Ranking Elements by Atomic Size

Problem Using only the periodic table (not Figure 8.13), rank each set of main-group elements in order of *decreasing* atomic size:
(a) Ca, Mg, Sr **(b)** K, Ga, Ca **(c)** Br, Rb, Kr **(d)** Sr, Ca, Rb

Plan To rank the elements by atomic size, we find them in the periodic table. They are main-group elements, so size increases down a group and decreases across a period.

Solution (a) Sr > Ca > Mg. These three elements are in Group 2A(2), and size decreases up the group.
(b) K > Ca > Ga. These three elements are in Period 4, and size decreases across a period.
(c) Rb > Br > Kr. Rb is largest because it has one more energy level (Period 5) and is farthest to the left. Kr is smaller than Br because Kr is farther to the right in Period 4.
(d) Rb > Sr > Ca. Ca is smallest because it has one fewer energy level. Sr is smaller than Rb because it is farther to the right.

Check From Figure 8.13, we see that the rankings are correct.

Follow-Up Problem 8.3 Using only the periodic table, rank the elements in each set in order of *increasing* size: **(a)** Se, Br, Cl; **(b)** I, Xe, Ba.

Periodicity of Atomic Size Figure 8.14 shows the variation in atomic size with atomic number. Note the up-and-down pattern as size drops across a period to the noble gas (*purple*) and then leaps up to the alkali metal (*brown*) that begins the next period. Also note the deviations from the smooth size decrease in each transition (*blue*) and inner transition (*green*) series.

Figure 8.14 Periodicity of atomic radius.

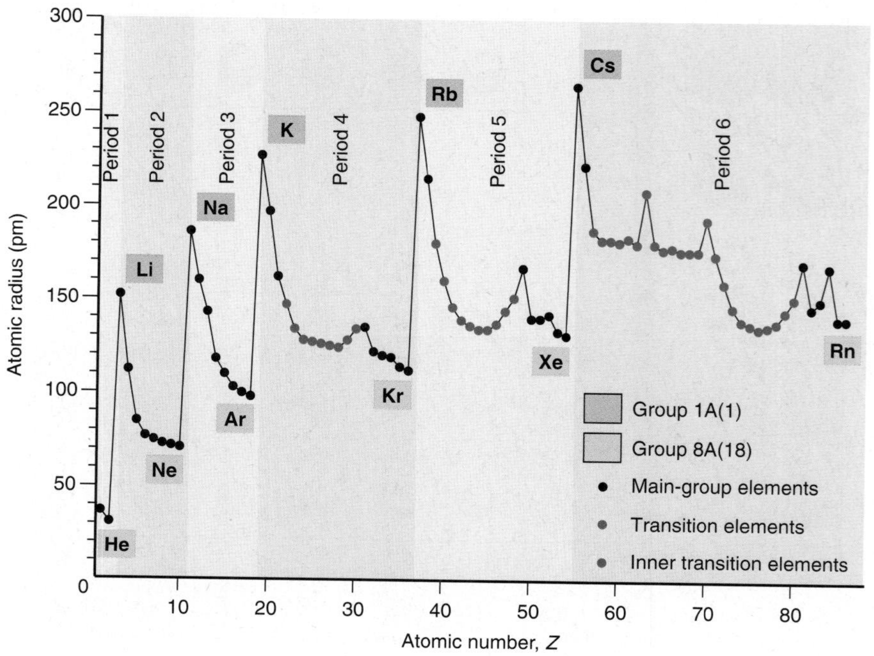

Trends in Ionization Energy

The **ionization energy (IE)** is the energy required for the *complete removal* of 1 mol of electrons from 1 mol of gaseous atoms or ions. Pulling an electron away from a nucleus *requires* energy to overcome their electrostatic attraction. Because energy flows *into* the system, the ionization energy is always positive (like ΔH of an endothermic reaction). (Chapter 7 viewed the ionization energy of the H atom as the energy difference between $n = 1$ and $n = \infty$, where the electron is completely removed.) The ionization energy is a key factor in an element's reactivity:

- *Atoms with a low IE tend to form cations during reactions.*
- *Atoms with a high IE (except the noble gases) tend to form anions.*

Many-electron atoms can lose more than one electron. The *first* ionization energy (IE_1) removes an outermost electron (highest energy sublevel) from a gaseous atom:

$$\text{Atom}(g) \longrightarrow \text{ion}^+(g) + e^- \qquad \Delta E = IE_1 > 0 \qquad (8.2)$$

The *second* ionization energy (IE_2) removes a second electron. Since this electron is pulled away from a positive ion, IE_2 is always larger than IE_1:

$$\text{Ion}^+(g) \longrightarrow \text{ion}^{2+}(g) + e^- \qquad \Delta E = IE_2 \text{ (always} > IE_1)$$

Periodicity of First Ionization Energy Figure 8.15 shows the variation in first ionization energy with atomic number. This up-and-down pattern—IE_1 rising across a period to the noble gas (*purple*) and then dropping down to the next alkali metal (*brown*)—is the *inverse* of the variation in atomic size (Figure 8.14): *as size decreases, it takes more energy to remove an electron because the nucleus is closer, so IE_1 increases.*

Let's examine the group and period trends and their exceptions:

1. *Down a group.* As we move *down* a main group, the n value increases, so atomic size does as well. As the distance from nucleus to outer electron increases, their attraction lessens, so the electron is easier to remove (Figure 8.16, *next page*):

Ionization energy generally ***decreases*** *down a group.*

The only significant exception occurs in Group 3A(13): IE_1 decreases from boron (B) to aluminum (Al), but not for the rest of the group. Filling the transition series in Periods 4, 5, and 6 causes a much higher Z_{eff} and an unusually small change in size, so outer electrons in the larger Group 3A members are held tighter.

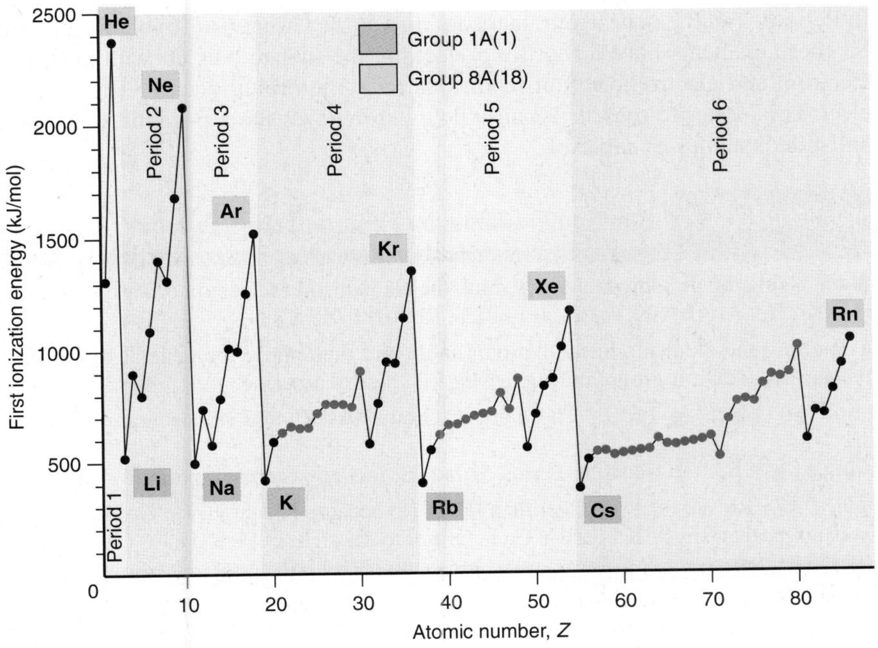

Figure 8.15 Periodicity of first ionization energy (IE_1). This trend is the *inverse* of the trend in atomic size (see Figure 8.14).

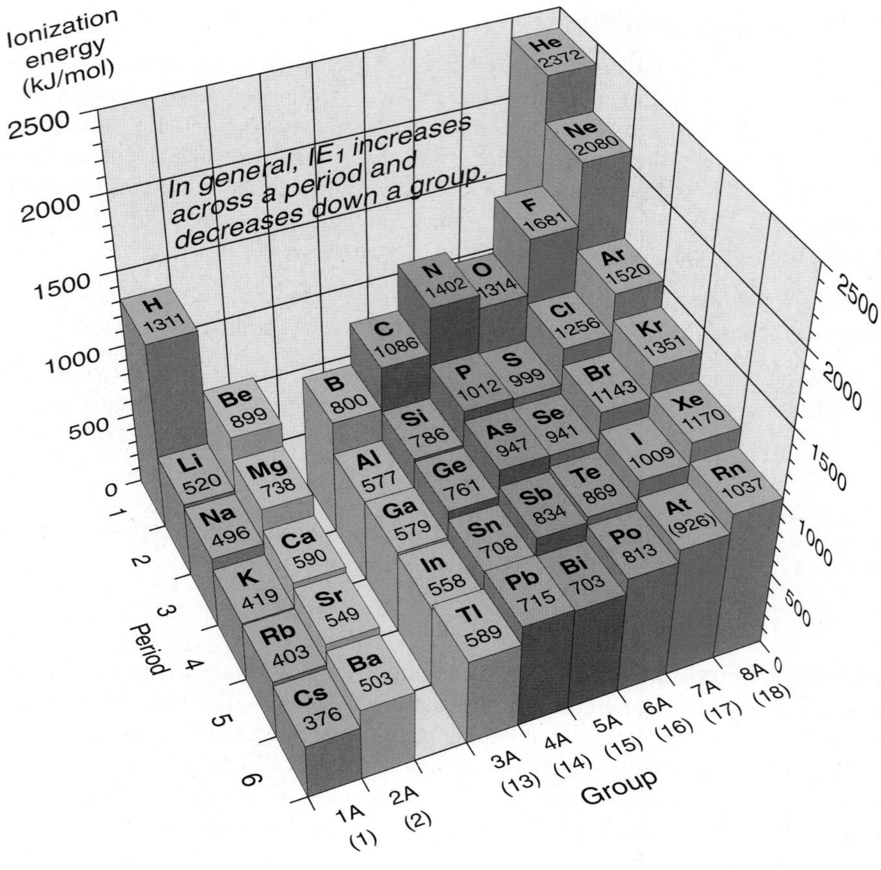

Figure 8.16 First ionization energies of the main-group elements.

2. *Across a period.* As we move left to right across a period, Z_{eff} increases and atomic size decreases. The attraction between nucleus and outer electron increases, so the electron is harder to remove:

Ionization energy generally ***increases*** *across a period.*

There are two exceptions to the otherwise smooth increase in IE_1 across periods:

- In Periods 2 and 3, there are dips at the Group 3A(13) elements, B and Al. These elements have the first *np* electrons, which are removed more easily because the resulting ion has a filled (stable) *ns* sublevel.
- In Periods 2 and 3, once again, there are dips at the Group 6A(16) elements, O and S. These elements have a fourth *np* electron, the first to pair up with another *np* electron, and electron-electron repulsions raise the orbital energy. The fourth *np* electron is easier to remove because doing so relieves the repulsions and leaves a half-filled (stable) *np* sublevel.

Sample Problem 8.4 Ranking Elements by First Ionization Energy

Problem Using the periodic table only, rank the elements in each set in order of *decreasing* IE_1: **(a)** Kr, He, Ar; **(b)** Sb, Te, Sn; **(c)** K, Ca, Rb; **(d)** I, Xe, Cs.

Plan We find the elements in the periodic table and then apply the general trends of decreasing IE_1 down a group and increasing IE_1 across a period.

Solution (a) He > Ar > Kr. These are in Group 8A(18), and IE_1 decreases down a group.

(b) Te > Sb > Sn. These are in Period 5, and IE_1 increases across a period.

(c) Ca > K > Rb. IE_1 of K is larger than IE_1 of Rb because K is higher in Group 1A(1). IE_1 of Ca is larger than IE_1 of K because Ca is farther to the right in Period 4.

(d) Xe > I > Cs. IE_1 of I is smaller than IE_1 of Xe because I is farther to the left. IE_1 of I is larger than IE_1 of Cs because I is farther to the right and in the previous period.

Check Because trends in IE_1 are generally the opposite of the trends in size, you can rank the elements by size and check that you obtain the reverse order.

Follow-Up Problem 8.4 Rank the elements in each set in order of *increasing* IE_1: **(a)** Sb, Sn, I; **(b)** Sr, Ca, Ba.

Successive Ionization Energies For a given element, IE_1, IE_2, and so on, increase because each electron is pulled away from a species with a higher positive charge. This increase includes an enormous jump *after* the outer (valence) electrons have been removed because *much* more energy is needed to remove an inner (core) electron (Figure 8.17).

Table 8.4 shows successive ionization energies for Period 2 and the first element in Period 3. Move across the values for any element, and you reach a point that separates relatively low from relatively high IE values *(shaded area)*. For example, follow the values for boron (B): IE_1 (0.80 MJ) is lower than IE_2 (2.43 MJ), which is lower than IE_3 (3.66 MJ), which is *much* lower than IE_4 (25.02 MJ). From this jump, we know that boron has three electrons in the highest energy level ($1s^22s^22p^1$). Because they are so difficult to remove, *core electrons are not involved in reactions.*

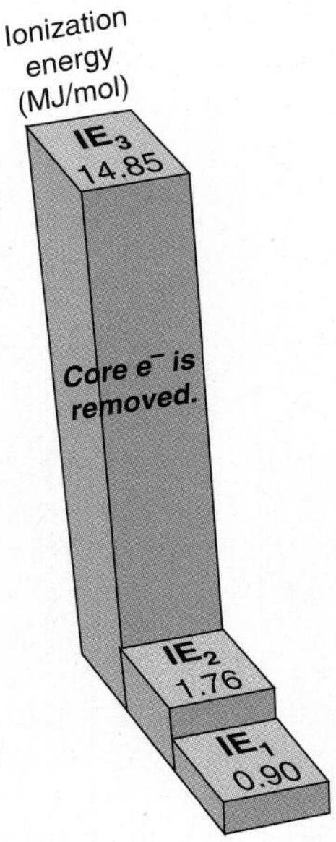

Figure 8.17 The first three ionization energies of beryllium. Beryllium has two valence electrons, so IE_3 is much larger than IE_2.

Sample Problem 8.5 Identifying an Element from Its Ionization Energies

Problem Name the Period 3 element with the following ionization energies (kJ/mol), and write its full electron configuration:

IE_1	IE_2	IE_3	IE_4	IE_5	IE_6
1012	1903	2910	4956	6278	22,230

Plan We look for a large jump in the IE values, which occurs after all valence electrons have been removed. Then we refer to the periodic table to find the Period 3 element with this number of valence electrons and write its electron configuration.

Solution The large jump occurs after IE_5, indicating that the element has five valence electrons and, thus, is in Group 5A(15). This Period 3 element is phosphorus (P; Z = 15). Its electron configuration is $1s^22s^22p^63s^23p^3$.

Follow-Up Problem 8.5 Element Q is in Period 3 and has the following ionization energies (in kJ/mol):

IE_1	IE_2	IE_3	IE_4	IE_5	IE_6
577	1816	2744	11,576	14,829	18,375

Name element Q, and write its full electron configuration.

Table 8.4 Successive Ionization Energies of the Elements Lithium Through Sodium

Z	Element	Number of Valence Electrons	IE_1	IE_2	IE_3	IE_4	IE_5	IE_6	IE_7	IE_8	IE_9	IE_{10}
			Ionization Energy (MJ/mol)*									
3	Li	1	0.52	7.30	11.81							
4	Be	2	0.90	1.76	14.85	21.01						
5	B	3	0.80	2.43	3.66	25.02	32.82					
6	C	4	1.09	2.35	4.62	6.22	37.83	47.28				
7	N	5	1.40	2.86	4.58	7.48	9.44	53.27	64.36			
8	O	6	1.31	3.39	5.30	7.47	10.98	13.33	71.33	84.08		
9	F	7	1.68	3.37	6.05	8.41	11.02	15.16	17.87	92.04	106.43	
10	Ne	8	2.08	3.95	6.12	9.37	12.18	15.24	20.00	23.07	115.38	131.43
11	Na	1	0.50	4.56	6.91	9.54	13.35	16.61	20.11	25.49	28.93	141.37

CORE ELECTRONS

*MJ/mol, or megajoules per mole = 10^3 kJ/mol.

Trends in Electron Affinity

The **electron affinity (EA)** is the energy change (kJ/mol) accompanying the *addition* of 1 mol of electrons to 1 mol of gaseous atoms or ions. The *first electron affinity* (EA_1) refers to the formation of 1 mol of monovalent (1−) gaseous anions:

$$\text{Atom}(g) + e^- \longrightarrow \text{ion}^-(g) \qquad \Delta E = EA_1$$

1A (1)	2A (2)	3A (13)	4A (14)	5A (15)	6A (16)	7A (17)	8A (18)
H −72.8							He (0.0)
Li −59.6	Be ≤0	B −26.7	C −122	N +7	O −141	F −328	Ne (+29)
Na −52.9	Mg ≤0	Al −42.5	Si −134	P −72.0	S −200	Cl −349	Ar (+35)
K −48.4	Ca −2.37	Ga −28.9	Ge −119	As −78.2	Se −195	Br −325	Kr (+39)
Rb −46.9	Sr −5.03	In −28.9	Sn −107	Sb −103	Te −190	I −295	Xe (+41)
Cs −45.5	Ba −13.95	Tl −19.3	Pb −35.1	Bi −91.3	Po −183	At −270	Rn (+41)

Figure 8.18 Electron affinities of the main-group elements (in kJ/mol). Values for Group 8A(18) are estimates, which is indicated by parentheses.

As with ionization energy, there is a first electron affinity, a second, and so forth. The first electron is *attracted* by the atom's nucleus, so in most cases, *EA_1 is negative* (energy is released), analogous to the negative ΔH for an exothermic reaction.* But, the second electron affinity (EA_2) is always positive because energy must be *absorbed* to overcome electrostatic repulsions and add another electron to a negative ion.

Factors other than Z_{eff} and atomic size affect electron affinities, so trends are not regular, as are those for size and IE_1. The many exceptions arise from changes in sublevel energy and electron-electron repulsion:

- *Down a group.* We might expect a smooth decrease (smaller negative number) down a group because size increases, and the nucleus is farther away from an electron being added. But only Group 1A(1) exhibits this behavior (Figure 8.18).
- *Across a period.* We might expect a regular increase (larger negative number) across a period because size decreases, and higher Z_{eff} should attract the electron being added more strongly. There is an overall left-to-right increase, but it is not at all regular.

Despite these irregularities, relative values of IE and EA show three general behavior patterns:

1. *Reactive nonmetals.* Members of Group 6A(16) and especially Group 7A(17) (the halogens) have high IEs and highly negative (exothermic) EAs: these elements lose electrons with difficulty but attract them strongly. Therefore, *in their ionic compounds, they form negative ions.*
2. *Reactive metals.* Members of Groups 1A(1) and 2A(2) have low IEs and slightly negative (exothermic) EAs: they lose electrons easily but attract them weakly, if at all. Therefore, *in their ionic compounds, they form positive ions.*
3. *Noble gases.* Members of Group 8A(18) have very high IEs and slightly positive (endothermic) EAs: *they tend **not** to lose or gain electrons.* In fact, only the larger members of the group (Kr, Xe, and Rn) form compounds at all.

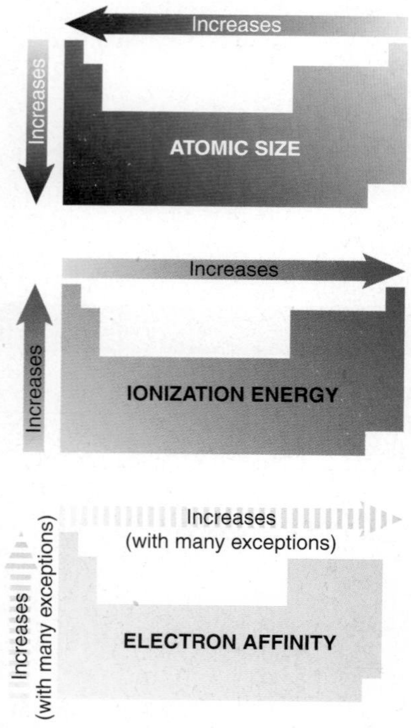

Figure 8.19 Trends in three atomic properties. For electron affinity, the dashed arrows indicate that there are numerous exceptions to expected trends.

Summary of Section 8.3

- Trends in three atomic properties are summarized in Figure 8.19.
- Atomic size (half the distance between nuclei of adjacent atoms) increases down a main group and decreases across a period. In a transition series, size remains relatively constant.
- First ionization energy (the energy required to remove the outermost electron from a mole of gaseous atoms) is inversely related to atomic size: IE_1 decreases down a main group and increases across a period.
- Successive ionization energies of an element show a very large increase after all valence electrons have been removed, because the first inner (core) electron is in an orbital of much lower energy and so is held very tightly.
- Electron affinity (the energy involved in adding an electron to a mole of gaseous atoms) shows many variations from expected trends.
- Based on the relative sizes of IEs and EAs, Group 1A(1) and 2A(2) elements tend to form cations and Group 6A(16) and 7A(17) elements tend to form anions in ionic compounds. Group 8A(18) elements are very unreactive.

*Some tables of EA_1 list them as positive values because energy would be *absorbed* to remove an electron from the anion.

8.4 • ATOMIC PROPERTIES AND CHEMICAL REACTIVITY

All physical and chemical behaviors of the elements and their compounds are based on electron configuration and effective nuclear charge. In this section, you'll see how atomic properties determine metallic behavior and the properties of ions.

Trends in Metallic Behavior

The three general classes of elements have distinguishing properties:

- *Metals,* found in the left and lower three-quarters of the periodic table, are typically shiny solids, have moderate to high melting points, are good conductors of heat and electricity, can be machined into wires and sheets, and lose electrons to nonmetals.
- *Nonmetals,* found in the upper right quarter of the table, are typically not shiny, have relatively low melting points, are poor conductors, are mostly crumbly solids or gases, and tend to gain electrons from metals.
- *Metalloids,* found between the other two classes, have intermediate properties.

Thus, *metallic behavior decreases left-to-right across a period and increases down a group in the periodic table* (Figure 8.20).

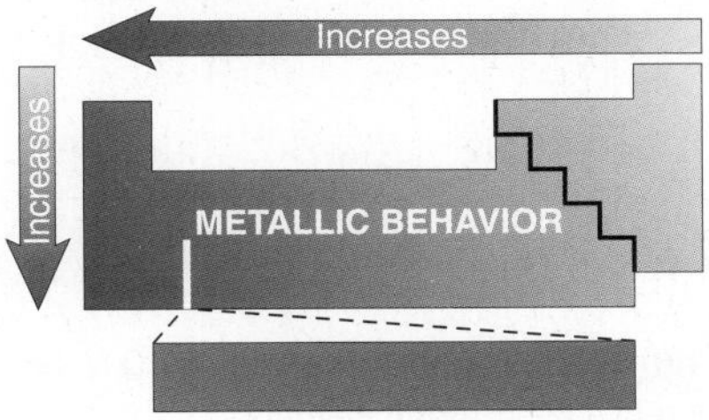

Figure 8.20 Trends in metallic behavior. (Hydrogen appears next to helium.)

Remember, though, that some elements don't fit these categories: as graphite, nonmetallic carbon is a good electrical conductor; the nonmetal iodine is shiny; metallic gallium melts in your hand; mercury is a liquid; and iron is brittle. Despite such exceptions, in this discussion, we'll make several generalizations about metallic behavior and its applications to redox behavior and the acid-base properties of oxides.

Relative Tendency to Lose or Gain Electrons Metals tend to lose electrons to nonmetals during reactions:

1. *Down a main group.* The increase in metallic behavior down a group is consistent with an increase in size and a decrease in IE and is most obvious in groups with more than one class of element, such as Group 5A(15) (Figure 8.21, *vertical*): *elements at the top can form anions, and those at the bottom can form cations.* Nitrogen (N) is a gaseous nonmetal, and phosphorus (P) is a soft nonmetal; both occur occasionally as 3− anions in their compounds. Arsenic (As) and antimony (Sb) are metalloids, with Sb the more metallic, and neither forms ions readily. Bismuth (Bi) is a typical metal, forming a 3+ cation in its mostly ionic compounds. Groups 3A(13), 4A(14), and 6A(16) show a similar trend. But even in Group 2A(2), which contains only metals, the tendency to form cations increases down the group: beryllium (Be) forms covalent compounds with nonmetals, whereas all compounds of barium (Ba) are ionic.

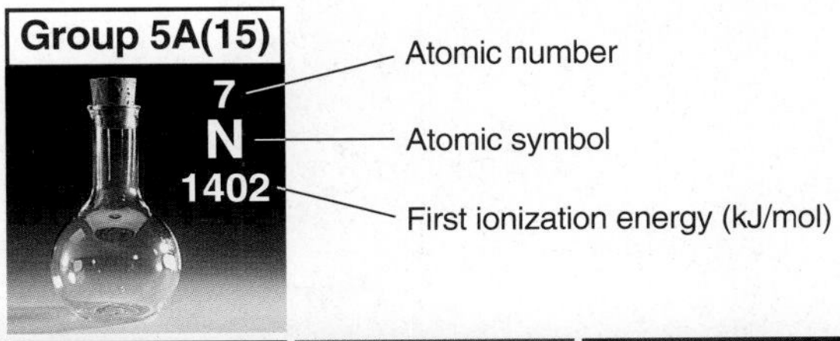

Figure 8.21 Metallic behavior in Group 5A(15) and Period 3. Moving down from N to Bi, there is an *increase* in metallic behavior. Moving across from Na to Cl, there is a *decrease* in metallic behavior.

2. *Across a period.* The decrease in metallic behavior across a period is consistent with a decrease in size, an increase in IE, and a more favorable (more negative) EA. Consider Period 3 (Figure 8.21, *horizontal*): *elements at the left tend to form cations, and those at the right tend to form anions.* Sodium and magnesium are metals that occur as Na^+ and Mg^{2+} in seawater, minerals, and organisms. Aluminum is metallic physically and occurs as Al^{3+} in some compounds, but it bonds covalently in most others. Silicon (Si) is a shiny metalloid that does not occur as

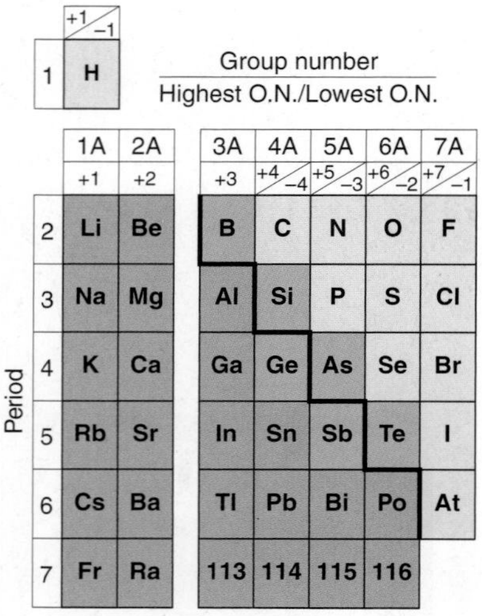

Figure 8.22 Highest and lowest O.N.s of reactive main-group elements.

a monatomic ion. Phosphorus is a white, waxy nonmetal that occurs rarely as P^{3-}, whereas crumbly, yellow sulfur forms S^{2-} in many compounds, and gaseous, yellow-green chlorine occurs in nature almost always as Cl^-.

Redox Behavior of the Main-Group Elements Closely related to an element's tendency to lose or gain electrons is its redox behavior—that is, whether it behaves as an oxidizing or reducing agent and the associated changes in its oxidation number (O.N.). You can find the highest and lowest oxidation numbers of many main-group elements from the periodic table (Figure 8.22):

- For most elements, the A-group number is the *highest* oxidation number (always positive) of any element in the group. The exceptions are O and F (see Table 4.3).
- For nonmetals and some metalloids, the A-group number minus 8 is the *lowest* oxidation number (always negative) of any element in the group.

For example, the highest oxidation number of S (Group 6A) is +6, as in SF_6, and the lowest is $6 - 8$, or -2, as in FeS and other metal sulfides.

Redox behavior is closely related to atomic properties:

- With their low IEs and small EAs, the members of Groups 1A(1) and 2A(2) lose electrons readily, so they are *strong reducing agents* and become oxidized.
- With their high IEs and large EAs, nonmetals in Groups 6A(16) and 7A(17) gain electrons readily, so they are *strong oxidizing agents* and become reduced.

Acid-Base Behavior of Oxides Metals are also distinguished from nonmetals by the acid-base behavior of their oxides in water:

Figure 8.23 **Oxide acidity.** In water, metal oxides are basic (*left*), and nonmetal oxides are acidic (*right*). The colors are due to the presence of acid-base indicators.

- Most main-group metals *transfer* electrons to oxygen, so their *oxides are ionic. In water, these oxides act as bases,* producing OH^- ions from O^{2-} and reacting with acids. Calcium oxide is an example (Figure 8.23, *left*).
- Nonmetals *share* electrons with oxygen, so *nonmetal oxides are covalent. They react with water to form acids,* producing H^+ ions and reacting with bases. Tetraphosphorus decaoxide is an example (Figure 8.23, *right*).

Some metals and many metalloids form oxides that are **amphoteric:** they can act as acids *or* bases in water.

Figure 8.24 shows the acid-base behavior of some common oxides of elements in Group 5A(15) and Period 3 with a gradient from blue (basic) to red (acidic):

1. *As elements become more metallic down a group (larger size and smaller IE), their oxides become more basic.* In Group 5A(15), dinitrogen pentaoxide, N_2O_5, forms the strong acid HNO_3:

$$N_2O_5(s) + H_2O(l) \longrightarrow 2HNO_3(aq)$$

Tetraphosphorus decaoxide, P_4O_{10}, forms the weaker acid H_3PO_4:

$$P_4O_{10}(s) + 6H_2O(l) \longrightarrow 4H_3PO_4(aq)$$

The oxide of the metalloid arsenic is weakly acidic, whereas that of the metalloid antimony is weakly basic. Bismuth, the most metallic of the group, forms a basic oxide that is insoluble in water but reacts with acid to yield a salt and water:

$$Bi_2O_3(s) + 6HNO_3(aq) \longrightarrow 2Bi(NO_3)_3(aq) + 3H_2O(l)$$

Figure 8.24 Acid-base behavior of some element oxides.

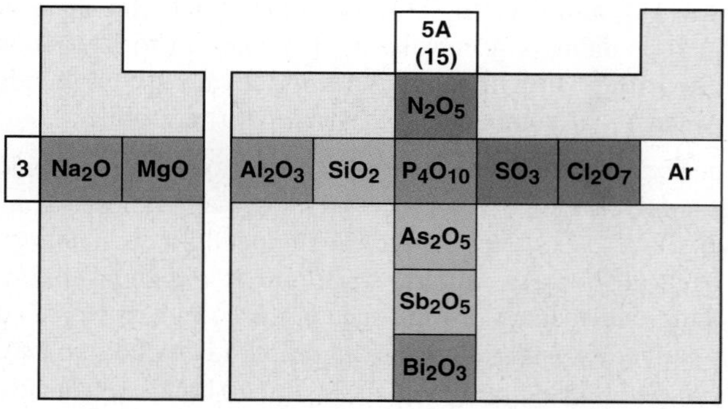

2. *As the elements become less metallic across a period (smaller size and higher IE), their oxides become more acidic.* In Period 3, Na_2O and MgO are strongly basic, and amphoteric aluminum oxide (Al_2O_3) reacts with acid or with base:

$$Al_2O_3(s) + 6HCl(aq) \longrightarrow 2AlCl_3(aq) + 3H_2O(l)$$

$$Al_2O_3(s) + 2NaOH(aq) + 3H_2O(l) \longrightarrow 2NaAl(OH)_4(aq)$$

Silicon dioxide is weakly acidic, forming a salt and water with base:

$$SiO_2(s) + 2NaOH(aq) \longrightarrow Na_2SiO_3(aq) + H_2O(l)$$

The common oxides of phosphorus, sulfur, and chlorine form acids of increasing strength: H_3PO_4, H_2SO_4, and $HClO_4$.

Properties of Monatomic Ions

So far we have focused on the reactants—the atoms—in the process of electron loss and gain. Now we focus on the products—the ions—considering their electron configurations, magnetic properties, and sizes.

Electron Configurations of Main-Group Ions Why does an ion have a particular charge: Na^+ not Na^{2+}, or F^- not F^{2-}? Why do some metals form two ions, such as Sn^{2+} and Sn^{4+}? The answer relates to the location of the element in the periodic table and the energy associated with losing or gaining electrons:

1. *Ions with a noble gas configuration.* Atoms of the noble gases have very low reactivity because their highest energy level is *filled* (ns^2np^6). Thus, *when elements at either end of a period form ions, they attain a filled outer level—a noble gas configuration.* These elements lie on either side of Group 8A(18), and their ions are **isoelectronic** (Greek *iso*, "same") with the nearest noble gas (Figure 8.25; see also Figure 2.13, p. 57).

- Elements in Groups 1A(1) and 2A(2) *lose* electrons and become isoelectronic with the *previous* noble gas. The Na^+ ion, for example, is isoelectronic with neon (Ne):

$$Na(1s^22s^22p^63s^1) \longrightarrow e^- + Na^+([He]2s^22p^6)\ [\text{isoelectronic with Ne}([He]2s^22p^6)]$$

- Elements in Groups 6A(16) and 7A(17) *gain* electrons and become isoelectronic with the *next* noble gas. The Br^- ion, for example, is isoelectronic with krypton (Kr):

$$Br\ ([Ar]\ 4s^23d^{10}4p^5) + e^- \longrightarrow Br^-\ ([Ar]\ 4s^23d^{10}4p^6)$$
$$[\text{isoelectronic with Kr}\ ([Ar]\ 4s^23d^{10}4p^6)]$$

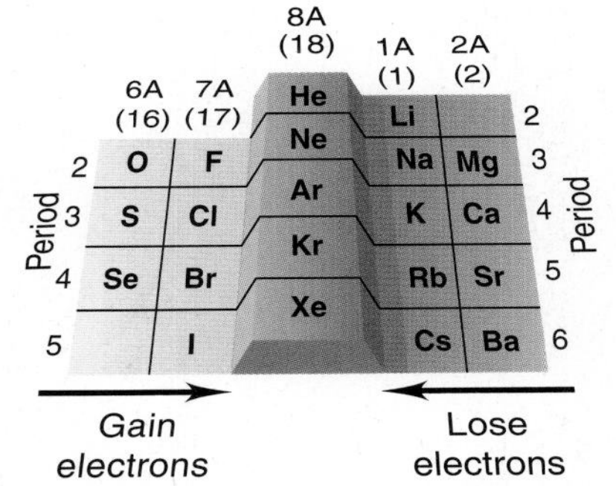

Figure 8.25 Main-group elements whose ions have noble gas electron configurations.

The energy needed to remove electrons from metals or add them to nonmetals determines the charges of the resulting ions:

- *Cations.* Removing another electron from Na^+ or from Mg^{2+} means removing a core electron, which requires too much energy: thus, $NaCl_2$ and MgF_3 do *not* exist.
- *Anions.* Similarly, adding another electron to F^- or to O^{2-} means putting it into the next higher energy level ($n = 3$). With 10 electrons ($1s^22s^22p^6$) acting as inner electrons, the nuclear charge would be shielded very effectively, and adding an outer electron would require too much energy: thus, we never see Na_2F or Mg_3O_2.

2. *Ions without a noble gas configuration.* Except for aluminum, the metals of Groups 3A(13) to 5A(15) do not form ions with noble gas configurations. Instead, they form cations with two different stable configurations:

- *Pseudo–noble gas configuration.* If the metal atom empties its highest energy level, it attains the stability of empty *ns* and *np* sublevels and filled inner $(n - 1)d$ sublevel. This $(n - 1)d^{10}$ configuration is called a **pseudo–noble gas configuration.** For example, tin (Sn; $Z = 50$) loses four electrons to form the tin(IV) ion (Sn^{4+}), which has empty 5*s* and 5*p* sublevels and a filled inner 4*d* sublevel:

$$Sn\ ([Kr]\ 5s^24d^{10}5p^2) \longrightarrow Sn^{4+}\ ([Kr]\ 4d^{10}) + 4e^-$$

- *Inert pair configuration.* Alternatively, the metal atom loses just its *np* electrons and attains a stable configuration with filled *ns* and $(n - 1)d$ sublevels. The retained ns^2 electrons are sometimes called an *inert pair*. For example, in the more common tin(II) ion (Sn^{2+}), the atom loses the two 5*p* electrons and has filled 5*s* and 4*d* sublevels:

$$\text{Sn ([Kr] } 5s^24d^{10}5p^2) \longrightarrow \text{Sn}^{2+} \text{ ([Kr] } 5s^24d^{10}) + 2e^-$$

Thallium, lead, and bismuth, the largest and, thus, most metallic members of Groups 3A(13) to 5A(15), form ions that retain the ns^2 pair: Tl^+, Pb^{2+}, and Bi^{3+}.

Once again, energy considerations explain these configurations. It would be energetically impossible for metals in Groups 3A(13) to 5A(15) to achieve noble gas configurations: tin, for example, would have to lose 14 electrons—ten 4*d* in addition to the two 5*p* and two 5*s*—to be isoelectronic with krypton (Kr; $Z = 36$), the previous noble gas.

Sample Problem 8.6 Writing Electron Configurations of Main-Group Ions

Problem Using condensed electron configurations, write equations representing the formation of the ion(s) of the following elements:
(a) Iodine ($Z = 53$) **(b)** Potassium ($Z = 19$) **(c)** Indium ($Z = 49$)

Plan We identify the element's position in the periodic table and recall that

- Ions of elements in Groups 1A(1), 2A(2), 6A(16), and 7A(17) are isoelectronic with the nearest noble gas.
- Metals in Groups 3A(13) to 5A(15) lose the *ns* and *np* electrons or just the *np*.

Solution **(a)** Iodine is in Group 7A(17), so it gains one electron, and I^- is isoelectronic with xenon:

$$\text{I ([Kr] } 5s^24d^{10}5p^5) + e^- \longrightarrow \text{I}^- \text{ ([Kr] } 5s^24d^{10}5p^6) \quad \text{(same as Xe)}$$

(b) Potassium is in Group 1A(1), so it loses one electron; K^+ is isoelectronic with argon:

$$\text{K ([Ar] } 4s^1) \longrightarrow \text{K}^+ \text{ ([Ar])} + e^-$$

(c) Indium is in Group 3A(13), so it loses either three electrons to form In^{3+} (with a pseudo–noble gas configuration) or one to form In^+ (with an inert pair):

$$\text{In ([Kr] } 5s^24d^{10}5p^1) \longrightarrow \text{In}^{3+} \text{ ([Kr] } 4d^{10}) + 3e^-$$

$$\text{In ([Kr] } 5s^24d^{10}5p^1) \longrightarrow \text{In}^{+} \text{ ([Kr] } 5s^24d^{10}) + e^-$$

Check Be sure that the number of electrons in the ion's electron configuration, plus the number gained or lost to form the ion, equals *Z*.

Follow-Up Problem 8.6 Using condensed electron configurations, write equations representing the formation of the ion(s) of the following elements:
(a) Ba ($Z = 56$) **(b)** O ($Z = 8$) **(c)** Pb ($Z = 82$)

Electron Configurations of Transition Metal Ions In contrast to many main-group ions, *transition metal ions rarely attain a noble gas configuration.* Aside from the Period 4 elements scandium, which forms Sc^{3+}, and titanium, which occasionally forms Ti^{4+}, *a transition element typically forms more than one cation by losing all of its ns and some of its (n − 1)d electrons.*

The reason, once again, is that energy costs are too high. Let's consider again the filling of Period 4. At the beginning of Period 4 (the same point holds in other periods), penetration makes the 4*s* sublevel *more stable* than the 3*d*. Therefore, the first and second electrons added enter the 4*s*, which is the outer sublevel. But, the 3*d* is an *inner* sublevel, so as it begins to fill, its electrons are not well shielded from the increasing nuclear charge.

A *crossover in sublevel energy* results: the 3*d* becomes *more stable* than the 4*s* in the transition series (Figure 8.26). This crossover has a major effect on the formation of Period 4 transition metal ions: because the 3*d* electrons are held tightly and shield those in the outer sublevel, *the 4s electrons of a transition metal are lost **before** the*

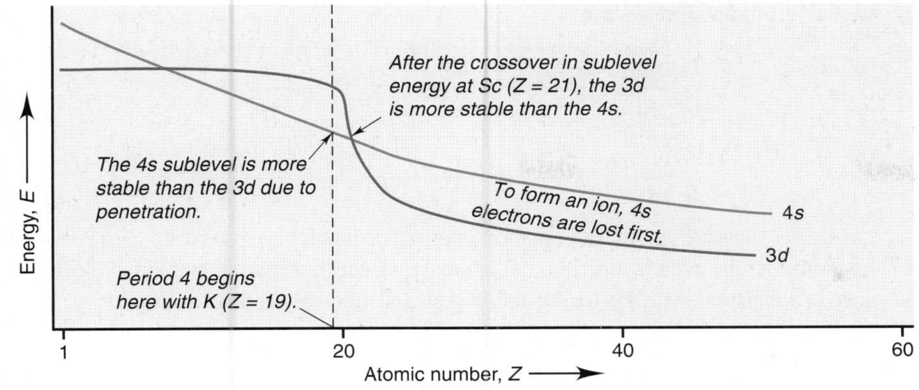

Figure 8.26 The crossover of sublevel energies in Period 4.

3d electrons. Thus, 4*s* electrons are added before 3*d* electrons to form the *atom* and are lost before them to form the *ion,* the so-called "first-in, first-out" rule.

Ion Formation: A Summary of Electron Loss or Gain The various ways that cations form have one point in common—*outer electrons are removed first.* Here is a summary of the rules for formation of any main-group or transition metal ion:

- Main-group *s*-block metals lose all electrons with the highest *n* value.
- Main-group *p*-block metals lose *np* electrons before *ns* electrons.
- Transition (*d*-block) metals lose *ns* electrons before $(n - 1)d$ electrons.
- Nonmetals gain electrons in the *p* orbitals of highest *n* value.

Magnetic Properties of Transition Metal Ions We learn a great deal about an element's electron configuration from atomic spectra, and magnetic studies provide additional evidence.

Recall that electron spin generates a tiny magnetic field, which causes a beam of H atoms to split in an external magnetic field (see Figure 8.1). Only a beam of a species (atoms, ions, or molecules) with one or more *unpaired* electrons will split. A beam of silver atoms (Ag; Z = 47) was used in the original 1921 experiment:

Ag (Z = 47) [Kr] $5s^14d^{10}$ [↑] [↑↓|↑↓|↑↓|↑↓|↑↓] [| |]
5*s* 4*d* 5*p*

Note the unpaired 5*s* electron. A beam of cadmium atoms (Cd; *Z* = 48) is not split because their 5*s* electrons are *paired* ([Kr] $5s^24d^{10}$).

A species with unpaired electrons exhibits **paramagnetism:** it is attracted by an external field. A species with all of its electrons paired exhibits **diamagnetism:** it is not attracted (and is slightly repelled) by the field (Figure 8.27). Many transition metals and their compounds are paramagnetic because their atoms and ions have unpaired electrons.

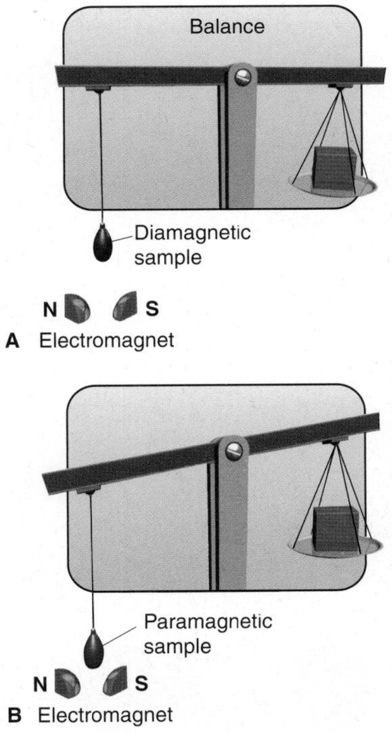

Figure 8.27 Measuring the magnetic behavior of a sample. The substance is weighed with the external magnetic field "off." **A,** If the substance is diamagnetic (has all *paired* electrons), its apparent mass is unaffected (or slightly reduced) with the field "on." **B,** If the substance is paramagnetic (has *unpaired* electrons), its apparent mass increases.

Let's see three examples of how magnetic studies might provide evidence for a proposed electron configuration:

1. *The Ti^{2+} ion.* Spectral analysis of titanium metal yields the electron configuration [Ar] $4s^23d^2$, and experiment shows that the metal is paramagnetic, which indicates the presence of unpaired electrons. Spectral analysis shows that the Ti^{2+} ion is [Ar] $3d^2$, indicating loss of the 4*s* electrons. In support of the spectra, magnetic studies show that Ti^{2+} compounds are paramagnetic. If Ti had lost its 3*d* electrons to form Ti^{2+}, its compounds would be diamagnetic:

$$\text{Ti ([Ar] } 4s^23d^2) \longrightarrow \text{Ti}^{2+} \text{ ([Ar] } 3d^2) + 2e^-$$

The partial orbital diagrams are

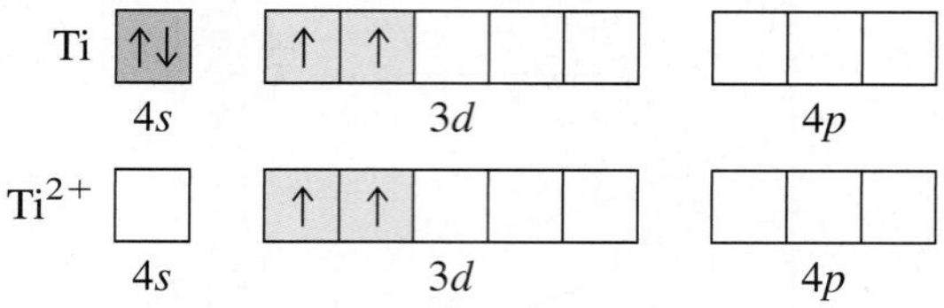

2. *The Fe^{3+} ion.* An increase in paramagnetism occurs when iron metal (Fe) becomes Fe^{3+} in compounds, which indicates an increase in the number of unpaired electrons. This fact is consistent with Fe losing its 4*s* pair and one electron of a 3*d* pair:

$$Fe\ ([Ar]\ 4s^23d^6) \longrightarrow Fe^{3+}\ ([Ar]\ 3d^5) + 3e^-$$

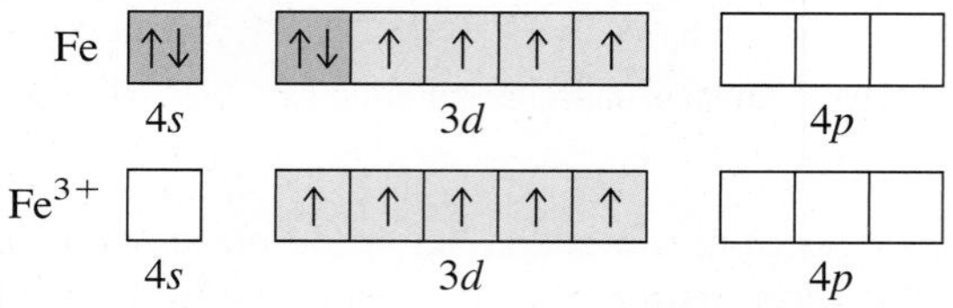

3. *The Cu^+ and Zn^{2+} ions.* Copper (Cu) metal is paramagnetic, but zinc (Zn) is diamagnetic. The Cu^+ and Zn^{2+} ions are diamagnetic, too. These observations are consistent with the ions being isoelectronic, which means 4*s* electrons were lost:

$$Cu\ ([Ar]\ 4s^13d^{10}) \longrightarrow Cu^+\ ([Ar]\ 3d^{10}) + e^-$$
$$Zn\ ([Ar]\ 4s^23d^{10}) \longrightarrow Zn^{2+}\ ([Ar]\ 3d^{10}) + 2e^-$$

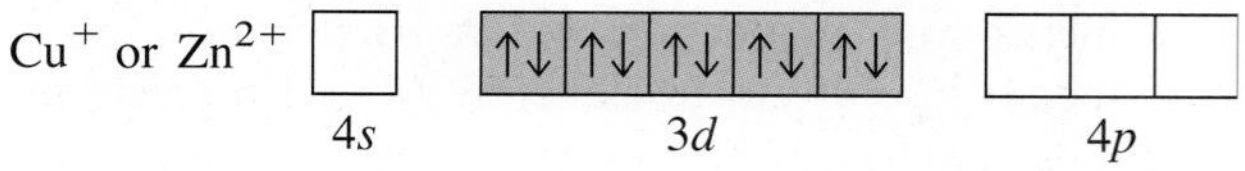

Sample Problem 8.7 Writing Electron Configurations and Predicting Magnetic Behavior of Transition Metal Ions

Problem Use condensed electron configurations to write an equation for the formation of each transition metal ion, and predict whether it is paramagnetic:
(a) Mn^{2+} ($Z = 25$) **(b)** Cr^{3+} ($Z = 24$) **(c)** Hg^{2+} ($Z = 80$)

Plan We first write the condensed electron configuration of the atom, recalling the irregularity for Cr. Then we remove electrons, beginning with *ns* electrons, to attain the ion charge. If unpaired electrons are present, the ion is paramagnetic.

Solution (a) $Mn\ ([Ar]\ 4s^23d^5) \longrightarrow Mn^{2+}\ ([Ar]\ 3d^5) + 2e^-$
There are five unpaired e^-, so Mn^{2+} is paramagnetic.

(b) $Cr\ ([Ar]\ 4s^13d^5) \longrightarrow Cr^{3+}\ ([Ar]\ 3d^3) + 3e^-$

There are three unpaired e^-, so Cr^{3+} is paramagnetic.

(c) $Hg\ ([Xe]\ 6s^24f^{14}5d^{10}) \longrightarrow Hg^{2+}\ ([Xe]\ 4f^{14}5d^{10}) + 2e^-$

The 4*f* and 5*d* sublevels are filled, so there are no unpaired e^-: Hg^{2+} is *not* paramagnetic.

Check We removed the *ns* electrons first, and the sum of the lost electrons and those in the electron configuration of the ion equals *Z*.

Follow-Up Problem 8.7 Write the condensed electron configuration of each transition metal ion, and predict whether it is paramagnetic:
(a) V^{3+} ($Z = 23$) **(b)** Ni^{2+} ($Z = 28$) **(c)** La^{3+} ($Z = 57$)

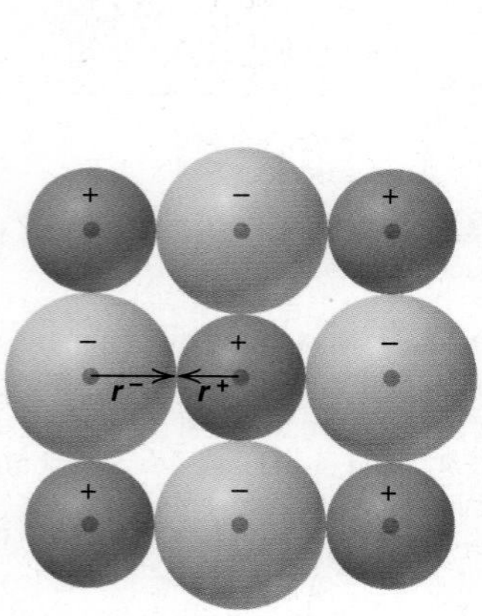

Figure 8.28 Ionic radius. Cation radius (r^+) and anion radius (r^-) together make up the distance between nuclei.

Ionic Size vs. Atomic Size The **ionic radius** is a measure of the size of an ion and is obtained from the distance between the nuclei of adjacent ions in a crystalline ionic compound (Figure 8.28). From the relation between effective nuclear charge (Z_{eff}) and atomic size, we can predict the size of an ion relative to its parent atom:

- *Cations are smaller than parent atoms.* When a cation forms, electrons are *removed from* the outer level. The resulting decrease in shielding and value of *nl* allows the nucleus to pull the remaining electrons closer.
- *Anions are larger than parent atoms.* When an anion forms, electrons are *added to* the outer level. The increases in shielding and electron repulsions means the electrons occupy more space.

Figure 8.29 shows the radii of some main-group ions and their parent atoms:

1. *Down a group, ionic size increases* because *n* increases.
2. *Across a period,* for instance, Period 3, the pattern is complex:
   - *Among cations,* the increase in Z_{eff} from left to right makes Na^+ larger than Mg^{2+}, which is larger than Al^{3+}.
   - *From last cation to first anion,* a great jump in size occurs: we are *adding* electrons rather than removing them, so repulsions increase sharply. For instance, P^{3-} has eight more electrons than Al^{3+}.
   - *Among anions,* the increase in Z_{eff} from left to right makes P^{3-} larger than S^{2-}, which is larger than Cl^-.
   - *Within an isoelectronic series,* these factors have striking results. Within the dashed outline in Figure 8.29, the ions are isoelectronic with neon. Period 2 anions are much larger than Period 3 cations because the same number of electrons are attracted by an increasing nuclear charge. The pattern is

$$3- > 2- > 1- > 1+ > 2+ > 3+$$

3. *Cation size decreases with charge.* When a metal forms more than one cation, *the greater the ionic charge, the smaller the ionic radius.* With the two ions of iron, for example, Fe^{3+} has one fewer electron, so shielding is reduced somewhat, and the same nucleus is attracting fewer electrons. As a result, Z_{eff} increases, so Fe^{3+} is smaller than Fe^{2+}.

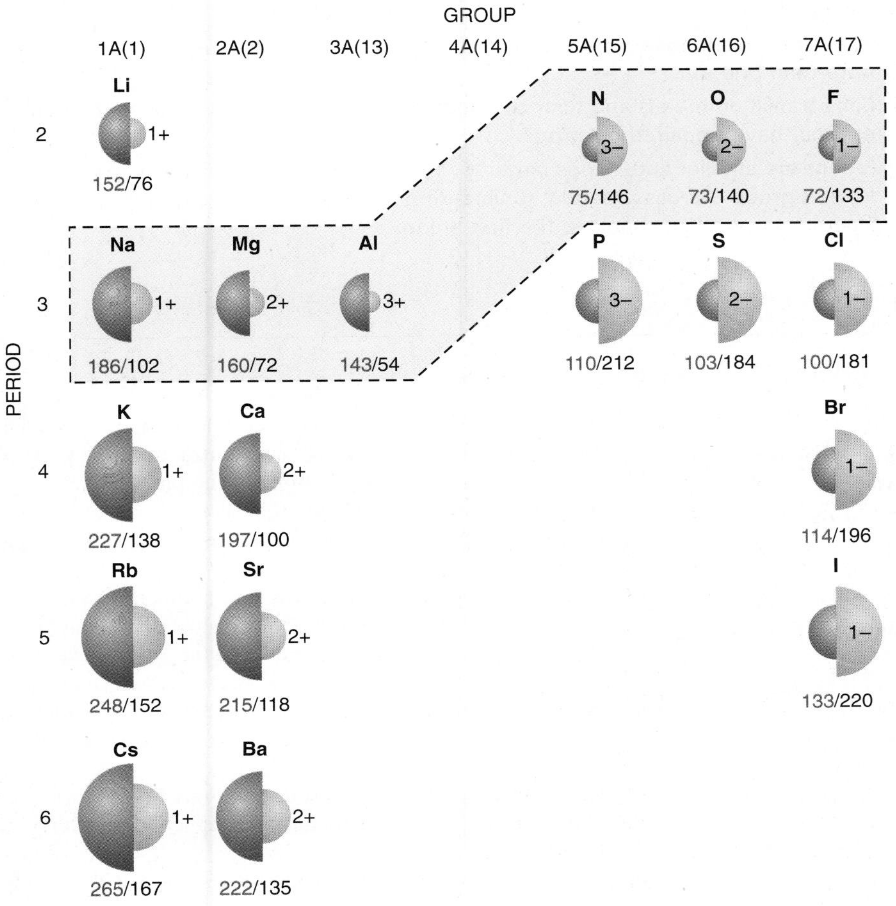

Figure 8.29 Ionic vs. atomic radii. Atomic radii (*color*) and ionic radii (*gray*) are given in picometers. Metal atoms (*blue*) form *smaller* positive ions, and nonmetal atoms (*red*) form *larger* negative ions. Ions in the dashed outline are *isoelectronic* with neon.

Sample Problem 8.8 Ranking Ions by Size

Problem Rank each set of ions in order of *decreasing* size, and explain your ranking:
(a) Ca^{2+}, Sr^{2+}, Mg^{2+} **(b)** K^+, S^{2-}, Cl^- **(c)** Au^+, Au^{3+}

Plan We find the position of each element in the periodic table and apply the ideas presented in the text.

Solution (a) Mg^{2+}, Ca^{2+}, and Sr^{2+} are all from Group 2A(2), so their sizes decrease up the group: $Sr^{2+} > Ca^{2+} > Mg^{2+}$.
(b) The ions K^+, S^{2-}, and Cl^- are isoelectronic. S^{2-} has a lower Z_{eff} than Cl^-, so it is larger. K^+ is a cation and has the highest Z_{eff}, so it is smallest: $S^{2-} > Cl^- > K^+$.
(c) Au^+ has a lower charge than Au^{3+}, so it is larger: $Au^+ > Au^{3+}$.

Follow-Up Problem 8.8 Rank the ions in each set in order of *increasing* size:
(a) Cl^-, Br^-, F^- **(b)** Na^+, Mg^{2+}, F^- **(c)** Cr^{2+}, Cr^{3+}

Summary of Section 8.4

- Metallic behavior correlates with large atomic size and low ionization energy. Thus, metallic behavior increases down a group and decreases across a period.
- Elements in Groups 1A(1) and 2A(2) are strong reducing agents; nonmetals in Groups 6A(16) and 7A(17) are strong oxidizing agents.
- Within the main groups, metal oxides are basic and nonmetal oxides acidic. Thus, oxides become more acidic across a period and more basic down a group.
- Many main-group elements form ions that are isoelectronic with the nearest noble gas. Removing (or adding) more electrons than needed to attain the noble gas configuration requires a prohibitive amount of energy.
- Metals in Groups 3A(13) to 5A(15) lose either their *np* electrons or both their *ns* and *np* electrons.
- Transition metals lose *ns* electrons before $(n - 1)d$ electrons and commonly form more than one ion.
- Many transition metals and their compounds are paramagnetic because their atoms (or ions) have unpaired electrons.
- Cations are smaller and anions larger than their parent atoms. Ionic radius increases down a group. Across a period, ionic radii generally decrease, but a large increase occurs from the last cation to the first anion.

CHAPTER REVIEW GUIDE

Learning Objectives

Relevant section (§) and/or sample problem (SP) numbers appear in parentheses.

Understand These Concepts

1. The meaning of the periodic law and the arrangement of elements by atomic number (Introduction)
2. The reason for the spin quantum number and its two possible values (§8.1)
3. How the exclusion principle applies to orbital filling (§8.1)
4. The effects of nuclear charge, shielding, and penetration on the splitting of energy levels; the meaning of effective nuclear charge (§8.1)
5. How the arrrangement of the periodic table is based on the order of sublevel energies (§8.2)
6. How sublevels are filled in main-group and transition elements; the importance of Hund's rule (§8.2)
7. How outer electron configuration within a group is related to chemical behavior (§8.2)
8. The distinction among inner, outer, and valence electrons (§8.2)
9. The meaning of atomic radius, ionization energy, and electron affinity (§8.3)
10. How *n* value and effective nuclear charge give rise to the periodic trends of atomic size and ionization energy (§8.3)
11. The importance of core electrons to the pattern of successive ionization energies (§8.3)
12. How atomic properties relate to the tendency to form ions (§8.3)
13. The general properties of metals and nonmetals (§8.4)
14. How vertical and horizontal trends in metallic behavior are related to ion formation and oxide acidity (§8.4)
15. How atomic size and IE relate to redox behavior (§8.4)
16. Why main-group ions are either isoelectronic with the nearest noble gas or have a pseudo–noble gas electron configuration (§8.4)
17. Why transition elements lose *ns* electrons first (§8.4)
18. The origin of paramagnetic and diamagnetic behavior (§8.4)
19. The relation between ionic and atomic size and the trends in ionic size (§8.4)

Master These Skills

1. Using orbital diagrams to determine the set of quantum numbers for any electron in an atom (SP 8.1)
2. Writing full and condensed electron configurations for an element (SP 8.2)
3. Using periodic trends to rank elements by atomic size and first ionization energy (SPs 8.3, 8.4)
4. Identifying an element from its successive ionization energies (SP 8.5)
5. Writing electron configurations of main-group and transition metal ions (SPs 8.6, 8.7)
6. Using periodic trends to rank ions by size (SP 8.8)

Key Terms

Page numbers appear in parentheses.

Introduction
periodic law (295)
electron configuration (295)

Section 8.1
spin quantum number (m_s) (296)
exclusion principle (297)
shielding (297)
effective nuclear charge (Z_{eff}) (297)
penetration (298)

Section 8.2
aufbau principle (299)
orbital diagram (299)
Hund's rule (300)
transition elements (303)
inner (core) electrons (306)
outer electrons (306)
valence electrons (306)
inner transition elements (306)
lanthanides (rare earths) (306)
actinides (306)

Section 8.3
metallic radius (308)
covalent radius (308)
ionization energy (IE) (311)
electron affinity (EA) (314)

Section 8.4
amphoteric (316)
isoelectronic (317)
pseudo–noble gas configuration (317)
paramagnetism (319)
diamagnetism (319)
ionic radius (320)

Key Equations and Relationships

Page numbers appear in parentheses.

8.1 Defining the energy order of sublevels in terms of the angular momentum quantum number (l value) (298):

Order of sublevel energies: $s < p < d < f$

8.2 Meaning of the first ionization energy (311):

$$\text{Atom}(g) \longrightarrow \text{ion}^+(g) + e^- \qquad \Delta E = \text{IE}_1 > 0$$

Brief Solutions to Follow-Up Problems

8.1 The element has eight electrons, so $Z = 8$: oxygen.

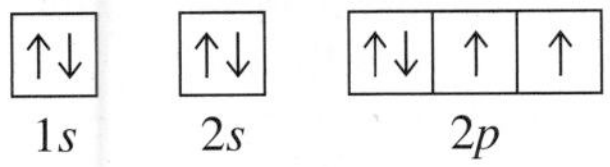

Sixth electron: $n = 2, l = 1, m_l = 0, +\frac{1}{2}$

8.2 (a) For Ni, $1s^22s^22p^63s^23p^64s^23d^8$; [Ar] $4s^23d^8$

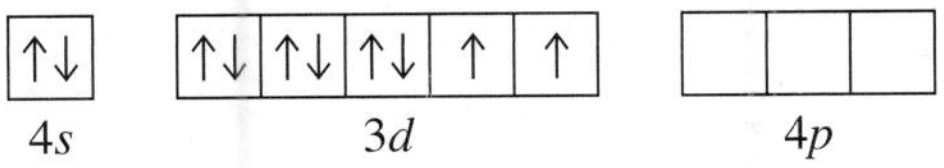

Ni has 18 inner electrons.
(b) For Sr, $1s^22s^22p^63s^23p^64s^23d^{10}4p^65s^2$; [Kr] $5s^2$

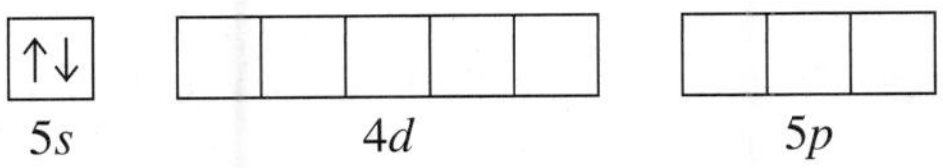

Sr has 36 inner electrons.

(c) For Po, $1s^22s^22p^63s^23p^64s^23d^{10}4p^65s^24d^{10}5p^66s^24f^{14}5d^{10}6p^4$; [Xe] $6s^24f^{14}5d^{10}6p^4$

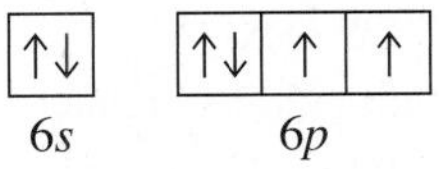

Po has 78 inner electrons.

8.3 (a) Cl < Br < Se; (b) Xe < I < Ba

8.4 (a) Sn < Sb < I; (b) Ba < Sr < Ca

8.5 Q is aluminum: $1s^22s^22p^63s^23p^1$

8.6 (a) Ba ([Xe] $6s^2$) $\longrightarrow$ Ba^{2+} ([Xe]) + $2e^-$
(b) O ([He] $2s^22p^4$) + $2e^-$ $\longrightarrow$ O^{2-} ([He] $2s^22p^6$) (same as Ne)
(c) Pb ([Xe] $6s^24f^{14}5d^{10}6p^2$) $\longrightarrow$ Pb^{2+} ([Xe] $6s^24f^{14}5d^{10}$) + $2e^-$
Pb ([Xe] $6s^24f^{14}5d^{10}6p^2$) $\longrightarrow$ Pb^{4+} ([Xe] $4f^{14}5d^{10}$) + $4e^-$

8.7 (a) V^{3+}: [Ar] $3d^2$; paramagnetic
(b) Ni^{2+}: [Ar] $3d^8$; paramagnetic
(c) La^{3+}: [Xe]; not paramagnetic (diamagnetic)

8.8 (a) $F^- < Cl^- < Br^-$
(b) $Mg^{2+} < Na^+ < F^-$
(c) $Cr^{3+} < Cr^{2+}$

PROBLEMS

Problems with **colored** numbers are answered in Appendix E and worked in detail in the Student Solutions Manual. Problem sections match those in the text and provide the numbers of relevant sample problems. Most offer Concept Review Questions, Skill-Building Exercises (grouped in pairs covering the same concept), and Problems in Context. The Comprehensive Problems are based on material from any section or previous chapter.

Introduction

Concept Review Questions

8.1 What would be your reaction to a claim that a new element had been discovered and it fit between tin (Sn) and antimony (Sb) in the periodic table?

8.2 Based on results of his study of atomic x-ray spectra, Moseley discovered a relationship that replaced atomic mass as the criterion for ordering the elements. By what criterion are the elements now ordered in the periodic table? Give an example of a sequence of element order that was confirmed by Moseley's findings.

Skill-Building Exercises (grouped in similar pairs)

8.3 Before Mendeleev published his periodic table, Döbereiner grouped elements with similar properties into "triads," in which the unknown properties of one member could be predicted by averaging known values of the properties of the others. To test this idea, predict the values of the following quantities:
(a) The atomic mass of K from the atomic masses of Na and Rb
(b) The melting point of Br_2 from the melting points of Cl_2 (−101.0°C) and I_2 (113.6°C) (actual value = −7.2°C)

8.4 To test Döbereiner's idea (Problem 8.3), predict:
(a) The boiling point of HBr from the boiling points of HCl (−84.9°C) and HI (−35.4°C) (actual value = −67.0°C)
(b) The boiling point of AsH_3 from the boiling points of PH_3 (−87.4°C) and SbH_3 (−17.1°C) (actual value = −55°C)

Characteristics of Many-Electron Atoms

Concept Review Questions

8.5 Summarize the rules for the allowable values of the four quantum numbers of an electron in an atom.

8.6 Which of the quantum numbers relate(s) to the electron only? Which relate(s) to the orbital?

8.7 State the exclusion principle. What does it imply about the number and spin of electrons in an atomic orbital?

8.8 What is the key distinction between sublevel energies in one-electron species, such as the H atom, and those in many-electron species, such as the C atom? What factors lead to this distinction? Would you expect the pattern of sublevel energies in Be^{3+} to be more like that in H or that in C? Explain.

8.9 Define *shielding* and *effective nuclear charge*. What is the connection between the two?

8.10 What is penetration? How is it related to shielding? Use the penetration effect to explain the difference in relative orbital energies of a 3*p* and a 3*d* electron in the same atom.

Skill-Building Exercises (grouped in similar pairs)

8.11 How many electrons in an atom can have each of the following quantum number or sublevel designations?
(a) $n = 2, l = 1$ (b) 3*d* (c) 4*s*

8.12 How many electrons in an atom can have each of the following quantum number or sublevel designations?
(a) $n = 2, l = 1, m_l = 0$ (b) 5*p* (c) $n = 4, l = 3$

8.13 How many electrons in an atom can have each of the following quantum number or sublevel designations?
(a) 4*p* (b) $n = 3, l = 1, m_l = +1$ (c) $n = 5, l = 3$

8.14 How many electrons in an atom can have each of the following quantum number or sublevel designations?
(a) 2*s* (b) $n = 3, l = 2$ (c) 6*d*

The Quantum-Mechanical Model and the Periodic Table

(Sample Problems 8.1 and 8.2)

Concept Review Questions

8.15 State the periodic law, and explain its relation to electron configuration. (Use Na and K in your explanation.)

8.16 State Hund's rule in your own words, and show its application in the orbital diagram of the nitrogen atom.

8.17 How does the aufbau principle, in connection with the periodic law, lead to the format of the periodic table?

8.18 For main-group elements, are outer electron configurations similar or different within a group? Within a period? Explain.

8.19 For which blocks of elements are outer electrons the same as valence electrons? For which are *d* electrons often included among the valence electrons?

8.20 What is the electron capacity of the *n*th energy level? What is the capacity of the fourth energy level?

Skill-Building Exercises (grouped in similar pairs)

8.21 Write a full set of quantum numbers for the following:
(a) The outermost electron in an Rb atom
(b) The electron gained when an S^- ion becomes an S^{2-} ion
(c) The electron lost when an Ag atom ionizes
(d) The electron gained when an F^- ion forms from an F atom

8.22 Write a full set of quantum numbers for the following:
(a) The outermost electron in an Li atom
(b) The electron gained when a Br atom becomes a Br^- ion
(c) The electron lost when a Cs atom ionizes
(d) The highest energy electron in the ground-state B atom

8.23 Write the full ground-state electron configuration for each:
(a) Rb (b) Ge (c) Ar

8.24 Write the full ground-state electron configuration for each:
(a) Br (b) Mg (c) Se

8.25 Write the full ground-state electron configuration for each:
(a) Cl (b) Si (c) Sr

8.26 Write the full ground-state electron configuration for each:
(a) S (b) Kr (c) Cs

8.27 Draw a partial (valence-level) orbital diagram, and write the condensed ground-state electron configuration for each:
(a) Ti (b) Cl (c) V

8.28 Draw a partial (valence-level) orbital diagram, and write the condensed ground-state electron configuration for each:
(a) Ba (b) Co (c) Ag

8.29 Draw a partial (valence-level) orbital diagram, and write the condensed ground-state electron configuration for each:
(a) Mn (b) P (c) Fe

8.30 Draw a partial (valence-level) orbital diagram, and write the condensed ground-state electron configuration for each:
(a) Ga (b) Zn (c) Sc

8.31 Draw the partial (valence-level) orbital diagram, and write the symbol, group number, and period number of the element:
(a) [He] $2s^22p^4$ (b) [Ne] $3s^23p^3$

8.32 Draw the partial (valence-level) orbital diagram, and write the symbol, group number, and period number of the element:
(a) [Kr] $5s^24d^{10}$ (b) [Ar] $4s^23d^8$

8.33 Draw the partial (valence-level) orbital diagram, and write the symbol, group number, and period number of the element:
(a) [Ne] $3s^23p^5$ (b) [Ar] $4s^23d^{10}4p^3$

8.34 Draw the partial (valence-level) orbital diagram, and write the symbol, group number, and period number of the element:
(a) [Ar] $4s^23d^5$ (b) [Kr] $5s^24d^2$

8.35 From each partial (valence-level) orbital diagram, write the condensed electron configuration and group number:

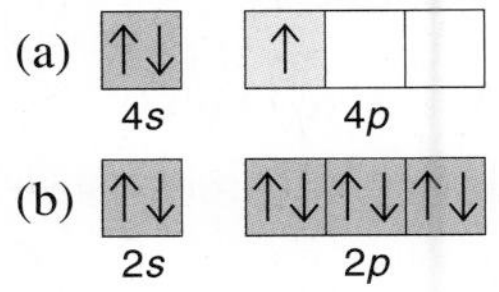

8.36 From each partial (valence-level) orbital diagram, write the condensed electron configuration and group number:

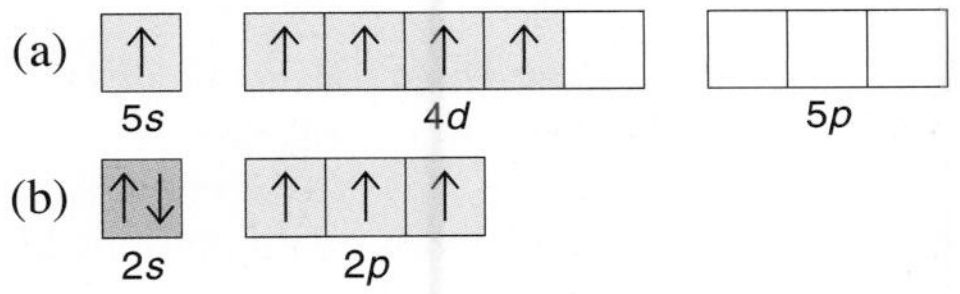

8.37 How many inner, outer, and valence electrons are present in an atom of each of the following elements?
(a) O (b) Sn (c) Ca (d) Fe (e) Se

8.38 How many inner, outer, and valence electrons are present in an atom of each of the following elements?
(a) Br (b) Cs (c) Cr (d) Sr (e) F

8.39 Identify each element below, and give the symbols of the other elements in its group:
(a) [He] $2s^22p^1$ (b) [Ne] $3s^23p^4$ (c) [Xe] $6s^25d^1$

8.40 Identify each element below, and give the symbols of the other elements in its group:
(a) [Ar] $4s^23d^{10}4p^4$ (b) [Xe] $6s^24f^{14}5d^2$ (c) [Ar] $4s^23d^5$

8.41 Identify each element below, and give the symbols of the other elements in its group:
(a) [He] $2s^22p^2$ (b) [Ar] $4s^23d^3$ (c) [Ne] $3s^23p^3$

8.42 Identify each element below, and give the symbols of the other elements in its group:
(a) [Ar] $4s^23d^{10}4p^2$ (b) [Ar] $4s^23d^7$ (c) [Kr] $5s^24d^5$

Problems in Context

8.43 After an atom in its ground state absorbs energy, it exists in an excited state. Spectral lines are produced when the atom returns to its ground state. The yellow-orange line in the sodium spectrum, for example, is produced by the emission of energy when excited sodium atoms return to their ground state. Write the electron configuration and the orbital diagram of the first excited state of sodium. (*Hint:* The outermost electron is excited.)

8.44 One reason spectroscopists study excited states is to gain information about the energies of orbitals that are unoccupied in an atom's ground state. Each of the following electron configurations represents an atom in an excited state. Identify the element, and write its condensed ground-state configuration:
(a) $1s^22s^22p^63s^13p^1$ (b) $1s^22s^22p^63s^23p^44s^1$
(c) $1s^22s^22p^63s^23p^64s^23d^44p^1$ (d) $1s^22s^22p^53s^1$

Trends in Three Atomic Properties

(Sample Problems 8.3 to 8.5)

Concept Review Questions

8.45 If the exact outer limit of an isolated atom cannot be measured, what criterion can we use to determine atomic radii? What is the difference between a covalent radius and a metallic radius?

8.46 Given the following partial (valence-level) electron configurations, (a) identify each element, (b) rank the four elements in order of increasing atomic size, and (c) rank them in order of increasing ionization energy:

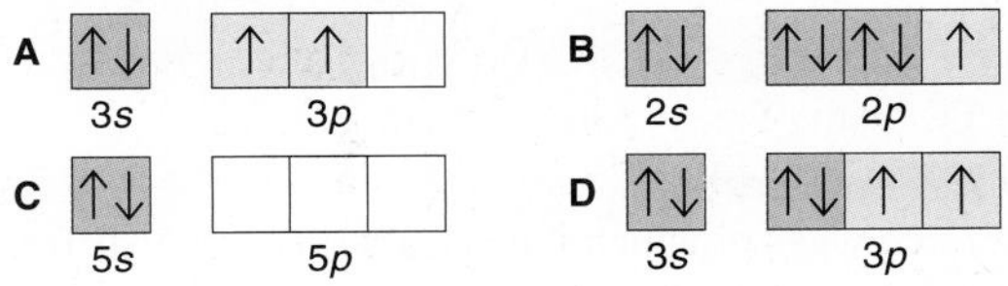

8.47 In what region of the periodic table will you find elements with relatively high IEs? With relatively low IEs?

8.48 (a) Why do successive IEs of a given element always increase? (b) When the difference between successive IEs of a given element is exceptionally large (for example, between IE_1 and IE_2 of K), what do we learn about its electron configuration? (c) The bars represent the relative magnitudes of the first five ionization energies of an atom:

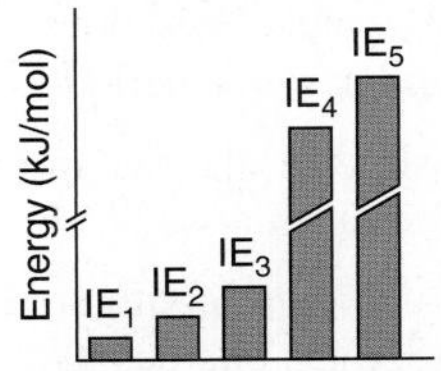

Identify the element and write its complete electron configuration, assuming it comes from (a) Period 2; (b) Period 3; (c) Period 4.

8.49 In a plot of IE_1 for the Period 3 elements (see Figure 8.15, p. 311), why do the values for elements in Groups 3A(13) and 6A(16) drop slightly below the generally increasing trend?

8.50 Which group in the periodic table has elements with high (endothermic) IE_1 and very negative (exothermic) first electron affinities (EA_1)? Give the charge on the ions these atoms form.

8.51 The EA_2 of an oxygen atom is positive, even though its EA_1 is negative. Why does this change of sign occur? Which other elements exhibit a positive EA_2? Explain.

8.52 How does *d*-electron shielding influence atomic size among the Period 4 transition elements?

Skill-Building Exercises (grouped in similar pairs)

8.53 Arrange each set in order of *increasing* atomic size:
(a) Rb, K, Cs (b) C, O, Be (c) Cl, K, S (d) Mg, K, Ca

8.54 Arrange each set in order of *decreasing* atomic size:
(a) Ge, Pb, Sn (b) Sn, Te, Sr (c) F, Ne, Na (d) Be, Mg, Na

8.55 Arrange each set of atoms in order of *increasing* IE_1:
(a) Sr, Ca, Ba (b) N, B, Ne (c) Br, Rb, Se (d) As, Sb, Sn

8.56 Arrange each set of atoms in order of *decreasing* IE_1:
(a) Na, Li, K (b) Be, F, C (c) Cl, Ar, Na (d) Cl, Br, Se

8.57 Write the full electron configuration of the Period 2 element with the following successive IEs (in kJ/mol):

$IE_1 = 801$ $IE_2 = 2427$ $IE_3 = 3659$
$IE_4 = 25{,}022$ $IE_5 = 32{,}822$

8.58 Write the full electron configuration of the Period 3 element with the following successive IEs (in kJ/mol):

$IE_1 = 738$ $IE_2 = 1450$ $IE_3 = 7732$
$IE_4 = 10{,}539$ $IE_5 = 13{,}628$

8.59 Which element in each of the following sets would you expect to have the *highest* IE_2?
(a) Na, Mg, Al (b) Na, K, Fe (c) Sc, Be, Mg

8.60 Which element in each of the following sets would you expect to have the *lowest* IE_3?
(a) Na, Mg, Al (b) K, Ca, Sc (c) Li, Al, B

Atomic Properties and Chemical Reactivity

(Sample Problems 8.6 to 8.8)

Concept Review Questions

8.61 List three ways in which metals and nonmetals differ.

8.62 Summarize the trend in metallic character as a function of position in the periodic table. Is it the same as the trend in atomic size? The trend in ionization energy?

8.63 Explain the relationship between atomic size and reducing strength in Group 1A(1). Explain the relationship between IE and oxidizing strength in Group 7A(17).

8.64 Summarize the acid-base behavior of the main-group metal and nonmetal oxides in water. How does oxide acidity in water change down a group and across a period?

8.65 What ions are possible for the two largest stable elements in Group 4A(14)? How does each arise?

8.66 What is a pseudo–noble gas configuration? Give an example of one ion from Group 3A(13) that has it.

8.67 How are measurements of paramagnetism used to support electron configurations derived spectroscopically? Use Cu(I) and Cu(II) chlorides as examples.

8.68 The charges of a set of isoelectronic ions vary from 3+ to 3−. Place the ions in order of increasing size.

Skill-Building Exercises (grouped in similar pairs)

8.69 Which element would you expect to be *more* metallic?
(a) Ca or Rb (b) Mg or Ra (c) Br or I

8.70 Which element would you expect to be *more* metallic?
(a) S or Cl (b) In or Al (c) As or Br

8.71 Which element would you expect to be *less* metallic?
(a) Sb or As (b) Si or P (c) Be or Na

8.72 Which element would you expect to be *less* metallic?
(a) Cs or Rn (b) Sn or Te (c) Se or Ge

8.73 Does the reaction of a main-group nonmetal oxide in water produce an acidic or a basic solution? Write a balanced equation for the reaction of a Group 6A(16) nonmetal oxide with water.

8.74 Does the reaction of a main-group metal oxide in water produce an acidic or a basic solution? Write a balanced equation for the reaction of a Group 2A(2) oxide with water.

8.75 Write the charge and full ground-state electron configuration of the monatomic ion most likely to be formed by each:
(a) Cl (b) Na (c) Ca

8.76 Write the charge and full ground-state electron configuration of the monatomic ion most likely to be formed by each:
(a) Rb (b) N (c) Br

8.77 Write the charge and full ground-state electron configuration of the monatomic ion most likely to be formed by each:
(a) Al (b) S (c) Sr

8.78 Write the charge and full ground-state electron configuration of the monatomic ion most likely to be formed by each:
(a) P (b) Mg (c) Se

8.79 How many unpaired electrons are present in a ground-state atom from each of the following groups?
(a) 2A(2) (b) 5A(15) (c) 8A(18) (d) 3A(13)

8.80 How many unpaired electrons are present in a ground-state atom from each of the following groups?
(a) 4A(14) (b) 7A(17) (c) 1A(1) (d) 6A(16)

8.81 Which of these are paramagnetic in their ground state?
(a) Ga (b) Si (c) Be (d) Te

8.82 Are compounds of these ground-state ions paramagnetic?
(a) Ti^{2+} (b) Zn^{2+} (c) Ca^{2+} (d) Sn^{2+}

8.83 Write the condensed ground-state electron configurations of these transition metal ions, and state which are paramagnetic:
(a) V^{3+} (b) Cd^{2+} (c) Co^{3+} (d) Ag^{+}

8.84 Write the condensed ground-state electron configurations of these transition metal ions, and state which are paramagnetic:
(a) Mo^{3+} (b) Au^{+} (c) Mn^{2+} (d) Hf^{2+}

8.85 Palladium (Pd; $Z = 46$) is diamagnetic. Draw partial orbital diagrams to show which of the following electron configurations is consistent with this fact:
(a) [Kr] $5s^2 4d^8$ (b) [Kr] $4d^{10}$ (c) [Kr] $5s^1 4d^9$

8.86 Niobium (Nb; $Z = 41$) has an anomalous ground-state electron configuration for a Group 5B(5) element: [Kr] $5s^1 4d^4$. What is the expected electron configuration for elements in this group? Draw partial orbital diagrams to show how paramagnetic measurements could support niobium's actual configuration.

8.87 Rank the ions in each set in order of *increasing* size, and explain your ranking:
(a) Li^+, K^+, Na^+ (b) Se^{2-}, Rb^+, Br^- (c) O^{2-}, F^-, N^{3-}

8.88 Rank the ions in each set in order of *decreasing* size, and explain your ranking:
(a) Se^{2-}, S^{2-}, O^{2-} (b) Te^{2-}, Cs^+, I^- (c) Sr^{2+}, Ba^{2+}, Cs^+

Comprehensive Problems

8.89 Name the element described in each of the following:
(a) Smallest atomic radius in Group 6A(16)
(b) Largest atomic radius in Period 6
(c) Smallest metal in Period 3
(d) Highest IE_1 in Group 4A(14)
(e) Lowest IE_1 in Period 5
(f) Most metallic in Group 5A(15)
(g) Group 3A(13) element that forms the most basic oxide
(h) Period 4 element with highest energy level filled
(i) Condensed ground-state electron configuration of [Ne] $3s^23p^2$
(j) Condensed ground-state electron configuration of [Kr] $5s^24d^6$
(k) Forms 2+ ion with electron configuration [Ar] $3d^3$
(l) Period 5 element that forms 3+ ion with pseudo–noble gas configuration
(m) Period 4 transition element that forms 3+ diamagnetic ion
(n) Period 4 transition element that forms 2+ ion with a half-filled *d* sublevel
(o) Heaviest lanthanide
(p) Period 3 element whose 2− ion is isoelectronic with Ar
(q) Alkaline earth metal whose cation is isoelectronic with Kr
(r) Group 5A(15) metalloid with the most acidic oxide

8.90 Use electron configurations to account for the stability of the lanthanide ions Ce^{4+} and Eu^{2+}.

8.91 When a nonmetal oxide reacts with water, it forms an oxoacid with the same oxidation number as the nonmetal. Give the name and formula of the oxide used to prepare each of these oxoacids: (a) hypochlorous acid; (b) chlorous acid; (c) chloric acid; (d) perchloric acid; (e) sulfuric acid; (f) sulfurous acid; (g) nitric acid; (h) nitrous acid; (i) carbonic acid; (j) phosphoric acid.

8.92 A fundamental relationship of electrostatics states that the energy required to separate opposite charges of magnitudes Q_1 and Q_2 that are a distance d apart is proportional to $\frac{Q_1 \times Q_2}{d}$. Use this relationship and any other factors to explain the following: (a) the IE_2 of He ($Z = 2$) is *more* than twice the IE_1 of H ($Z = 1$); (b) the IE_1 of He is *less* than twice the IE_1 of H.

8.93 The energy difference between the 5*d* and 6*s* sublevels in gold accounts for its color. Assuming this energy difference is about 2.7 eV (electron volt; 1 eV $= 1.602\times10^{-19}$ J), explain why gold has a warm yellow color.

8.94 Write the formula and name of the compound formed from the following ionic interactions: (a) The 2+ ion and the 1− ion are both isoelectronic with the atoms of a chemically unreactive Period 4 element. (b) The 2+ ion and the 2− ion are both isoelectronic with the Period 3 noble gas. (c) The 2+ ion is the smallest with a filled *d* sublevel; the anion forms from the smallest halogen. (d) The ions form from the largest and smallest ionizable atoms in Period 2.

8.95 The energy changes for many unusual reactions can be determined using Hess's law (Section 6.5).
(a) Calculate ΔE for the conversion of $F^-(g)$ into $F^+(g)$.
(b) Calculate ΔE for the conversion of $Na^+(g)$ into $Na^-(g)$.

8.96 Discuss each conclusion from a study of redox reactions:
(a) The sulfide ion functions only as a reducing agent.
(b) The sulfate ion functions only as an oxidizing agent.
(c) Sulfur dioxide functions as an oxidizing or a reducing agent.

8.97 The hot glowing gases around the Sun, the *corona*, can reach millions of degrees Celsius, high enough to remove many electrons from gaseous atoms. Iron ions with charges as high as 14+ have been observed in the corona. Which ions from Fe^+ to Fe^{14+} are paramagnetic? Which would be most strongly attracted to a magnetic field?

8.98 There are some exceptions to the trends of first and successive ionization energies. For each of the following pairs, explain which ionization energy would be higher:
(a) IE_1 of Ga or IE_1 of Ge
(b) IE_2 of Ga or IE_2 of Ge
(c) IE_3 of Ga or IE_3 of Ge
(d) IE_4 of Ga or IE_4 of Ge

8.99 Use Figure 8.16, p. 312, to find: (a) the longest wavelength of electromagnetic (EM) radiation that can ionize an alkali metal atom; (b) the longest wavelength of EM radiation that can ionize an alkaline earth metal atom; (c) the elements, other than the alkali and alkaline earth metals, that could also be ionized by the radiation of part (b); (d) the region of the EM spectrum in which these photons are found.

8.100 Rubidium and bromine atoms are depicted at right. (a) What monatomic ions do they form? (b) What electronic feature characterizes this pair of ions, and which noble gas are they related to? (c) Which pair best represents the relative ionic sizes?

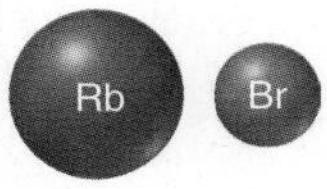

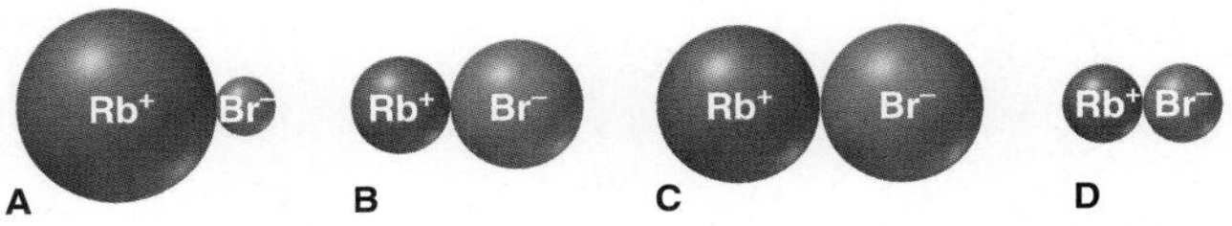

8.101 Partial (valence-level) electron configurations for four different ions are shown below:

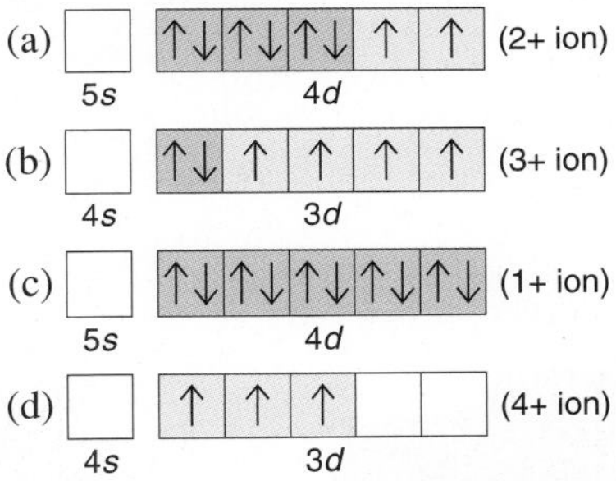

Identify the elements from which the ions are derived, and write the formula of the oxide each ion forms.

8.102 Data from the planet Zog for some main-group elements are shown below (Zoggian units are linearly related to Earth units but are not shown). Radio signals from Zog reveal that balloonium is a monatomic gas with two positive nuclear charges. Use the data to deduce the names that Earthlings give to these elements:

Name	Atomic Radius	IE_1	EA_1
Balloonium	10	339	0
Inertium	24	297	+4.1
Allotropium	34	143	−28.6
Brinium	63	70.9	−7.6
Canium	47	101	−15.3
Fertilium	25	200	0
Liquidium	38	163	−46.4
Utilium	48	82.4	−6.1
Crimsonium	72	78.4	−2.9

Models of Chemical Bonding

9

Concepts and skills to review before you study this chapter

- characteristics of ionic and covalent compounds; Coulomb's law (Section 2.7)
- polar covalent bonds and the polarity of water (Section 4.1)
- Hess's law, ΔH°_{rxn}, and ΔH°_f (Sections 6.5 and 6.6)
- atomic and ionic electron configurations (Sections 8.2 and 8.4)
- trends in atomic properties and metallic behavior (Sections 8.3 and 8.4)

Why do substances behave as they do? That is, why is table salt (or any other ionic substance) a hard, brittle, high-melting solid that conducts a current only when molten or dissolved in water? Why is candle wax (along with most covalent substances) low melting, soft, and nonconducting, even though diamond (and a few others of this type of covalent substance) is high melting and extremely hard? And why is copper (and most other metals) shiny, malleable, and able to conduct a current whether molten or solid? The answers lie in the *type of bonding within the substance*. In Chapter 8, we examined the properties of individual atoms and ions. But the behavior of matter really depends on how those atoms and ions bond.

IN THIS CHAPTER . . . We examine how atomic properties give rise to three models of chemical bonding—ionic, covalent, and metallic—and how each model explains the behavior of substances.

- We see how metals and nonmetals combine via three types of bonding and learn how to depict atoms and ions with Lewis symbols.
- We detail the steps in the formation of an ionic solid and focus on the importance of lattice energy.
- Covalent bonding occurs in the vast majority of compounds, so we look at how a bond forms and discuss the relations among bond order, energy, and length.
- We explore the relationship between bond energy and the enthalpy change of a reaction, with a focus on fuels and foods.
- We examine periodic trends in electronegativity and learn its role in the range of bonding, from pure covalent to ionic, and in bond polarity.
- We consider a simple bonding model that explains the properties of metals.

9.1 • ATOMIC PROPERTIES AND CHEMICAL BONDS

Before we examine the types of chemical bonding, we should start with the most fundamental question: why do atoms bond at all? In general, *bonding lowers the potential energy between positive and negative particles* (see Figure 1.3, p. 9), whether they are oppositely charged ions or nuclei and electron pairs. Just as the electron configuration and the strength of nucleus-electron attractions determine the properties of an atom, the type and strength of chemical bonds determine the properties of a substance.

Types of Bonding: Three Ways Metals and Nonmetals Combine

In general, there is a gradation from atoms of more metallic elements to atoms of more nonmetallic elements across a period *and* up a group (Figure 9.1, *next page*). Three types of bonding result from the three ways these two types of atoms can combine:

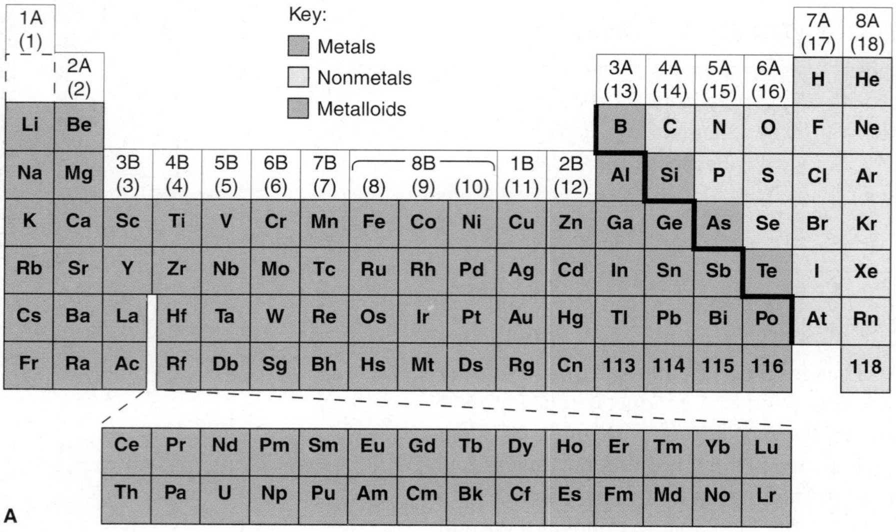

B

PROPERTY	METAL ATOM	NONMETAL ATOM
Atomic size	Larger	Smaller
Z_{eff}	Lower	Higher
IE	Lower	Higher
EA	Less negative	More negative

Figure 9.1 A comparison of metals and nonmetals. **A,** Location within the periodic table. **B,** Relative magnitudes of some atomic properties across a period.

1. *Metal with nonmetal: electron transfer and ionic bonding* (Figure 9.2A). We observe **ionic bonding** between atoms with large differences in their tendencies to lose or gain electrons. Such differences occur between reactive metals [Groups 1A(1) and 2A(2)] and nonmetals [Group 7A(17) and the top of Group 6A(16)]. A metal atom (low IE) loses its one or two valence electrons, and a nonmetal atom (highly negative EA) gains the electron(s). *Electron transfer* from metal to nonmetal occurs, and each atom forms an ion with a noble gas electron configuration. The electrostatic attractions between these positive and negative ions draw them into a three-dimensional array to form an ionic solid. Note that the chemical formula of an ionic compound is the *empirical formula* because it gives the cation-to-anion ratio.

2. *Nonmetal with nonmetal: electron sharing and covalent bonding* (Figure 9.2B). When two atoms differ little, or not at all, in their tendencies to lose or gain electrons, we observe *electron sharing* and **covalent bonding,** which occurs most commonly between nonmetal atoms. Each atom holds onto its own electrons tightly (high IE) and attracts other electrons (highly negative EA). The nucleus of each atom attracts the valence electrons of the other, which draws the atoms together. The shared electron pair is typically *localized* between the two atoms, linking them in a covalent bond of a particular length and strength. In most cases, separate molecules result when atoms bond covalently. Note that the chemical formula of a covalent compound is the *molecular formula* because it gives the actual numbers of atoms in each molecule.

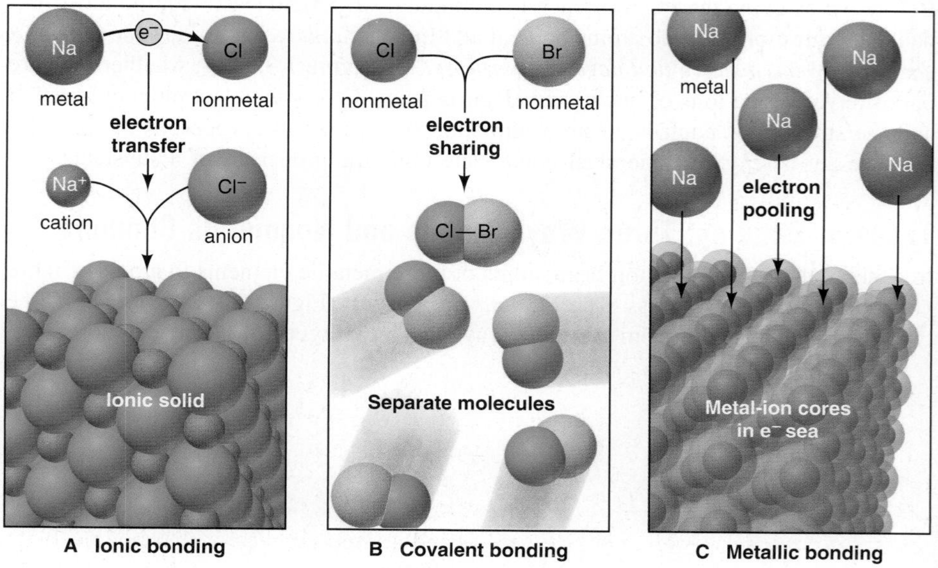

Figure 9.2 Three models of chemical bonding.

3. *Metal with metal: electron pooling and metallic bonding* (Figure 9.2C). Metal atoms are relatively large, and their few outer electrons are well shielded by filled inner levels (core electrons). Thus, they lose outer electrons easily (low IE) and do not gain them readily (slightly negative or positive EA). These properties lead metal atoms to share their valence electrons, but not by covalent bonding. In the simplest model of **metallic bonding,** the enormous number of atoms in a sample of a metal *pool* their valence electrons into a "sea" of electrons that "flows" between and around each metal-ion core (nucleus plus inner electrons), thereby attracting them together. Unlike the localized electrons in covalent bonding, electrons in metallic bonding are *delocalized,* moving freely throughout the entire piece of metal.

In the world of real substances, there are exceptions to these idealized models, so you can't always predict bond type from positions of the elements in the periodic table. As just one example, when the metal beryllium [Group 2A(2)] combines with the nonmetal chlorine [Group 7A(17)], there is more electron sharing than transferring—that is, the bonding is more covalent than ionic. Thus, just as we see gradations in atomic behavior within a group or period, we see gradations in type of bonding between atoms from different groups and periods (Figure 9.3).

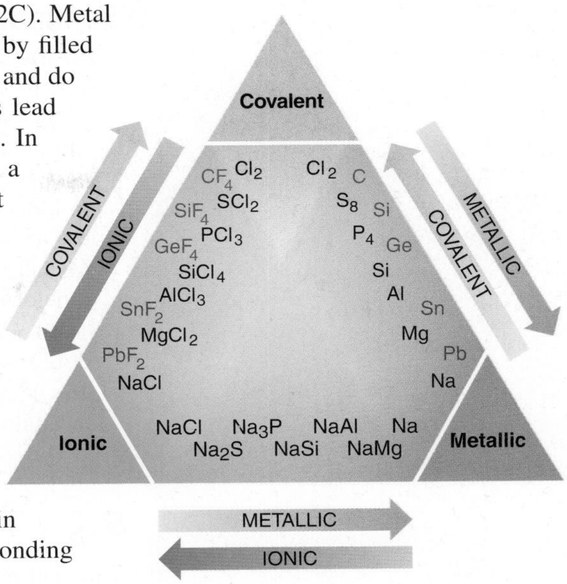

Figure 9.3 Gradations in bond type among Period 3 *(black type)* and Group 4A *(red type)* elements.

Lewis Symbols and the Octet Rule

Before examining each of the models, let's learn a method for depicting the valence electrons of interacting atoms that predicts how they bond. In a **Lewis electron-dot symbol** (named for the American chemist G. N. Lewis), the element symbol represents the nucleus *and* inner electrons, and dots around the symbol represent the valence electrons (Figure 9.4). Note that the pattern of dots is the same for elements within a group.

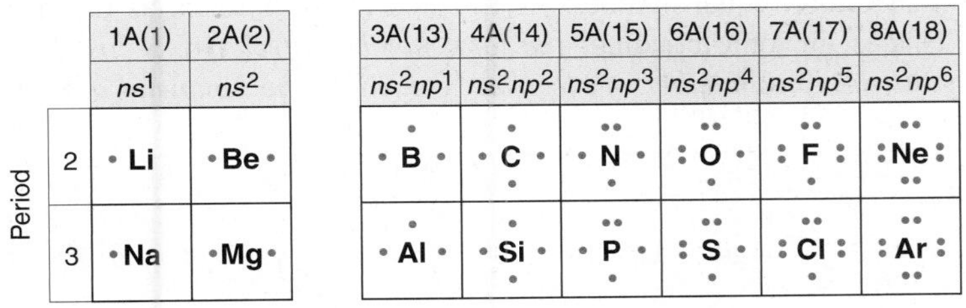

Figure 9.4 Lewis electron-dot symbols for elements in Periods 2 and 3.

We use these steps to write the Lewis symbol for any main-group element:

1. Note its A-group number (1A to 8A), which tells the number of valence electrons.
2. Place one dot at a time on each of the four sides (top, right, bottom, left) of the element symbol.
3. Keep adding dots, pairing them, until all are used up.

The specific placement of dots is not important; that is, in addition to the one shown in Figure 9.4, the Lewis symbol for nitrogen can *also* be written as

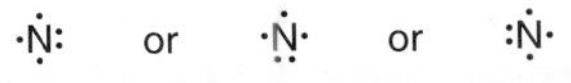

The Lewis symbol provides information about an element's bonding behavior:

- For a *metal,* the *total* number of dots is the number of electrons an atom loses to form a cation.
- For a *nonmetal,* the number of *unpaired* dots equals either the number of electrons an atom *gains* to form an anion or the number it *shares* to form covalent bonds.

The Lewis symbol for carbon illustrates the last point. Rather than one pair of dots and two unpaired dots, as its electron configuration seems to call for ([He] $2s^22p^2$), carbon has four unpaired dots because it forms four bonds. Larger nonmetals can form as many bonds as the number of dots in their Lewis symbol (Chapter 10).

In his pioneering studies, Lewis generalized much of bonding behavior into the **octet rule:** *when atoms bond, they lose, gain, or share electrons to attain a filled outer level of eight electrons* (*or two,* for H and Li). The octet rule holds for nearly all of the compounds of Period 2 elements and a large number of others as well.

Summary of Section 9.1

- Nearly all naturally occurring substances consist of atoms or ions bonded to others. Chemical bonding allows atoms to lower their energy.
- Ionic bonding occurs when metal atoms transfer electrons to nonmetal atoms, and the resulting ions attract each other and form an ionic solid.
- Covalent bonding is most common between nonmetal atoms and usually results in individual molecules. Bonded atoms share one or more pairs of electrons that are localized between them.
- Metallic bonding occurs when many metal atoms pool their valence electrons into a delocalized electron "sea" that holds all the atoms in the sample together.
- The Lewis electron-dot symbol of a main-group atom shows valence electrons as dots surrounding the element symbol.
- The octet rule says that, when bonding, many atoms lose, gain, or share electrons to attain a filled outer level of eight (or two) electrons.

9.2 • THE IONIC BONDING MODEL

The central idea of the ionic bonding model is the *transfer of electrons from metal atoms to nonmetal atoms to form ions that attract each other into a solid compound.* In most cases, for the main groups, the ion that forms has a filled outer level of either two or eight electrons, the number in the nearest noble gas (octet rule).

The transfer of an electron from a lithium atom to a fluorine atom is depicted in three ways in Figure 9.5. In each, Li loses its single outer electron and is left with a filled $n = 1$ level (two e^-), while F gains a single electron to fill its $n = 2$ level (eight e^-). In this case, each atom is one electron away from the configuration of its nearest noble gas, so the number of electrons lost by each Li equals the number gained by each F. Therefore, equal numbers of Li^+ and F^- ions form, as the formula LiF indicates. That is, in ionic bonding, *the total number of electrons lost by the metal atom(s) equals the total number of electrons gained by the nonmetal atom(s).*

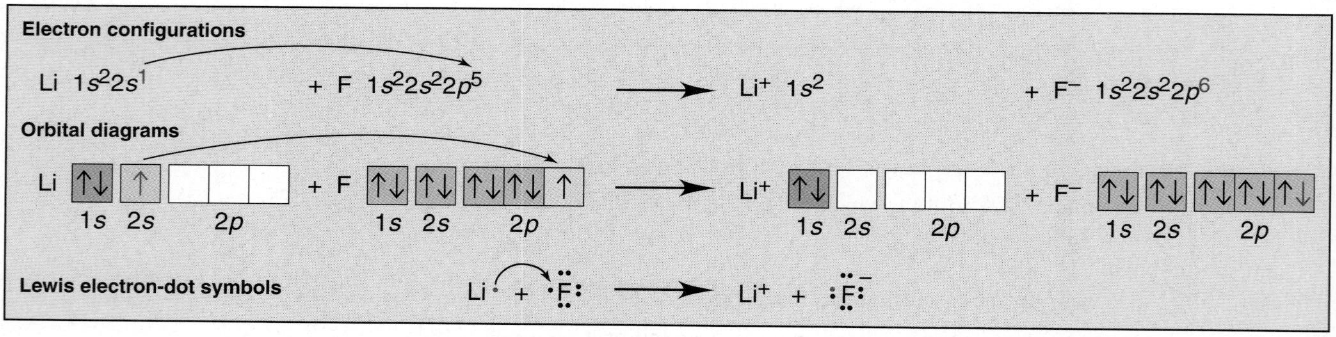

Figure 9.5 Three ways to depict electron transfer in the formation of Li^+ and F^-. The electron being transferred is shown in red.

Sample Problem 9.1 Depicting Ion Formation

Problem Use partial orbital diagrams and Lewis symbols to depict the formation of Na^+ and O^{2-} ions from the atoms, and give the formula of the compound formed.

Plan First we draw the orbital diagrams and Lewis symbols for Na and O atoms. To attain filled outer levels, Na loses one electron and O gains two. To make the number of electrons lost equal the number gained, two Na atoms are needed for each O atom.

Solution

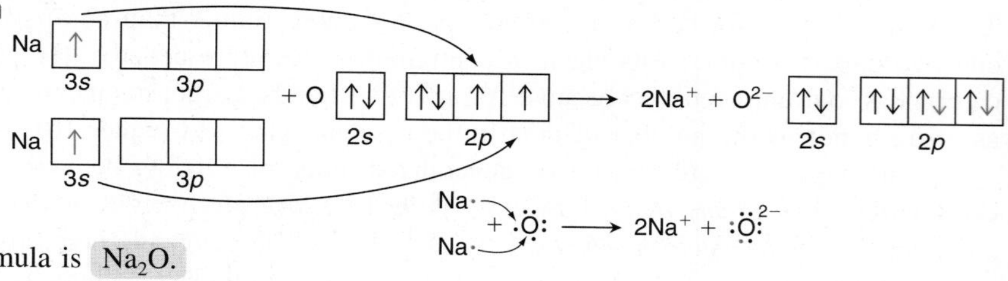

The formula is Na_2O.

Follow-Up Problem 9.1 Use condensed electron configurations and Lewis symbols to depict the formation of Mg^{2+} and Cl^- ions from the atoms, and give the formula of the compound formed.

Why Ionic Compounds Form: The Importance of Lattice Energy

You may be surprised to learn that energy is *absorbed* during electron transfer. So why does it occur? And, in view of this absorption of energy, why do ionic substances exist at all? As you'll see, the answer involves the enormous quantity of energy *released* after electron transfer, as the ions form a solid.

1. *The electron-transfer process.* Consider the electron-transfer process for the formation of lithium fluoride, which involves a gaseous Li atom losing an electron, and a gaseous F atom gaining it:

- The first ionization energy (IE_1) of Li is the energy absorbed when 1 mol of gaseous Li atoms loses 1 mol of valence electrons:

$$Li(g) \longrightarrow Li^+(g) + e^- \qquad IE_1 = 520 \text{ kJ}$$

- The first electron affinity (EA_1) of F is the energy released when 1 mol of gaseous F atoms gains 1 mol of electrons:

$$F(g) + e^- \longrightarrow F^-(g) \qquad EA_1 = -328 \text{ kJ}$$

- Taking the sum shows that electron transfer *by itself* requires energy:

$$Li(g) + F(g) \longrightarrow Li^+(g) + F^-(g) \qquad IE_1 + EA_1 = 192 \text{ kJ}$$

2. *Other steps that absorb energy.* The total energy needed prior to ion formation adds to the sum of IE_1 and EA_1: metallic lithium must be made into gaseous atoms (161 kJ/mol), and fluorine molecules must be broken into separate atoms (79.5 kJ/mol).

3. *Steps that release energy.* Despite these endothermic steps, the standard enthalpy of formation (ΔH_f°) of solid LiF is −617 kJ/mol; that is, 617 kJ is *released* when 1 mol of LiF(*s*) forms from its elements. Formation of LiF is typical of reactions between active metals and nonmetals: ionic solids form readily (Figure 9.6).

If the overall reaction releases energy, there must be some step that is exothermic enough to outweigh the endothermic steps. This step involves the *strong attraction between pairs of oppositely charged ions.* When 1 mol of $Li^+(g)$ and 1 mol of $F^-(g)$ form 1 mol of gaseous LiF molecules, a large quantity of heat is released:

$$Li^+(g) + F^-(g) \longrightarrow LiF(g) \qquad \Delta H^\circ = -755 \text{ kJ}$$

But, as you know, under ordinary conditions, LiF does not exist as gaseous molecules: *even more energy is released when the separate gaseous ions coalesce into a crystalline solid* because each ion attracts *several* oppositely charged ions:

$$Li^+(g) + F^-(g) \longrightarrow LiF(s) \qquad \Delta H^\circ = -1050 \text{ kJ}$$

The negative of this enthalpy change is 1050 kJ, the lattice energy of LiF. The **lattice energy ($\Delta H^\circ_{lattice}$)** is the enthalpy change that accompanies the reverse of this equation—1 mol of ionic solid separating into gaseous ions.

Figure 9.6 The exothermic formation of sodium bromide. **A,** Sodium (in beaker under mineral oil) and bromine. **B,** The reaction is rapid and vigorous.

Determining Lattice Energy with a Born-Haber Cycle The magnitude of the lattice energy is a measure of the strength of the ionic interactions and influences macroscopic properties, such as melting point, hardness, and solubility. Despite playing this crucial role in the formation of ionic compounds, lattice energy cannot be measured directly. One way to determine it applies Hess's law (see Section 6.5) in a **Born-Haber cycle,** a series of steps from elements to ionic solid for which all the enthalpies* are known except the lattice energy.

*Strictly speaking, ionization energy (IE) and electron affinity (EA) are internal energy changes (ΔE), not enthalpy changes (ΔH), but in these steps, $\Delta H = \Delta E$ because $\Delta V = 0$ (see Section 6.2).

Let's go through a Born-Haber cycle for the formation of lithium fluoride to calculate $\Delta H^\circ_{lattice}$. Figure 9.7 shows two possible paths, a direct combination reaction (ΔH°_f; *black arrow*) and a multistep path (*orange arrows*) in which one step is the unknown $\Delta H^\circ_{lattice}$. Hess's law tells us both paths involve the same overall enthalpy change:

$$\Delta H^\circ_f \text{ of LiF}(s) = \text{sum of } \Delta H^\circ \text{ values for multistep path}$$

Hess's law lets us choose *hypothetical* steps whose enthalpy changes we can measure, even though *they are* ***not*** *the actual steps that occur when lithium reacts with fluorine.* We identify each ΔH° by its step number in Figure 9.7:

Step 1. From solid Li to Li atoms. This step, called *atomization,* has the enthalpy change ΔH°_{atom}. It involves breaking metallic bonds, so it absorbs energy:

$$\text{Li}(s) \longrightarrow \text{Li}(g) \qquad \Delta H^\circ_{step\ 1} = \Delta H^\circ_{atom} = 161 \text{ kJ}$$

Step 2. From F_2 molecules to F atoms. This step involves breaking a covalent bond, so it absorbs energy; as we discuss later, this is the *bond energy* (BE) of F_2. Since we need 1 mol of F atoms to make 1 mol of LiF, we start with $\frac{1}{2}$ mol of F_2:

$$\tfrac{1}{2}\text{F}_2(g) \longrightarrow \text{F}(g) \qquad \Delta H^\circ_{step\ 2} = \tfrac{1}{2}(\text{BE of F}_2) = \tfrac{1}{2}(159 \text{ kJ}) = 79.5 \text{ kJ}$$

Step 3. From Li to Li^+. Removing the 2*s* electron from Li absorbs energy:

$$\text{Li}(g) \longrightarrow \text{Li}^+(g) + \text{e}^- \qquad \Delta H^\circ_{step\ 3} = \text{IE}_1 = 520 \text{ kJ}$$

Step 4. From F to F^-. Adding an electron to F releases energy:

$$\text{F}(g) + \text{e}^- \longrightarrow \text{F}^-(g) \qquad \Delta H^\circ_{step\ 4} = \text{EA}_1 = -328 \text{ kJ}$$

Step 5. From gaseous ions to ionic solid. Forming solid LiF from gaseous Li^+ and F^- releases a lot of energy. The enthalpy change for this step is unknown but is, by definition, the negative of the lattice energy:

$$\text{Li}^+(g) + \text{F}^-(g) \longrightarrow \text{LiF}(s) \qquad \Delta H^\circ_{step\ 5} = -\Delta H^\circ_{lattice} \text{ of LiF} = ?$$

The enthalpy change of the combination reaction (*black arrow*) is

$$\text{Li}(s) + \tfrac{1}{2}\text{F}_2(g) \longrightarrow \text{LiF}(s) \qquad \Delta H^\circ_{overall} = \Delta H^\circ_f = -617 \text{ kJ}$$

Figure 9.7 The Born-Haber cycle for lithium fluoride. The formation of LiF(*s*) from its elements can happen in one combination reaction *(black arrow)* or in five steps *(orange arrows)*. The unknown enthalpy change is $\Delta H^\circ_{step\ 5}$ ($-\Delta H^\circ_{lattice}$ of LiF).

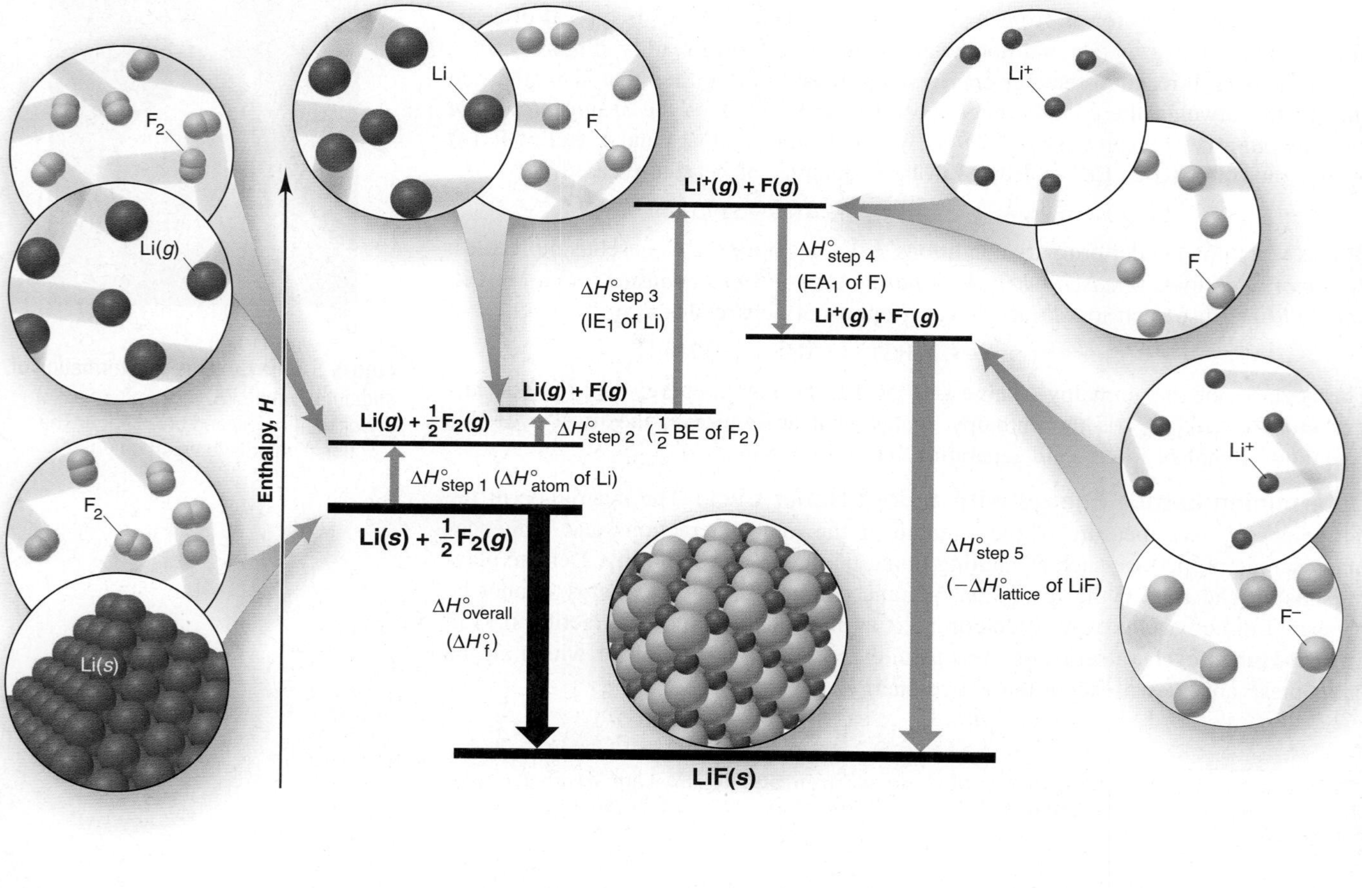

We set ΔH_f° equal to the sum of the ΔH° values for the steps and solve for $\Delta H_{lattice}^\circ$:

$$\Delta H_f^\circ = \Delta H_{step\ 1}^\circ + \Delta H_{step\ 2}^\circ + \Delta H_{step\ 3}^\circ + \Delta H_{step\ 4}^\circ + (-\Delta H_{lattice}^\circ \text{ of LiF})$$

Solving for $-\Delta H_{lattice}^\circ$ of LiF gives

$$\begin{aligned} -\Delta H_{lattice}^\circ \text{ of LiF} &= \Delta H_f^\circ - (\Delta H_{step\ 1}^\circ + \Delta H_{step\ 2}^\circ + \Delta H_{step\ 3}^\circ + \Delta H_{step\ 4}^\circ) \\ &= -617 \text{ kJ} - [161 \text{ kJ} + 79.5 \text{ kJ} + 520 \text{ kJ} + (-328 \text{ kJ})] \\ &= -1050 \text{ kJ} \end{aligned}$$

And changing the sign gives,

$$\Delta H_{lattice}^\circ \text{ of LiF} = -(-1050 \text{ kJ}) = 1050 \text{ kJ}$$

Note that *the lattice energy is, by far, the largest component of the multistep process.* (Problems 9.30 and 9.31 are among several that focus on Born-Haber cycles.)

The Born-Haber cycle shows that the energy *required* for elements to form ions is *supplied* by the attraction among the ions in the solid. And the "take-home lesson" is that *ionic solids exist* ***only*** *because the lattice energy far exceeds the total energy needed to form the ions.*

Periodic Trends in Lattice Energy

The lattice energy results from electrostatic interactions among ions, so its magnitude depends on ionic size, ionic charge, and ionic arrangement in the solid. Therefore, we expect to see periodic trends in lattice energy.

Explaining the Trends with Coulomb's Law Recall from Chapter 2 that **Coulomb's law** states that the electrostatic energy between particles A and B is directly proportional to the product of their charges and inversely proportional to the distance between them:

$$\text{Electrostatic energy} \propto \frac{\text{charge A} \times \text{charge B}}{\text{distance}}$$

Lattice energy is directly proportional to electrostatic energy. In an ionic solid, cations and anions lie as close to each other as possible, so the distance between them is the sum of the ionic radii (see Figure 8.28, p. 320):

$$\text{Electrostatic energy} \propto \frac{\text{cation charge} \times \text{anion charge}}{\text{cation radius} + \text{anion radius}} \propto \Delta H_{lattice}^\circ \quad (9.1)$$

This relationship helps us explain the effects of ionic size and charge on trends in lattice energy:

1. *Effect of ionic size.* As we move down a group, ionic radii increase, so the electrostatic energy between cations and anions decreases; thus, lattice energies should decrease as well. Figure 9.8 on the next page shows that, for the alkali-metal halides, lattice energy decreases down the group whether we hold the cation constant (LiF to LiI) or the anion constant (LiF to RbF).

2. *Effect of ionic charge.* Across a period, ionic charge changes. For example, lithium fluoride and magnesium oxide have cations and anions of about equal radii (Li^+ = 76 pm and Mg^{2+} = 72 pm; F^- = 133 pm and O^{2-} = 140 pm). The major difference is between singly charged Li^+ and F^- ions and doubly charged Mg^{2+} and O^{2-} ions. The difference in the lattice energies of the two compounds is striking:

$$\Delta H_{lattice}^\circ \text{ of LiF} = 1050 \text{ kJ/mol} \qquad \text{and} \qquad \Delta H_{lattice}^\circ \text{ of MgO} = 3923 \text{ kJ/mol}$$

This nearly fourfold increase in $\Delta H_{lattice}^\circ$ reflects the fourfold increase in the product of the charges (1 × 1 vs. 2 × 2) in the numerator of Equation 9.1.

Why Does MgO Exist? We might ask how ionic solids, like MgO, with its doubly charged ions, could even form. After all, forming 1 mol of Mg^{2+} involves the sum of the first *and* second ionization energies:

$$Mg(g) \longrightarrow Mg^{2+}(g) + 2e^- \qquad \Delta H^\circ = IE_1 + IE_2 = 738 \text{ kJ} + 1450 \text{ kJ} = 2188 \text{ kJ}$$

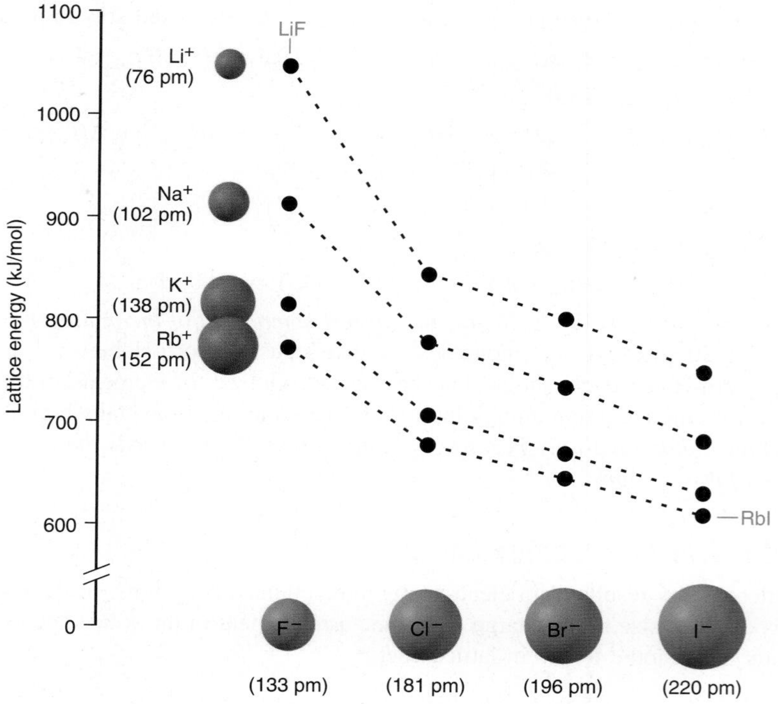

Figure 9.8 Trends in lattice energy. The lattice energies are shown for compounds formed from a given Group 1A(1) cation *(left side)* and one of the Group 7A(17) anions *(bottom)*. LiF (smallest ions) has the highest lattice energy, and RbI (largest ions) has the lowest.

And, while forming 1 mol of O^- ions is exothermic (first electron affinity, EA_1), adding a second mole of electrons (second electron affinity, EA_2) is endothermic because the electron is added to a negative ion. The overall formation of O^{2-} ions is endothermic:

$$\begin{array}{lll} O(g) + e^- \longrightarrow O^-(g) & \Delta H^\circ = EA_1 & = -141\ \text{kJ} \\ O^-(g) + e^- \longrightarrow O^{2-}(g) & \Delta H^\circ = EA_2 & = 878\ \text{kJ} \\ \hline O(g) + 2e^- \longrightarrow O^{2-}(g) & \Delta H^\circ = EA_1 + EA_2 & = 737\ \text{kJ} \end{array}$$

There are also the endothermic steps for converting Mg(*s*) to Mg(*g*) (148 kJ/mol) and breaking $\frac{1}{2}$ mol of O_2 molecules into O atoms (498 kJ/mol). Nevertheless, the 2+ and 2− ionic charges make the lattice energy so large ($\Delta H^\circ_{\text{lattice}}$ = 3923 kJ/mol) that solid MgO forms readily whenever Mg burns in air (ΔH°_f = −601 kJ/mol).

How the Model Explains the Properties of Ionic Compounds

The central role of any model is to explain the facts. With atomic-level views, we can see how the ionic bonding model accounts for the properties of ionic solids:

1. *Physical behavior.* As a typical ionic compound, a piece of rock salt (NaCl) is *hard* (does not dent), *rigid* (does not bend), and *brittle* (cracks without deforming). These properties arise from the strong attractive forces that hold the ions *in specific positions*. Moving them out of position requires overcoming these forces, so rock salt does not dent or bend. If enough force *is* applied, ions of like charge are brought next to each other, and repulsions between them crack the sample suddenly (Figure 9.9).

Figure 9.9 Why ionic compounds crack. **A,** Ionic compounds crack when struck with enough force. **B,** When a force moves like charges near each other, repulsions cause a crack.

A
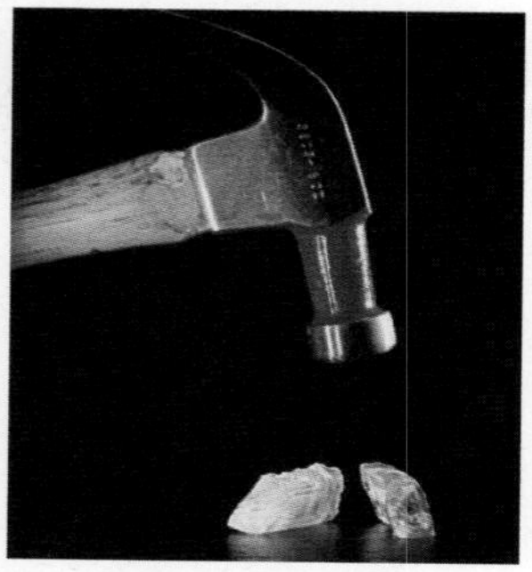

B
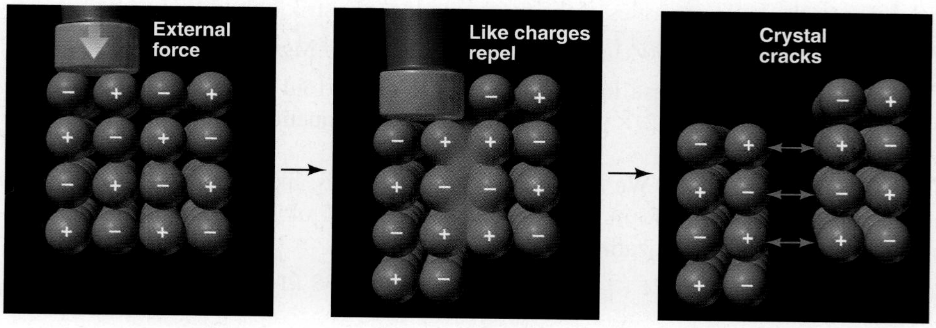

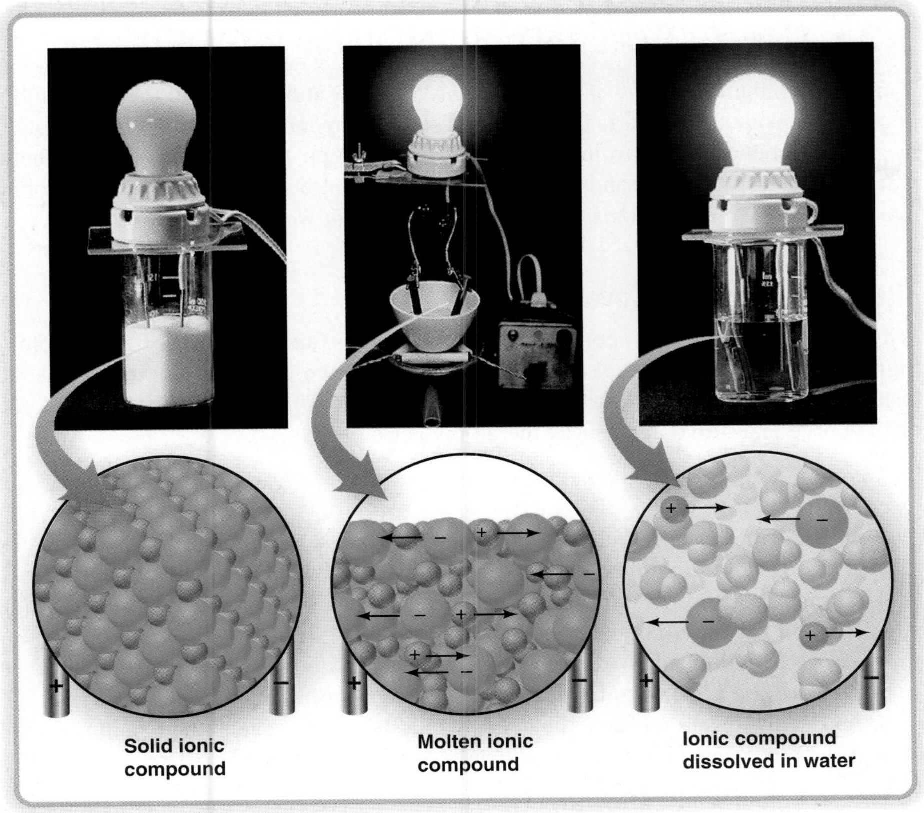

Figure 9.10 Electrical conductance and ion mobility.

2. *Electrical conductivity.* Ionic compounds typically *do not* conduct electricity in the solid state but *do* conduct when melted or dissolved. According to the model, the solid consists of fixed ions, but when it melts or dissolves, the ions can move and carry a current (Figure 9.10).

3. *Thermal conductivity.* Large amounts of energy would be needed to free the ions from their positions and separate them. Thus, we would expect ionic compounds to have high melting points and much higher boiling points (Table 9.1). In fact, the interionic attraction is so strong that the vapor consists of **ion pairs,** gaseous ionic molecules, rather than individual ions (Figure 9.11). In their normal state, as you know, ionic compounds are solid arrays of ions, and *no separate molecules exist.*

Table 9.1 Melting and Boiling Points of Some Ionic Compounds

Compound	mp (°C)	bp (°C)
CsBr	636	1300
NaI	661	1304
$MgCl_2$	714	1412
KBr	734	1435
$CaCl_2$	782	>1600
NaCl	801	1413
LiF	845	1676
KF	858	1505
MgO	2852	3600

Summary of Section 9.2

- In ionic bonding, a metal transfers electrons to a nonmetal, and the resulting ions attract each other to form a solid.
- Main-group elements often attain a filled outer level (either eight electrons or two) by forming ions with the electron configuration of the nearest noble gas.
- Ion formation by itself *absorbs* energy, but more than enough energy is *released* when the ions form a solid. The lattice energy, the energy required to separate the solid into gaseous ions, is the reason ionic solids exist.
- The lattice energy is determined by applying Hess's law in a Born-Haber cycle.
- Lattice energies increase with higher ionic charge and decrease with larger ionic radius.
- According to the ionic bonding model, the strong electrostatic attractions that keep ions in position explain why ionic solids are hard, conduct a current only when melted or dissolved, and have high melting and boiling points.
- Ion pairs form when an ionic compound vaporizes.

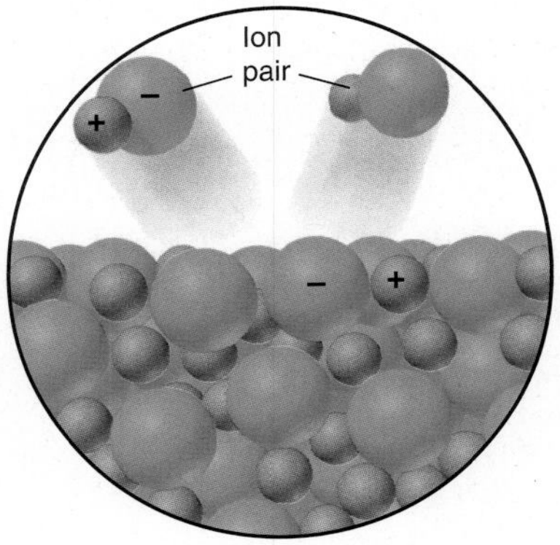

Figure 9.11 Ion pairs formed when an ionic compound vaporizes.

9.3 • THE COVALENT BONDING MODEL

Look through the *Handbook of Chemistry and Physics,* and you'll find that the number of covalent compounds dwarfs the number of ionic compounds. Molecules held together by covalent bonds range from tiny, diatomic hydrogen to biological and synthetic macromolecules with thousands of atoms. And covalent bonds occur in all polyatomic ions, too. Without doubt, *sharing electrons is the main way that atoms interact.*

The Formation of a Covalent Bond

Why does hydrogen gas consist of H_2 molecules and not separate H atoms? Figure 9.12 plots the potential energy of a system of two isolated H atoms versus the distance between their nuclei (see also Figure 2.14, p. 60). Let's start at the right end of the curve and move along it as the atoms get closer:

- *At point 1,* the atoms are far apart, and each acts as though the other were not present.
- *At point 2,* the distance between the atoms has decreased enough for each nucleus to start attracting the other atom's electron, which lowers the potential energy. As the atoms get closer, these attractions increase, but so do repulsions between the nuclei and between the electrons.
- *At point 3* (bottom of the energy "well"), the maximum attraction is achieved in the face of the increasing repulsion, and the system has its minimum energy.
- *At point 4,* if it were reached, the atoms would be too close, and the rise in potential energy from increasing repulsions would push them apart toward point 3 again.

Thus, a **covalent bond** arises from the balance between the nuclei attracting the electrons and electrons and nuclei repelling each other. (We'll return to Figure 9.12 shortly.)

Formation of a covalent bond always results in greater electron density ***between*** *the nuclei.* Figure 9.13 depicts this fact with a cross section of a space-filling model (A), an *electron density contour map* (B), and an *electron density relief map* (C).

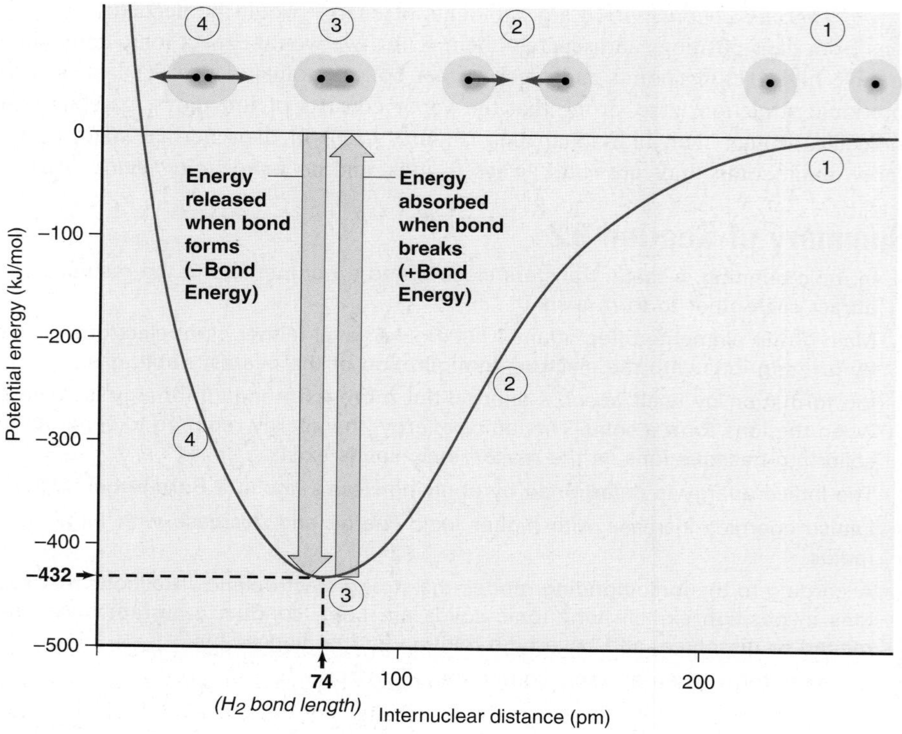

Figure 9.12 Covalent bond formation in H_2. The energy difference between points 1 and 3 is the H_2 *bond energy* (432 kJ/mol): it is released when the bond forms and absorbed to break the bond. The internuclear distance at point 3 is the H_2 *bond length* (74 pm).

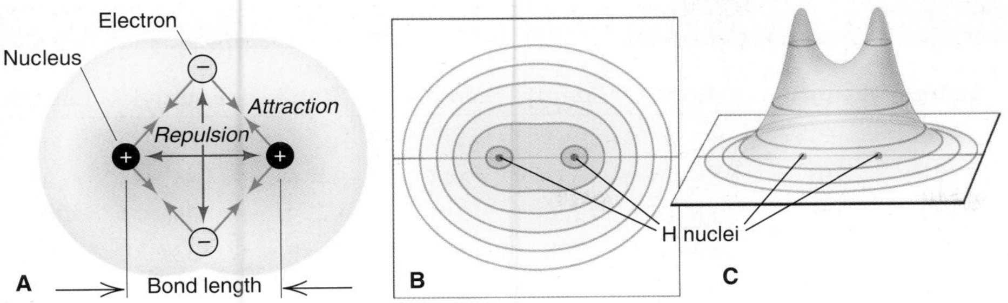

Figure 9.13 **Distribution of electron density in H_2.** **A,** At some distance (bond length), attractions balance repulsions. Electron density *(blue shading)* is high around and between the nuclei. **B,** Electron density doubles with each concentric curve. **C,** The highest regions of electron density are shown as peaks.

Bonding Pairs and Lone Pairs

To achieve a full outer (valence) level of electrons, *each atom in a covalent bond "counts" the shared electrons as belonging entirely to itself.* Thus, the two shared electrons in H_2 simultaneously fill the outer level of *both* H atoms, as clarified by the blue circles added below (which are *not* part of the Lewis structures). The **shared pair,** or **bonding pair,** is represented by a pair of dots or a line:

An outer-level electron pair that is *not* involved in bonding is called a **lone pair,** or **unshared pair.** The bonding pair in HF fills the outer level of the H atom *and,* together with three lone pairs, fills the outer level of the F atom as well:

In F_2 the bonding pair and three lone pairs fill the outer level of *each* F atom:

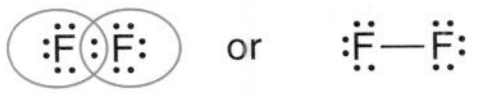

(This text generally shows bonding pairs as lines and lone pairs as dots.)

Properties of a Covalent Bond: Order, Energy, and Length

A covalent bond has three important properties that are closely related to one another and to the compound's reactivity—bond order, bond energy, and bond length.

1. *Bond order.* The **bond order** is the number of electron pairs being shared by a given pair of atoms:

- A **single bond,** as shown above in H_2, HF, or F_2, is the most common bond and consists of one bonding pair of electrons. Thus, a *single bond has a bond order of 1.*
- Many molecules (and ions) contain *multiple bonds,* in which more than one pair is shared between two atoms. Multiple bonds usually involve C, O, and/or N atoms. A **double bond** consists of two bonding electron pairs, four electrons shared between two atoms, so *the bond order is 2.* Ethylene (C_2H_4) contains a carbon-carbon double bond and four carbon-hydrogen single bonds:

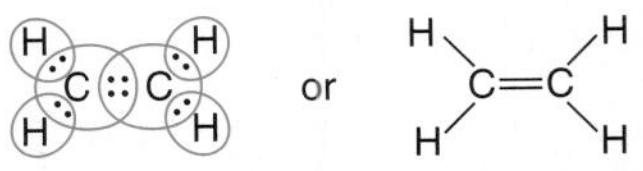

  Each carbon "counts" the four electrons in the double bond and the four in its two single bonds to hydrogens to attain an octet.
- A **triple bond** consists of three shared pairs: two atoms share six electrons, so *the bond order is 3.* The N_2 molecule has a triple bond, and each N atom also has a lone pair. Six shared and two unshared electrons give *each* N atom an octet:

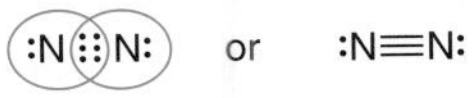

2. *Bond energy.* The strength of a covalent bond depends on the magnitude of the attraction between the nuclei and shared electrons. The **bond energy (BE)** (also called *bond enthalpy* or *bond strength*) is the energy needed to overcome this attraction and is defined as the standard enthalpy change for breaking the bond in 1 mol

Table 9.2 Average Bond Energies (kJ/mol) and Bond Lengths (pm)

Bond	Energy	Length	Bond	Energy	Length	Bond	Energy	Length	Bond	Energy	Length
Single Bonds											
H—H	432	74	N—H	391	101	Si—H	323	148	S—H	347	134
H—F	565	92	N—N	160	146	Si—Si	226	234	S—S	266	204
H—Cl	427	127	N—P	209	177	Si—O	368	161	S—F	327	158
H—Br	363	141	N—O	201	144	Si—S	226	210	S—Cl	271	201
H—I	295	161	N—F	272	139	Si—F	565	156	S—Br	218	225
			N—Cl	200	191	Si—Cl	381	204	S—I	~170	234
C—H	413	109	N—Br	243	214	Si—Br	310	216			
C—C	347	154	N—I	159	222	Si—I	234	240	F—F	159	143
C—Si	301	186							F—Cl	193	166
C—N	305	147	O—H	467	96	P—H	320	142	F—Br	212	178
C—O	358	143	O—P	351	160	P—Si	213	227	F—I	263	187
C—P	264	187	O—O	204	148	P—P	200	221	Cl—Cl	243	199
C—S	259	181	O—S	265	151	P—F	490	156	Cl—Br	215	214
C—F	453	133	O—F	190	142	P—Cl	331	204	Cl—I	208	243
C—Cl	339	177	O—Cl	203	164	P—Br	272	222	Br—Br	193	228
C—Br	276	194	O—Br	234	172	P—I	184	246	Br—I	175	248
C—I	216	213	O—I	234	194				I—I	151	266
Multiple Bonds											
C=C	614	134	N=N	418	122	C≡C	839	121	N≡N	945	110
C=N	615	127	N=O	607	120	C≡N	891	115	N≡O	631	106
C=O	745 (799 in CO_2)	123	O_2	498	121	C≡O	1070	113			

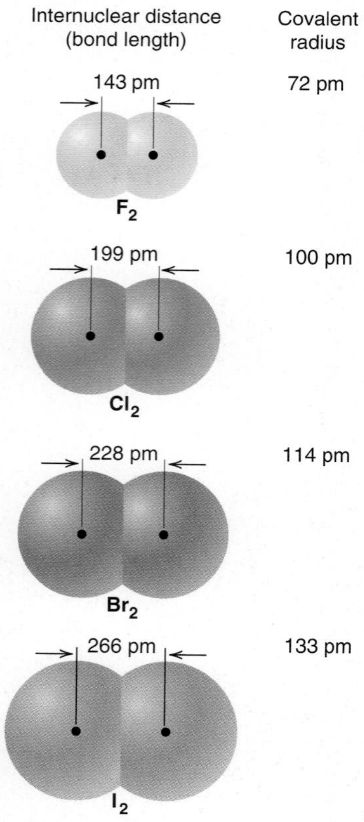

Figure 9.14 Bond length and covalent radius.

of gaseous molecules. Bond breakage is an *endothermic* process, so *bond energy is always positive:*

$$A{-}B(g) \longrightarrow A(g) + B(g) \qquad \Delta H^\circ_{\text{bond breaking}} = BE_{A-B}\ (\text{always} > 0)$$

The bond energy is the difference in energy between separated and bonded atoms (the potential energy difference between points 1 and 3, the energy "well" in Figure 9.12). *The same quantity of energy absorbed to break the bond is released when the bond forms.* Bond formation is an *exothermic* process, so *the sign of its enthalpy change is always negative:*

$$A(g) + B(g) \longrightarrow A{-}B(g) \qquad \Delta H^\circ_{\text{bond forming}} = -BE_{A-B}\ (\text{always} < 0)$$

Table 9.2 lists the energies of some common bonds. By definition,

- *Stronger bonds are lower in energy (have a deeper energy well).*
- *Weaker bonds are higher in energy (have a shallower energy well).*

The energy of a given bond varies slightly from molecule to molecule and even within the same molecule, so each value is an *average* bond energy.

3. *Bond length.* A covalent bond has a **bond length,** the distance between the nuclei of two bonded atoms. In Figure 9.12, bond length is the distance between the nuclei at the point of minimum energy (bottom of the well), and Table 9.2 shows the lengths of some covalent bonds. Like bond energies, these values are *average* bond lengths for a bond in different substances. Bond length is related to the sum of the radii of the bonded atoms. In fact, most atomic radii are calculated from measured bond lengths (see Figure 8.14C, p. 310). Bond lengths for a series of similar bonds, as in the halogens, increase with atomic size (Figure 9.14).

The order, energy, and length of a covalent bond are interrelated. Two nuclei are more strongly attracted to two shared pairs than to one, so double-bonded atoms are drawn closer together *and* are more difficult to pull apart than single-bonded atoms: *for a given pair of atoms, a higher bond order results in a shorter bond length and*

Table 9.3 The Relation of Bond Order, Bond Length, and Bond Energy

Bond	Bond Order	Average Bond Length (pm)	Average Bond Energy (kJ/mol)
C—O	1	143	358
C=O	2	123	745
C≡O	3	113	1070
C—C	1	154	347
C=C	2	134	614
C≡C	3	121	839
N—N	1	146	160
N=N	2	122	418
N≡N	3	110	945

a higher bond energy. Thus, as Table 9.3 shows, for a given pair of atoms, *a shorter bond is a stronger bond.*

In some cases, we can see a relation among atomic size, bond length, and bond energy by varying one of the atoms in a single bond while holding the other constant:

- *Variation within a group.* The trend in carbon-halogen single bond lengths, C—I > C—Br > C—Cl, parallels the trend in atomic size, I > Br > Cl, and is opposite to the trend in bond energy, C—Cl > C—Br > C—I.
- *Variation within a period.* Looking again at single bonds involving carbon, the trend in bond lengths, C—N > C—O > C—F, is opposite to the trend in bond energy, C—F > C—O > C—N.

Sample Problem 9.2 Comparing Bond Length and Bond Strength

Problem Without referring to Table 9.2, rank the bonds in each set in order of *decreasing* bond length and *decreasing* bond strength:
(a) S—F, S—Br, S—Cl **(b)** C=O, C—O, C≡O

Plan **(a)** S is singly bonded to three different halogen atoms, so the bond order is the same. Bond length increases and bond strength decreases as the halogen's atomic radius increases. **(b)** The same two atoms are bonded, but the bond orders differ. In this case, bond strength increases and bond length decreases as bond order increases.

Solution **(a)** Atomic size increases down a group, so F < Cl < Br.

Bond length: S—Br > S—Cl > S—F

Bond strength: S—F > S—Cl > S—Br

(b) By ranking the bond orders, C≡O > C=O > C—O, we obtain

Bond length: C—O > C=O > C≡O

Bond strength: C≡O > C=O > C—O

Check From Table 9.2, we see that the rankings are correct.

Comment Remember that for bonds involving pairs of different atoms, as in part (a), *the relationship between length and strength holds* only *for single bonds* and not in every case, so apply it carefully.

Follow-Up Problem 9.2 Rank the bonds in each set in order of *increasing* bond length and *increasing* bond strength: **(a)** Si—F, Si—C, Si—O; **(b)** N=N, N—N, N≡N.

How the Model Explains the Properties of Covalent Substances

The covalent bonding model proposes that electron sharing between pairs of atoms leads to *strong, localized bonds.* Most, but not all, covalent substances consist of individual molecules. These *molecular* covalent substances have very different *physical* properties than *network* covalent solids because different types of forces give rise to them.

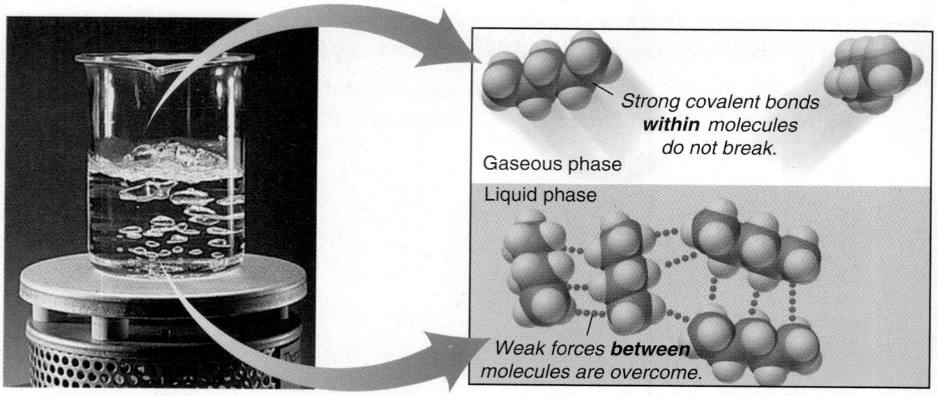

Figure 9.15 Strong forces within molecules and weak forces between them.

1. *Physical properties of molecular covalent substances.* At first glance, the model seems inconsistent with physical properties of covalent substances. Most are gases (such as methane and ammonia), liquids (such as benzene and water), or low-melting solids (such as sulfur and paraffin wax). If covalent bonds are so strong (~200 to 500 kJ/mol), why do covalent substances melt and boil at such low temperatures?

To answer this, we'll focus on two different forces: (1) *strong bonding forces* hold the atoms together within the molecule, and (2) *weak intermolecular forces* act between separate molecules in the sample. It is the weak forces *between* molecules that account for the physical properties of *molecular* covalent substances. For example, look what happens when pentane (C_5H_{12}) boils (Figure 9.15): weak forces *between* pentane molecules are overcome, not the strong C—C and C—H bonds *within* each pentane molecule.

2. *Physical properties of network covalent solids.* Some covalent substances do not consist of separate molecules. Rather, these *network covalent solids* are held together by covalent bonds *between atoms throughout the sample,* and their properties *do* reflect the strength of covalent bonds. Two examples are quartz and diamond (Figure 9.16). Quartz (SiO_2; *top*) has silicon-oxygen covalent bonds in three dimensions; no separate SiO_2 molecules exist. It is very hard and melts at 1550°C. Diamond (*bottom*) has covalent bonds connecting each carbon atom to four others. It is the hardest natural substance known and melts at around 3550°C. Thus, covalent bonds *are* strong, but most covalent substances consist of separate molecules with weak forces between them. (We discuss intermolecular forces in detail in Chapter 12.)

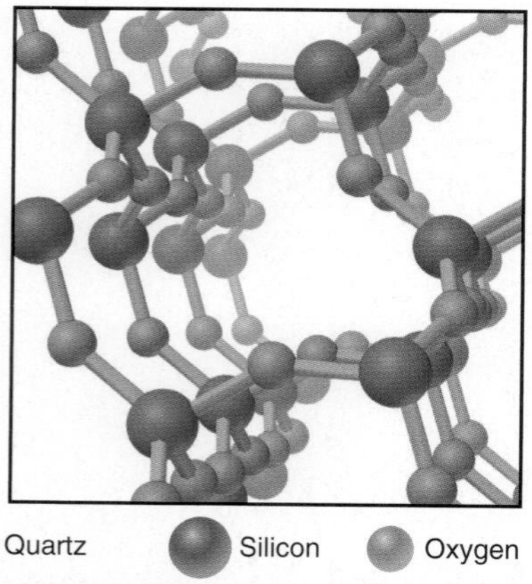

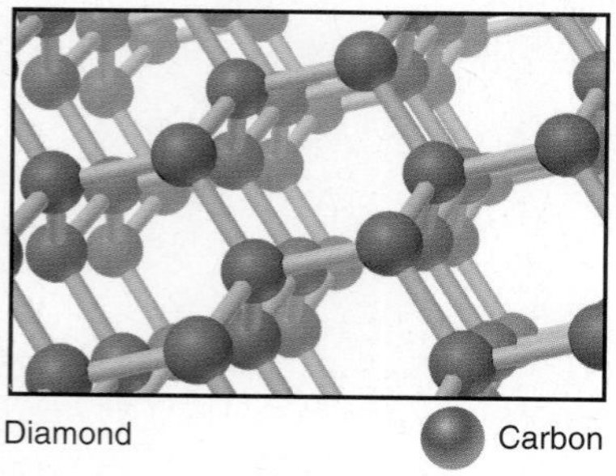

Figure 9.16 Covalent bonds of network covalent solids: quartz and diamond.

3. *Electrical conductivity.* An electric current is carried by either mobile electrons or mobile ions. Most covalent substances are poor electrical conductors, whether melted or dissolved, because their electrons are localized as either shared or unshared pairs, and no ions are present. The Tools of the Laboratory essay describes a tool used widely for studying the types of bonds in covalent substances.

Summary of Section 9.3

- A shared, localized pair of valence electrons holds the nuclei of two atoms together in a covalent bond, filling each atom's outer level.
- Bond order is the number of shared pairs between two atoms. Bond energy is the energy absorbed to separate the atoms; the same quantity of energy is released when the bond forms. Bond length is the distance between their nuclei.
- For a given pair of atoms, bond order is directly related to bond energy and inversely related to bond length.
- Molecular covalent substances are soft and low melting because of the weak forces *between* the molecules, not the strong bonding forces *within* them. Network covalent solids are hard and high melting because covalent bonds join all the atoms in the sample.
- Most covalent substances have low electrical conductivity because their electrons are localized and ions are absent.
- Atoms in a covalent bond vibrate, and the energies of these vibrations are studied with IR spectroscopy.

TOOLS OF THE LABORATORY | Infrared Spectroscopy

Infrared (IR) spectroscopy is an instrumental technique most often used to study covalently bonded molecules. The key components of an IR spectrometer are the same as those of other types of spectrometers (see Figure B7.3, p. 273). The source emits radiation of many wavelengths, but only those in the IR region are selected. The sample is typically a pure liquid or solid that absorbs varying amounts of certain IR wavelengths. An IR spectrum consists of peaks that indicate these various absorptions.

Molecular Vibrations and IR Absorption

An IR spectrum indicates the types of bonds in a molecule based on their vibrations. All molecules undergo movement through space, rotation around several axes, and vibrations of bonds. Consider a sample of ethane gas. The $H_3C—CH_3$ molecules zoom throughout the container, but let's disregard motion through space and focus on other motions. The whole molecule rotates and its two CH_3 groups rotate about the C—C bond. More important to IR spectroscopy, each pair of atoms is vibrating as though the bonds were springs. Figure B9.1 depicts the vibrations of diatomic and triatomic molecules; larger molecules vibrate in many more ways.

The energies of IR photons are in the range of these vibrational energies. *Each vibration has a frequency based on the type of motion, masses of the atoms, and strength of the bond.* The frequencies correspond to IR wavelengths between 2.5 and 25 μm. *The energy of these vibrations is quantized.* Just as an atom can absorb a photon whose energy equals the difference between *electron* energy levels, a molecule can absorb an IR photon whose energy equals the difference between *vibrational* energy levels.

IR Radiation and Global Warming

Carbon dioxide, O═C═O, is a linear molecule that bends and stretches symmetrically and asymmetrically when it absorbs IR radiation (Problem B9.2). Sunlight is absorbed by Earth's surface and re-emitted as heat, much of which is IR radiation. Atmospheric CO_2 absorbs this radiation and re-emits it, thus warming the atmosphere (see Chemical Connections, pp. 249–251).

Compound Identification

An IR spectrum can be used to identify a compound for three related reasons:

1. *Each kind of bond absorbs a specific range of wavelengths.* That is, a C—C bond absorbs a different range than does a C═C bond, a C—H bond, a C═O bond, and so forth.
2. *Different types of organic compounds have characteristic spectra.* The different groupings of atoms that define an alcohol, a carboxylic acid, an ether, and so forth (see Chapter 15) absorb differently.
3. *Each compound has a unique spectrum.* The IR spectrum acts like a fingerprint to identify the compound, because the quantity of each wavelength absorbed depends on the detailed molecular structure. For example, no other compound has the IR spectrum of acrylonitrile, a compound used to make plastics (Figure B9.2, *next page*).

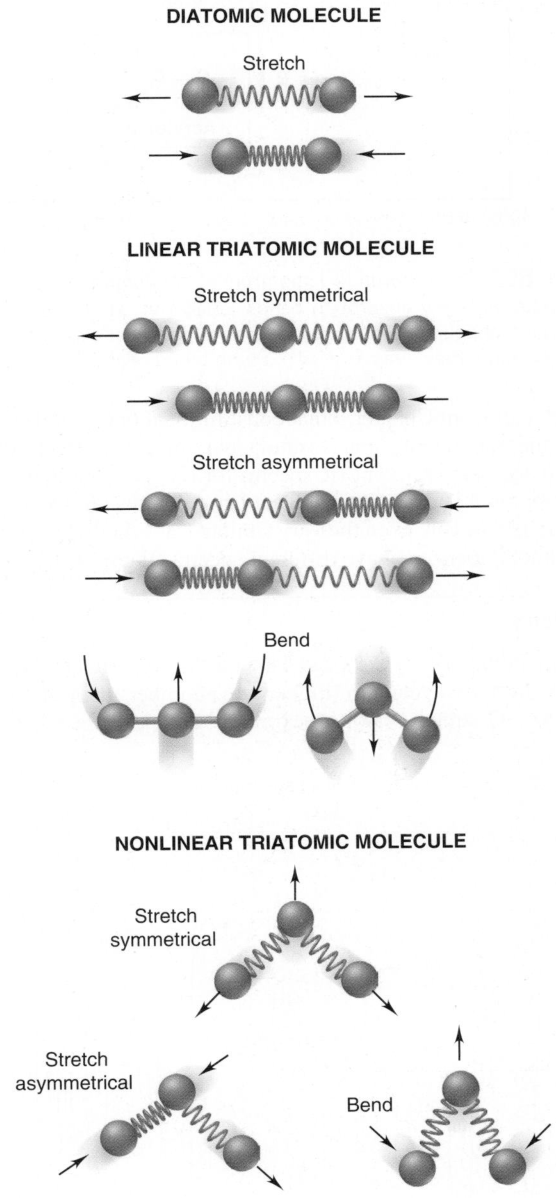

Figure B9.1 Vibrational motions in general diatomic and triatomic molecules.

(continued)

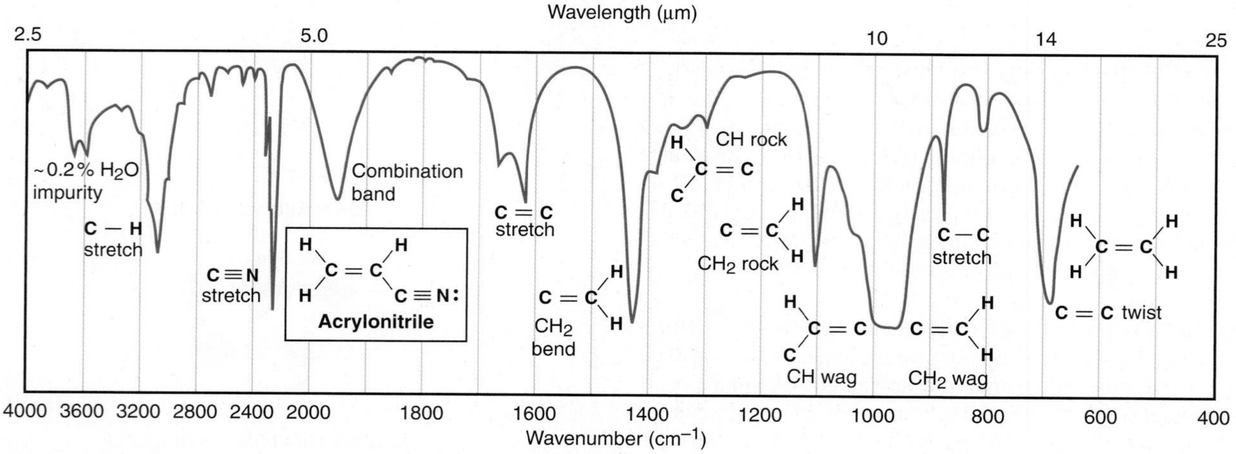

Figure B9.2 The infrared (IR) spectrum of acrylonitrile. In this typical IR spectrum, many absorption bands (peaks) of differing depths and sharpness appear. Most correspond to a particular type of vibration (stretch, bend, rock, wag, or twist). Some broad peaks (e.g., "combination band") represent several overlapping vibrations. The bottom axis is given as wavenumber, the inverse of wavelength, and has units of cm^{-1}. (The scale expands to the right of 2000 cm^{-1}.)

Recall from Chapter 3 that constitutional (structural) isomers have the same molecular formula but different structures. We should see very different IR spectra for the isomers diethyl ether and 2-butanol because their molecular structures are so dissimilar (Figure B9.3). But, even the very similar 1,3-dimethylbenzene and 1,4-dimethylbenzene have different spectra (Figure B9.4).

Problems

B9.1 In Figure B9.2, the peak labeled "C═C stretch" occurs at a shorter wavelength (higher wavenumber) than that labeled "C—C stretch," as it does in the IR spectrum of any substance with those bonds. Explain the relative positions of these peaks. In what relative position along the wavelength scale of Figure B9.2 would you expect to find a peak for a C≡C stretch? Explain.

B9.2 The vibrations of a CO_2 molecule are symmetrical stretch, bend, and asymmetrical stretch (Figure B9.1), with frequencies of $4.02\times10^{13}\ s^{-1}$, $2.00\times10^{13}\ s^{-1}$, and $7.05\times10^{13}\ s^{-1}$, respectively.
(a) What wavelengths correspond to these vibrations?
(b) Calculate the energy (in J) of each vibration. Which uses the least energy?

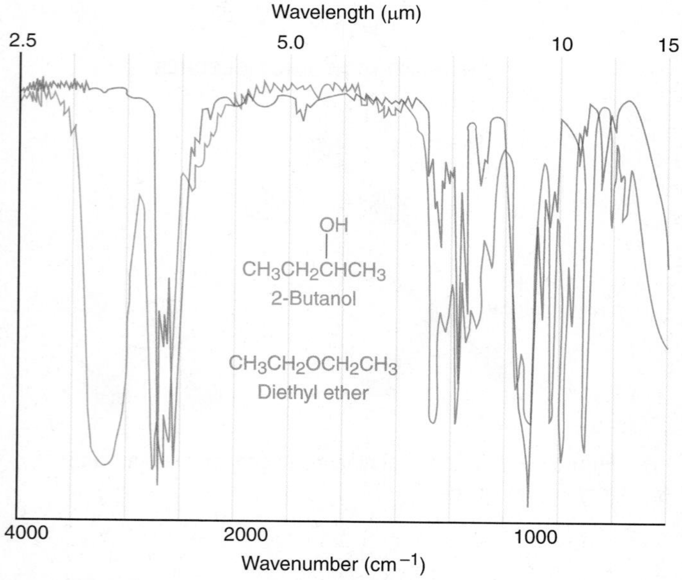

Figure B9.3 The infrared spectra of 2-butanol (*green*) and diethyl ether (*red*).

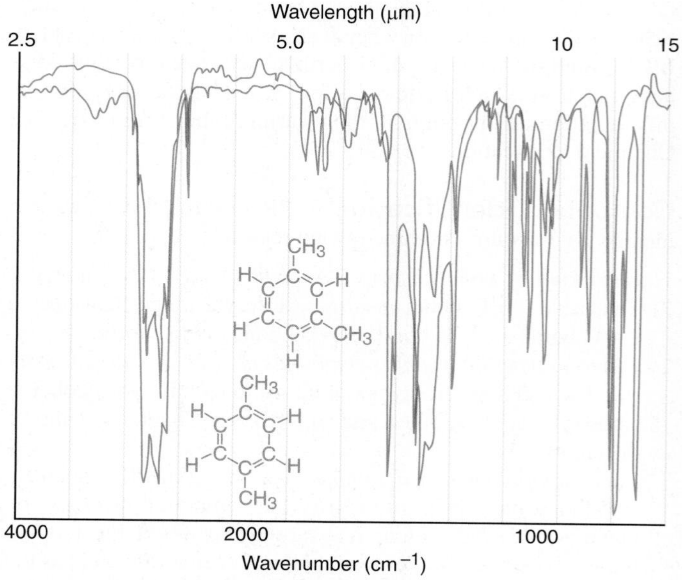

Figure B9.4 The infrared spectra of 1,3-dimethylbenzene (*green*) and 1,4-dimethylbenzene (*red*).

9.4 • BOND ENERGY AND CHEMICAL CHANGE

The relative strengths of the bonds in reactants and products determine whether heat is released or absorbed in a chemical reaction. In Chapter 20, you'll see that the change in bond energy is one of two factors determining whether the reaction occurs at all. In this section, we'll discuss the origin of the enthalpy of reaction (ΔH_{rxn}), use bond energies to calculate it, and look at the energy available from fuels and foods.

Changes in Bond Energy: Where Does ΔH°_{rxn} Come From?

In Chapter 6, we discussed the heat involved in a chemical change but never asked a central question: where does the enthalpy of reaction (ΔH°_{rxn}) come from? For example, when 1 mol of H_2 and 1 mol of F_2 react to form 2 mol of HF at 1 atm and 298 K,

$$H_2(g) + F_2(g) \longrightarrow 2HF(g) + 546 \text{ kJ}$$

where does the 546 kJ come from? We find the answer by looking closely at the energies of the molecules involved. A system's total internal energy is composed of its kinetic energy and potential energy. Let's see how these change during the formation of HF:

- *Kinetic energy.* The most important contributions to the kinetic energy are the molecules' movements in space, rotations, and vibrations. However, since kinetic energy is proportional to temperature, which is constant at 298 K, it doesn't change during the reaction.
- *Potential energy.* The most important contributions to the potential energy are phase changes and changes in the attraction between vibrating atoms, between nucleus and electrons (and between electrons) in each atom, between protons and neutrons in each nucleus, and between nuclei and the shared electron pair in each bond. Of these, there are no phase changes, vibrational forces vary only slightly as the bonded atoms change, and forces within the atoms and nuclei don't change at all. The only significant change in potential energy comes from changes in the attraction between the nuclei and the shared electron pair—the bond energy.

Thus, our answer to "where does ΔH°_{rxn} come from?" is that it doesn't really "come from" anywhere: *the heat released or absorbed during a chemical change is due to differences between reactant bond energies and product bond energies.*

Using Bond Energies to Calculate ΔH°_{rxn}

Hess's law allows us to think of any reaction as a two-step process, whether or not it actually occurs that way:

1. *A quantity of heat is absorbed ($\Delta H^\circ > 0$) to break the reactant bonds and form separate atoms.*
2. *A different quantity of heat is then released ($\Delta H^\circ < 0$) when the atoms form product bonds.*

The sum (symbolized by Σ) of these enthalpy changes is the enthalpy of reaction, ΔH°_{rxn}:

$$\Delta H^\circ_{rxn} = \Sigma\Delta H^\circ_{\text{reactant bonds broken}} + \Sigma\Delta H^\circ_{\text{product bonds formed}} \quad (9.2)$$

- In an exothermic reaction, the magnitude of $\Delta H^\circ_{\text{product bonds formed}}$ is *greater* than that of $\Delta H^\circ_{\text{reactant bonds broken}}$, so the sum, ΔH°_{rxn}, is *negative* (heat is released).
- In an endothermic reaction, the opposite situation is true, the magnitude of $\Delta H^\circ_{\text{product bonds formed}}$ is *smaller* than that of $\Delta H^\circ_{\text{reactant bonds broken}}$, so ΔH°_{rxn} is *positive* (heat is absorbed).

An equivalent form of Equation 9.2 uses bond energies:

$$\Delta H^\circ_{rxn} = \Sigma BE_{\text{reactant bonds broken}} - \Sigma BE_{\text{product bonds formed}}$$

(We need the minus sign because all bond energies are positive.)

Typically, only certain bonds break and form during a reaction, but with Hess' law, the following is a simpler method of calculating ΔH°_{rxn}:

1. Break **all** the reactant bonds to obtain individual atoms.
2. Use the atoms to form **all** the product bonds.
3. Add the bond energies, with appropriate signs, to obtain the enthalpy of reaction.

(This method assumes reactants and products do not change physical state; additional heat is involved when phase changes occur. We address this topic in Chapter 12.)

Let's use the method to calculate ΔH°_{rxn} for two reactions:

1. *Formation of HF.* When 1 mol of H—H bonds and 1 mol of F—F bonds absorb energy and break, the 2 mol of H atoms and 2 mol of F atoms form 2 mol of H—F bonds, which releases energy (Figure 9.17). We find the bond energy values in Table 9.2 (p. 340) and use a positive sign for bonds broken and a negative sign for bonds formed:

Bonds broken:

$$1 \times \text{H—H} = (1\ \text{mol})(432\ \text{kJ/mol}) = 432\ \text{kJ}$$
$$1 \times \text{F—F} = (1\ \text{mol})(159\ \text{kJ/mol}) = 159\ \text{kJ}$$
$$\Sigma\Delta H^\circ_{\text{reactant bonds broken}} = 591\ \text{kJ}$$

Bonds formed:

$$2 \times \text{H—F} = (2\ \text{mol})(-565\ \text{kJ/mol}) = \Sigma\Delta H^\circ_{\text{product bonds formed}} = -1130\ \text{kJ}$$

Applying Equation 9.2 gives

$$\Delta H^\circ_{rxn} = \Sigma\Delta H^\circ_{\text{reactant bonds broken}} + \Sigma\Delta H^\circ_{\text{product bonds formed}}$$
$$= 591\ \text{kJ} + (-1130\ \text{kJ}) = -539\ \text{kJ}$$

The small discrepancy between this bond energy value (-539 kJ) and the value from tabulated ΔH° values (-546 kJ) is due to variations in experimental method.

2. *Combustion of CH_4.* In this more complicated reaction, all the bonds in CH_4 and O_2 break, and the atoms form all the bonds in CO_2 and H_2O (Figure 9.18). Once again, we use Table 9.2 and appropriate signs for bonds broken and bonds formed:

Bonds broken:

$$4 \times \text{C—H} = (4\ \text{mol})(413\ \text{kJ/mol}) = 1652\ \text{kJ}$$
$$2 \times O_2 = (2\ \text{mol})(498\ \text{kJ/mol}) = 996\ \text{kJ}$$
$$\Sigma\Delta H^\circ_{\text{reactant bonds broken}} = 2648\ \text{kJ}$$

Bonds formed:

$$2 \times \text{C=O} = (2\ \text{mol})(-799\ \text{kJ/mol}) = -1598\ \text{kJ}$$
$$4 \times \text{O—H} = (4\ \text{mol})(-467\ \text{kJ/mol}) = -1868\ \text{kJ}$$
$$\Sigma\Delta H^\circ_{\text{product bonds formed}} = -3466\ \text{kJ}$$

Applying Equation 9.2 gives

$$\Delta H^\circ_{rxn} = \Sigma\Delta H^\circ_{\text{reactant bonds broken}} + \Sigma\Delta H^\circ_{\text{product bonds formed}}$$
$$= 2648\ \text{kJ} + (-3466\ \text{kJ}) = -818\ \text{kJ}$$

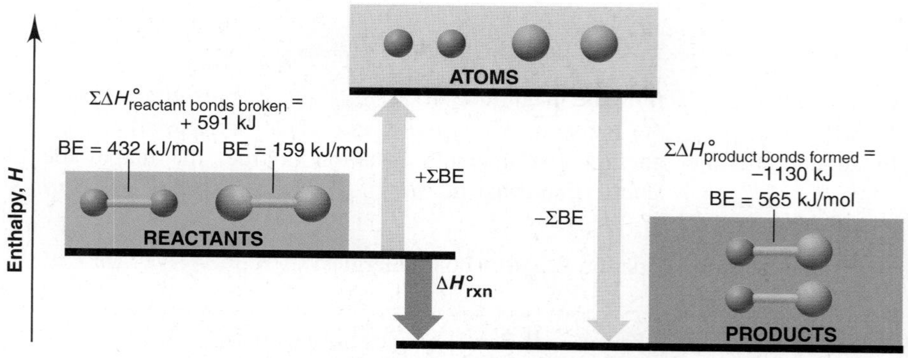

Figure 9.17 Using bond energies to calculate ΔH°_{rxn} for HF formation.

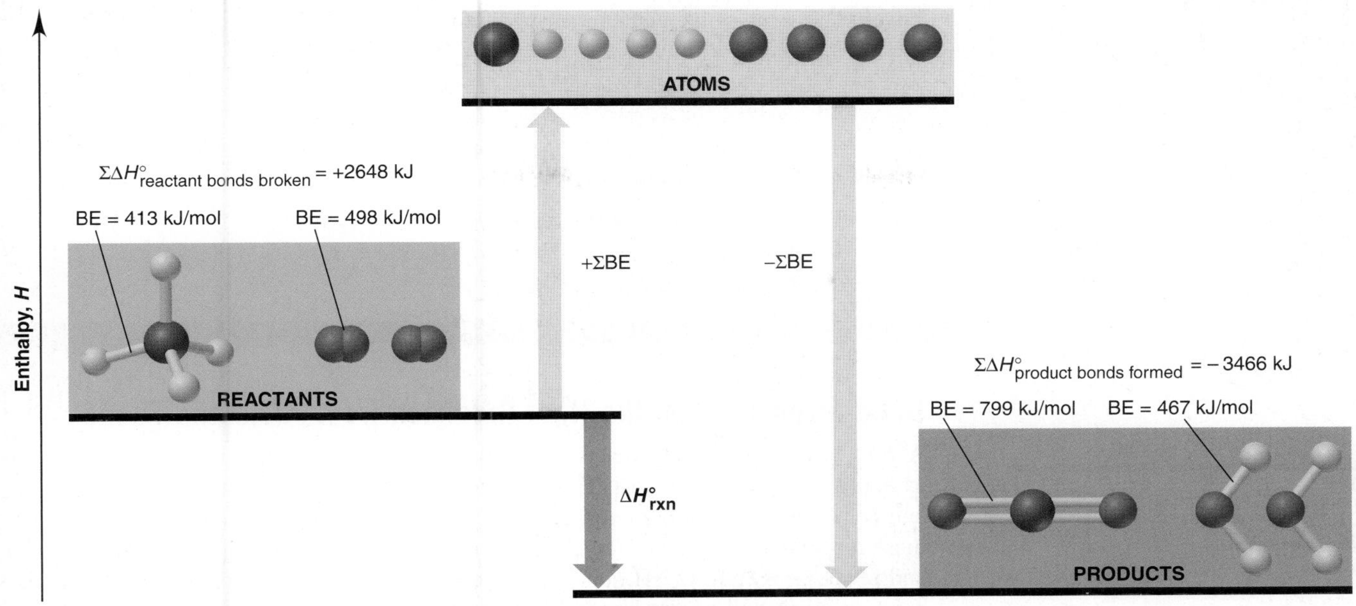

Figure 9.18 Using bond energies to calculate ΔH°_{rxn} for the combustion of methane.

In addition to variations in experimental method, there is a more basic reason for the discrepancy between the ΔH°_{rxn} obtained from bond energies (−818 kJ) and the value obtained by calorimetry (−802 kJ; Section 6.3). A bond energy is an *average* value for a given bond over many compounds. The value *in a particular substance* is usually close, but not equal, to the average. For example, the C—H bond energy of 413 kJ/mol is the average for C—H bonds in many molecules. In fact, 415 kJ is actually required to break 1 mol of C—H bonds in methane, or 1660 kJ for 4 mol of these bonds, which gives a ΔH°_{rxn} closer to the calorimetric value. Thus, it isn't surprising to find small discrepancies between ΔH°_{rxn} values obtained in different ways.

Sample Problem 9.3 Using Bond Energies to Calculate ΔH°_{rxn}

Problem Calculate ΔH°_{rxn} for the chlorination of methane to form chloroform:

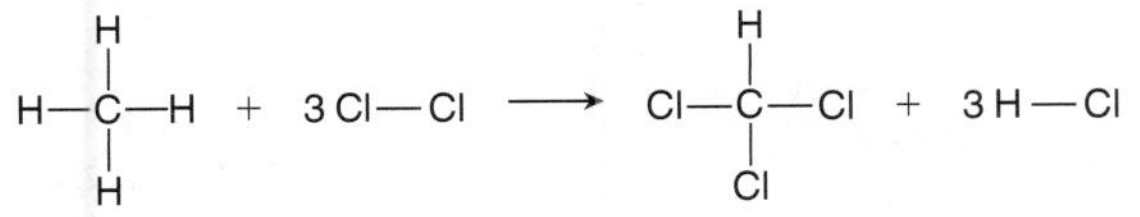

Plan *All* the reactant bonds break, and *all* the product bonds form. We find the bond energies in Table 9.2 and substitute the two sums, with correct signs, into Equation 9.2.

Solution Finding the standard enthalpy changes for bonds broken and for bonds formed:
For bonds broken, the bond energy values are

$$\begin{aligned} 4 \times \text{C—H} &= (4\ \text{mol})(413\ \text{kJ/mol}) = 1652\ \text{kJ} \\ 3 \times \text{Cl—Cl} &= (3\ \text{mol})(243\ \text{kJ/mol}) = 729\ \text{kJ} \\ \Sigma\Delta H^\circ_{\text{bonds broken}} &= 2381\ \text{kJ} \end{aligned}$$

For bonds formed, the values are

$$\begin{aligned} 3 \times \text{C—Cl} &= (3\ \text{mol})(-339\ \text{kJ/mol}) = -1017\ \text{kJ} \\ 1 \times \text{C—H} &= (1\ \text{mol})(-413\ \text{kJ/mol}) = -413\ \text{kJ} \\ 3 \times \text{H—Cl} &= (3\ \text{mol})(-427\ \text{kJ/mol}) = -1281\ \text{kJ} \\ \Sigma\Delta H^\circ_{\text{bonds formed}} &= -2711\ \text{kJ} \end{aligned}$$

Calculating ΔH°_{rxn}:

$$\begin{aligned} \Delta H^\circ_{\text{rxn}} &= \Sigma\Delta H^\circ_{\text{bonds broken}} + \Sigma\Delta H^\circ_{\text{bonds formed}} \\ &= 2381\ \text{kJ} + (-2711\ \text{kJ}) \\ &= -330\ \text{kJ} \end{aligned}$$

Check The signs of the enthalpy changes are correct: $\Sigma\Delta H^\circ_{\text{bonds broken}} > 0$, and $\Sigma\Delta H^\circ_{\text{bonds formed}} < 0$. More energy is released than absorbed, so $\Delta H^\circ_{\text{rxn}}$ is negative:

$$\sim 2400\text{ kJ} + [\sim(-2700\text{ kJ})] = -300\text{ kJ}$$

Follow-Up Problem 9.3 One of the most important industrial reactions is the formation of ammonia from its elements:

$$\text{N}{\equiv}\text{N} + 3\,\text{H—H} \longrightarrow 2\,\text{H—}\underset{\text{H}}{\underset{|}{\text{N}}}\text{—H}$$

Use bond energies to calculate $\Delta H^\circ_{\text{rxn}}$.

Bond Strengths and the Heat Released from Fuels and Foods

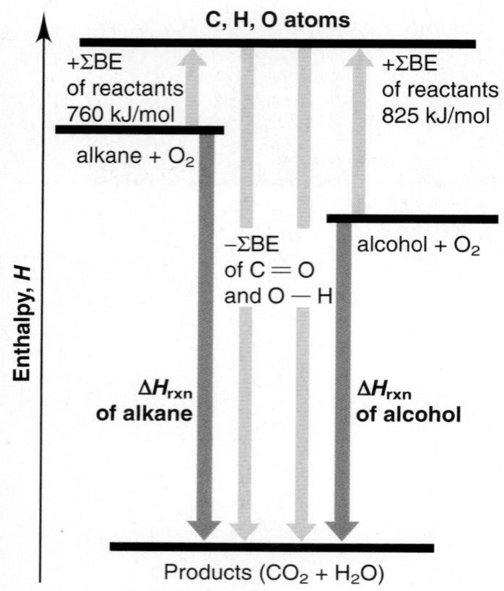

Figure 9.19 Relative bond strength and energy from fuels.

A *fuel* is a material that reacts with atmospheric oxygen to release energy *and* is available at a reasonable cost. The most common fuels for machines are hydrocarbons and coal, and the most common ones for organisms are fats and carbohydrates. All of these fuels are composed of large organic molecules with many C—C and C—H bonds and fewer C—O and O—H bonds. According to our two-step approach, when the fuel reacts with O_2, all of the bonds break, and the C, H, and O atoms form C═O and O—H bonds in the products (CO_2 and H_2O). Because their combustion is exothermic, the total of the bond energies in the products is *greater* than the total in the reactants. *Weaker bonds (less stable, more reactive) are easier to break than stronger bonds (more stable, less reactive) because they are already higher in energy.* Therefore, the bonds in CO_2 and H_2O are stronger (lower energy, more stable) than those in gasoline (or cooking oil) and O_2 (weaker, higher energy, less stable).

Fuels with more weak bonds yield more energy than fuels with fewer weak bonds. When a hydrocarbon burns, C—C and C—H bonds break; when an alcohol burns, C—O and O—H bonds break as well. Table 9.2 (p. 340) shows that the sum for C—C and C—H bonds (760 kJ/mol) is less than the sum for C—O and O—H bonds (825 kJ/mol). Therefore, it takes more energy to break the bonds of a fuel with a lot of C—O and O—H bonds. Thus, in general, *a fuel with fewer bonds to O releases more energy* (Figure 9.19).

Both fats and carbohydrates serve as high-energy foods and consist of chains or rings of C atoms attached to H atoms, with some C—O, C═O, and O—H bonds *(shown in red below):*

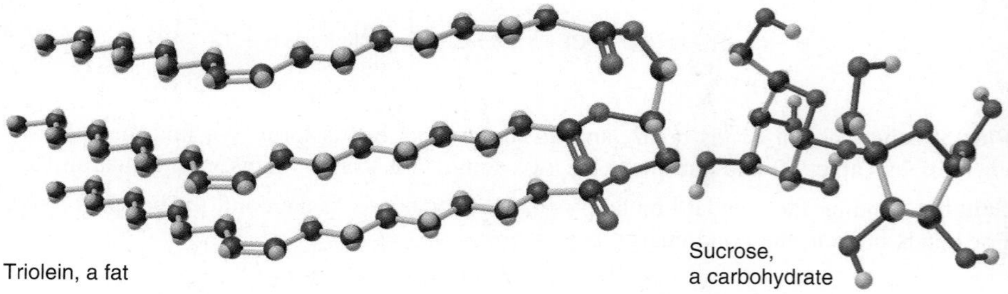

Triolein, a fat

Sucrose, a carbohydrate

Carbohydrates have fewer chains of C atoms and bonds to H and more bonds to O. Fats "contain more Calories" per gram than carbohydrates because fats have fewer bonds to O (Table 9.4).

Table 9.4 Enthalpies of Reaction for Combustion of Some Foods

Substance	ΔH_{rxn} (kJ/g)
Fats	
Vegetable oil	−37.0
Margarine	−30.1
Butter	−30.0
Carbohydrates	
Table sugar (sucrose)	−16.2
Brown rice	−14.9
Maple syrup	−10.4

Summary of Section 9.4

- The only component of internal energy that changes significantly during a reaction is the bond energies of reactants and products, and this change appears as the enthalpy of reaction, $\Delta H^\circ_{\text{rxn}}$.
- A reaction involves breaking reactant bonds and forming product bonds. Applying Hess's law, we use tabulated bond energies to calculate $\Delta H^\circ_{\text{rxn}}$.
- Bonds in fuels are weaker (less stable, higher energy) than bonds in the combustion products. Fuels with more weak bonds release more energy than fuels with fewer.

9.5 • BETWEEN THE EXTREMES: ELECTRONEGATIVITY AND BOND POLARITY

Scientific models are idealized descriptions of reality. The ionic and covalent bonding models portray compounds as formed by *either* complete electron transfer *or* complete electron sharing. But, in real substances, most atoms are joined by *polar covalent bonds*—partly ionic and partly covalent (Figure 9.20). In this section, we explore the "in-between" nature of these bonds and its importance in the properties of substances.

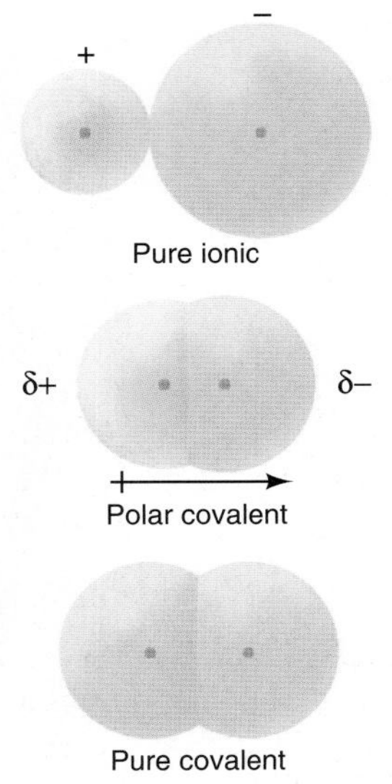

Figure 9.20 Bonding between the models. Pure ionic bonding (*top*) and pure covalent bonding (*bottom*) are far less common than polar covalent bonding (*middle*).

Electronegativity

Electronegativity (EN) is the relative ability of a bonded atom to attract shared electrons.* We might expect the H—F bond energy to be the average of an H—H bond (432 kJ/mol) and an F—F bond (159 kJ/mol), or 296 kJ/mol. But, the actual HF bond energy is 565 kJ/mol, or 269 kJ/mol *higher!* To explain this difference, the American chemist Linus Pauling reasoned this way: If F attracted the shared electron pair more strongly than H, that is, if F were more *electronegative* than H, the electrons would spend more time closer to F, and this unequal sharing would make the F end of the bond partially negative and the H end partially positive. The electrostatic attraction between these partial charged bond "poles" would *increase* the energy required to break the bond. From studies with many other compounds, Pauling derived a scale of *relative EN values* based on fluorine having the highest EN value, 4.0 (Figure 9.21).

*Electronegativity refers to a *bonded* atom attracting a shared pair; electron affinity refers to a gaseous atom gaining an electron to form an anion. Elements with a high EN also have a highly negative EA.

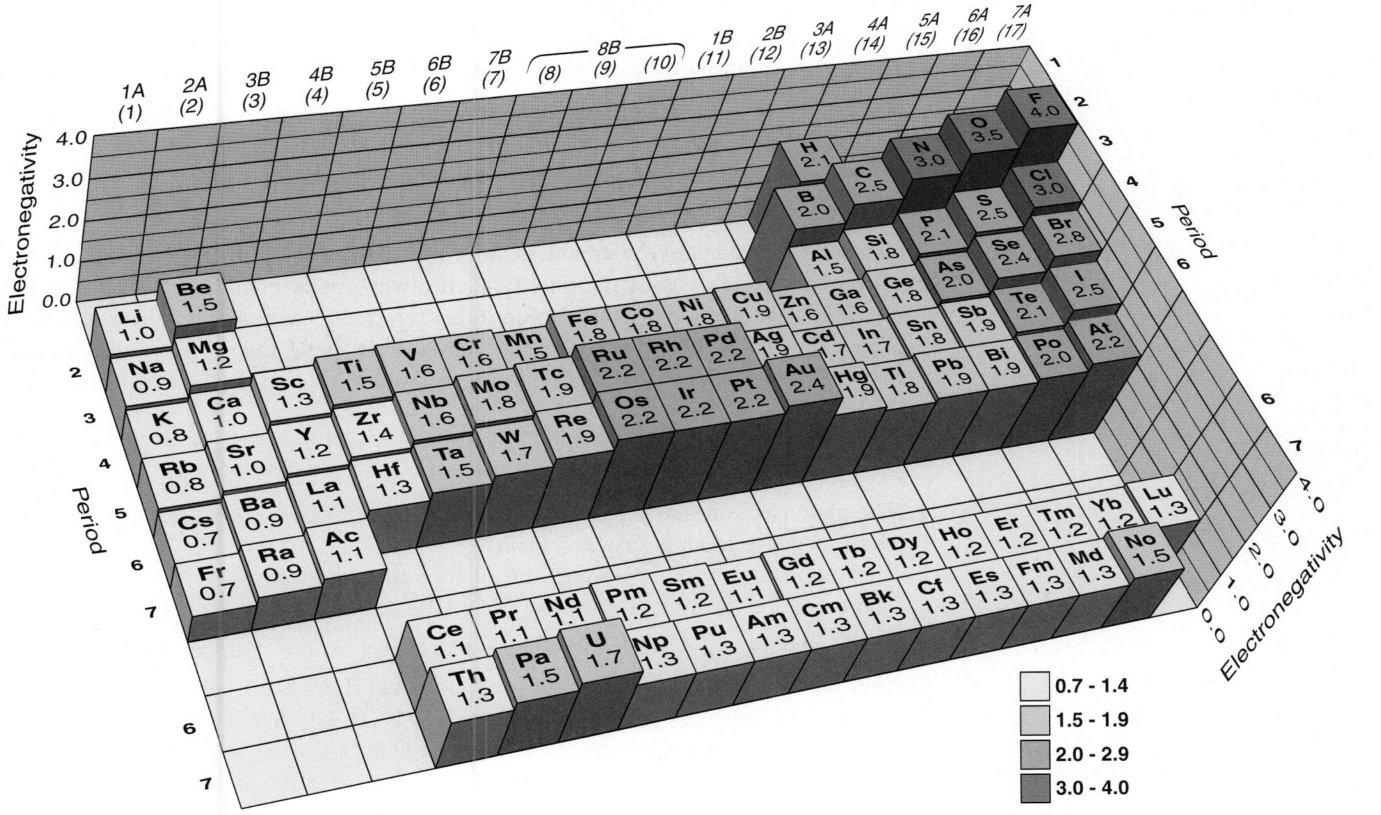

Figure 9.21 The Pauling electronegativity (EN) scale. The height of each post is proportional to the EN, which is shown on top. The key has several EN cutoffs. In the main groups, EN *increases* across and *decreases* down. The transition and inner transition elements show little change in EN. Here hydrogen is placed near elements with similar EN values.

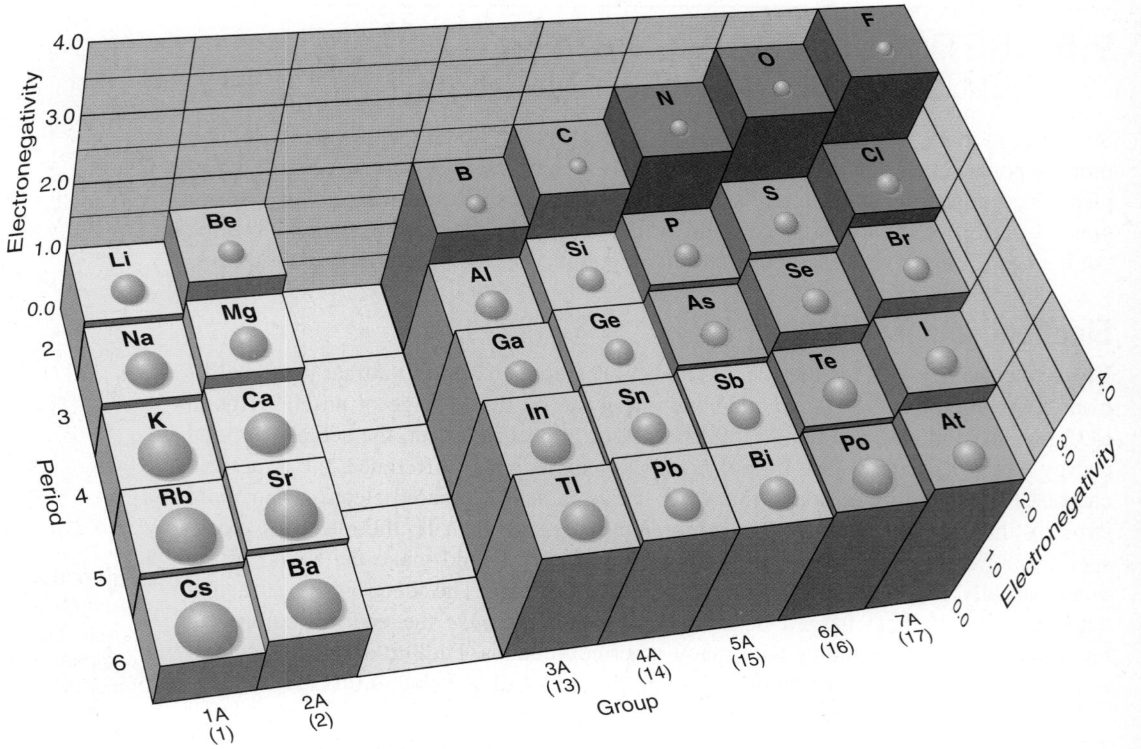

Figure 9.22 Electronegativity and atomic size.

Trends in Electronegativity In general, *electronegativity is inversely related to atomic size* because the nucleus of a smaller atom is closer to the shared pair than the nucleus of a larger atom, so it attracts the electrons more strongly (Figure 9.22):

- *Down a main group,* electronegativity (height of post) decreases as size (hemisphere on top of post) increases.
- *Across a period of main-group elements,* electronegativity increases.
- Nonmetals are *more* electronegative than metals.

The most electronegative element is fluorine, with oxygen a close second. Thus, except when it bonds with fluorine, oxygen always pulls bonding electrons toward itself. The least electronegative element (also referred to as the most *electropositive*) is francium, in the lower left corner of the periodic table, but it is radioactive and extremely rare, so for all practical purposes, cesium is the most electropositive.*

Electronegativity and Oxidation Number An important use of electronegativity is in determining an atom's oxidation number (O.N.; see Section 4.5):

1. The more electronegative atom in a bond is assigned *all* the *shared* electrons; the less electronegative atom is assigned *none.*
2. Each atom in a bond is assigned *all* of its *unshared* electrons.
3. The oxidation number is given by

$$\text{O.N.} = \text{no. of valence e}^- - (\text{no. of shared e}^- + \text{no. of unshared e}^-)$$

In HCl, for example, Cl is more electronegative than H. Cl has 7 valence electrons and is assigned 8 (2 shared + 6 unshared), so its O.N. is $7 - 8 = -1$. The H atom has 1 valence electron and is assigned none, so its O.N. is $1 - 0 = +1$.

*In 1934, the American physicist Robert S. Mulliken developed electronegativity values based on atomic properties: EN = (IE − EA)/2. By this approach as well, fluorine, with a high ionization energy (IE) and a large negative electron affinity (EA), has a high EN; and cesium, with a low IE and a small EA, has a low EN.

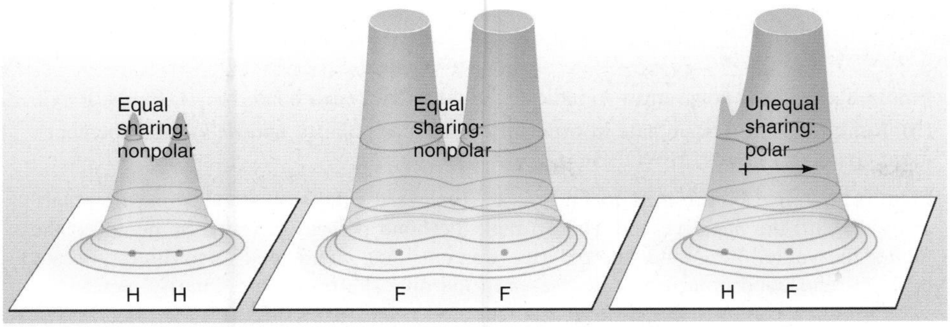

Figure 9.23 Electron density distributions in H_2, F_2, and HF. In HF, the electron density shifts from H to F. (The electron density peak for F has been cut off to limit the figure height.)

Bond Polarity and Partial Ionic Character

Whenever atoms of different electronegativities form a bond, such as H (2.1) and F (4.0) in HF, the bonding pair is shared *unequally*. This unequal distribution of electron density results in a **polar covalent bond.** It is depicted by a polar arrow (+⟶) pointing toward the partially negative pole or by δ+ and δ− symbols (see Figure 4.1):

H—F: (with polar arrow) or H—F: (with δ+ over H and δ− over F)

In the H—H and F—F bonds, where the atoms are identical, the bonding pair is shared *equally,* and a **nonpolar covalent bond** results. In Figure 9.23, relief maps show the distribution of electron density in H_2, F_2, and HF.

The Importance of Electronegativity Difference (ΔEN) The **electronegativity difference (ΔEN),** the difference between the EN values of the bonded atoms, is directly related to a bond's polarity. It ranges from 0.0 in a diatomic element, such as H_2, O_2, or Cl_2, all the way up to 3.3, the difference between the most electronegative atom, F (4.0), and the most electropositive, Cs (0.7), in the ionic compound CsF.

Another parameter closely related to ΔEN is the **partial ionic character** of a bond: *a greater ΔEN results in larger partial charges and higher partial ionic character.* Consider three Cl-containing gaseous molecules: ΔEN for LiCl(*g*) is 3.0 − 1.0 = 2.0; for HCl(*g*), it is 3.0 − 2.1 = 0.9; and for Cl_2(*g*), it is 3.0 − 3.0 = 0.0. Thus, the bond in LiCl has more ionic character than the one in HCl, which has more than the one in Cl_2.

Here are two approaches that quantify ionic character. Both use arbitrary cutoffs, which is not really consistent with the actual gradation in bonding:

1. *ΔEN range.* This approach divides bonds into mostly ionic, polar covalent, mostly covalent, and nonpolar covalent based on a range of ΔEN values (Figure 9.24).

2. *Percent ionic character.* This approach is based on the behavior of a diatomic molecule in an electric field. A plot of *percent ionic character* vs. ΔEN for several gaseous molecules shows that, as expected, *percent ionic character generally increases with ΔEN* (Figure 9.25A). A value of 50% divides ionic from covalent bonds. Note that a substance like Cl_2(*g*) has 0% ionic character, but none has 100% ionic character: *electron sharing occurs to some extent in every bond,* even in an alkali halide (Figure 9.25B).

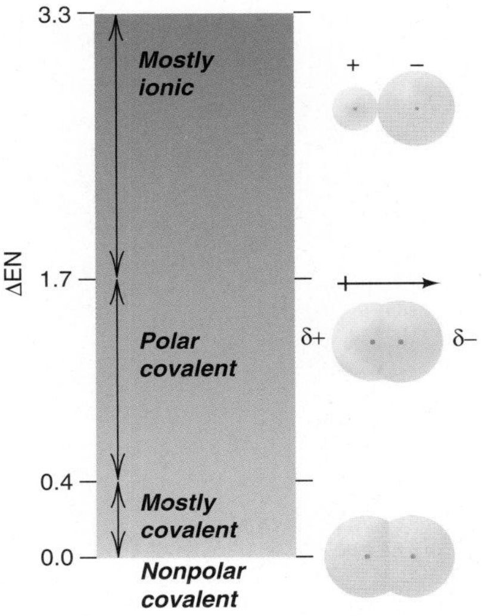

Figure 9.24 ΔEN ranges for classifying the partial ionic character of bonds.

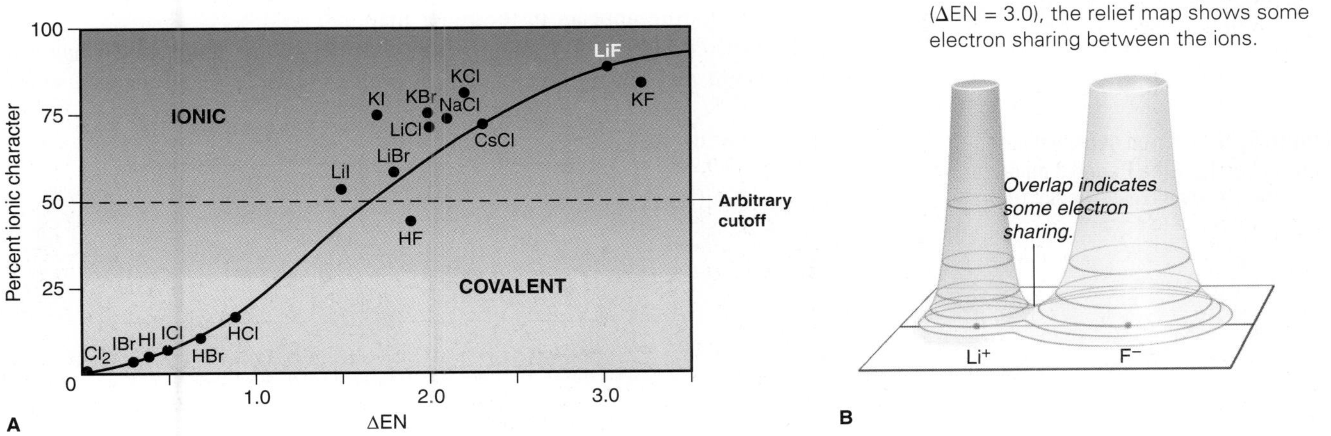

Figure 9.25 Percent ionic character as a function of ΔEN. **A,** ΔEN correlates with ionic character. **B,** Even in highly ionic LiF (ΔEN = 3.0), the relief map shows some electron sharing between the ions.

Sample Problem 9.4 Determining Bond Polarity from EN Values

Problem **(a)** Use a polar arrow to indicate the polarity of each bond: N—H, F—N, I—Cl. **(b)** Rank the following bonds in order of *increasing* polarity and *decreasing* percent ionic character: H—N, H—O, H—C.

Plan **(a)** We use Figure 9.21 to find the EN values for the atoms and point the polar arrow toward the negative end. **(b)** To rank the bond polarity, we determine ΔEN: the higher the value, the greater the polarity. Percent ionic character is also directly related to ΔEN (and bond polarity); it decreases in the opposite order that polarity increases.

Solution **(a)** The EN of N = 3.0 and the EN of H = 2.1, so $\overset{\longleftarrow\!+}{\text{N—H}}$

The EN of F = 4.0 and the EN of N = 3.0, so $\overset{\longleftarrow\!+}{\text{F—N}}$

The EN of I = 2.5 and the EN of Cl = 3.0, so $\overset{+\!\longrightarrow}{\text{I—Cl}}$

(b) The ΔEN values are 0.9 for H—N, 1.4 for H—O, and 0.4 for H—C.
The order of *increasing* bond polarity is H—C < H—N < H—O.
The order of *decreasing* percent ionic character is H—O > H—N > H—C.

Check In (b), we can check the order of bond polarity using periodic trends. Each bond involves H and a Period 2 atom. Since size decreases and EN increases across a period, the polarity is greatest for the bond to O (farthest to the right in Period 2).

Comment In Chapter 10, you'll see that the bond polarity contributes to the overall polarity of the molecule, which is a major factor determining behavior.

Follow-Up Problem 9.4 Arrange each set of bonds in order of increasing polarity, and indicate bond polarity with δ+ and δ− symbols:
(a) Cl—F, Br—Cl, Cl—Cl **(b)** Si—Cl, P—Cl, S—Cl, Si—Si

The Gradation in Bonding Across a Period

A metal and a nonmetal—elements from the left and right sides of the periodic table—have a relatively large ΔEN and typically form an ionic compound. Two nonmetals—both from the right side of the table—have a small ΔEN and form a covalent compound. When we combine chlorine with each of the other Period 3 elements, starting with sodium, we observe a steady decrease in ΔEN and a gradation in bond type from ionic through polar covalent to nonpolar covalent.

Figure 9.26 shows an electron density relief map of a bond in each of the common Period 3 chlorides; note the steady increase in the height of electron density *between* the peaks—the bonding region—which indicates an *increase in electron sharing.* Figure 9.27 shows samples of common Period 3 chlorides—NaCl, $MgCl_2$, $AlCl_3$, $SiCl_4$, PCl_3, and SCl_2, as well as Cl_2—along with the change in ΔEN and two physical properties:

- NaCl. Sodium chloride is a white (colorless) crystalline solid with a ΔEN of 2.1, a high melting point, and high electrical conductivity when molten—ionic by any criterion. However, just as for LiF (Figure 9.25B), a small but significant region of electron sharing appears in the relief map.
- $MgCl_2$. With a ΔEN of 1.8, magnesium chloride is still ionic, but it has a lower melting point and lower conductivity, as well as slightly more electron sharing.

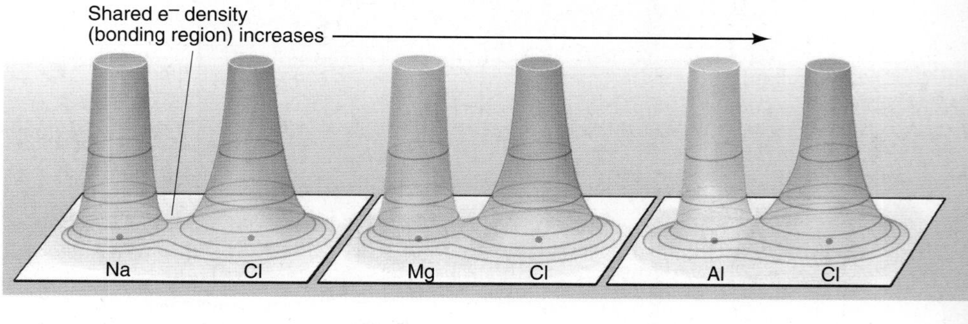

Figure 9.26 Electron density distributions in bonds of the Period 3 chlorides. Note the steady increase in electron sharing from left to right.

Figure 9.27 Properties of the Period 3 chlorides. As ΔEN decreases, melting point and electrical conductivity decrease because the bond type changes from ionic to polar covalent to nonpolar covalent.

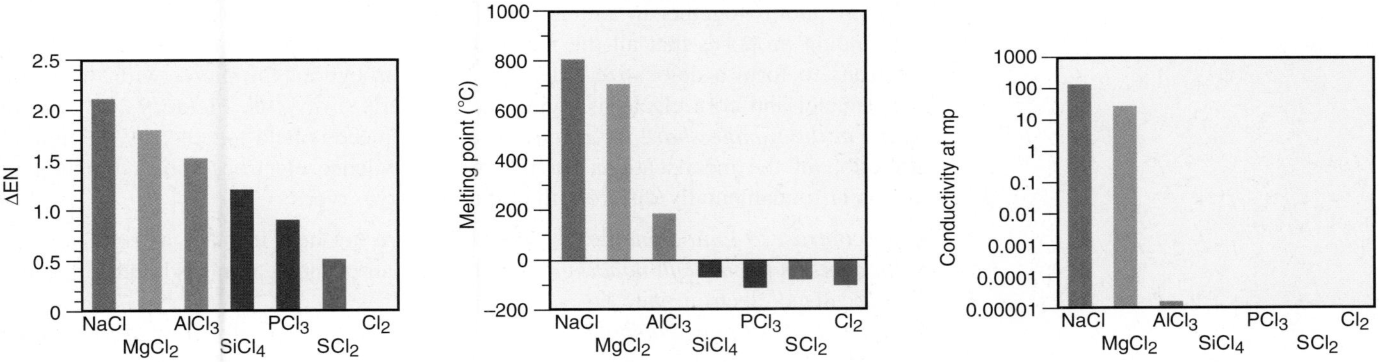

- $AlCl_3$. Rather than being a three-dimensional lattice of Al^{3+} and Cl^- ions, aluminum chloride, with a ΔEN value of 1.5, consists of layers of highly polar Al—Cl bonds. Weak forces between layers result in a much lower melting point, and the low conductivity implies few free ions. And, electron density between the nuclei is higher.
- $SiCl_4$, PCl_3, SCl_2, and Cl_2. The trend toward more covalent bonding continues through the remaining substances. Each occurs as separate molecules, which have no conductivity and such weak forces *between* them that melting points are below 0°C. In Cl_2, the bond is nonpolar (ΔEN = 0.0). The relief maps show the increasing height of the electron density in the bonding region.

Thus, *as ΔEN decreases, the bond becomes more covalent,* and the character of the substance changes from ionic solid to covalent gas.

Summary of Section 9.5

- Electronegativity is the ability of a bonded atom to attract shared electrons, which generates opposite partial charges at the ends of the bond and contributes to the bond energy.
- Electronegativity increases across a period and decreases down a group, the reverse of the trends in atomic size.
- The larger the ΔEN for two bonded atoms, the more polar the bond is and the greater its ionic character.
- For Period 3 chlorides, there is a gradation in bond type from ionic to polar covalent to nonpolar covalent.

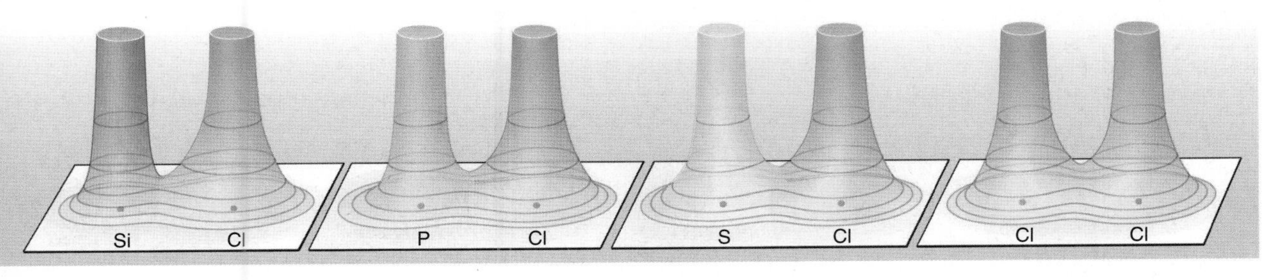

9.6 • AN INTRODUCTION TO METALLIC BONDING

In this section, you'll see how a simple, qualitative model for metallic bonding accounts for the properties of metals; a more detailed model is presented in Chapter 12.

The Electron-Sea Model

Metals can transfer electrons to nonmetals and form ionic solids, such as NaCl. And experiments with metals in the gas phase show that two metal atoms can even share their valence electrons to form gaseous, diatomic molecules, such as Na_2. But what holds the atoms together in a chunk of Na metal? The **electron-sea model** of metallic bonding proposes that all the metal atoms in the sample contribute their valence electrons to form a delocalized electron "sea" throughout the piece, with the metal ions (nuclei and core electrons) lying in an orderly array (see Figure 9.2C). *All the atoms in the sample share the electrons,* and the piece is held together by the mutual attraction of the metal cations for the mobile, valence electrons. Thus, bonding in metals is fundamentally different than the other two types:

- *In contrast to ionic bonding,* the metal ions are not held in place as rigidly.
- *In contrast to covalent bonding,* no particular pair of metal atoms is bonded through a localized electron pair.
- *Instead of forming compounds,* two or more metals typically form **alloys,** solid mixtures of variable composition. Alloys appear in car and airplane bodies, bridges, coins, jewelry, dental fillings, and many other familiar objects.

How the Model Explains the Properties of Metals

The physical properties of metals vary over a wide range. Two features of the electron-sea model that account for these properties are (1) the *regularity,* but not rigidity, of the metal-ion array and (2) the *number* and *mobility* of the valence electrons.

1. *Melting and boiling points.* Nearly all metals are solids with moderate to high melting points and much higher boiling points (Table 9.5). These properties are related to the energy of the metallic bonding. Melting points are only moderately high because the cations can move without breaking the attraction to the surrounding electrons. Boiling points are very high because each cation and its valence electron(s) must break away from the others. Gallium provides a striking example: it can melt in your hand (mp 29.8°C) but doesn't boil until over 2400°C.

Periodic trends are consistent with the strength of the bonding:

- *Down a group,* melting points decrease because the larger metal ions have a weaker attraction to the electron sea.
- *Across a period,* melting points increase. Alkaline earth metals [Group 2A(2)] have higher melting points than alkali metals [Group 1A(1)] because their 2+ cations have stronger attractions to twice as many valence electrons (Figure 9.28).

Table 9.5 Melting and Boiling Points of Some Metals

Element	mp (°C)	bp (°C)
Lithium (Li)	180	1347
Tin (Sn)	232	2623
Aluminum (Al)	660	2467
Barium (Ba)	727	1850
Silver (Ag)	961	2155
Copper (Cu)	1083	2570
Uranium (U)	1130	3930

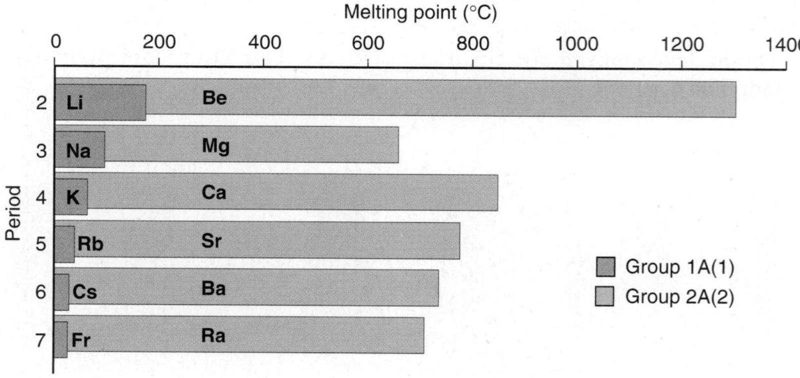

Figure 9.28 Melting points of Group 1A(1) and Group 2A(2) metals.

2. *Mechanical properties*. When a piece of metal is deformed by a hammer, the metal ions do not repel each other, but rather slide past each other through the electron sea and end up in new positions; thus metals dent and bend, as shown in Figure 9.29. Compare this behavior with the interionic repulsions that occur when an ionic solid is struck (see Figure 9.9, p. 336).

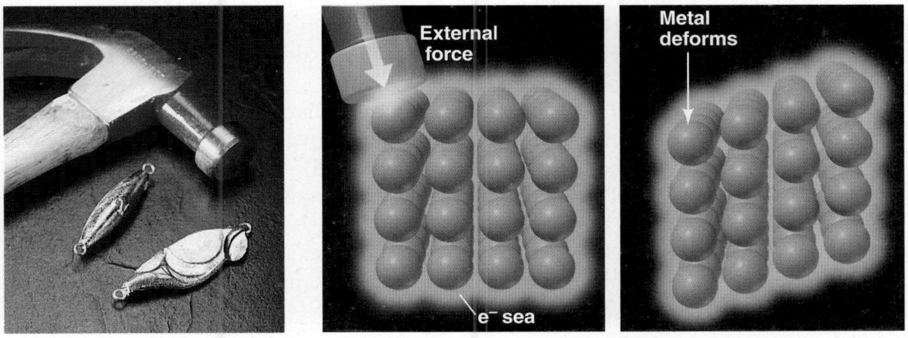

Figure 9.29 Why metals dent and bend rather than crack.

All the Group 1B(11) metals—copper, silver, and gold—are soft enough to be machined into sheets (malleable) and wires (ductile), but gold is in a class by itself. One gram of gold, about the size of a small ball-bearing, can be drawn into a wire 20 μm thick and 165 m long or hammered into a 1.0-m^2 sheet that is 230 atoms (about 70 nm) thick *(see photo)*!

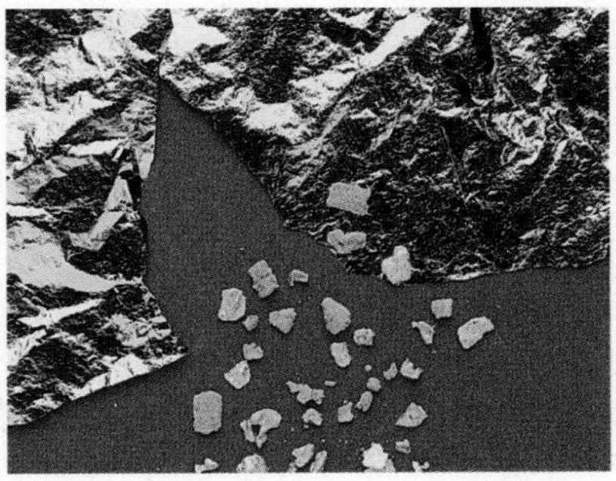

How thin is gold leaf?

3. *Electrical conductivity*. Unlike ionic and covalent substances, metals are good conductors of electricity in both the solid and liquid states because of their mobile electrons. When a piece of metal wire is attached to a battery, electrons flow from one terminal into the wire, replacing the electrons that flow from the wire into the other terminal. Foreign atoms disrupt the array of metal atoms and reduce conductivity. Copper used in electrical wiring is over 99.99% pure because traces of other atoms drastically restrict electron flow.

4. *Thermal conductivity*. Mobile electrons also make metals good conductors of heat. Place your hand on a piece of metal and a piece of wood that are both at room temperature. The metal feels colder because it conducts heat away from your hand much faster than the wood. The mobile, delocalized electrons in the metal disperse the heat from your hand more quickly than the localized electron pairs in the covalent bonds of wood.

Summary of Section 9.6

- According to the electron-sea model, the valence electrons of the metal atoms in a sample are highly delocalized and attract all the metal cations, holding them together.
- Metals have only moderately high melting points because the metal ions remain attracted to the electron sea even if their relative positions change.
- Boiling involves complete separation of individual cations with their valence electrons from all the others, so metals have very high boiling points.
- Metals can be deformed because the electron sea prevents repulsions among the cations.
- Metals conduct electricity and heat because their electrons are mobile.

CHAPTER REVIEW GUIDE

Learning Objectives

Relevant section (§) and/or sample problem (SP) numbers appear in parentheses.

Understand These Concepts

1. How differences in atomic properties lead to differences in bond type; the basic distinctions among the three types of bonding (§9.1)
2. The essential features of ionic bonding: electron transfer to form ions, and their electrostatic attraction to form a solid (§9.2)
3. How lattice energy is ultimately responsible for the formation of ionic compounds (§9.2)
4. How ionic compound formation is conceptualized as occurring in hypothetical steps (a Born-Haber cycle) to calculate the lattice energy (§9.2)
5. How Coulomb's law explains the periodic trends in lattice energy (§9.2)
6. Why ionic compounds are brittle and high melting and conduct electricity only when molten or dissolved in water (§9.2)
7. How nonmetal atoms form a covalent bond (§9.3)
8. How bonding and lone electron pairs fill the outer (valence) level of each atom in a molecule (§9.3)
9. The interrelationships among bond order, bond length, and bond energy (§9.3)
10. How the distinction between bonding and nonbonding forces explains the properties of covalent molecules and network covalent solids (§9.3)
11. How changes in bond strength account for the enthalpy of reaction (§9.4)
12. How a reaction can be divided conceptually into bond-breaking and bond-forming steps (§9.4)
13. The periodic trends in electronegativity and the inverse relationship of EN values to atomic sizes (§9.5)
14. How bond polarity arises from differences in the electronegativities of bonded atoms; the direction of bond polarity (§9.5)
15. The change in partial ionic character with ΔEN and the change from ionic to polar covalent to nonpolar covalent bonding across a period (§9.5)
16. The role of delocalized electrons in metallic bonding (§9.6)
17. How the electron-sea model explains why metals bend, have very high boiling points, and conduct electricity in solid or molten form (§9.6)

Master These Skills

1. Using Lewis electron-dot symbols to depict main-group atoms (§9.1)
2. Depicting the formation of ions with electron configurations, orbital diagrams, and Lewis symbols, and writing the formula of the ionic compound (SP 9.1)
3. Calculating lattice energy from the enthalpies of the steps to ionic compound formation (§9.2)
4. Ranking similar covalent bonds according to their length and strength (SP 9.2)
5. Using bond energies to calculate ΔH°_{rxn} (SP 9.3)
6. Determining bond polarity from EN values (SP 9.4)

Key Terms

Page numbers appear in parentheses.

Section 9.1
ionic bonding (330)
covalent bonding (330)
metallic bonding (331)
Lewis electron-dot symbol (331)
octet rule (331)

Section 9.2
lattice energy ($\Delta H^\circ_{lattice}$) (333)
Born-Haber cycle (333)
Coulomb's law (335)
ion pair (337)

Section 9.3
covalent bond (338)
bonding (shared) pair (339)
lone (unshared) pair (339)
bond order (339)
single bond (339)
double bond (339)
triple bond (339)
bond energy (BE) (339)
bond length (340)
infrared (IR) spectroscopy (343)

Section 9.5
electronegativity (EN) (349)
polar covalent bond (351)
nonpolar covalent bond (351)
electronegativity difference (ΔEN) (351)
partial ionic character (351)

Section 9.6
electron-sea model (354)
alloy (354)

Key Equations and Relationships

Page numbers appear in parentheses.

9.1 Relating the energy of attraction to the lattice energy (335):

$$\text{Electrostatic energy} \propto \frac{\text{cation charge} \times \text{anion charge}}{\text{cation radius} + \text{anion radius}} \propto \Delta H^\circ_{lattice}$$

9.2 Calculating enthalpy of reaction from bond enthalpies or bond energies (345):

$$\Delta H^\circ_{rxn} = \Sigma\Delta H^\circ_{\text{reactant bonds broken}} + \Sigma\Delta H^\circ_{\text{product bonds formed}}$$

or

$$\Delta H^\circ_{rxn} = \Sigma BE_{\text{reactant bonds broken}} - \Sigma BE_{\text{product bonds formed}}$$

Brief Solutions to Follow-Up Problems

9.1 Mg ([Ne] $3s^2$) + 2Cl ([Ne] $3s^23p^5$) $\longrightarrow$

Mg^{2+} ([Ne]) + $2Cl^-$ ([Ne] $3s^23p^6$)

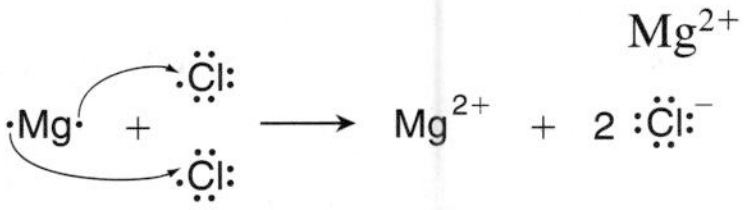

Formula: $MgCl_2$

9.2 (a) Bond length: Si—F < Si—O < Si—C
Bond strength: Si—C < Si—O < Si—F
(b) Bond length: N≡N < N=N < N—N
Bond strength: N—N < N=N < N≡N

9.3 N≡N + 3 H—H ⟶ 2 H—N(—H)—H

$\Sigma\Delta H^\circ_{\text{bonds broken}} = 1\ \text{N}{\equiv}\text{N} + 3\ \text{H—H}$
$= 945\ \text{kJ} + 1296\ \text{kJ} = 2241\ \text{kJ}$
$\Sigma\Delta H^\circ_{\text{bonds formed}} = 6\ \text{N—H} = -2346\ \text{kJ}$
$\Delta H^\circ_{\text{rxn}} = -105\ \text{kJ}$

9.4 (a) Cl—Cl < $\overset{\delta+}{\text{Br}}$—$\overset{\delta-}{\text{Cl}}$ < $\overset{\delta+}{\text{Cl}}$—$\overset{\delta-}{\text{F}}$

(b) Si—Si < $\overset{\delta+}{\text{S}}$—$\overset{\delta-}{\text{Cl}}$ < $\overset{\delta+}{\text{P}}$—$\overset{\delta-}{\text{Cl}}$ < $\overset{\delta+}{\text{Si}}$—$\overset{\delta-}{\text{Cl}}$

PROBLEMS

Problems with **colored** numbers are answered in Appendix E and worked in detail in the Student Solutions Manual. Problem sections match those in the text and provide the numbers of relevant sample problems. Most offer Concept Review Questions, Skill-Building Exercises (grouped in pairs covering the same concept), and Problems in Context. The Comprehensive Problems are based on material from any section or previous chapter.

Atomic Properties and Chemical Bonds

Concept Review Questions

9.1 In general terms, how does each of the following atomic properties influence the metallic character of the main-group elements in a period?
(a) Ionization energy
(b) Atomic radius
(c) Number of outer electrons
(d) Effective nuclear charge

9.2 Three solids are represented below. What is the predominant type of intramolecular bonding in each?

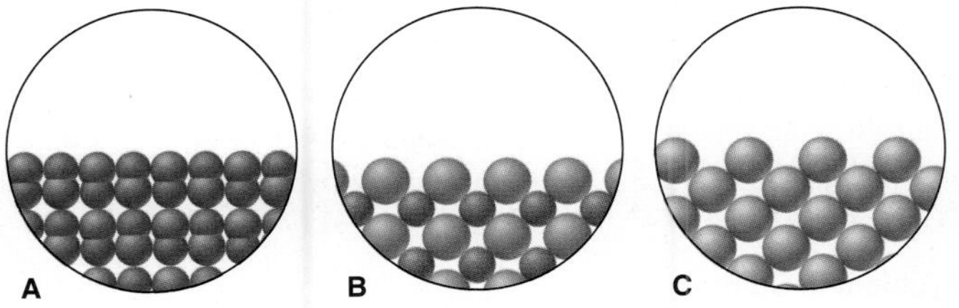

9.3 What is the relationship between the tendency of a main-group element to form a monatomic ion and its position in the periodic table? In what part of the table are the main-group elements that typically form cations? Anions?

Skill-Building Exercises (grouped in similar pairs)

9.4 Which member of each pair is *more* metallic?
(a) Na or Cs (b) Mg or Rb (c) As or N

9.5 Which member of each pair is *less* metallic?
(a) I or O (b) Be or Ba (c) Se or Ge

9.6 State the type of bonding—ionic, covalent, or metallic—you would expect in each: (a) CsF(*s*); (b) N_2(*g*); (c) Na(*s*).

9.7 State the type of bonding—ionic, covalent, or metallic—you would expect in each: (a) ICl_3(*g*); (b) N_2O(*g*); (c) LiCl(*s*).

9.8 State the type of bonding—ionic, covalent, or metallic—you would expect in each: (a) O_3(*g*); (b) $MgCl_2$(*s*); (c) BrO_2(*g*).

9.9 State the type of bonding—ionic, covalent, or metallic—you would expect in each: (a) Cr(*s*); (b) H_2S(*g*); (c) CaO(*s*).

9.10 Draw a Lewis electron-dot symbol for (a) Rb; (b) Si; (c) I.

9.11 Draw a Lewis electron-dot symbol for (a) Ba; (b) Kr; (c) Br.

9.12 Draw a Lewis electron-dot symbol for (a) Sr; (b) P; (c) S.

9.13 Draw a Lewis electron-dot symbol for (a) As; (b) Se; (c) Ga.

9.14 Give the group number and general electron configuration of an element with each electron-dot symbol: (a) ·X: (b) X·

9.15 Give the group number and general electron configuration of an element with each electron-dot symbol: (a) ·X: (b) ·X·

The Ionic Bonding Model

(Sample Problem 9.1)

Concept Review Questions

9.16 If energy is required to form monatomic ions from metals and nonmetals, why do ionic compounds exist?

9.17 (a) In general, how does the lattice energy of an ionic compound depend on the charges and sizes of the ions? (b) Ion arrangements of three general salts are represented below. Rank them in order of increasing lattice energy.

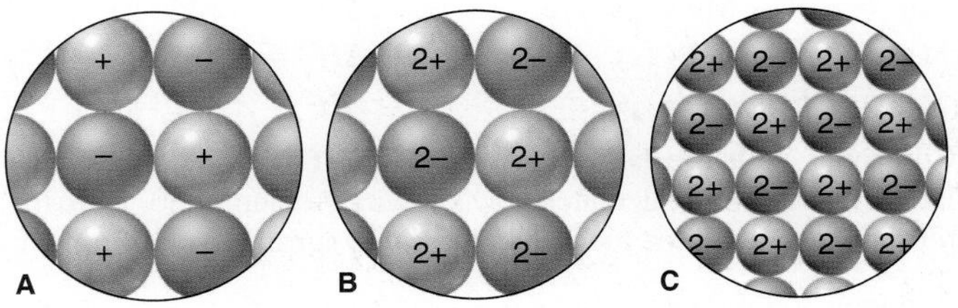

9.18 When gaseous Na^+ and Cl^- ions form gaseous NaCl ion pairs, 548 kJ/mol of energy is released. Why, then, does NaCl occur as a solid under ordinary conditions?

9.19 To form S^{2-} ions from gaseous sulfur atoms requires 214 kJ/mol, but these ions exist in solids such as K_2S. Explain.

Skill-Building Exercises (grouped in similar pairs)

9.20 Use condensed electron configurations and Lewis electron-dot symbols to depict the ions formed from each of the following atoms, and predict the formula of their compound:
(a) Ba and Cl (b) Sr and O (c) Al and F (d) Rb and O

9.21 Use condensed electron configurations and Lewis electron-dot symbols to depict the ions formed from each of the following atoms, and predict the formula of their compound:
(a) Cs and S (b) O and Ga (c) N and Mg (d) Br and Li

9.22 For each ionic compound formula, identify the main group to which X belongs: (a) XF_2; (b) MgX; (c) X_2SO_4.

9.23 For each ionic compound formula, identify the main group to which X belongs: (a) X_3PO_4; (b) $X_2(SO_4)_3$; (c) $X(NO_3)_2$.

9.24 For each ionic compound formula, identify the main group to which X belongs: (a) X_2O_3; (b) XCO_3; (c) Na_2X.

9.25 For each ionic compound formula, identify the main group to which X belongs: (a) CaX_2; (b) Al_2X_3; (c) XPO_4.

9.26 For each pair, choose the compound with the higher lattice energy, and explain your choice: (a) BaS or CsCl; (b) LiCl or CsCl.

9.27 For each pair, choose the compound with the higher lattice energy, and explain your choice: (a) CaO or CaS; (b) BaO or SrO.

9.28 For each pair, choose the compound with the lower lattice energy, and explain your choice: (a) CaS or BaS; (b) NaF or MgO.

9.29 For each pair, choose the compound with the lower lattice energy, and explain your choice: (a) NaF or NaCl; (b) K_2O or K_2S.

9.30 Use the following to calculate the $\Delta H^\circ_{\text{lattice}}$ of NaCl:

$Na(s) \longrightarrow Na(g)$	$\Delta H^\circ = 109$ kJ
$Cl_2(g) \longrightarrow 2Cl(g)$	$\Delta H^\circ = 243$ kJ
$Na(g) \longrightarrow Na^+(g) + e^-$	$\Delta H^\circ = 496$ kJ
$Cl(g) + e^- \longrightarrow Cl^-(g)$	$\Delta H^\circ = -349$ kJ
$Na(s) + \frac{1}{2}Cl_2(g) \longrightarrow NaCl(s)$	$\Delta H^\circ = -411$ kJ

Compared with the lattice energy of LiF (1050 kJ/mol), is the magnitude of the value for NaCl what you expected? Explain.

9.31 Use the following to calculate the $\Delta H^\circ_{\text{lattice}}$ of MgF_2:

$Mg(s) \longrightarrow Mg(g)$	$\Delta H^\circ = 148$ kJ
$F_2(g) \longrightarrow 2F(g)$	$\Delta H^\circ = 159$ kJ
$Mg(g) \longrightarrow Mg^+(g) + e^-$	$\Delta H^\circ = 738$ kJ
$Mg^+(g) \longrightarrow Mg^{2+}(g) + e^-$	$\Delta H^\circ = 1450$ kJ
$F(g) + e^- \longrightarrow F^-(g)$	$\Delta H^\circ = -328$ kJ
$Mg(s) + F_2(g) \longrightarrow MgF_2(s)$	$\Delta H^\circ = -1123$ kJ

Compared with the lattice energy of LiF (1050 kJ/mol) or the lattice energy you calculated for NaCl in Problem 9.30, does the relative magnitude of the value for MgF_2 surprise you? Explain.

Problems in Context

9.32 Aluminum oxide (Al_2O_3) is a widely used industrial abrasive (emery, corundum), for which the specific application depends on the hardness of the crystal. What does this hardness imply about the magnitude of the lattice energy? Would you have predicted from the chemical formula that Al_2O_3 is hard? Explain.

9.33 Born-Haber cycles were used to obtain the first reliable values for electron affinity by considering the EA value as the unknown and using a theoretically calculated value for the lattice energy. Use a Born-Haber cycle for KF and the following values to calculate a value for the electron affinity of fluorine:

$K(s) \longrightarrow K(g)$	$\Delta H^\circ = 90$ kJ
$K(g) \longrightarrow K^+(g) + e^-$	$\Delta H^\circ = 419$ kJ
$F_2(g) \longrightarrow 2F(g)$	$\Delta H^\circ = 159$ kJ
$K(s) + \frac{1}{2}F_2(g) \longrightarrow KF(s)$	$\Delta H^\circ = -569$ kJ
$K^+(g) + F^-(g) \longrightarrow KF(s)$	$\Delta H^\circ = -821$ kJ

The Covalent Bonding Model
(Sample Problem 9.2)

Concept Review Questions

9.34 Describe the interactions that occur between individual chlorine atoms as they approach each other and form Cl_2. What combination of forces gives rise to the energy holding the atoms together and to the final internuclear distance?

9.35 Define bond energy using the H—Cl bond as an example. When this bond breaks, is energy absorbed or released? Is the accompanying ΔH value positive or negative? How do the magnitude and sign of this ΔH value relate to the value that accompanies H—Cl bond formation?

9.36 For single bonds between similar types of atoms, how does the strength of the bond relate to the sizes of the atoms? Explain.

9.37 How does the energy of the bond between a given pair of atoms relate to the bond order? Why?

9.38 When liquid benzene (C_6H_6) boils, does the gas consist of molecules, ions, or separate atoms? Explain.

Skill-Building Exercises (grouped in similar pairs)

9.39 Using the periodic table only, arrange the members of each of the following sets in order of increasing bond *strength:*
(a) Br—Br, Cl—Cl, I—I (b) S—H, S—Br, S—Cl
(c) C═N, C—N, C≡N

9.40 Using the periodic table only, arrange the members of each of the following sets in order of increasing bond *length:*
(a) H—F, H—I, H—Cl (b) C—S, C═O, C—O
(c) N—H, N—S, N—O

Problem in Context

9.41 Formic acid (HCOOH; structural formula shown below) is secreted by certain species of ants when they bite.

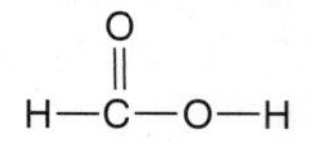

Rank the relative strengths of (a) the C—O and C═O bonds and (b) the H—C and H—O bonds. Explain these rankings.

Bond Energy and Chemical Change
(Sample Problem 9.3)

Concept Review Questions

9.42 Write a solution Plan (without actual numbers, but including the bond energies you would use and how you would combine them algebraically) for calculating the total enthalpy change of the following reaction:

$$H_2(g) + O_2(g) \longrightarrow H_2O_2(g) \qquad (H—O—O—H)$$

9.43 The text points out that, for similar types of substances, one with weaker bonds is usually more reactive than one with stronger bonds. Why is this generally true?

9.44 Why is there a discrepancy between a heat of reaction obtained from calorimetry and one obtained from bond energies?

Skill-Building Exercises (grouped in similar pairs)

9.45 Which of the following gases would you expect to have the greater heat of reaction per mole for combustion? Why?

methane or formaldehyde

9.46 Which of the following gases would you expect to have the greater heat of reaction per mole for combustion? Why?

ethanol or methanol

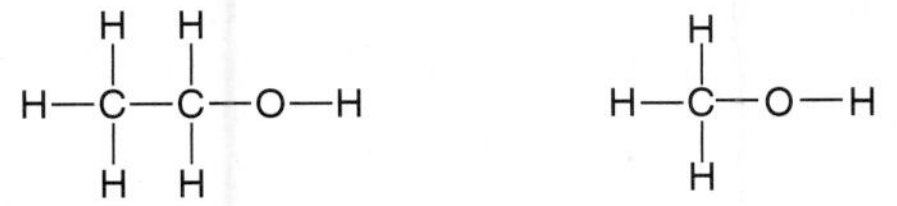

9.47 Use bond energies to calculate the heat of reaction:

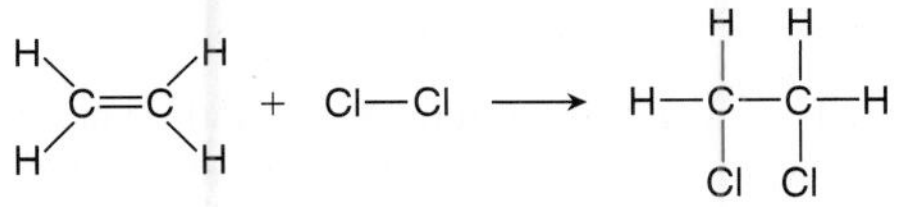

9.48 Use bond energies to calculate the heat of reaction:

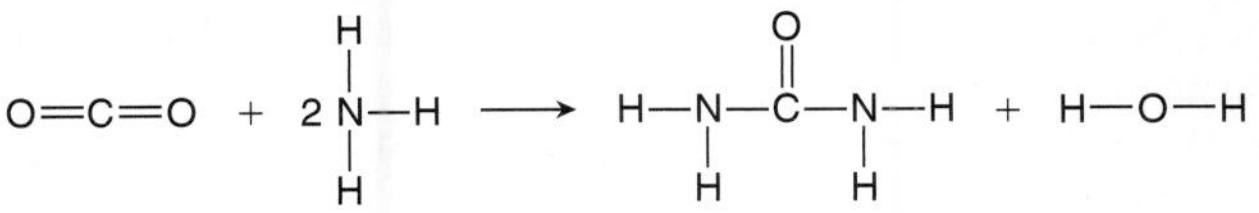

Problems in Context

9.49 An important industrial route to extremely pure acetic acid is the reaction of methanol with carbon monoxide:

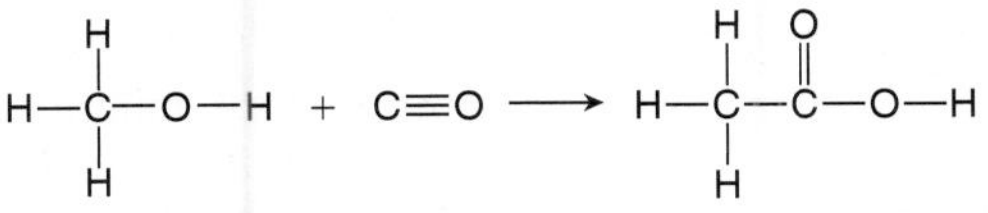

Use bond energies to calculate the enthalpy of reaction.

9.50 Sports trainers treat sprains and soreness with ethyl bromide. It is manufactured by reacting ethylene with hydrogen bromide:

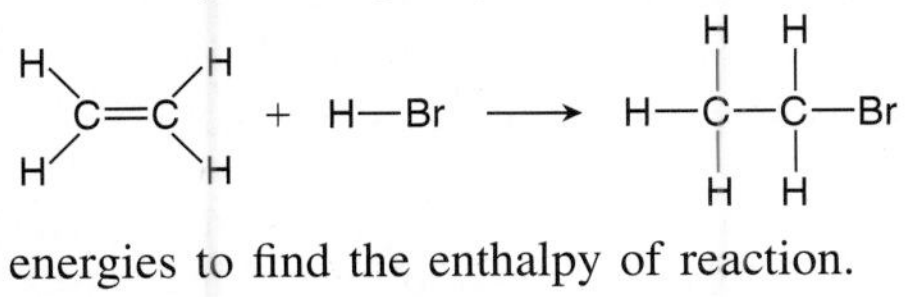

Use bond energies to find the enthalpy of reaction.

Between the Extremes: Electronegativity and Bond Polarity

(Sample Problem 9.4)

Concept Review Questions

9.51 Describe the vertical and horizontal trends in electronegativity (EN) among the main-group elements. According to Pauling's scale, what are the two most electronegative elements? The two least electronegative elements?

9.52 What is the general relationship between IE_1 and EN for the elements? Why?

9.53 Is the H—O bond in water nonpolar covalent, polar covalent, or ionic? Define each term, and explain your choice.

9.54 How does electronegativity differ from electron affinity?

9.55 How is the partial ionic character of a bond in a diatomic molecule related to ΔEN for the bonded atoms? Why?

Skill-Building Exercises (grouped in similar pairs)

9.56 Using the periodic table only, arrange the elements in each set in order of *increasing* EN: (a) S, O, Si; (b) Mg, P, As.

9.57 Using the periodic table only, arrange the elements in each set in order of *increasing* EN: (a) I, Br, N; (b) Ca, H, F.

9.58 Using the periodic table only, arrange the elements in each set in order of *decreasing* EN: (a) N, P, Si; (b) Ca, Ga, As.

9.59 Using the periodic table only, arrange the elements in each set in order of *decreasing* EN: (a) Br, Cl, P; (b) I, F, O.

9.60 Use Figure 9.21, p. 349, to indicate the polarity of each bond with a *polar arrow:* (a) N—B; (b) N—O; (c) C—S; (d) S—O; (e) N—H; (f) Cl—O.

9.61 Use Figure 9.21, p. 349, to indicate the polarity of each bond with *partial charges:* (a) Br—Cl; (b) F—Cl; (c) H—O; (d) Se—H; (e) As—H; (f) S—N.

9.62 Which is the more polar bond in each of the following pairs from Problem 9.60: (a) or (b); (c) or (d); (e) or (f)?

9.63 Which is the more polar bond in each of the following pairs from Problem 9.61: (a) or (b); (c) or (d); (e) or (f)?

9.64 Are the bonds in each of the following substances ionic, nonpolar covalent, or polar covalent? Arrange the substances with polar covalent bonds in order of increasing bond polarity:
(a) S_8 (b) RbCl (c) PF_3 (d) SCl_2 (e) F_2 (f) SF_2

9.65 Are the bonds in each of the following substances ionic, nonpolar covalent, or polar covalent? Arrange the substances with polar covalent bonds in order of increasing bond polarity:
(a) KCl (b) P_4 (c) BF_3 (d) SO_2 (e) Br_2 (f) NO_2

9.66 Rank the members of each set of compounds in order of *increasing* ionic character of their bonds. Use *polar arrows* to indicate the bond polarity of each:
(a) HBr, HCl, HI (b) H_2O, CH_4, HF (c) SCl_2, PCl_3, $SiCl_4$

9.67 Rank the members of each set of compounds in order of *decreasing* ionic character of their bonds. Use *partial charges* to indicate the bond polarity of each:
(a) PCl_3, PBr_3, PF_3 (b) BF_3, NF_3, CF_4 (c) SeF_4, TeF_4, BrF_3

Problem in Context

9.68 The energy of the C—C bond is 347 kJ/mol, and that of the Cl—Cl bond is 243 kJ/mol. Which of the following values might you expect for the C—Cl bond energy? Explain.
(a) 590 kJ/mol (sum of the values given)
(b) 104 kJ/mol (difference of the values given)
(c) 295 kJ/mol (average of the values given)
(d) 339 kJ/mol (greater than the average of the values given)

An Introduction to Metallic Bonding

Concept Review Questions

9.69 (a) List four physical characteristics of a solid metal. (b) List two chemical characteristics of a metallic element.

9.70 Briefly account for the following relative values:
(a) The melting points of Na and K are 89°C and 63°C, respectively.
(b) The melting points of Li and Be are 180°C and 1287°C, respectively.
(c) Li boils more than 1100°C higher than it melts.

9.71 Magnesium metal is easily deformed by an applied force, whereas magnesium fluoride is shattered. Why do these two solids behave so differently?

Comprehensive Problems

9.72 Geologists have a rule of thumb: when molten rock cools and solidifies, crystals of compounds with the smallest lattice energies appear at the bottom of the mass. Suggest a reason for this.

9.73 Acetylene gas (ethyne; HC≡CH) burns in an oxyacetylene torch to produce carbon dioxide and water vapor. The heat of reaction for the combustion of acetylene is 1259 kJ/mol. (a) Calculate the C≡C bond energy, and compare your value with that in Table 9.2, p. 340. (b) When 500.0 g of acetylene burns, how many kilojoules of heat are given off? (c) How many grams of CO_2 form? (d) How many liters of O_2 at 298 K and 18.0 atm are consumed?

9.74 Use Lewis electron-dot symbols to represent the formation of (a) BrF_3 from bromine and fluorine atoms; (b) AlF_3 from aluminum and fluorine atoms.

9.75 Even though so much energy is required to form a metal cation with a 2+ charge, the alkaline earth metals form halides with general formula MX_2, rather than MX.
(a) Use the following data to calculate the ΔH°_f of MgCl:

$$Mg(s) \longrightarrow Mg(g) \qquad \Delta H^\circ = 148\ kJ$$
$$Cl_2(g) \longrightarrow 2Cl(g) \qquad \Delta H^\circ = 243\ kJ$$
$$Mg(g) \longrightarrow Mg^+(g) + e^- \qquad \Delta H^\circ = 738\ kJ$$
$$Cl(g) + e^- \longrightarrow Cl^-(g) \qquad \Delta H^\circ = -349\ kJ$$
$$\Delta H^\circ_{lattice}\ of\ MgCl = 783.5\ kJ/mol$$

(b) Is MgCl favored energetically relative to Mg and Cl_2? Explain.
(c) Use Hess's law to calculate ΔH° for the conversion of MgCl to $MgCl_2$ and Mg (ΔH°_f of $MgCl_2 = -641.6$ kJ/mol).
(d) Is MgCl favored energetically relative to $MgCl_2$? Explain.

9.76 Gases react explosively if the heat released when the reaction begins is sufficient to cause more reaction, which leads to a rapid expansion of the gases. Use bond energies to calculate ΔH° of the following reactions, and predict which occurs explosively:
(a) $H_2(g) + Cl_2(g) \longrightarrow 2HCl(g)$
(b) $H_2(g) + I_2(g) \longrightarrow 2HI(g)$
(c) $2H_2(g) + O_2(g) \longrightarrow 2H_2O(g)$

9.77 By using photons of specific wavelengths, chemists can dissociate gaseous HI to produce H atoms with certain speeds. When HI dissociates, the H atoms move away rapidly, whereas the heavier I atoms move more slowly. (a) What is the longest wavelength (in nm) that can dissociate a molecule of HI? (b) If a photon of 254 nm is used, what is the excess energy (in J) over that needed for dissociation? (c) If this excess energy is carried away by the H atom as kinetic energy, what is its speed (in m/s)?

9.78 In developing the concept of electronegativity, Pauling used the term *excess bond energy* for the difference between the actual bond energy of X—Y and the average bond energies of X—X and Y—Y (see text discussion for the case of HF). Based on the values in Figure 9.21, p. 349, which of the following substances contains bonds with no excess bond energy?
(a) PH_3 (b) CS_2 (c) BrCl (d) BH_3 (e) Se_8

9.79 Use condensed electron configurations to predict the relative hardnesses and melting points of rubidium ($Z = 37$), vanadium ($Z = 23$), and cadmium ($Z = 48$).

9.80 Without stratospheric ozone (O_3), harmful solar radiation would cause gene alterations. Ozone forms when the bond in O_2 breaks and each O atom reacts with another O_2 molecule. It is destroyed by reaction with Cl atoms formed when the C—Cl bond in synthetic chemicals breaks. Find the wavelengths of light that can break the C—Cl bond and the bond in O_2.

9.81 "Inert" xenon actually forms many compounds, especially with highly electronegative fluorine. The ΔH°_f values for xenon difluoride, tetrafluoride, and hexafluoride are −105, −284, and −402 kJ/mol, respectively. Find the average bond energy of the Xe—F bonds in each fluoride.

9.82 The HF bond length is 92 pm, 16% shorter than the sum of the covalent radii of H (37 pm) and F (72 pm). Suggest a reason for this difference. Similar data show that the difference becomes smaller down the group, from HF to HI. Explain.

9.83 There are two main types of covalent bond breakage. In homolytic breakage (as in Table 9.2, p. 340), each atom in the bond gets one of the shared electrons. In some cases, the electronegativity of adjacent atoms affects the bond energy. In heterolytic breakage, one atom gets both electrons and the other gets none; thus, a cation and an anion form.
(a) Why is the C—C bond in $H_3C—CF_3$ (423 kJ/mol) stronger than that in $H_3C—CH_3$ (376 kJ/mol)?
(b) Use bond energy and any other data to calculate the enthalpy of reaction for the heterolytic cleavage of O_2.

9.84 Find the longest wavelengths of light that can cleave the bonds in elemental nitrogen, oxygen, and fluorine.

9.85 The work function (ϕ) of a metal is the minimum energy needed to remove an electron from its surface. (a) Is it easier to remove an electron from a gaseous silver atom or from the surface of solid silver ($\phi = 7.59\times10^{-19}$ J; IE = 731 kJ/mol)? (b) Explain the results in terms of the electron-sea model of metallic bonding.

9.86 Lattice energies can also be calculated for covalent solids using a Born-Haber cycle, and the network solid silicon dioxide has one of the highest $\Delta H^\circ_{lattice}$ values. Silicon dioxide is found in pure crystalline form as transparent rock quartz. Much harder than glass, this material was once prized for making lenses for optical devices and expensive spectacles. Use Appendix B and the following data to calculate $\Delta H^\circ_{lattice}$ of SiO_2:

$$Si(s) \longrightarrow Si(g) \qquad \Delta H^\circ = 454\ kJ$$
$$Si(g) \longrightarrow Si^{4+}(g) + 4e^- \qquad \Delta H^\circ = 9949\ kJ$$
$$O_2(g) \longrightarrow 2O(g) \qquad \Delta H^\circ = 498\ kJ$$
$$O(g) + 2e^- \longrightarrow O^{2-}(g) \qquad \Delta H^\circ = 737\ kJ$$

9.87 The average C—H bond energy in CH_4 is 415 kJ/mol. Use Table 9.2 (p. 340) and the following to calculate the average C—H bond energy in ethane (C_2H_6; C—C bond), in ethene (C_2H_4; C═C bond), and in ethyne (C_2H_2; C≡C bond):

$$C_2H_6(g) + H_2(g) \longrightarrow 2CH_4(g) \qquad \Delta H^\circ_{rxn} = -65.07 \text{ kJ/mol}$$
$$C_2H_4(g) + 2H_2(g) \longrightarrow 2CH_4(g) \qquad \Delta H^\circ_{rxn} = -202.21 \text{ kJ/mol}$$
$$C_2H_2(g) + 3H_2(g) \longrightarrow 2CH_4(g) \qquad \Delta H^\circ_{rxn} = -376.74 \text{ kJ/mol}$$

9.88 Carbon-carbon bonds form the "backbone" of nearly every organic and biological molecule. The average bond energy of the C—C bond is 347 kJ/mol. Calculate the frequency and wavelength of the least energetic photon that can break an average C—C bond. In what region of the electromagnetic spectrum is this radiation?

9.89 In a future hydrogen-fuel economy, the cheapest source of H_2 will certainly be water. It takes 467 kJ to produce 1 mol of H atoms from water. What is the frequency, wavelength, and minimum energy of a photon that can free an H atom from water?

9.90 Dimethyl ether (CH_3OCH_3) and ethanol (CH_3CH_2OH) are constitutional isomers (see Table 3.4, p. 103). (a) Use Table 9.2 (p. 340) to calculate ΔH°_{rxn} for the formation of each compound as a gas from methane and oxygen; water vapor also forms. (b) State which reaction is more exothermic. (c) Calculate ΔH°_{rxn} for the conversion of ethanol to dimethyl ether.

9.91 Enthalpies of reaction calculated from bond energies and from enthalpies of formation are often, but not always, close to each other.

(a) Industrial ethanol (CH_3CH_2OH) is produced by a catalytic reaction of ethylene (CH_2═CH_2) with water at high pressures and temperatures. Calculate ΔH°_{rxn} for this gas-phase hydration of ethylene to ethanol, using bond energies and then using enthalpies of formation.

(b) Ethylene glycol is produced by the catalytic oxidation of ethylene to ethylene oxide, which then reacts with water to form ethylene glycol:

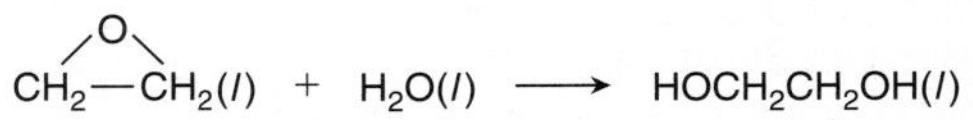

The ΔH°_{rxn} for this hydrolysis step, based on enthalpies of formation, is −97 kJ/mol. Calculate ΔH°_{rxn} for the hydrolysis using bond energies.

(c) Why are the two values relatively close for the hydration in part (a) but not close for the hydrolysis in part (b)?

The Shapes of Molecules

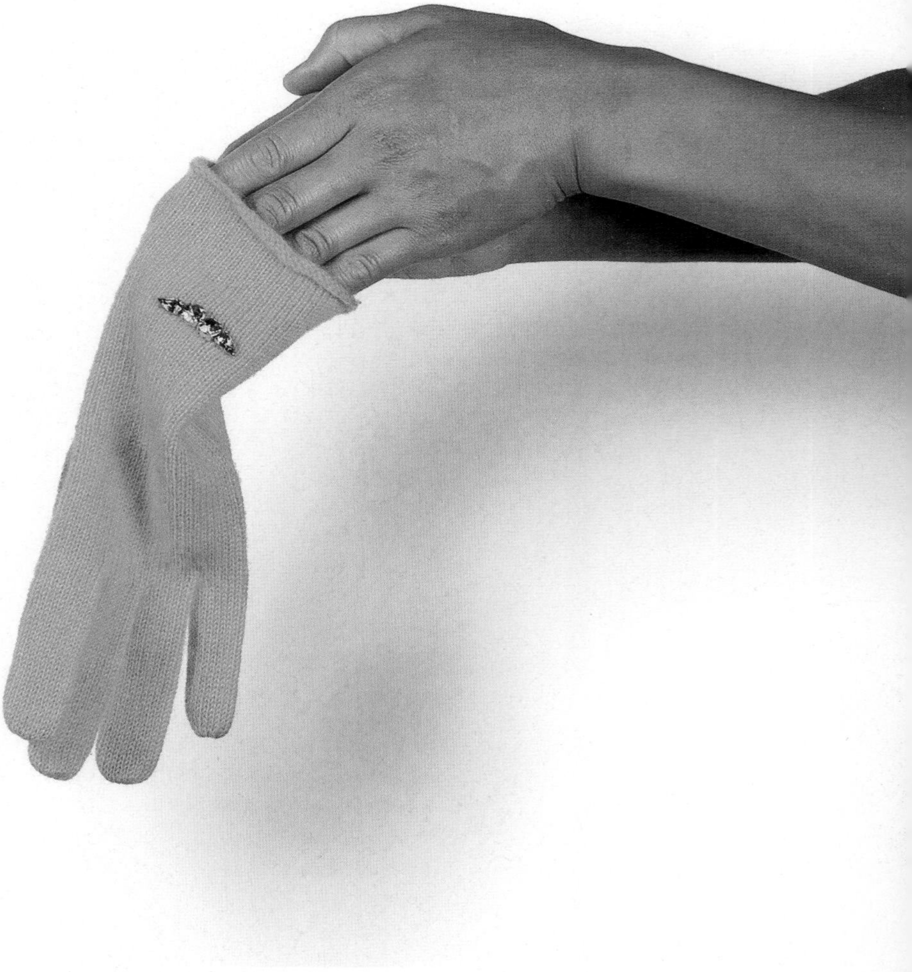

10

Concepts and skills to review before you study this chapter

- electron configurations of main-group elements (Section 8.2)
- electron-dot symbols (Section 9.1)
- octet rule (Section 9.1)
- bond order, bond length, and bond energy (Sections 9.3 and 9.4)
- polar covalent bonds and bond polarity (Section 9.5)

In the everyday world, the shapes of interacting objects often reflect their function—cup and saucer, mortar and pestle, or the matching shapes of hand and glove. The same is true in the molecular world. But, with all the symbols, lines, and dots you've been seeing, it's easy to forget that every molecule has a characteristic minute architecture. Each atom, bonding pair, and lone pair has its own position relative to the others, with definite angles and distances between them that are determined by the attractive and repulsive forces governing all matter. Molecular shape plays a crucial role in the interactions of reactants, the behavior of synthetic materials, and especially in the life-sustaining processes in cells.

IN THIS CHAPTER . . . We learn how to picture molecules by applying two approaches that explain their shapes, and we examine some effects of molecular shape on physical and biochemical behavior.

- We learn how to apply the octet rule to convert a molecular formula into a flat structural formula that shows atom attachments and electron-pair locations.
- We see how electron delocalization limits our ability to depict a molecule with a single structural formula and requires us to apply the concept of resonance.
- We introduce bond angle and apply a theory that converts two-dimensional formulas into three-dimensional shapes.
- We describe five basic classes of shapes that many molecules adopt, how multiple bonds and lone pairs affect them, and how to combine smaller molecular portions into the shapes of more complex molecules.
- We discuss the relation among bond polarity, shape, and molecular polarity and the effect of polarity on behavior.
- We describe a few examples of shape influencing biological function.

10.1 • DEPICTING MOLECULES AND IONS WITH LEWIS STRUCTURES

The first step toward visualizing a molecule is to convert its molecular formula to its **Lewis structure** (or **Lewis formula***), which shows electron-dot symbols for the atoms, the bonding pairs as lines, and the lone pairs that fill each atom's outer level (valence shell) as pairs of dots.

Applying the Octet Rule to Write Lewis Structures

To write a Lewis structure, we decide on the relative placement of the atoms in the molecule or polyatomic ion and then distribute the total number of valence electrons as bonding and lone pairs. In many, but not all, cases, the octet rule (Section 9.1) guides us in distributing the electrons. We begin with species that "obey" the octet rule, in which each atom fills its outer level with eight electrons (or two for hydrogen).

*A Lewis *structure* does ***not*** indicate the three-dimensional shape, so it may be more correct to call it a Lewis *formula*, but we follow convention and use the term *structure*.

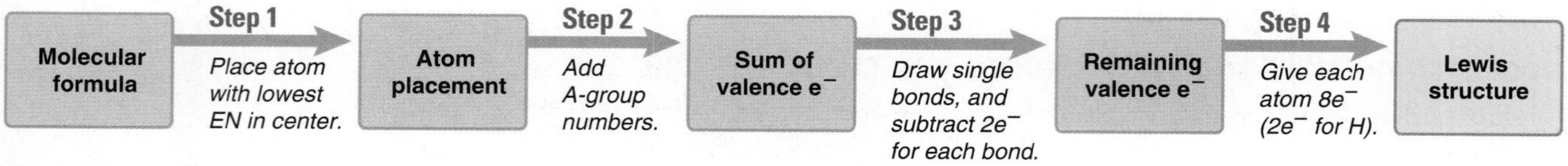

Figure 10.1 The steps in converting a molecular formula into a Lewis structure.

Molecules with Single Bonds Figure 10.1 lays out the steps for writing Lewis structures for species with only single bonds. Let's use nitrogen trifluoride, NF_3, to introduce the steps:

Step 1. Place the atoms relative to each other. For compounds with the general molecular formula AB_n, place the atom with the *lower group number* in the center because it needs more electrons to attain an octet; usually, this is also the atom with the *lower electronegativity*. In NF_3, the N (Group 5A; EN = 3.0) has five electrons and so needs three, whereas each F (Group 7A; EN = 4.0) has seven and needs only one; thus, N goes in the center with the three F atoms around it:

If the atoms have the same group number, as in SO_3, place the atom with the *higher period number* (also lower EN) in the center. H can form only one bond, so it is *never* a central atom.

Step 2. Determine the total number of valence electrons.

- For molecules, add up the valence electrons of the atoms. (Recall that the number of valence electrons equals the A-group number.) In NF_3, N has five valence electrons, and each F has seven:

$$[1 \times N(5e^-)] + [3 \times F(7e^-)] = 5e^- + 21e^- = 26 \text{ valence } e^-$$

- For polyatomic ions, *add* one e^- for each negative charge, or *subtract* one e^- for each positive charge.

Step 3. Draw a single bond from each surrounding atom to the central atom, and subtract $2e^-$ from the total for each bond to find the number of e^- remaining:

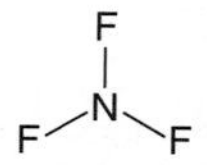

$$3 \text{ N—F bonds} \times 2e^- = 6e^- \quad \text{so} \quad 26e^- - 6e^- = 20e^- \text{ remaining}$$

Step 4. Distribute the remaining electrons in pairs so that each atom ends up with $8e^-$ (or $2e^-$ for H). First, place lone pairs on the *surrounding (more electronegative) atoms* to give each an octet. If any electrons remain, place them around the central atom—each F gets 3 pairs ($3 \times 6e^- = 18e^-$) and the N gets 1 ($2e^-$), for a total of $20e^-$. Then check that each atom has $8e^-$:

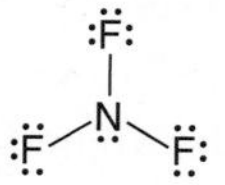

This is the Lewis structure for NF_3. It is a neutral species, so the total number of electrons (bonds plus lone pairs) equals the sum of the valence electrons:

$$6e^- \text{ in three bonds} + 20e^- \text{ in ten lone pairs} = 26 \text{ valence } e^-$$

If we were writing a Lewis structure for a polyatomic ion, we would also take the charge into account, as described in step 2.

Since Lewis structures do not indicate shape, an equally correct depiction of NF_3 is

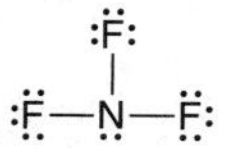

or any other that retains the *same connections among the atoms*—a central N atom connected by single bonds to each of three surrounding F atoms.

Using these four steps, you can write a Lewis structure for any singly bonded species with a central C, N, or O atom, as well as for some species with central atoms from higher periods. In nearly all their compounds,

- Hydrogen atoms form one bond.
- Carbon atoms form four bonds.
- Nitrogen atoms form three bonds.
- Oxygen atoms form two bonds.
- Surrounding halogens form one bond; fluorine is *always* a surrounding atom.

Sample Problem 10.1 Writing Lewis Structures for Molecules with One Central Atom

Problem Write a Lewis structure for CCl_2F_2, one of the compounds responsible for the depletion of stratospheric ozone.

Solution *Step 1.* Place the atoms relative to each other. In CCl_2F_2, carbon has the lowest group number and EN, so it is the central atom (*see margin*). The halogen atoms surround it, but their specific positions are not important.

Step 1:

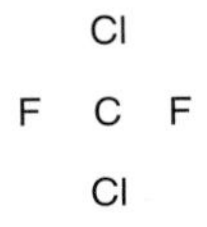

Step 2. Determine the total number of valence electrons (from A-group numbers): C is in Group 4A; F and Cl are in Group 7A. Therefore, we have

$$[1 \times C(4e^-)] + [2 \times F(7e^-)] + [2 \times Cl(7e^-)] = 32 \text{ valence } e^-$$

Step 3. Draw single bonds to the central atom (*see margin*) and subtract $2e^-$ for each bond:

Step 3:

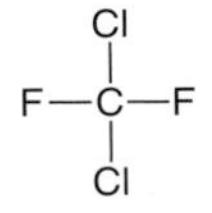

$$4 \text{ bonds} \times 2e^- = 8e^- \quad \text{so} \quad 32e^- - 8e^- = 24e^- \text{ remaining}$$

Step 4. Distribute the remaining electrons in pairs, beginning with the surrounding atoms, so that each atom has an octet. Each surrounding halogen gets 3 pairs (*see margin*).

Step 4:

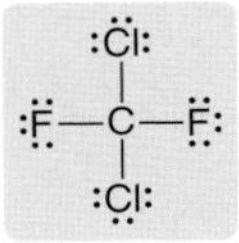

Check Always check that each atom has an octet. Bonding electrons belong to each atom in the bond. The total number in bonds ($8e^-$) and lone pairs ($24e^-$) equals 32 valence e^-. As expected, C has four bonds and the surrounding halogens have one each.

Follow-Up Problem 10.1 Write a Lewis structure for **(a)** H_2S; **(b)** OF_2; **(c)** $SOCl_2$.

In molecules with two or more central atoms bonded to each other, it is usually clear which atoms are central and which surrounding.

Sample Problem 10.2 Writing Lewis Structures for Molecules with More Than One Central Atom

Problem Write the Lewis structure for methanol (molecular formula CH_4O), an important industrial alcohol that can be used as a gasoline alternative in cars.

Solution *Step 1.* Place the atoms relative to each other. The H atoms can have only one bond, so C and O must be central and adjacent to each other. C has four bonds and O has two, so we arrange the H atoms accordingly (*see margin*).

Step 1:

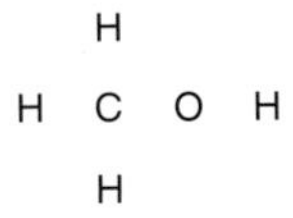

Step 2. Find the sum of valence electrons (C is in Group 4A, O is in Group 6A):

$$[1 \times C(4e^-)] + [1 \times O(6e^-)] + [4 \times H(1e^-)] = 14e^-$$

Step 3. Add single bonds (*see margin*) and subtract $2e^-$ for each bond:

Step 3:

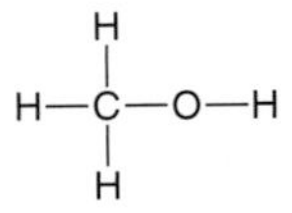

$$5 \text{ bonds} \times 2e^- = 10e^- \quad \text{so} \quad 14e^- - 10e^- = 4e^- \text{ remaining}$$

Step 4. Add the remaining electrons in pairs to fill each valence level. C already has an octet, and each H shares $2e^-$ with the C; so the remaining $4e^-$ form two lone pairs on O to give the Lewis structure for methanol (*see margin*).

Step 4:

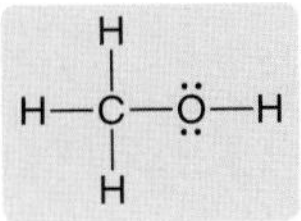

Check Each H atom has $2e^-$, and C and O each have $8e^-$. The total number of valence electrons is $14e^-$, which equals $10e^-$ in bonds plus $4e^-$ in two lone pairs. Each H has one bond, C has four, and O has two.

Follow-Up Problem 10.2 Write a Lewis structure for **(a)** hydroxylamine (NH_3O); **(b)** dimethyl ether (C_2H_6O; no O—H bonds).

Molecules with Multiple Bonds In most cases, if there are not enough electrons for the central atom(s) to attain an octet, a multiple bond is present, and we add the following step to the procedure for writing a Lewis structure:

Step 5. Cases involving multiple bonds. If a central atom does not end up with an octet, change a lone pair on a surrounding atom into another bonding pair to the central atom, thus forming a multiple bond.

Sample Problem 10.3 Writing Lewis Structures for Molecules with Multiple Bonds

Problem Write Lewis structures for the following:
(a) Ethylene (C_2H_4), the most important reactant in the manufacture of polymers
(b) Nitrogen (N_2), the most abundant atmospheric gas

Plan We show the structure resulting from steps 1 to 4: placing the atoms, counting the total valence electrons, making single bonds, and distributing the remaining valence electrons in pairs to attain octets. Then we continue with step 5, if needed.

Solution **(a)** For C_2H_4. After steps 1 to 4, we have

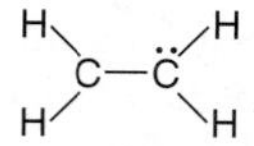

Step 5. Change a lone pair to a bonding pair. The right C has an octet, but the left C has only $6e^-$, so we change the lone pair to another bonding pair between the two C atoms:

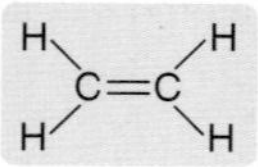

(b) For N_2. After steps 1 to 4, we have :N̈—N̈:
Step 5. Neither N has an octet, so we change a lone pair to a bonding pair, :N̈═N:
In this case, moving one lone pair to make a double bond still does not give the right N an octet, so we move a lone pair from the left N to make a triple bond, :N≡N:

Check **(a)** Each C has four bonds and counts the $4e^-$ in the double bond as part of its own octet. The valence electron total is $12e^-$, all in six bonds. **(b)** Each N counts the $6e^-$ in the triple bond as part of its own octet. The valence electron total is $10e^-$, which equals the electrons in three bonds and two lone pairs.

Follow-Up Problem 10.3 Write Lewis structures for **(a)** CO (the only common molecule in which C has three bonds); **(b)** HCN; **(c)** CO_2.

Resonance: Delocalized Electron-Pair Bonding

We often find that, for a molecule or polyatomic ion with *double bonds next to single bonds,* we can write more than one Lewis structure. Which, if any, is correct?

The Need for Resonance Structures To understand this issue, consider ozone (O_3), an air pollutant at ground level but an absorber of harmful ultraviolet (UV) radiation in the stratosphere. Two Lewis structures (with lettered O atoms for clarity) are

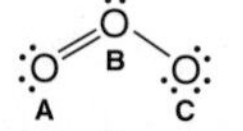

I

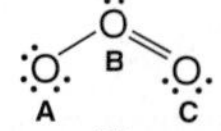

II

In structure I, oxygen B has a double bond to oxygen A and a single bond to oxygen C. In structure II, the single and double bonds are reversed. You can rotate I to get II, so these are *not* different types of ozone molecules, but different Lewis structures for the *same* molecule.

In fact, *neither* Lewis structure depicts O_3 accurately, because the two oxygen-oxygen bonds in O_3 are actually identical in length and energy. The bonds in O_3 have properties between an O—O bond and an O═O bond, something like a "one-and-a-half" bond. The molecule is shown more correctly with two Lewis structures, called

resonance structures (or **resonance forms**), and a two-headed resonance arrow (⟷) between them. Resonance structures *have the same relative placement of atoms but different locations of bonding and lone electron pairs.* You can convert one resonance form to another by moving lone pairs to bonding positions, and vice versa:

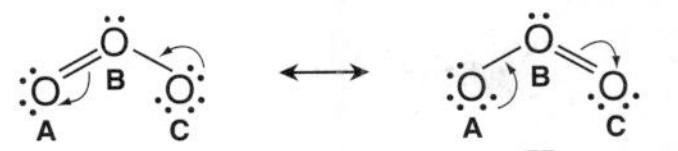

I II

Resonance structures are not real bonding depictions: O_3 does *not* change back and forth quickly from structure I to structure II. The actual molecule is a **resonance hybrid,** an average of the resonance forms.

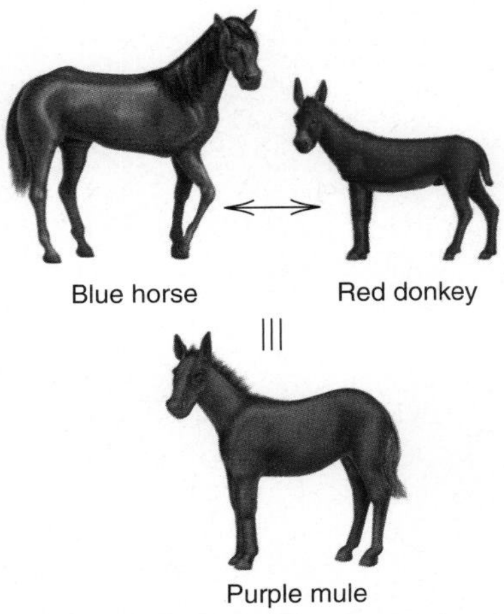

A Purple Mule, Not a Blue Horse and a Red Donkey A mule is a genetic mix, a hybrid, of a horse and a donkey; it is not a horse one instant and a donkey the next. Similarly, the color purple is a mix of red and blue, not red one instant and blue the next. In the same sense, a resonance hybrid is one molecular species, not one resonance form this instant and another resonance form the next. The problem is that we cannot depict the actual species, the hybrid, accurately with a single Lewis structure.

Electron Delocalization Our need for more than one Lewis structure to depict O_3 is due to **electron-pair delocalization.** In a single, double, or triple bond, each electron pair is *localized* between the bonded atoms. In a resonance hybrid, two of the electron pairs (one bonding and one lone pair) are *delocalized:* their density is "spread" over a few adjacent atoms. (This delocalization involves just a few e^- pairs, so it is *much* less extensive than the electron delocalization in metals that we saw in Section 9.6.)

In O_3, the result is two identical bonds, each consisting of a single bond (the localized pair) and a *partial bond* (the contribution from one of the delocalized pairs). We draw the resonance hybrid with a curved dashed line to show the delocalized pairs:

resonance hybrid 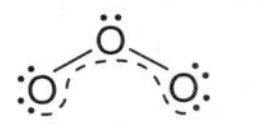

Resonance is very common. For example, benzene (C_6H_6, *shown below*) has two important resonance forms in which alternating single and double bonds have different positions. The actual molecule is an average of the two forms with six C—C bonds and three electron pairs delocalized over all six C atoms. The delocalized pairs are often shown as a dashed circle (or simply a circle):

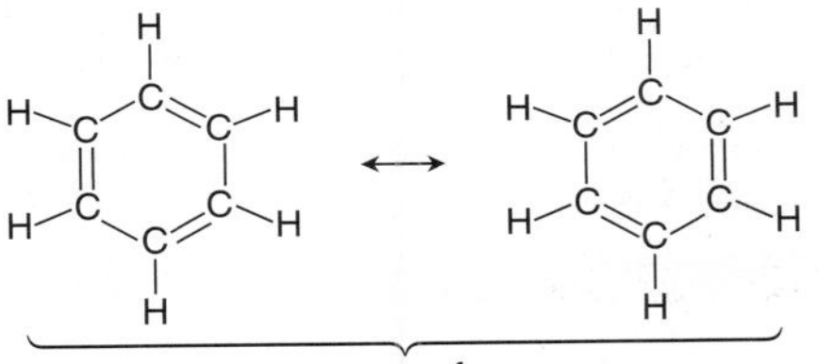

resonance forms

or

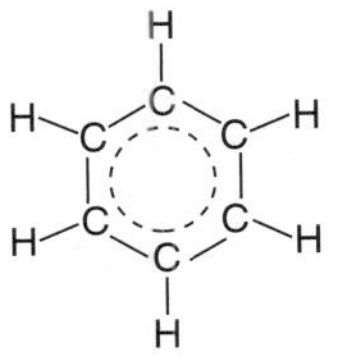

resonance hybrid

Fractional Bond Orders Partial bonding, as in resonance hybrids, often leads to fractional bond orders. For O_3, we have

$$\text{Bond order} = \frac{3 \text{ electron pairs}}{2 \text{ bonded-atom pairs}} = 1\tfrac{1}{2}$$

The carbon-to-carbon bond order in benzene is 9 electron pairs/6 bonded-atom pairs, or $1\frac{1}{2}$ also. For the carbonate ion, CO_3^{2-}, three resonance structures can be drawn. Each has 4 electron pairs shared among 3 bonded-atom pairs, so the bond order is $\frac{4}{3}$, or $1\frac{1}{3}$. One of the three resonance structures for CO_3^{2-} is

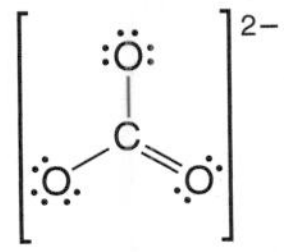

Note here (and in Sample Problem 10.4) that the Lewis structure of a polyatomic ion is written in *square brackets with the ion charge outside the brackets.*

Sample Problem 10.4 Writing Resonance Structures

Problem Write resonance structures for the nitrate ion, NO_3^-, and find the bond order.

Plan We write a Lewis structure, remembering to add $1e^-$ to the total number of valence electrons because of the 1− ionic charge. Then we move lone and bonding pairs to write other resonance forms and connect them with the resonance arrow. The bond order is the number of shared electron pairs divided by the number of atom pairs.

Solution After steps 1 to 4, we have

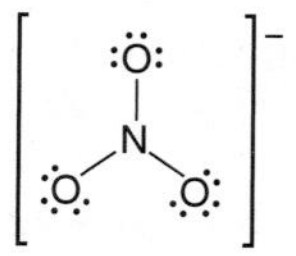

Step 5. Since N has only $6e^-$, we change a lone pair on one of the O atoms to a bonding pair to form a double bond, which gives each atom an octet. All the O atoms are equivalent, however, so we can move a lone pair from any one of the three and obtain three resonance structures:

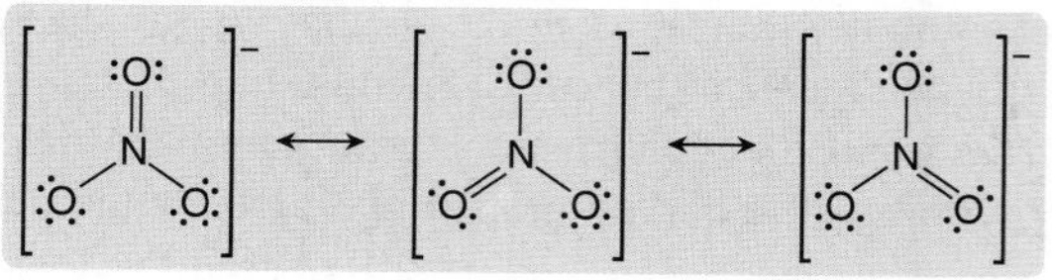

The bond order is

$$\frac{4 \text{ shared electron pairs}}{3 \text{ bonded-atom pairs}} = 1\tfrac{1}{3}$$

Check Each structure has the same relative placement of atoms, an octet around each atom, and $24e^-$ (the sum of the valence electron total and $1e^-$ from the ionic charge, distributed in four bonds and eight lone pairs).

Comment These three resonance forms contribute equally to the resonance hybrid because all of the surrounding atoms are identical. This is not always the case, as you'll see next.

Follow-Up Problem 10.4 One of the three resonance structures for CO_3^{2-} was shown just before Sample Problem 10.4. Draw the other two.

Formal Charge: Selecting the More Important Resonance Structure

If one resonance form "looks" more like the resonance hybrid than the others, it "weights" the average in its favor. One way to select the more important resonance form is by determining each atom's **formal charge,** the charge it would have *if the bonding electrons were shared equally*. We'll examine this concept and then see how formal charge compares with oxidation number.

Determining Formal Charge An atom's formal charge is its total number of valence electrons minus *all* of its unshared valence electrons and *half* of its shared valence electrons. Thus,

$$\text{Formal charge of atom} = \text{no. of valence } e^- - (\text{no. of unshared valence } e^- + \tfrac{1}{2}\text{ no. of shared valence } e^-) \quad \textbf{(10.1)}$$

For example, in O_3, the formal charge of oxygen A in resonance form I is

$$6 \text{ valence } e^- - (4 \text{ unshared } e^- + \tfrac{1}{2} \text{ of } 4 \text{ shared } e^-) = 6 - 4 - 2 = 0$$

The formal charges of all the atoms in the two O_3 resonance forms are

$O_A[6 - 4 - \tfrac{1}{2}(4)] = 0$

$O_B[6 - 2 - \tfrac{1}{2}(6)] = +1$

$O_C[6 - 6 - \tfrac{1}{2}(2)] = -1$

I II

$O_A[6 - 6 - \tfrac{1}{2}(2)] = -1$

$O_B[6 - 2 - \tfrac{1}{2}(6)] = +1$

$O_C[6 - 4 - \tfrac{1}{2}(4)] = 0$

Forms I and II have the same formal charges but on different O atoms, so they contribute equally to the resonance hybrid. *Formal charges must sum to the actual charge on the species:* zero for a molecule or the ionic charge for an ion.

Note that, in I, instead of oxygen's usual two bonds, O_B has three bonds and O_C has one. Only when an atom has a zero formal charge does it have its usual number of bonds; the same holds for C in CO_3^{2-}, N in NO_3^-, and so forth.

Choosing the More Important Resonance Form Three criteria help us choose the more important resonance structure:

- Smaller formal charges (positive *or* negative) are preferable to larger ones.
- The *same* nonzero formal charges on adjacent atoms are not preferred.
- A more negative formal charge should reside on a more electronegative atom.

As in the case of O_3, the resonance forms for CO_3^{2-}, NO_3^-, and benzene all have identical atoms surrounding the central atom(s) and, thus, have identical formal charges and are equally important contributors to the resonance hybrid. But, let's apply these criteria to the cyanate ion, NCO^-, which has two *different* atoms around the central one. Three resonance forms with formal charges are

Formal charges:
Resonance forms:

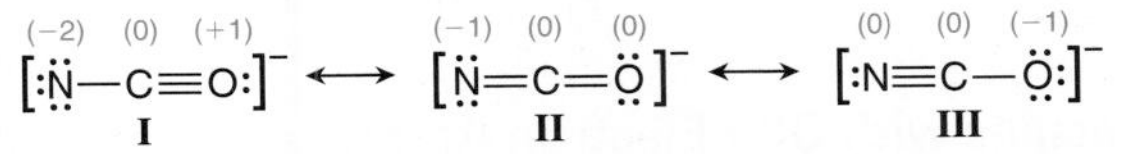

I II III

Form I is *not* an important contributor to the hybrid because it has a larger formal charge on N and a positive formal charge on the more electronegative O. Forms II and III have the same magnitude of charges, but III has a -1 charge on O, the more electronegative atom. Therefore, II and III are more important than I, and III is more important than II.

Formal Charge Versus Oxidation Number Formal charge (used to examine resonance structures) is *not* the same as oxidation number (used to monitor redox reactions):

- For a *formal charge,* bonding electrons are *shared equally* by the atoms (as if the bonding were *nonpolar covalent*), so each atom has half of them:

$$\text{Formal charge} = \text{valence } e^- - (\text{lone pair } e^- + \tfrac{1}{2}\text{ bonding } e^-)$$

- For an *oxidation number,* bonding electrons are *transferred completely* to the more electronegative atom (as if the bonding were *pure ionic*):

$$\text{Oxidation number} = \text{valence } e^- - (\text{lone pair } e^- + \text{bonding } e^-)$$

For the three cyanate ion resonance structures,

Formal charges:

Oxidation numbers:

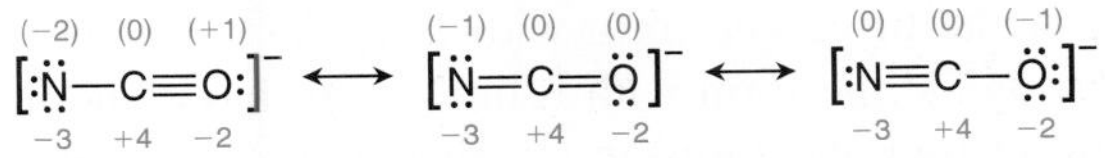

Notice that the oxidation numbers *do not* change from one resonance form to another (because the electronegativities *do not* change), but the formal charges *do* change (because the numbers of bonding and lone pairs *do* change).

Lewis Structures for Exceptions to the Octet Rule

The octet rule applies to most molecules (and ions) with Period 2 central atoms, but not every one, and not to many with central atoms from Period 3 and higher. Three important exceptions occur in molecules with (1) electron-deficient atoms, (2) odd-electron atoms, and (3) atoms with expanded valence shells. In this discussion, you'll also see that formal charge has limitations for selecting the best resonance form.

Molecules with Electron-Deficient Atoms Gaseous molecules containing either beryllium or boron as the central atom are often **electron deficient:** they have *fewer* than eight electrons around the central atom. The Lewis structures, with formal charges, of gaseous beryllium chloride* and boron trifluoride are

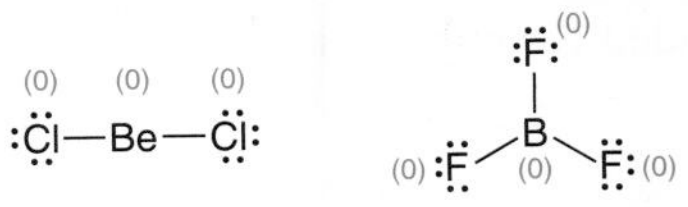

*Even though beryllium is in Group 2A(2), most Be compounds have considerable covalent bonding. For example, molten $BeCl_2$ does not conduct electricity, indicating a lack of ions.

There are only four electrons around Be and six around B. Surrounding halogen atoms don't form multiple bonds to the central atoms to give them an octet, because the halogens are much more electronegative. Formal charges make the following structures unlikely:

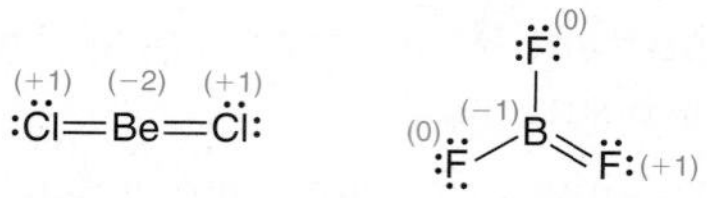

(Some data for BF_3 show a shorter than expected B—F bond. Shorter bonds indicate double-bond character, so the structure with the B═F bond may be a minor contributor to a resonance hybrid.) Electron-deficient atoms often attain an octet by forming additional bonds in reactions. When BF_3 reacts with ammonia, for instance, a compound forms in which boron attains an octet:*

Molecules with Odd-Electron Atoms A few molecules contain a central atom with an odd number of valence electrons, so they cannot have all their electrons in pairs. Most have a central atom from an odd-numbered group, such as N [Group 5A(15)] or Cl [Group 7A(17)]. These are called **free radicals**, species that contain a lone (unpaired) electron, which makes them paramagnetic (Section 8.4) and extremely reactive. Free radicals are dangerous because they can bond to an H atom in a biomolecule and extract it, which forms a new free radical. This step repeats and can disrupt genes and membranes. Recent studies suggest that free radicals may be involved in cancer and even aging. Antioxidants like vitamin E interrupt free-radical proliferation.

Consider the free radical nitrogen dioxide, NO_2, a major contributor to urban smog, that is formed when the NO in auto exhaust is oxidized. NO_2 has several resonance forms. Two differ in terms of which O atom is doubly bonded, as in the case of ozone. Two others have the lone electron residing on the N or on an O, so the resonance hybrid has the lone electron delocalized over these two atoms:

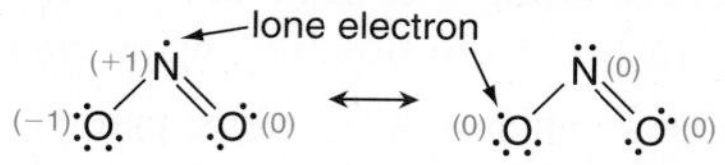

Let's see if formal charge considerations help us decide where the electron resides most of the time. The form with it on the singly bonded O has zero formal charges (*right*), while the form with it on N (*left*) has some nonzero charges. Thus, based on formal charge, the form on the right is more important. But, chemical facts suggest otherwise. Free radicals often react with each other to pair their lone electrons. When two NO_2 molecules react, the lone electrons pair up to form the N—N bond in dinitrogen tetraoxide (N_2O_4) and each N attains an octet:

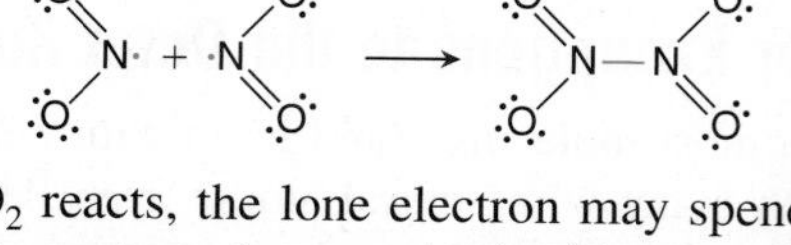

Thus, given the way NO_2 reacts, the lone electron may spend most of its time on N, making *that* form more important. Apparently, in this case, formal charge is not very useful for picking the most important resonance form; we'll see other cases below.

Expanded Valence Shells Many molecules (and ions) have more than eight valence electrons around the central atom. *An atom expands its valence shell to form more bonds, which releases energy.* The central atom must be large and have empty orbitals that can hold the additional pairs. Therefore, **expanded valence shells** occur only with *nonmetals from Period 3 or higher because they have d orbitals available.* Such a central atom may be bonded to more than four atoms, or to four or fewer.

*Reactions in which one species "donates" an electron pair to another to form a covalent bond are Lewis acid-base reactions, which we discuss fully in Chapter 18.

1. *Central atom bonded to more than four atoms.* Phosphorus pentachloride, PCl_5, is a fuming yellow-white solid used to manufacture lacquers and films. It forms when phosphorus trichloride, PCl_3, reacts with chlorine gas. The P in PCl_3 has an octet, but two more bonds to chlorine form and P expands its valence shell to 10 electrons in PCl_5. Note that when PCl_5 forms, *one* Cl—Cl bond breaks *(left side of the equation),* and *two* P—Cl bonds form *(right side),* for a net increase of one bond:

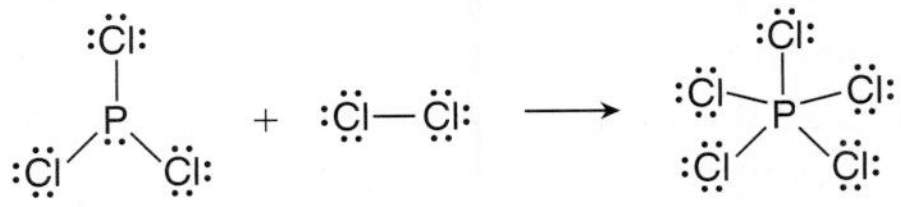

Sulfur hexafluoride, SF_6, a dense and inert gas, is used as an electrical insulator. Analogously to PCl_5, it forms when sulfur tetrafluoride, SF_4, reacts with F_2. The S in SF_4 already has an expanded valence shell of 10 electrons, but two more bonds to F expand the valence shell further to 12 electrons:

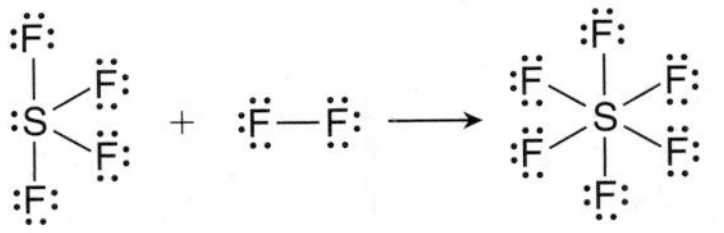

2. *Central atoms bonded to four or fewer atoms.* By applying the concept of formal charge, we can draw Lewis structures with expanded valence shells of central atoms bonded to *four or fewer* atoms. The S in SF_4 is one example, and others follow:

- *Sulfuric acid.* Two resonance forms of H_2SO_4, with formal charges, are

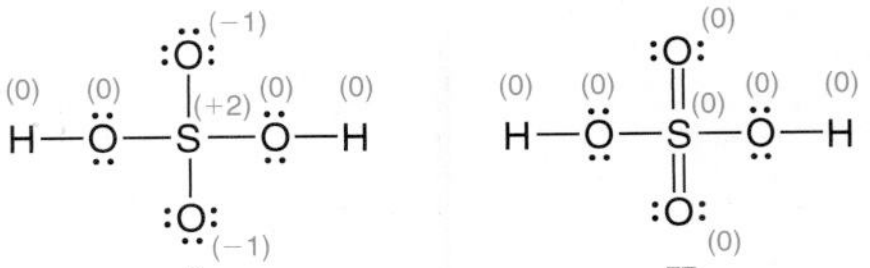

I II

Form I obeys the octet rule, but it has several nonzero formal charges. In form II, sulfur has 12 electrons (6 bonds) around it, but all zero formal charges. Thus, based on the formal charge rules alone, II contributes more than I to the resonance hybrid. More important than whether rules are followed, form II is consistent with observation. In gaseous H_2SO_4, the two sulfur-oxygen bonds *with* an H atom attached to the O are 157 pm long, whereas the two sulfur-oxygen bonds *without* an H atom are 142 pm long. This shorter bond indicates double-bond character, and other measurements indicate greater electron density in the bonds without the attached H.

- *Sulfate ion.* When sulfuric acid loses two H^+ ions, it forms the sulfate ion, SO_4^{2-}. Measurements indicate all the bonds in SO_4^{2-} are 149 pm long, between the length of an S═O bond (~142 pm) and that of an S—O bond (~157 pm). Six of the seven resonance forms consistent with these data have an expanded valence shell and zero formal charges. Two of the six (*left*) and the one that obeys the octet rule (*right*) are

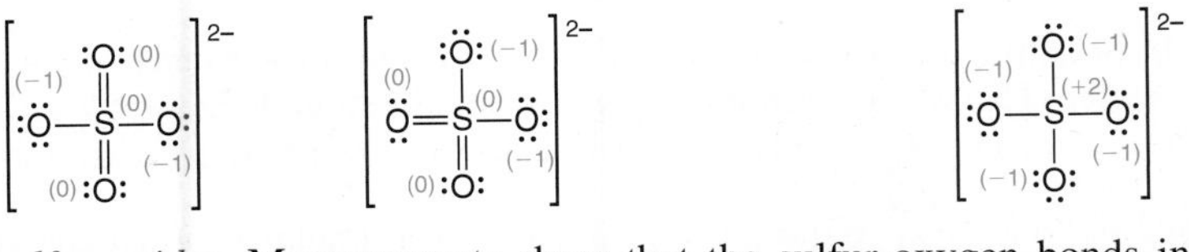

- *Two sulfur oxides.* Measurements show that the sulfur-oxygen bonds in SO_2 and SO_3 are all approximately 142 pm long, indicating S═O bonds. Lewis structures consistent with these data have zero formal charges *(two at left),* but others *(two at right)* obey the octet rule:

3. *Limitations of Lewis structures and formal charge.* Chemistry has been a central science for well over two centuries, yet controversies often arise over interpretation of

data, even in established areas like bonding and structure. We've seen that a single Lewis structure often cannot accurately depict a molecule, so we need several resonance forms to do so.

Formal charge rules have limitations, too. They were not useful in choosing the correct location for the lone electron in NO_2. And, quantum-mechanical calculations indicate that resonance forms with expanded valence shells that have zero formal charges look *less* like the actual species than forms that follow the octet rule but have higher formal charges. Shorter bonds arise, these findings suggest, not from double-bond character, but because the higher formal charges draw the bonded atoms closer. Such considerations favor the octet-rule forms for H_2SO_4, SO_4^{2-}, SO_2, and SO_3. Thus, formal charge may be a useful tool for selecting the most important resonance form, but it is far from perfect. Nevertheless, while keeping these contrary findings in mind, we will continue to draw structures based on formal charge rules because they provide a simple approach consistent with experimental data.

Sample Problem 10.5 Writing Lewis Structures for Octet-Rule Exceptions

Problem Write a Lewis structure and identify the octet-rule exception for **(a)** $SClF_5$; **(b)** H_3PO_4 (draw two resonance forms and select the more important); **(c)** $BFCl_2$.

Plan We write each Lewis structure and examine it for exceptions to the octet rule. **(a)** and **(b)** The central atoms are in Period 3, so they can have more than an octet. **(c)** The central atom is B, which can have fewer than an octet of electrons.

Solution (a) $SClF_5$ has an *expanded valence shell.* The Lewis structure is

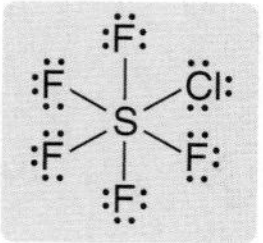

(b) H_3PO_4 has two resonance forms. The structures, with formal charges, are

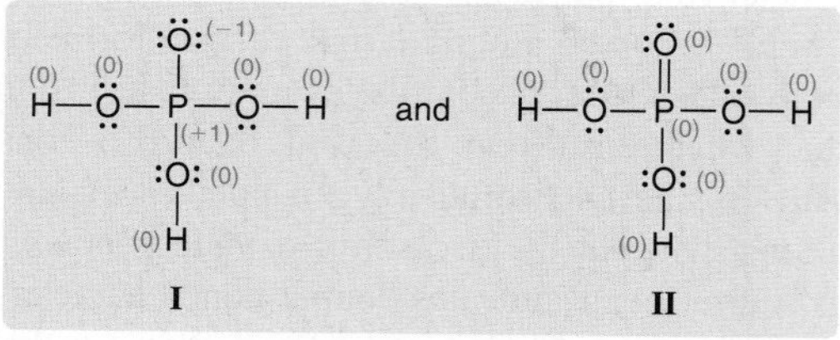

Structure I obeys the octet rule but has nonzero formal charges. Structure II has an expanded valence shell with zero formal charges. According to formal charge rules, structure II is the more important form.

(c) $BFCl_2$ is an *electron-deficient molecule;* B has only six electrons surrounding it:

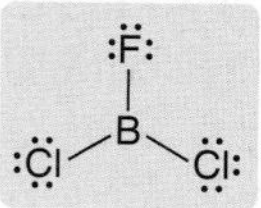

Comment In (b), structure II is consistent with bond-length measurements, which show one shorter (152 pm) phosphorus-oxygen bond and three longer (157 pm) ones. Nevertheless, as for H_2SO_4, calculations show that structure I may be more important.

Follow-Up Problem 10.5 Write a Lewis structure with minimal formal charges for **(a)** $POCl_3$; **(b)** ClO_2; **(c)** XeF_4.

Summary of Section 10.1

- A stepwise process converts a molecular formula into a Lewis structure, a two-dimensional representation of a molecule (or ion) that shows the placement of atoms and distribution of valence electrons among bonding and lone pairs.
- When two or more Lewis structures can be drawn for the same relative placement of atoms, the actual structure is a hybrid of those resonance forms.

- Formal charges can be useful for choosing the more important contributor to the hybrid, but experimental data always determine the choice.
- Molecules with an electron-deficient atom (central Be or B) or an odd-electron atom (free radicals) have less than an octet around the central atom but often attain an octet in reactions.
- In a molecule (or ion) with a central atom from Period 3 or higher, that atom can have more than eight valence electrons because it is larger and has empty *d* orbitals for expanding its valence shell.

10.2 • VALENCE-SHELL ELECTRON-PAIR REPULSION (VSEPR) THEORY

Virtually every biochemical process hinges to a great extent on the shapes of interacting molecules. Every medicine you take, odor you smell, or flavor you taste depends on part or all of one molecule fitting together with another. Biologists have found that complex behaviors in many organisms, such as mating, defense, navigation, and feeding, often depend on one molecule's shape matching that of another. In this section, we discuss a model for predicting the shape of a molecule.

To obtain the molecular shape, chemists start with the Lewis structure and apply **valence-shell electron-pair repulsion (VSEPR) theory.** Its basic principle is that, *to minimize repulsions, each group of valence electrons around a central atom is located as far as possible from the others.* A "group" of electrons is any number that occupies a localized region around an atom: single bond, double bond, triple bond,* lone pair, or even lone electron. The **molecular shape** is the three-dimensional arrangement of nuclei joined by the bonding groups.

Electron-Group Arrangements and Molecular Shapes

When two, three, four, five, or six objects attached to a central point maximize the space between them, five geometric patterns result, which Figure 10.2A shows with balloons. If the objects are valence-electron groups, repulsions maximize the space each occupies around the central atom, and we obtain the five *electron-group arrangements* seen in the great majority of molecules and polyatomic ions.

Classifying Molecular Shapes *The electron-group arrangement* is defined by the bonding *and* nonbonding electron groups, but the *molecular shape* is defined by the relative positions of the nuclei, which are connected by the bonding groups only. Figure 10.2B shows the molecular shapes that occur when *all* the surrounding electron groups are *bonding* groups. When some are *nonbonding* groups, no nucleus is attached so dif-

*The two electron pairs in a double bond (or the three pairs in a triple bond) occupy separate orbitals, so they remain near each other and act as one electron group (see Chapter 11).

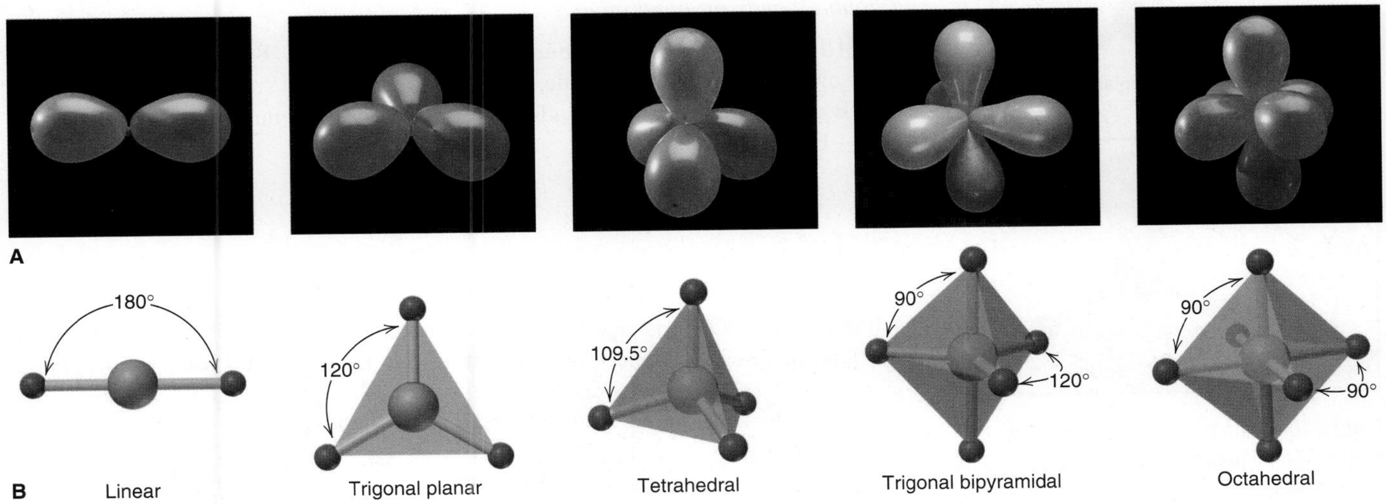

Figure 10.2 Electron-group repulsions and molecular shapes. A, Five geometric orientations arise when each balloon occupies as much space as possible. **B,** Mutually repelling bonding groups (*gray sticks*) attach a surrounding atom (*dark gray*) to the central atom (*red*). The name is the electron-group arrangement.

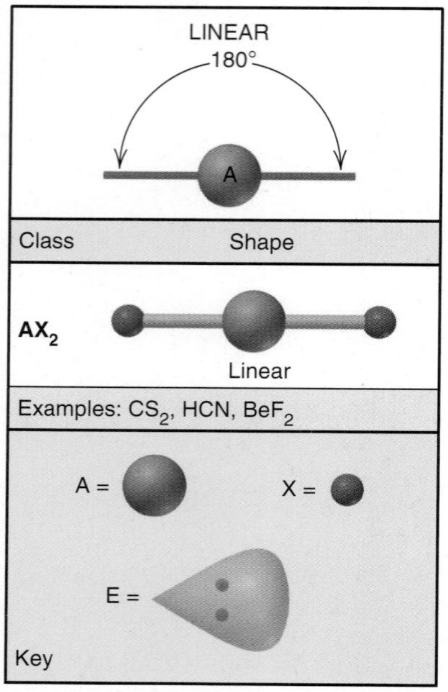

Figure 10.3 **The single molecular shape of the linear electron-group arrangement.** The key (*bottom*) for A, X, and E also refers to Figures 10.4, 10.5, 10.7, and 10.8.

ferent molecular shapes occur. Thus, *the same electron-group arrangement can give rise to different molecular shapes:* some with all bonding groups (as in Figure 10.2B) and others with bonding and nonbonding groups. To classify molecular shapes, we assign each a specific AX_mE_n designation, where m and n are integers, A is the central atom, X is a surrounding atom, and E is a nonbonding valence-electron group (usually a lone pair).

The Importance of Bond Angle The **bond angle** is the angle formed by the nuclei of two surrounding atoms with the nucleus of the central atom at the vertex. The angles shown for the shapes in Figure 10.2B are *ideal* bond angles determined by basic geometry alone. We observe them when all the bonding groups are the same and connected to the same type of atom. When this is not the case, the real bond angles deviate from the ideal angles:

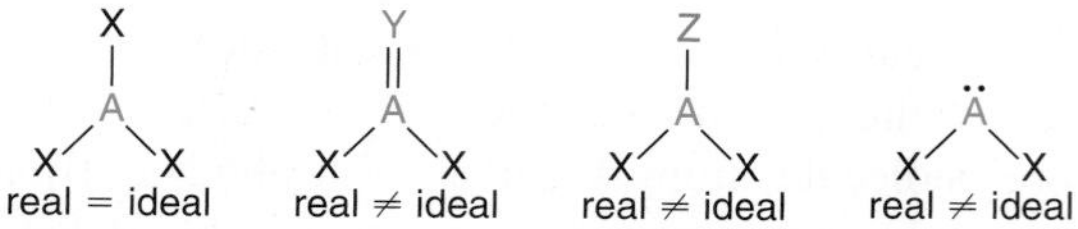

The Molecular Shape with Two Electron Groups (Linear Arrangement)

Two electron groups attached to a central atom point in opposite directions. This **linear arrangement** of electron groups results in a molecule with a **linear shape** and a bond angle of 180°. Figure 10.3 shows the general form (*top*) and shape (*middle*) with VSEPR shape class (AX_2), and gives the formulas of some linear molecules.

Gaseous beryllium chloride ($BeCl_2$) is a linear molecule. Recall that gaseous Be compounds are electron deficient, with two electron pairs around the central Be:

In carbon dioxide, the central C atom forms two double bonds with the O atoms:

Each double bond acts as one electron group and is 180° away from the other. The lone pairs on the O atoms of CO_2 or on the Cl atoms of $BeCl_2$ are *not* involved in the molecular shape: only electron groups around the *central* atom affect shape.

Molecular Shapes with Three Electron Groups (Trigonal Planar Arrangement)

Three electron groups around a central atom point to the corners of an equilateral triangle, which gives the **trigonal planar arrangement** and an ideal bond angle of 120° (Figure 10.4). This arrangement has two molecular shapes—one with all bonding groups and the other with one lone pair. It allows us to see *the effects of lone pairs and double bonds on bond angles.*

1. *All bonding groups: trigonal planar shape (AX_3).* Boron trifluoride (BF_3), another electron-deficient molecule, is an example. It has six electrons around the central B atom in three single bonds to F atoms. The four nuclei lie in a plane, and each F—B—F angle is 120°:

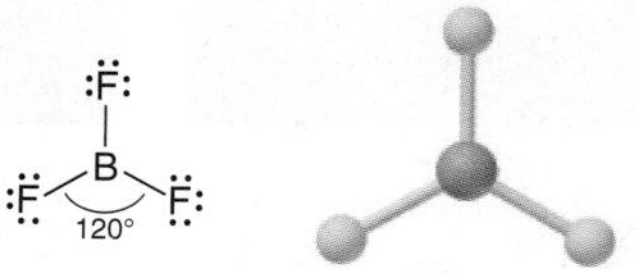

The nitrate ion (NO_3^-) is one of several polyatomic ions with the trigonal planar shape. One of three resonance forms of the nitrate ion (Sample Problem 10.4) is

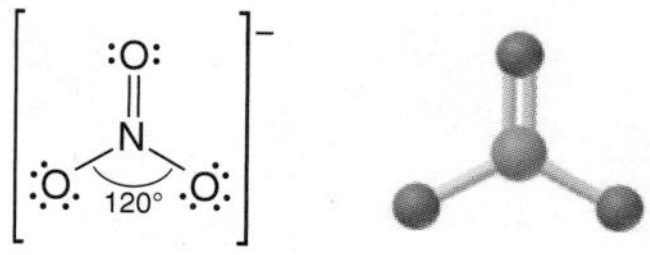

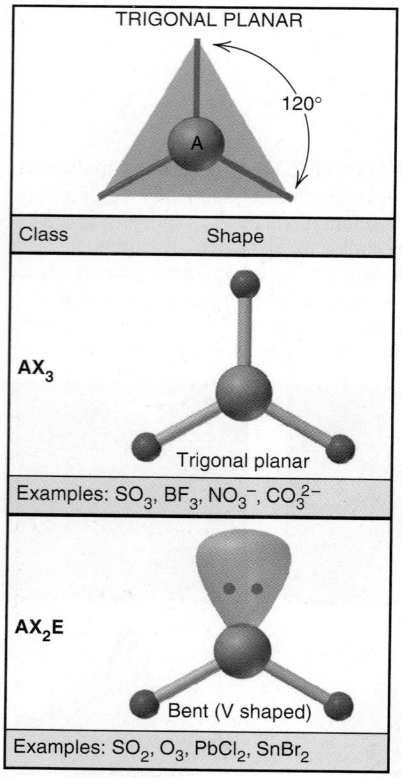

Figure 10.4 **The two molecular shapes of the trigonal planar electron-group arrangement.**

The resonance hybrid has three identical bonds of bond order $1\frac{1}{3}$, so the ideal bond angle is observed.

2. *One lone pair: bent or V shape (AX_2E).* Gaseous tin(II) chloride is a molecule with a **bent shape,** or **V shape,** with three electron groups in a trigonal plane and a lone pair at one of the triangle's corners. A lone pair often has a major effect on bond angle. Because it is held by only one nucleus, a lone pair is less confined than a bonding pair and so exerts stronger repulsions. In general, *a lone pair repels bonding pairs more than bonding pairs repel each other, so it decreases the angle between bonding pairs.* Note the 95° bond angle in $SnCl_2$, which is considerably less than the ideal 120°:

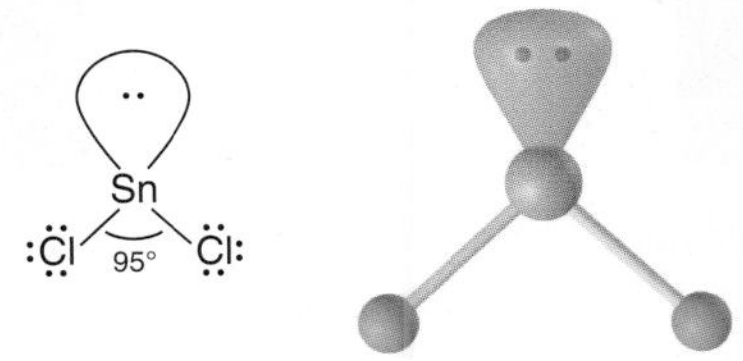

Effect of Double Bonds on Bond Angle When the surrounding atoms and electron groups are not identical, the bond angles may also be affected. Consider formaldehyde (CH_2O), whose uses include the manufacture of countertops and the production of methanol. Its trigonal planar shape is due to two types of surrounding atoms (O and H) and two types of electron groups (single and double bonds):

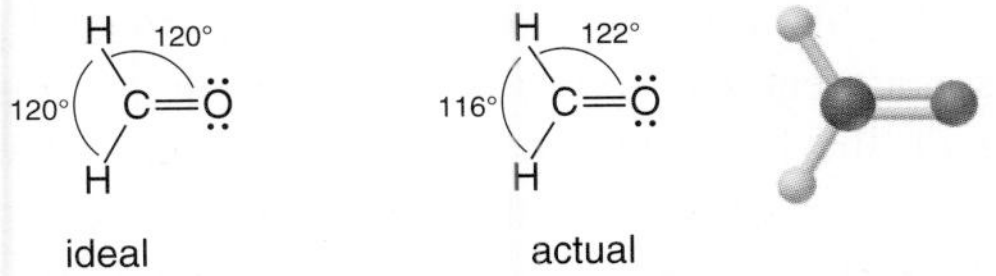

The actual H—C—H bond angle is less than the ideal 120° because *the greater electron density of a double bond repels electrons in single bonds more than the single bonds repel each other.*

Molecular Shapes with Four Electron Groups (Tetrahedral Arrangement)

Shapes based on two or three electron groups lie in a plane, but four electron groups require three dimensions to maximize separation. Consider methane, whose Lewis structure (*below, left*) shows four bonds pointing to the corners of a square, which suggests 90° bond angles. But, *Lewis structures do **not** depict shape.* In three dimensions, the four electron groups lie at the corners of a *tetrahedron,* a polyhedron with four faces made of equilateral triangles, giving bond angles of 109.5° (Figure 10.5).

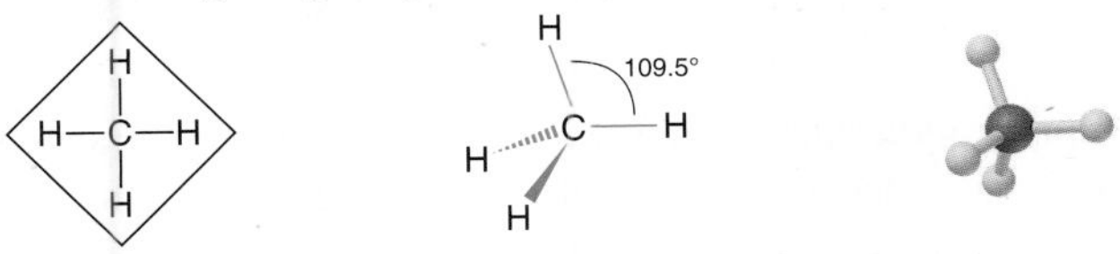

A *perspective drawing* for methane (*above, middle*) indicates depth by using solid and dashed wedges for bonds out of the plane of the page. The normal bond lines (*blue*) are in the plane of the page; the solid wedge (*green*) is the bond from the C atom in the plane of the page to the H above that plane; and the dashed wedge (*red*) is the bond from the C to the H below the plane of the page. The ball-and-stick model (*above, right*) shows the tetrahedral shape more clearly.

*All molecules or ions with four electron groups around a central atom adopt the **tetrahedral arrangement**.* There are three shapes with this arrangement:

1. *All bonding groups: tetrahedral shape (AX_4).* Methane has a tetrahedral shape, a very common geometry in organic molecules. In Sample Problem 10.1, we drew the Lewis structure for CCl_2F_2, without regard to relative placement of the four halogen atoms around the carbon atom. Because Lewis structures are flat, it may seem like you can write two different ones for CCl_2F_2, but they represent the same molecule, as a twist of the wrist reveals (Figure 10.6, *next page*).

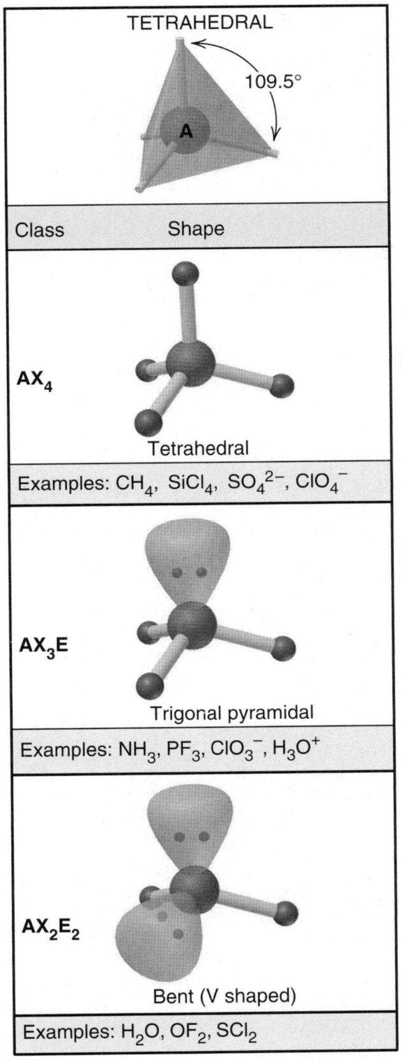

Figure 10.5 The three molecular shapes of the tetrahedral electron-group arrangement.

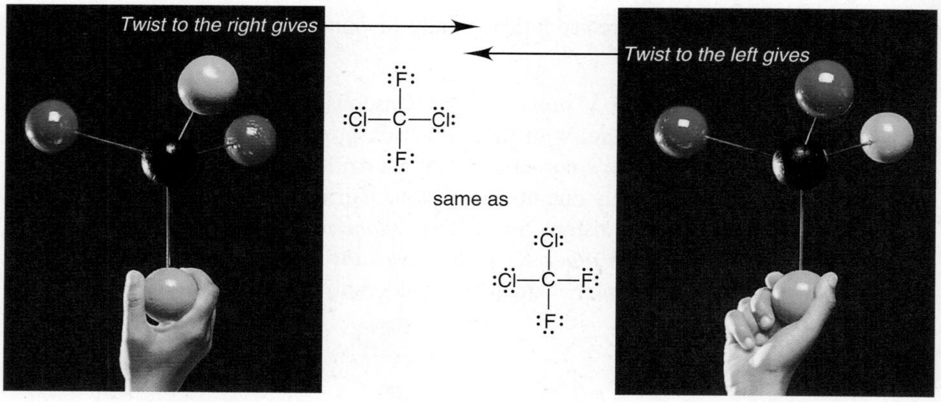

Figure 10.6 Lewis structures do not indicate molecular shape. In this model, Cl is green and F is yellow.

2. *One lone pair: trigonal pyramidal shape (AX_3E).* Ammonia (NH_3) is an example of a molecule with a **trigonal pyramidal shape,** a tetrahedron with one vertex "missing." Stronger repulsions by the lone pair make the H—N—H bond angle slightly less than the ideal 109.5°. The lone pair forces the N—H pairs closer to each other, and the bond angle is 107.3°. NF_3 (see page 364) also has a trigonal pyramidal shape.

Picturing shapes is a great way to visualize a reaction. For instance, when ammonia reacts with an acid, the lone pair on N forms a bond to the H^+ and yields the ammonium ion (NH_4^+), one of many tetrahedral polyatomic ions. As the lone pair becomes a bonding pair, the H—N—H angle expands from 107.3° to 109.5°:

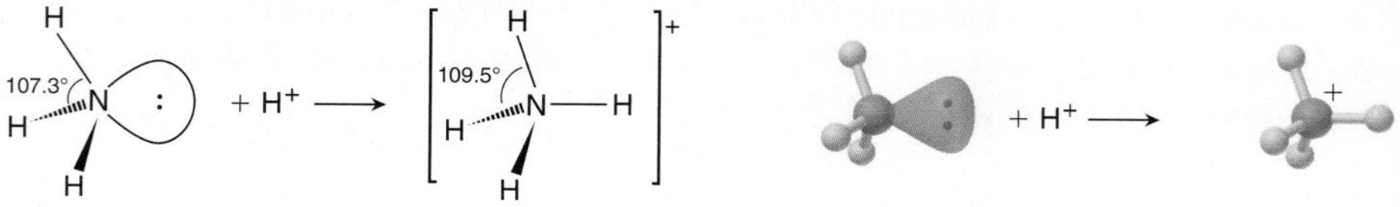

3. *Two lone pairs: bent or V shape (AX_2E_2).* Water is the most important V-shaped molecule with the tetrahedral arrangement. [Note that, in the trigonal planar arrangement, the V shape has two bonding groups and *one* lone pair (AX_2E), and its ideal bond angle is 120°, not 109.5°.] Repulsions from two lone pairs are greater than from one, and the H—O—H bond angle is 104.5°, less than the H—N—H angle in NH_3:

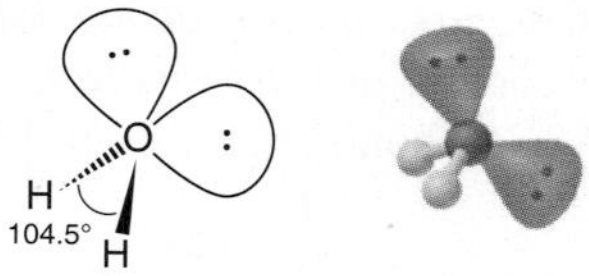

Thus, for similar molecules within a given electron-group arrangement, electron-electron repulsions cause deviations from ideal bond angles in the following order:

Lone pair–lone pair > lone pair–bonding pair > bonding pair–bonding pair **(10.2)**

Molecular Shapes with Five Electron Groups (Trigonal Bipyramidal Arrangement)

All molecules with five or six electron groups have a central atom from Period 3 or higher because only those atoms have *d* orbitals available to expand the valence shell.

Relative Positions of Electron Groups Five mutually repelling electron groups form the **trigonal bipyramidal arrangement,** in which two trigonal pyramids share a common base (Figure 10.7). This is the only case in which *there are two different positions for electron groups and two ideal bond angles.* Three **equatorial groups** lie in a trigonal plane that includes the central atom, and two **axial groups** lie above and below this plane. Therefore, a 120° bond angle separates equatorial groups, and a 90° angle separates axial from equatorial groups. Two factors come into play:

- The greater the bond angle, the weaker the repulsions, so *equatorial-equatorial (120°) repulsions are weaker than axial-equatorial (90°) repulsions.*
- The stronger repulsions from lone pairs means that, when possible, *lone pairs occupy equatorial positions.*

Shapes for the Trigonal Bipyramidal Arrangement The tendency for lone pairs to occupy equatorial positions, and thus minimize stronger axial-equatorial repulsions, governs three of the four shapes for this arrangement.

1. *All bonding groups: trigonal bipyramidal shape (AX_5).* Phosphorus pentachloride (PCl_5) has a trigonal bipyramidal shape. With five identical surrounding atoms, the bond angles are ideal:

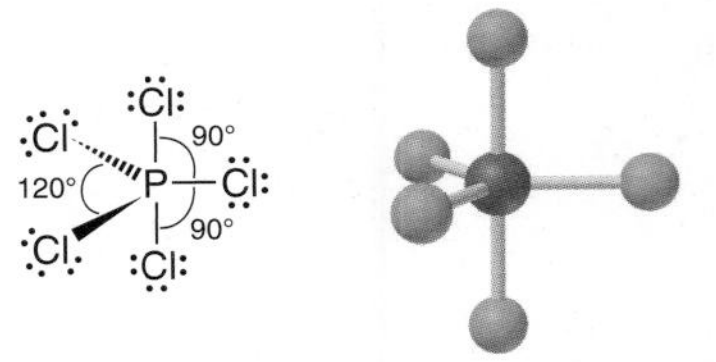

2. *One lone pair: seesaw shape (AX_4E).* Sulfur tetrafluoride (SF_4), a strong fluorinating agent, has the **seesaw shape;** in Figure 10.7, the "seesaw" is tipped on an end. This is the first example of *lone pairs occupying equatorial positions* to minimize repulsions. The lone pair repels all four bonding pairs, reducing the bond angles to 101.5° and 86.8°:

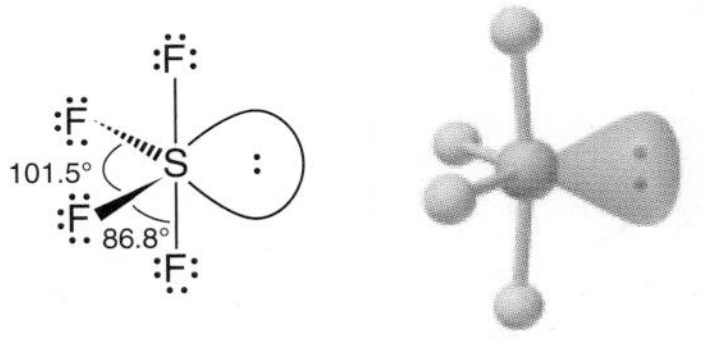

3. *Two lone pairs: T shape (AX_3E_2).* Bromine trifluoride (BrF_3), one of many compounds with fluorine bonded to a larger halogen, has a **T shape.** Since both lone pairs occupy equatorial positions, we see a greater decrease in the axial-equatorial bond angle, down to 86.2°:

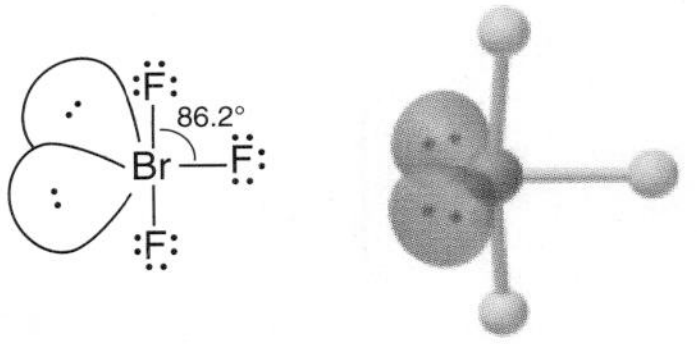

4. *Three lone pairs: linear shape (AX_2E_3).* The triiodide ion (I_3^-), which forms when I_2 dissolves in aqueous I^- solution, is linear. With three equatorial lone pairs and two axial bonding pairs, the three nuclei form a straight line and a 180° X—A—X bond angle:

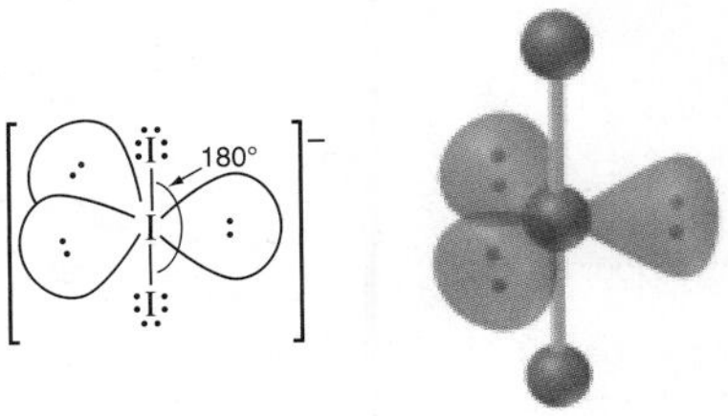

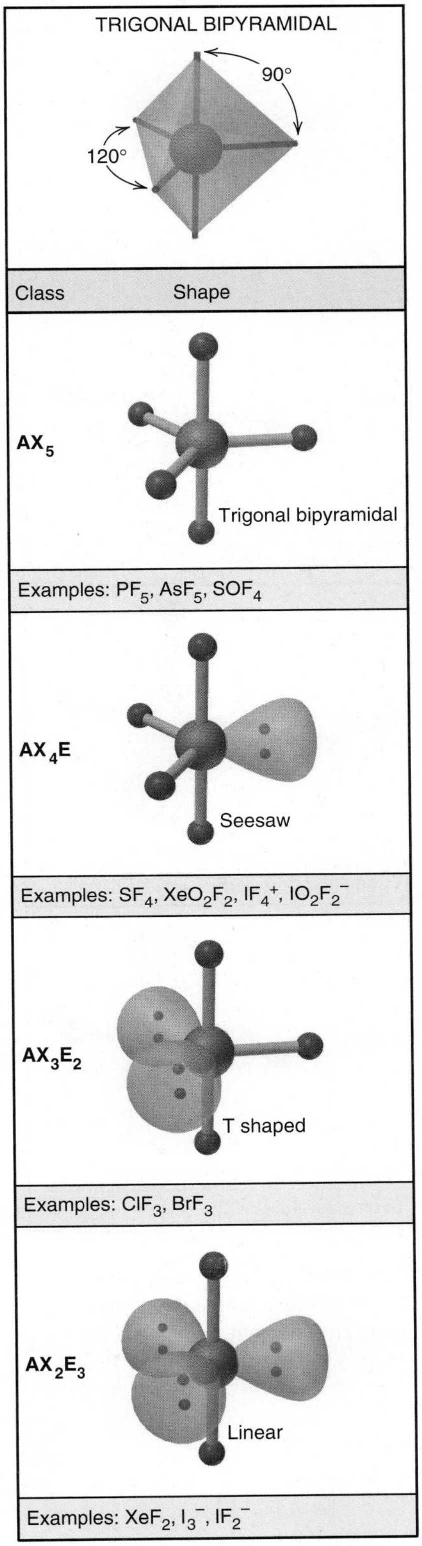

Figure 10.7 The four molecular shapes of the trigonal bipyramidal electron-group arrangement.

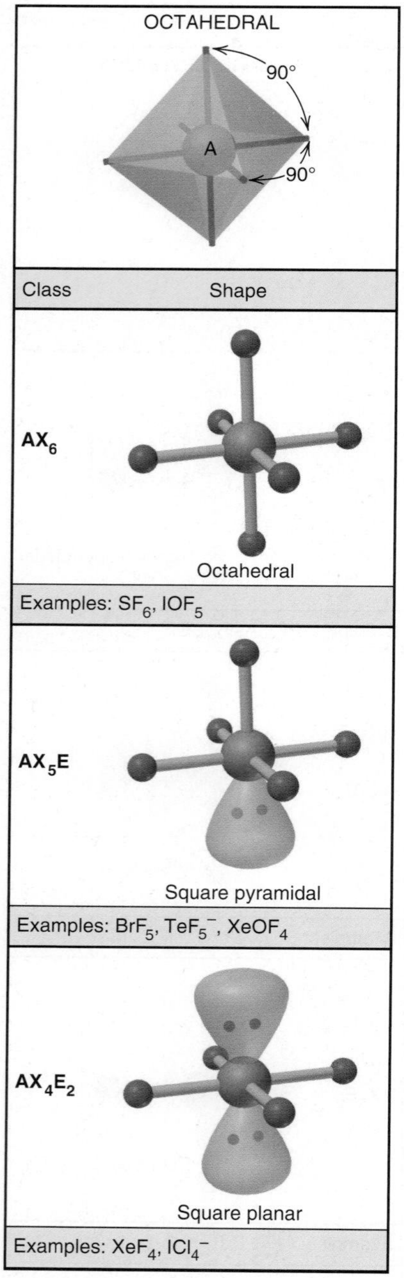

Figure 10.8 The three molecular shapes of the octahedral electron-group arrangement.

Molecular Shapes with Six Electron Groups (Octahedral Arrangement)

Six electron groups form the **octahedral arrangement.** An *octahedron* is a polyhedron with eight equilateral triangles for faces and six identical vertices (Figure 10.8). Each of the six groups points to a corner, which gives a 90° ideal bond angle.

1. *All bonding groups: octahedral shape (AX_6).* When seesaw-shaped SF_4 reacts with more F_2 (see pp. 371 and 377), the central S atom expands its valence shell further to form octahedral sulfur hexafluoride (SF_6):

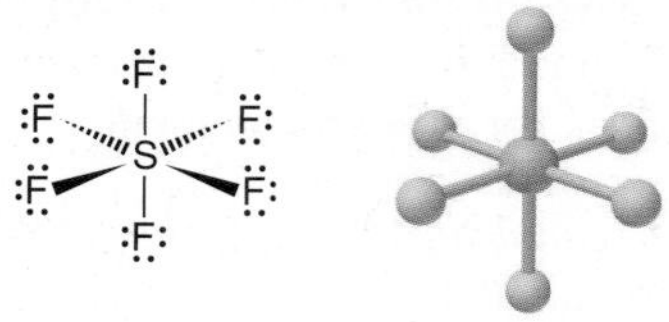

2. *One lone pair: square pyramidal shape (AX_5E).* Iodine pentafluoride (IF_5) has a **square pyramidal shape.** Note that it makes no difference where one lone pair resides because all the bond angles are 90°. The lone pair reduces the bond angles to 81.9°:

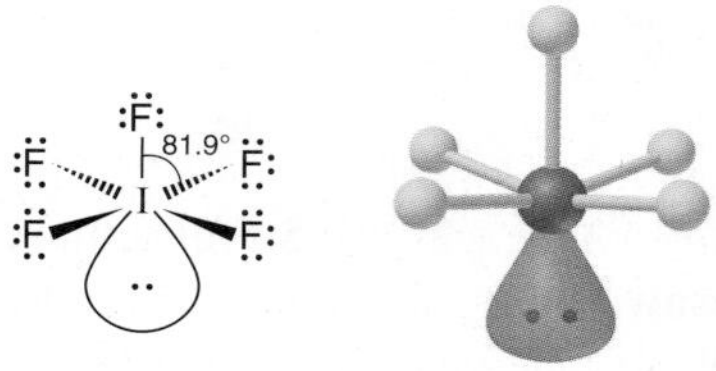

3. *Two lone pairs: square planar shape (AX_4E_2).* Xenon tetrafluoride (XeF_4) has a **square planar shape.** To avoid stronger 90° lone pair–lone pair repulsions, two lone pairs lie *opposite* each other:

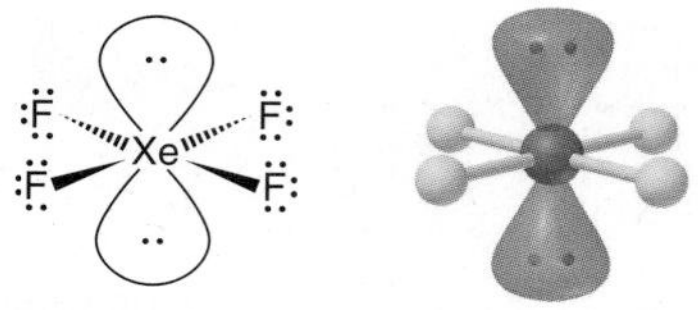

Figure 10.9 displays the shapes possible for elements in different periods, and Figure 10.10 summarizes the molecular shapes we've discussed.

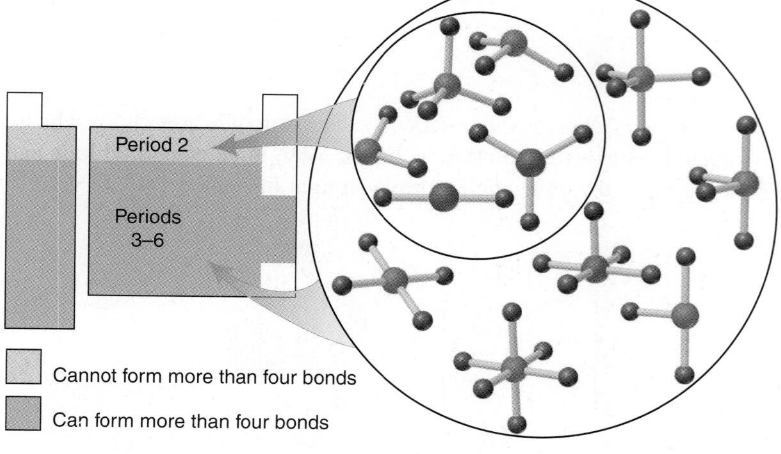

Figure 10.9 Molecular shapes for central atoms in Period 2 and in higher periods.

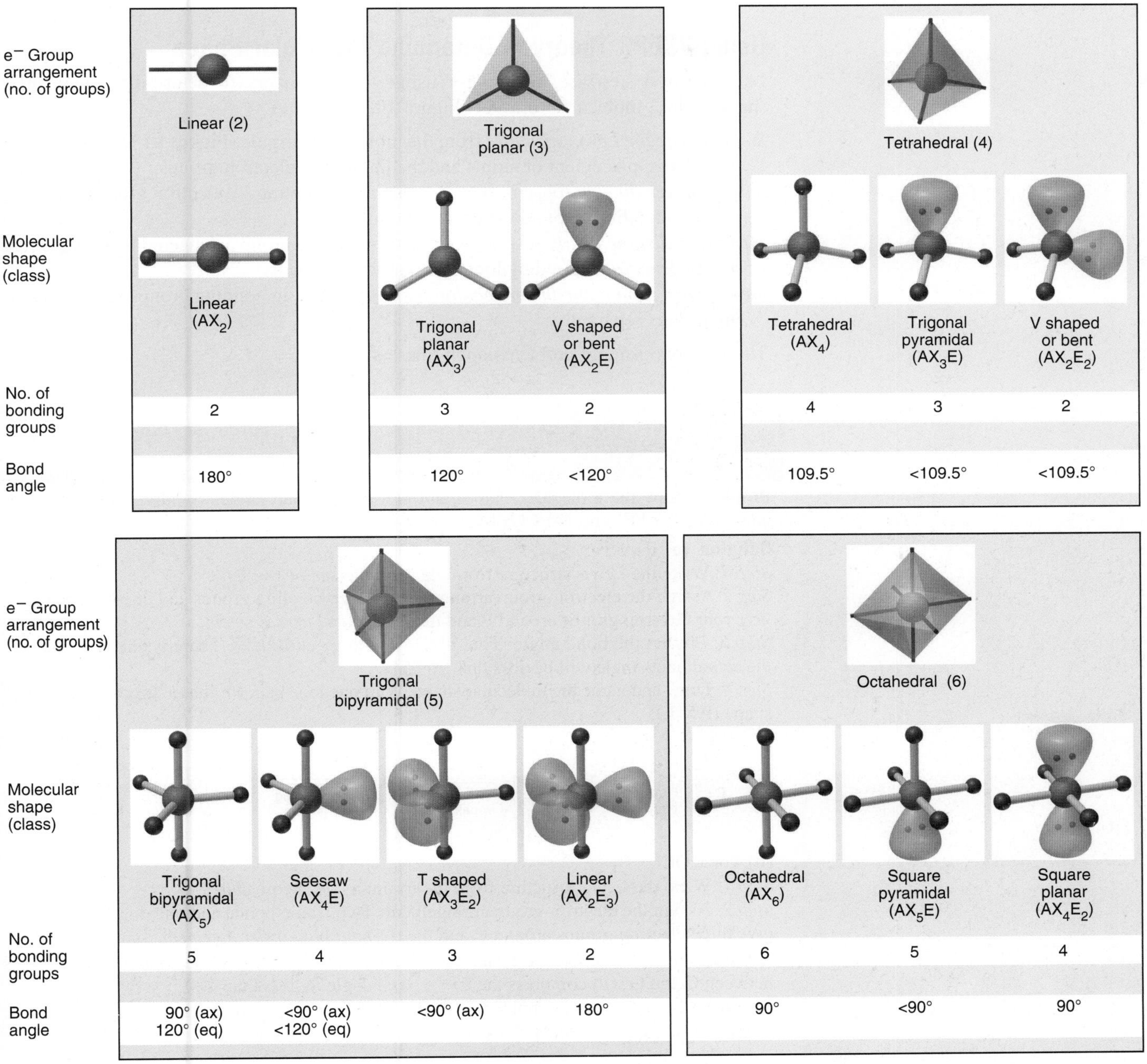

Figure 10.10 A summary of common molecular shapes with two to six electron groups.

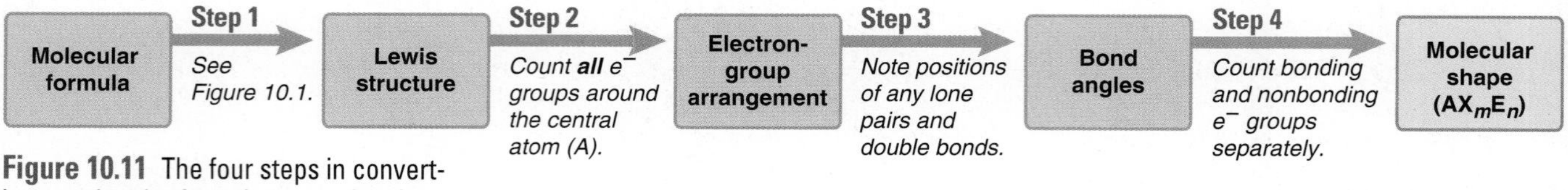

Figure 10.11 The four steps in converting a molecular formula to a molecular shape.

Using VSEPR Theory to Determine Molecular Shape

Let's apply a stepwise method for using VSEPR theory to determine a molecular shape from a molecular formula (Figure 10.11):

Step 1. Write the Lewis structure from the molecular formula (Figure 10.1, p. 364) to see the relative placement of atoms and the number of electron groups.
Step 2. Assign an electron-group arrangement by counting *all* electron groups (bonding plus nonbonding) around the central atom.
Step 3. Predict the ideal bond angle from the electron-group arrangement and *the effect of any deviation* caused by lone pairs or double bonds.
Step 4. Draw and name the molecular shape by counting bonding groups and nonbonding groups separately.

The next two sample problems apply these steps.

Sample Problem 10.6 Examining Shapes with Two, Three, or Four Electron Groups

Problem Draw the molecular shapes and predict the bond angles (relative to the ideal angles) of **(a)** PF_3 and **(b)** $COCl_2$.

Solution (a) For PF_3.
Step 1. Write the Lewis structure from the formula (*see below, left*).
Step 2. Assign the electron-group arrangement: Three bonding groups and one lone pair give four electron groups around P and the *tetrahedral arrangement*.
Step 3. Predict the bond angle: The ideal bond angle is 109.5°. There is one lone pair, so the actual bond angle will be less than 109.5°.
Step 4. Draw and name the molecular shape: With one lone pair, PF_3 has a trigonal pyramidal shape (AX_3E):

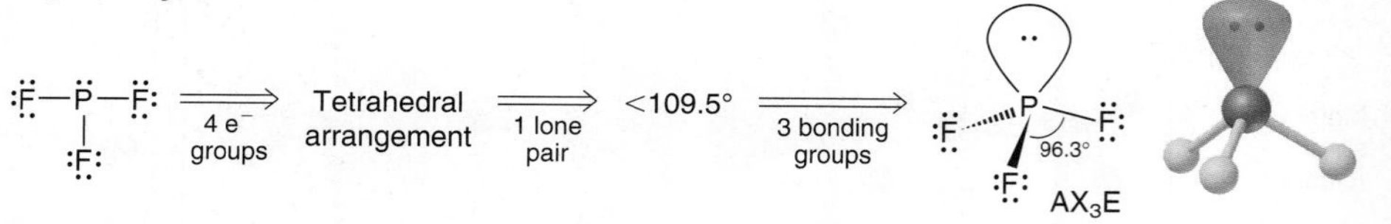

(b) For $COCl_2$.
Step 1. Write the Lewis structure from the formula (*see below, left*).
Step 2. Assign the electron-group arrangement: Two single bonds and one double bond give three electron groups around C and the *trigonal planar arrangement.*
Step 3. Predict the bond angles: The ideal bond angle is 120°, but the double bond between C and O will compress the Cl—C—Cl angle to less than 120°.
Step 4. Draw and name the molecular shape: With three electron groups and no lone pairs, $COCl_2$ has a trigonal planar shape (AX_3):

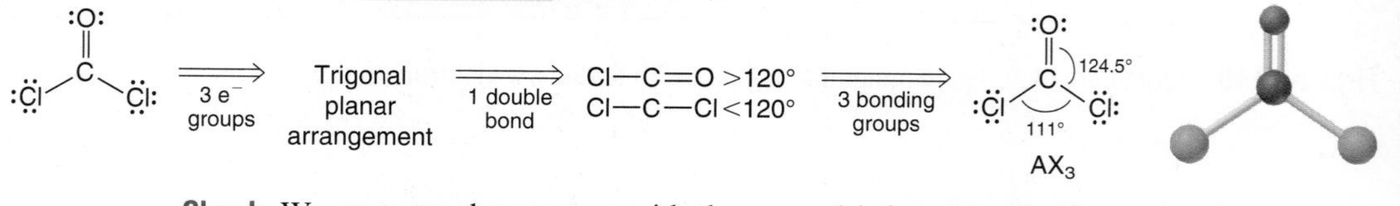

Check We compare the answers with the general information in Figure 10.10.

Comment Be sure the Lewis structure is correct because it determines the other steps.

Follow-Up Problem 10.6 Draw the molecular shapes and predict the bond angles (relative to the ideal angles) of **(a)** CS_2; **(b)** $PbCl_2$; **(c)** CBr_4; **(d)** SF_2.

Sample Problem 10.7 Examining Shapes with Five or Six Electron Groups

Problem Draw the molecular shapes and predict the bond angles (relative to the ideal angles) of **(a)** SbF_5 and **(b)** BrF_5.

Plan We proceed as in Sample Problem 10.6, being sure to minimize the number of axial-equatorial repulsions.

Solution (a) For SbF_5.
Step 1. Lewis structure (*see below, left*).
Step 2. Electron-group arrangement: With five electron groups, this is the *trigonal bipyramidal* arrangement.
Step 3. Bond angles: All the groups and surrounding atoms are identical, so the bond angles are ideal: 120° between equatorial groups and 90° between axial and equatorial groups.
Step 4. Molecular shape: Five electron groups and no lone pairs give the trigonal bipyramidal shape (AX_5):

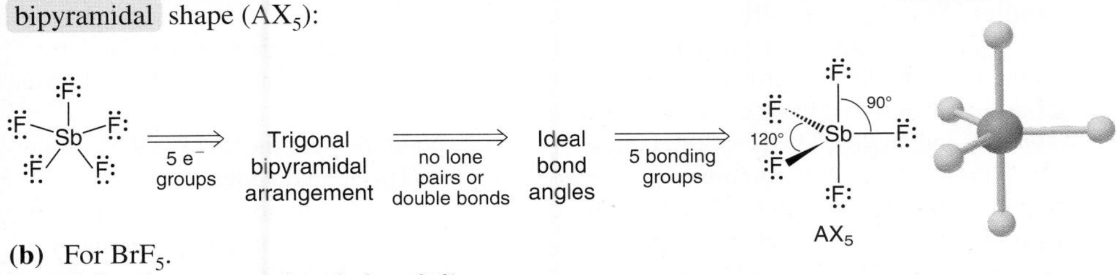

(b) For BrF_5.
Step 1. Lewis structure (*see below, left*).
Step 2. Electron-group arrangement: Six electron groups give the *octahedral* arrangement.
Step 3. Bond angles: The lone pair will make all bond angles less than the ideal 90°.
Step 4. Molecular shape: With one lone pair, BrF_5 has the square pyramidal shape (AX_5E):

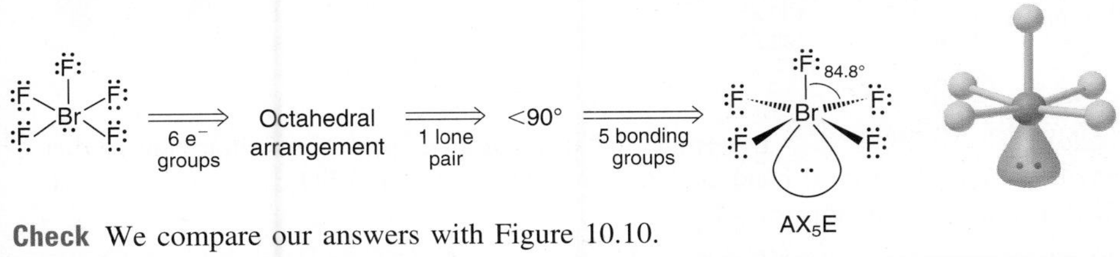

Check We compare our answers with Figure 10.10.

Comment We will also see the linear, tetrahedral, square planar, and octahedral shapes in an important group of substances, called *coordination compounds,* in Chapter 23.

Follow-Up Problem 10.7 Draw the molecular shapes and predict the bond angles (relative to the ideal angles) of **(a)** ICl_2^-; **(b)** ClF_3; **(c)** SOF_4.

Molecular Shapes with More Than One Central Atom

The shapes of molecules with more than one central atom are composites of the shapes around each of the atoms. Here are two examples:

1. Ethane (CH_3CH_3; molecular formula C_2H_6) is a component of natural gas. With four bonding groups and no lone pairs around the two central carbons, ethane is shaped like two overlapping tetrahedra (Figure 10.12A).

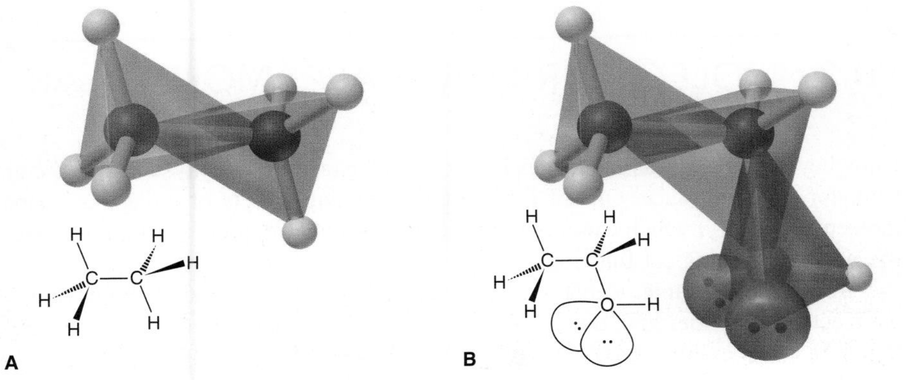

Figure 10.12 The tetrahedral shapes around the central atoms and the overall shapes of ethane **(A)** and ethanol **(B)**.

2. Ethanol (CH_3CH_2OH; molecular formula C_2H_6O), the intoxicating substance in beer, wine, and whiskey, has three central atoms (Figure 10.12B). The CH_3— group is tetrahedrally shaped, and the —CH_2— group has four bonding groups around its central C atom, so it is also tetrahedrally shaped. The O atom has two bonding groups and two lone pairs around it, so the —OH group has a V shape (AX_2E_2).

Sample Problem 10.8 Predicting Molecular Shapes with More Than One Central Atom

Problem Determine the shape around each central atom in acetone, $(CH_3)_2CO$.

Plan There are three central C atoms, two of which are in CH_3— groups. We determine the shape around one central atom at a time.

Solution *Step 1.* Lewis structure (*see below, left*).

Step 2. Electron-group arrangement: Each CH_3— group has four electron groups around its central C, so its electron-group arrangement is *tetrahedral.* The third C atom has three electron groups around it, so it has the *trigonal planar arrangement.*

Step 3. Bond angles: The H—C—H angle in CH_3— should be near the ideal 109.5°. The C=O double bond will compress the C—C—C angle to less than the ideal 120°.

Step 4. Shapes around central atoms: With four electron groups and no lone pairs, the shape around C in each CH_3— is tetrahedral (AX_4). With three electron groups and no lone pairs, the shape around the middle C is trigonal planar (AX_3):

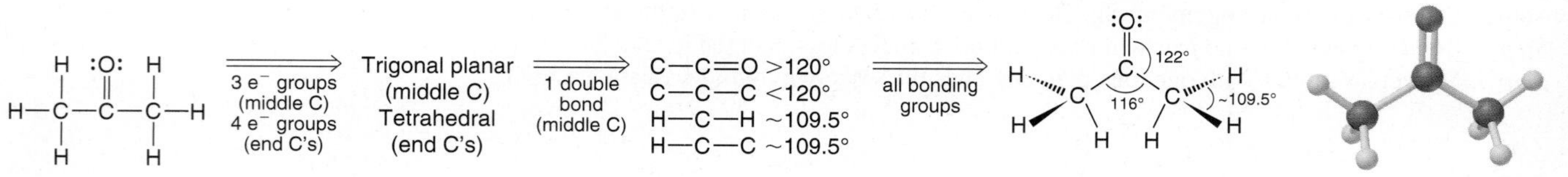

Follow-Up Problem 10.8 Determine the shape around each central atom and predict any deviations from ideal bond angles in the following: **(a)** H_2SO_4; **(b)** propyne (C_3H_4; there is one C≡C bond); **(c)** S_2F_2.

Summary of Section 10.2

- VSEPR theory proposes that each electron group (single bond, multiple bond, lone pair, or lone electron) around a central atom remains as far from the others as possible.
- Five electron-group arrangements are possible when two, three, four, five, or six electron groups surround a central atom. Each arrangement is associated with one or more molecular shapes, depending on the numbers of bonding and lone pairs.
- Ideal bond angles are based on the regular geometric arrangements. Deviations from them occur when surrounding atoms and/or electron groups are not identical.
- Lone pairs and double bonds exert stronger repulsions than single bonds.
- Shapes of larger molecules are composites of the shapes around each central atom.

10.3 • MOLECULAR SHAPE AND MOLECULAR POLARITY

Knowing the shape of its molecules is key to understanding the physical and chemical behavior of a substance. One of the most far-reaching effects of molecular shape is molecular polarity, which can influence melting and boiling points, solubility, reactivity, and even biological function.

Recall from Chapter 9 that a covalent bond is *polar* when the atoms have different electronegativities and, thus, share the electrons unequally. In diatomic molecules, such as HF, the only bond is polar, so the molecule is polar. In larger molecules, *both shape and bond polarity determine* **molecular polarity,** an imbalance of charge over the whole molecule or large portion of it. Polar molecules become oriented in an electric field, with their partially charged ends pointing toward the oppositely charged plates (Figure 10.13). **Dipole moment (μ)** is a measure of molecular polarity, given in the unit *debye* (D)* derived from SI units of charge (coulomb, C) and length (m): $1\ D = 3.34\times10^{-30}\ C\cdot m$.

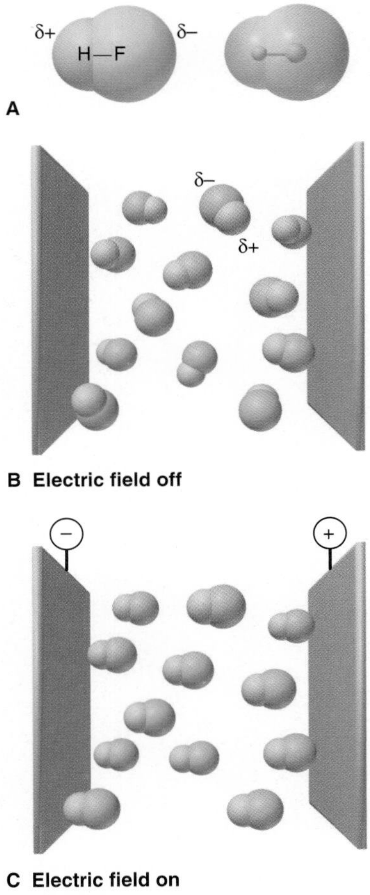

Figure 10.13 The orientation of polar molecules in an electric field.
A, Space-filling (*left*) and electron-density models (*right*) of the polar HF molecule. **B,** With the external electric field off, HF molecules are oriented randomly. **C,** With the field on, the molecules, on average, become oriented.

Bond Polarity, Bond Angle, and Dipole Moment

The presence of polar bonds does not *always* result in a polar molecule; we must also consider shape and the atoms surrounding the central atom. Here are three cases:

1. *CO_2: polar bonds, nonpolar molecule.* In carbon dioxide, the electronegativity difference between C (EN = 2.5) and O (EN = 3.5) makes each C=O bond polar. But CO_2 is linear, so the bonds point 180° from each other. The two bond polarities are counterbalanced, and the molecule has *no net dipole moment* (μ = 0 D). The electron density model shows regions of high negative charge (*red*) distributed equally on either side of the central region of high positive charge (*blue*):

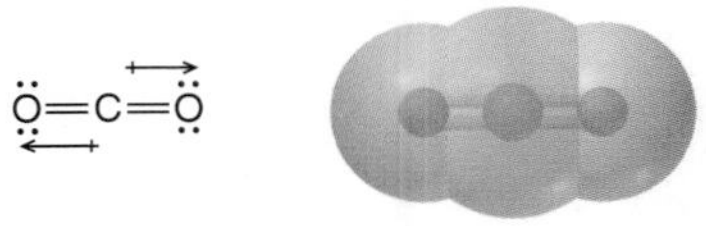

2. *H_2O: polar bonds, polar molecule.* Water also has two polar bonds, but it *is* polar (μ = 1.85 D). In each O—H bond, electron density is pulled from H (EN = 2.1) toward O (EN = 3.5). Bond polarities are *not* counterbalanced because the molecule is V shaped (also see Figure 4.1, p. 138). The bond polarities are partially reinforced, making the O end partially negative and the other end (the region between the H atoms) partially positive:

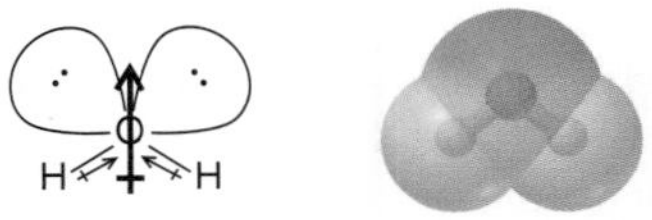

(The molecular polarity of water has some amazing effects, from determining the composition of the oceans to supporting life itself, as you'll see in Chapter 12.)

3. *Same shapes, different polarities.* When different molecules have the same shape, the identities of the surrounding atoms affect polarity. Carbon tetrachloride (CCl_4) and chloroform ($CHCl_3$) are tetrahedral molecules with very different polarities. In CCl_4, all the surrounding atoms are Cl atoms. Each C—Cl bond is polar (ΔEN = 0.5), but the molecule is nonpolar (μ = 0 D) because the bond polarities counterbalance each other. In $CHCl_3$, an H replaces one Cl, disrupting the balance and giving chloroform a significant dipole moment (μ = 1.01 D):

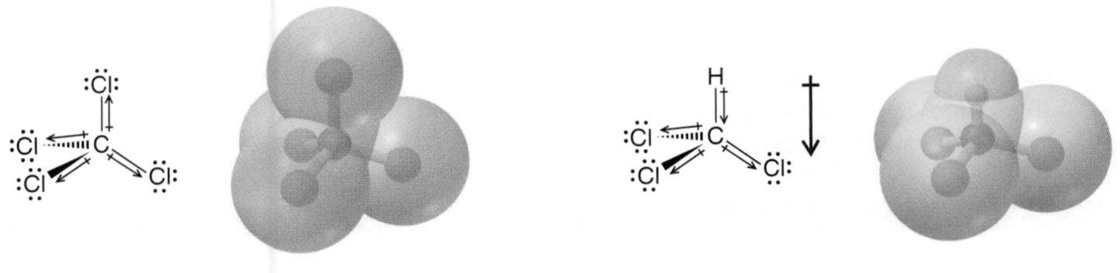

*The unit is named for the Dutch-American scientist Peter Debye (1884–1966) who won the Nobel Prize in 1936 for contributions to the fields of molecular structure and solution behavior.

Sample Problem 10.9 Predicting the Polarity of Molecules

Problem For each of the following, use the molecular shape and EN values and trends (Figure 9.20, p. 349) to predict the direction of bond and molecular polarity, if present:
(a) Ammonia, NH_3
(b) Boron trifluoride, BF_3
(c) Carbonyl sulfide, COS (atom sequence SCO)

Plan We draw and name the molecular shape and point a polar arrow toward the atom with higher EN in each bond. If the bond polarities balance one another, the molecule is nonpolar; if they reinforce each other, we show the direction of the molecular polarity.

Solution **(a)** For NH_3. The molecular shape is trigonal pyramidal. N (EN = 3.0) is more electronegative than H (EN = 2.1), so the bond polarities point toward N and partially reinforce each other; thus the molecular polarity points toward N:

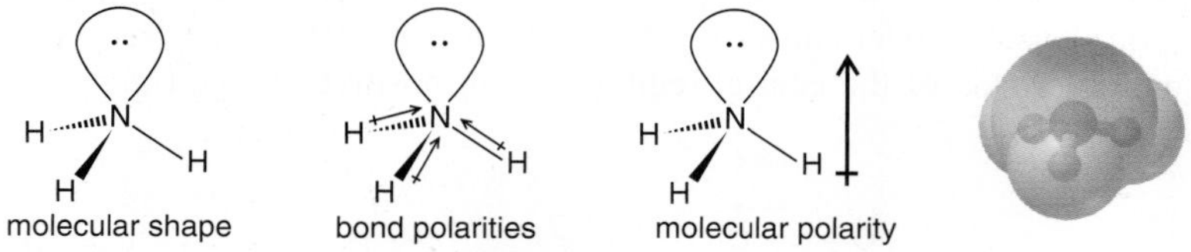

Therefore, ammonia is polar.
(b) For BF_3. The molecular shape is trigonal planar. F (EN = 4.0) is farther to the right in Period 2 than B (EN = 2.0), so it is more electronegative; thus, each bond polarity points toward F. However, the bond angle is 120°, so the three bond polarities balance each other, and BF_3 has no molecular polarity:

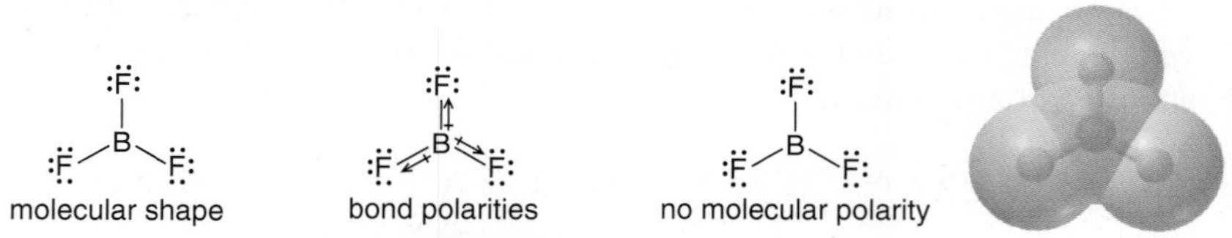

Therefore, boron trifluoride is nonpolar.
(c) For COS. The molecular shape is linear. With C and S having the same EN, the C=S bond is nonpolar, but the C=O bond is quite polar (ΔEN = 1.0), so there is a net molecular polarity toward the O:

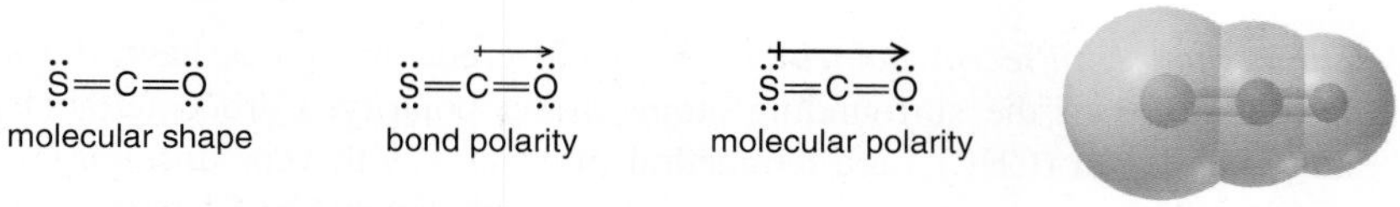

Therefore, carbonyl sulfide is polar.

Check The electron density models confirm our conclusions. Note that, in (b), the negative (*red*) regions surround the central B (*blue*) symmetrically.

Follow-Up Problem 10.9 Show the bond polarities and molecular polarity, if any, for each of the following:
(a) Dichloromethane (CH_2Cl_2)
(b) Iodine oxide pentafluoride (IOF_5)
(c) Nitrogen tribromide (NBr_3).

The Effect of Molecular Polarity on Behavior

Earlier we mentioned that molecular polarity influences physical behavior. Let's see how a molecular property like dipole moment affects a macroscopic property like boiling point. Consider the two dichloroethylenes shown below. They have the *same* molecular formula ($C_2H_2Cl_2$) but *different* physical and chemical properties; that is, they are constitutional isomers (Section 3.3). Both molecules are planar, with a trigonal planar shape around each C atom. The *trans* isomer is nonpolar (μ = 0 D) because the polar C—Cl bonds balance each other. The *cis* isomer is polar (μ = 1.90 D) because the bond polarities partially reinforce each other, with the molecular polarity pointing between the Cl atoms.

A liquid boils when it forms bubbles against the atmospheric pressure. To enter the bubble, the molecules in the liquid must overcome the weak attractive forces *between* them. Because of their polarity, the *cis* molecules attract each other more strongly than the *trans* molecules do. Since more energy is needed to overcome the stronger attractions, we expect the *cis* isomer to have a higher boiling point: *cis*-1,2-dichloroethylene boils 13°C higher than *trans*-1,2-dichloroethylene.

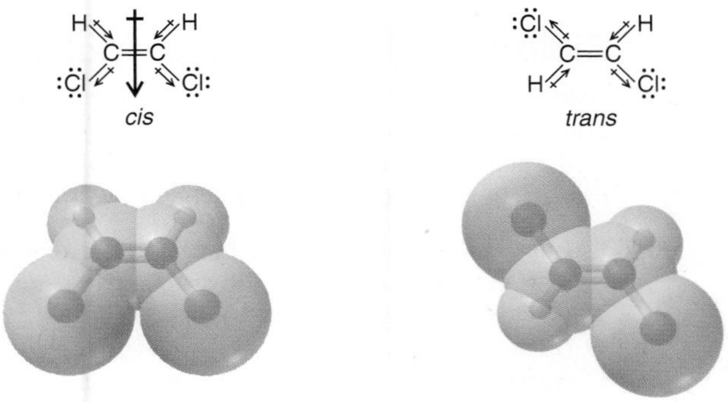

Figure 10.14 shows the chain of influences of atomic properties on the behavior of substances. We extend these relationships in Chapter 12, and the upcoming Chemical Connections essay discusses some biological effects of molecular shape and polarity.

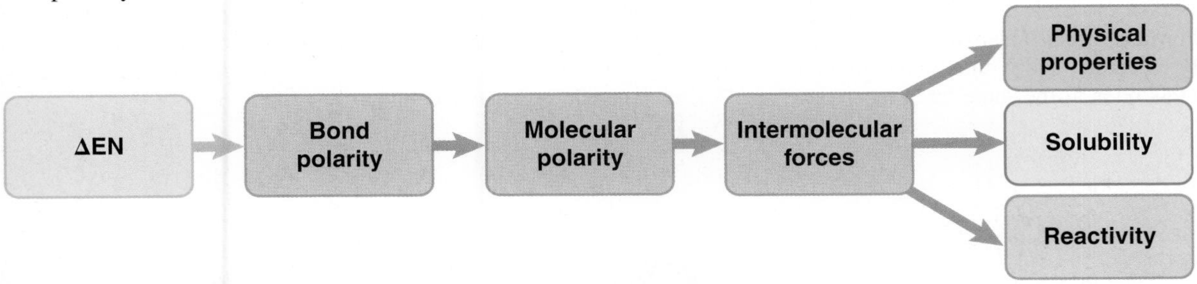

Figure 10.14 The influence of atomic properties on macroscopic behavior.

Summary of Section 10.3

- Bond polarity and molecular shape determine molecular polarity, which is measured as a dipole moment.
- A molecule with polar bonds is not necessarily a polar molecule. When bond polarities counterbalance each other, the molecule is nonpolar; when they reinforce each other, the molecule is polar.
- Molecular shape and polarity can affect physical properties, such as boiling point, and they play a central role in biological function.

CHEMICAL CONNECTIONS TO SENSORY PHYSIOLOGY | Molecular Shape, Biological Receptors, and the Sense of Smell

A biological cell can be thought of as a membrane-bound sack filled with an aqueous fluid containing many molecules of various shapes. Many complex processes begin when a molecular "key" fits into a molecular "lock" with a complementary shape. Typically, the key is a small molecule circulating in cellular or other bodily fluid, and the lock, the *biological receptor,* is a large molecule often embedded in a membrane. The *receptor site* is a small region of the receptor with a shape that matches the molecular key. Thousands of molecules per second collide with the receptor site, but when one with the correct shape does, the receptor "grabs" it through intermolecular attractions, and the biological response begins.

Molecular Shape and the Sense of Smell

Molecular shapes fitting together is crucial to the sense of smell (olfaction). To have an odor, a substance must be a gas or a volatile liquid or solid and must be at least slightly soluble in the aqueous film of the nasal passages. And the odorous molecule, or a portion of it, must fit into one of the receptor sites on nerve endings in this area. When this happens, nerve impulses travel to the brain, which interprets them as a specific odor.

Over half a century ago, a new theory proposed that molecular shape (and sometimes polarity), but *not* composition, determines odor. It stated that any molecule producing one of seven primary odors—camphor-like, musky, floral, minty, ethereal, pungent, and putrid—matches a receptor site of a particular shape. Figure B10.1 shows three of the seven sites holding a molecule with that odor.

Several predictions of the theory proved to be correct:

- If different substances fit a given receptor, they have the same odor. The four molecules in Figure B10.2 fit the camphor-like receptor and smell like moth repellent.
- If different parts of a molecule fit different receptors, it has a mixed odor. Portions of benzaldehyde fit the camphor-like, floral, and minty receptors, and it smells like almonds; other molecules with this odor fit the same three receptors.

But, other predictions were not confirmed. For example, an odor predicted from the shape was often not the odor smelled. The reason is that molecules may not have the same shape in solution at the receptor as they have in the gas phase.

Evidence from the 1990s suggests that the original model is far too simple. The 2004 Nobel Prize in medicine or physiology was given to Richard Axel and Linda B. Buck for showing that olfaction involves about 1000 different receptors and molecules fitting various combinations of them produce the over 10,000 odors humans smell.

Thus, although the process is much more complex than originally thought, the central idea that odor depends on molecular shape is valid and is being actively researched in the food, cosmetics, and insecticide industries.

Biological Significance of Molecular Shape

Countless other examples show that no chemical property is more crucial to living systems than molecular shape. Here are just a few of the many biochemical processes controlled by one molecule fitting into a receptor site on another:

- Enzymes are proteins that bind cellular reactants and speed their reaction. An early step in energy metabolism involves glucose binding to the "active" site of the enzyme hexokinase (Figure B10.3).
- Nerve impulses are transmitted when small molecules released from one nerve fit into receptors on the next. Mind-altering drugs act by chemically disrupting the molecular fit at such nerve receptors in the brain.
- One type of immune response is triggered when a molecule on a bacterial surface binds to the receptors on "killer" cells in the bloodstream.
- Hormones regulate processes by fitting into and activating specific receptors on target tissues and organs.
- Genes function when certain nucleic acid molecules fit into specific regions of others.

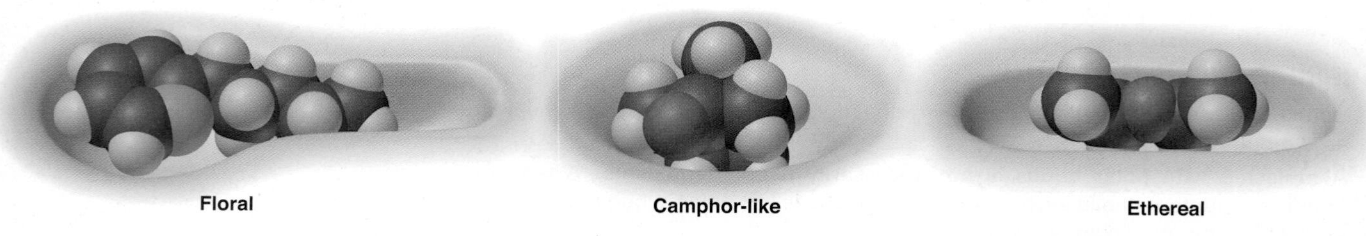

Figure B10.1 Shapes of some olfactory receptor sites.

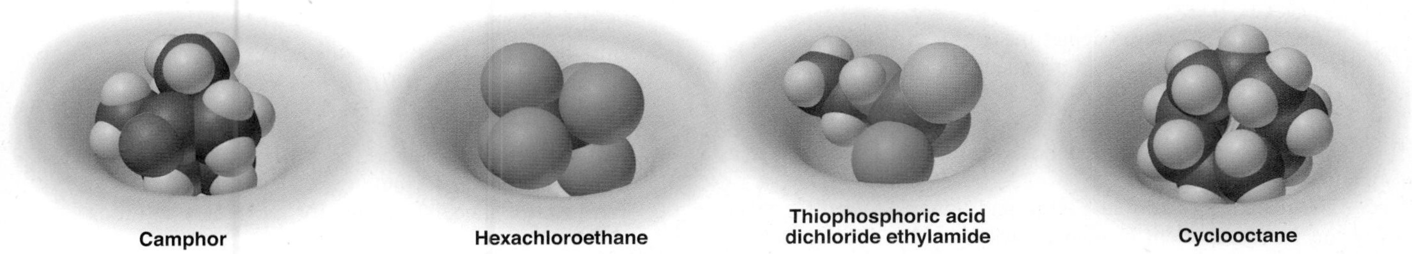

Figure B10.2 Different molecules with the same odor.

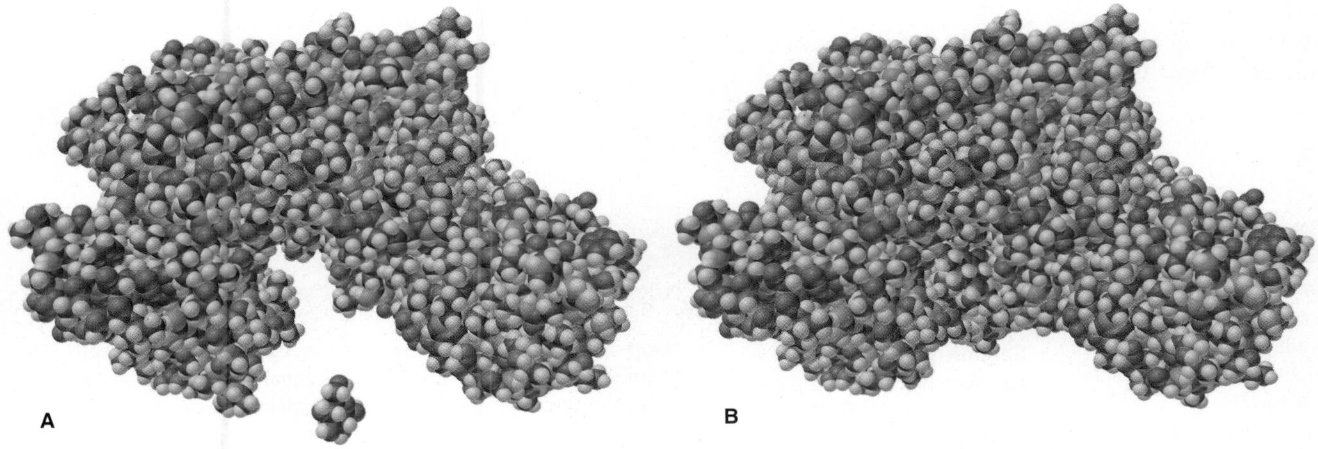

Figure B10.3 Molecular shape and enzyme action. **A,** A small sugar molecule (*bottom*) is shown near a specific region of an enzyme molecule. **B,** When the sugar lands in that region, the reaction begins.

Problems

B10.1 As you'll learn in Chapter 11, groups joined by a single bond rotate freely around the bond, but those joined by double bonds don't. Peptide bonds make up a major portion of protein chains. Determine the molecular shape around the central C and N atoms in the two resonance forms of the peptide bond:

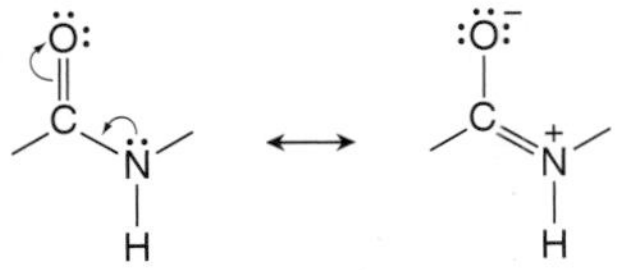

B10.2 Lewis structures of mescaline, a hallucinogenic compound in peyote cactus, and dopamine, a neurotransmitter in the mammalian brain, are shown below. Suggest a reason for mescaline's ability to disrupt nerve impulses.

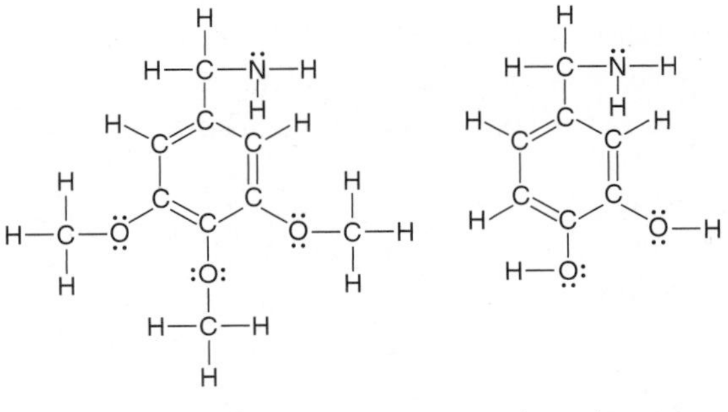

CHAPTER REVIEW GUIDE

Learning Objectives

Relevant section (§) and/or sample problem (SP) numbers appear in parentheses.

Understand These Concepts

1. How Lewis structures depict the atoms, bonding pairs, and lone electron pairs in a molecule or polyatomic ion (§10.1)
2. How resonance and electron delocalization explain bond properties in many compounds with double bonds adjacent to single bonds (§10.1)
3. The meaning of formal charge and how it is used to select the most important resonance structure; the difference between formal charge and oxidation number (§10.1)
4. The octet rule and its three major exceptions—molecules with a central atom that has an electron deficiency, an odd number of electrons, or an expanded valence shell (§10.1)
5. How electron-group repulsions lead to molecular shapes (§10.2)
6. The five electron-group arrangements and their associated molecular shapes (§10.2)
7. Why double bonds and lone pairs cause deviations from ideal bond angles (§10.2)
8. How bond polarities and molecular shape combine to give a molecule polarity (§10.3)

Master These Skills

1. Using a stepwise method for writing a Lewis structure from a molecular formula (SPs 10.1–10.3, 10.5)
2. Writing resonance structures for molecules and ions (SP 10.4)
3. Calculating the formal charge of any atom in a molecule or ion (SP 10.5)
4. Predicting molecular shapes from Lewis structures (SPs 10.6–10.8)
5. Using molecular shape and electronegativity values to predict the polarity of a molecule (SP 10.9)

Key Terms

Page numbers appear in parentheses.

Section 10.1

Lewis structure (Lewis formula) (363)
resonance structure (resonance form) (367)
resonance hybrid (367)
electron-pair delocalization (367)
formal charge (368)
electron deficient (369)
free radical (370)
expanded valence shell (370)

Section 10.2

valence-shell electron-pair repulsion (VSEPR) theory (373)
molecular shape (373)
bond angle (374)
linear arrangement (374)
linear shape (374)
trigonal planar arrangement (374)
bent shape (V shape) (375)
tetrahedral arrangement (375)
trigonal pyramidal shape (376)
trigonal bipyramidal arrangement (376)
equatorial group (376)
axial group (377)
seesaw shape (377)
T shape (377)
octahedral arrangement (378)
square pyramidal shape (378)
square planar shape (378)

Section 10.3

molecular polarity (383)
dipole moment (μ) (383)

Key Equations and Relationships

Page numbers appear in parentheses.

10.1 Calculating the formal charge on an atom (368):

$$\text{Formal charge of atom} = \text{no. of valence } e^- - (\text{no. of unshared valence } e^- + \tfrac{1}{2}\text{ no. of shared valence } e^-)$$

10.2 Ranking the effect of electron-pair repulsions on bond angle (376):

Lone pair–lone pair > lone pair–bonding pair > bonding pair–bonding pair

Brief Solutions to Follow-Up Problems

10.1 (a) (b) (c)

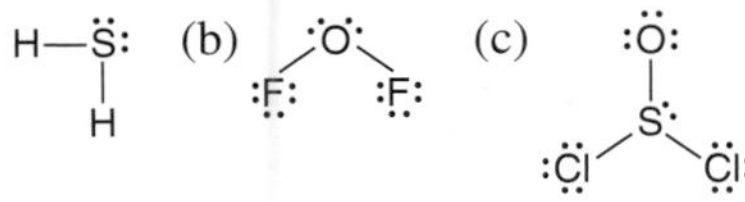

10.2 (a) (b)

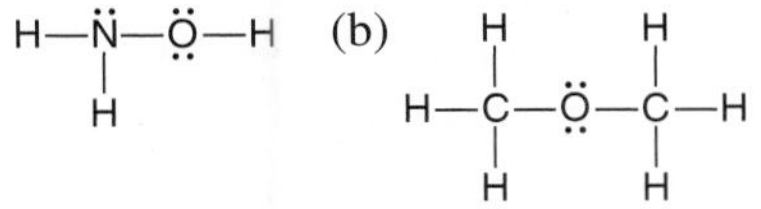

10.3 (a) :C≡O: (b) H—C≡N: (c) :O=C=O:

10.4

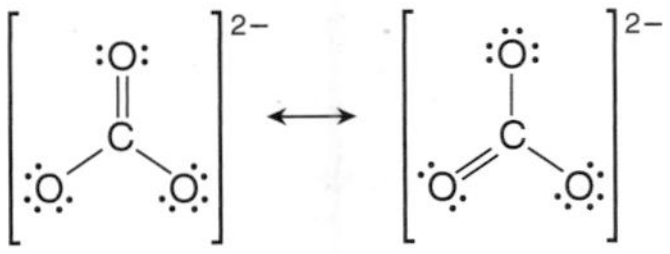

10.5 (a)

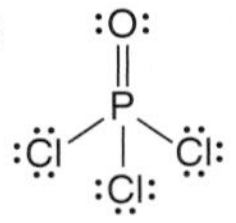

(b)

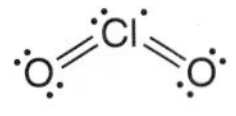

(c)

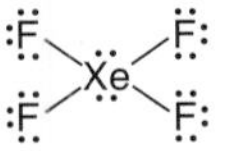

10.6 (a) S=C=S

Linear, 180°

(b)

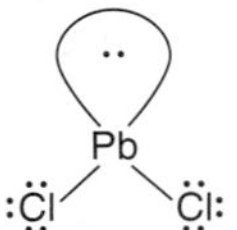

V shaped, <120°

(c)

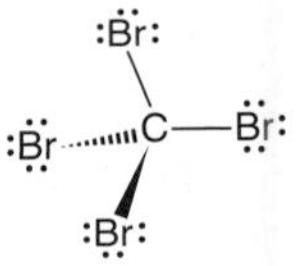

Tetrahedral, 109.5°

(d)

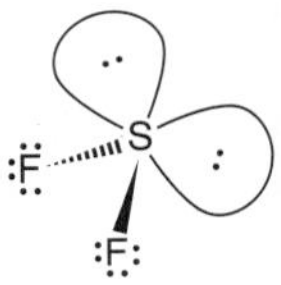

V shaped, <109.5°

10.7

(a)

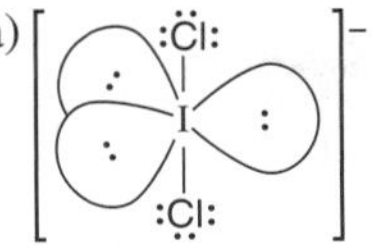

Linear, 180°

(b)

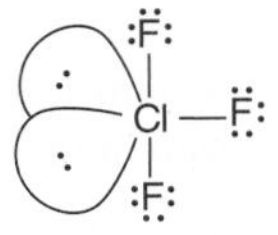

T shaped, <90°

(c)

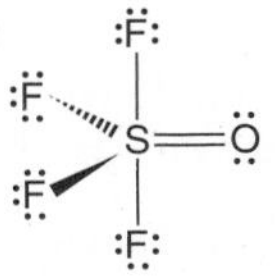

Trigonal bipyramidal
F_{eq}—S—F_{eq} angle <120°
F_{ax}—S—F_{eq} angle <90°

10.8 (a)

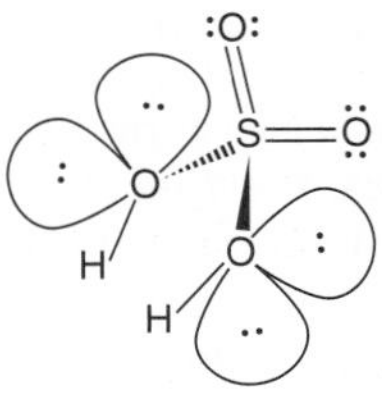

S is tetrahedral; double bonds compress O—S—O angle to <109.5°. Shape around each O in an —OH is V shape; lone pairs compress H—O—S angle to <109.5°.

(b)

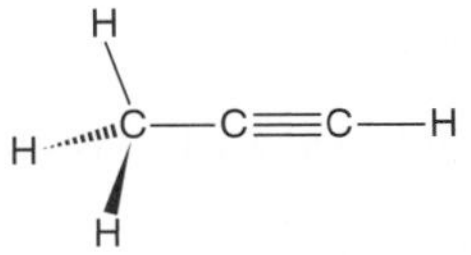

Shape around C in CH_3— is tetrahedral, with angles ~109.5°; other C atoms are linear, 180°.

(c)

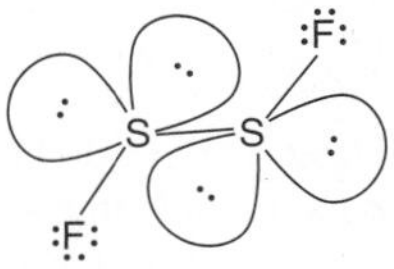

V shape around each S; F—S—S angle <109.5°.

10.9

(a)

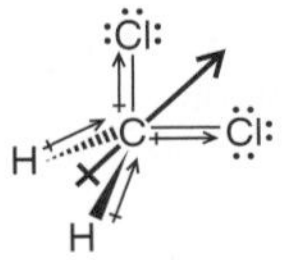

(b)

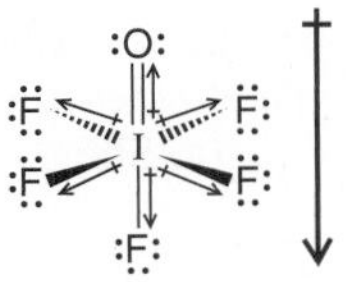

(c)

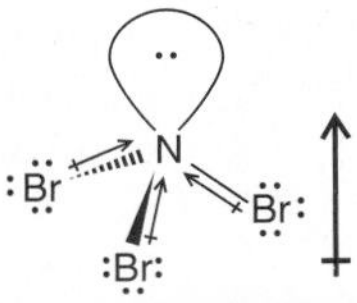

PROBLEMS

Problems with **colored** numbers are answered in Appendix E and worked in detail in the Student Solutions Manual. Problem sections match those in the text and provide the numbers of relevant sample problems. Most offer Concept Review Questions, Skill-Building Exercises (grouped in pairs covering the same concept), and Problems in Context. The Comprehensive Problems are based on material from any section or previous chapter.

Depicting Molecules and Ions with Lewis Structures

(Sample Problems 10.1 to 10.5)

Concept Review Questions

10.1 Which of these atoms *cannot* serve as a central atom in a Lewis structure: (a) O; (b) He; (c) F; (d) H; (e) P? Explain.

10.2 When is a resonance hybrid needed to adequately depict the bonding in a molecule? Using NO_2 as an example, explain how a resonance hybrid is consistent with the actual bond length, bond strength, and bond order.

10.3 In which of these bonding patterns does X obey the octet rule?

(a) (b) (c) (d) (e) (f) (g) (h)

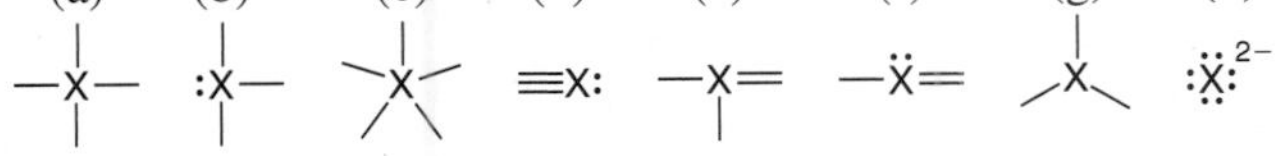

10.4 What is required for an atom to expand its valence shell? Which of the following atoms can expand its valence shell: F, S, H, Al, Se, Cl?

Skill-Building Exercises (grouped in similar pairs)

10.5 Draw a Lewis structure for (a) SiF_4; (b) $SeCl_2$; (c) COF_2 (C is central).

10.6 Draw a Lewis structure for (a) PH_4^+; (b) C_2F_4; (c) SbH_3.

10.7 Draw a Lewis structure for (a) PF_3; (b) H_2CO_3 (both H atoms are attached to O atoms); (c) CS_2.

10.8 Draw a Lewis structure for (a) CH_4S; (b) S_2Cl_2; (c) $CHCl_3$.

10.9 Draw Lewis structures of all the important resonance forms of (a) NO_2^+; (b) NO_2F (N is central).

10.10 Draw Lewis structures of all the important resonance forms of (a) HNO_3 ($HONO_2$); (b) $HAsO_4^{2-}$ ($HOAsO_3^{2-}$).

10.11 Draw Lewis structures of all the important resonance forms of (a) N_3^-; (b) NO_2^-.

10.12 Draw Lewis structures of all the important resonance forms of (a) HCO_2^- (H is attached to C); (b) $HBrO_4$ ($HOBrO_3$).

10.13 Draw the Lewis structure with lowest formal charges, and determine the charge of each atom in (a) IF_5; (b) AlH_4^-.

10.14 Draw the Lewis structure with lowest formal charges, and determine the charge of each atom in (a) OCS; (b) NO.

10.15 Draw the Lewis structure with lowest formal charges, and determine the charge of each atom in (a) CN^-; (b) ClO^-.

10.16 Draw the Lewis structure with lowest formal charges, and determine the charge of each atom in (a) BF_4^-; (b) ClNO.

10.17 Draw a Lewis structure for a resonance form of each ion with the lowest possible formal charges, show the charges, and give oxidation numbers of the atoms: (a) BrO_3^-; (b) SO_3^{2-}.

10.18 Draw a Lewis structure for a resonance form of each ion with the lowest possible formal charges, show the charges, and give oxidation numbers of the atoms: (a) AsO_4^{3-}; (b) ClO_2^-.

10.19 These species do not obey the octet rule. Draw a Lewis structure for each, and state the type of octet-rule exception:
(a) BH_3 (b) AsF_4^- (c) $SeCl_4$

10.20 These species do not obey the octet rule. Draw a Lewis structure for each, and state the type of octet-rule exception:
(a) PF_6^- (b) ClO_3 (c) H_3PO_3 (one P—H bond)

10.21 These species do not obey the octet rule. Draw a Lewis structure for each, and state the type of octet-rule exception:
(a) BrF_3 (b) ICl_2^- (c) BeF_2

10.22 These species do not obey the octet rule. Draw a Lewis structure for each, and state the type of octet-rule exception:
(a) O_3^- (b) XeF_2 (c) SbF_4^-

Problems in Context

10.23 Molten beryllium chloride reacts with chloride ion from molten NaCl to form the $BeCl_4^{2-}$ ion, in which the Be atom attains an octet. Show the net ionic reaction with Lewis structures.

10.24 Despite many attempts, the perbromate ion (BrO_4^-) was not prepared in the laboratory until about 1970. (In fact, articles were published explaining theoretically why it could never be prepared!) Draw a Lewis structure for BrO_4^- in which all atoms have lowest formal charges.

10.25 Cryolite (Na_3AlF_6) is an indispensable component in the electrochemical production of aluminum. Draw a Lewis structure for the AlF_6^{3-} ion.

10.26 Phosgene is a colorless, highly toxic gas that was employed against troops in World War I and it is used today as a key reactant in organic syntheses. From the following resonance structures, select the one with the lowest formal charges:

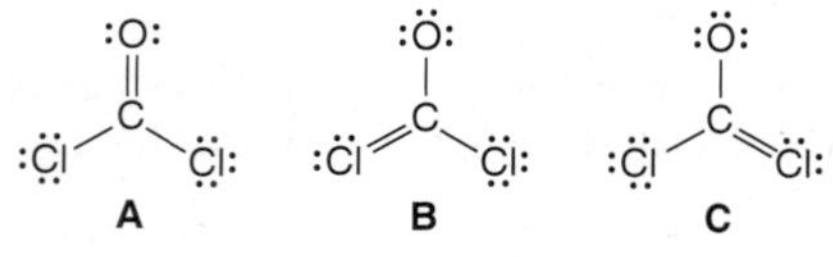

Valence-Shell Electron-Pair Repulsion (VSEPR) Theory

(Sample Problems 10.6 to 10.8)

Concept Review Questions

10.27 If you know the formula of a molecule or ion, what is the first step in predicting its shape?

10.28 In what situation is the name of the molecular shape the same as the name of the electron-group arrangement?

10.29 Which of the following numbers of electron groups can give rise to a bent (V-shaped) molecule: two, three, four, five, six? Draw an example for each case, showing the shape classification (AX_mE_n) and the ideal bond angle.

10.30 Name all the molecular shapes that have a tetrahedral electron-group arrangement.

10.31 Consider the following molecular shapes:

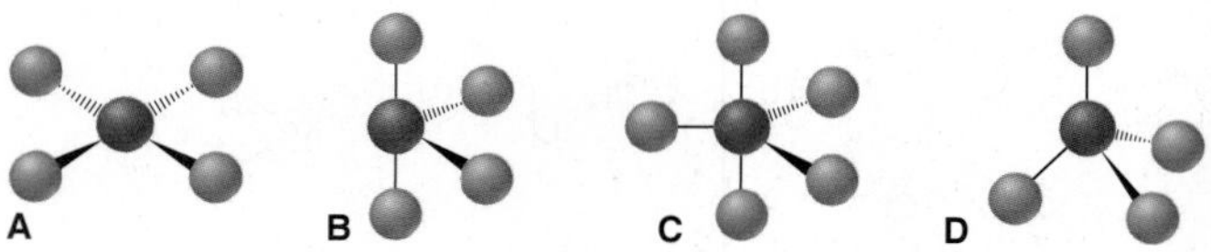

(a) Which has the most electron pairs (both shared and unshared) around the central atom?
(b) Which has the most unshared pairs around the central atom?
(c) Do any have only shared pairs around the central atom?

10.32 Use wedge-bond perspective drawings (if necessary) to sketch the atom positions in a general molecule of formula (not shape class) AX_n that has each of the following shapes:
(a) V shaped (b) trigonal planar (c) trigonal bipyramidal
(d) T shaped (e) trigonal pyramidal (f) square pyramidal

10.33 What would you expect to be the electron-group arrangement around atom A in each of the following cases? For each arrangement, give the ideal bond angle and the direction of any expected deviation:

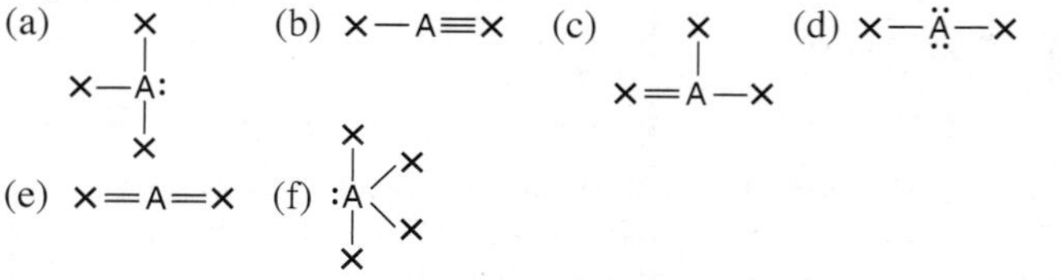

Skill-Building Exercises (grouped in similar pairs)

10.34 Determine the electron-group arrangement, molecular shape, and ideal bond angle(s) for each of the following:
(a) O_3 (b) H_3O^+ (c) NF_3

10.35 Determine the electron-group arrangement, molecular shape, and ideal bond angle(s) for each of the following:
(a) SO_4^{2-} (b) NO_2^- (c) PH_3

10.36 Determine the electron-group arrangement, molecular shape, and ideal bond angle(s) for each of the following:
(a) CO_3^{2-} (b) SO_2 (c) CF_4

10.37 Determine the electron-group arrangement, molecular shape, and ideal bond angle(s) for each of the following:
(a) SO_3 (b) N_2O (N is central) (c) CH_2Cl_2

10.38 Name the shape and give the AX_mE_n classification and ideal bond angle(s) for each of the following general molecules:

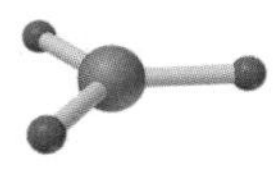
(a)

(b)

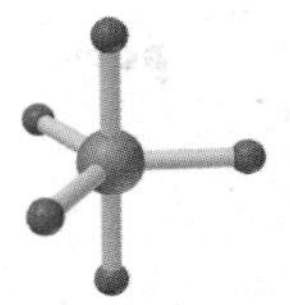
(c)

10.39 Name the shape and give the AX_mE_n classification and ideal bond angle(s) for each of the following general molecules:

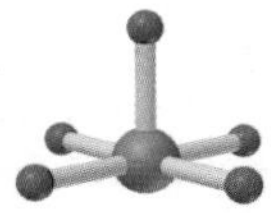
(a)

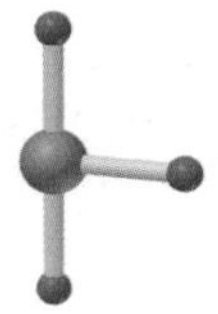
(b)

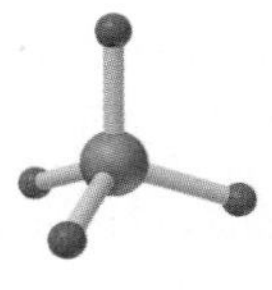
(c)

10.40 Determine the shape, ideal bond angle(s), and the direction of any deviation from those angles for each of the following:
(a) ClO_2^- (b) PF_5 (c) SeF_4 (d) KrF_2

10.41 Determine the shape, ideal bond angle(s), and the direction of any deviation from those angles for each of the following:
(a) ClO_3^- (b) IF_4^- (c) $SeOF_2$ (d) TeF_5^-

10.42 Determine the shape around each central atom in each molecule, and explain any deviation from ideal bond angles:
(a) CH_3OH (b) N_2O_4 (O_2NNO_2)

10.43 Determine the shape around each central atom in each molecule, and explain any deviation from ideal bond angles:
(a) H_3PO_4 (no H—P bond) (b) $CH_3—O—CH_2CH_3$

10.44 Determine the shape around each central atom in each molecule, and explain any deviation from ideal bond angles:
(a) CH_3COOH (b) H_2O_2

10.45 Determine the shape around each central atom in each molecule, and explain any deviation from ideal bond angles:
(a) H_2SO_3 (no H—S bond) (b) N_2O_3 ($ONNO_2$)

10.46 Arrange the following AF_n species in order of *increasing* F—A—F bond angles: BF_3, BeF_2, CF_4, NF_3, OF_2.

10.47 Arrange the following ACl_n species in order of *decreasing* Cl—A—Cl bond angles: SCl_2, OCl_2, PCl_3, $SiCl_4$, $SiCl_6^{2-}$.

10.48 State an ideal value for each of the bond angles in each molecule, and note where you expect deviations:

(a)
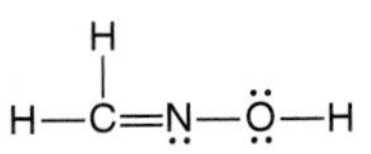

(b)
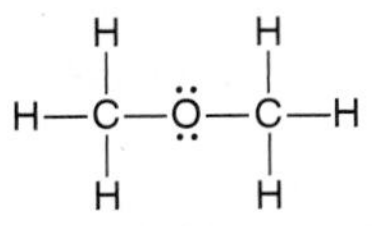

(c)
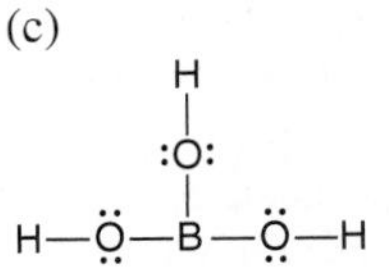

10.49 State an ideal value for each of the bond angles in each molecule, and note where you expect deviations:

(a)
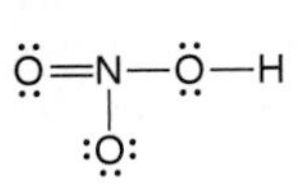

(b)
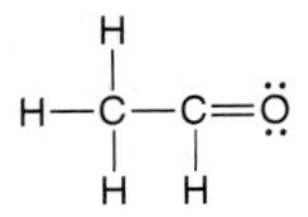

(c)
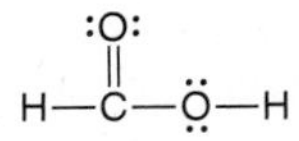

Problems in Context

10.50 Because both tin and carbon are members of Group 4A(14), they form structurally similar compounds. However, tin exhibits a greater variety of structures because it forms several ionic species. Predict the shapes and ideal bond angles, including any deviations, for the following:
(a) $Sn(CH_3)_2$ (b) $SnCl_3^-$ (c) $Sn(CH_3)_4$
(d) SnF_5^- (e) SnF_6^{2-}

10.51 In the gas phase, phosphorus pentachloride exists as separate molecules. In the solid phase, however, the compound is composed of alternating PCl_4^+ and PCl_6^- ions. What change(s) in molecular shape occur(s) as PCl_5 solidifies? How does the Cl—P—Cl angle change?

Molecular Shape and Molecular Polarity

(Sample Problem 10.9)

Concept Review Questions

10.52 For molecules of general formula AX_n (where $n > 2$), how do you determine if a molecule is polar?

10.53 How can a molecule with polar covalent bonds not be polar? Give an example.

10.54 Explain in general why the shape of a biomolecule is important to its function.

Skill-Building Exercises (grouped in similar pairs)

10.55 Consider the molecules SCl_2, F_2, CS_2, CF_4, and BrCl.
(a) Which has bonds that are the most polar?
(b) Which molecules have a dipole moment?

10.56 Consider the molecules BF_3, PF_3, BrF_3, SF_4, and SF_6.
(a) Which has bonds that are the most polar?
(b) Which molecules have a dipole moment?

10.57 Which molecule in each pair has the greater dipole moment? Give the reason for your choice.
(a) SO_2 or SO_3 (b) ICl or IF
(c) SiF_4 or SF_4 (d) H_2O or H_2S

10.58 Which molecule in each pair has the greater dipole moment? Give the reason for your choice.
(a) ClO_2 or SO_2 (b) HBr or HCl
(c) $BeCl_2$ or SCl_2 (d) AsF_3 or AsF_5

Problems in Context

10.59 There are three different dichloroethylenes (molecular formula $C_2H_2Cl_2$), which we can designate X, Y, and Z. Compound X has no dipole moment, but compound Z does. Compounds X and Z each combine with hydrogen to give the same product:

$$C_2H_2Cl_2\ (\text{X or Z}) + H_2 \longrightarrow ClCH_2—CH_2Cl$$

What are the structures of X, Y, and Z? Would you expect compound Y to have a dipole moment?

10.60 Dinitrogen difluoride, N_2F_2, is the only stable, simple inorganic molecule with an N=N bond. The compound occurs in *cis* and *trans* forms.
(a) Draw the molecular shapes of the two forms of N_2F_2.
(b) Predict the direction of the polarity, if any, of each form.

Comprehensive Problems

10.61 In addition to ammonia, nitrogen forms three other hydrides: hydrazine (N_2H_4), diazene (N_2H_2), and tetrazene (N_4H_4).

(a) Use Lewis structures to compare the strength, length, and order of the nitrogen-nitrogen bonds in hydrazine, diazene, and N_2.
(b) Tetrazene (atom sequence H_2NNNNH_2) decomposes above 0°C to hydrazine and nitrogen gas. Draw a Lewis structure for tetrazene, and calculate ΔH°_{rxn} for this decomposition.

10.62 Draw a Lewis structure for each species: (a) PF_5; (b) CCl_4; (c) H_3O^+; (d) ICl_3; (e) BeH_2; (f) PH_2^-; (g) $GeBr_4$; (h) CH_3^-; (i) BCl_3; (j) BrF_4^+; (k) XeO_3; (l) TeF_4.

10.63 Give the molecular shape of each species in Problem 10.62.

10.64 Consider the following reaction of silicon tetrafluoride:

$$SiF_4 + F^- \longrightarrow SiF_5^-$$

(a) Which depiction below best illustrates the change in molecular shape around Si? (b) Give the name and AX_mE_n designation of each shape in the depiction chosen in part (a).

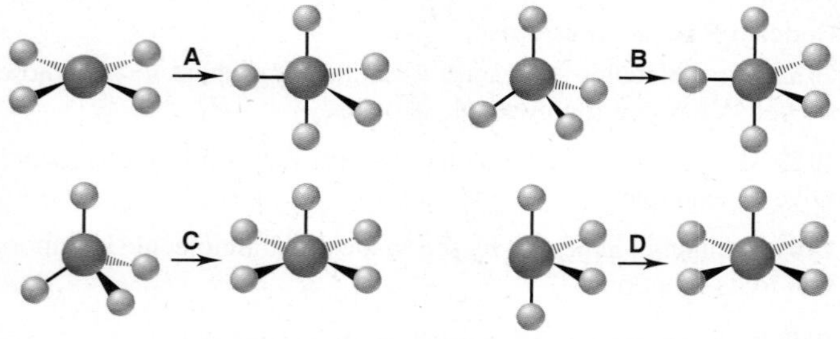

10.65 Both aluminum and iodine form chlorides, Al_2Cl_6 and I_2Cl_6, with "bridging" Cl atoms. The Lewis structures are

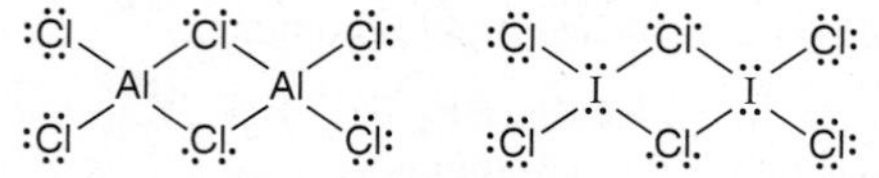

(a) What is the formal charge on each atom? (b) Which of these molecules has a planar shape? Explain.

10.66 The VSEPR model was developed before any xenon compounds had been prepared. Thus, these compounds provided an excellent test of the model's predictive power. What would you have predicted for the shapes of XeF_2, XeF_4, and XeF_6?

10.67 When SO_3 gains two electrons, SO_3^{2-} forms. (a) Which depiction shown below best illustrates the change in molecular shape around S? (b) Does molecular polarity change during this reaction?

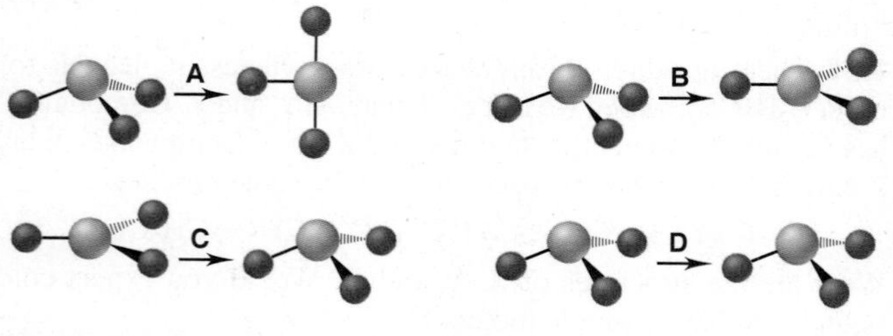

10.68 The actual bond angle in NO_2 is 134.3°, and in NO_2^- it is 115.4°, although the ideal bond angle is 120° in both. Explain.

10.69 "Inert" xenon actually forms several compounds, especially with the highly electronegative elements oxygen and fluorine. The simple fluorides XeF_2, XeF_4, and XeF_6 are all formed by direct reaction of the elements. As you might expect from the size of the xenon atom, the Xe—F bond is not a strong one. Calculate the Xe—F bond energy in XeF_6, given that the enthalpy of formation is −402 kJ/mol.

10.70 Propylene oxide is used to make many products, including plastics such as polyurethane. One method for synthesizing it involves oxidizing propene with hydrogen peroxide:

$$CH_3-CH{=}CH_2 + H_2O_2 \longrightarrow CH_3-\underset{\diagdown O \diagup}{CH-CH_2} + H_2O$$

(a) What is the molecular shape and ideal bond angle around each carbon atom in propylene oxide?
(b) Predict any deviation from the ideal for the actual C—C—C bond angles (assume the three atoms in the ring form an equilateral triangle).

10.71 Chloral, $Cl_3C—CH{=}O$, reacts with water to form the sedative and hypnotic agent chloral hydrate, $Cl_3C—CH(OH)_2$. Draw Lewis structures for these substances, and describe the change in molecular shape, if any, that occurs around each of the carbon atoms during the reaction.

10.72 Like several other bonds, carbon-oxygen bonds have lengths and strengths that depend on the bond order. Draw Lewis structures for the following species, and arrange them in order of increasing carbon-oxygen bond length and then by increasing carbon-oxygen bond strength: (a) CO; (b) CO_3^{2-}; (c) H_2CO; (d) CH_4O; (e) HCO_3^- (H attached to O).

10.73 In the 1980s, there was an international agreement to destroy all stockpiles of mustard gas, $ClCH_2CH_2SCH_2CH_2Cl$. When this substance contacts the moisture in eyes, nasal passages, and skin, the —OH groups of water replace the Cl atoms and create high local concentrations of hydrochloric acid, which cause severe blistering and tissue destruction. Write a balanced equation for this reaction, and calculate ΔH°_{rxn}.

10.74 The four bonds of carbon tetrachloride (CCl_4) are polar, but the molecule is nonpolar because the bond polarity is canceled by the symmetric tetrahedral shape. When other atoms substitute for some of the Cl atoms, the symmetry is broken and the molecule becomes polar. Use Figure 9.21 (p. 349) to rank the following molecules from the least polar to the most polar: CH_2Br_2, CF_2Cl_2, CH_2F_2, CH_2Cl_2, CBr_4, CF_2Br_2.

10.75 Ethanol (CH_3CH_2OH) is being used as a gasoline additive or alternative in many parts of the world.
(a) Use bond energies to find ΔH°_{rxn} for the combustion of gaseous ethanol. (Assume H_2O forms as a gas.)
(b) In its standard state at 25°C, ethanol is a liquid. Its vaporization requires 40.5 kJ/mol. Correct the value from part (a) to find the enthalpy of reaction for the combustion of liquid ethanol.
(c) How does the value from part (b) compare with the value you calculate from standard enthalpies of formation (Appendix B)?
(d) "Greener" methods produce ethanol from corn and other plant material, but the main industrial method involves hydrating ethylene from petroleum. Use Lewis structures and bond energies to calculate ΔH°_{rxn} for the formation of gaseous ethanol from ethylene gas with water vapor.

10.76 In the following compounds, the C atoms form a single ring. Draw a Lewis structure for each compound, identify cases for which resonance exists, and determine the carbon-carbon bond order(s): (a) C_3H_4; (b) C_3H_6; (c) C_4H_6; (d) C_4H_4; (e) C_6H_6.

10.77 An experiment requires 50.0 mL of 0.040 *M* NaOH for the titration of 1.00 mmol of acid. Mass analysis of the acid shows 2.24% hydrogen, 26.7% carbon, and 71.1% oxygen. Draw the Lewis structure of the acid.

10.78 A gaseous compound has a composition by mass of 24.8% carbon, 2.08% hydrogen, and 73.1% chlorine. At STP, the gas has a density of 4.3 g/L. Draw a Lewis structure that fits these facts. Would another structure be equally satisfactory? Explain.

10.79 Perchlorates are powerful oxidizing agents used in fireworks, flares, and the booster rockets of space shuttles. Lewis structures for the perchlorate ion (ClO_4^-) can be drawn with all single bonds or with one, two, or three double bonds. Draw each of these possible resonance forms, use formal charges to determine the most important, and calculate its average bond order.

10.80 Methane burns in oxygen to form carbon dioxide and water vapor. Hydrogen sulfide burns in oxygen to form sulfur dioxide and water vapor. Use bond energies (Table 9.2, p. 340) to determine the enthalpy of each reaction per mole of O_2 (assume Lewis structures with zero formal charges; BE of S=O is 552 kJ/mol).

10.81 Use Lewis structures to determine which *two* of the following are unstable: (a) SF_2; (b) SF_3; (c) SF_4; (d) SF_5; (e) SF_6.

10.82 A major short-lived, neutral species in flames is OH.
(a) What is unusual about the electronic structure of OH?
(b) Use the standard enthalpy of formation of OH(*g*) (39.0 kJ/mol) and bond energies to calculate the O—H bond energy in OH(*g*).
(c) From the average value for the O—H bond energy in Table 9.2 (p. 340) and your value for the O—H bond energy in OH(*g*), find the energy needed to break the first O—H bond in water.

10.83 Pure HN_3 (atom sequence HNNN) is explosive. In aqueous solution, it is a weak acid that yields the azide ion, N_3^-. Draw resonance structures to explain why the nitrogen-nitrogen bond lengths are equal in N_3^- but unequal in HN_3.

10.84 Except for nitrogen, the elements of Group 5A(15) all form pentafluorides, and most form pentachlorides. The chlorine atoms of PCl_5 can be replaced with fluorine atoms one at a time to give, successively, PCl_4F, PCl_3F_2, . . . , PF_5. (a) Given the sizes of F and Cl, would you expect the first two F substitutions to be at axial or equatorial positions? Explain. (b) Which of the five fluorine-containing molecules have no dipole moment?

10.85 Dinitrogen monoxide (N_2O) supports combustion in a manner similar to oxygen, with the nitrogen atoms forming N_2. Draw three resonance structures for N_2O (one N is central), and use formal charges to decide the relative importance of each. What correlation can you suggest between the most important structure and the observation that N_2O supports combustion?

10.86 Oxalic acid ($H_2C_2O_4$) is found in toxic concentrations in rhubarb leaves. The acid forms two ions, $HC_2O_4^-$ and $C_2O_4^{2-}$, by the sequential loss of H^+ ions. Draw Lewis structures for the three species, and comment on the relative lengths and strengths of their carbon-oxygen bonds. The connections among the atoms are shown below with single bonds only.

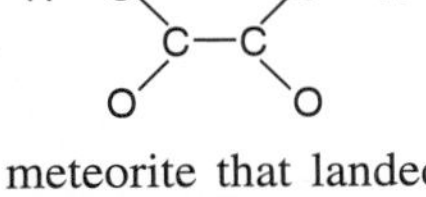

10.87 The Murchison meteorite that landed in Australia in 1969 contained 92 different amino acids, including 21 found in Earth organisms. A skeleton structure (single bonds only) of one of these extraterrestrial amino acids is shown below.

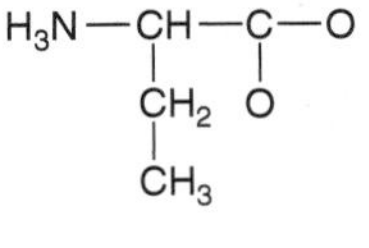

Draw a Lewis structure, and identify any atoms having a nonzero formal charge.

10.88 Hydrazine (N_2H_4) is used as a rocket fuel because it reacts very exothermically with oxygen to form nitrogen gas and water vapor. The heat released and the increase in number of moles of gas provide thrust. Calculate the enthalpy of reaction.

10.89 A student isolates a product with the molecular shape shown at right (F is orange). (a) If the species is a neutral compound, can the black sphere represent selenium (Se)? (b) If the species is an anion, can the black sphere represent N? (c) If the black sphere represents Br, what is the charge of the species?

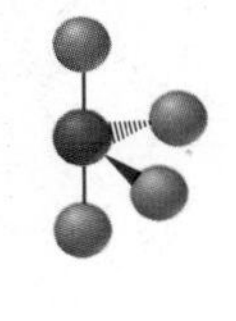

10.90 When gaseous sulfur trioxide is dissolved in concentrated sulfuric acid, disulfuric acid forms:

$$SO_3(g) + H_2SO_4(l) \longrightarrow H_2S_2O_7(l)$$

Use bond energies (Table 9.2, p. 340) to determine ΔH°_{rxn}. (The S atoms in $H_2S_2O_7$ are bonded through an O atom. Assume Lewis structures with zero formal charges; BE of S=O is 552 kJ/mol.)

10.91 A molecule of formula AY_3 is found experimentally to be polar. Which molecular shapes are possible and which are impossible for AY_3?

10.92 Consider the following molecular shapes:

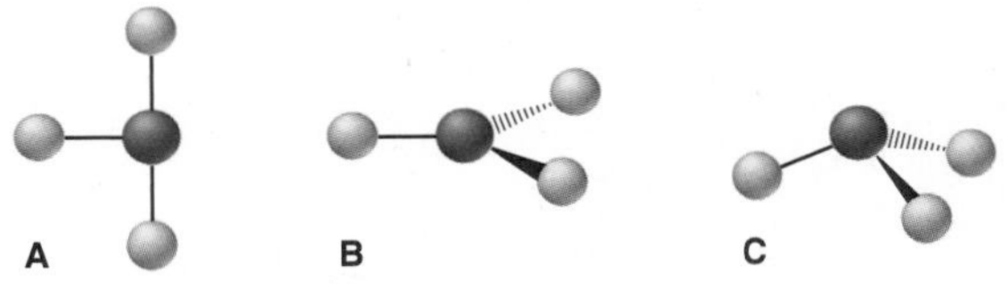

(a) Match each shape with one of the following species: XeF_3^+, $SbBr_3$, $GaCl_3$.
(b) Which, if any, is polar?
(c) Which has the most valence electrons around the central atom?

10.93 Hydrogen cyanide can be catalytically reduced with hydrogen to form methylamine. Use Lewis structures and bond energies to determine ΔH°_{rxn} for

$$HCN(g) + 2H_2(g) \longrightarrow CH_3NH_2(g)$$

10.94 Ethylene, C_2H_4, and tetrafluoroethylene, C_2F_4, are used to make the polymers polyethylene and polytetrafluoroethylene (Teflon), respectively.
(a) Draw the Lewis structures for C_2H_4 and C_2F_4, and give the ideal H—C—H and F—C—F bond angles.
(b) The actual H—C—H and F—C—F bond angles are 117.4° and 112.4°, respectively. Explain these deviations.

10.95 Using bond lengths in Table 9.2 (p. 340) and assuming ideal geometry, calculate each of the following distances:
(a) Between H atoms in C_2H_2
(b) Between F atoms in SF_6 (two answers)
(c) Between equatorial F atoms in PF_5

10.96 Phosphorus pentachloride, a key industrial compound with annual world production of about 2×10^7 kg, is used to make other compounds. It reacts with sulfur dioxide to produce phosphorus oxychloride ($POCl_3$) and thionyl chloride ($SOCl_2$). Draw a Lewis structure, and name the molecular shape of each product.

Theories of Covalent Bonding

11

Concepts and skills to review before you study this chapter

- atomic orbital shapes (Section 7.4)
- exclusion principle (Section 8.1)
- Hund's rule (Section 8.2)
- Lewis structures (Section 10.1)
- resonance in covalent bonding (Section 10.1)
- molecular shapes (Section 10.2)
- molecular polarity (Section 10.3)

All scientific models have limitations because they are simplifications of reality. The VSEPR theory, covered in Chapter 10, accounts for molecular shapes, but it doesn't explain how they arise from interactions of atomic orbitals. After all, the orbitals described in Chapter 7 aren't oriented toward the corners of, say, an octahedron, like the ones shown at left for the sulfur in SF_6. Moreover, knowing the shape doesn't help us explain the magnetic and spectral properties of molecules; only an understanding of their orbitals and energy levels can.

The two theories presented in this chapter focus on different questions and complement each other. Don't be concerned if we need several models to explain a complex phenomenon like bonding. In every science, one model may account for some aspect of a topic better than another, and several are employed to explain a wider range of phenomena.

IN THIS CHAPTER . . . We introduce two theories of bonding in molecules based on the interactions of the orbitals of their atoms.

- We discuss valence bond (VB) theory, which rationalizes molecular shapes through interactions of atomic orbitals during bonding to form hybrid orbitals.
- We apply VB theory to sigma and pi bonds, the two types of covalent bonds.
- We see why parts of molecules don't rotate freely around multiple bonds, which has major effects on reactivity, physical properties, and biological behavior.
- We discuss molecular orbital (MO) theory, which explains molecular energy levels and properties through formation of orbitals that spread over the whole molecule.
- We apply MO theory to understand key properties of some diatomic and simple polyatomic molecules.

11.1 • VALENCE BOND (VB) THEORY AND ORBITAL HYBRIDIZATION

What *is* a covalent bond, and what characteristic gives it strength? And how can we explain *molecular* shapes based on the interactions of *atomic* orbitals? The most useful approach for answering these questions is based on quantum mechanics (Chapter 7) and called **valence bond (VB) theory.**

The Central Themes of VB Theory

The basic principle of VB theory is that *a covalent bond forms when orbitals of two atoms overlap and a pair of electrons occupy the overlap region.* In the terminology of quantum mechanics, overlap of the two orbitals means their wave functions are *in phase* (constructive interference), so the amplitude between the nuclei increases (see Figure 7.5, p. 265). The central themes of VB theory derive from this principle:

1. *Opposing spins of the electron pair.* As the exclusion principle (Section 8.1) prescribes, the space formed by the overlapping orbitals *has a maximum capacity for two electrons that have opposite (paired) spins.* In the simplest case, a molecule of H_2 forms when the 1*s* orbitals of two H atoms overlap, and the electrons, with their spins paired, spend more time in the overlap region (up and down arrows in Figure 11.1).

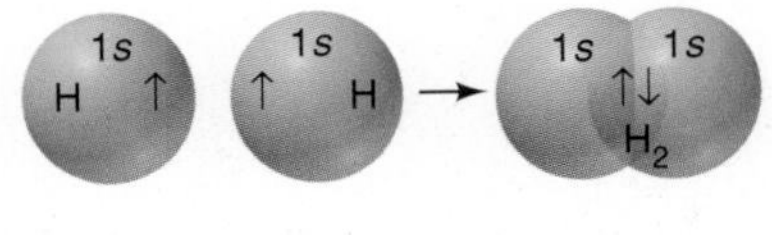

Figure 11.1 Orbital overlap and spin pairing in H_2.

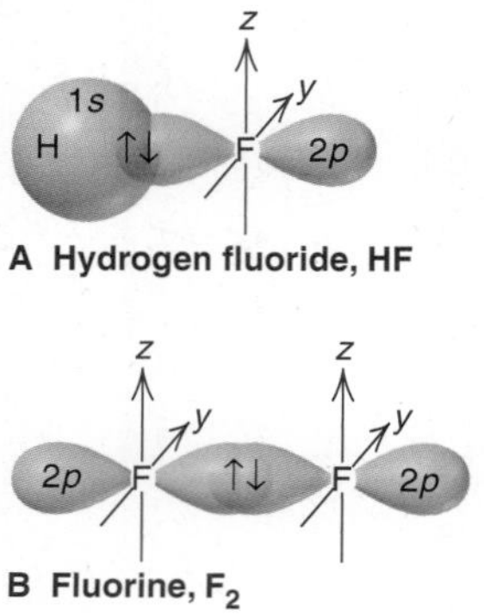

Figure 11.2 Orbital orientation and maximum overlap. (The $2p_x$ orbital is shown bonding; the other two $2p$ orbitals of F are omitted for clarity.)

2. *Maximum overlap of bonding orbitals.* Bond strength depends on the attraction between nuclei and shared electrons, so *the greater the orbital overlap, the stronger the bond.* Extent of overlap depends on orbital shape and direction. An *s* orbital is spherical, so its orientation is the same in any direction, but *p* and *d* orbitals have specified directions. Thus, a *p* or *d* orbital involved in a bond is oriented so as to maximize overlap. In HF, for example, the 1*s* orbital of H overlaps a half-filled 2*p* orbital of F *along its long axis* (Figure 11.2A). In F_2, the two half-filled 2*p* orbitals interact end to end, that is, *along the long axes* of the orbitals (Figure 11.2B).

3. *Hybridization of atomic orbitals.* To account for the bonding in diatomic molecules, we picture direct overlap of *s* and/or *p* orbitals of isolated atoms. But how can we account for the shape of a molecule like methane from the shapes and orientations of C and H atomic orbitals? A C atom ([He] $2s^22p^2$) has two valence electrons in the spherical 2*s* orbital and one each in two of the three mutually perpendicular 2*p* orbitals. If the half-filled *p* orbitals overlap the 1*s* orbitals of two H atoms, *two* C—H bonds would form with a 90° H—C—H bond angle. But methane has the formula CH_4, not CH_2, and its bond angle is 109.5°.

To explain such facts, Linus Pauling proposed that, during bonding, *the valence atomic orbitals in the isolated atoms become* ***different*** *when they are in the molecule.* Quantum-mechanical calculations show that if we mathematically "mix" certain combinations of orbitals, we form new ones whose spatial orientations *do* match the observed molecular shapes. The process of orbital mixing is called **hybridization,** and the new atomic orbitals are called **hybrid orbitals.**

4. *Features of hybrid orbitals.* Here are some central points about hybrid orbitals that arise during bonding:

- The *number* of hybrid orbitals formed *equals* the number of atomic orbitals mixed.
- The *type* of hybrid orbitals formed *varies* with the types of atomic orbitals mixed.
- The *shape* and *orientation* of a hybrid orbital *maximizes* overlap with the orbital of the other atom in the bond.

You can think of hybridization as a process in which atomic orbitals mix, hybrid orbitals form, they overlap other orbitals, and electrons enter the overlap region with opposing spins, thus forming stable bonds. In truth, hybridization is a concept to explain the results we calculate that predict the molecular shapes we observe.

Types of Hybrid Orbitals

We postulate the type of hybrid orbitals in a molecule *after* we observe its shape. Note that the orientations of the five types of hybrid orbitals we discuss next correspond to the five electron-group arrangements in VSEPR theory.

***sp* Hybridization** When two electron groups surround the central atom, we observe a linear shape, which means the bonding orbitals must have a linear orientation.

1. *Orbitals mixed and orbitals formed.* VB theory proposes two *nonequivalent* orbitals of a central atom, one *s* and one *p*, mix and form two *equivalent* ***sp* hybrid orbitals** that are oriented 180° apart (Figure 11.3A). The shape of these hybrid orbitals, with one large and one small lobe, differs markedly from the shapes of the atomic orbitals. The orbital orientations increase electron density *in the bonding direction.*

2. *Overlap of orbitals from central and surrounding atoms: $BeCl_2$.* In beryllium chloride, the Be atom is *sp* hybridized. Figure 11.3B depicts the hybridization of Be in an orbital box diagram, and part C shows an orbital box diagram with shaded contours instead of arrows. Bond formation with Cl is shown in part D. The filled 2*s* and one of the three empty 2*p* orbitals of Be mix and form two half-filled *sp* orbitals. Two empty unhybridized 2*p* orbitals of Be lie perpendicular to each other and to the *sp* hybrids. The hybrid orbitals overlap the half-filled 3*p* orbital in each of two Cl atoms. The four electrons—two from Be and one from each Cl—appear as pairs with opposite spins in the two overlap regions. (The 3*p* and *sp* hybrid orbitals that are partially colored on the left become fully colored on the right, after the bonds form and each orbital is filled with two electrons.)

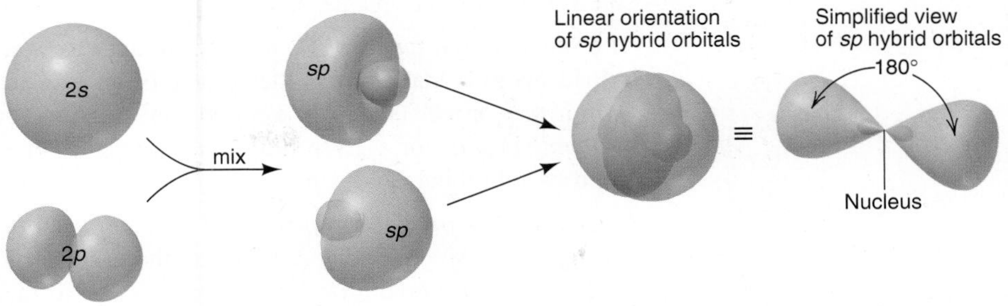

A Formation of *sp* hybrid orbitals

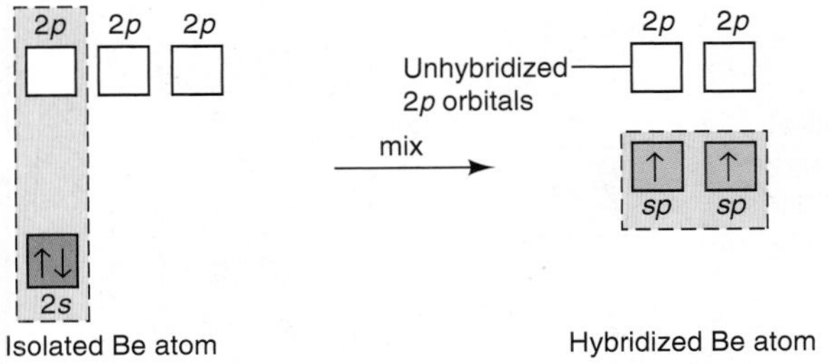

B Orbital box diagram

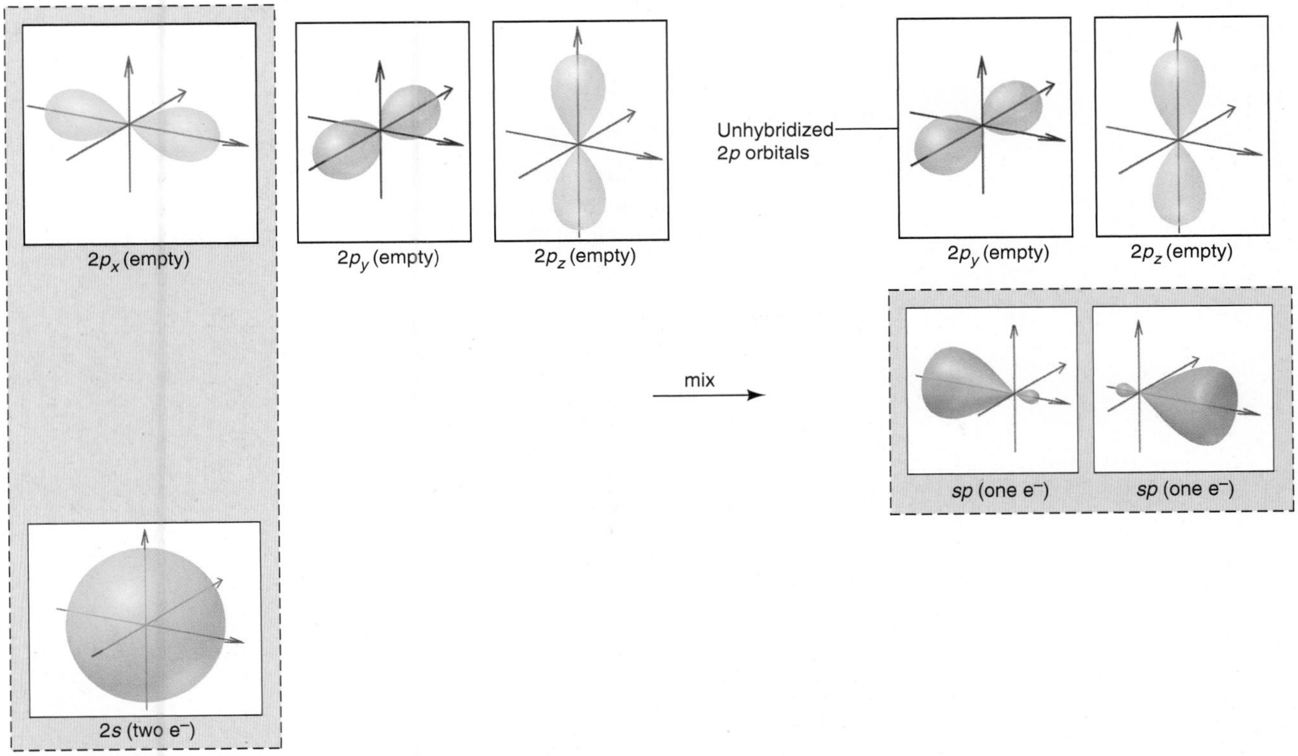

C Box diagram with orbital contours

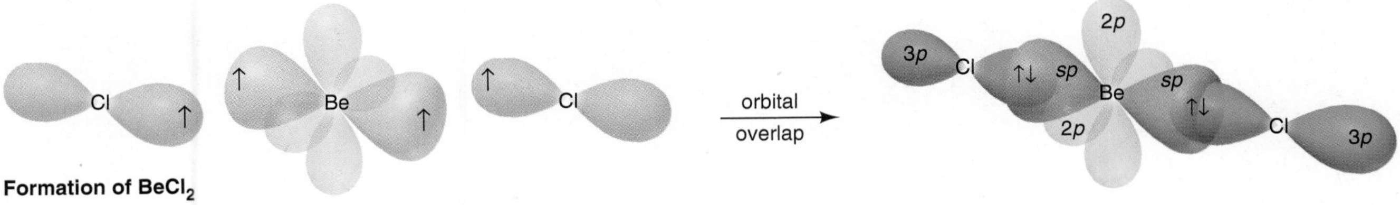

D Formation of $BeCl_2$

Figure 11.3 Formation and orientation of *sp* hybrid orbitals and the bonding in $BeCl_2$. **A,** One 2*s* and one 2*p* atomic orbital mix to form two *sp* hybrid orbitals. (The simplified hybrid orbitals at far right are used elsewhere, often even without the small lobe.) **B,** The orbital box diagram for hybridization of Be, drawn vertically. **C,** The orbital box diagram with orbital contours. **D,** Overlap of Be and Cl orbitals to form $BeCl_2$. (Only the Cl 3*p* orbital involved in bonding is shown.)

sp^2 Hybridization We use this type of hybridization to rationalize the two shapes possible for the trigonal planar electron-group arrangement.

1. *Orbitals mixed and orbitals formed.* Mixing one s and two p orbitals gives three **sp^2 hybrid orbitals** that point to the corners of an equilateral triangle, their axes 120° apart. (In hybrid orbitals, unlike in electron configurations, superscripts refer to the number of *atomic orbitals* of a given type, *not* the number of *electrons* in the orbital: thus, one s and two p orbitals give s^1p^2, or sp^2.) The third $2p$ orbital remains unhybridized.

2. *Overlap of orbitals from central and surrounding atoms: BF_3.* The central B atom in BF_3 is sp^2 hybridized, with the three sp^2 orbitals in a trigonal plane and the third $2p$ orbital unhybridized and perpendicular to this plane (Figure 11.4). Each half-filled sp^2 orbital overlaps the half-filled $2p$ orbital of an F atom, and the six valence electrons—three from B and one from each of the three F atoms—form three bonding pairs.

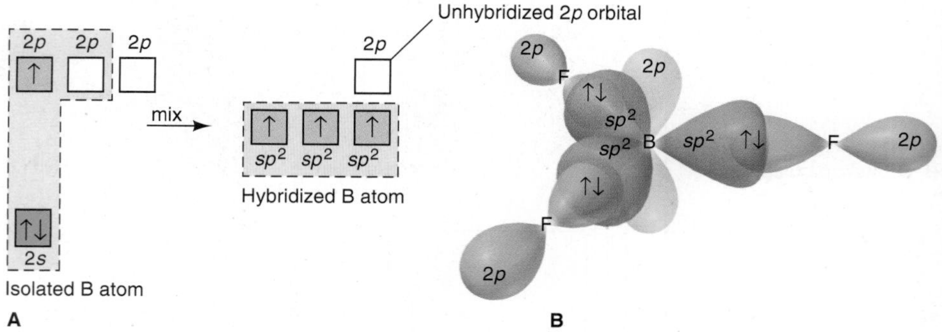

Figure 11.4 The sp^2 hybrid orbitals in BF_3. **A,** The orbital box diagram shows the formation of three sp^2 hybrid orbitals. One $2p$ orbital is unhybridized and empty. **B,** Contour depiction of BF_3.

3. *Placement of lone pairs.* To account for other molecular shapes within a given electron-group arrangement, one or more hybrid orbitals contains a lone pair. In ozone (O_3), for example, the central O is sp^2 hybridized and a lone pair fills one of the three sp^2 orbitals.

sp^3 Hybridization The type of hybridization that accounts for the shape of methane applies to any species with a tetrahedral electron-group arrangement.

1. *Orbitals mixed and orbitals formed.* Mixing one s and three p orbitals gives four **sp^3 hybrid orbitals** that point to the corners of a tetrahedron.

2. *Overlap of orbitals from central and surrounding atoms: CH_4.* The C atom in methane is sp^3 hybridized. Its four valence electrons half-fill the four sp^3 hybrids, which overlap the half-filled $1s$ orbitals of four H atoms to form four C—H bonds (Figure 11.5).

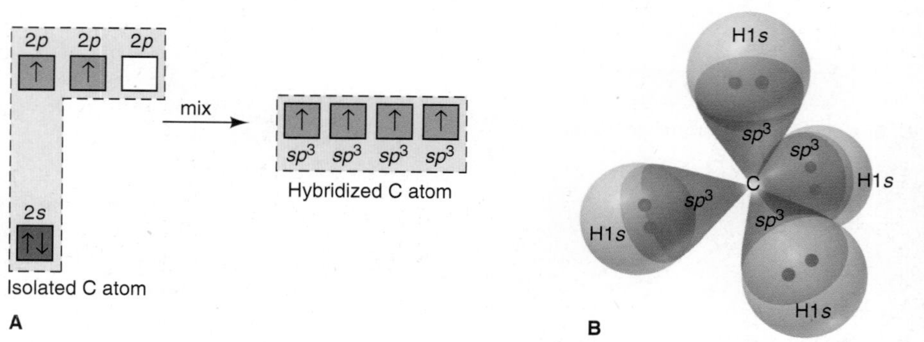

Figure 11.5 The sp^3 hybrid orbitals in CH_4. **A,** The orbital box diagram shows formation of four sp^3 hybrids. **B,** Contour depiction of CH_4, with electron pairs shown as dots.

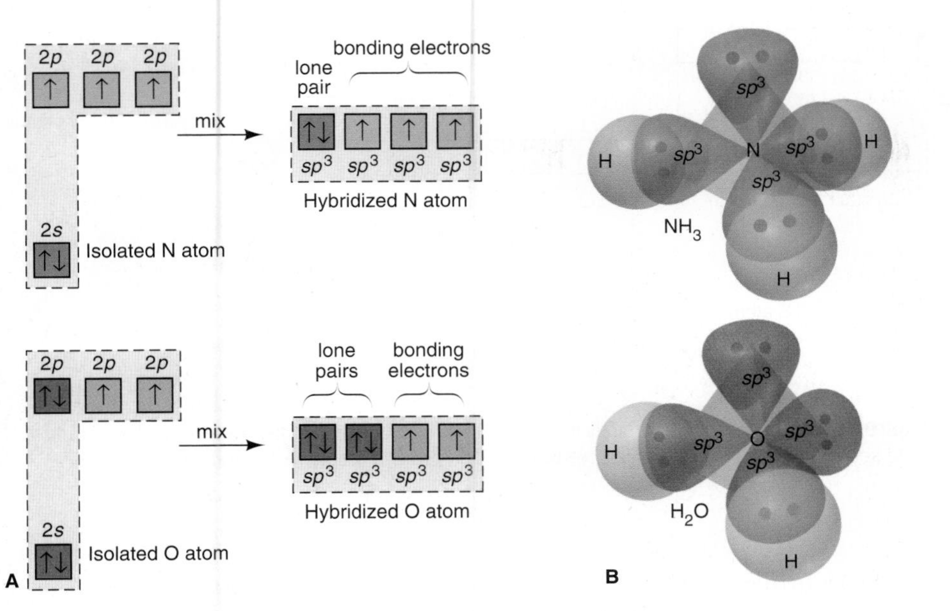

Figure 11.6 The sp^3 hybrid orbitals in NH_3 and H_2O. **A,** The orbital box diagrams show sp^3 hybridization, with lone pairs filling one (NH_3) or two (H_2O) hybrid orbitals. **B,** Contour depictions.

3. *Placement of lone pairs.* The trigonal pyramidal shape of NH_3 arises when a lone pair fills any one of the four sp^3 orbitals of N, and the bent shape of H_2O arises when lone pairs fill any two of the sp^3 orbitals of O (Figure 11.6).

sp^3d Hybridization Molecules with shapes due to the trigonal bipyramidal electron-group arrangement have central atoms from Period 3 or higher. VB theory proposes that *d* orbitals, as well as *s* and *p* orbitals, are mixed to form hybrid orbitals.

1. *Orbitals mixed and orbitals formed.* Mixing one 3*s*, the three 3*p*, and one of the five 3*d* orbitals gives five **sp^3d hybrid orbitals,** which point to the corners of a trigonal bipyramid.

2. *Overlap of orbitals from central and surrounding atoms: PCl_5.* The P atom in PCl_5 is sp^3d hybridized. Each hybrid orbital overlaps a 3*p* orbital of a Cl atom, and ten valence electrons—five from P and one from each of the five Cl atoms—form five P—Cl bonds (Figure 11.7).

3. *Placement of lone pairs.* Seesaw, T-shaped, and linear molecules have lone pairs in, respectively, one, two, or three of the central atom's sp^3d orbitals.

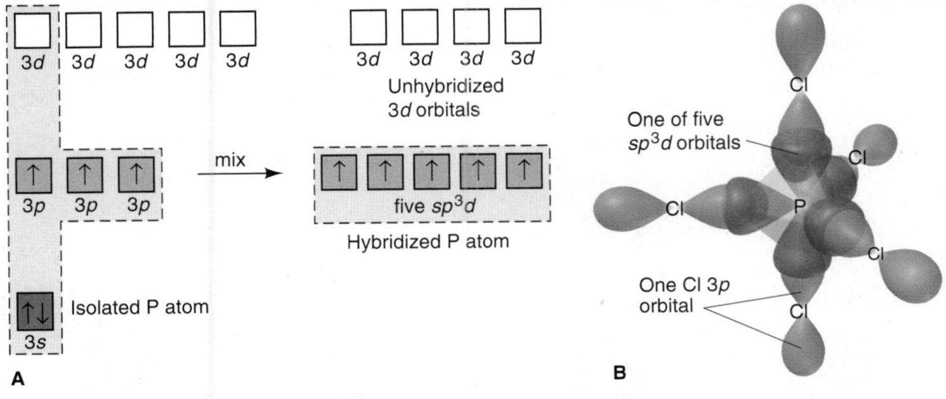

Figure 11.7 The sp^3d hybrid orbitals in PCl_5. **A,** The orbital box diagram shows the formation of five half-filled sp^3d orbitals. Four 3*d* orbitals are unhybridized and empty. **B,** Contour depiction of PCl_5. (For clarity, unhybridized 3*d* orbitals, the other two Cl 3*p* orbitals, and the five bonding P—Cl pairs are not shown.)

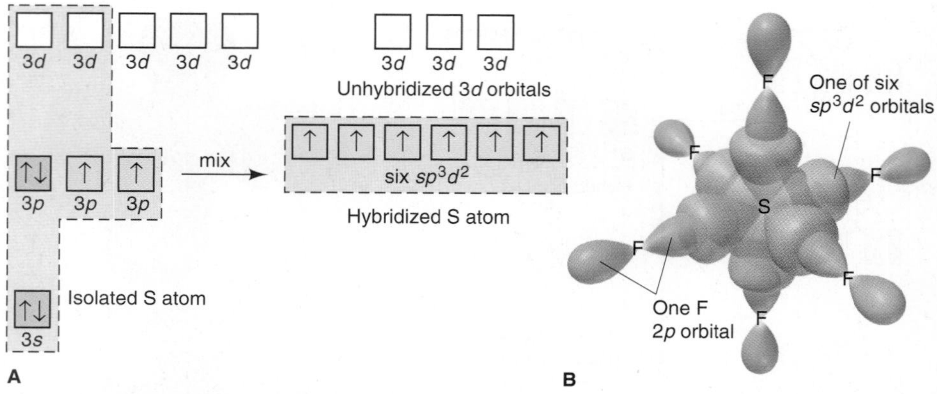

Figure 11.8 The sp^3d^2 hybrid orbitals in SF_6. **A,** The orbital box diagram shows formation of six half-filled sp^3d^2 orbitals; three 3*d* orbitals remain unhybridized and empty. **B,** Contour depiction of SF_6.

sp^3d^2 Hybridization The VB model proposes that molecules with shapes having the octahedral electron-group arrangement also use *d* orbitals to form hybrids.

1. *Orbitals mixed and orbitals formed.* Mixing one 3*s*, the three 3*p*, and two 3*d* orbitals gives six **sp^3d^2 hybrid orbitals,** which point to the corners of an octahedron.

2. *Overlap of orbitals from central and surrounding atoms: SF_6.* The S atom in SF_6 is sp^3d^2 hybridized. Each half-filled hybrid orbital overlaps a half-filled 2*p* orbital of an F atom, and 12 valence electrons—six from S and one from each of the six F atoms—form six S—F bonds (Figure 11.8).

3. *Placement of lone pairs.* Square pyramidal and square planar molecules have lone pairs in one and two of the central atom's sp^3d^2 orbitals, respectively.

Table 11.1 summarizes the numbers and types of atomic orbitals that mix to form the five types of hybrid orbitals. Figure 11.9 shows three conceptual steps from a molecular formula to the hybrid orbitals in the molecule, and Sample Problem 11.1 focuses on the last step of that process.

Table 11.1 Composition and Orientation of Hybrid Orbitals

	Linear	Trigonal Planar	Tetrahedral	Trigonal Bipyramidal	Octahedral
Atomic orbitals mixed	one *s* one *p*	one *s* two *p*	one *s* three *p*	one *s* three *p* one *d*	one *s* three *p* two *d*
Hybrid orbitals formed	two *p*	three sp^2	four sp^3	five sp^3d	six sp^3d^2
Unhybridized orbitals remaining	two *p*	one *p*	none	four *d*	three *d*
Orientation		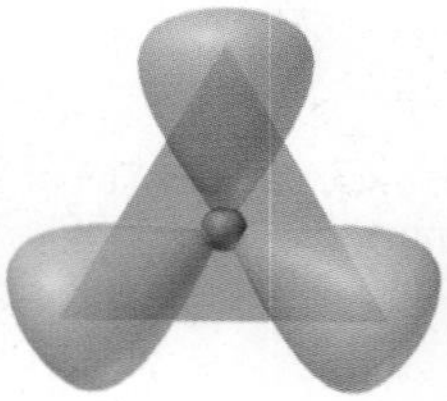	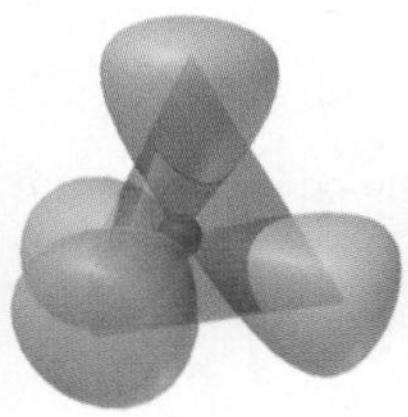	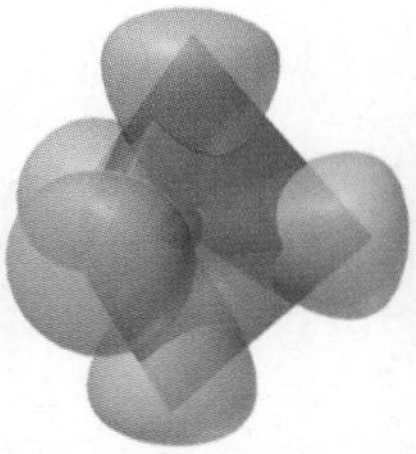	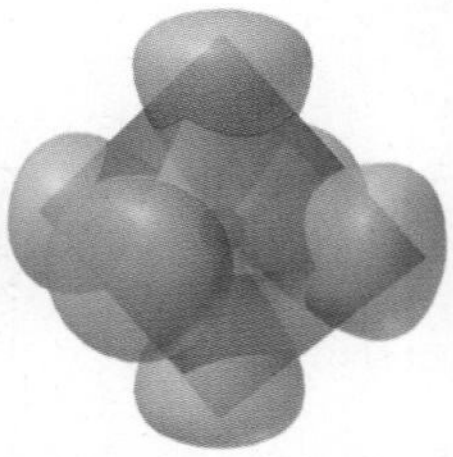

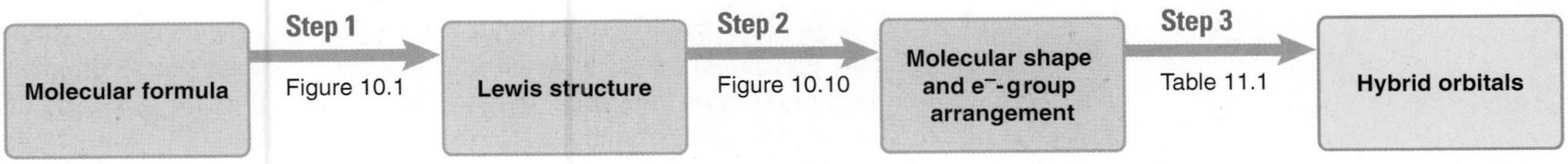

Figure 11.9 From molecular formula to hybrid orbitals. (See Figures 10.1, p. 364, and 10.10, p. 379.)

Sample Problem 11.1 Postulating Hybrid Orbitals in a Molecule

Problem Use partial orbital diagrams to describe how mixing the atomic orbitals of the central atom(s) leads to the hybrid orbitals in each of the following:
(a) Methanol, CH_3OH **(b)** Sulfur tetrafluoride, SF_4

Plan Prior to the Solution steps below, we have used the molecular formula to draw the Lewis structure and determined the electron-group arrangement of each central atom. Then, starting from there, we use Table 11.1 to postulate the type of hybrid orbitals. We write the partial orbital diagram for each central atom before and after the orbitals are hybridized.

Solution (a) For CH_3OH. The electron-group arrangement is tetrahedral around both the C and the O atom, so each mixed one 2*s* and three 2*p* to become sp^3 hybridized. The C atom has four half-filled sp^3 orbitals:

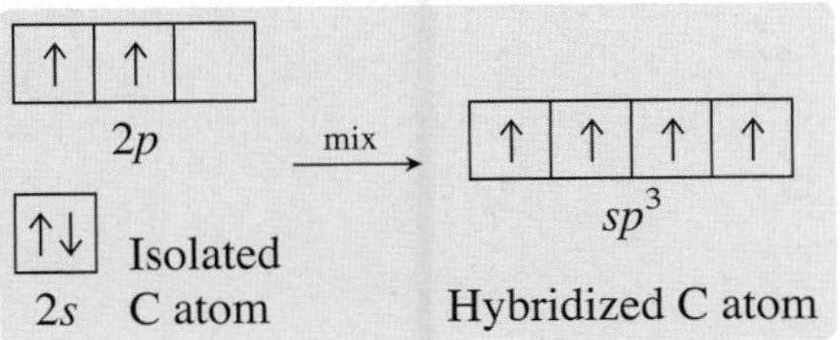

The O atom has two half-filled sp^3 orbitals and two filled with lone pairs:

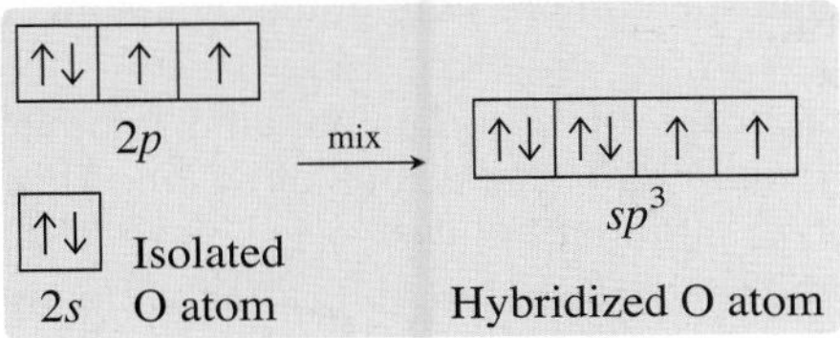

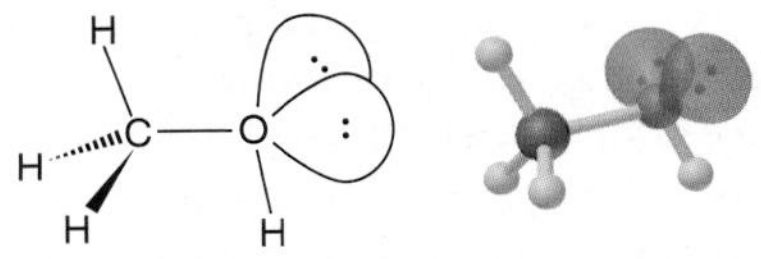

(b) For SF_4. The electron-group arrangement is trigonal bipyramidal, so the central S atom is sp^3d hybridized, which means one 3*s*, three 3*p*, and one 3*d* orbital are mixed. One hybrid orbital is filled with a lone pair, and four are half-filled. Four unhybridized 3*d* orbitals remain empty:

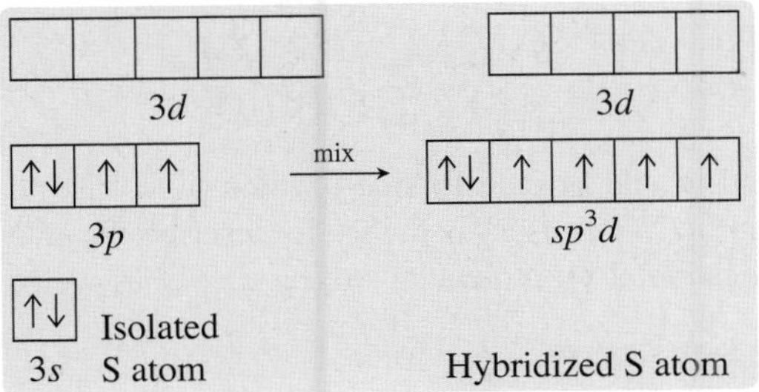

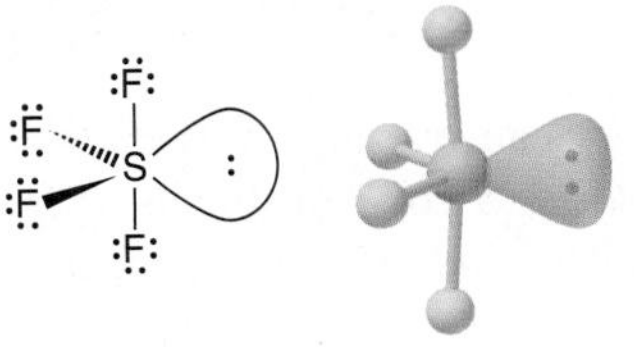

Follow-Up Problem 11.1 Use partial orbital diagrams to show how the atomic orbitals of the central atom mix to form hybrid orbitals in **(a)** beryllium fluoride, BeF_2; **(b)** silicon tetrachloride, $SiCl_4$; **(c)** xenon tetrafluoride, XeF_4.

Limitations to the Concept of Hybridization We rely on the VSEPR and VB theories to rationalize an observed molecular shape. In some cases, however, the theories may not be consistent with other findings.

1. *Hybridization does not apply: large nonmetal hydrides.* Consider the Lewis structure and bond angle of H_2S:

Based on VSEPR theory, we would predict that, as in H_2O, the four electron groups around H_2S point to the corners of a tetrahedron, and the two lone pairs compress the H—S—H bond angle below the ideal 109.5°. Based on VB theory, we would propose that the 3*s* and 3*p* orbitals of the S atom mix and form four sp^3 hybrids, two of which are filled with lone pairs, while the other two overlap 1*s* orbitals of two H atoms and are filled with bonding pairs.

But observation does *not* support these arguments. The bond angle of 92° is close to the 90° angle between *unhybridized p* orbitals. Similar angles occur in the hydrides of other large nonmetals of Groups 5A(15) and 6A(16). Why apply a theory if the facts don't warrant it? Real factors—bond length, atomic size, and electrostatic repulsions—influence shape. Larger atoms form longer bonds to H, which decreases repulsions; thus, overlap of *unhybridized* orbitals explains these shapes.

2. *d-Orbital hybridization is less important: rationalizing shapes with expanded valence shells.* Quantum-mechanical calculations show that *d*-orbitals have such high energies that they do not hybridize effectively with the *much* more stable *s* and *p* orbitals of a given *n* value. Thus, for example, some have proposed that SF_6 is most stable when the bonding orbitals of the central S use a combination of *sp*-hybrid orbitals and unhybridized 3*p*-orbitals instead of sp^3d^2 hybrid orbitals. Others prefer explanations that involve molecular orbitals or even ionic structures. These topics are beyond the scope of this text, and while they are being actively debated, we will continue to use the traditional, though limited, approach of including *d*-orbital hybridization for molecules with expanded valence shells.

Summary of Section 11.1

- VB theory explains that a covalent bond forms when two atomic orbitals overlap and two electrons with paired (opposite) spins spend more time in the overlapped regions.
- To explain molecular shape, the theory proposes that, during bonding, atomic orbitals mix to form hybrid orbitals with a different shape and direction. This process gives rise to greater overlap and, thus, stronger bonds.
- Based on the observed molecular shape (and the related electron-group arrangement), we postulate the type of hybrid orbital that accounts for the shape. In many cases, especially molecules with larger central atoms, the concept of hybridization has major limitations.

11.2 • MODES OF ORBITAL OVERLAP AND THE TYPES OF COVALENT BONDS

Orbitals can overlap by two *modes*—end to end or side to side—which gives rise to two types of covalent bonds—*sigma* and *pi*. We'll use VB theory to describe the two types here and, as you'll see, they are described by molecular orbital theory as well.

Orbital Overlap in Single and Multiple Bonds

Ethane (C_2H_6), ethylene (C_2H_4), and acetylene (C_2H_2) have different shapes. Ethane is tetrahedral at both carbons with bond angles near the ideal 109.5°. Ethylene is trigonal planar at both carbons with bond angles near the ideal 120°. Acetylene is linear with bond angles of 180°:

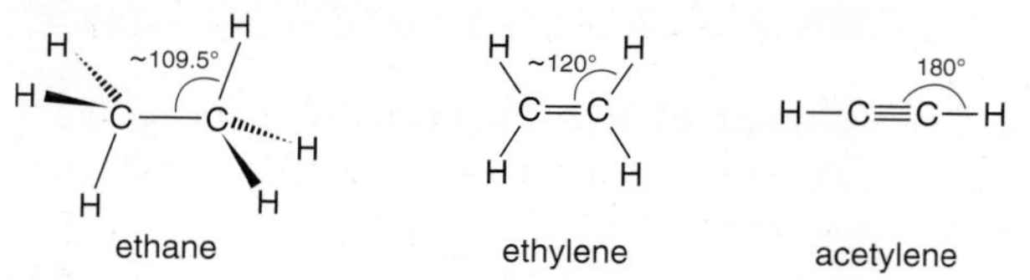

In these molecules, two modes of orbital overlap result in two types of bonds.

End-to-End Overlap and Sigma (σ) Bonding Both C atoms of ethane are sp^3 hybridized (Figure 11.10). The C—C bond arises from overlap of the end of one sp^3 orbital with the end of the other. *End-to-end* overlap forms a **sigma (σ) bond,** which has its *highest electron density along the bond axis* and is shaped like an ellipse rotated

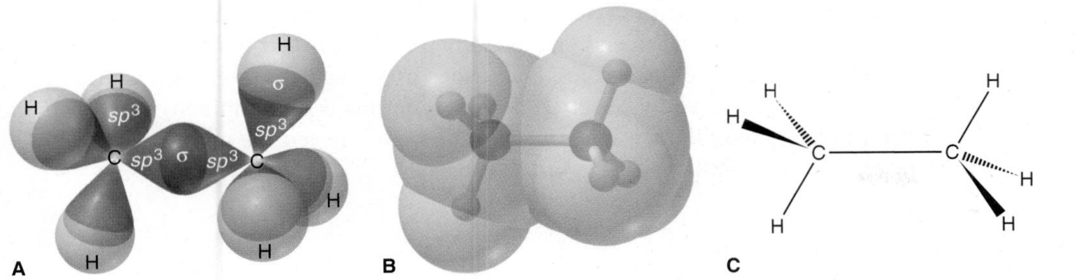

Figure 11.10 The σ bonds in ethane (C_2H_6). **A,** Depiction using atomic contours. **B,** An electron density model shows very slightly positive (*blue*) and negative (*red*) regions. **C,** Wedge-bond perspective drawing.

about its long axis (like a football). *All single bonds are σ bonds,* including the six C—H bonds in ethane.

Side-to-Side Overlap and Pi (π) Bonding For this type of bonding, we'll examine ethylene and acetylene:

1. *In ethylene,* each C atom is sp^2 hybridized. The four valence electrons of C half-fill the three sp^2 orbitals *and* the unhybridized $2p$ orbital, which lies perpendicular to the sp^2 plane (Figure 11.11). Two sp^2 orbitals of each C form C—H σ bonds. The third sp^2 orbital forms a σ bond with the other C. With the σ-bonded C atoms near each other, their half-filled $2p$ orbitals overlap *side to side,* which forms a **pi (π) bond.** It has *two regions (lobes) of electron density,* one above and one below the σ-bond axis. *The two electrons in one π bond occupy both lobes. A double bond consists of one σ bond and one π bond,* which increases electron density between the nuclei (Figure 11.11D). The two electron pairs act as one electron group because each pair occupies a different orbital, which reduces repulsions.

Figure 11.11 The σ and π bonds in ethylene (C_2H_4). **A,** The C—C σ bond and the four C—H σ bonds are shown with the unhybridized $2p$ orbitals. **B,** An accurate depiction of the $2p$ orbitals shows the side-to-side overlap; σ bonds are shown in ball-and-stick form. **C,** Two overlapping regions comprise *one* π bond, which is occupied by two electrons. **D,** With four electrons (one σ bond and one π bond) between the C atoms, electron density (*red*) is higher. **E,** Wedge-bond perspective drawing.

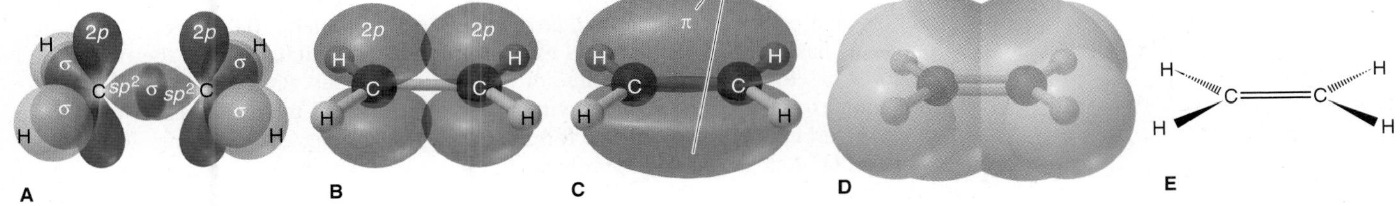

2. *In acetylene,* each C atom is *sp* hybridized, and its four valence electrons half-fill the two *sp* hybrids *and* the two unhybridized $2p$ orbitals (Figure 11.12). Each C forms a C—H σ bond with one *sp* orbital and a C—C σ bond with the other. Side-to-side overlap of one pair of $2p$ orbitals gives one π bond, with electron density above and below the σ bond. Side-to-side overlap of the other pair of $2p$ orbitals gives another π bond, 90° away from the first, with electron density in front and back of the σ bond. The result is a *cylindrically symmetrical* H—C≡C—H molecule. Note the greater electron density between the C atoms created by the six bonding electrons. Any triple bond *consists of one σ and two π bonds.*

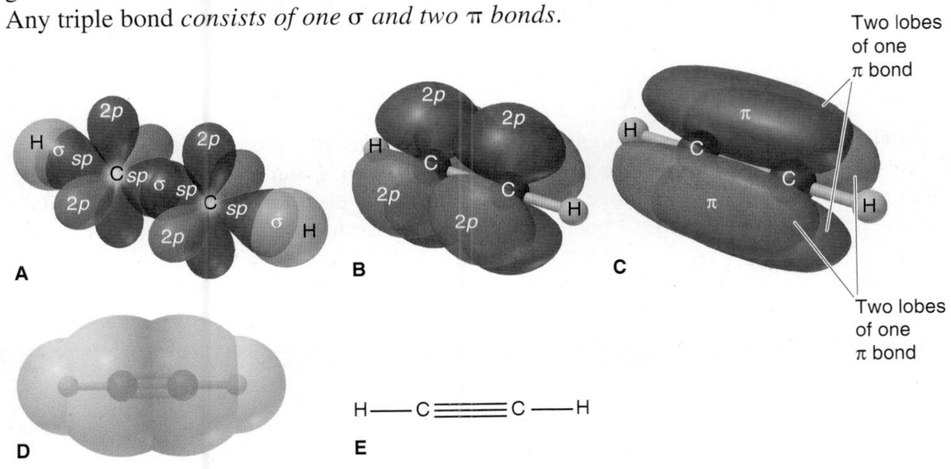

Figure 11.12 The σ bonds and π bonds in acetylene (C_2H_2). **A,** A contour depiction shows the C—C σ bond, the two C—H σ bonds, and two unhybridized $2p$ orbitals (one pair is in *red* for clarity). **B,** The $2p$ orbitals (accurate form) overlap side to side; σ bonds are shown by a ball-and-stick model. **C,** Overlapping regions of two π bonds, one black and the other red. **D,** The molecule has cylindrical symmetry. Six electrons (one σ bond and two π bonds) create even higher electron density (*red*) between the C atoms. **E,** Bond-line drawing.

Mode of Overlap, Bond Strength, and Bond Order Because orbitals overlap less side to side than end to end, a π bond is weaker than a σ bond; thus, for carbon-carbon bonds, a double bond is less than twice as strong as a single bond (Table 9.2, p. 340). Figure 11.13 shows electron density relief maps of the three types of carbon-carbon bonds; note the increasing electron density between the nuclei from single to double to triple bond.

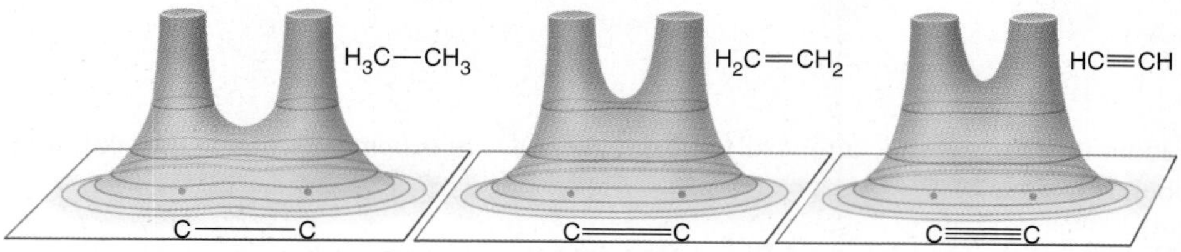

Figure 11.13 Electron density and bond order in ethane, ethylene, and acetylene.

Lone-pair repulsions, bond polarities, and other factors affect overlap between other pairs of atoms. Nevertheless, as a rough approximation, in terms of bond order (BO), a double bond (BO = 2) is about twice as strong as a single bond (BO = 1), and a triple bond (BO = 3) is about three times as strong.

Sample Problem 11.2 Describing the Types of Bonds in Molecules

Problem Describe the types of bonds and orbitals in acetone, $(CH_3)_2CO$.

Plan We use the shape around each central atom to postulate the hybrid orbitals used and use unhybridized orbitals to form the C=O bond.

Solution The shapes are tetrahedral around each C of the two CH_3 (methyl) groups and trigonal planar around the middle C (see Sample Problem 10.8, p. 382). Thus, the middle C has three sp^2 orbitals and one unhybridized p orbital. Each of the two methyl C atoms has four sp^3 orbitals. Three of these form σ bonds with the $1s$ orbitals of H atoms; the fourth forms a σ bond with an sp^2 orbital of the middle C. Thus, two of the three sp^2 orbitals of the middle C form σ bonds to the other two C atoms.

The O atom is also sp^2 hybridized and has an unhybridized p orbital that can form a π bond. Two of the O atom's sp^2 orbitals hold lone pairs, and the third forms a σ bond with the third sp^2 orbital of the middle C atom. The unhybridized, half-filled $2p$ orbitals of C and O form a π bond. The σ and π bonds constitute the C=O bond:

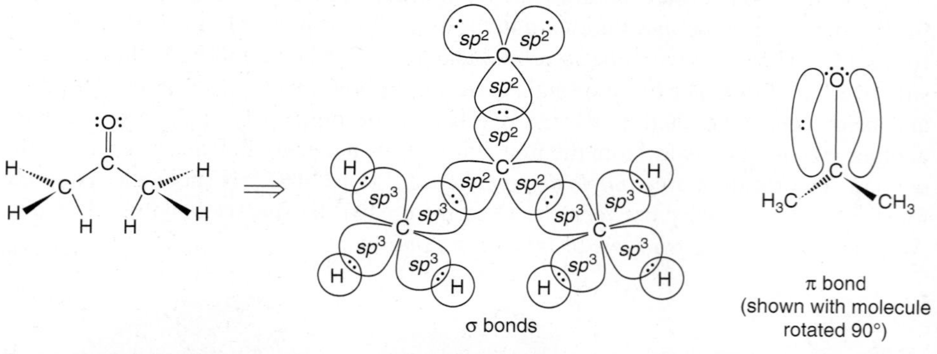

Comment Why would the O atom in acetone be hybridized? After all, it could use two perpendicular p orbitals for the σ and π bonds with C and leave the other p and the s orbital to hold the two lone pairs. Instead, having each lone pair in an sp^2 orbital oriented away from the C=O bond lowers electron-electron repulsions.

Follow-Up Problem 11.2 Describe the types of bonds and orbitals in **(a)** hydrogen cyanide, HCN, and **(b)** carbon dioxide, CO_2.

Orbital Overlap and Molecular Rotation

The type of overlap—end-to-end or side-to-side—affects rotation around the bond:

- *Sigma bond.* A σ *bond allows free rotation* because the extent of overlap is not affected. If you could hold one CH_3 group of ethane, the other CH_3 could spin without affecting the overlap of the C—C σ bond (see Figure 11.10).
- *Pi bond.* A π *bond restricts rotation* because *p* orbitals must be parallel to each other to overlap most effectively. Holding one CH_2 group in ethylene and trying to spin the other decreases the side-to-side overlap and breaks the π bond. For this reason, distinct *cis* and *trans* structures exist for compounds such as 1,2-dichloroethylene (Section 10.3). As Figure 11.14 shows, the π bond allows two *different* arrangements of atoms around the C atoms, which has a major effect on molecular polarity (see p. 385). Rotation around a triple bond is not meaningful: each triple-bonded C atom is bonded to one other group in a linear arrangement, so there can be no difference in the relative positions of attached groups.

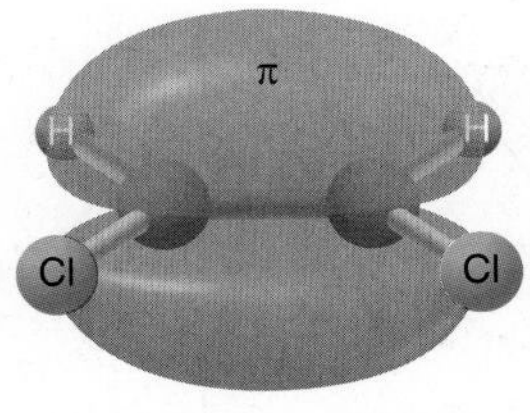

cis-1,2-Dichloroethylene

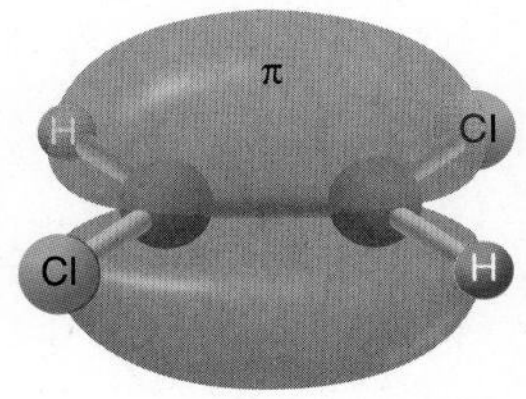

trans-1,2-Dichloroethylene

Figure 11.14 Restricted rotation around a π bond. *Cis*- and *trans*-1,2-dichloroethylene are different molecules because the π bond restricts rotation.

Summary of Section 11.2

- End-to-end overlap of atomic orbitals forms a σ bond, which allows free rotation of the bonded parts of the molecule.
- Side-to-side overlap forms a π bond, which restricts rotation.
- A multiple bond consists of a σ bond and either one π bond (double bond) or two (triple bond). Multiple bonds have greater electron density between the nuclei than single bonds do and, thus, higher bond energies.

11.3 • MOLECULAR ORBITAL (MO) THEORY AND ELECTRON DELOCALIZATION

Scientists choose the model that best answers a question: VSEPR for one about molecular shape and VB theory for one about orbital overlap. But neither adequately explains magnetic and spectral properties, and both understate the importance of electron delocalization. To deal with phenomena like these, which involve molecular energy levels, chemists choose **molecular orbital (MO) theory.** The MO model is a quantum-mechanical treatment for molecules similar to the one for atoms (Chapter 8): just as an atom has atomic orbitals (AOs) of given energies and shapes that are occupied by the atom's electrons, a molecule has **molecular orbitals (MOs)** of given energies and shapes that are occupied by the molecule's electrons.

There is a key distinction between VB and MO theories:

- VB theory pictures a molecule as a group of atoms bonded through *localized* overlapping of valence-shell atomic and/or hybrid orbitals occupied by electrons.
- MO theory pictures a molecule as a collection of nuclei with orbitals *delocalized* over the whole molecule and occupied by electrons.

Despite its usefulness, MO theory has a drawback in that MOs are more difficult to visualize than the shapes of VSEPR theory or the hybrid orbitals of VB theory.

The Central Themes of MO Theory

Several key ideas of MO theory appear in its description of H_2 and other simple species: how MOs form, what their energies and shapes are, and how they fill with electrons.

Formation of Molecular Orbitals Just as we need approximations to solve the Schrödinger equation for any atom with more than one electron, we need an approximation to determine the MOs of even the simplest molecule, H_2. The approximation is

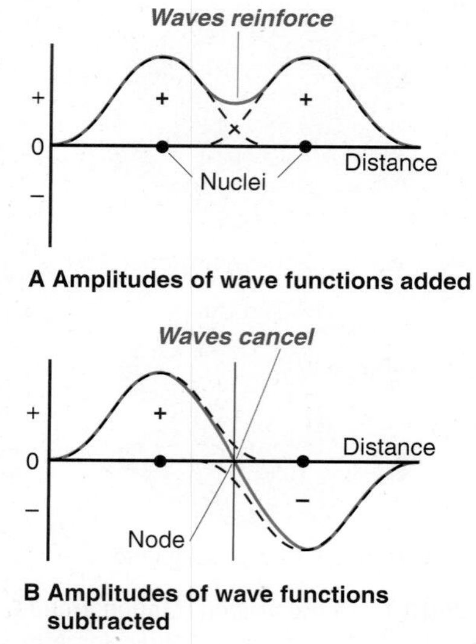

Figure 11.15 An analogy between light waves and atomic wave functions.

to mathematically *combine* (add or subtract) AOs (atomic wave functions) of nearby atoms to form MOs (molecular wave functions). Thus, when two H nuclei lie near each other, their AOs overlap and combine in two ways:

- *Adding the wave functions together.* This combination forms a **bonding MO,** which has *a region of high electron density between the nuclei.* Additive overlap is analogous to light waves reinforcing each other, which makes the amplitude higher and the light brighter. For electron waves, the overlap *increases* the probability that the electrons are between the nuclei (Figure 11.15A).
- *Subtracting the wave functions from each other.* This combination forms an **antibonding MO,** which has *a node, a region of zero electron density, between the nuclei* (Figure 11.15B). Subtractive overlap is analogous to light waves canceling each other, causing the light to disappear. With electron waves, the probability that the electrons lie between the nuclei *decreases* to zero.

The two possible combinations for hydrogen atoms H_A and H_B are

AO of H_A + AO of H_B = bonding MO of H_2 (more e^- density between nuclei)

AO of H_A − AO of H_B = antibonding MO of H_2 (less e^- density between nuclei)

Notice that *the number of AOs combined always equals the number of MOs formed:* two H atomic orbitals combine to form two H_2 molecular orbitals.

Shape and Energy of H_2 Molecular Orbitals Bonding and antibonding MOs have different shapes and energies. Figure 11.16 shows these orbitals for H_2:

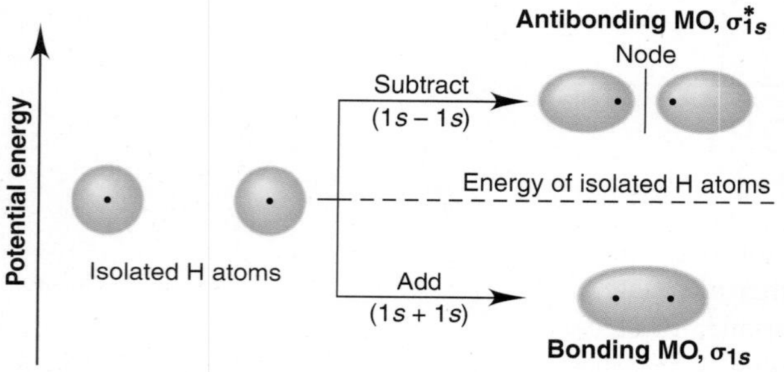

Figure 11.16 Contours and energies of H_2 bonding and antibonding MOs.

- *Bonding MO.* A bonding MO is *lower in energy* than the AOs that form it. Because it is spread mostly *between* the nuclei, nuclear repulsions decrease while nucleus-electron attractions increase. Moreover, two electrons in this MO can delocalize their charges over a larger volume than in nearby, separate AOs, which lowers electron repulsions. Because of these electrostatic effects, when electrons occupy this orbital, the H_2 molecule is *more stable* than the separate H atoms.
- *Antibonding MO.* An antibonding MO is *higher in energy* than the AOs that form it. With most of its electron density *outside* the internuclear region, it has a node between the nuclei, and nuclear repulsions increase. Therefore, when electrons occupy this orbital, the H_2 molecule is *less stable* than the separate H atoms.

Both the bonding and antibonding MOs of H_2 are **sigma (σ) MOs** because they are cylindrically symmetrical about an imaginary line between the nuclei. The bonding MO is denoted by σ_{1s}; that is, a σ MO derived from 1*s* AOs. Antibonding orbitals are denoted with a superscript star: the antibonding MO derived from 1*s* AOs is σ^*_{1s} (spoken "sigma, one ess, star").

For AOs to interact enough to form MOs, they must be similar in *energy* and *orientation.* The 1*s* orbitals of two H atoms have identical energy and orientation, so they interact strongly. We'll revisit this requirement for molecules composed of many-electron atoms.

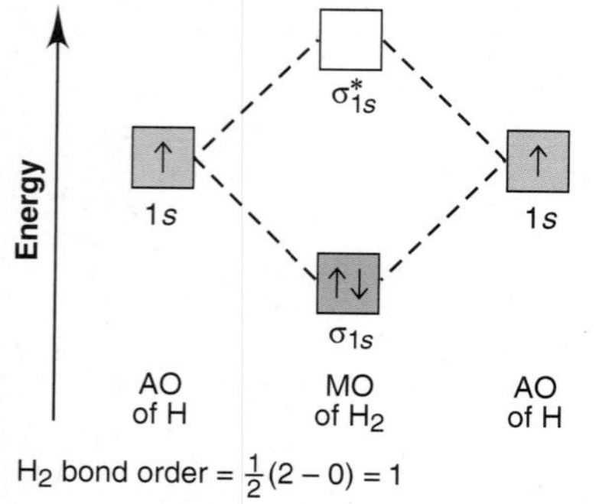

Figure 11.17 MO diagram for H_2. The vertical placement of the boxes indicates relative energies. Orbital occupancy is shown with arrows and color (dark = full, pale = half-filled, none = empty).

Electrons in Molecular Orbitals Several aspects of MO theory—filling of MOs, energy-level diagrams, electron configuration, and bond order—relate to earlier ideas:

1. *Filling MOs with electrons.* Electrons enter MOs just as they do AOs:

- MOs are filled in order of increasing energy (aufbau principle).
- An MO can hold a maximum of two electrons with opposite spins (exclusion principle).
- Orbitals of equal energy are half-filled, with spins parallel, before any of them are filled (Hund's rule).

2. *MO energy-level diagrams.* A **molecular orbital (MO) diagram** shows the relative energy and number of electrons in each MO, as well as the AOs from which they formed. In the MO diagram for H_2 (Figure 11.17), two electrons, one from the AO of each H, fill the H_2 bonding MO, while the antibonding MO remains empty.

3. *Electron configuration*. Just as we write an electron configuration for an atom, we can write one for a molecule. The symbol of each occupied MO is written in parentheses, with the number of electrons in it as a superscript outside: the electron configuration of H_2 is $(\sigma_{1s})^2$.

4. *Bond order*. In a Lewis structure, bond order is the number of electron pairs per atom-to-atom linkage. The **MO bond order** is the number of electrons in bonding MOs minus the number in antibonding MOs, divided by two:

$$\text{Bond order} = \tfrac{1}{2}[(\text{no. of e}^- \text{ in bonding MO}) - (\text{no. of e}^- \text{ in antibonding MO})] \quad (11.1)$$

Here are three key points about MO bond order:

- Bond order > 0: the molecule is more stable than the separate atoms, so it *will* form. For H_2, the bond order is $\tfrac{1}{2}(2-0) = 1$.
- Bond order = 0: the molecule is as stable as the separate atoms, so it will *not* form (occurs when equal numbers of electrons occupy bonding and antibonding MOs).
- In general, the *higher* the bond order, the *stronger* the bond is.

Do He_2^+ and He_2 Exist? One of the early triumphs of MO theory was its ability to *predict* the existence of He_2^+, the helium molecule-ion, which consists of two He nuclei and three electrons. Let's use MO diagrams to see why He_2^+ exists but He_2 doesn't:

- In He_2^+, the 1*s* AOs form MOs (Figure 11.18A). The three electrons are distributed as a pair in the σ_{1s} MO and a lone electron in the σ^*_{1s} MO. The bond order is $\tfrac{1}{2}(2-1) = \tfrac{1}{2}$. Thus, He_2^+ has a relatively weak bond, but it should exist. Indeed, this species has been observed frequently when He atoms collide with He^+ ions. Its electron configuration is $(\sigma_{1s})^2(\sigma^*_{1s})^1$.
- In He_2, with four electrons in the σ_{1s} and σ^*_{1s} MOs, both the bonding and antibonding orbitals are filled (Figure 11.18B). Stabilization from the electron pair in the bonding MO is canceled by destabilization from the electron pair in the antibonding MO. With a zero bond order $[\tfrac{1}{2}(2-2) = 0]$, we predict, and experiment has so far confirmed, that a covalent He_2 molecule does not exist.

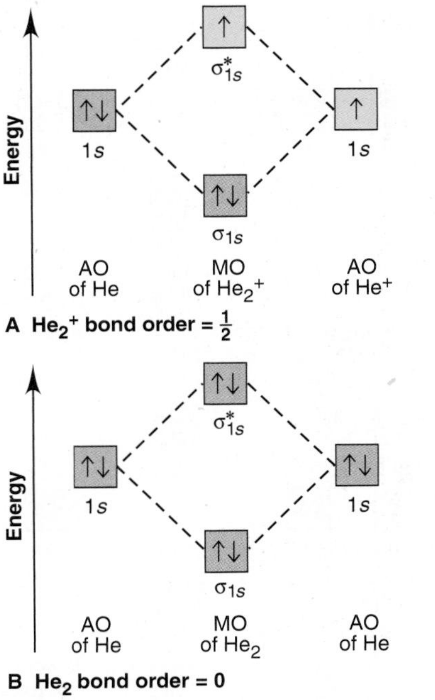

Figure 11.18 MO diagrams for He_2^+ and He_2.

Sample Problem 11.3 Predicting Stability of Species Using MO Diagrams

Problem Use MO diagrams to find bond orders and predict whether H_2^+ and H_2^- exist. If either exists, write its electron configuration.

Plan Since the 1*s* AOs form the MOs, the MO diagrams are similar to the one for H_2. We find the number of electrons in each species and distribute them one at a time to the MOs in order of increasing energy. We obtain the bond order with Equation 11.1 and write the electron configuration as described in the text.

Solution For H_2^+. H_2 has two e^-, so H_2^+ has only one, which enters the bonding MO (*see diagram, below left*). The bond order is $\tfrac{1}{2}(1-0) = \tfrac{1}{2}$, so we predict that H_2^+ exists. The electron configuration is $(\sigma_{1s})^1$.

For H_2^-. H_2 has two e^-, so H_2^- has three. We place two paired e^- in the bonding MO and one unpaired e^- in the antibonding MO (*see diagram, below right*). The bond order is $\tfrac{1}{2}(2-1) = \tfrac{1}{2}$, so we predict that H_2^- exists. The electron configuration is $(\sigma_{1s})^2(\sigma^*_{1s})^1$.

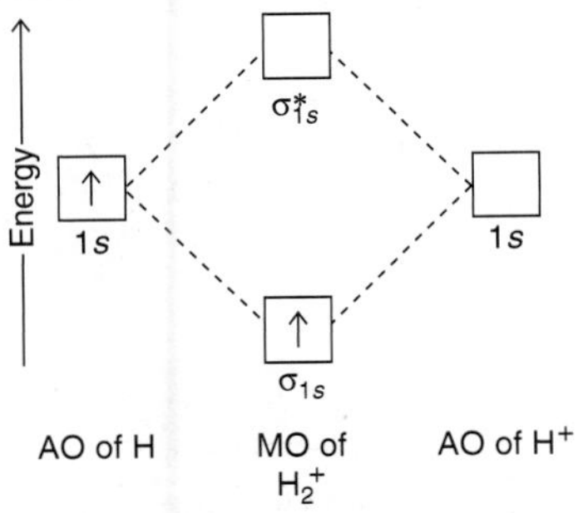

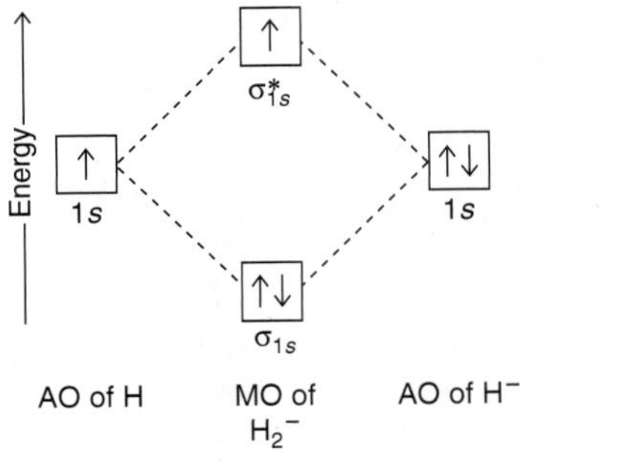

Check The number of electrons in the MOs equals the number of electrons in the AOs.

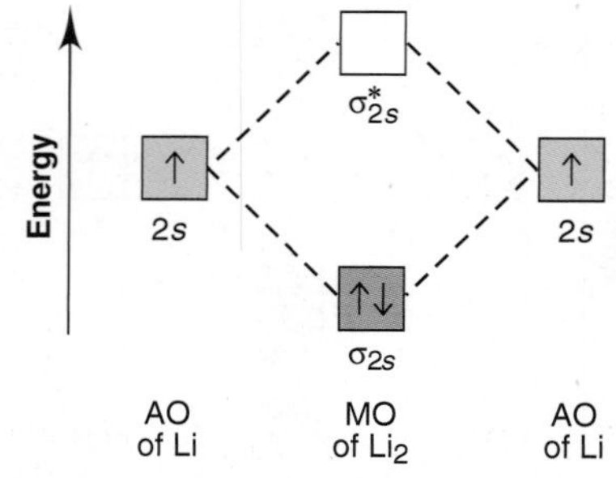

A Li_2 **bond order = 1**

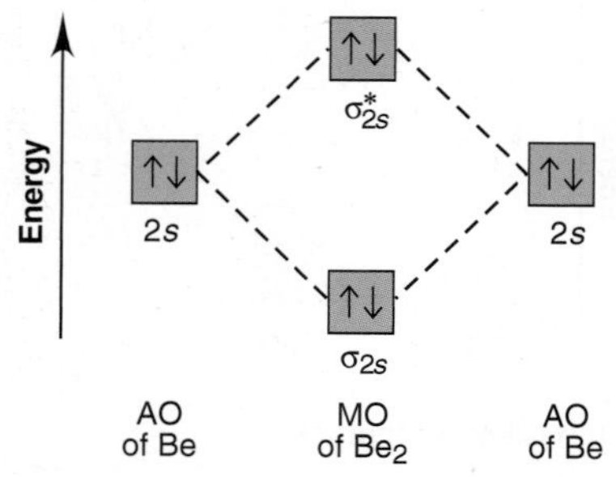

B Be_2 **bond order = 0**

Figure 11.19 Bonding in *s*-block homonuclear diatomic molecules. Only outer (valence) AOs interact enough to form MOs.

Comment Both species have been detected spectroscopically, H_2^+ in the material around stars and H_2^- in the laboratory.

Follow-Up Problem 11.3 Use an MO diagram to find the bond order and predict whether two H^- ions could form H_2^{2-}. If it does exist, write its electron configuration.

Homonuclear Diatomic Molecules of Period 2 Elements

Homonuclear diatomic molecules are composed of two identical atoms. In addition to H_2 from Period 1, you're familiar with N_2, O_2, and F_2 from Period 2 as the elemental forms under standard conditions. Others in Period 2—Li_2, Be_2, B_2, C_2, and Ne_2—are observed, if at all, at high temperatures. We'll divide them into molecules from the *s* block, Groups 1A(1) and 2A(2), and the *p* block, Groups 3A(13) through 8A(18).

Bonding in the *s*-Block Homonuclear Diatomic Molecules Both Li and Be occur as metals under normal conditions, but MO theory can examine their stability as diatomic gases, dilithium (Li_2) and diberyllium (Be_2).

These atoms have electrons in inner (1*s*) and outer (2*s*) AOs, but we ignore the inner ones because, in general, *only outer (valence) AOs interact enough to form MOs.* Like those formed from 1*s* AOs, these 2*s* AOs form σ MOs, cylindrically symmetrical around the internuclear axis.

- In Li_2, the two valence electrons fill the bonding (σ_{2s}) MO, with opposing spins, leaving the antibonding (σ^*_{2s}) MO empty (Figure 11.19A). The bond order is $\frac{1}{2}(2 - 0) = 1$. In fact, Li_2 *has* been observed; the electron configuration is $(\sigma_{2s})^2$.
- In Be_2, the four valence electrons fill the σ_{2s} and σ^*_{2s} MOs (Figure 11.19B), giving an orbital occupancy similar to that in He_2. The bond order is $\frac{1}{2}(2 - 2) = 0$, and the ground state of Be_2 has never been observed.

Shape and Energy of MOs from Atomic *p*-Orbital Combinations As we move to boron, atomic 2*p* orbitals are occupied. Recall that *p* orbitals can overlap by two modes, which correspond to two ways their wave functions combine (Figure 11.20):

- End-to-end combination gives a pair of σ MOs, the σ_{2p} and σ^*_{2p}.
- Side-to-side combination gives a pair of **pi (π) MOs,** π_{2p} and π^*_{2p}.

Despite the different shapes, MOs derived from *p* orbitals are like those from *s* orbitals. Bonding MOs have most of the electron density *between* the nuclei, and antibonding MOs have most *outside* the internuclear region, with a node between the nuclei.

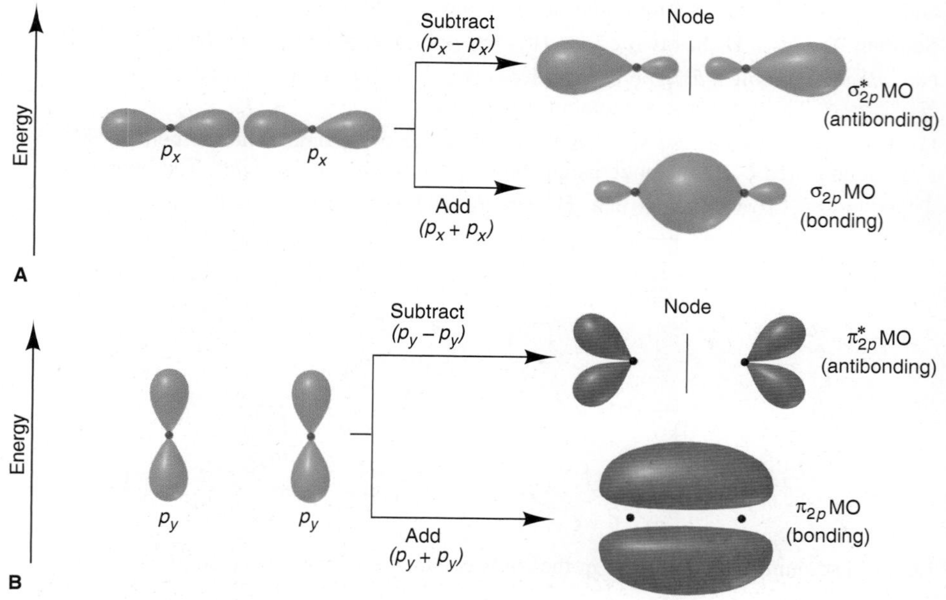

Figure 11.20 Shapes and energies of σ and π MOs from combinations of 2*p* atomic orbitals. **A,** The *p* orbitals lying along the internuclear axis (designated p_x) overlap end to end and form σ_{2p} and σ^*_{2p} MOs. **B,** The *p* orbitals perpendicular to the internuclear axis overlap side to side and form two π MOs. (The p_y interactions, shown here, are the same as for the p_z, for a total of four π MOs.)

The order of energy levels for MOs, whether bonding or antibonding, is based on the order of AO energy levels *and* on the mode of the *p*-orbital overlap:

- MOs formed from 2*s* orbitals are *lower in energy* than MOs formed from 2*p* orbitals because 2*s* AOs are lower in energy than 2*p* AOs.
- Bonding MOs are *lower in energy* than antibonding MOs: σ_{2p} is lower in energy than σ^*_{2p} and π_{2p} is lower than π^*_{2p}.
- Atomic *p* orbitals overlap more extensively end to end than side to side. Thus, the σ_{2p} MO is usually lower in energy than the π_{2p} MO. We also find that the destabilizing effect of the σ^*_{2p} MO is greater than that of the π^*_{2p} MO.

Thus, the energy order for MOs derived from 2*p* orbitals is typically

$$\sigma_{2p} < \pi_{2p} < \pi^*_{2p} < \sigma^*_{2p}$$

Each atom has three mutually perpendicular 2*p* orbitals. When the six *p* orbitals in two atoms combine, the two that interact end to end form one σ and one σ* MO, and the two pairs of orbitals that interact side to side form two π MOs and two π* MOs. Placing these orientations within the energy order gives the *expected* MO diagram for the *p*-block Period 2 homonuclear diatomic molecules (Figure 11.21A).

Recall that only AOs of similar energy interact enough to form MOs. This fact leads to two energy orders:

1. ***Without*** *s and p orbital mixing: O_2, F_2, and Ne_2*. The order in Figure 11.21A assumes that *s* and *p* AOs are so different in energy that they do not interact; we say the orbitals do not *mix*. Lying at the right of Period 2, O, F, and Ne are relatively small. Thus, as electrons start to pair up in the half-filled 2*p* orbitals, strong repulsions raise the energy of the 2*p* orbitals high enough above the 2*s* orbitals to prevent orbital mixing.

2. ***With*** *s and p orbital mixing: B_2, C_2, and N_2*. B, C, and N atoms are relatively large, with 2*p* AOs only half-filled, so repulsions are weaker. As a result, orbital energies are close enough for some mixing to occur between the 2*s* of one atom and the end-on 2*p* of the other. The effect is to *lower* the energy of the σ_{2s} and σ^*_{2s} MOs and *raise* the energy of the σ_{2p} and σ^*_{2p} MOs; the π MOs are not affected. The MO diagram for B_2, C_2, and N_2 reflects this mixing (Figure 11.21B). The only difference from the MO diagram for O_2, F_2, and Ne_2 is the *reverse in energy order* of the σ_{2p} and π_{2p} MOs.

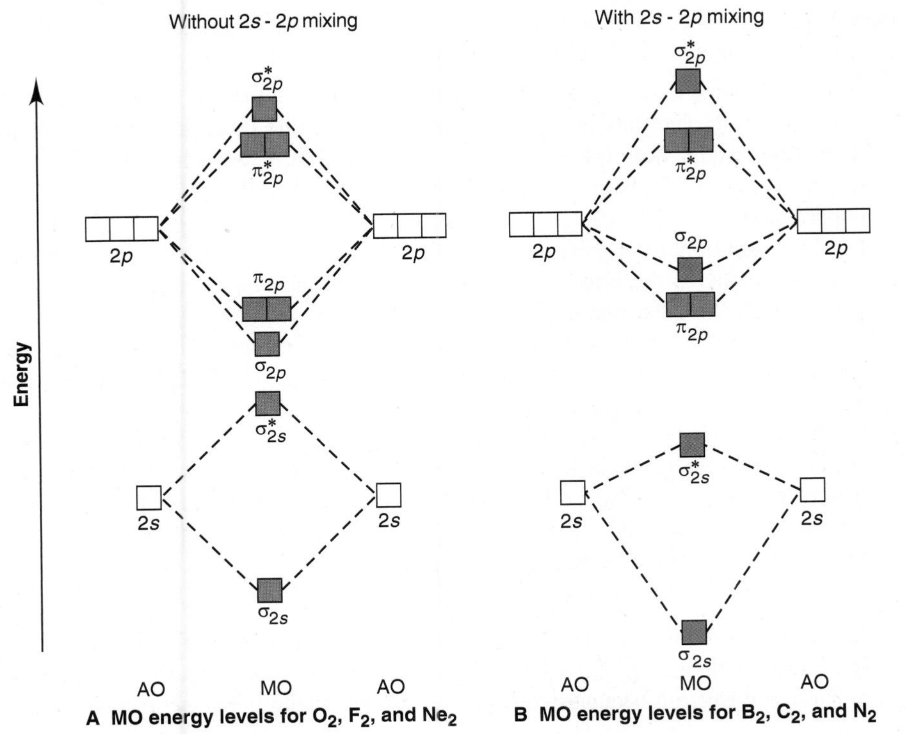

Figure 11.21 Relative MO energy levels for Period 2 homonuclear diatomic molecules. (For clarity, the MOs affected by mixing are shown in *purple*.)

Figure 11.22 MO occupancy and some properties of B_2 through Ne_2. Energy order and occupancy of MOs are above bar graphs of bond energy and length, bond order, magnetic properties, and outer (valence) electron configuration.

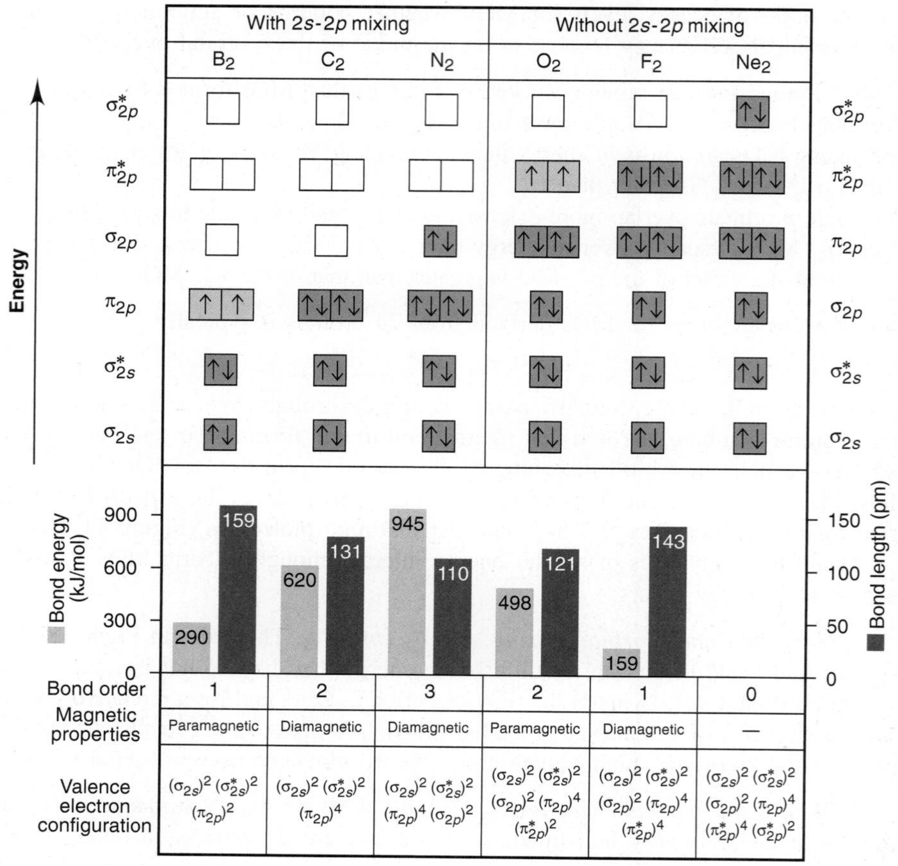

Bonding in the *p*-Block Homonuclear Diatomic Molecules Figure 11.22 shows the MOs, electron occupancy, and some properties of B_2 through Ne_2. Note that

1. *Higher* bond order correlates with *greater* bond energy and *shorter* bond length.

2. Orbital occupancy correlates with magnetic properties. Recall from Chapter 8 that if a substance has unpaired electrons, it is *paramagnetic,* and if all electrons are paired, the substance is *diamagnetic;* the same applies to molecules. Let's examine the MO occupancy and some properties of these molecules:

- *B_2*. The B_2 molecule has six outer electrons: four fill the σ_{2s} and σ^*_{2s} MOs. The remaining two electrons occupy the two π_{2p} MOs, one in each orbital, in keeping with Hund's rule. With four electrons in bonding MOs and two in antibonding MOs, the bond order of B_2 is $\frac{1}{2}(4 - 2) = 1$. As expected from the two lone electrons, B_2 is paramagnetic.
- *C_2*. Two additional electrons in C_2 fill the two π_{2p} MOs. With two more bonding electrons than B_2, the bond order of C_2 is 2 and the bond is stronger and shorter. But with all the electrons paired, C_2 is diamagnetic.
- *N_2*. Two more electrons in N_2 fill the σ_{2p} MO, so the molecule is also diamagnetic. The bond order of 3 is consistent with the triple bond in the Lewis structure and with a stronger, shorter bond.
- *O_2*. With this molecule, we see the power of MO theory over VB theory and others based on electrons in localized orbitals. It is impossible to write one Lewis structure consistent with the fact that O_2 is double bonded and paramagnetic. We can write one with a double bond and paired electrons, and another with a single bond and two unpaired electrons:

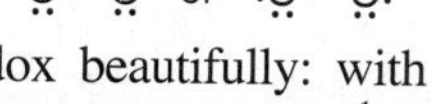

MO theory resolves this paradox beautifully: with eight electrons in bonding MOs and four in antibonding MOs, the bond order is $\frac{1}{2}(8 - 4) = 2$, and it is paramagnetic because *one* electron occupies each of *two* π^*_{2p} MOs with unpaired (parallel) spins. A thin stream of liquid O_2 will remain suspended between the poles of a powerful magnet (Figure 11.23). As expected, the bond is weaker and longer than the one in N_2.

- *F_2*. Two more electrons in F_2 fill the π^*_{2p} orbitals, so it is diamagnetic. The bond has an order of 1 and is weaker and longer than the one in O_2. Note that this bond is shorter, yet about half as strong as the single bond in B_2. We might have expected it to be stronger because F is smaller than B. But 18 electrons in the smaller volume of F_2 cause greater repulsions than the 10 in B_2, so the F_2 bond is weaker.
- *Ne_2*. The final member of the Period 2 series doesn't exist for the same reason He_2 doesn't: all the MOs are filled, which gives a bond order of zero.

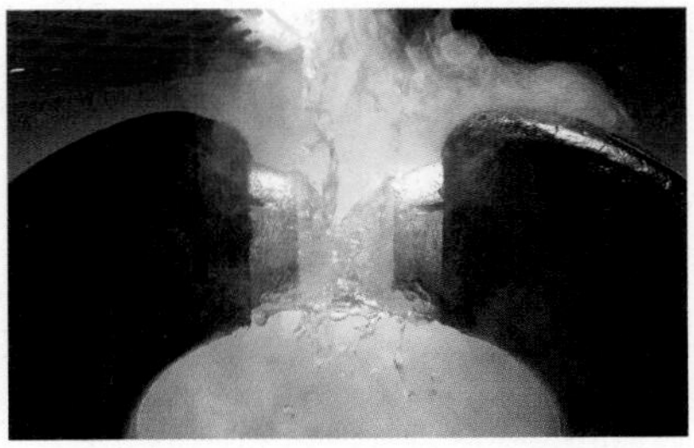

Figure 11.23 The paramagnetic properties of O_2.

Sample Problem 11.4 Using MO Theory to Explain Bond Properties

Problem Explain the following data with diagrams showing the occupancy of MOs:

	N_2	N_2^+	O_2	O_2^+
Bond energy (kJ/mol)	945	841	498	623
Bond length (pm)	110	112	121	112

Plan The data show that removing an electron from each parent molecule has opposite effects: N_2^+ has a weaker, longer bond than N_2, but O_2^+ has a stronger, shorter bond than O_2. We determine the valence electrons in each species, draw the sequence of MO energy levels (showing orbital mixing in N_2 but not in O_2), and fill them with electrons. To explain the data, we calculate bond orders, which relate directly to bond energy and inversely to bond length.

Solution Determining the valence electrons:

N has 5 valence e^-, so N_2 has 10 and N_2^+ has 9

O has 6 valence e^-, so O_2 has 12 and O_2^+ has 11

Drawing and filling the MO diagrams:

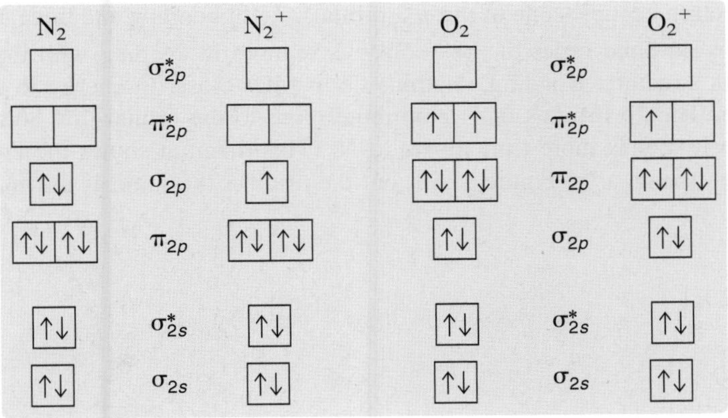

Calculating bond orders:

$\frac{1}{2}(8-2)=3$ $\quad \frac{1}{2}(7-2)=2.5$ $\quad \frac{1}{2}(8-4)=2$ $\quad \frac{1}{2}(8-3)=2.5$

Explaining the data:

1. When N_2 becomes N_2^+, a *bonding* electron is removed, so the bond order decreases. Thus, N_2^+ has a weaker, longer bond than N_2.
2. When O_2 becomes O_2^+, an *antibonding* electron is removed, so the bond order increases. Thus, O_2^+ has a stronger, shorter bond than O_2.

Check The answers make sense in terms of bond order, bond energy, and bond length. Check that the total number of bonding and antibonding electrons equals the number of valence electrons calculated.

Follow-Up Problem 11.4 Determine the bond orders for the following species: F_2^{2-}, F_2^-, F_2, F_2^+, F_2^{2+}. List the species in order of increasing bond energy and in order of increasing bond length.

Two Heteronuclear Diatomic Molecules: HF and NO

Heteronuclear diatomic molecules have asymmetric MO diagrams because the AOs of the *different* atoms have unequal energies. Atoms with greater effective nuclear charge (Z_{eff}) pull their electrons closer, so they have more stable (lower energy) AOs (Section 8.1) and higher EN values (Section 9.5). Let's examine the bonding in HF and NO.

Bonding in HF To form the MOs in HF, we decide which AOs will combine. The high Z_{eff} of F holds its electrons so tightly that the $1s$, $2s$, and $2p$ orbitals of F have lower energy than the $1s$ of H. The half-filled F $2p$ orbital interacts with the H $1s$ through end-on overlap, which forms σ and σ^* MOs. The two filled $2p$ orbitals of F are called **nonbonding MOs.** Because they are not involved in bonding, they have the same energy as the isolated AOs (Figure 11.24A).

The bonding MO is closer in energy to the AOs of F, so the F $2p$ orbital contributes more to the HF bond than the H $1s$ does. In polar covalent molecules, *bonding MOs are closer in energy to the AOs of the more electronegative atom.* In effect, fluorine's greater electronegativity lowers the energy of the bonding MO and draws the bonding electrons closer.

Bonding in NO Nitrogen monoxide (nitric oxide) is highly reactive because of its lone electron. Two possible Lewis structures for NO, with formal charges (Section 10.1), are

$$\overset{0}{:\dot{N}}=\overset{0}{\ddot{O}}: \quad \text{or} \quad \overset{-1}{:\ddot{N}}=\overset{+1}{\dot{O}}:$$
$$\text{I} \qquad\qquad\qquad \text{II}$$

Both structures show a double bond, but the *measured* bond energy suggests a bond order *higher* than 2. Moreover, it is not clear where the lone electron resides, although the lower formal charges for structure I suggest that it is on the N.

The MO diagram is asymmetric, with the AOs of the more electronegative O lower in energy (Figure 11.24B). When the 11 valence electrons fill the MOs of NO, the lone electron occupies one of the π^*_{2p} orbitals. Eight bonding and three antibonding electrons give a bond order of $\frac{1}{2}(8 - 3) = 2.5$, more in keeping with the data than either Lewis structure. Bonding electrons lie in MOs closer in energy to the AOs of the O atom. The $2p$ orbitals of N contribute more to the orbital that holds the lone electron, so it spends more time closer to N. (This diagram shows the energy order *with* $2s$–$2p$ mixing, as in Figure 11.21, but the result is the same as the order without mixing.)

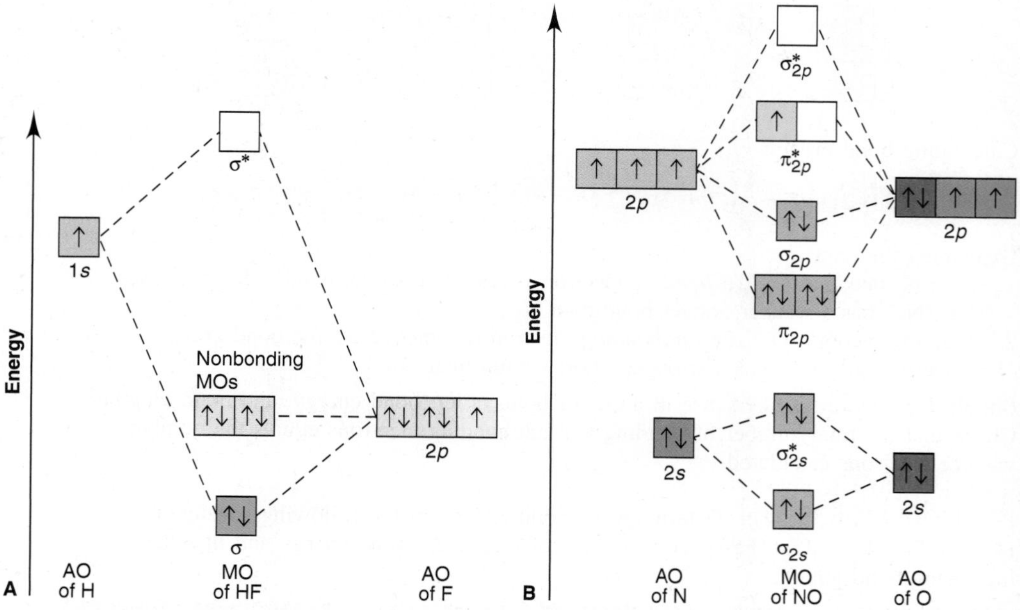

Figure 11.24 The MO diagrams for HF and NO. **A,** In HF, the bonding MO is closer in energy to the $2p$ orbital of F. (The $2s$ AO of F is not shown.) **B,** In NO, the lone electron occupies an MO closer in energy to the $2p$ of N.

Two Polyatomic Molecules: Benzene and Ozone

The orbital shapes and MO diagrams for polyatomic molecules are too complex for a detailed treatment here. But we'll briefly discuss how the model eliminates the need for resonance forms and helps explain the effects of the absorption of energy.

Recall that we cannot draw one Lewis structure for either benzene or ozone, so we draw separate forms of a resonance hybrid. The VB model also uses resonance because it relies on *localized* bonds. In contrast, MO theory pictures a structure of delocalized σ and π MOs. Figure 11.25 shows the lowest energy π-bonding MOs in benzene and ozone. The extended areas of electron density allow delocalization of one π-bonding electron pair over the entire molecule, thus eliminating the need for separate resonance forms:

- *In benzene*, the upper and lower hexagonal lobes of this MO lie above and below the σ plane of the six C nuclei.
- *In ozone*, the two lobes of this MO extend over and under the three O nuclei.

The full MO diagrams for these molecules help us rationalize how bonding electrons in O_3 become excited and occupy empty antibonding orbitals when the molecule absorbs UV radiation in the stratosphere, and why the UV spectrum of benzene has its characteristic absorption bands.

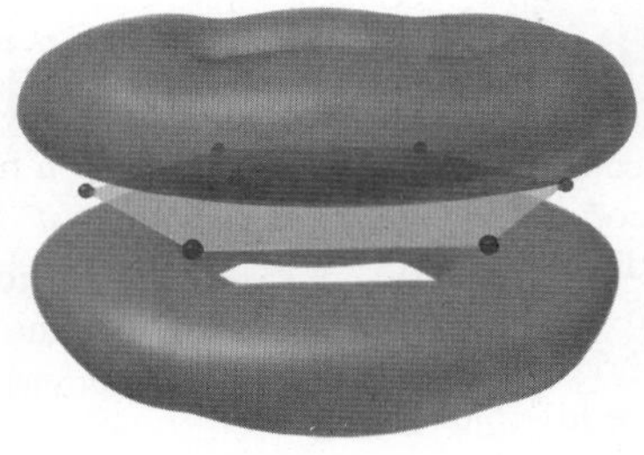

Benzene, C_6H_6

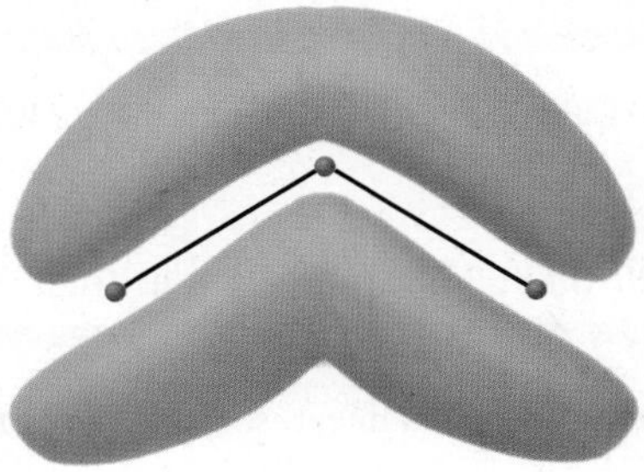

Ozone, O_3

Figure 11.25 The lowest energy π-bonding MOs in benzene and ozone.

Summary of Section 11.3

- Molecular orbital (MO) theory treats a molecule as a collection of nuclei with MOs delocalized over the entire structure.
- Atomic orbitals of comparable energy can be added or subtracted to obtain bonding or antibonding MOs, respectively.
- Bonding MOs, whether σ or π, have most of the electron density between the nuclei and are lower in energy than the AOs; most of the electron density in antibonding MOs does not lie between the nuclei, so these MOs are higher in energy.
- MOs are filled in order of their energy with paired electrons having opposite spins.
- MO diagrams show energy levels and orbital occupancy. Diagrams for the Period 2 homonuclear diatomic molecules explain bond energy, bond length, and magnetic behavior.
- In heteronuclear diatomic molecules, the more electronegative atom contributes more to the bonding MOs.
- MO theory eliminates the need for resonance forms to depict larger molecules.

CHAPTER REVIEW GUIDE

Learning Objectives

Relevant section (§) and/or sample problem (SP) numbers appear in parentheses.

Understand These Concepts

1. The main ideas of valence bond theory—orbital overlap, opposing electron spins, and hybridization—as a means of rationalizing molecular shapes (§11.1)
2. How orbitals mix to form hybrid orbitals with different spatial orientations (§11.1)
3. The distinction between end-to-end and side-to-side overlap and the origin of sigma (σ) and pi (π) bonds in simple molecules (§11.2)
4. How these two modes of orbital overlap lead to single, double, and triple bonds (§11.2)
5. Why π bonding restricts rotation around double bonds (§11.2)
6. The distinction between the localized bonding of VB theory and the delocalized bonding of MO theory (§11.3)
7. How addition or subtraction of AOs forms bonding or antibonding MOs (§11.3)
8. The shapes of MOs formed from combinations of two *s* orbitals and combinations of two *p* orbitals (§11.3)
9. How MO bond order predicts the stability of molecular species (§11.3)
10. How MO theory explains the bonding and magnetic properties of homonuclear and heteronuclear diatomic molecules of Period 2 elements (§11.3)

Master These Skills

1. Using molecular shape to postulate the hybrid orbitals used by a central atom (SP 11.1)
2. Describing the types of orbitals and bonds in a molecule (SP 11.2)
3. Drawing MO diagrams, writing electron configurations, and calculating bond orders of molecular species (SP 11.3)
4. Explaining bond and magnetic properties with MO theory (SP 11.4)

Key Terms

Page numbers appear in parentheses.

Section 11.1
valence bond (VB) theory (395)
hybridization (396)
hybrid orbital (396)
sp hybrid orbital (396)
sp^2 hybrid orbital (398)
sp^3 hybrid orbital (398)
sp^3d hybrid orbital (399)
sp^3d^2 hybrid orbital (400)

Section 11.2
sigma (σ) bond (402)
pi (π) bond (403)

Section 11.3
molecular orbital (MO) theory (405)
molecular orbital (MO) (405)
bonding MO (406)
antibonding MO (406)
sigma (σ) MO (406)
molecular orbital (MO) diagram (406)
MO bond order (407)
homonuclear diatomic molecule (408)
pi (π) MO (408)
nonbonding MO (412)

Key Equations and Relationships

Page numbers appear in parentheses.

11.1 Calculating the MO bond order (407): Bond order $= \frac{1}{2}[(\text{no. of e}^- \text{ in bonding MO}) - (\text{no. of e}^- \text{ in antibonding MO})]$

Brief Solutions to Follow-Up Problems

11.1 (a) Shape is linear, so Be is *sp* hybridized.

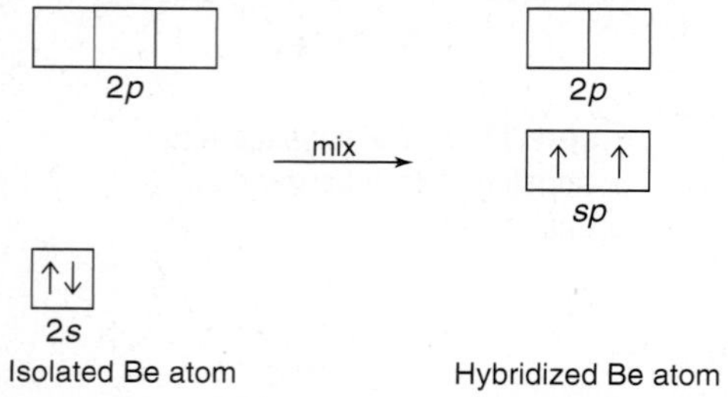

(b) Shape is tetrahedral, so Si is sp^3 hybridized.

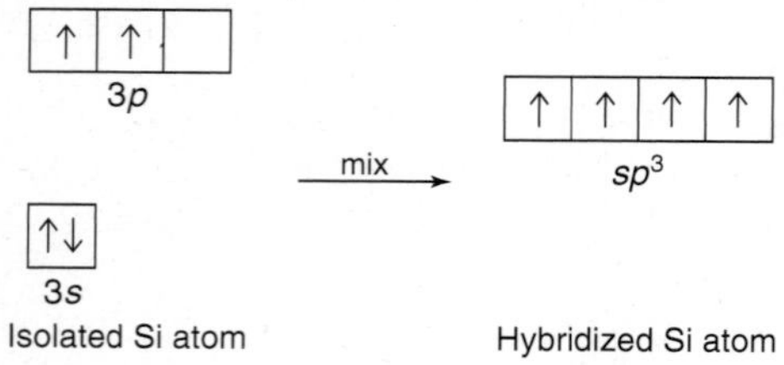

(c) Shape is square planar, so Xe is sp^3d^2 hybridized.

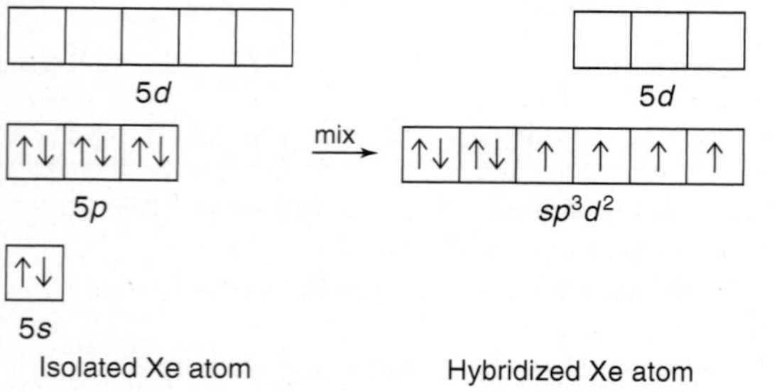

11.2 (a) H—C≡N:

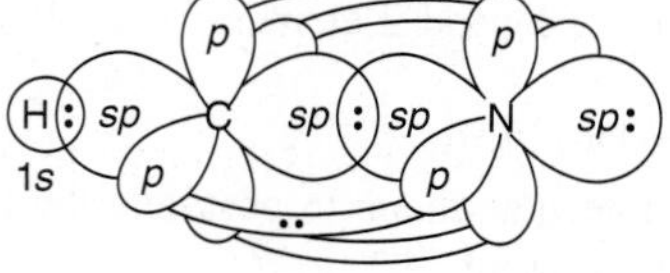

HCN is linear, so C is *sp* hybridized. N is also *sp* hybridized. One *sp* of C overlaps the 1*s* of H to form a σ bond. The other *sp* of C overlaps one *sp* of N to form a σ bond. The other *sp* of N holds a lone pair. Two unhybridized *p* orbitals of N and two of C overlap to form two π bonds.

(b) Ö=C=Ö

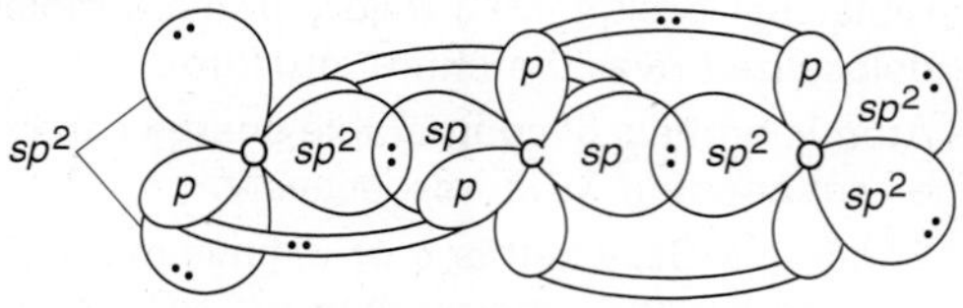

CO_2 is linear, so C is *sp* hybridized. Both O atoms are sp^2 hybridized. Each *sp* of C overlaps one sp^2 of an O to form two σ bonds. Each of the two unhybridized *p* orbitals of C forms a π bond with the unhybridized *p* of one of the two O atoms. Two sp^2 of each O hold lone pairs.

11.3

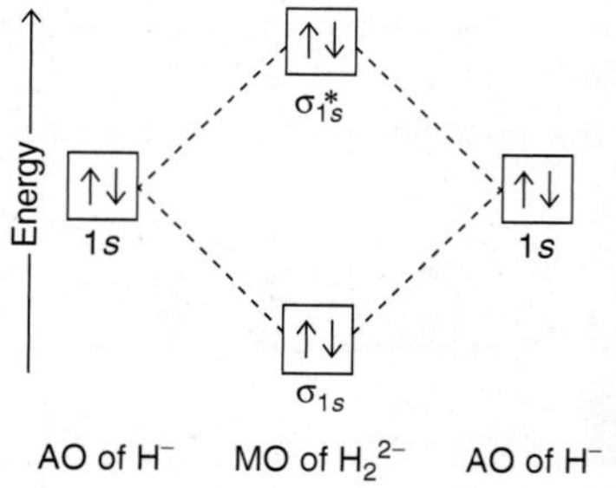

Does not exist: bond order $= \frac{1}{2}(2 - 2) = 0$.

11.4 Bond orders: $F_2^{2-} = 0$; $F_2^- = \frac{1}{2}$; $F_2 = 1$; $F_2^+ = 1\frac{1}{2}$
$F_2^{2+} = 2$

Bond energy: $F_2^{2-} < F_2^- < F_2 < F_2^+ < F_2^{2+}$

Bond length: $F_2^{2+} < F_2^+ < F_2 < F_2^-$; F_2^{2-} does not exist

PROBLEMS

Problems with **colored** numbers are answered in Appendix E and worked in detail in the Student Solutions Manual. Problem sections match those in the text and provide the numbers of relevant sample problems. Most offer Concept Review Questions, Skill-Building Exercises (grouped in pairs covering the same concept), and Problems in Context. The Comprehensive Problems are based on material from any section or previous chapter.

Valence Bond (VB) Theory and Orbital Hybridization

(Sample Problem 11.1)

Concept Review Questions

11.1 What type of central-atom orbital hybridization corresponds to each electron-group arrangement: (a) trigonal planar; (b) octahedral; (c) linear; (d) tetrahedral; (e) trigonal bipyramidal?

11.2 What is the orbital hybridization of a central atom that has one lone pair and bonds to: (a) two other atoms; (b) three other atoms; (c) four other atoms; (d) five other atoms?

11.3 How do carbon and silicon differ with regard to the *types* of orbitals available for hybridization? Explain.

11.4 How many hybrid orbitals form when four atomic orbitals of a central atom mix? Explain.

Skill-Building Exercises (grouped in similar pairs)

11.5 Give the number and type of hybrid orbital that forms when each set of atomic orbitals mixes:
(a) two *d*, one *s*, and three *p* (b) three *p* and one *s*

11.6 Give the number and type of hybrid orbital that forms when each set of atomic orbitals mixes:
(a) one *p* and one *s* (b) three *p*, one *d*, and one *s*

11.7 What is the hybridization of nitrogen in each of the following: (a) NO; (b) NO_2; (c) NO_2^-?

11.8 What is the hybridization of carbon in each of the following: (a) CO_3^{2-}; (b) $C_2O_4^{2-}$; (c) NCO^-?

11.9 What is the hybridization of chlorine in each of the following: (a) ClO_2; (b) ClO_3^-; (c) ClO_4^-?

11.10 What is the hybridization of bromine in each of the following: (a) BrF_3; (b) BrO_2^-; (c) BrF_5?

11.11 Which types of atomic orbitals of the central atom mix to form hybrid orbitals in (a) $SiClH_3$; (b) CS_2; (c) SCl_3F; (d) NF_3?

11.12 Which types of atomic orbitals of the central atom mix to form hybrid orbitals in (a) Cl_2O; (b) $BrCl_3$; (c) PF_5; (d) SO_3^{2-}?

11.13 Phosphine (PH_3) reacts with borane (BH_3) as follows:

$$PH_3 + BH_3 \longrightarrow H_3P{-}BH_3$$

(a) Which of the illustrations below depicts the change, if any, in the orbital hybridization of P during this reaction? (b) Which depicts the change, if any, in the orbital hybridization of B?

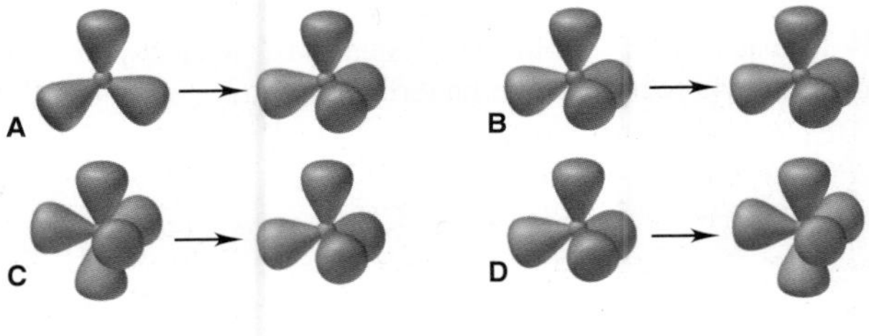

11.14 The illustrations below depict differences in orbital hybridization of some tellurium (Te) fluorides. (a) Which depicts the difference, if any, between TeF_6 (*left*) and TeF_5^- (*right*)? (b) Which depicts the difference, if any, between TeF_4 (*left*) and TeF_6 (*right*)?

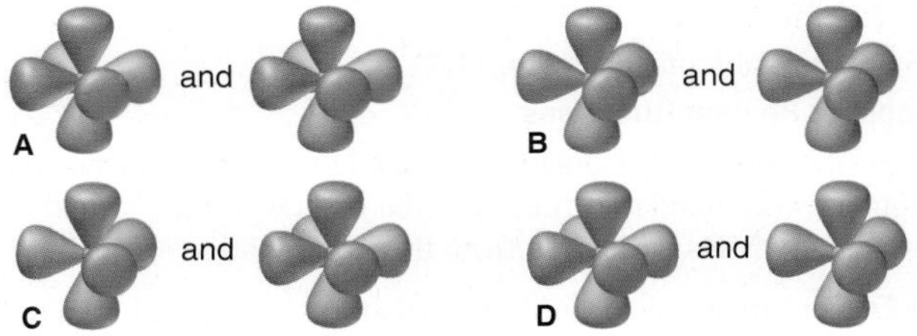

11.15 Use partial orbital diagrams to show how the atomic orbitals of the central atom lead to hybrid orbitals in (a) $GeCl_4$; (b) BCl_3; (c) CH_3^+.

11.16 Use partial orbital diagrams to show how the atomic orbitals of the central atom lead to hybrid orbitals in (a) BF_4^-; (b) PO_4^{3-}; (c) SO_3.

11.17 Use partial orbital diagrams to show how the atomic orbitals of the central atom lead to hybrid orbitals in (a) $SeCl_2$; (b) H_3O^+; (c) IF_4^-.

11.18 Use partial orbital diagrams to show how the atomic orbitals of the central atom lead to hybrid orbitals in (a) $AsCl_3$; (b) $SnCl_2$; (c) PF_6^-.

Problems in Context

11.19 Methyl isocyanate, $CH_3{-}\ddot{N}{=}C{=}\ddot{O}{:}$, is an intermediate in the manufacture of many pesticides. In 1984 a leak from a manufacturing plant resulted in the death of more than 2000 people in Bhopal, India. What are the hybridizations of the N atom and the two C atoms in methyl isocyanate? Sketch the molecular shape.

Modes of Orbital Overlap and the Types of Covalent Bonds

(Sample Problem 11.2)

Concept Review Questions

11.20 Are these statements true or false? Correct any false ones.
(a) Two σ bonds comprise a double bond.
(b) A triple bond consists of one π bond and two σ bonds.
(c) Bonds formed from atomic *s* orbitals are always σ bonds.
(d) A π bond restricts rotation about the σ-bond axis.
(e) A π bond consists of two pairs of electrons.
(f) End-to-end overlap results in a bond with electron density above and below the bond axis.

Skill-Building Exercises (grouped in similar pairs)

11.21 Describe the hybrid orbitals used by the central atom and the type(s) of bonds formed in (a) NO_3^-; (b) CS_2; (c) CH_2O.

11.22 Describe the hybrid orbitals used by the central atom and the type(s) of bonds formed in (a) O_3; (b) I_3^-; (c) $COCl_2$ (C is central).

11.23 Describe the hybrid orbitals used by the central atom(s) and the type(s) of bonds formed in (a) FNO; (b) C_2F_4; (c) $(CN)_2$.

11.24 Describe the hybrid orbitals used by the central atom(s) and the type(s) of bonds formed in (a) BrF_3; (b) $CH_3C{\equiv}CH$; (c) SO_2.

Problem in Context

11.25 2-Butene ($CH_3CH{=}CHCH_3$) is a starting material in the manufacture of lubricating oils and many other compounds. Draw two different structures for 2-butene, indicating the σ and π bonds in each.

Molecular Orbital (MO) Theory and Electron Delocalization

(Sample Problems 11.3 and 11.4)

Concept Review Questions

11.26 Two *p* orbitals from one atom and two *p* orbitals from another atom are combined to form molecular orbitals for the joined atoms. How many MOs will result from this combination? Explain.

11.27 Certain atomic orbitals on two atoms were combined to form the following MOs. Name the atomic orbitals used and the MOs formed, and explain which MO has higher energy:

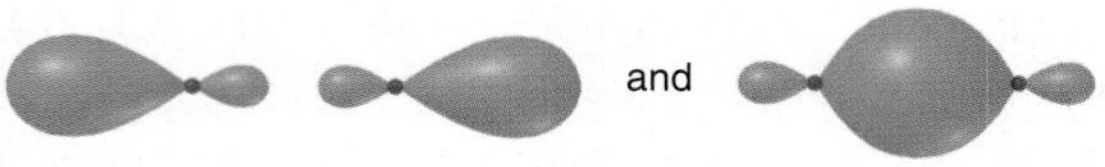

11.28 How do the bonding and antibonding MOs formed from a given pair of AOs compare to each other with respect to (a) energy; (b) presence of nodes; (c) internuclear electron density?

11.29 Antibonding MOs always have at least one node. Can a bonding MO have a node? If so, draw an example.

Skill-Building Exercises (grouped in similar pairs)

11.30 How many electrons does it take to fill (a) a σ bonding MO; (b) a π antibonding MO; (c) the MOs formed from combination of the 1*s* orbitals of two atoms?

11.31 How many electrons does it take to fill (a) the MOs formed from combination of the 2*p* orbitals of two atoms; (b) a σ^*_{2p} MO; (c) the MOs formed from combination of the 2*s* orbitals of two atoms?

11.32 The molecular orbitals depicted below are derived from 2*p* atomic orbitals in F_2^+. (a) Give the orbital designations. (b) Which is occupied by at least one electron in F_2^+? (c) Which is occupied by only one electron in F_2^+?

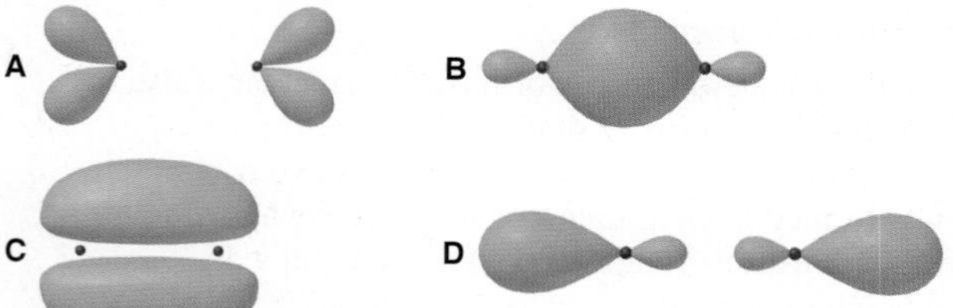

11.33 The molecular orbitals depicted below are derived from $n = 2$ atomic orbitals. (a) Give the orbital designations. (b) Which is highest in energy? (c) Lowest in energy? (d) Rank the MOs in order of increasing energy for B_2.

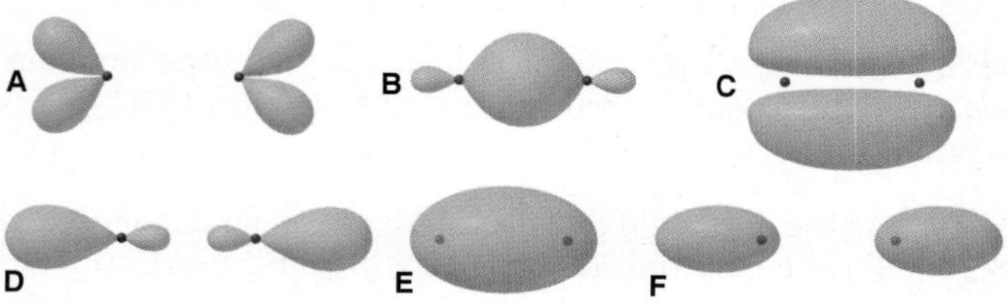

11.34 Use MO diagrams and the bond orders you obtain from them to answer: (a) Is Be_2^+ stable? (b) Is Be_2^+ diamagnetic? (c) What is the outer (valence) electron configuration of Be_2^+?

11.35 Use MO diagrams and the bond orders you obtain from them to answer: (a) Is O_2^- stable? (b) Is O_2^- paramagnetic? (c) What is the outer (valence) electron configuration of O_2^-?

11.36 Use MO diagrams to place C_2^-, C_2, and C_2^+ in order of (a) increasing bond energy; (b) increasing bond length.

11.37 Use MO diagrams to place B_2^+, B_2, and B_2^- in order of (a) decreasing bond energy; (b) decreasing bond length.

Comprehensive Problems

11.38 Predict the shape, state the hybridization of the central atom, and give the ideal bond angle(s) and any expected deviations for:
(a) BrO_3^- (b) $AsCl_4^-$ (c) SeO_4^{2-} (d) BiF_5^{2-}
(e) SbF_4^+ (f) AlF_6^{3-} (g) IF_4^+

11.39 Butadiene (*right*) is a colorless gas used to make synthetic rubber and many other compounds. (a) How many σ bonds and π bonds does the molecule have? (b) Are *cis-trans* arrangements about the double bonds possible? Explain.

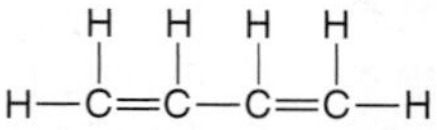

11.40 Epinephrine (or adrenaline; *below*) is a naturally occurring hormone that is also manufactured commercially for use as a heart stimulant, a nasal decongestant, and a glaucoma treatment.

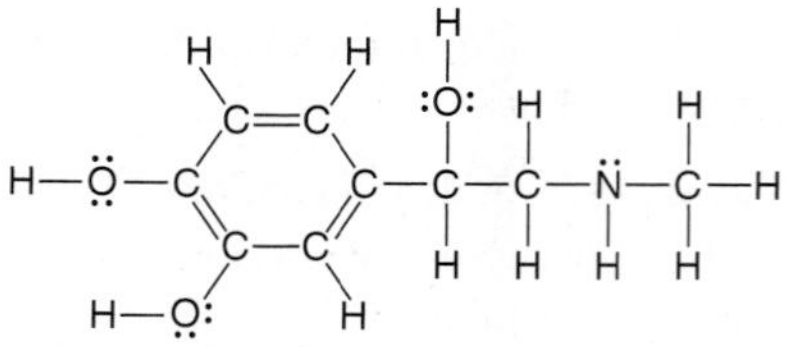

(a) What is the hybridization of each C, O, and N atom? (b) How many σ bonds does the molecule have? (c) How many π electrons are delocalized in the ring?

11.41 Use partial orbital diagrams to show how the atomic orbitals of the central atom lead to the hybrid orbitals in:
(a) IF_2^- (b) ICl_3 (c) $XeOF_4$ (d) BHF_2

11.42 Isoniazid (*below*) is an antibacterial agent that is very useful against many common strains of tuberculosis. (a) How many σ bonds are in the molecule? (b) What is the hybridization of each C and N atom?

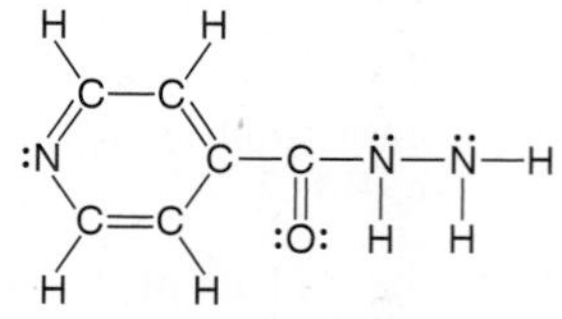

11.43 Hydrazine, N_2H_4, and carbon disulfide, CS_2, form a cyclic molecule (*below*). (a) Draw Lewis structures for N_2H_4 and CS_2. (b) How do electron-group arrangement, molecular shape, and hybridization of N change when N_2H_4 reacts to form the product? (c) How do electron-group arrangement, molecular shape, and hybridization of C change when CS_2 reacts to form the product?

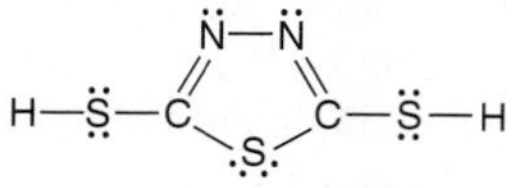

11.44 In each of the following equations, what hybridization change, if any, occurs for the underlined atom?
(a) $\underline{B}F_3 + NaF \longrightarrow Na^+BF_4^-$
(b) $\underline{P}Cl_3 + Cl_2 \longrightarrow PCl_5$
(c) $H\underline{C}{\equiv}CH + H_2 \longrightarrow H_2C{=}CH_2$
(d) $\underline{Si}F_4 + 2F^- \longrightarrow SiF_6^{2-}$
(e) $\underline{S}O_2 + \frac{1}{2}O_2 \rightarrow SO_3$

11.45 The ionosphere lies about 100 km above Earth's surface. This layer consists mostly of NO, O_2, and N_2, and photoionization creates NO^+, O_2^+, and N_2^+. (a) Use MO theory to compare the bond orders of the molecules and ions. (b) Does the magnetic behavior of each species change when its ion forms?

11.46 Glyphosate (*below*) is a common herbicide that is relatively harmless to animals but deadly to most plants. Describe the shape around and the hybridization of the P, N, and three numbered C atoms.

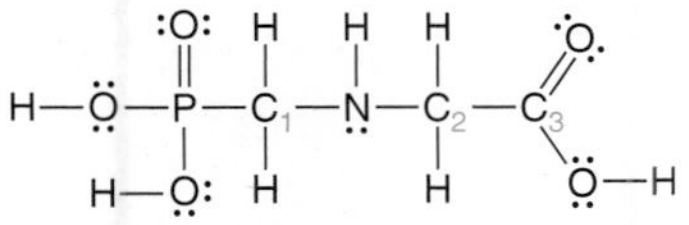

11.47 Tryptophan is one of the amino acids found in proteins:

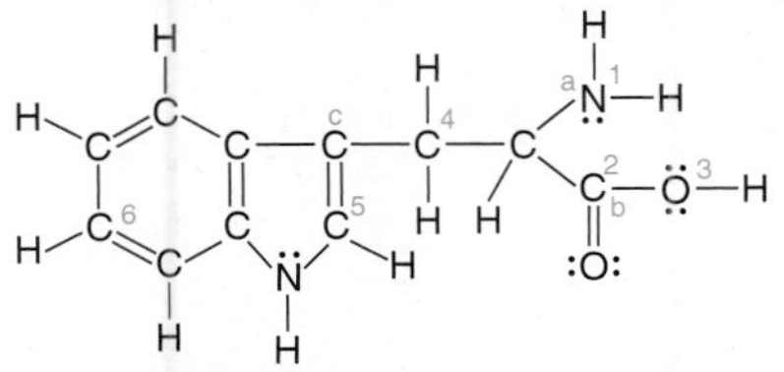

(a) What is the hybridization of each of the numbered C, N, and O atoms? (b) How many σ bonds are present in tryptophan? (c) Predict the bond angles at points a, b, and c.

11.48 Some species with two oxygen atoms only are the oxygen molecule, O_2, the peroxide ion, O_2^{2-}, the superoxide ion, O_2^-, and the dioxygenyl ion, O_2^+. Draw an MO diagram for each, rank them in order of increasing bond length, and find the number of unpaired electrons in each.

11.49 Molecular nitrogen, carbon monoxide, and cyanide ion are isoelectronic. (a) Draw an MO diagram for each. (b) CO and CN^- are toxic. What property may explain why N_2 isn't?

11.50 There is concern in health-related government agencies that the American diet contains too much meat, and numerous recommendations have been made urging people to consume more fruit and vegetables. One of the richest sources of vegetable protein is soy, available in many forms. Among these is soybean curd, or tofu, which is a staple of many Asian diets. Chemists have isolated an anticancer agent called *genistein* from tofu, which may explain the much lower incidence of cancer among people in the Far East. A valid Lewis structure for genistein is

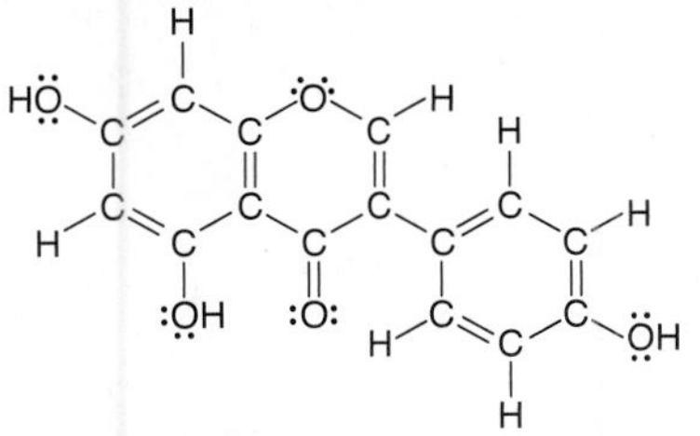

(a) Is the hybridization of each C in the right-hand ring the same? Explain. (b) Is the hybridization of the O atom in the center ring the same as that of the O atoms in OH groups? Explain. (c) How many carbon-oxygen σ bonds are there? How many carbon-oxygen π bonds? (d) Do all the lone pairs on oxygens occupy the same type of hybrid orbital? Explain.

11.51 An organic chemist synthesizes the molecule below:

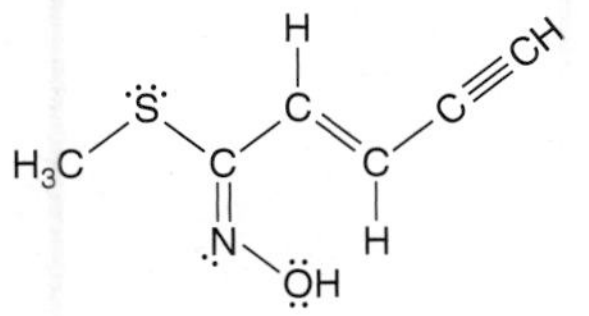

(a) Which of the orientations of hybrid orbitals shown below are present in the molecule? (b) Are there any present that are not shown below? If so, what are they? (c) How many of each type of hybrid orbital are present?

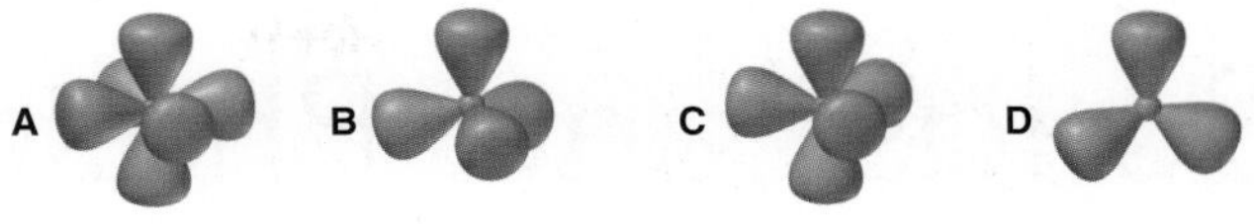

11.52 Simple proteins consist of amino acids linked together in a long chain; a small portion of such a chain is

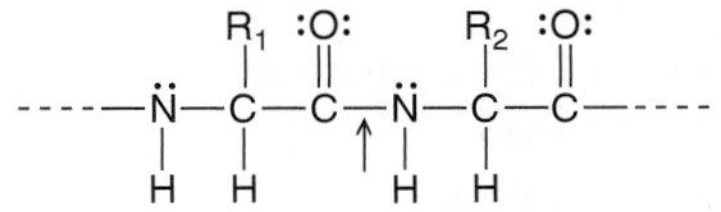

Experiment shows that rotation about the C—N bond (indicated by the arrow) is somewhat restricted. Explain with resonance structures, and show the types of bonding involved.

11.53 Sulfur forms oxides, oxoanions, and halides. What is the hybridization of the central S in SO_2, SO_3, SO_3^{2-}, SCl_4, SCl_6, and S_2Cl_2 (atom sequence Cl—S—S—Cl)?

11.54 The compound 2,6-dimethylpyrazine (*below*) gives chocolate its odor and is used in flavorings. (a) Which atomic orbitals mix to form the hybrid orbitals of N? (b) In what type of hybrid orbital do the lone pairs of N reside? (c) Is C in CH_3 hybridized the same as any C in the ring? Explain.

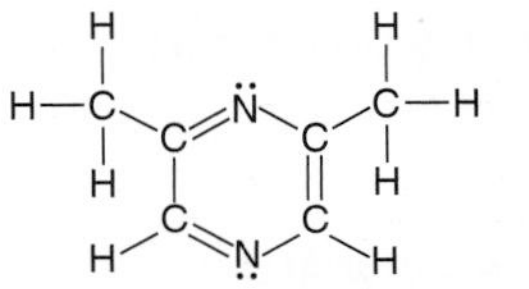

11.55 Acetylsalicylic acid (aspirin), the most widely used medicine in the world, has the Lewis structure shown below. (a) What is the hybridization of each C and each O atom? (b) How many localized π bonds are present? (c) How many C atoms have a trigonal planar shape around them? A tetrahedral shape?

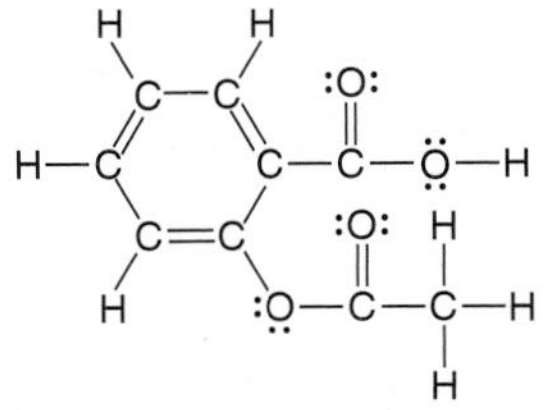

11.56 Linoleic acid is an essential fatty acid found in many vegetable oils, such as soy, peanut, and cottonseed. A key structural feature of the molecule is the *cis* orientation around its two double bonds, where R_1 and R_2 represent two different groups that form the rest of the molecule.

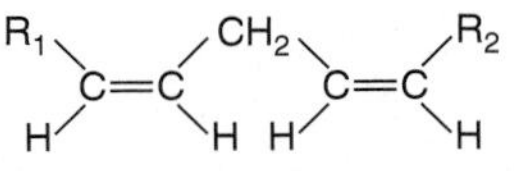

(a) How many different compounds are possible, changing only the *cis-trans* arrangements around these two double bonds?
(b) How many are possible for a similar compound with three double bonds?

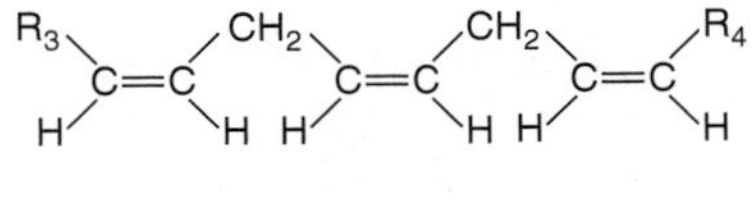

Intermolecular Forces: Liquids, Solids, and Phase Changes

12

Concepts and skills to review before you study this chapter

- properties of gases, liquids, and solids (Section 5.1)
- kinetic-molecular theory of gases (Section 5.5)
- kinetic and potential energy (Section 6.1)
- enthalpy change, heat capacity, and Hess's law (Sections 6.2, 6.3, and 6.5)
- diffraction of light (Section 7.1)
- Coulomb's law (Section 9.2)
- chemical bonding models (Chapter 9)
- molecular polarity (Section 10.3)
- molecular orbital treatment of diatomic molecules (Section 11.3)

All the matter in and around you occurs in one or more of the three physical states—gas, liquid, or solid. Under different conditions, many substances can occur in any of the states. We're all familiar with the states of water: we inhale and exhale gaseous water; drink, excrete, and wash with liquid water; and shovel, slide on, or cool our drinks with solid water. And, given the right conditions, even other solids (gold jewelry, table salt), liquids (gasoline, antifreeze), and gases (air, CO_2 bubbles) can exist in one or both of the other states.

The three states were introduced in Chapter 1 and their properties were compared when we examined gases in Chapter 5. You saw there that the particles in gases are, on average, very far apart. Now, we examine liquids and solids, which are called *condensed* states because their *particles are very close together.*

IN THIS CHAPTER . . . We explore the interplay of forces that give rise to the three states of matter and their changes, with special attention to liquids and solids.

- We use kinetic-molecular theory to see how relative magnitudes of potential and kinetic energy account for the behavior of gases, liquids, and solids and how temperature is related to phase changes.
- We calculate the heat associated with warming or cooling a phase and with a phase change.
- We highlight the effects of temperature and pressure on phases and their changes with phase diagrams.
- We describe the types and relative strengths of the intermolecular forces that occur within pure substances.
- We see how intermolecular forces give rise to the properties of liquids.
- As a special case, we trace the unique and vital physical properties of water to the electron configurations of its atoms.
- We discuss the properties of solids, emphasizing the relationship between type of bonding and predominant intermolecular force, and we examine the methods used to study crystal structure.
- We introduce key features of several kinds of advanced materials—semiconductors, liquid crystals, ceramics, polymers, and nanostructures.

12.1 • AN OVERVIEW OF PHYSICAL STATES AND PHASE CHANGES

Each physical state is called a **phase,** a physically distinct, homogeneous part of system. The water in a closed container constitutes one phase; the water vapor above the liquid is a second phase; add some ice, and there are three.

In this section, you'll see that interactions between the potential energy and the kinetic energy of the particles give rise to the properties of each phase:

- The *potential energy* in the form of **intermolecular forces** (or, more generally, *interparticle forces*) tends to draw the molecules together. According to Coulomb's law, the electrostatic potential energy depends on the charges of the particles and the distances between them (Section 9.2).
- The *kinetic energy* associated with the random motion of the molecules tends to disperse them. It is related to their average speed and is proportional to the absolute temperature (Section 5.5).

These interactions also explain **phase changes,** changes in physical state from one phase to another—liquid to solid, solid to gas, and so forth.

A Kinetic-Molecular View of the Three States Imagine yourself among the particles in any of the three states of water. Look closely and you'll discover two types of electrostatic forces at work:

1. *Intra*molecular (bonding) forces exist *within* each molecule. The *chemical* behavior of the three states is identical because each consists of the same bent, polar H—O—H molecules held together by identical covalent bonding forces.
2. *Inter*molecular (nonbonding) forces exist *between* the molecules. The *physical* behavior of the states is different because the strengths of these forces differ from state to state.

Whether a substance occurs as a gas, liquid, or solid depends on the interplay of the potential and kinetic energy:

- *In a gas,* the potential energy (energy of attraction) is small relative to the kinetic energy (energy of motion); thus, on average, the particles are far apart. This large distance has several macroscopic consequences: a gas fills its container, is highly compressible, and flows easily through another gas (Table 12.1).
- *In a liquid,* attractions are stronger because the particles are touching, but they have enough kinetic energy to move randomly around each other. Thus, a liquid conforms to the shape of its container but has a surface, it resists an applied force and thus compresses very slightly, and it flows, but *much* more slowly than gases.
- *In a solid,* the attractions dominate the motion so much that the particles are fixed in position relative to one another, just jiggling in place. Thus, a solid has its own shape, compresses even less than liquids, and does not flow significantly.

How does ability to flow influence composition in nature?

The environment provides a perfect demonstration of these differences in ability to flow (*see photo*). Atmospheric gases mix so well that the lowest 80 km of air has a uniform composition. Much less mixing in the oceans allows the composition at various depths to support different species. And rocks intermingle so little that adjacent strata remain separated for millions of years.

Table 12.1 A Macroscopic Comparison of Gases, Liquids, and Solids

State	Shape and Volume	Compressibility	Ability to Flow
Gas	Conforms to shape and volume of container	High	High
Liquid	Conforms to shape of container; volume limited by surface	Very low	Moderate
Solid	Maintains its own shape and volume	Almost none	Almost none

Types of Phase Changes and Their Enthalpies When we consider phase changes, understanding the effect of temperature is critical:

- As *temperature increases,* the average kinetic energy does too, so the faster moving particles overcome attractions more easily.
- As *temperature decreases,* particles slow, so attractions can pull them together.

Each phase change has a name and an associated enthalpy change:

1. *Gas to liquid, and vice versa.* As the temperature drops, the molecules in the gas phase come together and form a liquid in the process of **condensation;** the opposite process, changing from a liquid to a gas, is **vaporization.**

2. *Liquid to solid, and vice versa.* As the temperature drops further, the particles move slower and become fixed in position in the process of **freezing;** the opposite change is called **melting,** or **fusion.** In common speech, *freezing* implies low temperature because we think of water. But, molten metals, for example, freeze (solidify) at much higher temperatures and have medical, industrial, and artistic applications, such as gold dental crowns, steel auto bodies, and bronze statues.

3. *Gas to solid, and vice versa.* All three states of water are familiar because they are stable under ordinary conditions. Carbon dioxide, on the other hand, is familiar as a gas and a solid (dry ice), but liquid CO_2 occurs only at pressures of 5.1 atm or greater. At ordinary conditions, solid CO_2 changes directly to a gas, a process called **sublimation.** Freeze-dried foods are prepared by sublimation. The opposite process, changing from a gas directly into a solid, is called **deposition**—ice crystals form on a cold window from the deposition of water vapor (Figure 12.1A).

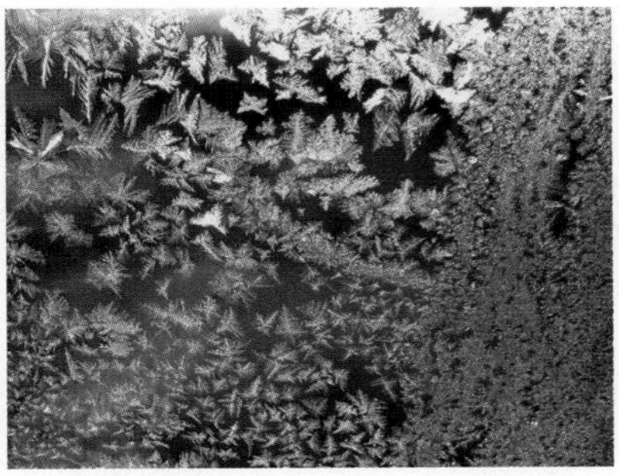

A Deposition

B Vaporization

Figure 12.1 Two familiar phase changes.

The accompanying enthalpy changes are either exothermic or endothermic:

- *Exothermic changes.* As the molecules of a gas attract each other into a liquid, and then become fixed in a solid, the system of particles *loses* energy, which is released as heat. Thus, *condensing, freezing, and depositing are exothermic changes.*
- *Endothermic changes.* Heat must be absorbed by the system to overcome the attractive forces that keep the particles fixed in place in a solid or near each other in a liquid. Thus, *melting, vaporizing, and subliming are endothermic changes.*

Sweating has a cooling effect because heat from your body vaporizes the water. To achieve this cooling, cats lick themselves and dogs pant (Figure 12.1B).

For a pure substance, each phase change is accompanied by a standard enthalpy change, given in units of *kilojoules per mole* (measured at 1 atm and the temperature of the change). For vaporization, it is the **heat** (or *enthalpy*) **of vaporization (ΔH°_{vap}),** and for fusion (melting), it is the **heat** (or *enthalpy*) **of fusion (ΔH°_{fus}).** In the case of water, we have

$$H_2O(l) \longrightarrow H_2O(g) \qquad \Delta H = \Delta H^\circ_{vap} = 40.7 \text{ kJ/mol (at 100°C)}$$
$$H_2O(s) \longrightarrow H_2O(l) \qquad \Delta H = \Delta H^\circ_{fus} = 6.02 \text{ kJ/mol (at 0°C)}$$

The reverse processes, condensing and freezing, have enthalpy changes of the *same magnitude but opposite sign:*

$$H_2O(g) \longrightarrow H_2O(l) \qquad \Delta H = -\Delta H^\circ_{vap} = -40.7 \text{ kJ/mol}$$
$$H_2O(l) \longrightarrow H_2O(s) \qquad \Delta H = -\Delta H^\circ_{fus} = -6.02 \text{ kJ/mol}$$

Water behaves typically in that it takes much less energy to melt the solid than to vaporize the liquid: $\Delta H^\circ_{fus} < \Delta H^\circ_{vap}$; that is, it takes less energy to reduce the intermolecular forces enough for the molecules to move out of their fixed positions (melt a solid) than to separate them completely (vaporize a liquid) (Figure 12.2).

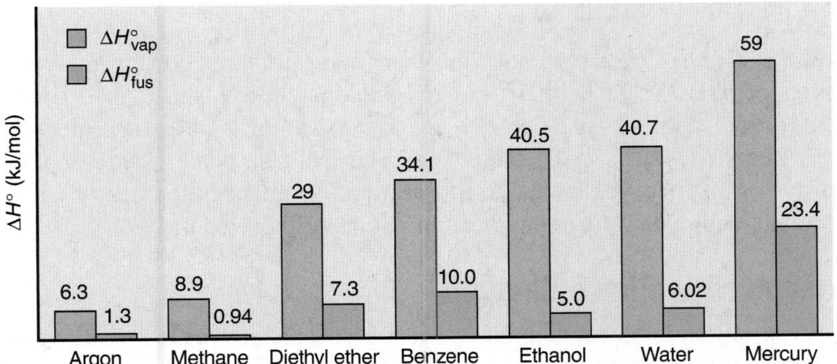

Figure 12.2 Heats of vaporization and fusion for several common substances.

The **heat** (or *enthalpy*) **of sublimation (ΔH°_{subl})** is the enthalpy change when 1 mol of a substance sublimes, and the negative of this value is the change when 1 mol of the substance deposits. Since sublimation can be considered a combination of melting and vaporizing, Hess's law (Section 6.5) says that the heat of sublimation equals the sum of the heats of fusion and vaporization:

$$\begin{array}{lll} \text{Solid} \longrightarrow \text{liquid} & \Delta H^\circ_{fus} \\ \text{Liquid} \longrightarrow \text{gas} & \Delta H^\circ_{vap} \\ \hline \text{Solid} \longrightarrow \text{gas} & \Delta H^\circ_{subl} \end{array}$$

Figure 12.3 on the next page summarizes the phase changes and their enthalpy changes.

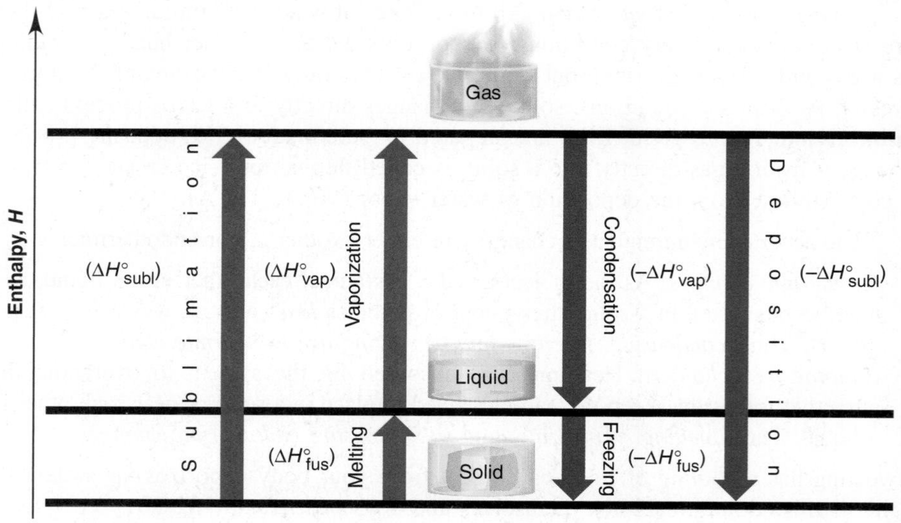

Figure 12.3 Phase changes and their enthalpy changes. Fusion (or melting), vaporization, and sublimation are endothermic changes (positive ΔH°), whereas freezing, condensation, and deposition are exothermic changes (negative ΔH°).

Summary of Section 12.1

- Because of the relative magnitudes of intermolecular forces (potential energy) and average speed (kinetic energy), the particles in a gas are far apart and moving randomly, those in a liquid are in contact and moving relative to each other, and those in a solid are in contact and in fixed positions. These molecular-level differences account for macroscopic differences in shape, compressibility, and ability to flow.
- When a solid becomes a liquid (melting, or fusion), a liquid becomes a gas (vaporization), or a solid becomes a gas (sublimation), energy is absorbed to overcome intermolecular forces and increase the average distance between particles. As particles come closer together in the reverse changes (freezing, condensation, and deposition), energy is released. Each phase change is associated with a given enthalpy change under specified conditions.

12.2 • QUANTITATIVE ASPECTS OF PHASE CHANGES

Many phase changes occur around you every day, accompanied by the release or absorption of heat. When it rains, water vapor has condensed to a liquid, which changes back to a gas as puddles dry up. In the spring, solid water melts, and in winter, it freezes again. And the same phase changes take place whenever you make a pot of tea or a tray of ice cubes. In this section, we quantify the heat involved in a phase change and examine the equilibrium nature of the process.

Heat Involved in Phase Changes

We apply a kinetic-molecular approach to phase changes with a **heating-cooling curve,** which shows the changes in temperature of a sample when heat is absorbed or released at a constant rate. Let's examine what happens when 2.50 mol of gaseous water in a closed container undergoes a change from 130°C to −40°C at a constant pressure of 1 atm. We'll divide this process into five heat-releasing (exothermic) stages (Figure 12.4):

Stage 1. Gaseous water cools. Water molecules zoom chaotically at a range of speeds, smashing into each other and the container walls. At the starting temperature, the most probable speed of the molecules, and thus their average kinetic energy (E_k), is high enough to overcome the potential energy (E_p) of attractions. As the temperature falls, the average E_k decreases and attractions become more important. The change is

$$H_2O(g)\,[130^\circ C] \longrightarrow H_2O(g)\,[100^\circ C]$$

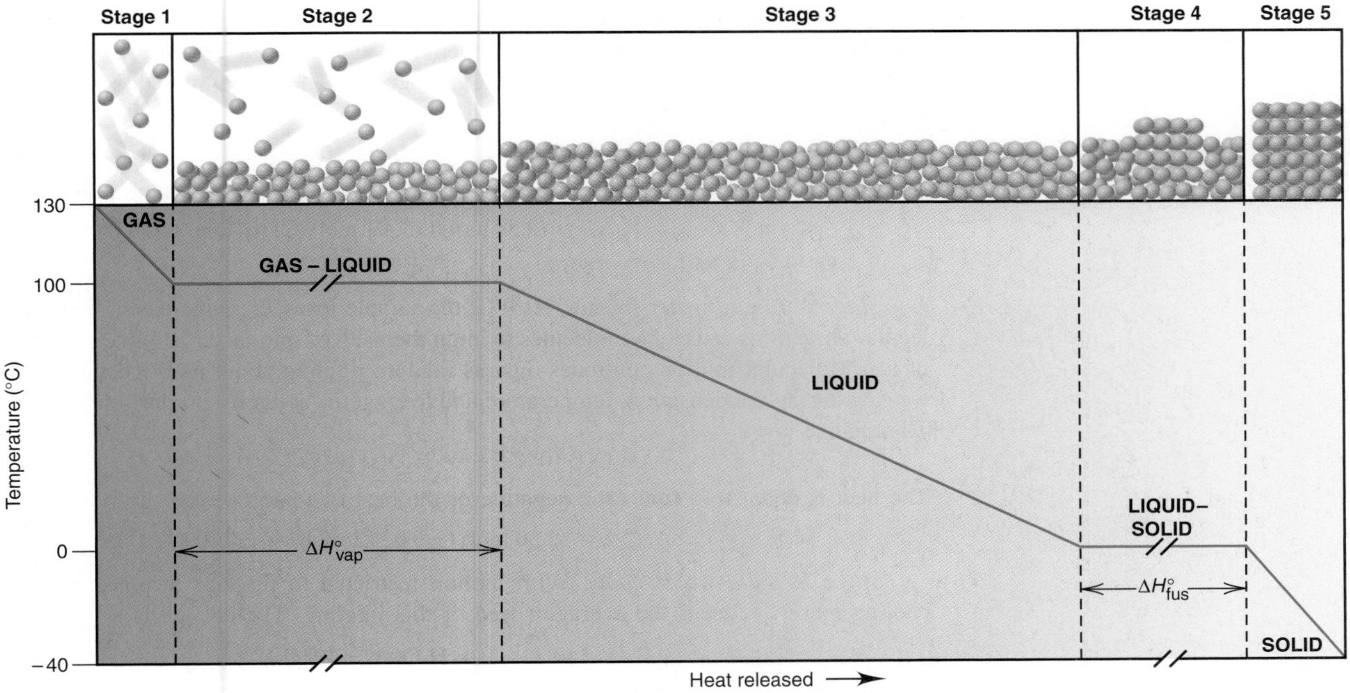

Figure 12.4 A cooling curve for the conversion of gaseous water to ice. A plot of temperature vs. heat released as gaseous water changes to ice is shown, with a molecular-level depiction for each stage. The slopes of the lines in stages 1, 3, and 5 reflect the molar heat capacities of the phases. Although not drawn to scale, the line in stage 2 is longer than the line in stage 4 because ΔH°_{vap} of water is greater than ΔH°_{fus}. A plot of temperature vs. heat absorbed starting at −40°C would have the same steps but in reverse order.

The heat (q) is the product of the amount (number of moles, n) of water, the molar heat capacity of *gaseous* water, $C_{water(g)}$, and the temperature change, ΔT ($T_{final} - T_{initial}$):

$$q = n \times C_{water(g)} \times \Delta T = (2.50 \text{ mol})(33.1 \text{ J/mol}\cdot{}^\circ\text{C})(100^\circ\text{C} - 130^\circ\text{C})$$
$$= -2482 \text{ J} = -2.48 \text{ kJ}$$

The minus sign indicates that heat is released.*

Stage 2. Gaseous water condenses. At the condensation point, intermolecular attractions cause the slowest of the molecules to aggregate into microdroplets and then a bulk liquid. Note that, during the phase change,

- The temperature of the sample, and thus its average E_k, is constant. At the same temperature, molecules move farther between collisions in a gas than in a liquid, but their *average* speed is the same.
- Releasing heat from the sample decreases the average E_p as the molecules approach each other.

Thus, at 100°C, gaseous and liquid water have the same average E_k, but the liquid has lower average E_p. The change is

$$H_2O(g)\ [100^\circ C] \longrightarrow H_2O(l)\ [100^\circ C]$$

The heat is the amount (n) times the negative of the heat of vaporization ($-\Delta H^\circ_{vap}$):

$$q = n(-\Delta H^\circ_{vap}) = (2.50 \text{ mol})(-40.7 \text{ kJ/mol}) = -102 \text{ kJ}$$

This stage contributes the *greatest portion of the total heat released* because of the large decrease in E_p as the molecules become so much closer in the liquid than they were in the gas.

*For purposes of canceling, the units for molar heat capacity, C, include °C, rather than K, but this doesn't affect the magnitude of C because these two units represent the same temperature increment.

Stage 3. Liquid water cools. The molecules in the liquid state continue to lose heat, which appears as a decrease in temperature, that is, as a decrease in the most probable molecular speed and, thus, the average E_k. The temperature decreases as long as the sample remains liquid. The change is

$$H_2O(l)\ [100°C] \longrightarrow H_2O(l)\ [0°C]$$

The heat depends on amount (n), the molar heat capacity of *liquid* water, and ΔT:

$$q = n \times C_{water(l)} \times \Delta T = (2.50\ mol)(75.4\ J/mol{\cdot}°C)(0°C - 100°C)$$
$$= -18{,}850\ J = -18.8\ kJ$$

Stage 4. Liquid water freezes. At 0°C, the sample loses E_p as increasing intermolecular attractions cause the molecules to align themselves into the crystalline structure of ice. Molecular motion continues only as random jiggling about fixed positions. As we saw during condensation, temperature and average E_k are constant during freezing. The change is

$$H_2O(l)\ [0°C] \longrightarrow H_2O(s)\ [0°C]$$

The heat is equal to n times the negative of the heat of fusion ($-\Delta H^\circ_{fus}$):

$$q = n(-\Delta H^\circ_{fus}) = (2.50\ mol)(-6.02\ kJ/mol) = -15.0\ kJ$$

Stage 5. Solid water cools. With motion restricted to jiggling in place, further cooling merely reduces the average speed of this jiggling. The change is

$$H_2O(s)\ [0°C] \longrightarrow H_2O(s)\ [-40°C]$$

The heat depends on n, the molar heat capacity of *solid* water, and ΔT:

$$q = n \times C_{water(s)} \times \Delta T = (2.50\ mol)(37.6\ J/mol{\cdot}°C)(-40°C - 0°C)$$
$$= -3760\ J = -3.76\ kJ$$

According to Hess's law, the total heat released is the sum of the heats released for the individual stages. The sum of q for stages 1 to 5 is -142 kJ. Two key points stand out for this or any similar process, whether exothermic or endothermic:

- *Within a phase,* heat flow is accompanied by *a change in temperature,* which is associated with a change in average E_k, as *the most probable speed of the molecules changes.* The heat released or absorbed depends on the amount of substance, the molar heat capacity *for that phase,* and the change in temperature.
- *During a phase change,* heat flow occurs at a *constant temperature,* which is associated with a change in average E_p, as *the average distance between molecules changes.* Both phases are present and (as you'll see below) are in equilibrium during the change. The heat released or absorbed depends on the amount of substance and the enthalpy change for that phase change.

Let's work a molecular-scene sample problem to make sure these ideas are clear.

Sample Problem 12.1 Finding the Heat of a Phase Change Depicted by Molecular Scenes

Problem The scenes below represent a phase change of water. Select data from the previous discussion to find the heat (in kJ) released or absorbed when 24.3 g of H_2O undergoes this change.

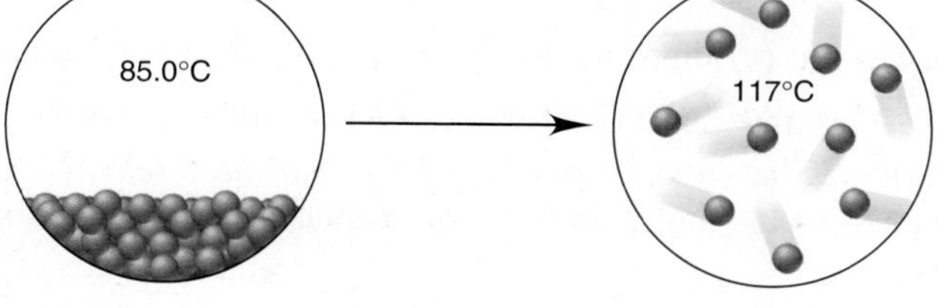

Plan From the molecular scenes, data in the text, and the given mass (24.3 g) of water, we have to find the heat that accompanies this change. The scenes show a disorderly, condensed phase at 85.0°C changing to separate molecules at 117°C. Thus, the phase change they depict is vaporization, an endothermic process. The text data are given per mole, so we first convert the mass (g) of water to amount (mol). There are three stages: (1) heating the liquid from 85.0°C to 100.°C, (2) converting liquid water at 100.°C to gaseous water at 100.°C, and (3) heating the gas from 100.°C to 117°C (*see margin*). We add the values of q for these stages to obtain the total heat.

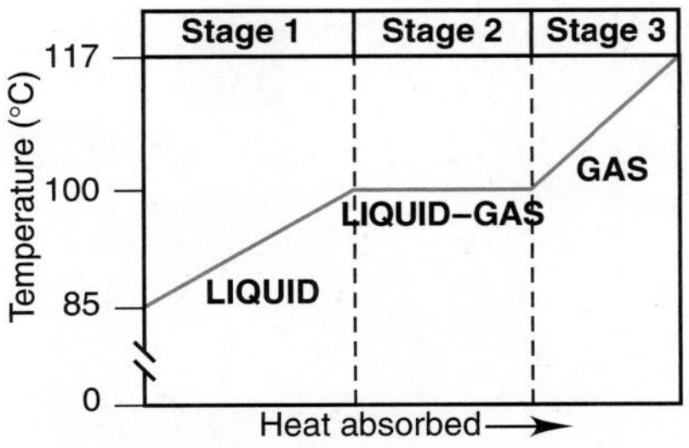

Solution Converting from mass (g) of H_2O to amount (mol):

$$\text{Amount (mol) of } H_2O = 24.3 \text{ g } H_2O \times \frac{1 \text{ mol}}{18.02 \text{ g } H_2O} = 1.35 \text{ mol}$$

Finding the flow accompanying stage 1, $H_2O(l)\,[85.0°C] \longrightarrow H_2O(l)\,[100.°C]$:

$$q = n \times C_{\text{water}(l)} \times \Delta T = (1.35 \text{ mol})(75.4 \text{ J/mol·°C})(100.°C - 85.0°C)$$
$$= 1527 \text{ J} = 1.53 \text{ kJ}$$

Finding the heat accompanying stage 2, $H_2O(l)\,[100.°C] \longrightarrow H_2O(g)\,[100.°C]$:

$$q = n(\Delta H^\circ_{\text{vap}}) = (1.35 \text{ mol})(40.7 \text{ kJ/mol}) = 54.9 \text{ kJ}$$

Finding the heat accompanying stage 3, $H_2O(g)\,[100.°C] \longrightarrow H_2O(g)\,[117°C]$:

$$q = n \times C_{\text{water}(g)} \times \Delta T = (1.35 \text{ mol})(33.1 \text{ J/mol·°C})(117°C - 100.°C)$$
$$= 759.6 \text{ J} = 0.760 \text{ kJ}$$

Adding the three heats together to find the total heat of the process:

$$\text{Total heat (kJ)} = 1.53 \text{ kJ} + 54.9 \text{ kJ} + 0.760 \text{ kJ} = \boxed{57.2 \text{ kJ}}$$

Check The heat should have a positive value because it is absorbed. Be sure to round to check each value of q; for example, in stage 1, 1.33 mol × 75 J/mol·°C × 15°C = 1500 J. Note that the phase change itself (stage 2) requires the most energy and, thus, dominates the final answer. The $\Delta H^\circ_{\text{vap}}$ units include kJ, whereas the molar heat capacity units include J, which is a thousandth as large.

Follow-Up Problem 12.1 The scenes below represent a phase change of water. Select data from the text discussion to find the heat (in kJ) released or absorbed when 2.25 mol of H_2O undergoes this change.

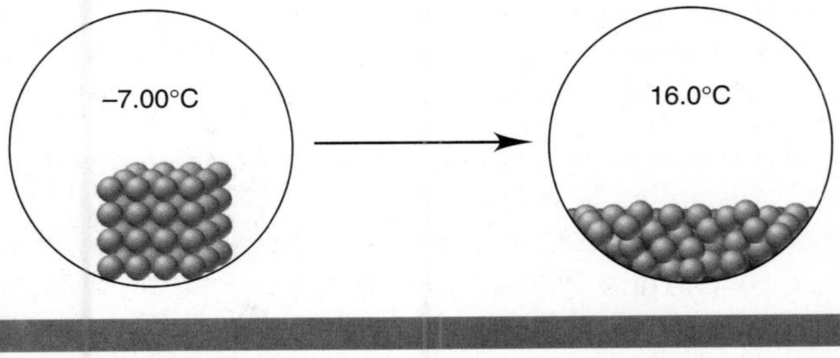

The Equilibrium Nature of Phase Changes

In everyday experience, phase changes take place in *open* containers—the outdoors, a pot on a stove, the freezer compartment of a refrigerator—so they are not reversible. But, in a *closed* container, *phase changes* ***are*** *reversible and reach equilibrium,* just as chemical changes do. In this discussion, we examine the three phase equilibria.

Liquid-Gas Equilibria Vaporization and condensation are familar events. Let's see how these processes differ in open and closed systems of a liquid in a flask:

1. *Open system: nonequilibrium process.* Picture an *open* flask containing a pure liquid at constant temperature. Within their range of speeds, some molecules at the surface have a high enough E_k to overcome attractions and vaporize. Nearby molecules fill the gap, and with heat supplied by the constant-temperature surroundings, the process continues until the entire liquid phase is gone.

2. *Closed system: equilibrium process.* Now picture a *closed* flask at constant temperature and assume a vacuum exists above a liquid (Figure 12.5A, *next page*). Two processes take place: Some molecules at the surface have a high enough E_k to *vaporize*. After a short time, molecules in the vapor collide with the surface, and the slower ones are attracted strongly enough to *condense*.

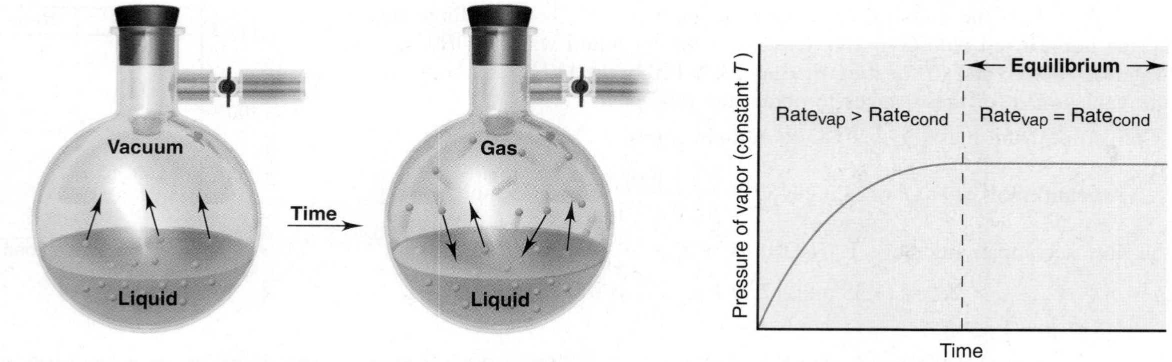

A Molecules in the liquid vaporize. **B** Molecules vaporize and condense at the same rate. **C** Plot of pressure vs. time.

Figure 12.5 Liquid-gas equilibrium.
A, Molecules leave the surface at a constant rate and the pressure rises. **B,** At equilibrium, the same number of molecules leave and enter the liquid in a given time. **C,** Pressure increases until, at equilibrium, it is constant.

At first, these two processes occur at different rates. The number of molecules in a given surface area is constant, so the number of molecules leaving the surface per unit time—the rate of vaporization—is also constant, and the pressure increases. With time, the number of molecules colliding with and entering the surface—the rate of condensation—increases as the vapor becomes more populated, so the increase in pressure slows. Eventually, the rate of condensation equals the rate of vaporization; from this time onward, *the pressure is constant* (Figure 12.5B).

Macroscopically, the situation at this point seems static, but at the molecular level, molecules are entering and leaving the liquid at equal rates. The system has reached a state of *dynamic equilibrium:*

$$\text{liquid} \rightleftharpoons \text{gas}$$

The pressure exerted by the vapor at equilibrium is called the *equilibrium vapor pressure,* or just the **vapor pressure,** of the liquid at that temperature. Figure 12.5C depicts the entire process graphically. If we started with a larger flask, the number of molecules in the vapor would be greater at equilibrium. But, as long as the temperature is constant and some liquid is present, the vapor pressure will be the same.

3. *Disturbing a system at equilibrium.* Let's see what happens if we alter certain conditions, called "disturbing" the system:

- *Decrease in pressure.* Suppose we pump some vapor out of the flask, immediately lowering the pressure. (In a cylinder fitted with a piston, we lower the pressure by moving the piston outward, thus increasing the volume.) The rate of condensation temporarily falls below the rate of vaporization (the forward process is faster) because fewer molecules enter the liquid than leave it. The pressure rises until, after a short time, the condensation rate increases enough for equilibrium to be reached again.
- *Increase in pressure.* Suppose we pump more vapor in (or move the piston inward, thus decreasing the volume), thereby immediately raising the pressure. The rate of condensation temporarily exceeds the rate of vaporization because more molecules enter the liquid than leave it (the reverse process is faster). Soon, however, the condensation rate decreases until the pressure again reaches the equilibrium value.

This general behavior of a liquid and its vapor is seen in any system at equilibrium: *when a system at equilibrium is disturbed, it counteracts the disturbance until it re-establishes equilibrium.* We'll return to this key idea often in later chapters.

The Effects of Temperature and Intermolecular Forces on Vapor Pressure

While the vapor pressure is not affected by the removal or addition of gas, it is affected by two other factors—a change in temperature and a change in the gas, that is, in the types of intermolecular forces:

1. *Effect of temperature.* Temperature has a major effect on vapor pressure because it changes the fraction of molecules moving fast enough to escape the liquid and, by the same token, the fraction moving slowly enough to be recaptured. In Figure 12.6, we see the familiar skewed bell-shaped curve of the distribution of molecular speeds (see also Figure 5.6, page 188). At the higher temperature, T_2, more molecules have

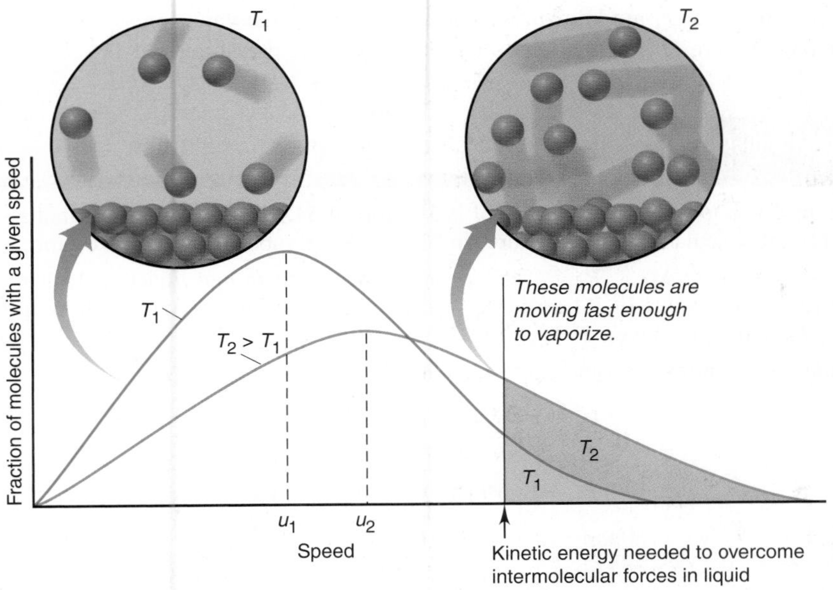

Figure 12.6 The effect of temperature on the distribution of molecular speeds.

enough energy to leave the surface. Thus, in general, *the higher the temperature is, the higher the vapor pressure:*

$$\text{higher } T \Longrightarrow \text{higher } P$$

2. *Effect of intermolecular forces.* At a given T, all substances have the same average E_k. Therefore, molecules with weaker intermolecular forces are held less tightly at the surface and vaporize more easily. In general, *the weaker the intermolecular forces are, the higher the vapor pressure:*

$$\text{weaker forces} \Longrightarrow \text{higher } P$$

Figure 12.7 shows the vapor pressure of three liquids as a function of temperature:

- The effect of temperature is seen in the steeper rise as the temperature increases.
- The effect of intermolecular forces is seen in the values of the vapor pressure, the short, horizontal dashed lines intersecting the vertical (pressure) axis at a given temperature *(vertical dashed line at 20°C)*: the intermolecular forces in diethyl ether (highest vapor pressure) are weaker than those in ethanol, which are weaker than those in water (lowest vapor pressure).

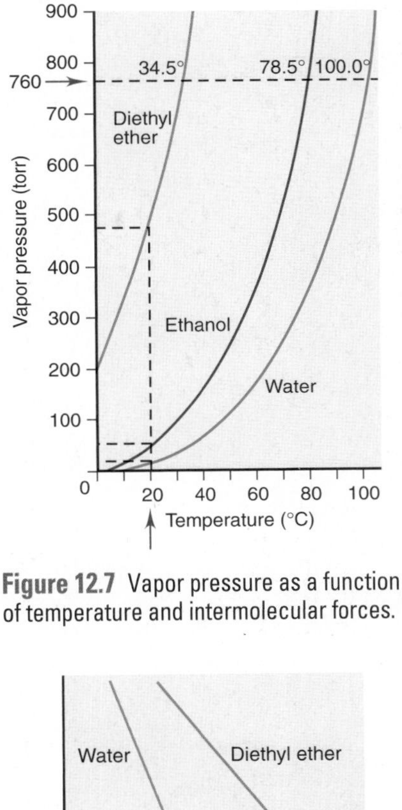

Figure 12.7 Vapor pressure as a function of temperature and intermolecular forces.

Quantifying the Effect of Temperature The nonlinear relationship between P and T is converted to a linear one with the **Clausius-Clapeyron equation:**

$$\ln P = \frac{-\Delta H_{\text{vap}}}{R}\left(\frac{1}{T}\right) + C$$
$$y \quad = \quad m \quad\quad x \quad + b$$

where ln P is the natural logarithm of the vapor pressure, ΔH_{vap} is the heat of vaporization, R is the universal gas constant (8.314 J/mol·K), T is the absolute temperature, and C is a constant (not related to heat capacity). The equation is often used to find the heat of vaporization. The equation for a straight line is shown under it in blue, with $y = \ln P$, $x = 1/T$, m (the slope) $= -\Delta H_{\text{vap}}/R$, and b (the y-axis intercept) $= C$. A plot of ln P vs. $1/T$ gives a straight line, as shown for diethyl ether and water in Figure 12.8.

A two-point version of the Clausius-Clapeyron equation allows us to calculate ΔH_{vap} if vapor pressures at two temperatures are known:

$$\ln \frac{P_2}{P_1} = \frac{-\Delta H_{\text{vap}}}{R}\left(\frac{1}{T_2} - \frac{1}{T_1}\right) \quad (12.1)$$

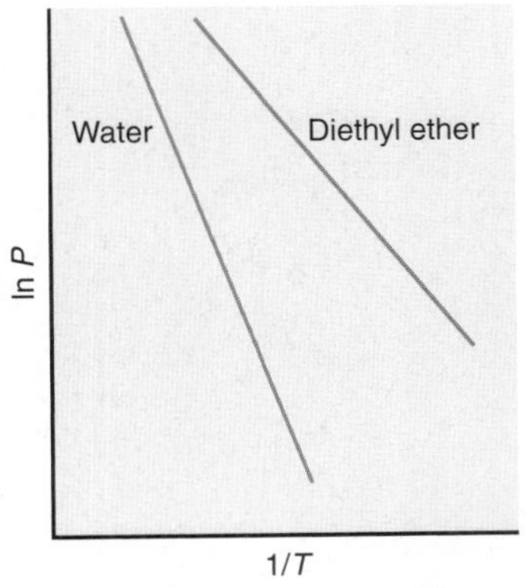

Figure 12.8 **Linear plots of the relationship between vapor pressure and temperature.** The slope is steeper for water because its ΔH_{vap} is greater.

If ΔH_{vap} and P_1 at T_1 are known, we can also calculate the vapor pressure (P_2) at any other temperature (T_2) or the temperature at any other pressure.

Sample Problem 12.2 Applying the Clausius-Clapeyron Equation

Problem The vapor pressure of ethanol is 115 torr at 34.9°C. If ΔH_{vap} of ethanol is 40.5 kJ/mol, calculate the temperature (in °C) when the vapor pressure is 760 torr.

Plan We are given ΔH_{vap}, P_1, P_2, and T_1 and substitute them into Equation 12.1 to solve for T_2. The value of R here is 8.314 J/mol·K, so we must convert T_1 to K to obtain T_2, and then convert T_2 back to °C.

Solution Substituting the values into Equation 12.1 and solving for T_2:

$$\ln \frac{P_2}{P_1} = \frac{-\Delta H_{vap}}{R}\left(\frac{1}{T_2} - \frac{1}{T_1}\right)$$

$$T_1 = 34.9°\text{C} + 273.15 = 308.0 \text{ K}$$

$$\ln \frac{760 \text{ torr}}{115 \text{ torr}} = \left(-\frac{40.5\times10^3 \text{ J/mol}}{8.314 \text{ J/mol·K}}\right)\left(\frac{1}{T_2} - \frac{1}{308.0 \text{ K}}\right)$$

$$1.888 = (-4.87\times10^3)\left[\frac{1}{T_2} - (3.247\times10^{-3})\right]$$

$$T_2 = 350. \text{ K}$$

Converting T_2 from K to °C:

$$T_2 = 350. \text{ K} - 273.15 = 77°\text{C}$$

Check Round off to check the math. The change is in the right direction: higher P should occur at higher T. As we discuss next, a substance has a vapor pressure of 760 torr at its *normal boiling point.* Checking the *CRC Handbook of Chemistry and Physics* shows that the boiling point of ethanol is 78.5°C, very close to our answer.

Follow-Up Problem 12.2 At 34.1°C, the vapor pressure of water is 40.1 torr. What is the vapor pressure at 85.5°C? The ΔH_{vap} of water is 40.7 kJ/mol.

Vapor Pressure and Boiling Point Let's discuss what is happening when a liquid boils and then see the effect of pressure on boiling point.

1. *How a liquid boils.* In an *open* container, the weight of the atmosphere bears down on a liquid surface. As the temperature rises, molecules move more quickly throughout the liquid. At some temperature, the average E_k of the molecules in the liquid is great enough for them to form bubbles of vapor *in the interior,* and the liquid boils. At any lower temperature, the bubbles collapse as soon as they start to form because the external pressure is greater than the vapor pressure inside the bubbles. Thus, the **boiling point** *is the temperature at which the vapor pressure equals the external pressure,* which is usually that of the atmosphere. As in condensation and freezing, once boiling begins, the temperature of the liquid remains constant until all of the liquid is gone.

2. *Effect of pressure on boiling point.* The boiling point of a liquid varies with elevation. At high elevations, a lower atmospheric pressure is exerted on the liquid surface, so molecules in the interior need less kinetic energy to form bubbles. Thus, *the boiling point depends on the applied pressure.*

In mountainous regions, food takes *more* time to cook because the boiling point is lower and the boiling liquid is not as hot; for instance, in Boulder, Colorado (elevation 5430 ft, or 1655 m), water boils at 94°C. On the other hand, in a pressure cooker, food takes *less* time to cook because the boiling point is higher at the higher pressure. The *normal boiling point* is observed at standard atmospheric pressure (760 torr, or 101.3 kPa; *long, horizontal dashed line* in Figure 12.7).

Solid-Liquid Equilibria The particles in a crystal are continually jiggling about their fixed positions. As the temperature rises, the particles jiggle more rapidly, until some have enough kinetic energy to break free of their positions. At this point, melting begins. As more molecules enter the liquid (molten) phase, some collide with the solid and become fixed in position again. Because the phases remain in contact, a dynamic equilibrium is established when the melting rate equals the freezing rate. The temperature at which this occurs is called the **melting point.** The temperature remains fixed at the melting point until all the solid melts.

Because liquids and solids are nearly incompressible, pressure has little effect on the rates of melting and freezing: a plot of pressure vs. temperature for a solid-liquid phase change is typically a *nearly* vertical straight line.

Figure 12.9 Iodine subliming. After the solid sublimes, I_2 vapor deposits on a cold surface (water-filled inner test tube).

Solid-Gas Equilibria Sublimation is not very familiar because solids have *much* lower vapor pressures than liquids. A substance sublimes rather than melts because the intermolecular attractions are not great enough to keep the molecules near each other when they leave the solid state. Some solids *do* have high enough vapor pressures to sublime at ordinary conditions, including dry ice (carbon dioxide), iodine (Figure 12.9), and moth repellants, all nonpolar molecules with weak intermolecular forces.

The plot of pressure vs. temperature for a solid-gas phase change reflects the large effect of temperature on vapor pressure; thus, it resembles the liquid-gas curve in rising steeply with higher temperatures.

Phase Diagrams: Effect of Pressure and Temperature on Physical State

The **phase diagram** of a substance combines the liquid-gas, solid-liquid, and solid-gas curves and gives the conditions of temperature and pressure at which each phase is stable and where phase changes occur.

The Phase Diagram for CO_2 and Most Substances The diagram for CO_2, which is typical of most substances, has four general features (Figure 12.10):

1. *Regions of the diagram.* Each region presents the conditions of pressure and temperature for which the phase is stable. If another phase is placed under those conditions, it will change to the stable phase. In general, the solid is stable at low temperature and high pressure, the gas at high temperature and low pressure, and the liquid at intermediate conditions.

2. *Lines between regions.* The lines are the phase-transition curves discussed earlier. Any point along a line shows the pressure and temperature at which the phases are in equilibrium. The solid-liquid line has a slightly *positive* slope (slants to the *right* with increasing pressure) because, for most substances, the solid is more dense than the liquid: an increase in pressure converts the liquid to the solid. (Water is *the* major exception.)

3. *The triple point.* The three phase-transition curves meet at the **triple point,** at which all three phases are in equilibrium. As strange as it sounds, at the triple point in Figure 12.10, CO_2 is subliming and depositing, melting and freezing, and vaporizing and condensing simultaneously! Substances with several solid and/or liquid forms can have more than one triple point.

The CO_2 phase diagram shows why dry ice (solid CO_2) doesn't melt under ordinary conditions. The triple-point pressure is 5.1 atm, so liquid CO_2 doesn't occur at 1 atm because it is not stable. The horizontal dashed line at 1.0 atm crosses the solid-gas line, so when solid CO_2 is heated, it sublimes at $-78°C$ rather than melts. If our normal atmospheric pressure were 5.2 atm, liquid CO_2 *would* occur.

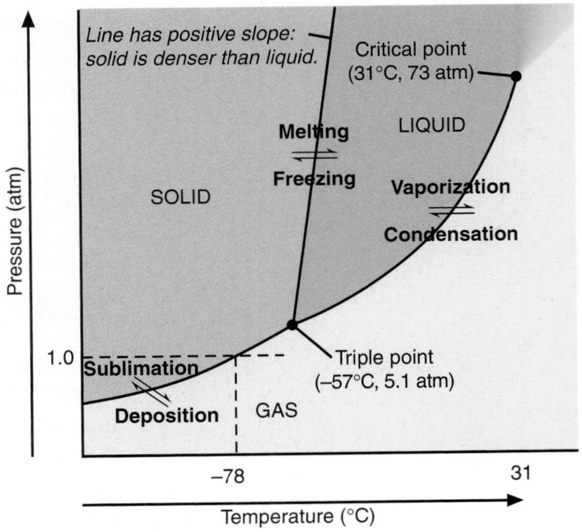

Figure 12.10 Phase diagram for CO_2. (The slope of the solid-liquid line is exaggerated, and the axes are not linear in both this figure and Figure 12.11.)

4. *The critical point.* Heat a liquid in a closed container and its density decreases. At the same time, more of the liquid vaporizes, so the density of the vapor increases. At the **critical point,** the two densities become equal and the phase boundary disappears. The temperature at

the critical point is the *critical temperature* (T_c), and the pressure is the *critical pressure* (P_c). The average E_k is so high at this point that the vapor cannot be condensed at any pressure. The two most common gases in air have critical temperatures far below room temperature: O_2 cannot be condensed above −119°C, and N_2 above −147°C.

Beyond the critical temperature, a *supercritical fluid* (SCF) exists rather than separate liquid and gaseous phases. An SCF expands and contracts like a gas and has unusual solvent properties. Supercritical CO_2 is used to extract caffeine from coffee beans, nicotine from tobacco, and fats from potato chips, and acts as a dry cleaning agent. Lower the pressure, and the SCF disperses as a harmless gas. Supercritical H_2O dissolves nonpolar substances, even though liquid water cannot. Studies are under way to use supercritical H_2O for removing nonpolar organic toxins, such as PCBs, from industrial waste.

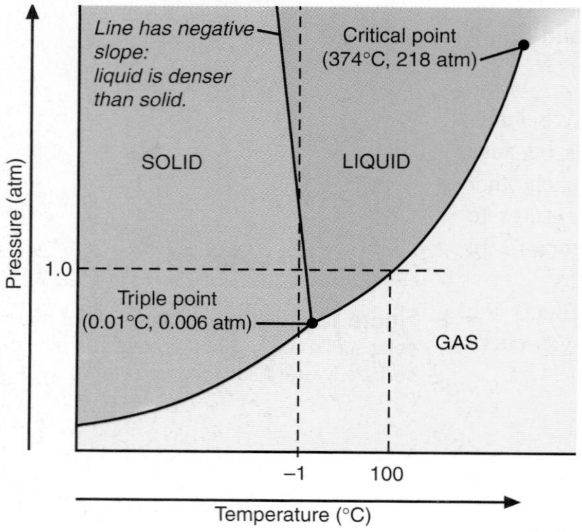

Figure 12.11 Phase diagram for H_2O.

The Solid-Liquid Line for Water The phase diagram for water differs from others in one major respect that reveals a key property. Unlike almost any other substance, the solid form is *less dense* than the liquid; that is, *water expands upon freezing*. Thus, the solid-liquid line has a *negative* slope (slants to the *left* with increasing pressure): an increase in pressure converts the solid to the liquid, and the higher the pressure, the lower the temperature at which water freezes (Figure 12.11). The vertical dashed line at −1°C crosses the solid-liquid line, which means that ice melts with only an increase in pressure.

The triple point of water occurs at low pressure (0.006 atm). Therefore, when solid water is heated at 1.0 atm (*horizontal dashed line*), the solid-liquid line is crossed at 0°C, the normal melting point. Thus, ice melts rather than sublimes. The horizontal dashed line then crosses the liquid-gas curve at 100°C, the normal boiling point.

Summary of Section 12.2

- A heating-cooling curve depicts the change in temperature when a substance absorbs or releases heat at a constant rate. Within a phase, temperature (and average E_k) changes. During a phase change, temperature (and average E_k) is constant, but E_p changes. The total enthalpy change for the system is found using Hess's law.
- In a closed container, the liquid and gas phases of a substance reach equilibrium. The vapor pressure, the pressure of the gas at equilibrium, is related directly to temperature and inversely to the strength of the intermolecular forces.
- The Clausius-Clapeyron equation relates the vapor pressure to the temperature and is often used to find ΔH_{vap}.
- A liquid in an open container boils when its vapor pressure equals the external pressure.
- Solid-liquid equilibrium occurs at the melting point. Some solids sublime because they have very weak intermolecular forces.
- The phase diagram of a substance shows the phase that is stable at any P and T, the conditions at which phase changes occur, and the conditions at the critical point and the triple point. Water differs from most substances in that its solid phase is less dense than its liquid phase, so its solid-liquid line has a negative slope.

12.3 • TYPES OF INTERMOLECULAR FORCES

In Chapter 9, we saw that bonding (*intra*molecular) forces are due to the attraction between cations and anions (ionic bonding), nuclei and electron pairs (covalent bonding), or metal cations and delocalized electrons (metallic bonding). But the nature of the phases and their changes are due primarily to *inter*molecular (nonbonding) forces, which arise from the attraction between molecules with partial charges or between ions and molecules. Coulomb's law explains why the two types of forces differ in magnitude:

- *Bonding forces are relatively strong* because larger charges are closer together.
- *Intermolecular forces are relatively weak* because smaller charges are farther apart.

How Close Can Molecules Approach Each Other?

To see the minimum distance *between* molecules, consider solid Cl_2. When we measure the distances between two Cl nuclei, we obtain two different values (Figure 12.12A):

- *Bond length and covalent radius.* The shorter distance, called the *bond length,* is between *two bonded Cl atoms in the **same** molecule.* One-half this distance is the *covalent radius.*
- *Van der Waals distance and radius.* The longer distance is between *two nonbonded Cl atoms in **adjacent** molecules.* It is called the *van der Waals (VDW) distance.* At this distance, intermolecular attractions balance electron-cloud repulsions; thus, the VDW distance is as close as one Cl_2 molecule can approach another. The **van der Waals radius** is one-half the closest distance between nuclei of identical *nonbonded* atoms. The VDW radius of an atom is *always larger than its covalent radius.* Like covalent radii, VDW radii decrease across a period and increase down a group (Figure 12.12B).

As we discuss intermolecular forces (also called *van der Waals forces*), consult Table 12.2, which compares them with bonding forces.

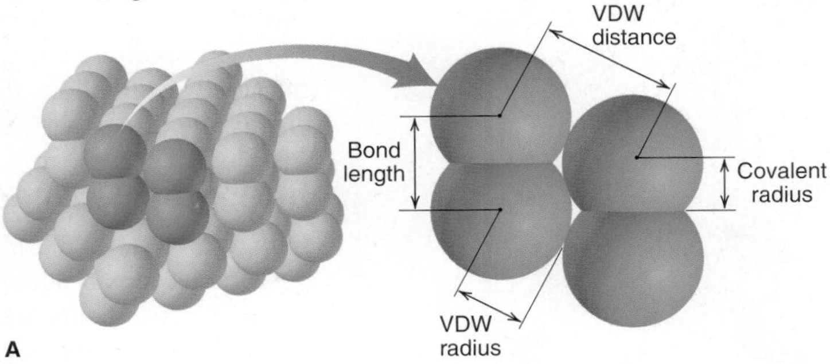

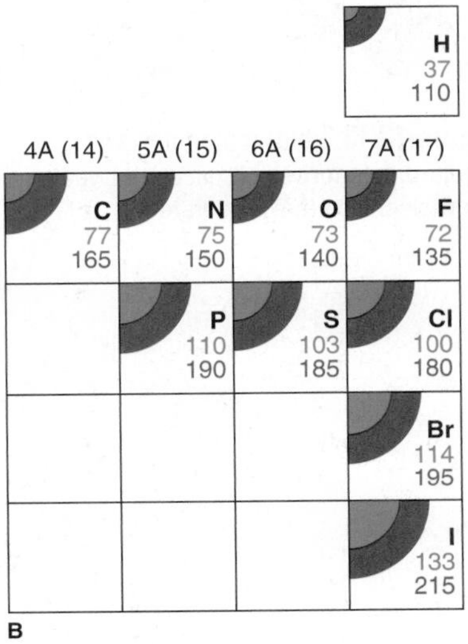

Figure 12.12 Covalent and van der Waals radii and their periodic trends. **A,** The van der Waals (VDW) radius is one-half the distance between adjacent *nonbonded* atoms ($\frac{1}{2}$ × VDW distance). **B,** Like covalent radii (*blue quarter-circles and numbers*), VDW radii (*red quarter-circles and numbers*) increase down a group and decrease across a period.

Table 12.2 Comparison of Bonding and Nonbonding (Intermolecular) Forces

Force	Model	Basis of Attraction	Energy (kJ/mol)	Example
Bonding				
Ionic	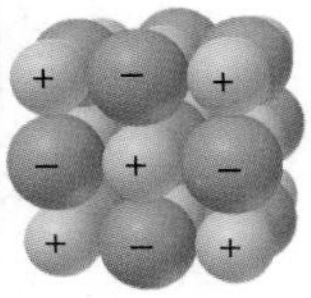	Cation–anion	400–4000	NaCl
Covalent	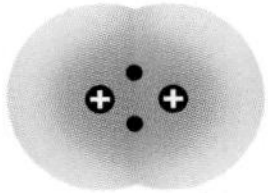	Nuclei–shared e^- pair	150–1100	H—H
Metallic	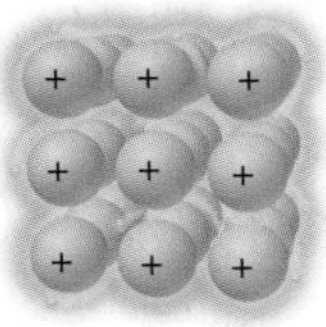	Cations–delocalized electrons	75–1000	Fe
Nonbonding (Intermolecular)				
Ion-dipole		Ion charge–dipole charge	40–600	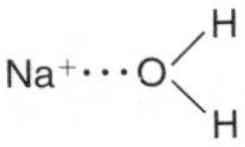
H bond	$\overset{\delta-}{—A}—\overset{\delta+}{H}\cdots\cdots:\overset{\delta-}{B}—$	Polar bond to H–dipole charge (high EN of N, O, F)	10–40	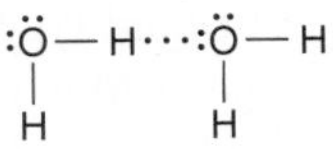
Dipole-dipole		Dipole charges	5–25	I—Cl···I—Cl
Ion–induced dipole		Ion charge–polarizable e^- cloud	3–15	$Fe^{2+}\cdots O_2$
Dipole–induced dipole	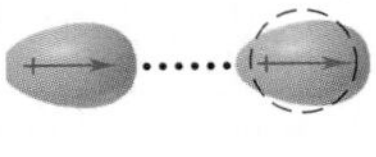	Dipole charge–polarizable e^- cloud	2–10	H—Cl···Cl—Cl
Dispersion (London)		Polarizable e^- clouds	0.05–40	F—F···F—F

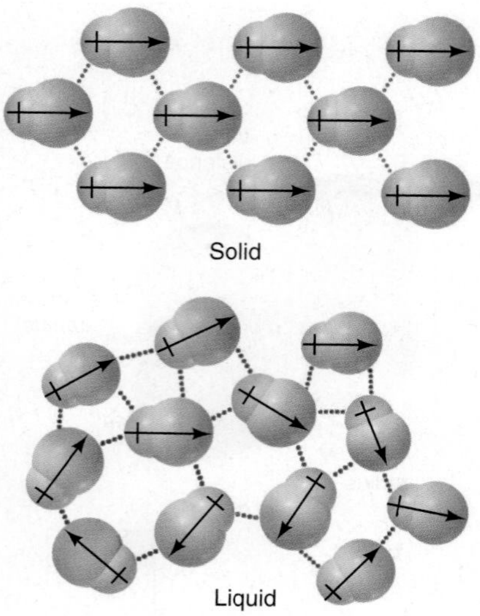

Figure 12.13 Polar molecules and dipole-dipole forces. (Spaces between the molecules are exaggerated.)

Ion-Dipole Forces

When an ion and a nearby polar molecule (dipole) attract each other, an **ion-dipole force** results. The most important example takes place when an ionic compound dissolves in water. The ions become separated because the attractions between the ions and the oppositely charged poles of the H_2O molecules are stronger than the attractions between the ions themselves. Ion-dipole forces in solutions and their associated energy are discussed fully in Chapter 13.

Dipole-Dipole Forces

In Figure 10.13 (p. 383), an external electric field orients gaseous polar molecules. The polar molecules in liquids and solids lie near each other, and their partial charges act as tiny electric fields and give rise to **dipole-dipole forces:** the positive pole of one molecule attracts the negative pole of another (Figure 12.13). The orientation is more orderly in a solid than in a liquid because the average kinetic energy is lower.

These forces depend on the magnitude of the molecular dipole moment. For compounds of similar molar mass, the greater the molecular dipole moment, the greater the dipole-dipole forces, so the more energy it takes to separate the molecules; thus the boiling point is higher. Methyl chloride, for instance, has a smaller dipole moment than acetaldehyde and boils at a lower temperature (Figure 12.14).

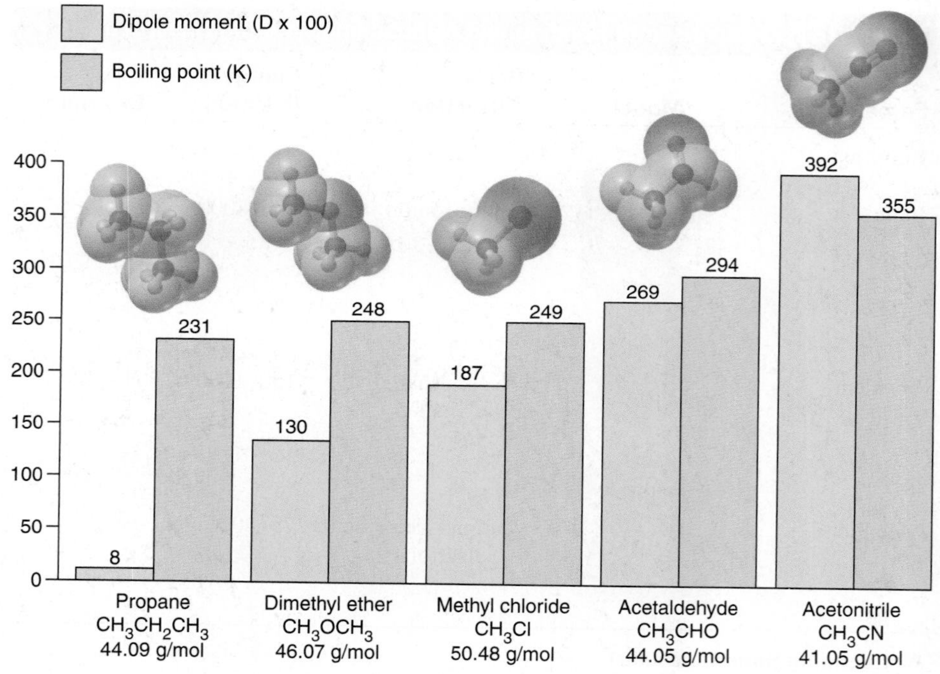

Figure 12.14 Dipole moment and boiling point. (Relative strength of the dipole moments is indicated by color intensities in the electron-density models.)

The Hydrogen Bond

A special type of dipole-dipole force arises between molecules that have *an H atom bonded to a small, highly electronegative atom with lone electron pairs, specifically N, O, or F.* The H—N, H—O, and H—F bonds are very polar. When the partially positive H of one molecule is attracted to the partially negative lone pair on the N, O, or F of another molecule, a **hydrogen bond (H bond)** forms. Thus, the atom sequence of an H bond (dotted line) is —B:····H—A—, where A *and* B are N, O, or F. Three examples are

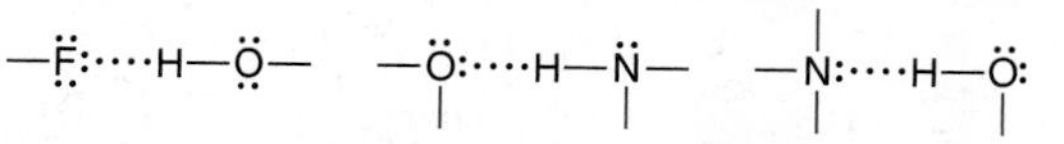

The small sizes of N, O, and F are essential to H bonding for two reasons:

1. The atoms are so electronegative that their covalently bonded H is highly positive.
2. The lone pair on the N, O, or F of the other molecule can come close to the H.

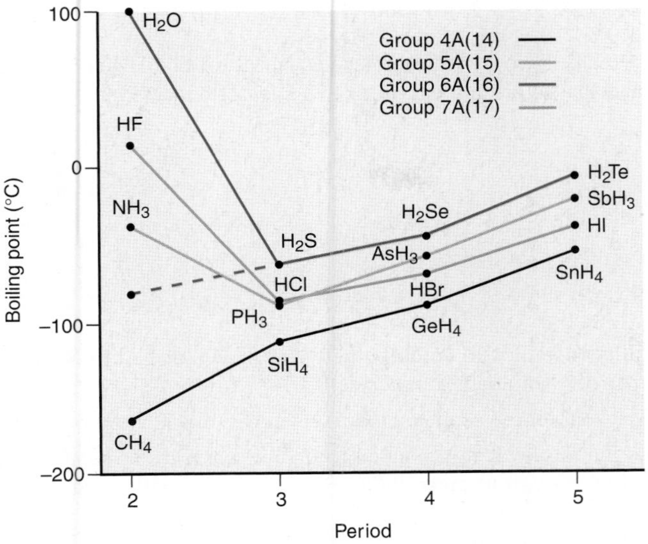

Figure 12.15 Hydrogen bonding and boiling point. NH_3, H_2O, and HF have exceptionallly high boiling points because they form H bonds.

The Significance of Hydrogen Bonding Hydrogen bonding has a profound impact in many systems. We'll examine one effect on physical properties and preview its importance in biological systems, which we address in Chapters 13 and 15.

Figure 12.15 shows the effect of H bonding on the boiling points of the binary hydrides of Groups 4A(14) through 7A(17). For reasons we'll discuss shortly, boiling points rise with molar mass, as the Group 4A(14) hydrides show. However, the first member in each of the other groups—NH_3, H_2O, and HF—deviates enormously from this expected trend. Within samples of these substances, the molecules form strong H bonds, so it takes more energy for the molecules to separate and enter the gas phase. For example, on the basis of molar mass alone, we would expect water to boil about 200°C lower than it actually does (*red dashed line*). (In Section 12.5 we'll discuss the effects that H bonds in water have in nature.)

The significance of hydrogen bonding in biological systems cannot be emphasized too strongly. In Chapter 13, you'll see that it is a key feature in the structure and function of the biological macromolecules—proteins and nucleic acids. It is also responsible for the action of many *enzymes,* the proteins that speed metabolic reactions.

Sample Problem 12.3 Drawing Hydrogen Bonds Between Molecules of a Substance

Problem Which of the following substances exhibits H bonding? For any that do, show the H bonds between two of its molecules.

(a) C_2H_6 **(b)** CH_3OH **(c)** $CH_3\overset{\overset{\large O}{\|}}{C}{-}NH_2$

Plan If the molecule does *not* contain N, O, or F, it cannot form H bonds. If it contains any of these atoms covalently bonded to H, we draw two molecules in the —B:····H—A— pattern.

Solution (a) For C_2H_6. No N, O, or F, so no H bonds can form.

(b) For CH_3OH. The H covalently bonded to the O in one molecule forms an H bond to the lone pair on the O of an adjacent molecule:

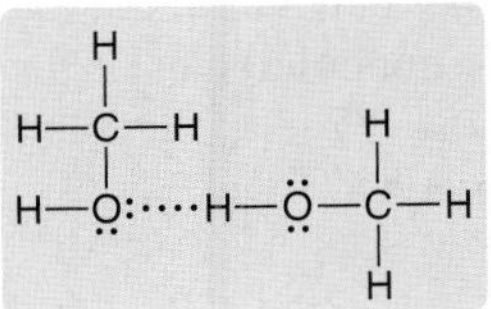

(c) For $CH_3C(=O)—NH_2$. Two of these molecules can form one H bond between an H bonded to N and the O, or they can form two such H bonds:

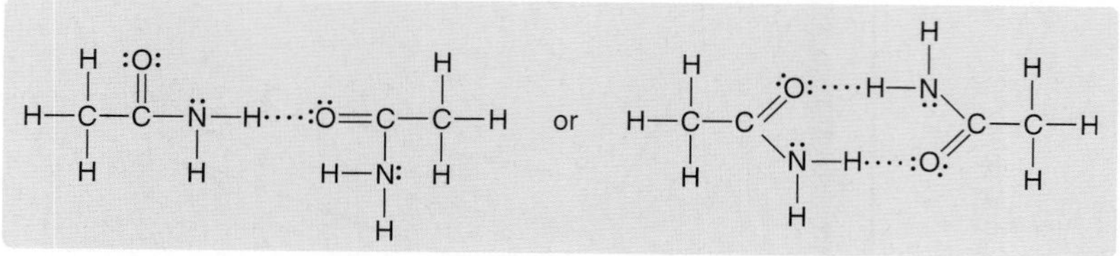

A third possibility (not shown) could be between an H attached to N in one molecule and the lone pair of N in another molecule.

Check The —B:····H—A— sequence (with A and B either N, O, or F) is present.

Comment Note that H covalently bonded to C *does not form H bonds* because carbon is not electronegative enough to make the C—H bond sufficiently polar.

Follow-Up Problem 12.3 Which of these substances exhibits H bonding? Draw the H bond(s) between two molecules of the substance where appropriate.

(a) $CH_3C(=O)—OH$ **(b)** CH_3CH_2OH **(c)** $CH_3C(=O)CH_3$

Polarizability and Induced Dipole Forces

Even though electrons are attracted to nuclei and localized in bonding and lone pairs, we often picture them as "clouds" of negative charge because they are in constant motion. A nearby electric field can *induce* a distortion in the cloud, pulling electron density toward a positive pole of a field or pushing it away from a negative one:

- *For a nonpolar molecule,* the distortion induces a temporary dipole moment.
- *For a polar molecule,* it enhances the dipole moment already present.

In addition to charged plates connected to a battery, the source of the electric field can be the charge of an ion or the partial charges of a polar molecule.

How easily an electron cloud can be distorted is called its **polarizability.** Smaller atoms (or ions) are less polarizable than larger ones because their electrons are closer to the nucleus and therefore held more tightly. Thus, we observe several trends:

- Polarizability *increases down a group* because atomic size increases and larger electron clouds are easier to distort.
- Polarizability *decreases across a period* because increasing Z_{eff} makes the atoms smaller and holds the electrons more tightly.
- Cations are *less* polarizable than their parent atoms because they are smaller; anions are *more* polarizable because they are larger.

Ion–induced dipole and dipole–induced dipole forces are the two types of charge-induced dipole forces; they are most important in solution, so we'll focus on them in Chapter 13. Nevertheless, *polarizability affects all intermolecular forces.*

Dispersion (London) Forces

So far, we've discussed forces that depend on the existing charge of an ion or a polar molecule. But what forces cause nonpolar substances like octane, chlorine, and argon to condense and solidify? As you'll see, polarizability plays the central role in the most universal intermolecular force.

The intermolecular force responsible for the condensed states of nonpolar substances is the **dispersion force** (or **London force,** named for Fritz London, the physicist who explained its quantum-mechanical basis). Dispersion forces *are present between all particles (atoms, ions, and molecules)* because they are caused by the *motion of electrons in atoms.* Let's examine key aspects of this force:

1. *Source.* Picture one atom in a sample of, say, argon gas. Over time, its 18 electrons are distributed uniformly, so the atom is nonpolar. But at any instant, there may be more electrons on one side of the nucleus than the other, which gives the atom an *instantaneous dipole.* When a pair of argon atoms is far apart, they don't influence each other, but when close together, *the instantaneous dipole in one atom induces a dipole in its neighbor,* and they attract each other. This process spreads to other atoms and throughout the sample. At low temperatures, these attractions keep the atoms together (Figure 12.16). Thus, dispersion forces are *instantaneous dipole–induced dipole forces.*

2. *Prevalence.* While they are the *only* force existing between nonpolar particles, *dispersion forces contribute to the energy of attraction in all substances* because they exist between *all* particles. In fact, except for the forces between small, highly polar molecules or between molecules forming H bonds, the *dispersion force is the dominant intermolecular force.* Calculations show, for example, that 85% of the attraction between HCl molecules is due to dispersion forces and only 15% to dipole-dipole forces. Even for water, 75% of the attraction comes from H bonds and 25% from dispersion forces.

3. *Relative strength.* The relative strength of dispersion forces depends on the polarizability of the particles, so they are weak for small particles, like H_2 and He, but stronger for larger particles, like I_2 and Xe. *Polarizability depends on the number of electrons, which correlates closely with molar mass* because heavier particles are either larger atoms or molecules with more atoms and, thus, more electrons. For this reason, as molar mass increases down the Group 4A(14) hydrides (see Figure 12.15), or down the halogens or the noble gases, dispersion forces increase and so do boiling points (Figure 12.17).

4. *Effect of molecular shape.* For a pair of nonpolar substances with the same molar mass, a molecular shape that has more area over which electron clouds can be distorted allows stronger attractions. For example, the two five-carbon alkanes, *n*-pentane and neopentane (2,2-dimethylpropane) are structural isomers—same molecular formula (C_5H_{12}) but different properties. *n*-Pentane is more cylindrical and neopentane more spherical (Figure 12.18). Thus, two *n*-pentane molecules make more contact than do two neopentane molecules, so dispersion forces act at more points, and *n*-pentane has a higher boiling point.

Figure 12.19 on the next page shows how to determine the intermolecular forces in a sample.

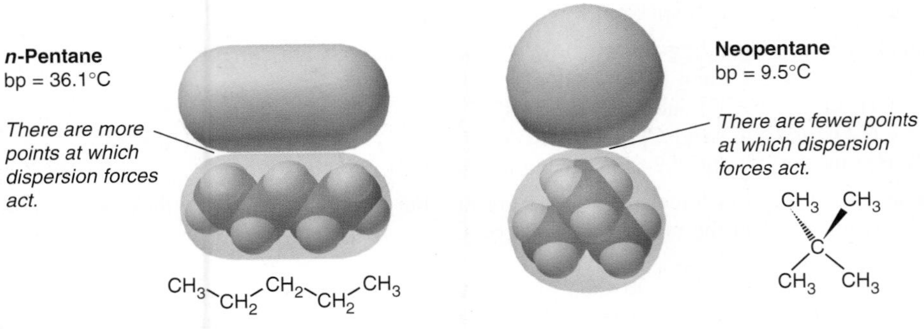

Figure 12.18 Molecular shape, intermolecular contact, and boiling point.

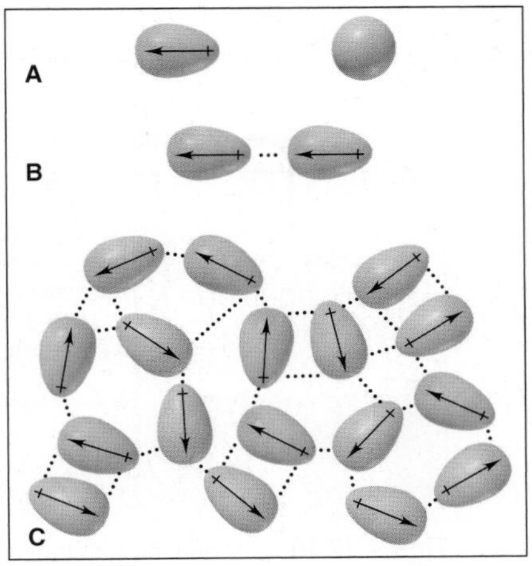

Figure 12.16 Dispersion forces among nonpolar particles. A, When atoms are far apart, an instantaneous dipole in one atom (*left*) doesn't influence another. **B,** When atoms are close together, the instantaneous dipole in one atom induces a dipole in the other. **C,** The process occurs through the sample.

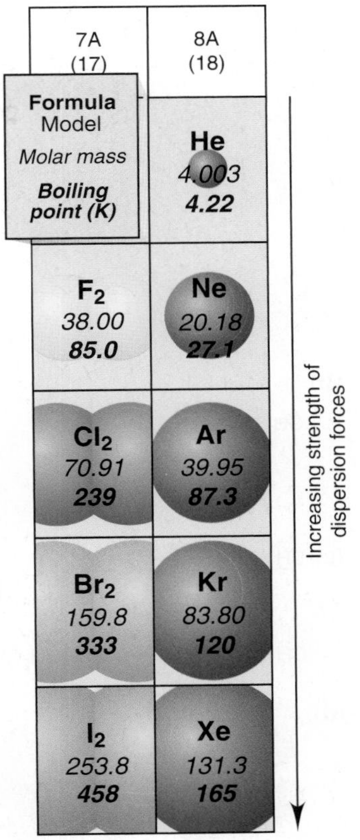

Figure 12.17 Molar mass and trends in boiling point.

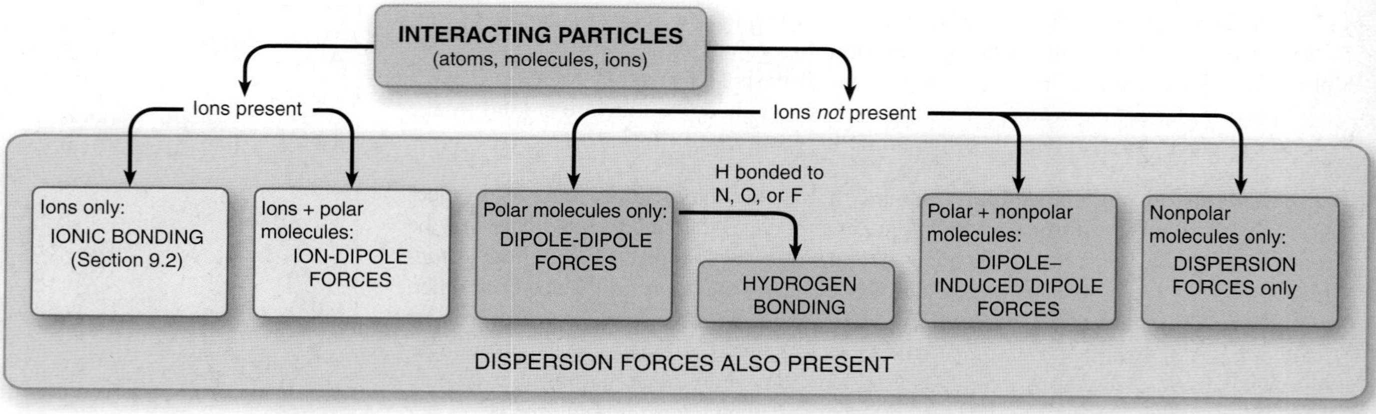

Figure 12.19 Determining the intermolecular forces in a sample.

Sample Problem 12.4 Predicting the Types of Intermolecular Forces

Problem For each substance, identify the key bonding and/or intermolecular force(s), and predict which one of the pair has the higher boiling point:

(a) $MgCl_2$ or PCl_3
(b) CH_3NH_2 or CH_3F
(c) CH_3OH or CH_3CH_2OH
(d) Hexane ($CH_3CH_2CH_2CH_2CH_2CH_3$) or 2,2-dimethylbutane

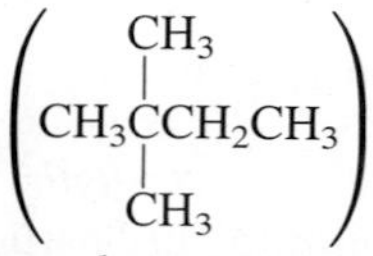

Plan We examine the formulas and structures for key differences between members of the pair: Are ions present? Are molecules polar or nonpolar? Is N, O, or F bonded to H? Do the molecules have different masses or shapes?
To rank boiling points, we consult Figure 12.19 and Table 12.2. Remember that

- Bonding forces are stronger than intermolecular forces.
- Hydrogen bonding is a strong type of dipole-dipole force.
- Dispersion forces are decisive when the difference is molar mass or molecular shape.

Solution (a) $MgCl_2$ consists of Mg^{2+} and Cl^- ions held together by ionic bonding forces; PCl_3 consists of polar molecules, so intermolecular dipole-dipole forces are present. The forces in $MgCl_2$ are stronger, so it should have a higher boiling point.
(b) CH_3NH_2 and CH_3F both consist of polar molecules of about the same molar mass. CH_3NH_2 has N—H bonds, so it can form H bonds (*see margin*). CH_3F contains a C—F bond but no H—F bond, so dipole-dipole forces occur but not H bonds. Therefore, CH_3NH_2 should have the higher boiling point.
(c) CH_3OH and CH_3CH_2OH molecules both contain an O—H bond, so they can form H bonds (*see margin*). CH_3CH_2OH has an additional $—CH_2—$ group and thus a larger molar mass, which correlates with stronger dispersion forces; therefore, it should have a higher boiling point.
(d) Hexane and 2,2-dimethylbutane are nonpolar molecules of the same molar mass but different molecular shapes (*see margin*). Cylindrical hexane molecules make more intermolecular contact than more compact 2,2-dimethylbutane molecules do, so hexane should have stronger dispersion forces and a higher boiling point.

(b)

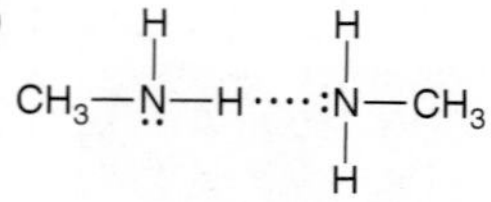

(c)

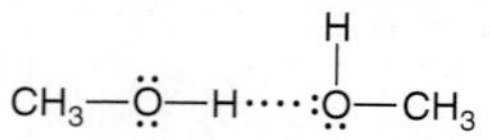

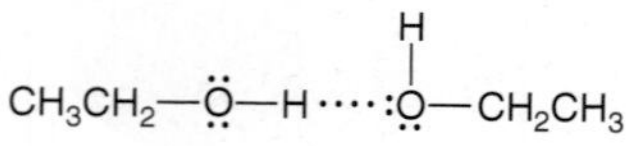

(d)

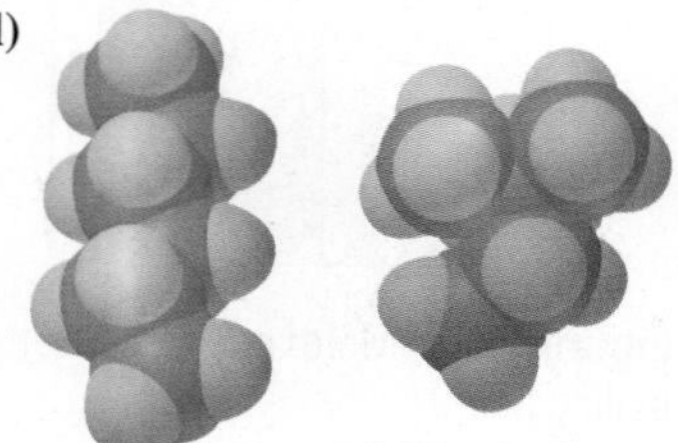

Hexane 2,2-Dimethylbutane

Check The actual boiling points show that our predictions are correct:
(a) $MgCl_2$ (1412°C) and PCl_3 (76°C)
(b) CH_3NH_2 (−6.3°C) and CH_3F (−78.4°C)
(c) CH_3OH (64.7°C) and CH_3CH_2OH (78.5°C)
(d) Hexane (69°C) and 2,2-dimethylbutane (49.7°C)

Comment Dispersion forces are *always* present, but in parts (a) and (b), they are much less significant than the other forces that occur.

Follow-Up Problem 12.4 In each pair, identify the intermolecular forces present for each substance, and predict which substance has the higher boiling point:
(a) CH_3Br or CH_3F **(b)** $CH_3CH_2CH_2OH$ or $CH_3CH_2OCH_3$ **(c)** C_2H_6 or C_3H_8

Summary of Section 12.3

- The van der Waals radius determines the shortest distance over which intermolecular forces operate; it is always larger than the covalent radius.
- Intermolecular forces are much weaker than bonding (intramolecular) forces.
- Ion-dipole forces occur between ions and polar molecules.
- Dipole-dipole forces occur between oppositely charged poles on polar molecules.
- Hydrogen bonding, a special type of dipole-dipole force, occurs when H bonded to N, O, or F is attracted to the lone pair of N, O, or F in another molecule.
- Electron clouds can be distorted (polarized) in an electric field.
- Ion– and dipole–induced dipole forces arise between a charge and the dipole it induces in another molecule.
- Dispersion (London) forces are instantaneous dipole–induced dipole forces that occur among all particles and increase with number of electrons (molar mass). Molecular shape determines the extent of contact between molecules and can be a factor in the strength of dispersion forces.

12.4 • PROPERTIES OF THE LIQUID STATE

Of the three states, only liquids combine the ability to flow with the effects of strong intermolecular forces. We understand this state least at the molecular level. Because of the *random* arrangement of the particles in a gas, any region of the sample is virtually identical to any other. And, different regions of a crystalline solid are identical because of the *orderly* arrangement of the particles (Section 12.6). Liquids, however, have regions that are orderly one moment and random the next. Despite this complexity, many macroscopic properties, such as surface tension, capillarity, and viscosity are well understood.

Surface Tension

Intermolecular forces have different effects on a molecule at the surface compared with one in the interior (Figure 12.20):

- An interior molecule is attracted by others on all sides.
- A surface molecule is only attracted by others below and to the sides, so it experiences a *net attraction downward.*

Figure 12.20 The molecular basis of surface tension.

Therefore, to increase attractions and become more stable, a surface molecule tends to move into the interior. For this reason, *a liquid surface has the fewest molecules and, thus, the smallest area possible.* In effect, the surface behaves like a "taut skin" covering the interior.

The only way to increase the surface area is for molecules to move up by breaking attractions in the interior, which requires energy. The **surface tension** is the energy required to increase the surface area and has units of J/m^2 (Table 12.3). In general, *the stronger the forces are between particles, the more energy it takes to increase the surface area, so the greater the surface tension.* Water has a high surface tension because its molecules form multiple H bonds. *Surfactants* (*surface-active* agents), such as soaps, petroleum recovery agents, and fat emulsifiers, decrease the surface tension of water by congregating at the surface and disrupting the H bonds.

Table 12.3 Surface Tension and Forces Between Particles

Substance	Formula	Surface Tension (J/m^2) at 20°C	Major Force(s)
Diethyl ether	$CH_3CH_2OCH_2CH_3$	1.7×10^{-2}	Dipole-dipole; dispersion
Ethanol	CH_3CH_2OH	2.3×10^{-2}	H bonding
Butanol	$CH_3CH_2CH_2CH_2OH$	2.5×10^{-2}	H bonding; dispersion
Water	H_2O	7.3×10^{-2}	H bonding
Mercury	Hg	48×10^{-2}	Metallic bonding

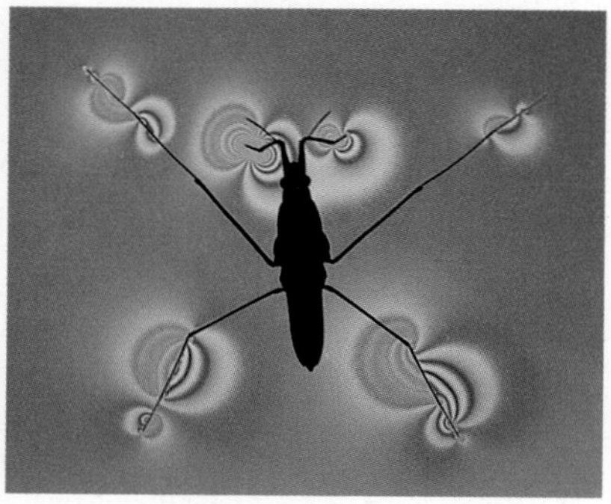

A water strider's widespread legs don't exert enough pressure to exceed the surface tension.

Surface tension is the cause of many familiar phenomena. Bubbles are round because this shape minimizes the surface area around the gas, and surface tension is the reason some insects can walk on water (*see photo*).

Capillarity

The rising of a liquid against the pull of gravity through a narrow space, such as a thin tube, is called *capillary action,* or **capillarity.** Capillarity results from a competition between the intermolecular forces within the liquid (cohesive forces) and those between the liquid and the tube walls (adhesive forces). Let's look at the difference between the capillarities of water and mercury in glass:

1. *Water in glass.* When you place a narrow glass tube in water, why does the liquid rise up the tube and form a concave meniscus? Glass is mostly silicon dioxide (SiO_2), so water molecules form adhesive H bonding forces with the O atoms of the glass. As a result, a thin film of water creeps up the wall. At the same time, cohesive H bonding forces between water molecules, which give rise to surface tension, make the surface taut. These adhesive and cohesive forces combine to raise the water level and produce the concave meniscus (Figure 12.21A). The liquid rises until gravity pulling down is balanced by adhesive forces pulling up.

2. *Mercury in glass.* When you place a glass tube in a dish of mercury, why does the liquid drop below the level in the dish and form a convex meniscus? The cohesive forces among the mercury atoms are metallic bonds, so they are *much* stronger than the mostly dispersion adhesive forces between mercury and glass. As a result, the liquid pulls away from the walls. At the same time, the surface atoms are being pulled toward the interior by mercury's high surface tension, so the level drops. These combined forces produce the concave meniscus seen in a laboratory barometer (Figure 12.21B).

Capillarity plays a key role in many everyday events. The adhesive (dipole–induced dipole) forces between water and a nonpolar surface are much weaker than the cohesive (H-bond) forces within water. As a result, water pulls away from a nonpolar surface and forms beaded droplets, as on a freshly waxed car or on the waxy coating of a leaf after a rainfall. Even more familiar, after a shower, capillary action draws water away from your body through the closely spaced fibers in the cotton towel, which is made of cellulose molecules, so the water molecules also form H bonds with the —OH groups of cellulose.

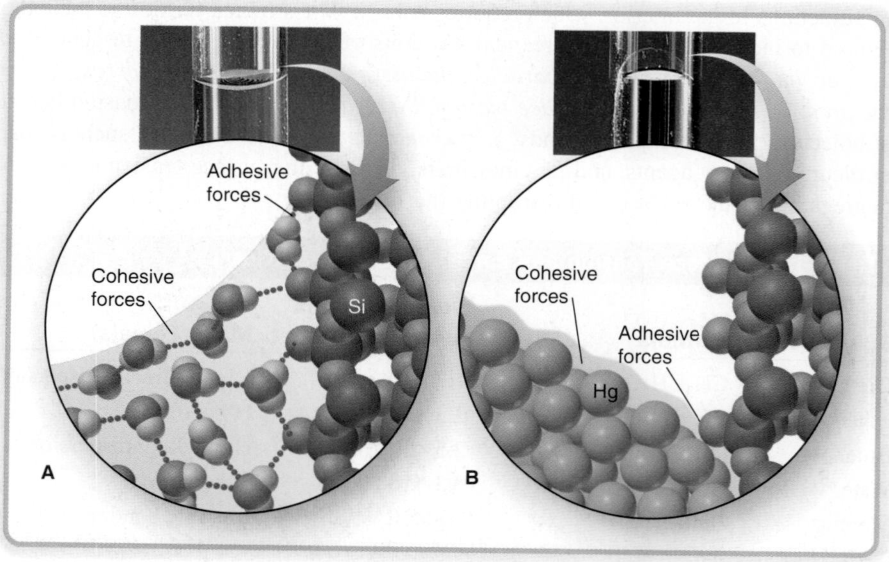

Figure 12.21 Capillary action and the shape of the water or mercury meniscus in glass. **A,** Water displays a concave meniscus. **B,** Mercury displays a convex meniscus.

Viscosity

Viscosity is the resistance of a fluid to flow, and it results from intermolecular attractions that impede the movement of molecules around and past each other. Both gases and liquids flow, but liquid viscosities are *much* higher because there are many more points for intermolecular forces to act due to the much shorter distances. Let's examine two factors—temperature and molecular shape—that influence viscosity:

- *Effect of temperature. Viscosity decreases with heating* (Table 12.4). Faster moving molecules overcome intermolecular forces more easily, so the resistance to flow decreases. Next time you heat cooking oil, watch the oil flow more easily and spread out in the pan as it warms.
- *Effect of molecular shape.* Small, spherical molecules make little contact and pour easily, like buckshot from a bowl. Long molecules make more contact and become entangled and pour slowly, like cooked spaghetti from a bowl. Thus, given the same types of intermolecular forces, liquids consisting of longer molecules have higher viscosities.

To protect engine parts during long drives, motor oils contain *polymeric viscosity improvers*. As the oil warms, these additive molecules change from compact spheres to long strands that become tangled with the long hydrocarbon molecules of the oil. Greater dispersion forces increase the viscosity to compensate for the oil thinning due to heating.

Table 12.4 Viscosity of Water at Several Temperatures

Temperature (°C)	Viscosity (N·s/m²)*
20	1.00×10^{-3}
40	0.65×10^{-3}
60	0.47×10^{-3}
80	0.35×10^{-3}

*The units of viscosity are newton-seconds per square meter.

Summary of Section 12.4

- Surface tension is a measure of the energy required to increase a liquid's surface area. Greater intermolecular forces within a liquid create higher surface tension.
- Capillarity, the rising of a liquid through a narrow space, occurs when the forces between a liquid and a surface (adhesive) are greater than those within the liquid (cohesive).
- Viscosity, the resistance to flow, depends on molecular shape and decreases with temperature. Stronger intermolecular forces create higher viscosity.

12.5 • THE UNIQUENESS OF WATER

Water is absolutely amazing stuff, with some of the most unusual properties of any substance, but it is so familiar we take it for granted. Like any substance, its properties arise inevitably from those of its atoms. Each O and H atom attains a filled outer level by sharing electrons in single bonds. With two bonding pairs and two lone pairs around O and a large electronegativity difference in each O—H bond, the H_2O molecule is bent and highly polar. This arrangement is crucial because it allows each molecule to engage in four H bonds with its neighbors (Figure 12.22). From these basic atomic and molecular facts emerges unique and remarkable macroscopic behavior.

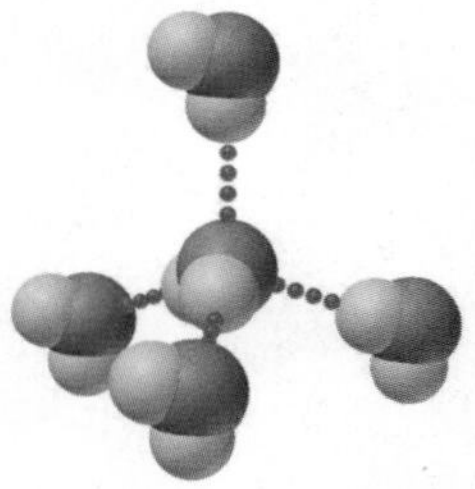

Figure 12.22 H-bonding ability of water. One H_2O molecule can form four H bonds to other molecules, resulting in a tetrahedral arrangement.

Solvent Properties of Water

The *great solvent power* of water results from its polarity and H-bonding ability:

- It dissolves ionic compounds through ion-dipole forces that separate the ions from the solid and keep them in solution (see Figure 4.2, p. 138).
- It dissolves polar nonionic substances, such as ethanol (CH_3CH_2OH) and glucose ($C_6H_{12}O_6$), by H bonding.
- It dissolves nonpolar atmospheric gases to a limited extent through dipole–induced dipole and dispersion forces.

Water is the environmental and biological solvent, forming the complex solutions we know as oceans, lakes, and cytoplasm. Aquatic animals could not survive without dissolved O_2, nor could aquatic plants without dissolved CO_2. Tiny marine animals form coral reefs made of carbonates from dissolved CO_2 and HCO_3^-. Life began in a "primordial soup," an aqueous mixture of simple molecules from which emerged larger molecules capable of self-sustaining reactions. From a chemical point of view, all organisms, from bacteria to humans, are highly organized systems of membranes enclosing and compartmentalizing complex aqueous solutions.

Thermal Properties of Water

When a substance is heated, some of the added energy increases average molecular speed, some increases molecular vibration and rotation, and some is used to overcome intermolecular forces.

1. *Specific heat capacity*. Because water has so many strong H bonds, its *specific heat capacity* is higher than any common liquid. With oceans covering 70% of Earth's surface, daytime energy from the Sun causes relatively small changes in temperature, allowing life to survive. On the waterless, airless Moon, temperatures range from 100°C to −150°C during a complete lunar day. Even in Earth's deserts, day-night temperature differences of 40°C are common.

2. *Heat of vaporization*. Numerous strong H bonds give water a very *high heat of vaporization*. Two examples show why this is crucial. The average adult has 40 kg of body water and generates about 10,000 kJ of heat a day from metabolism. If this heat were used to increase the average E_k of water molecules in the body, the rise in body temperaure of tens of degrees would mean immediate death. Instead, the heat is converted to E_p as it breaks H bonds and evaporates sweat, resulting in a stable body temperature and minimal loss of body fluid. On a planetary scale, the Sun's energy vaporizes ocean water in warm latitudes, and the potential energy is released as heat to warm cooler regions when the vapor condenses to rain. This global-scale cycling of water powers many weather patterns.

Surface Properties of Water

Hydrogen bonding is also responsible for water's *high surface tension* and *high capillarity*. Except for some molten metals and salts, water has the highest surface tension of any liquid. It keeps plant debris resting on a pond surface, providing shelter and nutrients for fish and insects. High capillarity means water rises through the tiny spaces between soil particles, so plant roots can absorb deep groundwater during dry periods.

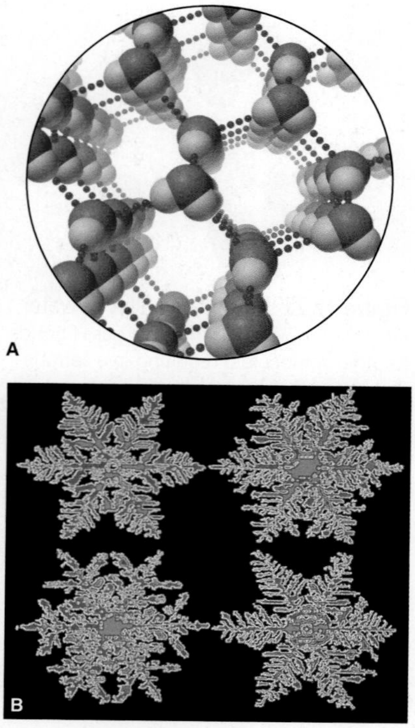

Figure 12.23 **The hexagonal structure of ice.** **A,** The open, hexagonal molecular structure of ice. **B,** The beauty of six-pointed snowflakes reflects this hexagonal structure.

The Unusual Density of Solid Water

In the solid state, the tetrahedral pattern of H bonding (see Figure 12.22) leads to the hexagonal, *open structure* of ice (Figure 12.23A), and the symmetrical beauty of snowflakes (Figure 12.23B) reflects this hexagonal organization. The large spaces within ice make *the solid less dense than the liquid* and explain the negative slope of the solid-liquid line in the phase diagram for water (see Figure 12.11, p. 430). As pressure is applied, some H bonds break, so the ordered crystal structure is disrupted, and the ice liquefies. When ice melts at 0°C, the loosened molecules pack much more closely, filling spaces in the collapsing solid structure. As a result, liquid water is most dense (1.000 g/mL) at around 4°C (3.98°C). With more heating, the density decreases through normal thermal expansion. This behavior has major effects in nature:

- *Surface ice of lakes*. When the surface of a lake freezes in winter, the ice floats. If the solid were denser than the liquid, as is true for nearly every other substance, the surface water would freeze and sink until the entire lake was solid. Aquatic life would not survive from year to year.
- *Nutrient turnover*. As lake water becomes colder in early winter, it becomes more dense *before* it freezes. Similarly, in spring, less dense ice thaws to form more dense water *before* the water expands. During both of these seasonal density changes, the top layer of water reaches maximum density first and sinks. The next layer of water rises because it is slightly less dense, reaches 4°C, and likewise sinks. This alternation of sinking and rising distributes nutrients and dissolved oxygen.
- *Soil formation*. When rain fills crevices in rocks and freezes, an outward force is applied that is relieved when the ice melts. In time, this repeated freeze-thaw stress cracks the rock. Over eons, this effect helps produce sand and soil.

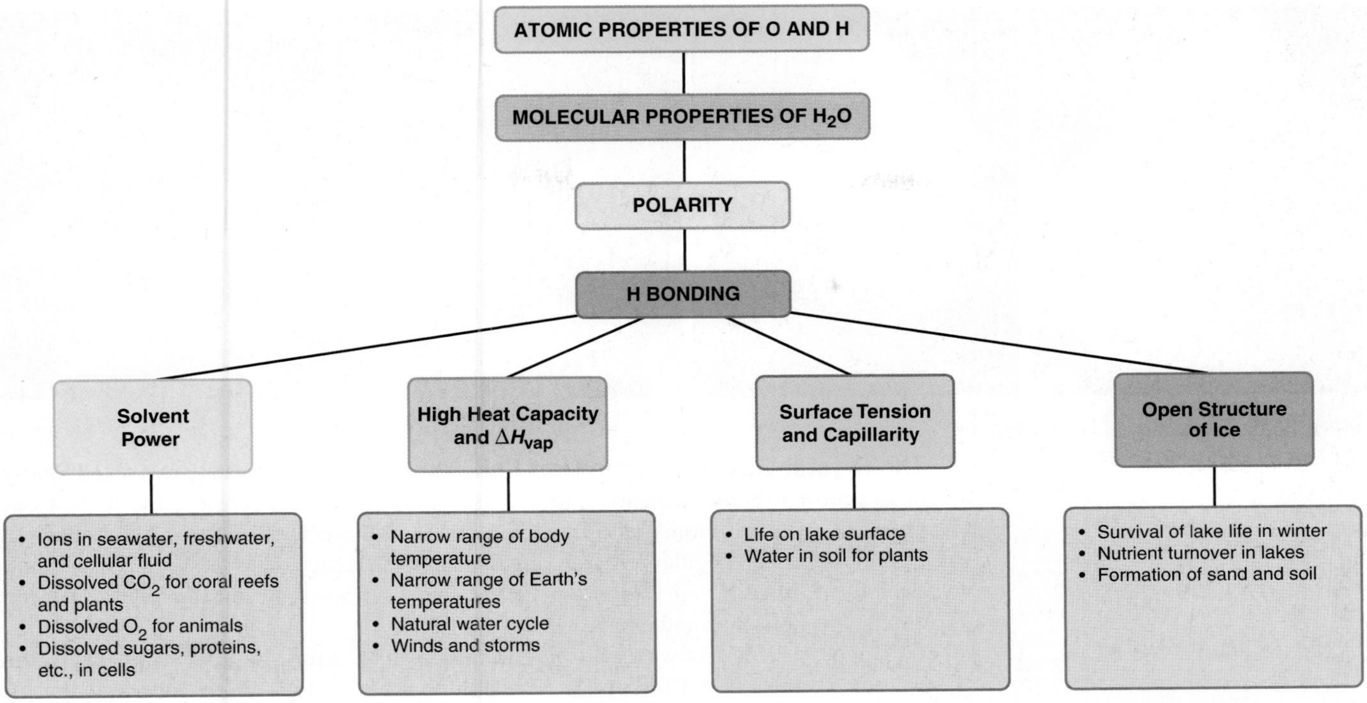

Figure 12.24 The unique macroscopic behavior of water that emerges from its atomic and molecular properties.

The far-reaching consequences of the properties of water illustrate chemistry's central theme: the macroscopic world we know is the cumulative outcome of the atomic world we seek to know (Figure 12.24).

Summary of Section 12.5

- The atomic properties of H and O result in water's bent molecular shape, polarity, and H-bonding ability.
- These properties give water the ability to dissolve many ionic and polar compounds.
- Water's high specific heat capacity and heat of vaporization give Earth and its organisms a narrow temperature range.
- The high surface tension and capillarity are essential to plants and animals.
- Because water expands on freezing, lake life survives in winter, nutrients mix from seasonal density changes, and soil forms through freeze-thaw stress on rocks.

12.6 • THE SOLID STATE: STRUCTURE, PROPERTIES, AND BONDING

Stroll through a museum's mineral collection, and you'll be struck by the variety and beauty of crystalline solids. In this section, we discuss the structural features of these and other solids and the intermolecular forces that create them. We also consider the main bonding model that explains many properties of solids.

Structural Features of Solids

We can divide solids into two broad categories:

- **Crystalline solids** have well defined shapes because their particles—atoms, molecules, or ions—occur in an orderly arrangement (Figure 12.25, *next page*).
- **Amorphous solids** have poorly defined shapes because their particles lack an orderly arrangement throughout the sample.

Figure 12.25 The beauty of crystalline solids. **A,** Wulfanite. **B,** Barite (*left*) on calcite (*right*). **C,** Beryl (emerald). **D,** Quartz (amethyst).

The Crystal Lattice and the Unit Cell The particles in a crystal are packed tightly in an orderly, three-dimensional array. As the simplest case, consider the particles as *identical* spherical atoms, and imagine a point at the center of each. The collection of points forms a regular pattern called the crystal **lattice.** The lattice consists of *all points with identical surroundings;* that is, there is no way to tell if you moved from one lattice point to another.

Figure 12.26A shows a portion of a lattice and the **unit cell,** the *smallest* portion that gives the crystal if it is repeated in all directions. A two-dimensional analogy for a unit cell and the resulting crystal lattice appears in a checkerboard (Figure 12.26B), a section of tiled floor, a strip of wallpaper, or any other pattern that is constructed from a repeating unit.

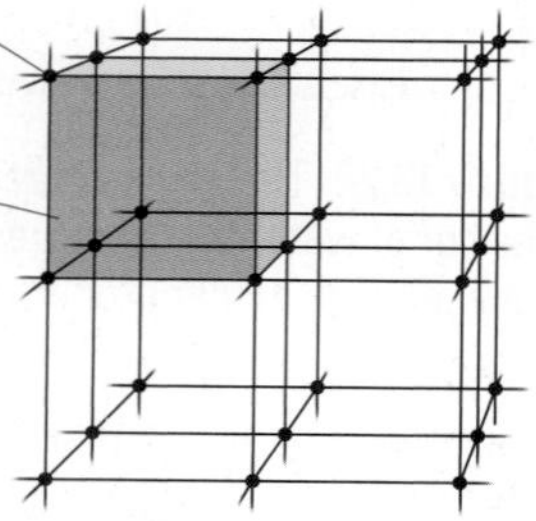

A Portion of 3-D lattice

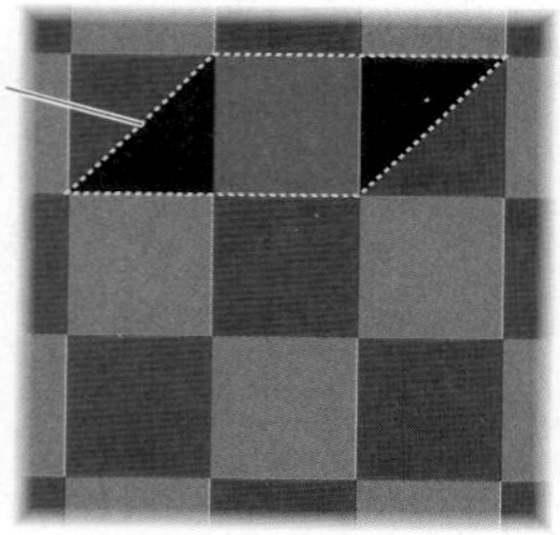

B 2-D analogy for unit cell and lattice

Figure 12.26 The crystal lattice and the unit cell. **A,** A small portion of a lattice is shown as points connected by lines, with a unit cell (*colored*). **B,** A checkerboard analogy for a lattice.

There are 7 crystal systems and 14 types of unit cells that occur in nature, but we will be concerned primarily with the *cubic system*. The solid states of a majority of metallic elements, some covalent compounds, and many ionic compounds occur as cubic lattices. A key parameter of any lattice is the **coordination number**, the number of *nearest* neighbors of a particle. There are three types of cubic unit cells within the cubic system:

1. In the **simple cubic unit cell** (Figure 12.27A), the centers of eight identical particles define the corners of a cube (shown in the expanded view, *top row*). The particles touch along the cube edges (see the space-filling view, *second row*), but they do not touch diagonally along the cube faces or through its center. An expanded portion of the crystal (*third row*) shows that the coordination number of each particle is 6: four in its own layer, one in the layer above, and one in the layer below.
2. In the **body-centered cubic unit cell** (Figure 12.27B), identical particles lie at each corner *and* in the center of the cube. Those at the corners do not touch each other, but they all touch the one in the center. Each particle is surrounded by eight nearest neighbors, four above and four below, so the coordination number is 8.
3. In the **face-centered cubic unit cell** (Figure 12.27C), identical particles lie at each corner *and* in the center of each face but not in the center of the cube. Particles at the corners touch those in the faces but not each other. The coordination number is 12.

How many particles make up a unit cell? For particles of the same size, *the higher the coordination number is, the greater the number of particles in a given volume.* Since one unit cell touches another, with no gaps, a particle at a corner or face is *shared* by adjacent cells. In the cubic unit cells, the particle at each corner is part of eight adjacent cells (Figure 12.27, *third row*), so one-eighth of each particle belongs to each cell (*bottom row*). There are eight corners in a cube, so

- A simple cubic unit cell contains $8 \times \frac{1}{8}$ particle $= 1$ particle.
- A body-centered cubic unit cell contains $8 \times \frac{1}{8}$ particle $= 1$ particle plus 1 particle in the center, for a total of 2 particles.
- A face-centered cubic unit cell contains $8 \times \frac{1}{8}$ particle $= 1$ particle plus one-half particle in each of the six faces, or $6 \times \frac{1}{2}$ particle $= 3$ particles, for a total of 4 particles.

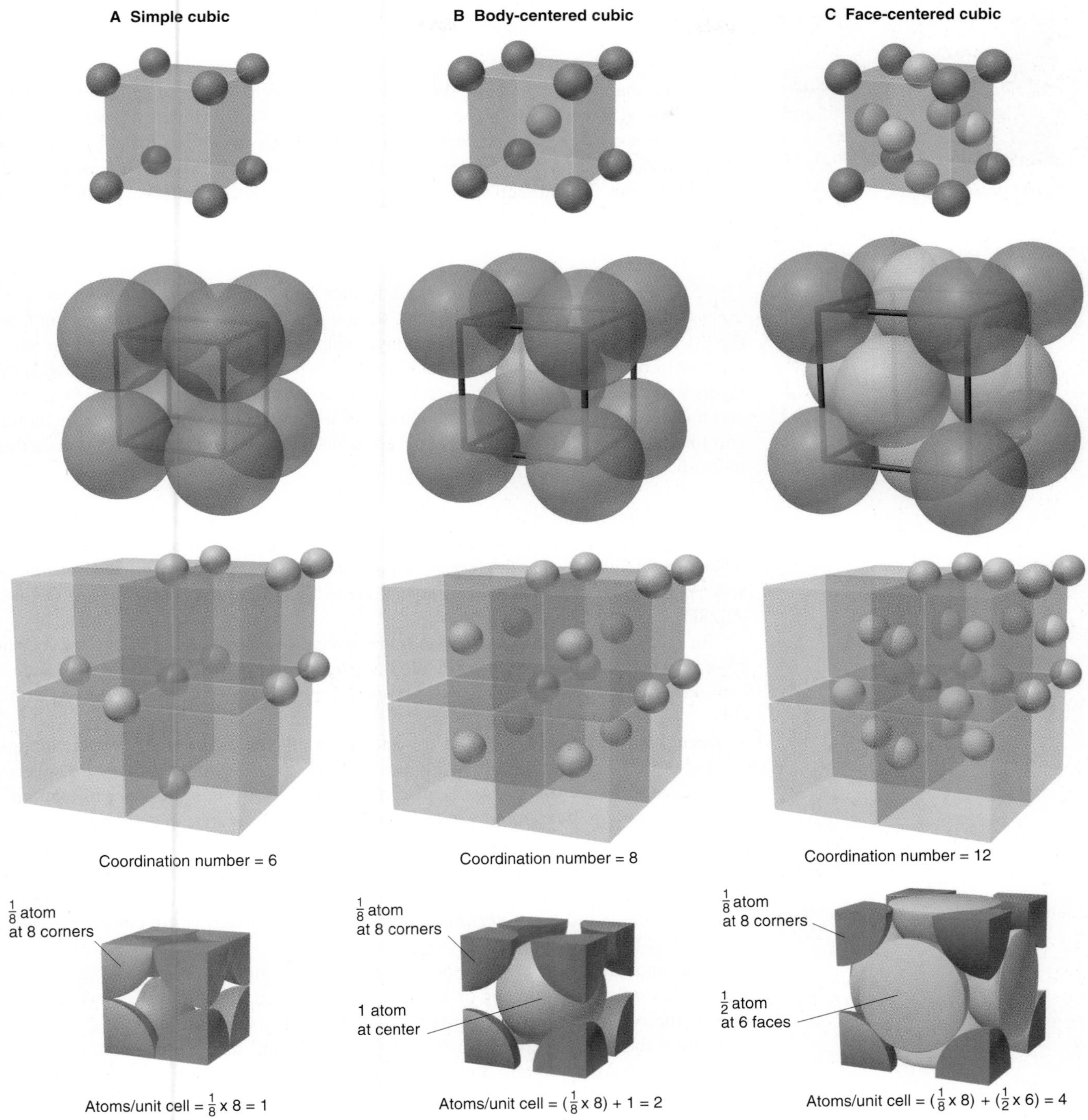

Figure 12.27 The three cubic unit cells. **A,** Simple cubic unit cell. **B,** Body-centered cubic unit cell. **C,** Face-centered cubic unit cell. *Top row:* Cubic arrangements of atoms in expanded view. *Second row:* Space-filling view of these cubic arrangements. All atoms are identical but, for clarity, corner atoms are blue, body-centered atoms pink, and face-centered atoms yellow. *Third row:* A unit cell (*shaded blue*) in an expanded portion of the crystal. The number of nearest neighbors around one particle (*dark blue in center*) is the coordination number. *Bottom row:* The total numbers of atoms in the actual unit cell. The simple cubic has one atom, the body-centered has two, and the face-centered has four.

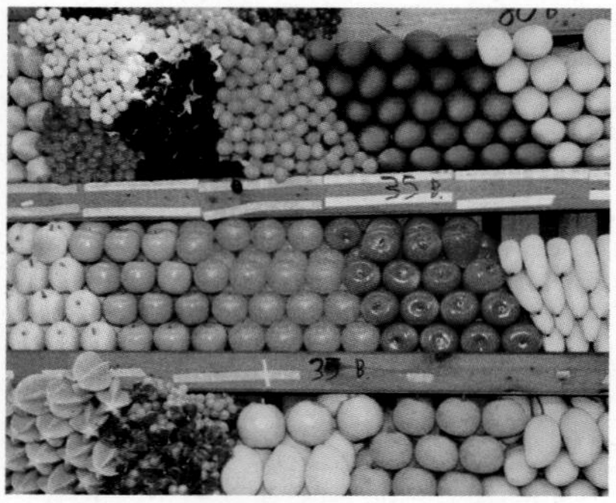

The efficient packing of fruit.

Packing Efficiency and the Creation of Unit Cells Unit cells result from the ways atoms pack together, which are similar to the ways that macroscopic spheres—marbles, golf balls, fruit—are packed (*see photo*). Let's pack *identical* spheres to create the three cubic unit cells and the hexagonal unit cell and determine the **packing efficiency,** the percentage of the total volume occupied by the spheres themselves:

1. *The simple cubic unit cell.* When we arrange the first layer of spheres in vertical and horizontal rows, large diamond-shaped spaces are formed (Figure 12.28A, *cutaway portion*). If we place the next layer of spheres *directly above* the first, we obtain an arrangement based on the *simple* cubic unit cell (Figure 12.28B). The spheres occupy only 52% of the unit-cell volume, so 48% is empty space between them. This is a very inefficient way to pack spheres, so neither fruit nor atoms are typically packed this way.

2. *The body-centered cubic unit cell.* Rather than placing the second layer (colored *green* for clarity) directly above the first, we use space more efficiently by placing it on the diamond-shaped spaces in the first layer (Figure 12.28C). Then we pack the third layer onto the diamond-shaped spaces in the second, which makes the first and third layers line up vertically. This arrangement is based on the *body-centered* cubic unit cell, and its packing efficiency is much higher at 68%. Several metallic elements, including chromium, iron, and all the Group 1A(1) elements, have a crystal structure based on this unit cell.

3. *The hexagonal and face-centered cubic unit cells.* Spheres are packed most efficiently in these cells. First, in the bottom layer (labeled *a*, *orange*), we shift every other row laterally so that the large diamond-shaped spaces become smaller triangular spaces. Then we place the second layer (labeled *b*, *green*) over these spaces (Figure 12.28D).

In layer *b*, notice that some spaces are orange because they lie above *spheres* in layer *a*, whereas other spaces are white because they lie above *spaces* in layer *a*. We can place the third layer in either of two ways, which gives rise to two different unit cells:

- *Hexagonal unit cell.* If we place the third layer of spheres (*orange*) over the orange spaces (look down and left to Figure 12.28E), they lie directly over the spheres in layer *a*. Every other layer is placed identically (an *abab. . .* layering pattern), and we obtain **hexagonal closest packing,** which is based on the *hexagonal* unit cell.
- *Face-centered unit cell.* If we place the third layer of spheres (*blue*) over the white spaces in layer *b* (look down and right to Figure 12.28F), the placement is different from layers *a* and *b* (an *abcabc. . .* pattern) and we obtain **cubic closest packing,** which is based on the *face-centered cubic* unit cell.

The packing efficiency of both hexagonal and cubic closest packing is 74%, and the coordination number of both is 12. Most metallic elements crystallize in one or the other of these arrangements. Magnesium, titanium, and zinc are some that adopt the hexagonal structure; nickel, copper, and lead adopt the cubic structure, as do many ionic compounds and other substances, such as CO_2, CH_4, and most noble gases.

In Sample Problem 12.5, we use density and our knowledge of unit cells to find an atomic radius.

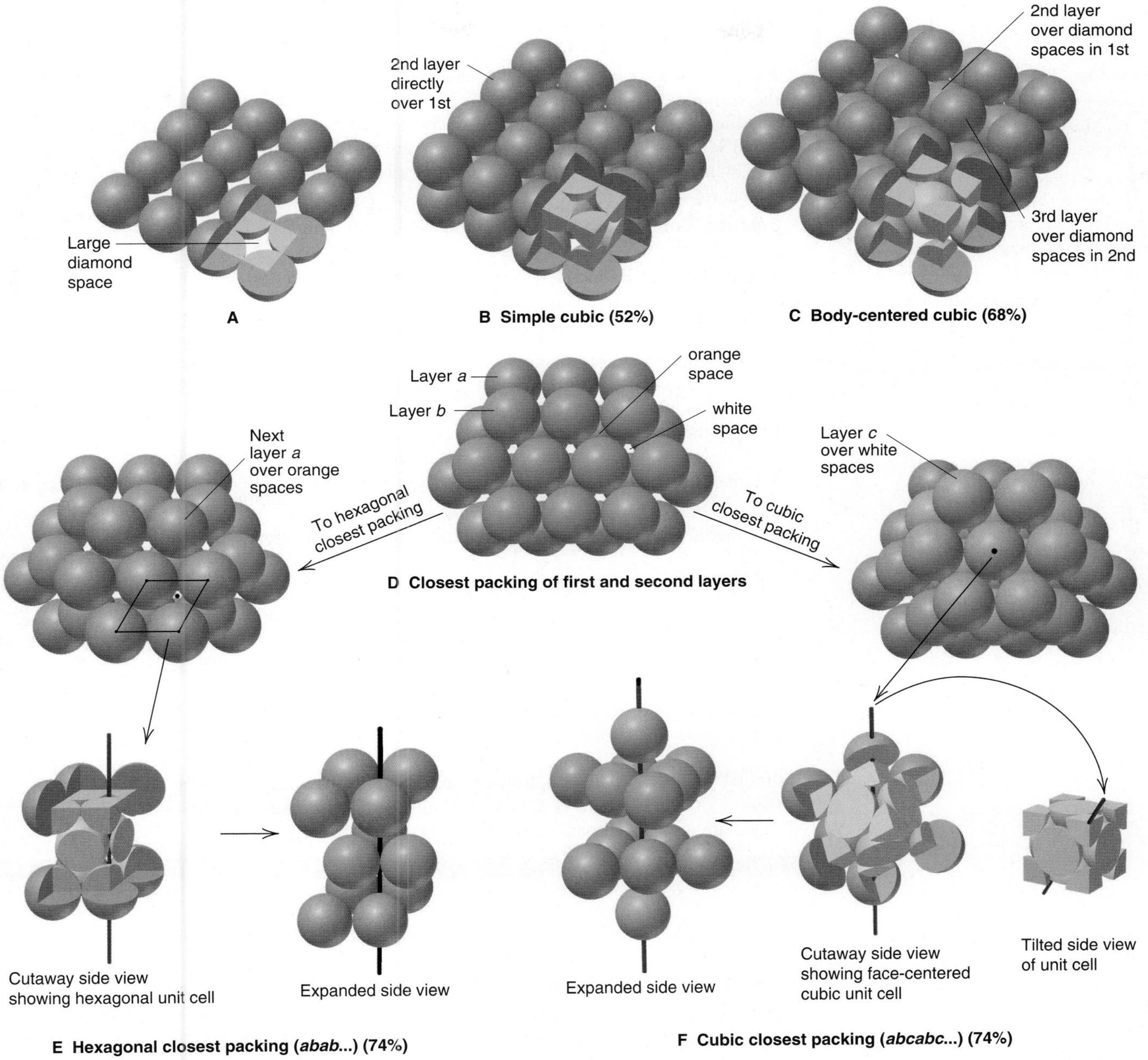

Figure 12.28 **Packing spheres to obtain three cubic and hexagonal unit cells.** **A,** In the first layer, each sphere lies next to another horizontally and vertically; note the large diamond-shaped spaces (*see cutaway*). **B,** If the spheres in the next layer lie directly over those in the first, the packing is based on the simple cubic unit cell (*pale orange cube, lower right corner*). **C,** If the spheres in the next layer lie in the diamond-shaped spaces of the first layer, the packing is based on the *body-centered cubic* unit cell (*lower right corner*). **D,** The closest possible packing of the first layer (*layer a, orange*) is obtained by shifting every other row in part A to obtain smaller triangular spaces. The spheres of the second layer (*layer b, green*) are placed above these spaces; note the orange and white spaces that result. **E,** When the third layer (*next layer a, orange*) is placed over the orange spaces, we obtain an *abab. . .* pattern and the hexagonal unit cell. **F,** When the third layer (*layer c, blue*) covers the white spaces, we get an *abcabc. . .* pattern and the face-centered cubic unit cell.

Road Map

Density (g/cm^3) of Ba metal

↓ find reciprocal and multiply by $\mathcal{M}$ (g/mol)

Volume (cm^3) per mole of Ba metal

↓ multiply by packing efficiency

Volume (cm^3) per mole of Ba atoms

↓ divide by Avogadro's number

Volume (cm^3) of Ba atom

↓ $V = \frac{4}{3}\pi r^3$

Radius (cm) of Ba atom

Sample Problem 12.5 Determining Atomic Radius

Problem Barium is the largest nonradioactive alkaline earth metal. It has a body-centered cubic unit cell and a density of 3.62 g/cm^3. What is the atomic radius of barium? (Volume of a sphere: $V = \frac{4}{3}\pi r^3$.)

Plan An atom is spherical, so we can find its radius from its volume. If we multiply the reciprocal of density (volume/mass) by the molar mass (mass/mole), we find the volume/mole of Ba metal. The metal crystallizes in the body-centered cubic structure, so 68% of this volume is occupied by 1 mol of the Ba atoms themselves (see Figure 12.28C). Dividing by Avogadro's number gives the volume of one Ba atom, from which we find the radius.

Solution Combining steps to find the volume of 1 mol of Ba metal:

$$\text{Volume/mole of Ba metal} = \frac{1}{\text{density}} \times \mathcal{M} = \frac{1\ \text{cm}^3}{3.62\ \text{g Ba}} \times \frac{137.3\ \text{g Ba}}{1\ \text{mol Ba}} = 37.9\ \text{cm}^3/\text{mol Ba}$$

Finding the volume (cm^3) of 1 mol of Ba *atoms:*

$$\text{Volume/mole of Ba atoms} = \text{cm}^3/\text{mol Ba} \times \text{packing efficiency}$$
$$= 37.9\ \text{cm}^3/\text{mol Ba} \times 0.68 = 26\ \text{cm}^3/\text{mol Ba atoms}$$

Finding the volume of one Ba atom:

$$\text{Volume of Ba atom} = \frac{26\ \text{cm}^3}{1\ \text{mol Ba atoms}} \times \frac{1\ \text{mol Ba atoms}}{6.022\times10^{23}\ \text{Ba atoms}} = 4.3\times10^{-23}\ \text{cm}^3/\text{Ba atom}$$

Finding the atomic radius of Ba from the volume of a sphere:

$$V \text{ of Ba atom} = \tfrac{4}{3}\pi r^3 \qquad \text{so} \qquad r^3 = \frac{3V}{4\pi}$$

Thus,

$$r = \sqrt[3]{\frac{3V}{4\pi}} = \sqrt[3]{\frac{3(4.3\times10^{-23}\ \text{cm}^3)}{4 \times 3.14}} = 2.2\times10^{-8}\ \text{cm}$$

Check The order of magnitude is correct for an atom ($\sim10^{-8}$ cm $\approx 10^{-10}$ m). The actual value for barium is, in fact, 2.22×10^{-8} cm (see Figure 8.9).

Follow-Up Problem 12.5 Iron crystallizes in a body-centered cubic structure. The volume of one Fe atom is 8.38×10^{-24} cm^3, and the density of Fe is 7.874 g/cm^3. Calculate an approximate value for Avogadro's number.

Our understanding of crystal structures comes from our ability to "see" them. Two techniques for doing this are described in Tools of the Laboratory.

The edge length of the unit cell is obtained from x-ray crystallography. We can then apply the Pythagorean theorem and some arithmetic to find atomic (or ionic) radii in the three cubic unit cells (Figure 12.29). Sample Problem 12.6 shows this approach.

Figure 12.29 Edge length and atomic (ionic) radius in the three cubic unit cells.

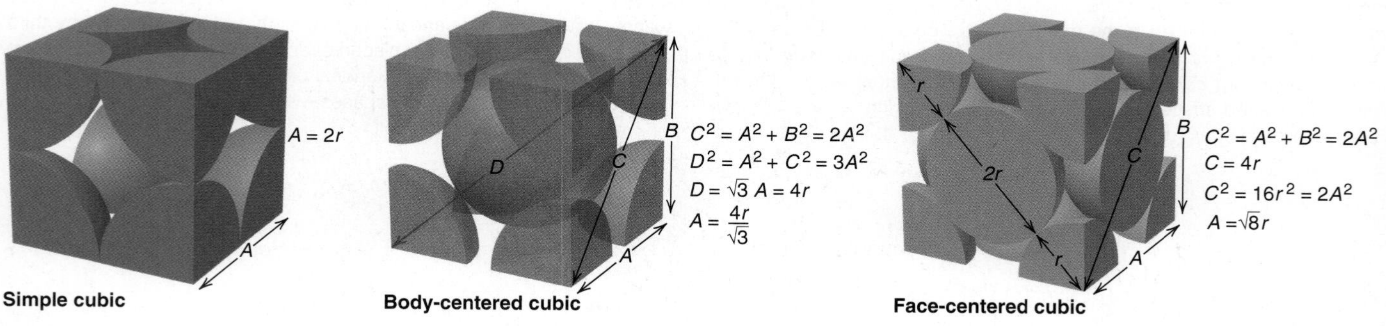

TOOLS OF THE LABORATORY | X-Ray Diffraction Analysis and Scanning Tunneling Microscopy

Various tools exist for measuring atomic-scale dimensions, and two of the most powerful are **x-ray diffraction analysis** and **scanning tunneling microscopy.**

X-Ray Diffraction Analysis

In Chapter 7, we saw how diffraction patterns of bright and dark regions appear when light passes through slits spaced as far apart as the wavelength (see Figure 7.5, p. 265). X-ray wavelengths are about the same size as the spaces between layers of spheres in a crystal, so we use the spaces as "slits" to diffract x-rays.

As one example, let's use this approach to measure the distance (d) between two adjacent layers of atoms in a simplified lattice (Figure B12.1). Two waves impinge on the crystal at an angle θ and are diffracted at that angle by the layers. When the first wave strikes the top layer and the second strikes the next layer, they are *in phase* (peaks aligned with peaks and troughs with troughs). If they are still in phase after being diffracted, they form a spot on a photographic plate. This will occur only if the additional distance traveled by the second wave ($DE + EF$ in the figure) is a whole number of wavelengths, $n\lambda$, where n is a positive integer referred to as the *order* of the diffraction. From trigonometry, we find that

$$n\lambda = 2d \sin \theta$$

where θ is the angle of incoming light and d, the unknown, is the distance between layers. This is the *Bragg equation,* named for W. H. Bragg and his son W. L. Bragg, who shared the Nobel Prize in physics in 1915 for their work on crystal structure analysis.

Rotating the crystal changes θ and produces different sets of spots. Eventually, the complete diffraction pattern reveals distances and angles in the lattice (Figure B12.2). X-ray diffraction analysis is used in many studies, but its greatest recent impact is uncovering the structures of DNA and proteins.

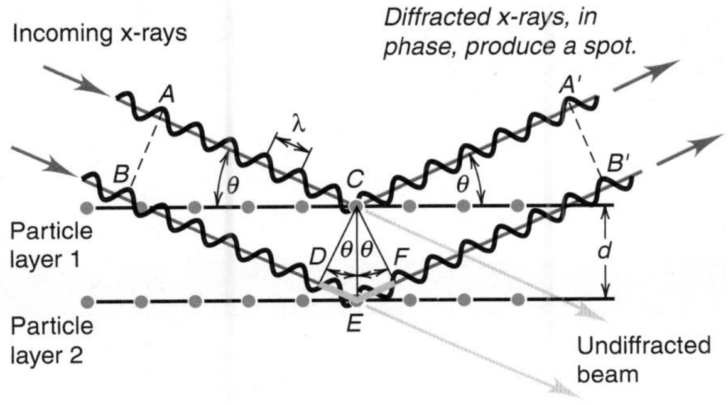

Figure B12.1 Diffraction of x-rays by crystal planes.

Scanning Tunneling Microscopy

This technique, invented by Gerd Binnig and Heinrich Rohrer, who won the Nobel Prize in physics in 1986, is used to observe surfaces. It is based on the idea that an electron has a small, but finite, probability of being so far from its nucleus that it can move ("tunnel") closer to another atom.

In practice, an extremely sharp tungsten-tipped probe, the source of the tunneling electrons, is placed very close (about

(continued)

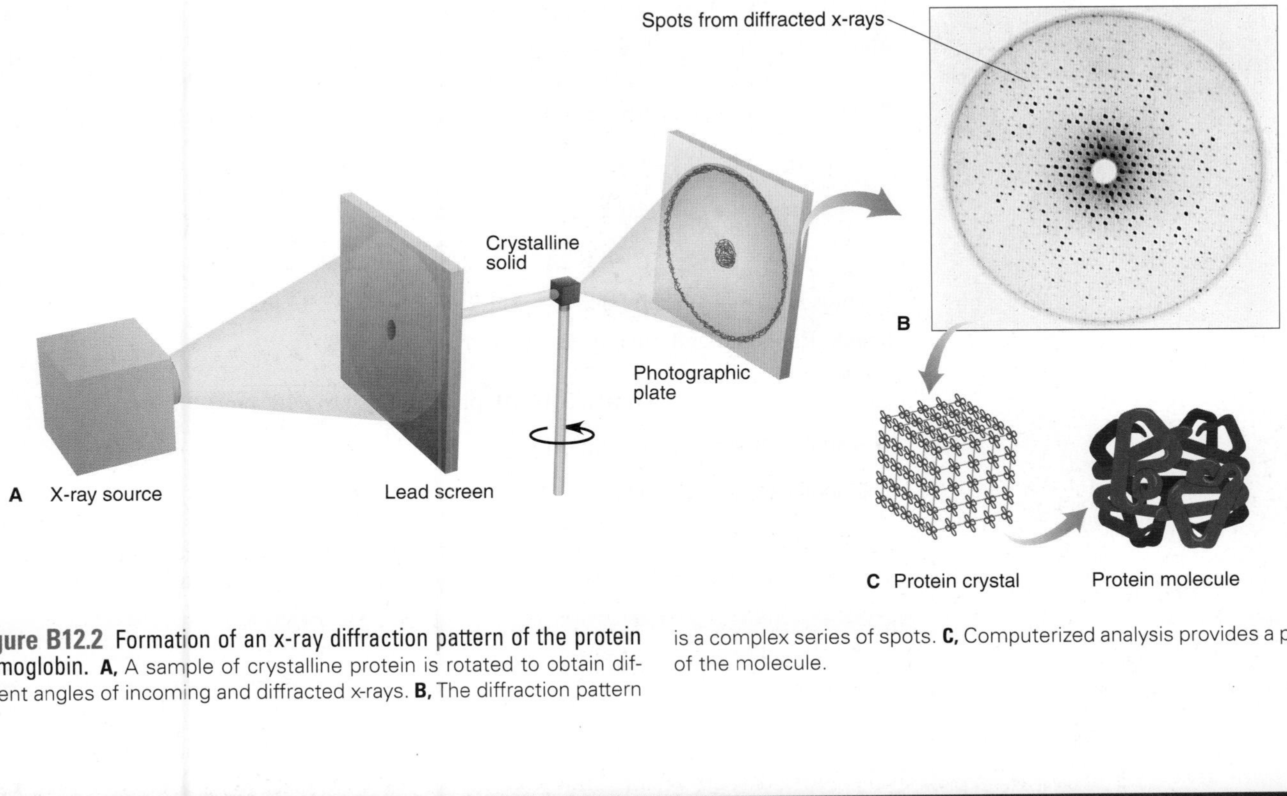

Figure B12.2 Formation of an x-ray diffraction pattern of the protein hemoglobin. **A,** A sample of crystalline protein is rotated to obtain different angles of incoming and diffracted x-rays. **B,** The diffraction pattern is a complex series of spots. **C,** Computerized analysis provides a picture of the molecule.

0.5 nm) to the surface under study. A small applied electric potential increases the probability that the electrons will tunnel across this minute gap. The probe moves tiny distances up and down to maintain the constant current across the gap, thus following the surface at the atomic scale. This movement is monitored electronically, and after many scans, a three-dimensional map of the surface is obtained. The method has revealed images of atoms and molecules coated on surfaces and is being used to study the nature of defects and many other surface features (Figure B12.3).

Figure B12.3 A scanning tunneling micrograph of cesium atoms (*red*) on gallium arsenide.

Problems

B12.1 X-rays of wavelength $\lambda = 0.709\times10^{-10}$ m undergo a first-order ($n = 1$) diffraction of 11.6° when aimed at crystalline nickel. What is the spacing between layers of Ni atoms?

B12.2 A first-order ($n = 1$) diffraction of x-rays aimed at a crystal of NaCl occurs at 15.9°.
(a) What is the wavelength (in pm) of the x-rays?
(b) At what angle would a second-order ($n = 2$) diffraction appear?

Sample Problem 12.6 Determining Atomic Radius from the Unit Cell

Problem Copper adopts cubic closest packing, and the edge length of the unit cell is 361.5 pm. What is the atomic radius of copper?

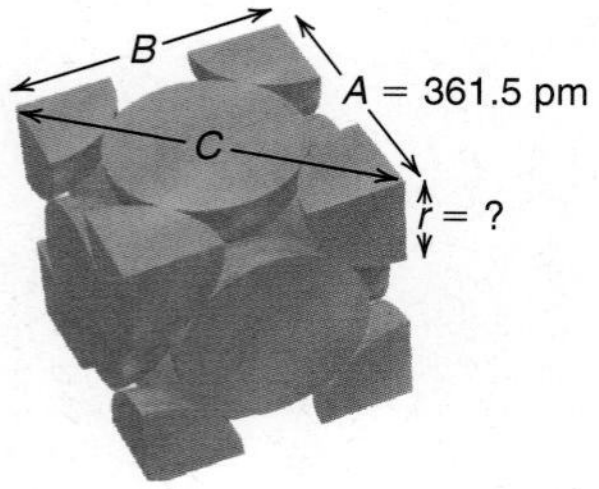

Plan Cubic closest packing has a face-centered cubic unit cell, and we know the edge length. With Figure 12.29 and $A = 361.5$ pm, we solve for r (*see margin*).

Solution Using the Pythagorean theorem to find C, the diagonal of the cell's face:

$$C = \sqrt{A^2 + B^2}$$

The unit cell is a cube, so $A = B$. Therefore,

$$C = \sqrt{2A^2} = \sqrt{2(361.5\text{ pm})^2} = 511.2\text{ pm}$$

Finding r: $C = 4r$. Therefore, $r = 511.2\text{ pm}/4 = 127.8\text{ pm.}$

Check Rounding and quickly checking the math gives

$$C = \sqrt{2(4\times10^2\text{ pm})^2} = \sqrt{2(16\times10^4\text{ pm}^2)}$$

or ~500–600 pm; thus, $r \approx$ 125–150 pm.

The actual value for copper is 128 pm (see Figure 8.15, p. 311).

Follow-Up Problem 12.6 Iron crystallizes in a body-centered cubic structure. If the atomic radius of Fe is 126 pm, find the edge length (in nm) of the unit cell.

Types and Properties of Crystalline Solids

The five most important types of solids are defined by the type(s) of particle(s) in the crystal (Table 12.5). We'll highlight interparticle forces and physical properties.

Atomic Solids Individual atoms held together only by *dispersion forces* form an **atomic solid,** and the noble gases [Group 8A(18)] are the only substances that form such solids. The very weak forces among the atoms mean melting and boiling points and heats of vaporization and fusion are all very low, rising smoothly with increasing molar mass. Argon crystallizes in a cubic closest packed structure (Figure 12.30), as do the other noble gases.

Figure 12.30 Cubic closest packing of frozen argon (face-centered cubic unit cell).

Molecular Solids In the many thousands of **molecular solids,** individual molecules occupy the lattice points. Various combinations of dipole-dipole, dispersion, and H-bonding forces account for a wide range of physical properties. Dispersion forces in nonpolar substances lead to melting points that generally increase with molar mass (Table 12.5). Among polar molecules, dipole-dipole forces and, where possible, H bonding occur. Most molecular solids have much higher melting points than atomic solids (noble gases) but much lower melting points than other types of solids. Methane crystallizes in a face-centered cubic structure with the center of each carbon as the lattice point (Figure 12.31).

Figure 12.31 Cubic closest packing (face-centered unit cell) of frozen CH_4.

Ionic Solids To maximize attractions in a binary **ionic solid,** cations are surrounded by as many anions as possible, and vice versa, with *the smaller of the ions (usually the cation) lying in the spaces (holes) formed by the packing of the larger (usually the anion).* The unit cell is the smallest portion that maintains the composition; that is, *the unit cell has the same cation/anion ratio as the empirical formula.*

Table 12.5 Characteristics of the Major Types of Crystalline Solids

Type	Particle(s)	Interparticle Forces	Physical Properties	Examples [mp, °C]
Atomic	Atoms	Dispersion	Soft, very low mp, poor thermal and electrical conductors	Group 8A(18) (Ne [−249] to Rn [−71])
Molecular	Molecules	Dispersion, dipole-dipole, H bonds	Fairly soft, low to moderate mp, poor thermal and electrical conductors	*Nonpolar** O_2 [−219], C_4H_{10} [−138] Cl_2 [−101], C_6H_{14} [−95], P_4 [44.1] *Polar* SO_2 [−73], $CHCl_3$ [−64], HNO_3 [−42], H_2O [0.0], CH_3COOH [17]
Ionic	Positive and negative ions	Ion-ion attraction	Hard and brittle, high mp, good thermal and electrical conductors when molten	NaCl [801] CaF_2 [1423] MgO [2852]
Metallic	Atoms	Metallic bond	Soft to hard, low to very high mp, excellent thermal and electrical conductors, malleable and ductile	Na [97.8] Zn [420] Fe [1535]
Network covalent	Atoms	Covalent bond	Very hard, very high mp, usually poor thermal and electrical conductors	SiO_2 (quartz) [1610] C (diamond) [~4000]

*Nonpolar molecular solids are arranged in order of increasing molar mass. Note the correlation with increasing melting point (mp).

As a result of cation-anion contact, the interparticle forces (ionic bonds) are *much* stronger than the van der Waals forces in atomic or molecular solids. The properties of ionic solids are a direct consequence of the *fixed ion positions* and *very strong attractive forces,* which create a high lattice energy. Thus, ionic solids typically have high melting points and low electrical conductivities. When a large quantity of heat is supplied and the ions gain enough kinetic energy to break free of their positions, the solid melts and the mobile ions conduct a current. Ionic compounds are hard because only a strong external force can change the relative positions of the huge number of ions attracting one another. If enough force *is* applied to move them, ions of like charge are brought near each other, and their repulsions crack the crystal (see Figure 9.8, p. 336).

Ionic solids often adopt cubic closest packed crystal structures. We'll describe two examples with a 1/1 ratio of ions and then two with a 2/1 (or 1/2) ratio:

1. The *sodium chloride structure* is found in many ionic compounds, including most alkali [Group 1A(1)] halides and hydrides, alkaline earth [Group 2A(2)] oxides and sulfides, and several transition-metal oxides and sulfides. To visualize this structure, imagine Cl^- anions and Na^+ cations in separate face-centered cubic arrays. Now picture the two arrays penetrating each other, the smaller Na^+ ions ending up in the holes between the larger Cl^- ions (Figure 12.32A). Thus, each Na^+ is surrounded by six Cl^-, and vice versa (coordination number = 6). Figure 12.32B is a space-filling depiction of the unit cell: four Cl^- $[(8 \times \frac{1}{8}) + (6 \times \frac{1}{2}) = 4\ Cl^-]$ and four Na^+ $[(12 \times \frac{1}{4}) + 1$ in the center $= 4\ Na^+]$, give a 1/1 ion ratio.

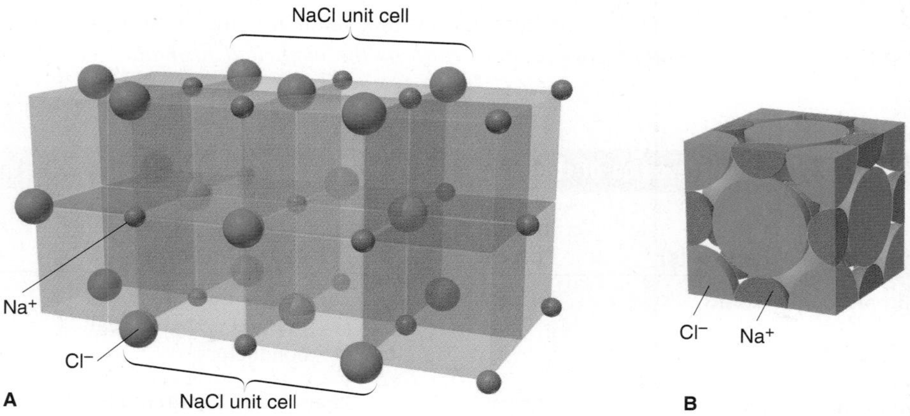

Figure 12.32 The sodium chloride structure. **A,** Expanded view. **B,** Space-filling model of the NaCl unit cell.

2. The *zinc blende (ZnS) structure* can be pictured as two face-centered cubic arrays, one of Zn^{2+} ions (*gray*) and the other of S^{2-} ions (*yellow*), penetrating each other such that each ion is tetrahedrally surrounded by four of the other ions (coordination number = 4) (Figure 12.33). There are four $[(8 \times \frac{1}{8}) + (6 \times \frac{1}{2}) = 4]\ S^{2-}$ ions and four Zn^{2+} ions for a 1/1 ion ratio. Many other compounds, including AgI, CdS, and the copper(I) halides, adopt the zinc blende structure.

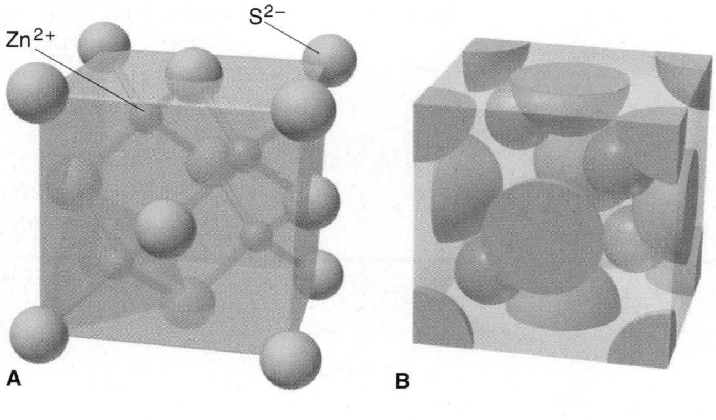

Figure 12.33 The zinc blende structure. **A,** Expanded view (with bonds shown for clarity). **B,** The unit cell is expanded a bit to show interior ions.

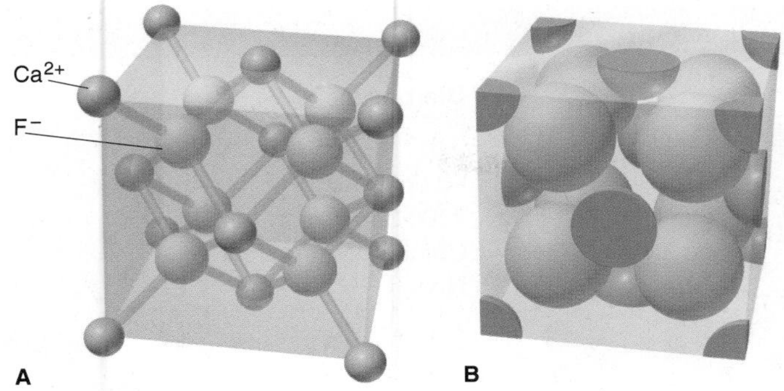

Figure 12.34 The fluorite structure. **A,** Expanded view (with bonds shown for clarity). **B,** The unit cell is expanded a bit to show interior ions.

3. The *fluorite* (CaF_2) *structure* is common among salts with a 1/2 cation/anion ratio that have relatively large cations and small anions, such as SrF_2 and $BaCl_2$. In CaF_2, the unit cell is a face-centered cubic array of Ca^{2+} ions with F^- ions occupying *all* eight available holes (Figure 12.34). This results in a Ca^{2+}/F^- ratio of 4/8, or 1/2.

4. The *antifluorite structure* is common in compounds with a 2/1 cation/anion ratio and a relatively large anion (such as K_2S). The ion arrangment is the opposite of that in the fluorite structure: the cations occupy all eight holes formed by the cubic closest packing of the anions.

Metallic Solids Most metallic elements crystallize in one of the two closest packed structures (Figure 12.35). In contrast to the weak dispersion forces in atomic solids, powerful metallic bonding forces hold atoms together in **metallic solids.** The properties of metals—high electrical and thermal conductivity, luster, and malleability—result from their delocalized electrons (Section 9.6). Melting points and hardnesses are related to the packing efficiency and number of valence electrons. For example, Group 2A metals are harder and melt higher than Group 1A metals (see Figure 9.27, pp. 352–353), because the 2A metals have twice as many delocalized valence electrons.

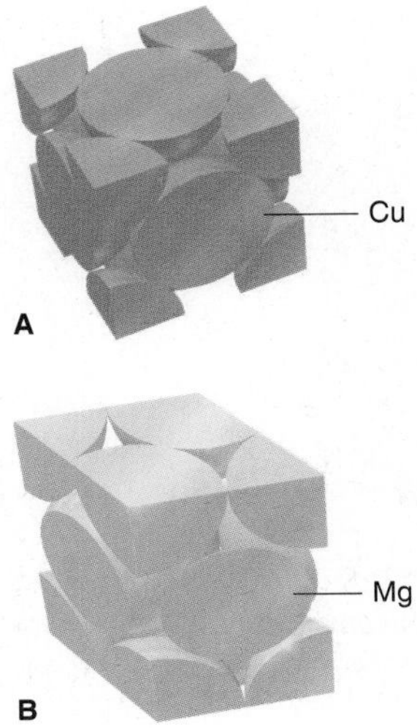

Figure 12.35 Crystal structures of metals. **A,** Copper adopts cubic closest packing. **B,** Magnesium adopts hexagonal closest packing.

Network Covalent Solids Strong covalent bonds link the atoms together in a **network covalent solid;** thus, separate particles are not present. These substances adopt a variety of crystal structures depending on the details of their bonding.

As a consequence of strong bonding, all network covalent solids have extremely high melting and boiling points, but their conductivity and hardness vary. Two examples with the same composition but strikingly different properties are the two common crystalline forms of elemental carbon, graphite and diamond:

- *Graphite* occurs as stacked flat sheets of hexagonal carbon rings with a strong σ-bond framework and delocalized π bonds, reminiscent of benzene; the arrangement looks like chicken wire or honeycomb. Whereas the π-bonding electrons of benzene are delocalized over one ring, those of graphite are delocalized over the entire sheet. Thus, graphite conducts electricity well—it is a common electrode material—but only in the plane of the sheets. The sheets interact via dispersion forces, and impurities, such as O_2, between the sheets allow them to slide past each other, which explains why graphite is soft and used as a lubricant.
- *Diamond* adopts a face-centered cubic unit cell, with each C tetrahedrally bonded to four others in an endless array. Throughout the crystal, strong single bonds make diamond the hardest natural substance known. Like most network covalent solids, diamond does not conduct electricity because the bonding electrons are localized.

These properties are compared in Table 12.6 on the next page.

The most important network covalent solids are the *silicates,* which consist of extended arrays of covalently bonded silicon and oxygen atoms. Quartz (SiO_2) is a common example. We'll discuss silicates, which form the structure of clays, rocks, and many minerals, when we consider the chemistry of silicon in Chapter 14.

Table 12.6 Comparison of the Properties of Diamond and Graphite

Property	Graphite	Diamond
Density (g/cm^3)	2.27	3.51
Hardness	<1 (very soft)	10 (hardest)
Melting point (K)	4100	4100
Color	Shiny black	Colorless transparent
Electrical conductivity	High (along sheet)	None
ΔH°_{rxn} for combustion (kJ/mol)	−393.5	−395.4
ΔH°_f (kJ/mol)	0 (standard state)	1.90

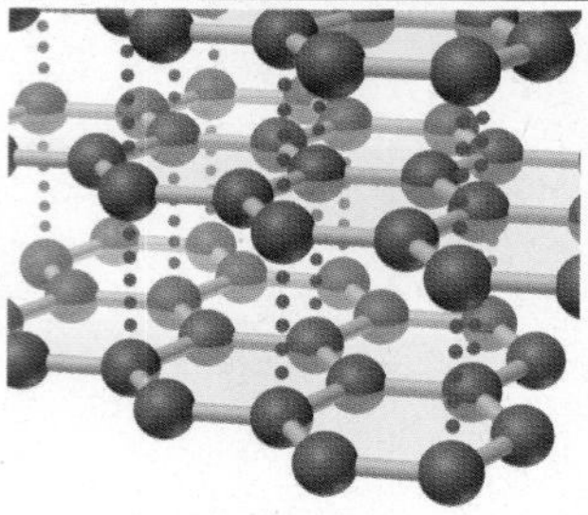

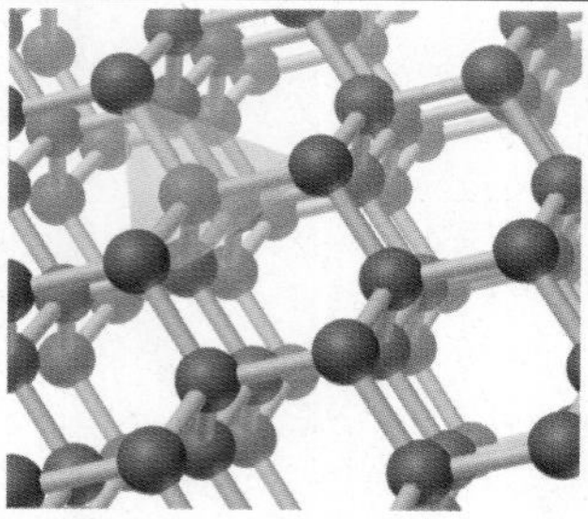

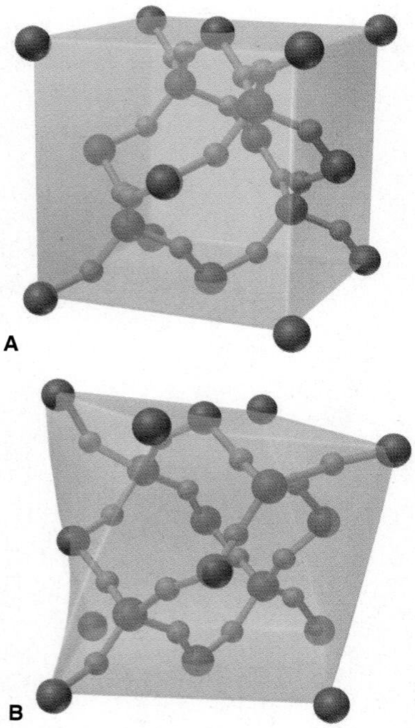

Figure 12.36 **Crystalline and amorphous silicon dioxide.** **A,** Cristobalite, a crystalline form of silica (SiO_2), shows cubic closest packing. **B,** Quartz glass is amorphous with a generally disordered structure.

Amorphous Solids

Amorphous solids are noncrystalline. Many have small, somewhat ordered regions interspersed among large disordered regions. Charcoal, rubber, and glass are examples.

The process that forms quartz glass is typical of many amorphous solids. Crystalline quartz (SiO_2), which adopts cubic closest packing, is melted and the viscous liquid is cooled rapidly to prevent it from recrystallizing. The chains of Si and O atoms cannot orient themselves quickly enough, so they solidify in a distorted jumble containing gaps and misaligned rows (Figure 12.36). The absence of regularity confers some properties of a liquid; in fact, glasses are sometimes referred to as *supercooled liquids.*

Bonding in Solids: Molecular Orbital Band Theory

Chapter 9 introduced a qualitative model of metallic bonding, with metal ions submerged in a "sea" of mobile, delocalized valence electrons. Molecular orbital (MO) theory offers a more quantitative, and therefore more useful, model called **band theory.** We'll focus on bonding in metals and the conductivity of metals, metalloids, and nonmetals.

Formation of Valence and Conduction Bands Recall from Section 11.3 that when two atoms form a diatomic molecule, their atomic orbitals (AOs) combine to form an equal number of molecular orbitals (MOs). Figure 12.37 shows the formation of MOs in lithium. To form Li_2, each Li atom has four valence orbitals (one 2*s* and three

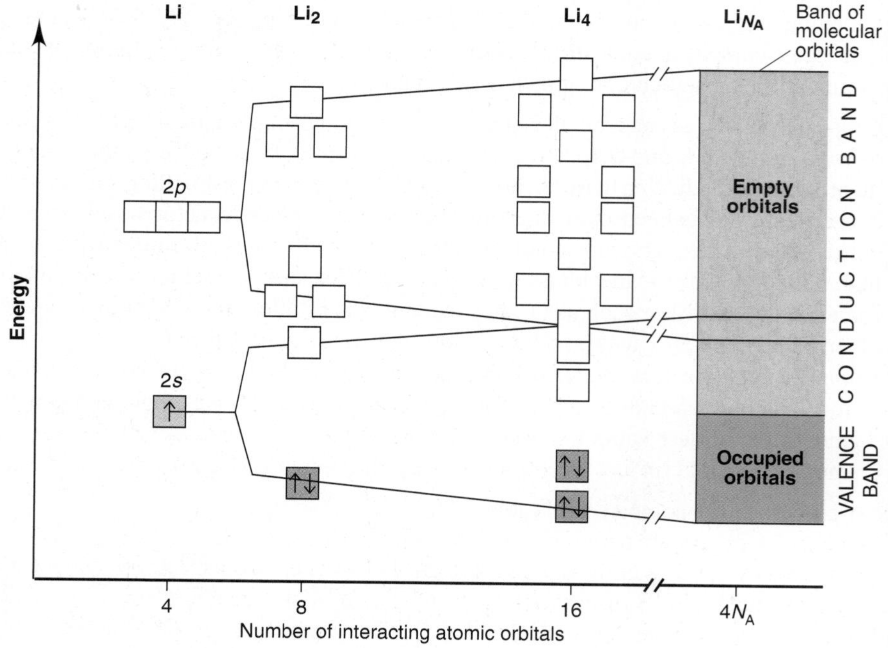

Figure 12.37 The band of molecular orbitals in lithium metal.

2*p*) that combine to form eight MOs, four bonding and four antibonding. The order of MOs shows 2*s*-2*p* mixing (Figure 11.21B, p. 409). Two more Li atoms form Li_4, a slightly larger aggregate, with 16 delocalized MOs. As more Li atoms join the cluster, more MOs are created, and their energy levels lie closer and closer together. Extending this process to 7 g (1 mol) of lithium results in 6×10^{23} Li atoms (Li_{N_A}) combining to form an extremely large number (4 × Avogadro's number) of delocalized MOs. *The energies of the MOs are so close that they form a continuum, or band, of MOs.*

The lower energy MOs are occupied by the $2s^1$ valence electrons and make up the **valence band.** The empty MOs that are higher in energy make up the **conduction band.** In Li metal, the valence band is derived from the 2*s* AOs, and the conduction band is derived from 2*s* and mostly 2*p* AOs. In Li_2, two valence electrons fill the lowest energy bonding MO and leave the antibonding MO empty. In Li metal, 1 mol of valence electrons fills the valence band and leaves the conduction band empty.

How Band Theory Explains Metallic Properties The key to understanding the properties of metals is that *the valence and conduction bands are contiguous,* that is, the highest level of one touches the lowest of the other. This means that, given an infinitesimal quantity of energy, electrons jump from the filled valence band to the unfilled conduction band: the electrons are completely delocalized.

- *Electrical conductivity.* Metals conduct so well because an applied field easily excites the highest energy valence electrons into empty conduction orbitals, allowing them to move through the sample.
- *Luster.* With so many closely spaced levels available, electrons absorb and release photons of many frequencies as they move between the valence and conduction bands.
- *Malleability.* Under an applied force, layers of positive metal ions move past each other, always protected from mutual repulsions by the delocalized electrons.
- *Thermal conductivity.* When a metal wire is heated, the highest energy electrons are excited and their extra energy is transferred as kinetic energy along the wire's length.

Conductivity of Solids and the Size of the Energy Gap Like metal atoms, large numbers of nonmetal and metalloid atoms can form bands of MOs. Band theory explains differences in electrical conductivity and the effect of temperature among these three classes of substances in terms of the presence of an energy gap between their valence and conduction bands (Figure 12.38):

1. *Conductors (metals).* The valence and conduction bands of a **conductor** have *no energy gap* between them, so electrons flow when a tiny electrical potential difference is applied. When the temperature is raised, greater random motion of the atoms hinders electron movement: conductivity *decreases* when a metal is heated.
2. *Semiconductors (metalloids).* In a **semiconductor,** a *small energy gap* exists between the valence and conduction bands. Thermally excited electrons can cross the gap, allowing a small current to flow: in contrast to a conductor, conductivity *increases* when a semiconductor is heated.
3. *Insulators (nonmetals).* In an **insulator,** a *large energy gap* exists between the bands: no current is observed even when the substance is heated.

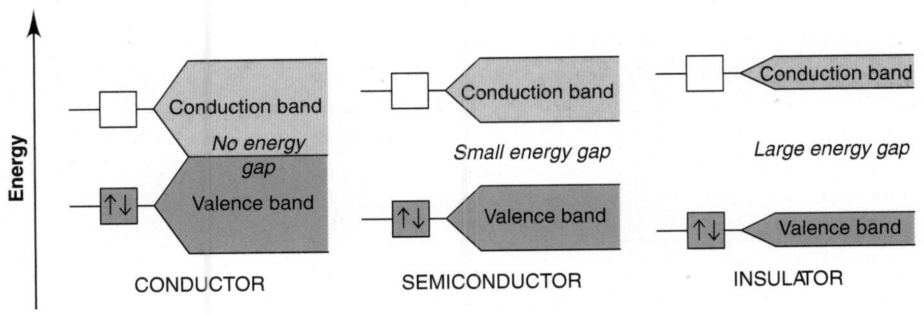

Figure 12.38 Electrical conductivity in a conductor, semiconductor, and insulator.

Another type of electrical conductivity, called **superconductivity,** has been the focus of intensive research for the past few decades. When metals conduct at ordinary temperatures, moving electrons collide with vibrating atoms; the reduction in their flow appears as resistive heating and represents a loss of energy.

For many years, to conduct with no energy loss—to superconduct—required minimizing atom movement by cooling with liquid helium (bp = 4 K; price ≈ \$11/L). Then, in 1986, certain ionic oxides that superconduct near the boiling point of liquid nitrogen (bp = 77 K; price = \$0.20/L) were prepared. Like metal conductors, oxide superconductors, such as $YBa_2Cu_3O_7$, have no gap between bands. In 1989, oxides with Bi and Tl instead of Y and Ba were synthesized and found to superconduct at 125 K; and in 1993, an oxide with Hg, Ba, and Ca, in addition to Cu and O, superconducted at 133 K. Such materials could transmit electricity with no loss of energy, allowing power plants to be located far from cities. They could be part of ultrasmall microchips for ultrafast computers, electromagnets to levitate superfast trains, and inexpensive medical diagnostic equipment with superb image clarity. However, the oxides are brittle and not easy to machine, and when warmed, the superconductivity may disappear and not return on cooling. Addressing these and related problems will involve chemists, physicists, and engineers for many years.

Summary of Section 12.6

- Particles in crystalline solids lie at points that form a structure of repeating unit cells.
- The three types of unit cells of the cubic system are simple, body-centered, and face-centered. The highest packing efficiency occurs with cubic (face-centered) and hexagonal closest packing.
- Bond angles and distances in a crystal are determined with x-ray diffraction analysis and scanning tunneling microscopy. These data are used to determine atomic radii.
- Atomic [Group 8A(18)] solids adopt cubic closest packing, with atoms held together by weak dispersion forces.
- Molecular solids have molecules at the lattice points and often adopt cubic closest packing. Combinations of intermolecular forces (dispersion, dipole-dipole, and H bonding) result in physical properties that vary greatly.
- Ionic solids crystallize with one ion filling holes in the cubic closest packed array of the other. High melting points, hardness, and low conductivity arise from strong ionic attractions.
- Most metals have a closest packed structure. Their physical properties result from the high packing efficiency and the presence of delocalized electrons.
- Atoms of network covalent solids are covalently bonded throughout the sample, so these substances have very high melting and boiling points.
- Amorphous solids have little regularity in their structure.
- Band theory proposes that atomic orbitals of many atoms combine to form a continuum, or band, of molecular orbitals. Metals are electrical conductors because electrons move freely from the filled (valence) band to the empty (conduction) band. Insulators have a large energy gap between the two portions, and semiconductors have a small gap, which can be bridged by heating.

12.7 • ADVANCED MATERIALS

In the last few decades, the exciting field of materials science has grown from solid-state chemistry, physics, and engineering. Objects that were once considered futuristic fantasies are becoming realities: powerful, ultrafast computers smaller than this book; cars powered by sunlight and made of nonmetallic parts stronger than steel and lighter than aluminum; ultrasmall machines constructed by manipulating individual atoms and molecules. In this section, we briefly discuss some of these remarkable materials.

Electronic Materials

The ideal of a perfectly ordered crystal is attainable only if the crystal is grown very slowly under carefully controlled conditions. When crystals form more rapidly, **crystal defects** inevitably form. Planes of particles are misaligned, particles are out of place or missing entirely, and foreign particles replace those that belong in the lattice. Although defects usually weaken a substance, they can be introduced intentionally to improve materials, giving them increased strength, hardness, or conductivity. Centuries of metal-working exemplify the traditional importance of defects, which is the basis of modern electronic materials.

Introducing Defects in Welding and Alloying In the process of *welding* two metals together, *vacancies* form near the surface when atoms vaporize, and then these vacancies move deeper as atoms from lower rows rise to fill the gaps. Welding causes the two types of metal atoms to intermingle and fill each other's vacancies. Metal *alloying* introduces several kinds of crystal defects, as when some atoms of a second metal occupy lattice sites of the first. Often, the alloy is harder than the pure metal; an example is brass, an alloy of copper with zinc. One reason the welded metals are stronger and the alloy is harder is that the second metal contributes additional valence electrons for metallic bonding.

Doped Semiconductors By controlling the number of valence electrons through the creation of specific types of crystal defects, chemists and engineers can greatly increase the conductivity of a semiconductor. Pure silicon [Si; Group 4A(14)], conducts poorly at room temperature because an energy gap separates its filled valence band from its conduction band (Figure 12.39A). Its conductivity can be greatly enhanced by **doping,** adding small amounts of other elements to increase or decrease the number of valence electrons in the bands:

- *n-Type semiconductor: increasing the number of valence electrons.* When Si is doped with phosphorus [or another Group 5A(15) element], P atoms occupy some of the lattice sites. Since P has one more valence electron than Si, this additional electron must enter an empty orbital in the conduction band, thus bridging the energy gap and increasing conductivity. Such doping creates an *n-type semiconductor,* so called because extra *n*egative charges (electrons) are present (Figure 12.39B).
- *p-Type semiconductor: decreasing the number of valence electrons.* When Si is doped with gallium [or another Group 3A(13) element], Ga atoms occupy some sites (Figure 12.39C). Since Ga has one fewer valence electron than Si, some of the orbitals in the valence band are empty, which creates a positive site. Si electrons can migrate to these empty orbitals, thereby increasing conductivity. Such doping creates a *p-type semiconductor,* so called because the empty orbitals act as *p*ositive holes.

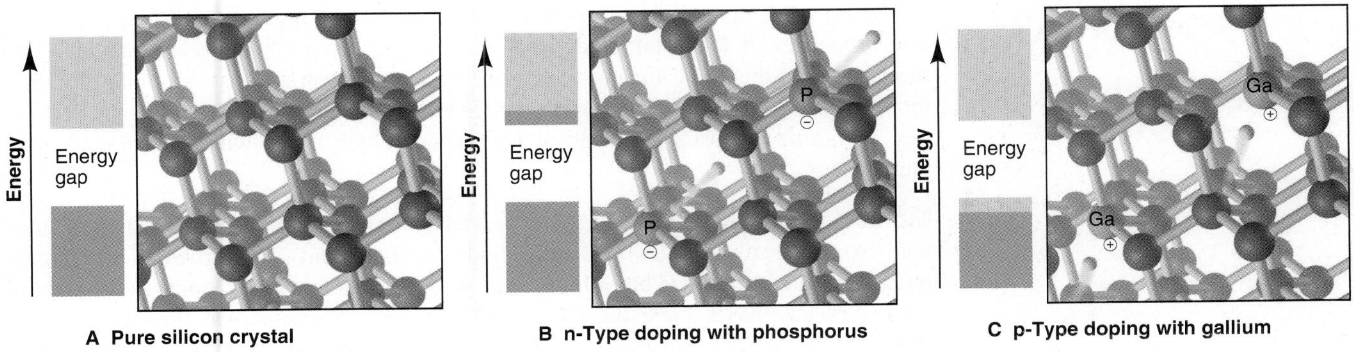

Figure 12.39 Crystal structures and band representations of doped semiconductors. **A,** Pure silicon has an energy gap between its valence and conduction bands, which keeps conductivity low at room temperature. **B,** Doping silicon with phosphorus (*purple*) adds additional valence electrons. **C,** Doping silicon with gallium (*orange*) removes electrons from the valence band and introduces positive holes.

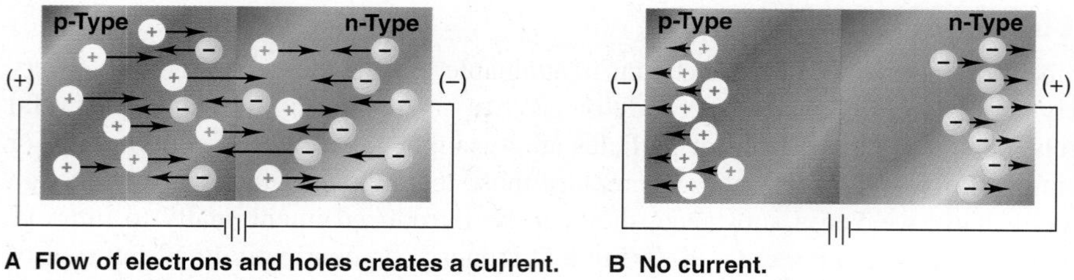

Figure 12.40 The p-n junction. Placing a p-type semiconductor adjacent to an n-type creates a p-n junction.

In contact with each other, an n-type and a p-type semiconductor form a *p-n junction.* When the negative terminal of a battery is connected to the n-type portion and the positive terminal to the p-type portion, electrons (*yellow, negative spheres*) flow freely in the n-to-p direction, which has the simultaneous effect of moving holes (*white, positive spheres*) in the p-to-n direction (Figure 12.40A). No current flows if the terminals are reversed (Figure 12.40B). Such unidirectional current flow makes a p-n junction act as a *rectifier,* a device that converts alternating current into direct current. A p-n junction in a modern integrated circuit can be made smaller than a square 10 μm on a side.

A modern computer chip the size of a nickel may incorporate millions of p-n junctions in the form of *transistors*. One of the most common types, an n-p-n transistor, is made by sandwiching a p-type portion between two n-type portions to form adjacent p-n junctions. The current flowing through one junction controls the current flowing through the other and results in an amplified signal.

One of the more common types of *solar cell* is, in essence, a p-n junction with an n-type surface exposed to a light source. Light provides the energy to free electrons from the n-type region and accelerate them through an external circuit into the p-type region, thus producing a current.

Liquid Crystals

Incorporated in the membrane of every cell in your body and in the display of every electronic device are **liquid crystals.** These materials flow like liquids but, like crystalline solids, pack at the molecular level with a high degree of order.

Ordering of the Particles Let's examine how particles are ordered in the three physical states and how this affects their properties. Both gases and liquids are *isotropic*—their physical properties are the same in every direction within the phase. For example, the viscosity of a gas or a liquid is the same regardless of direction. Glasses and other amorphous solids are also isotropic because they have no regular lattice structure.

In contrast, crystalline solids have a high degree of order among their particles. The properties of a crystal *do* depend on direction, so a crystal is *anisotropic.* The facets in a cut diamond, for instance, arise because the crystal cracks in one direction more easily than in another. Liquid crystals are anisotropic in several physical properties, including electrical and optical properties, which differ with direction through the phase.

Molecular Characteristics Liquid crystal phases consist of individual molecules with two characteristics: (1) a long, cylindrical shape and (2) a structure that fosters intermolecular attractions but inhibits perfect crystalline packing. Molecules that form liquid crystal phases have rodlike shapes and certain groups—in the cases shown in Figure 12.41, flat, benzene-like ring systems—that keep the molecules extended. Many of these molecules also have polarity associated with the long molecular axis. A strong electric field can orient these polar molecules like compass needles in a magnetic field.

The viscosity of a liquid crystal phase is lowest in the direction parallel to the long axis. Like moistened microscope slides, it is easier for the molecules to slide along each other (because the total attractive force remains the same), than it is for

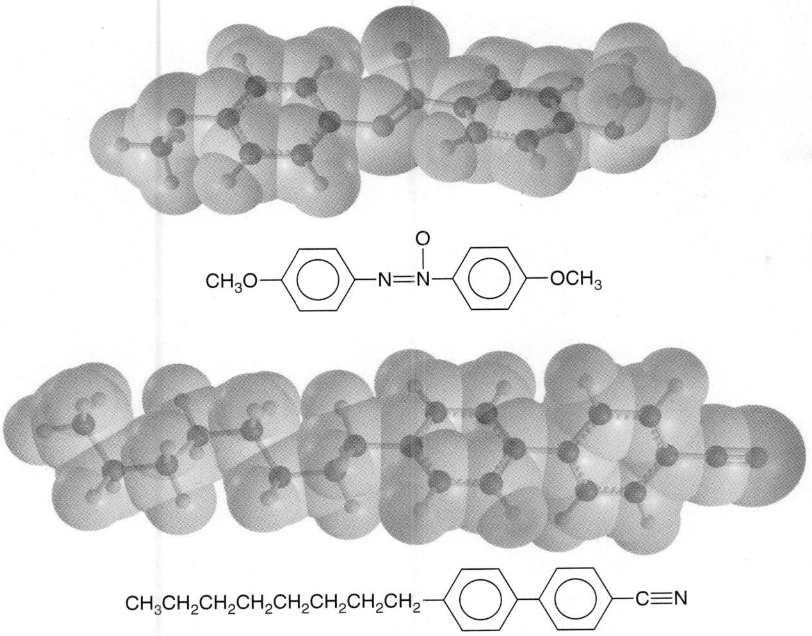

Figure 12.41 Structures of two typical molecules that form liquid crystal phases. Note the long, extended shapes and the regions of high (*red*) and low (*blue*) electron density.

them to pull apart from each other sideways. As a result, the molecules tend to align while the phase flows.

Controlling Conditions to Form Phases Liquid crystal phases can arise in two general ways, and, sometimes, either way can occur in the same substance:

1. *Thermotropic phases* develop as a result of a change in temperature. As a crystalline solid is heated, the molecules leave their lattice sites, but the intermolecular interactions are still strong enough to keep the molecules aligned with each other along their long axes. Like any other phase, the liquid crystal phase has sharp transition temperatures, but they occur over a relatively small temperature range. Further heating provides enough kinetic energy for the molecules to become disordered, as in a normal liquid. The typical range for liquid crystal phases of pure substances is from $<1°C$ to as much as 10°C, but mixing phases of two or more substances can greatly extend this range. For this reason, the liquid crystal phases used within display devices, as well as those within cell membranes, consist of mixtures of molecules.

2. *Lyotropic phases* occur in solution as the result of changes in concentration, but the conditions for forming such a phase vary for different substances. For example, when purified, some biomolecules that exist in cell membranes form lyotropic phases in water at the temperature that occurs within the organism. At the other extreme, Kevlar, a fiber used in bulletproof vests and high-performance sports equipment, forms a lyotropic phase in concentrated H_2SO_4 solution.

In some cases, a substance that forms a given liquid crystal phase under one set of conditions forms other phases under different conditions. Thus, a given thermotropic liquid crystal substance can pass from disordered liquid through a series of distinct liquid crystal phases to an ordered crystal through a decrease in temperature. A lyotropic substance can undergo similar changes through an increase in concentration.

Types of Order in Liquid Crystal Phases Molecules that form liquid crystal phases can exhibit various types of order. Three common types are nematic, cholesteric, and smectic:

1. In a *nematic phase,* the molecules lie in the same direction but their ends are not aligned, much like a school of fish swimming in synchrony (Figure 12.42A, *next page*). The nematic phase is the least ordered type of liquid crystal phases.

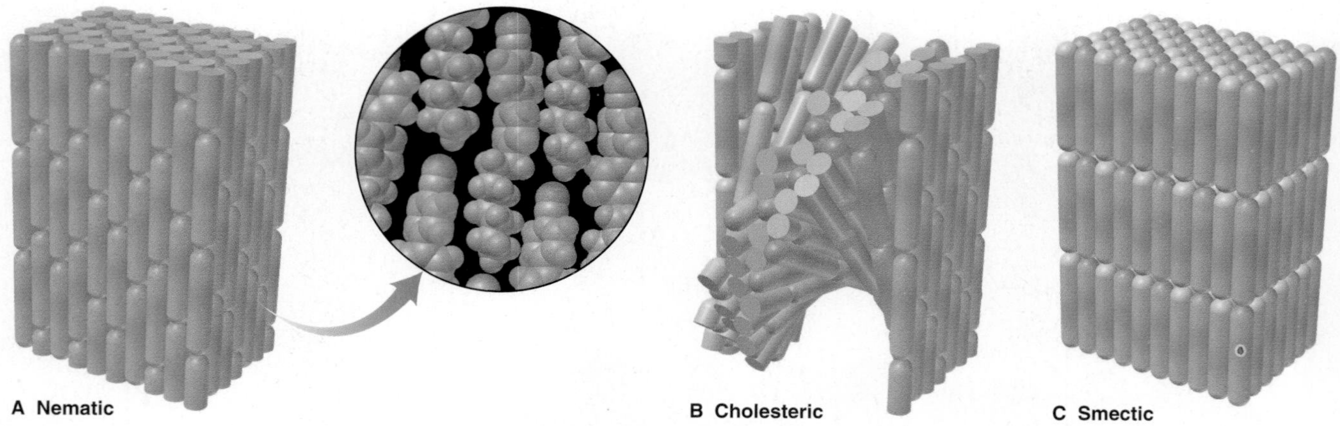

Figure 12.42 The three common types of ordering in liquid crystal phases.

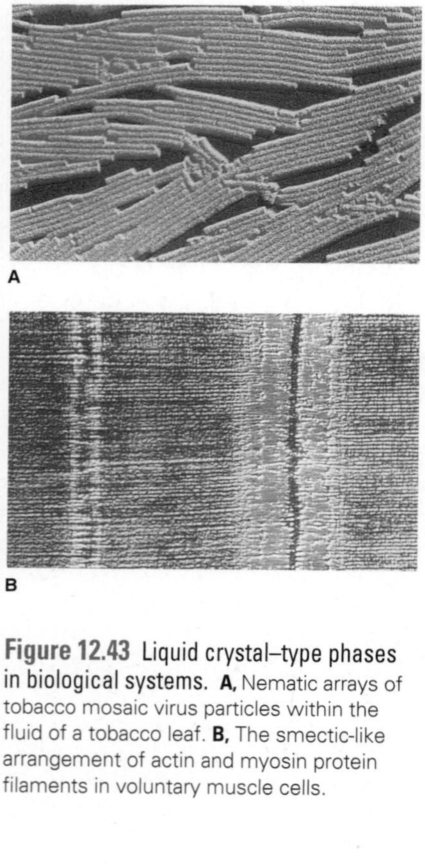

Figure 12.43 Liquid crystal–type phases in biological systems. **A,** Nematic arrays of tobacco mosaic virus particles within the fluid of a tobacco leaf. **B,** The smectic-like arrangement of actin and myosin protein filaments in voluntary muscle cells.

2. In a *cholesteric phase,* which is somewhat more ordered, the molecules lie in layers that each exhibit nematic-type ordering. Rather than lying in parallel fashion, however, each layer is rotated by a fixed angle with respect to the next layer to give a helical (corkscrew) arrangement. A cholesteric phase is often called a *twisted nematic phase* (Figure 12.42B).
3. In a *smectic phase,* which is the most ordered, the molecules lie parallel to each other, *with* their ends aligned, in layers that are stacked directly over each other (Figure 12.42C). The long molecular axis has a well-defined angle (shown in the figure as 90°) with respect to the plane of the layer. The molecules in Figure 12.41 form nematic or smectic phases. Liquid crystal–type phases appear in many biological systems (Figure 12.43).

Applications of Liquid Crystals The ability to control the orientation of the molecules in a liquid crystal allows us to produce materials with high strength or unique optical properties:

1. *High-strength applications* involve the use of extremely long molecules called *polymers.* While in a thermotropic liquid crystal phase and during their flow through the processing equipment, these molecules become highly aligned, like the fibers in wood. Cooling solidifies them into fibers, rods, and sheets that can be shaped into materials with superior mechanical properties. Sporting equipment, supersonic aircraft parts, and the sails used in the America's Cup races are fabricated from these polymeric materials. (We discuss the structure and physical behavior of polymers later in this section and their synthesis in Chapter 15.)

2. *Optical applications* include the liquid crystal displays (LCDs) used in countless devices, such as watches, calculators, cell phones, and computers. All depend on *changes in molecular orientation in an electric field.* Figure 12.44 shows a small portion of a wristwatch LCD. Layers of nematic phases are sandwiched between thin glass plates that incorporate transparent electrodes. The long molecular axis lies parallel to the plane of the plates. The distance between plates (6–8 μm) allows the molecular axis within each succeeding layer to twist just enough for the molecular orientation at the bottom plate to be 90° from that at the top plate. Above and below this "sandwich" are thin polarizing filters that allow light waves oriented in only one direction to pass through. The filters are placed in a "crossed" arrangement, so that light passing through the top filter must twist 90° to pass through the bottom filter. This whole grouping of filters, plates, and liquid crystal phase lies on a mirror.

A current generated by the watch battery controls the orientation of the molecules. With the current on in one region of the display, the molecules become oriented *toward* the field, and thus block the light from passing through to the bottom filter, so that region appears dark. With the current off in another region, light passes through the molecules and bottom filter to the mirror and back again, so that region appears bright.

Cholesteric liquid crystals are used in applications that involve color changes with temperature. The twisted molecular orientation "unwinds" with heating, and the extent of the unwinding determines the color. Liquid crystal thermometers include a mixture of substances to widen their range of temperatures. Newer uses include "mapping" the area of a tumor, detecting faulty connections in electronic circuit boards, and nondestructive testing of materials under stress.

Ceramic Materials

First developed by Stone Age people, **ceramics** are nonmetallic, nonpolymeric solids hardened by high temperature. Clay ceramics consist of silicate microcrystals suspended in a glassy cementing medium. In "firing" a ceramic pot, for example, a kiln heats the object made of an aluminosilicate clay, such as kaolinite, to 1500°C and the clay loses water:

$$Si_2Al_2O_5(OH)_4(s) \longrightarrow Si_2Al_2O_7(s) + 2H_2O(g)$$

During the heating process, the structure rearranges to an extended network of Si-centered and Al-centered tetrahedra of O atoms (Section 14.6).

Bricks, porcelain, glazes, and other clay ceramics are hard and resistant to heat and chemicals. Today's high-tech ceramics have these characteristics in addition to superior electrical and magnetic properties (Table 12.7). As just one example, consider the unusual electrical behavior of certain zinc oxide (ZnO) composites. Ordinarily a semiconductor, ZnO can be doped so that it becomes a conductor. Imbedding particles of the doped oxide into an insulating ceramic produces a variable resistor: at low voltage, the material conducts poorly, but at high voltage, it conducts well. The changeover voltage can be "preset" by controlling the size of the ZnO particles and the thickness of the insulating medium.

Preparing Modern Ceramics Among the important modern ceramics are silicon carbide (SiC) and nitride (Si_3N_4), boron nitride (BN), and the superconducting oxides. They are prepared by standard chemical methods that involve driving off a volatile component during the reaction:

1. *SiC ceramics* are made from compounds used in silicone polymer manufacture (we'll discuss these polymers in Section 14.6):

$$n(CH_3)_2SiCl_2(l) + 2nNa(s) \longrightarrow 2nNaCl(s) + [(CH_3)_2Si]_n(s)$$

This product is heated to 800°C to form the ceramic:

$$[(CH_3)_2Si]_n \longrightarrow nCH_4(g) + nH_2(g) + nSiC(s)$$

Silicon carbide can also be prepared by the direct reaction of silicon and graphite under vacuum:

$$Si(s) + C(\text{graphite}) \xrightarrow{\sim 1500^\circ C} SiC(s)$$

Table 12.7 Some Uses of Modern Ceramics and Ceramic Mixtures

Ceramic	Applications
SiC, Si_3N_4, TiB_2, Al_2O_3	Whiskers (fibers) to strengthen Al and other ceramics
Si_3N_4	Car engine parts; turbine rotors for "turbo" cars; electronic sensor units
Si_3N_4, BN, Al_2O_3	Support or layering materials (as insulators) in electronic microchips
SiC, Si_3N_4, TiB_2, ZrO_2, Al_2O_3, BN	Cutting tools, edge sharpeners (as coatings and whole devices), scissors, surgical tools, industrial "diamond"
BN, SiC	Armor-plating reinforcement fibers (as in Kevlar composites)
ZrO_2, Al_2O_3	Surgical implants (hip and knee joints)

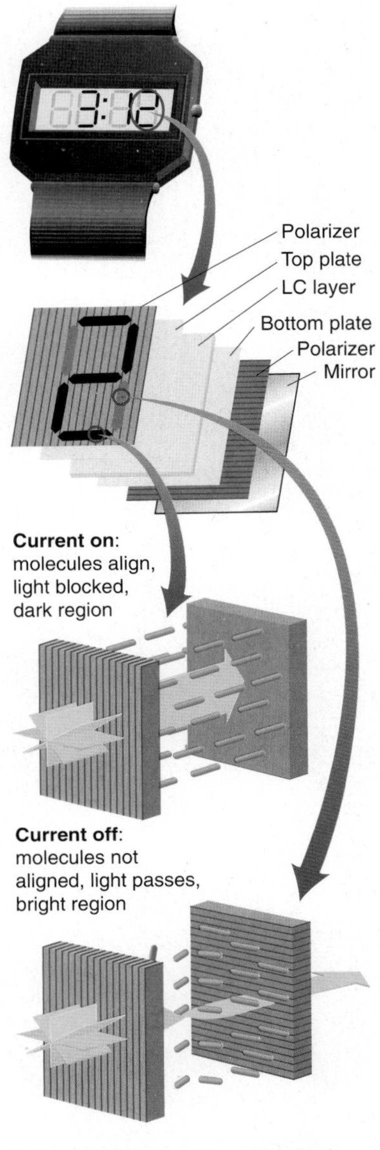

Figure 12.44 A liquid crystal display (LCD). A close-up of the "2" on a wristwatch LCD reveals two polarizers sandwiching two glass plates, which sandwich a liquid crystal (LC) layer, all lying on a mirror. When light waves enter the first polarizer, waves oriented in one direction emerge to enter the LC layer. Enlarging a dark region (*top blow-up*) shows the LC molecules aligned, keeping light waves from passing through; thus, the viewer sees no light. Enlarging a bright region (*bottom blow-up*) shows the LC molecules rotating the plane of the light waves, which can then pass through and reach the viewer.

The nitride is also prepared by reaction of the elements:

$$3Si(s) + 2N_2(g) \xrightarrow{>1300^\circ C} Si_3N_4(s)$$

2. *BN ceramics* are produced through the reaction of boron trichloride or boric acid with ammonia:

$$B(OH)_3(s) + 3NH_3(g) \longrightarrow B(NH_2)_3(s) + 3H_2O(g)$$

Heat drives off some of the bound nitrogen as NH_3 to yield the ceramic:

$$B(NH_2)_3(s) \xrightarrow{\Delta} 2NH_3(g) + BN(s)$$

3. One type of *superconducting oxide* is made by heating a mixture of barium carbonate with copper and yttrium oxides, followed by further heating in the presence of O_2:

$$4BaCO_3(s) + 6CuO(s) + Y_2O_3(s) \xrightarrow{\Delta} 2YBa_2Cu_3O_{6.5}(s) + 4CO_2(g)$$

$$YBa_2Cu_3O_{6.5}(s) + \tfrac{1}{4}O_2(g) \xrightarrow{\Delta} YBa_2Cu_3O_7(s)$$

Ceramic Structures and Uses Structures of several ceramic materials are shown in Figure 12.45.

1. *Silicon carbide* has a diamond-like structure. Network covalent bonding gives this material great strength. It is made into thin fibers, called *whiskers,* to reinforce other ceramics and prevent cracking in a composite structure, much like steel rods reinforcing concrete.

2. *Silicon nitride* is virtually inert chemically, retains its strength and wear resistance for extended periods above 1000°C, is dense and hard, and acts as an electrical insulator. Many automakers are testing it in high-efficiency car and truck engines because of its low weight, tolerance of high operating temperature, and little need for lubrication.

3. *BN ceramics* exist in two structures, analogous to the common crystalline forms of carbon. In the graphite-like form, BN has extraordinary properties as an electrical insulator. At high temperature and very high pressure (1800°C and 8.5×10^4 atm), it converts to a diamond-like structure, which is extremely hard and durable. Both forms are virtually invisible to radar.

4. *Superconducting oxides* often contain copper in an unusual oxidation state. In $YBa_2Cu_3O_7$, for instance, assuming oxidation states of +3 for Y, +2 for Ba, and −2 for O, the three Cu atoms have a total oxidation state of +7. This is allocated as $Cu(II)_2Cu(III)$, with one Cu in the unusual +3 state. X-ray diffraction analysis indicates that a distortion in the structure makes four of the oxide ions unusually close to the Y^{3+} ion, which aligns the Cu ions into chains within the crystal. It is suspected that a specific half-filled 3*d* orbital in Cu oriented toward a neighboring O^{2-} ion may be associated with superconductivity.

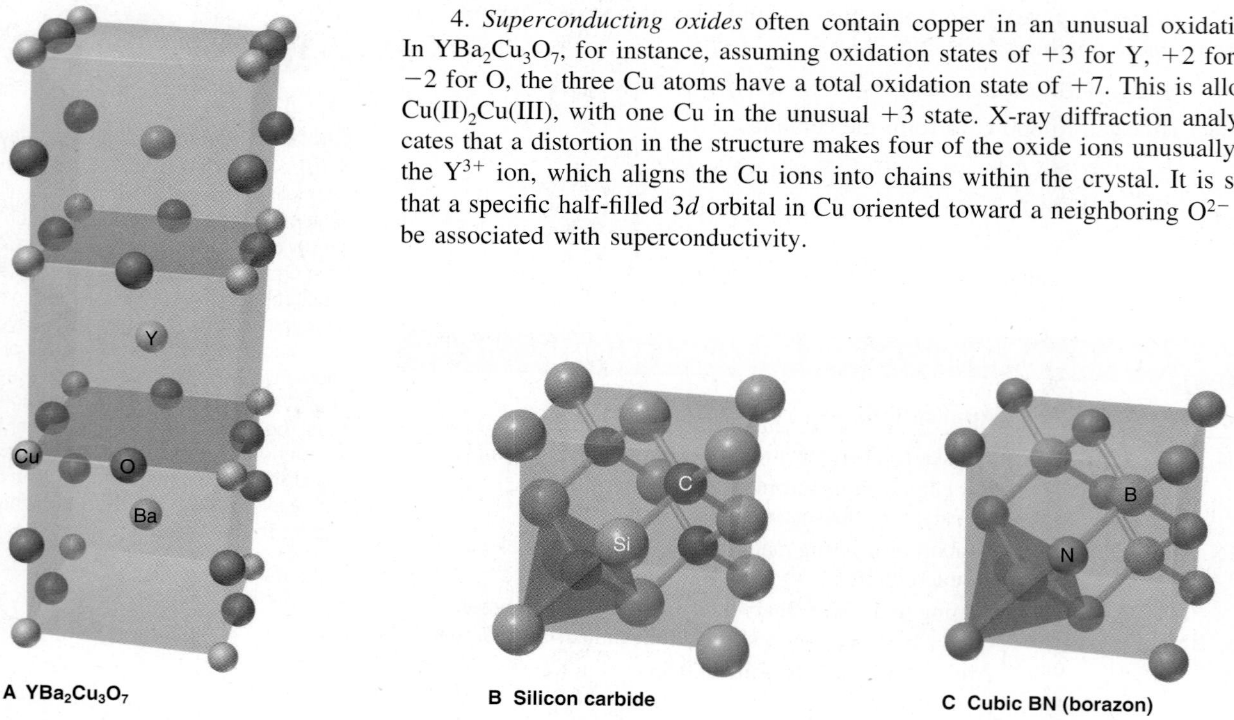

Figure 12.45 Expanded view of the atom arrangements in some modern ceramic materials.

Because of brittleness, it is difficult to fashion these ceramics into wires, but methods for making films and ribbons have been developed. The brittleness arises from the strength of the ionic-covalent bonding and the resulting inability to deform. Under stress, a microfine defect widens until the material cracks. One new method forms defect-free superconducting oxide ceramics using controlled packing and heat-treating of extremely small, uniform oxide particles coated with organic polymers. Another method is aimed at arresting a widening crack. The ceramics are embedded with zirconia (ZrO_2), whose crystal structure expands up to 5% under mechanical stress. When an advancing crack reaches them, the zirconia particles pinch it shut. A third method prepares the material of precisely grown crystals of Al_2O_3 and $GdAlO_3$, which become entangled during the solidification process. The resulting material bends without cracking above 1800 K.

Polymeric Materials

A **polymer** (Greek, "many parts") is an extremely large molecule, or **macromolecule,** consisting of a covalently linked chain of smaller molecules, called **monomers** (Greek, "one part"). The monomer is the *repeat unit* of the polymer, and a polymer may have hundreds to hundreds of thousands of repeat units. Many types of monomers give polymers the complete repertoire of intermolecular forces.

- *Synthetic* polymers are created in the laboratory.
- *Natural* polymers (or *biopolymers*) are created within organisms.

In this section, we examine the physical nature of synthetic polymers and explore the role of intermolecular forces in their properties and uses. In Chapter 15, we'll examine the types of monomers, the preparation of synthetic polymers, and the monomers, structures, and functions of some biopolymers.

Dimensions of a Polymer Chain Polymers differ from smaller molecules in terms of molar mass, chain length, shape, and size. We'll discuss these, using polyethylene, by far the most common synthetic polymer, as an example.

1. *Polymer mass.* The molar mass of a polymer chain ($\mathcal{M}_{\text{polymer}}$, in g/mol, often referred to as the *molecular weight*) depends on the molar mass of the repeat unit ($\mathcal{M}_{\text{repeat}}$) and the **degree of polymerization (*n*),** the number of repeat units in the chain:

$$\mathcal{M}_{\text{polymer}} = \mathcal{M}_{\text{repeat}} \times n$$

For example, the molar mass of the ethylene repeat unit ($-CH_2-CH_2-$) is 28 g/mol. If an individual polyethylene chain in a plastic grocery bag has a degree of polymerization of 7100, the molar mass of that chain is

$$\mathcal{M}_{\text{polymer}} = \mathcal{M}_{\text{repeat}} \times n = (28\text{ g/mol})\,(7.1\times10^3) = 2.0\times10^5\text{ g/mol}$$

Table 12.8 shows some other examples.

Table 12.8 Molar Masses of Some Common Polymers

Name	$\mathcal{M}_{\text{polymer}}$ (g/mol)	*n*	Uses
Acrylates	2×10^5	2×10^3	Rugs, carpets
Polyamide (nylons)	1.5×10^4	1.2×10^2	Tires, fishing line
Polycarbonate	1×10^5	4×10^2	Compact discs
Polyethylene	3×10^5	1×10^4	Grocery bags
Polyethylene (ultrahigh molecular weight)	5×10^6	2×10^5	Hip joints
Poly(ethylene terephthalate)	2×10^4	1×10^2	Soda bottles
Polystyrene	3×10^5	3×10^3	Packing, coffee cups
Poly(vinyl chloride)	1×10^5	1.5×10^3	Plumbing

However, even though the monomer repeat unit in any given chain has the same molar mass, the degree of polymerization often varies considerably from chain to chain. Thus, *a sample of a synthetic polymer has a distribution of chain lengths and molar masses.* Polymer chemists use various definitions of the *average* molar mass, and a common one is the *number-average molar mass*, $\mathcal{M}_n$:

$$\mathcal{M}_n = \frac{\text{total mass of all chains}}{\text{number of moles of chains}}$$

If the number-average molar mass of the polyethylene in grocery bags is, say, 1.6×10^5 g/mol, the chains may vary in molar mass from about 7.0×10^4 to 3.0×10^5 g/mol.

2. *Polymer chain length.* The long axis of a polymer chain is called its *backbone.* The length of an *extended* backbone is simply the number of repeat units (degree of polymerization, n) times the length of each repeat unit (l_0). For instance, the length of an ethylene repeat unit is about 250 pm, so the extended length of our particular grocery-bag polyethylene chain is

$$\text{Length of extended chain} = n \times l_0 = (7.1\times10^3)\,(2.5\times10^2 \text{ pm}) = 1.8\times10^6 \text{ pm}$$

Comparing this length with the thickness of the chain, which is about 40 pm, shows the threadlike nature of the extended chain (length about 50,000 times width).

3. *Coiled shape and size.* A polymer molecule, however, whether pure or in solution, doesn't exist as an extended chain. In principle, the shape of the molecule arises from free rotation around all the single bonds. Thus, as each repeat unit rotates randomly, the chain continuously changes direction, turning back on itself many times and eventually arriving at the **random coil** shape that most polymers adopt (Figure 12.46). In reality, rotation is not completely free because intermolecular forces between chain portions, between different chains, and/or between chain and solvent have significant effects on the actual shape of a polymer chain.

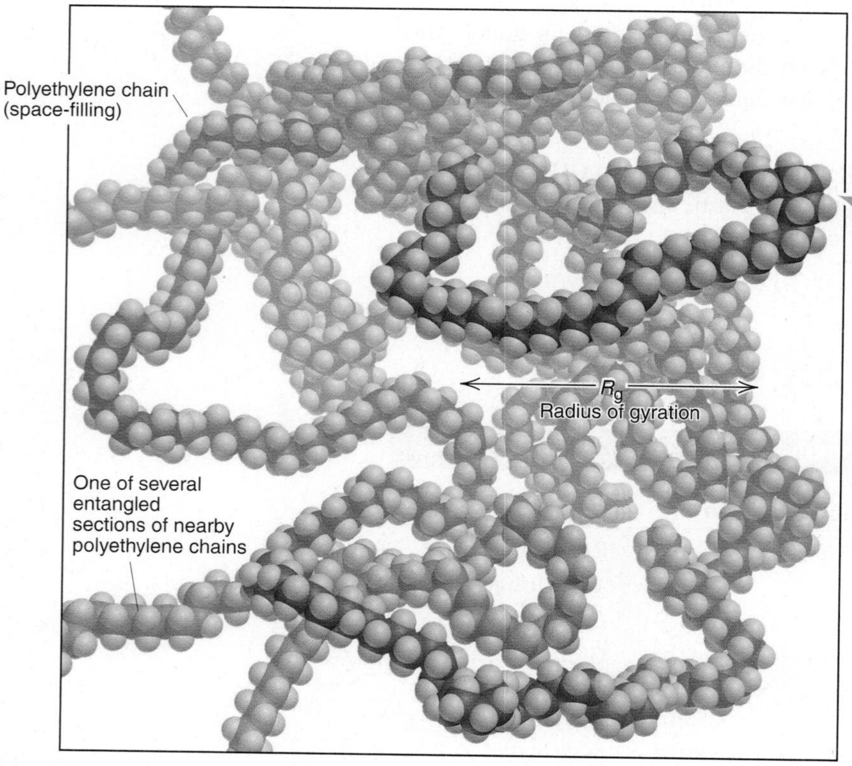

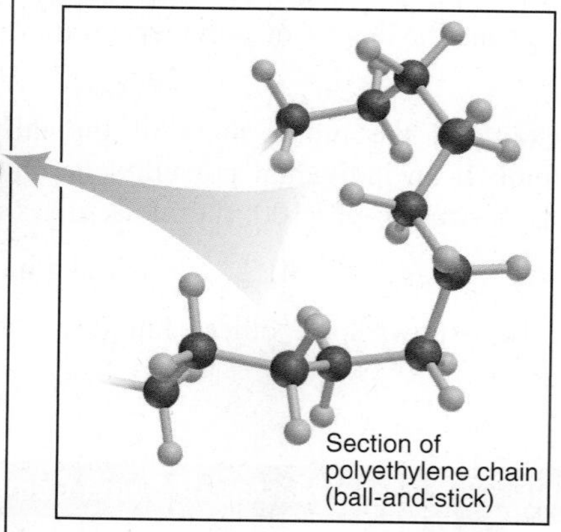

Figure 12.46 The random-coil shape of a polymer chain. Note the random coiling of the chain's carbon atoms (*black*). Sections of several nearby chains (*red, green,* and *yellow*) are entangled with this chain, kept near one another by dispersion forces. In reality, entangling chains fill any gaps shown here.

The size of the coiled chain is expressed by its **radius of gyration, R_g,** the average distance from the center of mass of the molecule to the outer edge of the coil (Figure 12.46). Even though R_g is reported as a single value for a given polymer, it represents an average value for many chains. The mathematical expression for the radius of gyration includes the length of each repeat unit and the degree of polymerization:*

$$R_g = \sqrt{\frac{nl_0^2}{6}}$$

As expected, the radius of gyration increases with the degree of polymerization, and thus with the molar mass as well. Light-scattering measurements correlate with these calculated results, so for many polymers the radius of gyration can be determined experimentally.

For our grocery-bag polyethylene chain, we have

$$R_g = \sqrt{\frac{nl_0^2}{6}} = \sqrt{\frac{(7.1\times10^3)(2.5\times10^2\ \text{pm})^2}{6}} = 8.6\times10^3\ \text{pm}$$

Doubling the radius gives a diameter of 1.7×10^4 pm for the coiled chain, less than one-hundredth the length of the extended chain!

Polymer Crystallinity A sample of a given polymer is not just a disorderly jumble of chains. If the molecular structure allows neighboring chains to pack together and if the chemical groups lead to favorable dipole-dipole, H-bonding, and/or dispersion forces, portions of the chains can align regularly and exhibit crystallinity.

However, the crystallinity of a polymer is very different from the crystal structures we discussed earlier. In those structures, the orderly array extends over many atoms or molecules, and the unit cell includes at least one atom or molecule. In contrast, the orderly regions of a polymer rarely involve even one whole molecule (Figure 12.47). At best, a polymer is *semicrystalline,* because parts of the molecule align with parts of neighboring molecules (or with other parts of the same chain), while most of the chain remains as a random coil.

*The mathematical derivation of R_g is beyond the scope of this text, but it is analogous to the two-dimensional "walk of the drunken sailor." With each step, the sailor stumbles in random directions and, given enough time, ends up very close to the starting position. The radius of gyration quantifies how far the end of the polymer chain (the sailor) has gone from the origin.

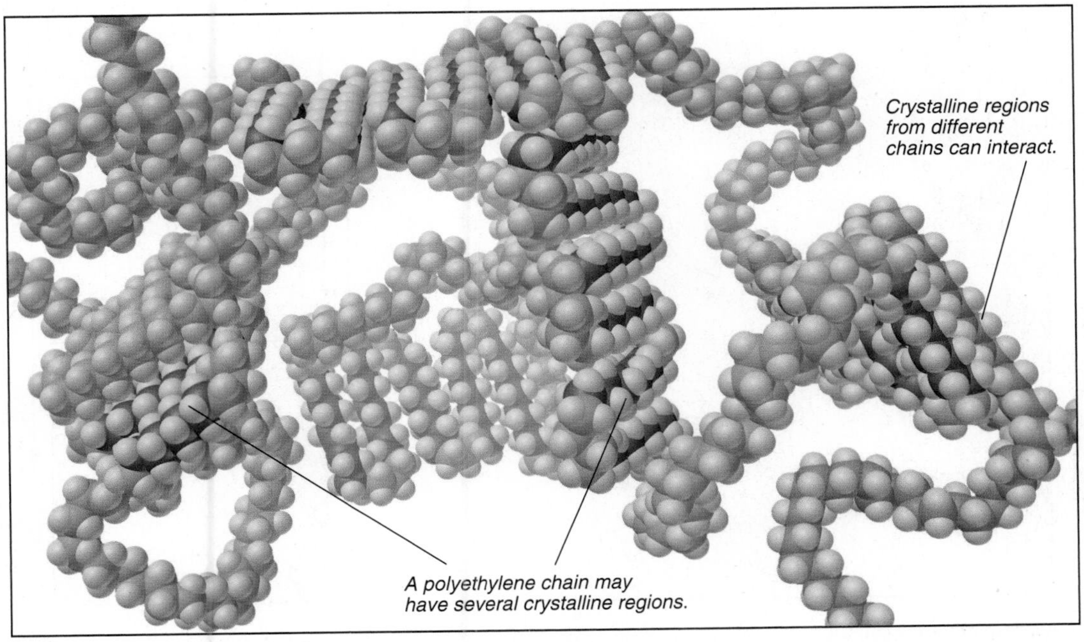

Figure 12.47 The semicrystallinity of a polymer chain. Several crystalline regions (*darker color*) have randomly coiled regions between them. Crystalline regions from nearby chains (*red* and *yellow*) align with those in the main chain.

Viscosity of Pure and Dissolved Polymers Some of the most important uses of polymers arise from their ability to change the viscosity of a solvent in which they are dissolved and to undergo temperature-dependent changes in their own viscosity.

1. *Dissolved polymers.* When an appreciable amount of polymer (about 5–15 mass %) dissolves, the viscosity of the solution is much higher than that of the pure solvent. In fact, polymers are added to increase the viscosity of many common materials, such as motor oil, paint, and salad dressing. As the random coil of a polymer moves through a solution, solvent molecules are attracted to it through intermolecular forces (Figure 12.48). Thus, as the solution flows, the polymer coil drags along solvent molecules that are interacting with other solvent molecules and other coils, and flow is reduced. Increasing the polymer concentration increases the viscosity because coils are more likely to become entangled.

Viscosity is a property of a particular polymer-solvent pair at a given temperature. The size (radius of gyration) of a random coil in solution increases with molar mass, and so does the viscosity. To improve polymer manufacture, chemists have developed equations to predict the viscosity of polymers of different molar masses in a variety of solvents (see Problem 12.142).

2. *Pure polymers.* Intermolecular forces also play a major role in the flow of a pure polymer sample. At temperatures high enough to melt them, many polymers exist as viscous liquids, flowing more like honey than water. The forces between the chains, as well as the entangling of chains, hinder the flow. As the temperature decreases, the intermolecular attractions exert a greater effect, and the eventual result is a rigid solid. If the chains don't crystallize, the resulting material is called a *polymer glass.* The transition from a liquid to a glass occurs over a narrow temperature range (10–20°C) for a given polymer; temperature at the midpoint of the range is

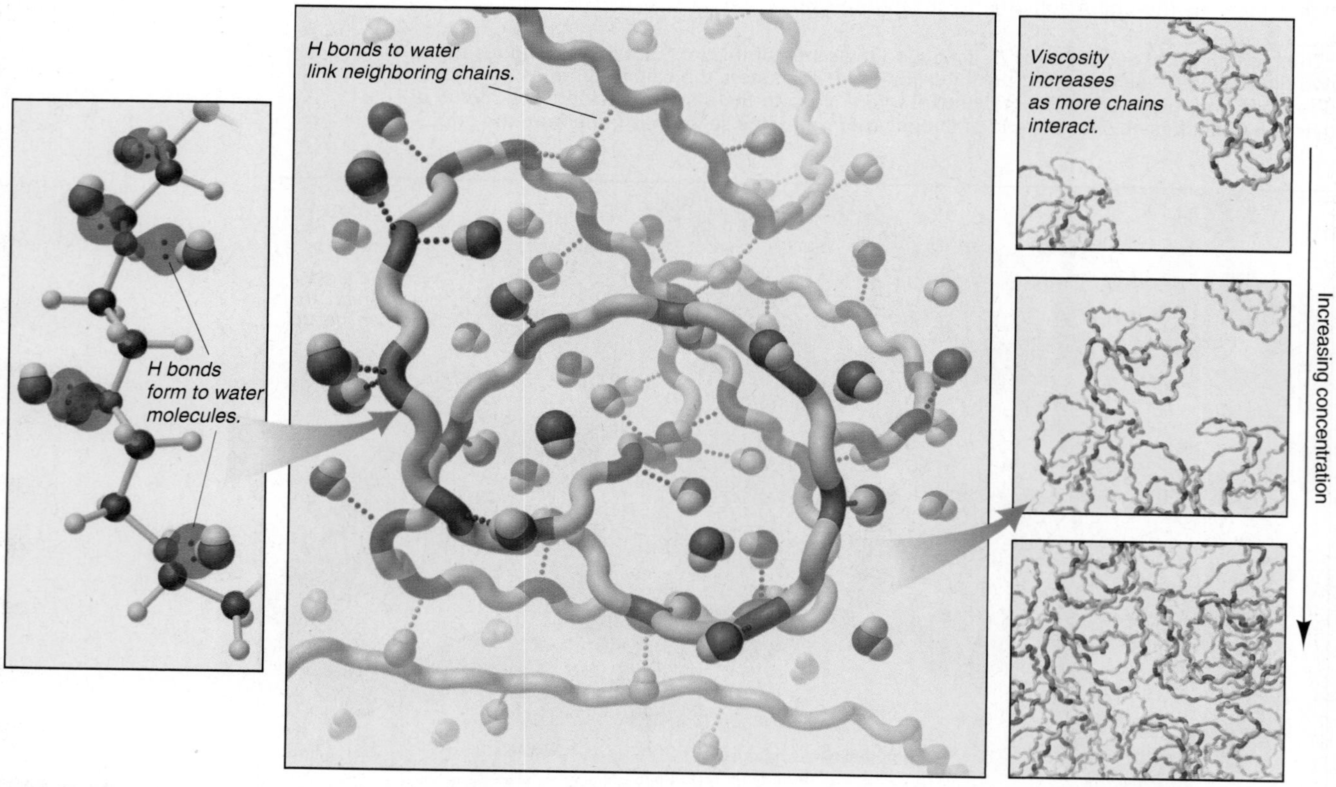

Figure 12.48 The viscosity of a polymer in aqueous solution. A section of a poly(ethylene oxide) chain *(left panel)* forms H bonds between the lone pairs of the chain's O atoms and the H atoms of water molecules. A polymer chain *(blue and red coiled rod, center panel)* forms many H bonds with water molecules that allow the chain to interact with other chains. As the concentration of polymer increases *(three right panels)*, the viscosity of the solution increases.

called the *glass transition temperature,* T_g. Like window glass, many polymer glasses are transparent, such as polystyrene in drinking cups and polycarbonate in eyeglass lenses.

Plasticity of Polymers The flow-related properties of polymers give rise to their familiar **plastic** mechanical behavior. The word "plastic" refers to a material that, when deformed, retains its new shape; in contrast, when an "elastic" object is deformed, it returns to its original shape. Many polymers can be deformed (stretched, bent, twisted) when warm and retain their deformed shape when cooled. In this way, they are made into milk bottles, car parts, and countless other everyday objects.

Molecular Architecture of Polymers A polymer's architecture—its overall spatial layout and molecular structure—is crucial to its properties. In addition to linear chains, more complex architectures arise through branching and crosslinking:

1. **Branches** are smaller chains appended to a polymer backbone. As the number of branches increases, the chains cannot pack as well, so the degree of crystallinity decreases and the polymer is less rigid. A small amount of branching occurs as a side reaction in the preparation of high-density polyethylene (HDPE). It is still largely linear and rigid enough for use in milk containers. In contrast, much more branching is intentionally induced to prepare low-density polyethylene (LDPE). The chains cannot pack well, so crystallinity is low. This polymer is used in flexible, transparent food storage bags.

Dendrimers are prepared from monomers with three or more attachment points, so each monomer forms branches. In essence, then, dendrimers have no backbone and consist only of branches. A dendrimer has a constantly increasing number of branches and an incredibly large number of end groups at its outer edge. Chemists use dendrimers to bind one polymer to another to create films and fibers and to deliver drugs in medical applications.

2. **Crosslinks** can be thought of as branches that link one chain to another. The extent of crosslinking leads to remarkable differences in properties. A small degree of crosslinking often yields a *thermoplastic* polymer, one that still flows at high temperatures. But, as the extent of crosslinking increases, a thermoplastic polymer is transformed into a *thermoset* polymer, one that can no longer flow because it has become a single network. Below their glass transition temperatures, some thermosets are extremely rigid and strong, making them ideal as matrix materials in high-strength composites (*see photo*).

Above their glass transition temperatures, many thermosets become **elastomers,** polymers that can be stretched and immediately spring back to their initial shapes when released, like a trampoline or a rubber band. When you stretch a rubber band, individual polymer chains flow for only a short distance before the connectivity of the network returns them to their original positions. Table 12.9 lists some elastomers.

Bicycle helmet containing a thermoset polymer.

Table 12.9 Some Common Elastomers

Name	T_g (°C)	Uses
Poly(dimethyl siloxane)	−123	Breast implants
Polybutadiene	−106	Rubber bands
Polyisoprene	−65	Surgical gloves
Polychloroprene (neoprene)	−43	Footwear; medical tubing

Impact of Monomer Sequence Differences in monomer sequences influence polymer properties as well. A *homopolymer* consists of one type of monomer (A—A—A—A—A— · · ·), whereas a **copolymer** consists of two or more types. The simplest copolymer is called an *AB block copolymer* because a chain (block) of monomer A and a chain of monomer B are linked at one point:

$$\cdots —A—A—A—A—A—B—B—B—B—B— \cdots$$

If the intermolecular forces between the A and B portions of the chain are weaker than those between different regions within each portion, the A and B portions form their own random coils. This ability makes AB block copolymers ideal *adhesives* for joining two polymer surfaces covalently. An ABA block copolymer has A chains linked at each end of a B chain:

$$\cdots\text{—A—A—A—B—(B)}_n\text{—B—A—A—A—}\cdots$$

Some of these block copolymers act as *thermoplastic elastomers,* materials shaped at high temperature that become elastomers at room temperature; many are used in the modern footwear industry.

Silicone polymers are described briefly in Chapter 14, and organic reactions that form polymer chains from monomers are examined in Chapter 15.

Nanotechnology: Designing Materials Atom by Atom

Nanotechnology is the science and engineering of nanoscale systems, whose sizes range from 1 to 100 nm. (Recall that 1 nm is 10^{-9} m—about one-billionth the width of your dorm-room desk or one-millionth the width of your pen tip. A nanometer is to a meter as a marble is to Earth!) Nanotechnology joins scientists from physics, materials science, chemistry, biology, environmental science, medicine, and many branches of engineering.

Nanoscale materials behave neither like atoms, which are smaller (1×10^1 nm), nor like crystals, which are at least 1×10^5 nm. The different behavior is due to a surface area that is similar to their interior volume—for example, a 5-nm particle has about half of its atoms on its surface. Cut a piece of ordinary aluminum foil into pieces just large enough to see with a light microscope and they still behave like the original piece. But, if you could cut the original piece into 20–30-nm pieces, they would explode. Indeed, aluminum nanoparticles are used in fireworks and propellants.

As so often happens in science, a technological advance allows a new field to blossom. Nanotechnologists can use the scanning tunneling microscope (see Tools of the Laboratory, pp. 447–448) and the similar scanning probe and atomic force microscopes to examine the chemical and physical properties of nanostructures and build them up, in many cases, atom by atom.

Two features of nanoscale engineering occur routinely in nature:

1. *Self-assembly* is the ability of smaller, simpler parts to organize themselves into a larger, more complex whole. On the molecular scale, self-assembly refers to atoms or small molecules aggregating through intermolecular forces. Oppositely charged regions on two such particles make contact to form a larger particle, which in turn aggregates with another to form a still larger one.
2. *Controlled orientation* is the positioning of two molecules near each other long enough for intermolecular forces to result in a change, often a bond breaking or forming. All enzymes function this way.

Because this new field changes many times faster than a textbook does, we can only provide a glimpse of a few exciting research directions in nanotechnology.

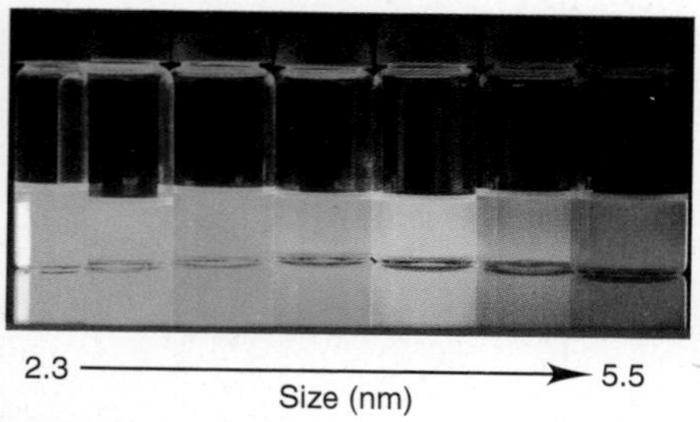

Figure 12.49 The colors of quantum dots. The smaller the dots, the shorter the emitted wavelengths.

Nanoscale Optical Materials *Quantum dots* are nanoparticles of semiconducting materials, such as gallium arsenide (GaAs) or gallium selenide (GaSe), that are smaller than 10 nm. Rather than having a band of energy levels, the dot has discrete energy levels, much like a single atom. As in atoms, the energy levels can be studied with spectroscopy; unlike atoms, quantum dots can be modified chemically. When high-energy (short-wavelength) UV light irradiates a suspension of quantum dots, they become excited and emit radiation of lower energy (longer wavelength). Most importantly, the emitted wavelengths depend on the size of the dots: the larger the particles, the longer the wavelength emitted. Thus, the color of the emitted light can be "tuned" by varying the dimensions of the nanoparticles (Figure 12.49). One use for quantum dots is the imaging of specific cells. The dot is encapsulated in a coating and then bonded to a particular protein used by a target organ. The cells in the target incorporate the protein, along with its attached quantum dot, and the location of the protein is viewed spectroscopically.

Nanostructured Materials *Nanostructuring,* the construction of bulk materials from nanoscale building blocks, increases strength, ductility, plasticity, and many other properties. The resulting *nanocomposites* behave as liquid magnets, ductile cements, conducting elastomers, and many other unique materials.

One example mimics a familiar natural material. Bones are natural nanocomposites of hydroxyapatite (a type of calcium phosphate) and other minerals. Synthetic nanocrystalline hydroxyapatite has been made with weight-bearing properties identical to bone that provides a framework for natural bone tissue to grow into and heal a fracture. Another material, called a *ferrofluid,* consists of magnetic nanoparticles (usually magnetite, Fe_3O_4) dispersed in a viscous fluid. When placed in a magnetic field, the particles align to conform to the shape of the field (Figure 12.50). Ferrofluids find uses in automobile shock absorbers, magnetic plastics, audio speakers, computer hard drives, high-vacuum valves, and many other devices.

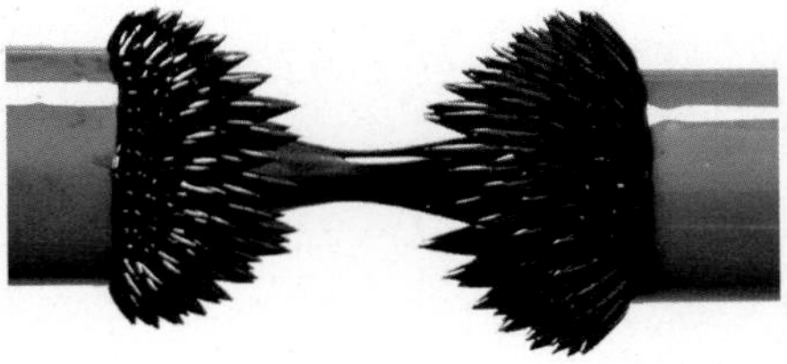

Figure 12.50 The magnetic behavior of a ferrofluid. Nanoparticles of magnetite (Fe_3O_4) dispersed in a viscous fluid are suspended between the poles of a magnet.

High-Surface-Area Materials Carbon nanotubes have remarkable mechanical and electrical properties. But, a possible future application involves storing H_2 gas for hydrogen-powered vehicles. Currently, H_2 is stored in metal cylinders at high pressures (>70 atm). Porous solids, such as carbon nanotubes, can store the same amount of gas at much lower pressures because they have surface areas of 4500 m^2/g—about four football fields per gram of material! Thus, a medium-sized container of nanotubes could store a large amount of H_2 fuel under conditions safe enough for a family car.

Other high-surface-area materials being developed are porous membranes for water purification or batteries and multilayer films that incorporate photosynthetic molecules for high-efficiency solar cells. A very exciting development is the molecule-specific biosensor, which can detect as little as 10^{-14} mol of DNA using color changes in gold nanoparticles. Such biosensors could circulate freely in the bloodstream to measure levels of specific disease-related molecules, deliver drugs to individual cells, and even alter individual genes.

Nanomachines In nature, the virus is a marvel of nanoscale engineering, designed for delivering genetic material to infect a host cell. For example, the T4 virus latches onto a bacterial cell with its tail fibers, bores through the bacterial membrane with its end plate, and then injects the payload of DNA, packaged in its head, into the bacterium. These complex functions are performed by a biological "machine" measuring 60×200 nm. Researchers are exploring ways for viruses to deliver medicinal agents to specific cells. In other feats of nanoscale engineering, researchers have created nanovalves, nanopropellers, and even a nanocar, complete with a chassis, axles, and buckyball wheels, that is only 4 nm wide and is "driven" on a gold surface under the direction of an atomic force microscope (Figure 12.51).

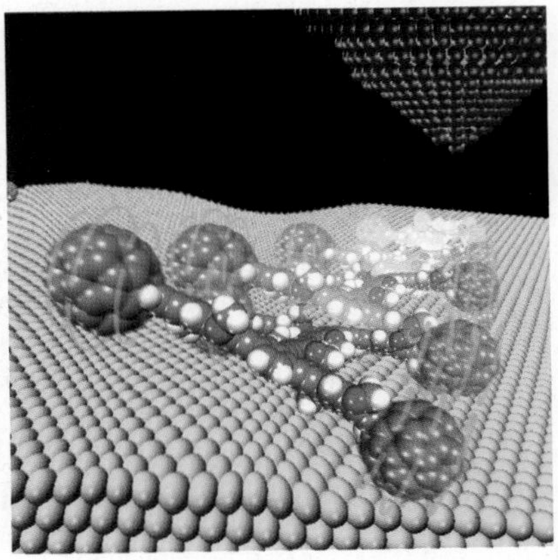

Figure 12.51 Driving a nanocar.

Summary of Section 12.7

- Doping increases the conductivity of semiconductors and is essential to modern electronic materials. Doping silicon with Group 5A(15) atoms introduces negative sites (n-type semiconductor) by adding valence electrons to the conduction band, whereas doping with Group 3A(13) atoms adds positive holes (p-type semiconductor) by emptying some orbitals in the valence band. Placing these two types of semiconductors in contact with one another forms a p-n junction. Sandwiching a p-type portion between two n-type portions forms a transistor.

- Liquid crystal phases flow like liquids but have molecules ordered like crystalline solids. Typically, the molecules have rodlike shapes, and their intermolecular forces keep them aligned. Thermotropic phases are prepared by heating the solid; lyotropic phases form when the solvent concentration is varied. The nematic, cholesteric, and smectic phases of liquid crystals differ in their molecular order. Liquid crystal applications depend on controlling the orientation of the molecules.
- Ceramics are very resistant to heat and chemicals. Most are network covalent solids formed at high temperature from simple reactants. They add lightweight strength to other materials.
- Polymers are extremely large molecules that adopt the shape of a random coil, as a result of intermolecular forces. A polymer sample has an average molar mass because it consists of chains with a range of lengths. The high viscosity of a polymer arises from attractions between chains or, in the case of a dissolved polymer, between chains and solvent. By varying the degrees of branching, crosslinking, and ordering (crystallinity), chemists tailor polymers with specific properties.
- Nanoscale materials can be made through construction processes involving self-assembly and controlled orientation of molecules.

CHAPTER REVIEW GUIDE

Learning Objectives

Relevant section (§) and/or sample problem (SP) numbers appear in parentheses.

Understand These Concepts

1. How the interplay between kinetic and potential energy underlies the properties of the three states of matter and their phase changes (§12.1)
2. The processes involved, both within a phase and during a phase change, when heat is added or removed from a pure substance (§12.2)
3. The meaning of vapor pressure and how phase changes are dynamic equilibrium processes (§12.2)
4. How temperature and intermolecular forces influence vapor pressure (§12.2)
5. The relation between vapor pressure and boiling point (§12.2)
6. How a phase diagram shows the phases of a substance at differing conditions of pressure and temperature (§12.2)
7. The distinction between bonding and intermolecular forces on the basis of Coulomb's law and the meaning of the van der Waals radius of an atom (§12.3)
8. The types and relative strengths of intermolecular forces acting in a substance (dipole-dipole, H-bonding, dispersion), the impact of H bonding on physical properties, and the meaning of polarizability (§12.3)
9. The meanings of surface tension, capillarity, and viscosity and how intermolecular forces influence their magnitudes (§12.4)
10. How the important macroscopic properties of water arise from atomic and molecular properties (§12.5)
11. The meaning of *crystal lattice* and the characteristics of the three types of cubic unit cells (§12.6)
12. How packing of spheres gives rise to the hexagonal and cubic unit cells (§12.6)
13. Types of crystalline solids and how their intermolecular forces give rise to their properties (§12.6)
14. How band theory accounts for the properties of metals and the relative conductivities of metals, nonmetals, and metalloids (§12.6)
15. The structures, properties, and functions of modern materials (doped semiconductors, liquid crystals, ceramics, polymers, and nanostructures) (§12.7)

Master These Skills

1. Calculating the overall enthalpy change when heat is gained or lost by a pure substance (§12.2 and SP 12.1)
2. Using the Clausius-Clapeyron equation to examine the relationship between vapor pressure and temperature (SP 12.2)
3. Using a phase diagram to predict the physical state and/or phase change of a substance (§12.2)
4. Determining whether a substance can form H bonds and drawing the H-bonded structures (SP 12.3)
5. Predicting the types and relative strength of the bonding and intermolecular forces acting within a substance from its structure (SP 12.4)
6. Finding the number of particles in a unit cell (§12.6)
7. Calculating atomic radius from the crystal structure of an element (SP 12.5, 12.6)

Key Terms

Page numbers appear in parentheses.

Section 12.1
phase (419)
intermolecular forces (419)
phase change (420)
condensation (420)
vaporization (420)
freezing (420)
melting (fusion) (420)
sublimation (421)
deposition (421)
heat of vaporization (ΔH°_{vap}) (421)
heat of fusion (ΔH°_{fus}) (421)
heat of sublimation (ΔH°_{subl}) (421)

Section 12.2
heating-cooling curve (422)
vapor pressure (426)
Clausius-Clapeyron equation (427)
boiling point (428)
melting point (429)
phase diagram (429)
triple point (429)
critical point (429)

Section 12.3
van der Waals radius (431)
ion-dipole force (432)
dipole-dipole force (432)
hydrogen bond (H bond) (432)
polarizability (434)
dispersion (London) force (435)

Section 12.4
surface tension (437)
capillarity (438)
viscosity (439)

Section 12.6
crystalline solid (441)
amorphous solid (441)
lattice (442)
unit cell (442)
coordination number (442)
simple cubic unit cell (442)
body-centered cubic unit cell (442)
face-centered cubic unit cell (442)
packing efficiency (444)
hexagonal closest packing (444)
cubic closest packing (444)
x-ray diffraction analysis (447)
scanning tunneling microscopy (447)
atomic solid (449)
molecular solid (449)
ionic solid (449)
metallic solid (451)
network covalent solid (451)
band theory (452)
valence band (453)
conduction band (453)
conductor (453)
semiconductor (453)
insulator (453)
superconductivity (454)

Section 12.7
crystal defect (455)
doping (455)
liquid crystal (456)
ceramic (459)
polymer (461)
macromolecule (461)
monomer (461)
degree of polymerization (n) (461)
random coil (462)
radius of gyration (R_g) (463)
plastic (465)
branch (465)
crosslink (465)
elastomer (465)
copolymer (465)
nanotechnology (466)

Key Equations and Relationships

Page number appears in parentheses.

12.1 Using the vapor pressure at one temperature to find the vapor pressure at another temperature (two-point form of the Clausius-Clapeyron equation) (427):

$$\ln \frac{P_2}{P_1} = \frac{-\Delta H_{vap}}{R}\left(\frac{1}{T_2} - \frac{1}{T_1}\right)$$

Brief Solutions to Follow-Up Problems

12.1 The scenes represent solid water at −7.00°C melting to liquid water at 16.0°C, so there are three stages.

Stage 1, $H_2O(s)$ [−7.00°C] ⟶ $H_2O(s)$ [0.00°C]:

$$q = n \times C_{water(s)} \times \Delta T = (2.25 \text{ mol})(37.6 \text{ J/mol·°C})(7.00\text{°C}) = 592 \text{ J} = 0.592 \text{ kJ}$$

Stage 2, $H_2O(s)$ [0.00°C] ⟶ $H_2O(l)$ [0.00°C]:

$$q = n(\Delta H^\circ_{fus}) = (2.25 \text{ mol})(6.02 \text{ kJ/mol}) = 13.5 \text{ kJ}$$

Stage 3, $H_2O(l)$ [0.00°C] ⟶ $H_2O(l)$ [16.0°C]:

$$q = n \times C_{water(l)} \times \Delta T = (2.25 \text{ mol})(75.4 \text{ J/mol·°C})(16.0\text{°C}) = 2714 \text{ J} = 2.71 \text{ kJ}$$

Total heat (kJ) = 0.592 kJ + 13.5 kJ + 2.71 kJ = 16.8 kJ

12.2

$$\ln \frac{P_2}{P_1} = \left(\frac{-40.7\times10^3 \text{ J/mol}}{8.314 \text{ J/mol·K}}\right) \times \left(\frac{1}{273.15 + 85.5 \text{ K}} - \frac{1}{273.15 + 34.1 \text{ K}}\right)$$

$$= (-4.90\times10^3 \text{ K})(-4.6\times10^{-4} \text{ K}^{-1}) = 2.28$$

$$\frac{P_2}{P_1} = 9.8; \text{ thus, } P_2 = 40.1 \text{ torr} \times 9.8 = 3.9\times10^2 \text{ torr}$$

12.3 (a)

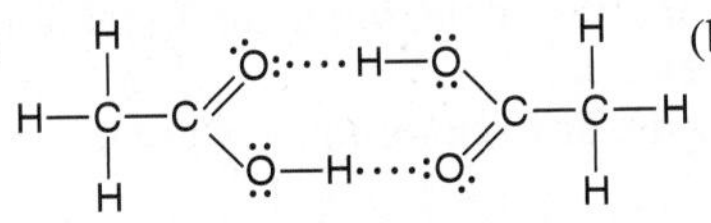

(b)

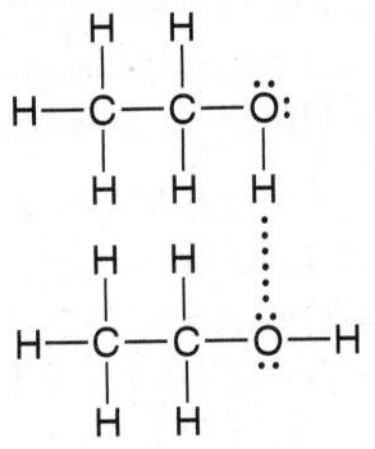

(c) No H bonding

12.4 (a) Dipole-dipole, dispersion; CH_3Br
(b) H bonds, dipole-dipole, dispersion; $CH_3CH_2CH_2OH$
(c) Dispersion; C_3H_8

12.5

$$\text{Avogadro's no.} = \frac{1 \text{ cm}^3}{7.874 \text{ g Fe}} \times \frac{55.85 \text{ g Fe}}{1 \text{ mol Fe}} \times 0.68 \times \frac{1 \text{ Fe atom}}{8.38\times10^{-24} \text{ cm}^3} = 5.8\times10^{23} \text{ Fe atoms/mol Fe}$$

12.6 From Figure 12.29B,

$$A = \frac{4r}{\sqrt{3}} = \frac{4(126 \text{ pm})}{\sqrt{3}} = 291 \text{ pm}$$

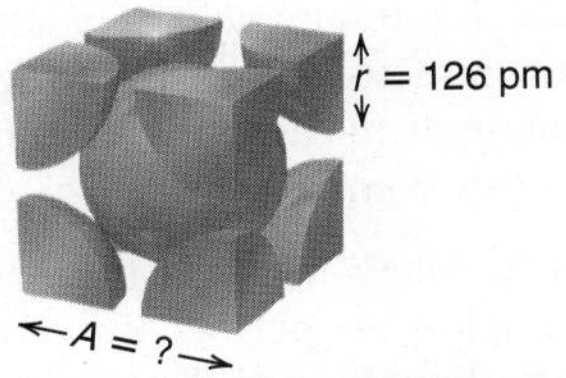

PROBLEMS

Problems with **colored** numbers are in Appendix E and worked in detail in the Student Solutions Manual. Problem sections match those in the text and provide the numbers of relevant sample problems. Most offer Concept Review Questions, Skill-Building Exercises (grouped in pairs covering the same concept), and Problems in Context. The Comprehensive Problems are based on material from any section or previous chapter.

Overview of Physical States and Phase Changes

Concept Review Questions

12.1 How does the energy of attraction between particles compare with their energy of motion in a gas and in a solid? As part of your answer, identify two macroscopic properties that differ between a gas and a solid.

12.2 (a) Why are gases more easily compressed than liquids? (b) Why do liquids have a greater ability to flow than solids?

12.3 What type of forces, intramolecular or intermolecular:
(a) Prevent ice cubes from adopting the shape of their container?
(b) Are overcome when ice melts?
(c) Are overcome when liquid water is vaporized?
(d) Are overcome when gaseous water is converted to hydrogen gas and oxygen gas?

12.4 (a) Why is the heat of fusion (ΔH_{fus}) of a substance smaller than its heat of vaporization (ΔH_{vap})?
(b) Why is the heat of sublimation (ΔH_{subl}) of a substance greater than its ΔH_{vap}?
(c) At a given temperature and pressure, how does the magnitude of the heat of vaporization of a substance compare with that of its heat of condensation?

Skill-Building Exercises (grouped in similar pairs)

12.5 Which forces are intramolecular and which intermolecular?
(a) Those preventing oil from evaporating at room temperature
(b) Those preventing butter from melting in a refrigerator
(c) Those allowing silver to tarnish
(d) Those preventing O_2 in air from forming O atoms

12.6 Which forces are intramolecular and which intermolecular?
(a) Those allowing fog to form on a cool, humid evening
(b) Those allowing water to form when H_2 is sparked
(c) Those allowing liquid benzene to crystallize when cooled
(d) Those responsible for the low boiling point of hexane

12.7 Name the phase change in each of these events: (a) Dew appears on a lawn in the morning. (b) Icicles change into liquid water. (c) Wet clothes dry on a summer day.

12.8 Name the phase change in each of these events: (a) A diamond film forms on a surface from gaseous carbon atoms in a vacuum. (b) Mothballs in a bureau drawer disappear over time. (c) Molten iron from a blast furnace is cast into ingots ("pigs").

Problems in Context

12.9 Liquid propane, a widely used fuel, is produced by compressing gaseous propane. During the process, approximately 15 kJ of energy is released for each mole of gas liquefied. Where does this energy come from?

12.10 Many heat-sensitive and oxygen-sensitive solids, such as camphor, are purified by warming under vacuum. The solid vaporizes directly, and the vapor crystallizes on a cool surface. What phase changes are involved in this method?

Quantitative Aspects of Phase Changes

(Sample Problems 12.1 and 12.2)

Concept Review Questions

12.11 Describe the changes (if any) in potential energy and in kinetic energy among the molecules when gaseous PCl_3 condenses to a liquid at a fixed temperature.

12.12 When benzene is at its melting point, two processes occur simultaneously and balance each other. Describe these processes on the macroscopic and molecular levels.

12.13 Liquid hexane (bp = 69°C) is placed in a closed container at room temperature. At first, the pressure of the vapor phase increases, but after a short time, it stops changing. Why?

12.14 Explain the effect of strong intermolecular forces on each of these parameters: (a) critical temperature; (b) boiling point; (c) vapor pressure; (d) heat of vaporization.

12.15 Match each numbered point in the phase diagram for compound Q with the correct molecular depiction below:

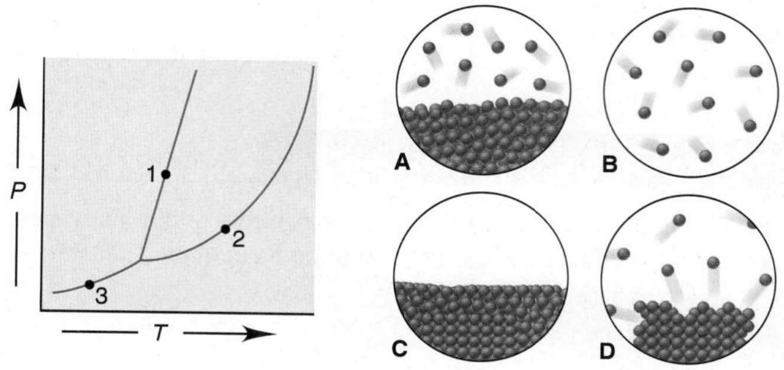

12.16 A liquid is in equilibrium with its vapor in a closed vessel at a fixed temperature. The vessel is connected by a stopcock to an evacuated vessel. When the stopcock is opened, will the final pressure of the vapor be different from the initial value if (a) some liquid remains; (b) all the liquid is first removed? Explain.

12.17 The phase diagram for substance A has a solid-liquid line with a positive slope, and that for substance B has a solid-liquid line with a negative slope. What macroscopic property can distinguish A from B?

12.18 Why does water vapor at 100°C cause a more severe burn than liquid water at 100°C?

Skill-Building Exercises (grouped in similar pairs)

12.19 From the data below, calculate the total heat (in J) needed to convert 22.00 g of ice at −6.00°C to liquid water at 0.500°C:

mp at 1 atm:	0.0°C	ΔH°_{fus}:	6.02 kJ/mol
c_{liquid}:	4.21 J/g·°C	c_{solid}:	2.09 J/g·°C

12.20 From the data below, calculate the total heat (in J) needed to convert 0.333 mol of gaseous ethanol at 300°C and 1 atm to liquid ethanol at 25.0°C and 1 atm:

bp at 1 atm:	78.5°C	ΔH°_{vap}:	40.5 kJ/mol
c_{gas}:	1.43 J/g·°C	c_{liquid}:	2.45 J/g·°C

12.21 A liquid has a ΔH°_{vap} of 35.5 kJ/mol and a boiling point of 122°C at 1.00 atm. What is its vapor pressure at 113°C?

12.22 Diethyl ether has a ΔH°_{vap} of 29.1 kJ/mol and a vapor pressure of 0.703 atm at 25.0°C. What is its vapor pressure at 95.0°C?

12.23 What is the ΔH°_{vap} of a liquid that has a vapor pressure of 621 torr at 85.2°C and a boiling point of 95.6°C at 1 atm?

12.24 Methane (CH_4) has a boiling point of −164°C at 1 atm and a vapor pressure of 42.8 atm at −100°C. What is the heat of vaporization of CH_4?

12.25 Use these data to draw a qualitative phase diagram for ethylene (C_2H_4). Is $C_2H_4(s)$ more or less dense than $C_2H_4(l)$?

bp at 1 atm:	−103.7°C
mp at 1 atm:	−169.16°C
Critical point:	9.9°C and 50.5 atm
Triple point:	−169.17°C and 1.20×10^{-3} atm

12.26 Use these data to draw a qualitative phase diagram for H_2. Does H_2 sublime at 0.05 atm? Explain.

mp at 1 atm:	13.96 K
bp at 1 atm:	20.39 K
Triple point:	13.95 K and 0.07 atm
Critical point:	33.2 K and 13.0 atm
Vapor pressure of solid at 10 K:	0.001 atm

Problems in Context

12.27 Sulfur dioxide is produced in enormous amounts for sulfuric acid production. It melts at −73°C and boils at −10.°C. Its ΔH°_{fus} is 8.619 kJ/mol and its ΔH°_{vap} is 25.73 kJ/mol. The specific heat capacities of the liquid and gas are 0.995 J/g·K and 0.622 J/g·K, respectively. How much heat is required to convert 2.500 kg of solid SO_2 at the melting point to a gas at 60.°C?

12.28 Butane is a common fuel used in cigarette lighters and camping stoves. Normally supplied in metal containers under pressure, the fuel exists as a mixture of liquid and gas, so high temperatures may cause the container to explode. At 25.0°C, the vapor pressure of butane is 2.3 atm. What is the pressure in the container at 135°C (ΔH°_{vap} = 24.3 kJ/mol)?

12.29 Use Figure 12.10, p. 429, to answer the following:
(a) Carbon dioxide is sold in steel cylinders under pressures of approximately 20 atm. Is there liquid CO_2 in the cylinder at room temperature (~20°C)? At 40°C? At −40°C? At −120°C?
(b) Carbon dioxide is also sold as solid chunks, called *dry ice,* in insulated containers. If the chunks are warmed by leaving them in an open container at room temperature, will they melt?
(c) If a container is nearly filled with dry ice and then sealed and warmed to room temperature, will the dry ice melt?
(d) If dry ice is compressed at a temperature below its triple point, will it melt?

Types of Intermolecular Forces

(Sample Problems 12.3 and 12.4)

Concept Review Questions

12.30 Why are covalent bonds typically much stronger than intermolecular forces?

12.31 (a) Name the type of force depicted in each scene below. (b) Rank the forces in order of increasing strength.

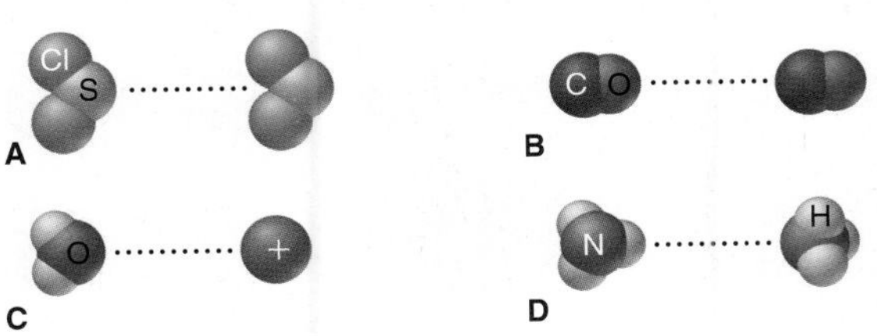

12.32 Oxygen and selenium are members of Group 6A(16). Water forms H bonds, but H_2Se does not. Explain.

12.33 In solid I_2, is the distance between the two I nuclei of one I_2 molecule longer or shorter than the distance between two I nuclei of adjacent I_2 molecules? Explain.

12.34 Polar molecules exhibit dipole-dipole forces. Do they also exhibit dispersion forces? Explain.

12.35 Distinguish between *polarizability* and *polarity*. How does each influence intermolecular forces?

12.36 How can one nonpolar molecule induce a dipole in a nearby nonpolar molecule?

Skill-Building Exercises (grouped in similar pairs)

12.37 What is the strongest interparticle force in each substance?
(a) CH_3OH (b) CCl_4 (c) Cl_2

12.38 What is the strongest interparticle force in each substance?
(a) H_3PO_4 (b) SO_2 (c) $MgCl_2$

12.39 What is the strongest interparticle force in each substance?
(a) CH_3Cl (b) CH_3CH_3 (c) NH_3

12.40 What is the strongest interparticle force in each substance?
(a) Kr (b) BrF (c) H_2SO_4

12.41 Which member of each pair of compounds forms intermolecular H bonds? Draw the H-bonded structures in each case:
(a) $CH_3CH(OH)CH_3$ (OH on the middle carbon) or CH_3SCH_3 (b) HF or HBr

12.42 Which member of each pair of compounds forms intermolecular H bonds? Draw the H-bonded structures in each case:
(a) $(CH_3)_2NH$ or $(CH_3)_3N$ (b) $HOCH_2CH_2OH$ or FCH_2CH_2F

12.43 Which forces oppose vaporization of each substance?
(a) Hexane (b) Water (c) $SiCl_4$

12.44 Which forces oppose vaporization of each substance?
(a) Br_2 (b) SbH_3 (c) CH_3NH_2

12.45 Which has the greater polarizability? Explain.
(a) Br^- or I^- (b) $CH_2{=}CH_2$ or $CH_3{-}CH_3$ (c) H_2O or H_2Se

12.46 Which has the greater polarizability? Explain.
(a) Ca^{2+} or Ca (b) CH_3CH_3 or $CH_3CH_2CH_3$ (c) CCl_4 or CF_4

12.47 Which member in each pair of liquids has the *higher* vapor pressure at a given temperature? Explain.
(a) C_2H_6 or C_4H_{10} (b) CH_3CH_2OH or CH_3CH_2F
(c) NH_3 or PH_3

12.48 Which member in each pair of liquids has the *lower* vapor pressure at a given temperature? Explain.
(a) $HOCH_2CH_2OH$ or $CH_3CH_2CH_2OH$
(b) CH_3COOH or $(CH_3)_2C{=}O$ (c) HF or HCl

12.49 Which substance has the *lower* boiling point? Explain.
(a) LiCl or HCl (b) NH_3 or PH_3 (c) Xe or I_2

12.50 Which substance has the *higher* boiling point? Explain.
(a) CH_3CH_2OH or $CH_3CH_2CH_3$ (b) NO or N_2
(c) H_2S or H_2Te

12.51 Which substance has the *lower* boiling point? Explain.
(a) $CH_3CH_2CH_2CH_3$ or cyclobutane ($CH_2{-}CH_2$ / $CH_2{-}CH_2$, ring) (b) NaBr or PBr_3
(c) H_2O or HBr

12.52 Which substance has the *higher* boiling point? Explain.
(a) CH_3OH or CH_3CH_3 (b) FNO or ClNO
(c)
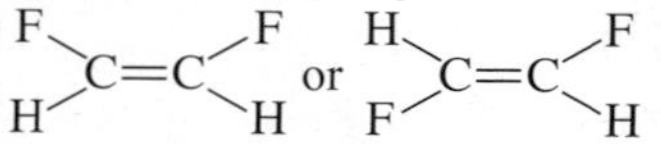

Problems in Context

12.53 For pairs of molecules in the gas phase, average H-bond dissociation energies are 17 kJ/mol for NH_3, 22 kJ/mol for H_2O, and 29 kJ/mol for HF. Explain this increase in H-bond strength.

12.54 Dispersion forces are the only intermolecular forces present in motor oil, yet it has a high boiling point. Explain.

12.55 Why does the antifreeze ingredient ethylene glycol ($HOCH_2CH_2OH$; $\mathcal{M} = 62.07$ g/mol) have a boiling point of 197.6°C, whereas propanol ($CH_3CH_2CH_2OH$; $\mathcal{M} = 60.09$ g/mol), a compound with a similar molar mass, has a boiling point of only 97.4°C?

Properties of the Liquid State

Concept Review Questions

12.56 Before the phenomenon of surface tension was understood, physicists described the surface of water as being covered with a "skin." What causes this skinlike phenomenon?

12.57 Small, equal-sized drops of oil, water, and mercury lie on a waxed floor. How does each liquid behave? Explain.

12.58 Why does an aqueous solution of ethanol (CH_3CH_2OH) have a lower surface tension than water?

12.59 Why are units of energy per area (J/m^2) used for surface tension values?

12.60 Does the *strength* of the intermolecular forces in a liquid change as the liquid is heated? Explain. Why does liquid viscosity decrease with rising temperature?

Skill-Building Exercises (grouped in similar pairs)

12.61 Rank the following in order of *increasing* surface tension at a given temperature, and explain your ranking:
(a) $CH_3CH_2CH_2OH$ (b) $HOCH_2CH(OH)CH_2OH$
(c) $HOCH_2CH_2OH$

12.62 Rank the following in order of *decreasing* surface tension at a given temperature, and explain your ranking:
(a) CH_3OH (b) CH_3CH_3 (c) $H_2C{=}O$

12.63 Rank the compounds in Problem 12.61 in order of *decreasing* viscosity at a given temperature; explain your ranking.

12.64 Rank the compounds in Problem 12.62 in order of *increasing* viscosity at a given temperature; explain your ranking.

Problems in Context

12.65 Soil vapor extraction (SVE) is used to remove volatile organic pollutants, such as chlorinated solvents, from soil at hazardous waste sites. Vent wells are drilled, and a vacuum pump is applied to the subsurface. (a) How does this remove pollutants? (b) Why does heating combined with SVE speed the process?

12.66 Use Figure 12.2, p. 421 to answer the following: (a) Does it take more heat to melt 12.0 g of CH_4 or 12.0 g of Hg? (b) Does it take more heat to vaporize 12.0 g of CH_4 or 12.0 g of Hg? (c) What is the principal intermolecular force in each sample?

12.67 Pentanol ($C_5H_{11}OH$; $\mathcal{M} = 88.15$ g/mol) has nearly the same molar mass as hexane (C_6H_{14}; $\mathcal{M} = 86.17$ g/mol) but is more than 12 times as viscous at 20°C. Explain.

The Uniqueness of Water

Concept Review Questions

12.68 For what types of substances is water a good solvent? For what types is it a poor solvent? Explain.

12.69 A water molecule can engage in as many as four H bonds. Explain.

12.70 Warm-blooded animals have a narrow range of body temperature because their bodies have a high water content. Explain.

12.71 What property of water keeps plant debris on the surface of lakes and ponds? What is the ecological significance of this?

12.72 A drooping plant can be made upright by watering the ground around it. Explain.

12.73 Describe the molecular basis of the property of water responsible for the presence of ice on the surface of a frozen lake.

12.74 Describe in molecular terms what occurs when ice melts.

The Solid State: Structure, Properties, and Bonding

(Sample Problems 12.5 and 12.6)

Concept Review Questions

12.75 What is the difference between an amorphous solid and a crystalline solid on the macroscopic and molecular levels? Give an example of each.

12.76 How are a solid's unit cell and crystal structure related?

12.77 For structures consisting of identical atoms, how many atoms are contained in the simple, body-centered, and face-centered cubic unit cells? Explain how you obtained the values.

12.78 An element has a crystal structure in which the width of the cubic unit cell equals the diameter of an atom. What type of unit cell does it have?

12.79 What specific difference in the positioning of spheres gives a crystal structure based on the face-centered cubic unit cell less empty space than one based on the body-centered cubic unit cell?

12.80 Both solid Kr and solid Cu consist of individual atoms. Why do their physical properties differ so much?

12.81 What is the energy gap in band theory? Compare its size in superconductors, conductors, semiconductors, and insulators.

12.82 Predict the effect (if any) of an increase in temperature on the electrical conductivity of (a) a conductor; (b) a semiconductor; (c) an insulator.

12.83 Besides the type of unit cell, what information is needed to find the density of a solid consisting of identical atoms?

Skill-Building Exercises (grouped in similar pairs)

12.84 What type of crystal lattice does each metal form? (The number of atoms per unit cell is given in parentheses.)
(a) Ni (4) (b) Cr (2) (c) Ca (4)

12.85 What is the number of atoms per unit cell for each metal?
(a) Polonium, Po (b) Manganese, Mn (c) Silver, Ag

12.86 When cadmium oxide reacts to form cadmium selenide, a change in unit cell occurs, as depicted below:

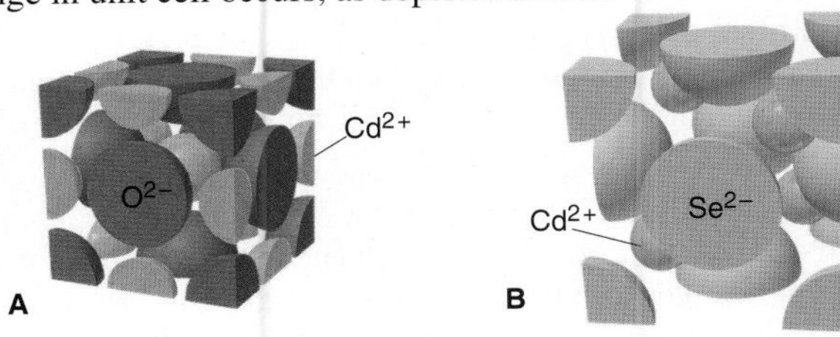

(a) What is the change in unit cell?
(b) Does the coordination number of cadmium change? Explain.

12.87 As molten iron cools to 1674 K, it adopts one type of cubic unit cell; then, as the temperature drops below 1181 K, it changes to another, as depicted below:

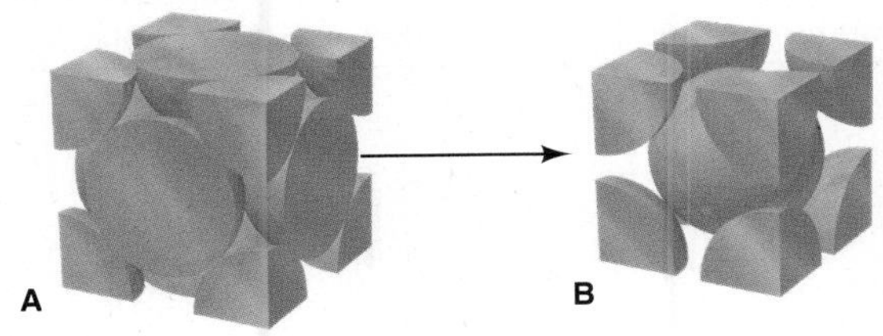

(a) What is the change in unit cell?
(b) Which crystal structure has the greater packing efficiency?

12.88 Of the five major types of crystalline solid, which does each of the following form, and why: (a) Ni; (b) F_2; (c) CH_3OH; (d) Sn; (e) Si; (f) Xe?

12.89 Of the five major types of crystalline solid, which does each of the following form, and why: (a) SiC; (b) Na_2SO_4; (c) SF_6; (d) cholesterol ($C_{27}H_{45}OH$); (e) KCl; (f) BN?

12.90 Zinc oxide adopts the zinc blende crystal structure (Figure P12.90). How many Zn^{2+} ions are in the ZnO unit cell?

12.91 Calcium sulfide adopts the sodium chloride crystal structure (Figure P12.91). How many S^{2-} ions are in the CaS unit cell?

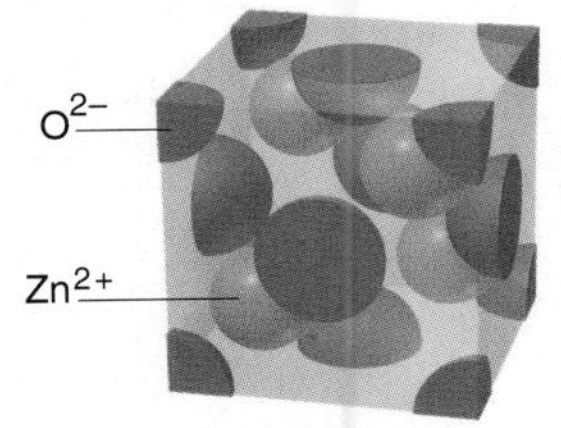

Figure P12.90

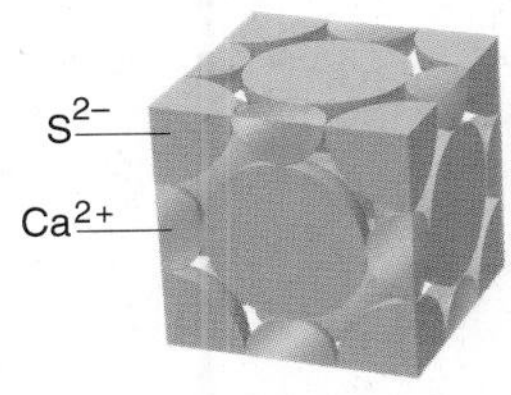

Figure P12.91

12.92 Zinc selenide (ZnSe) crystallizes in the zinc blende structure (see Figure P12.90) and has a density of 5.42 g/cm^3.
(a) How many Zn and Se ions are in each unit cell?
(b) What is the mass of a unit cell?
(c) What is the volume of a unit cell?
(d) What is the edge length of a unit cell?

12.93 An element crystallizes in a face-centered cubic lattice and has a density of 1.45 g/cm^3. The edge of its unit cell is 4.52×10^{-8} cm.
(a) How many atoms are in each unit cell?
(b) What is the volume of a unit cell?
(c) What is the mass of a unit cell?
(d) Calculate an approximate atomic mass for the element.

12.94 Classify each of the following as a conductor, insulator, or semiconductor: (a) phosphorus; (b) mercury; (c) germanium.

12.95 Classify each of the following as a conductor, insulator, or semiconductor: (a) carbon (graphite); (b) sulfur; (c) platinum.

12.96 Predict the effect (if any) of an increase in temperature on the electrical conductivity of (a) antimony; (b) tellurium; (c) bismuth.

12.97 Predict the effect (if any) of a decrease in temperature on the electrical conductivity of (a) silicon; (b) lead; (c) germanium.

Problems in Context

12.98 Polonium, the Period 6 member of Group 6A(16), is a rare radioactive metal that is the only element with a crystal structure based on the simple cubic unit cell. If its density is 9.142 g/cm^3, calculate an approximate atomic radius for polonium.

12.99 The coinage metals—copper, silver, and gold—crystallize in a cubic closest packed structure. Use the density of copper (8.95 g/cm^3) and its molar mass (63.55 g/mol) to calculate an approximate atomic radius for copper.

12.100 One of the most important enzymes in the world—nitrogenase, the plant protein that catalyzes nitrogen fixation—contains active clusters of iron, sulfur, and molybdenum atoms. Crystalline molybdenum (Mo) has a body-centered cubic unit cell (d of Mo = 10.28 g/cm^3). (a) Determine the edge length of the unit cell. (b) Calculate the atomic radius of Mo.

12.101 Tantalum (Ta; d = 16.634 g/cm^3 and $\mathcal{M}$ = 180.9479 g/mol) has a body-centered cubic structure with a unit-cell edge length of 3.3058 Å. Use these data to calculate Avogadro's number.

Advanced Materials

Concept Review Questions

12.102 When tin is added to copper, the resulting alloy (bronze) is much harder than copper. Explain.

12.103 In the process of doping a semiconductor, certain impurities are added to increase its electrical conductivity. Explain this process for an n-type and a p-type semiconductor.

12.104 State two molecular characteristics of substances that typically form liquid crystals. How is each related to function?

12.105 Distinguish between isotropic and anisotropic substances. To which category do liquid crystals belong?

12.106 How are the properties of high-tech ceramics the same as those of traditional clay ceramics, and how are they different? Refer to specific substances in your answer.

12.107 Why is the average molar mass of a polymer sample different from the molar mass of an individual chain?

12.108 How does the random coil shape relate to the radius of gyration of a polymer chain?

12.109 What factor(s) influence the viscosity of a polymer solution? What factor(s) influence the viscosity of a molten polymer? What is a polymer glass?

12.110 Use an example to show how branching and crosslinking can affect the physical behavior of a polymer.

Skill-Building Exercises (grouped in similar pairs)

12.111 Silicon and germanium are both semiconducting elements from Group 4A(14) that can be doped to improve their conductivity. Would each of the following form an n-type or a p-type semiconductor: (a) Ge doped with P; (b) Si doped with In?

12.112 Would each of the following form an n-type or a p-type semiconductor: (a) Ge doped with As; (b) Si doped with B?

12.113 The repeat unit in a polystyrene coffee cup has the formula $C_6H_5CHCH_2$. If the molar mass of the polymer is 3.5×10^5 g/mol, what is the degree of polymerization?

12.114 The monomer of poly(vinyl chloride) has the formula C_2H_3Cl. If there are 1565 repeat units in a single chain of the polymer, what is the molecular mass (in amu) of that chain?

12.115 The polypropylene (repeat unit CH_3CHCH_2) in a plastic toy has a molar mass of 2.8×10^5 g/mol and a repeat unit length of 0.252 pm. Calculate the radius of gyration.

12.116 The polymer that is used to make 2-L soda bottles [poly(ethylene terephthalate)] has a repeat unit with molecular formula $C_{10}H_8O_4$ and length 1.075 nm. Calculate the radius of gyration of a chain with molar mass of 2.30×10^4 g/mol.

Comprehensive Problems

12.117 A 0.75-L bottle is cleaned, dried, and closed in a room where the air is 22°C and 44% relative humidity (that is, the water vapor in the air is 0.44 of the equilibrium vapor pressure at 22°C). The bottle is then brought outside and stored at 0.0°C.
(a) What mass of liquid water condenses inside the bottle?
(b) Would liquid water condense at 10°C? (See Table 5.2, p. 200.)

12.118 In an experiment, 5.00 L of N_2 is saturated with water vapor at 22°C and then compressed to half its volume at constant *T*. (a) What is the partial pressure of H_2O in the compressed gas mixture? (b) What mass of water vapor condenses to liquid?

12.119 Barium is the largest nonradioactive alkaline earth metal. It has a body-centered cubic unit cell and a density of 3.62 g/cm^3. What is the atomic radius of barium? (Volume of a sphere: $V = \frac{4}{3}\pi r^3$.)

12.120 Two important characteristics used to evaluate the risk of fire or explosion are a compound's *lower flammable limit* (LFL) and *flash point.* The LFL is the minimum percentage by volume in air that is ignitable. Below that, the mixture is too "lean" to burn. The flash point is the temperature at which the air over a confined liquid becomes ignitable. *n*-Hexane boils at 68.7°C at 1 atm. At 20.0°C, its vapor pressure is 121 mmHg. The LFL of *n*-hexane is 1.1%. Calculate the flash point of *n*-hexane.

12.121 Bismuth is used to calibrate instruments employed in high-pressure studies because it has several well-characterized crystalline phases. Its phase diagram (*right*) shows the liquid phase and five solid phases that are stable above 1 katm (1000 atm) and up to 300°C.
(a) Which solid phases are stable at 25°C? (b) Which phase is stable at 50 katm and 175°C? (c) As the pressure is reduced from 100 to 1 katm at 200°C, what phase transitions does bismuth undergo? (d) What phases are present at each of the triple points?

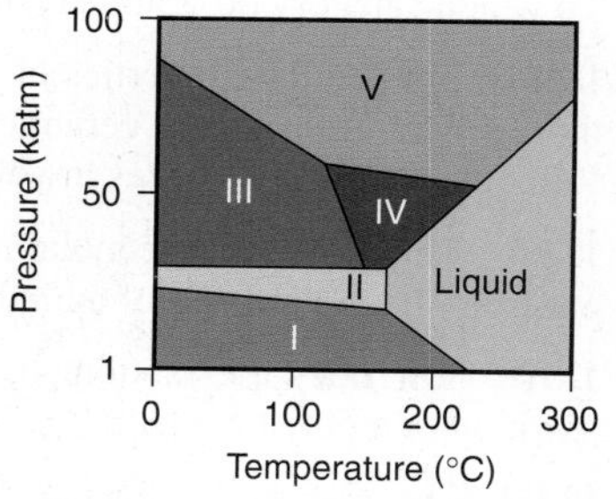

12.122 In making computer chips, a 4.00-kg cylindrical ingot of ultrapure n-type doped silicon that is 5.20 inches in diameter is sliced into wafers 1.12×10^{-4} m thick.
(a) Assuming no waste, how many wafers can be made?
(b) What is the mass of a wafer (*d* of Si = 2.34 g/cm^3; *V* of a cylinder = $\pi r^2 h$)?
(c) A key step in making p-n junctions for the chip is chemical removal of the oxide layer on the wafer through treatment with gaseous HF. Write a balanced equation for this reaction.
(d) If 0.750% of the Si atoms are removed during the treatment in part (c), how many moles of HF are required per wafer, assuming 100% reaction yield?

12.123 Methyl salicylate, $C_8H_8O_3$, the odorous constituent of oil of wintergreen, has a vapor pressure of 1.00 torr at 54.3°C and 10.0 torr at 95.3°C. (a) What is its vapor pressure at 25°C? (b) What is the minimum number of liters of air that must pass over a sample of the compound at 25°C to vaporize 1.0 mg of it?

12.124 Mercury (Hg) vapor is toxic and readily absorbed from the lungs. At 20.°C, mercury (ΔH_{vap} = 59.1 kJ/mol) has a vapor pressure of 1.20×10^{-3} torr, which is high enough to be hazardous. To reduce the danger to workers in processing plants, Hg is cooled to lower its vapor pressure. At what temperature would the vapor pressure of Hg be at the safer level of 5.0×10^{-5} torr?

12.125 Polytetrafluoroethylene (Teflon) has a repeat unit with the formula $F_2C—CF_2$. A sample of the polymer consists of fractions with the following distribution of chains:

Fraction	Average no. of repeat units	Amount (mol) of polymer
1	273	0.10
2	330	0.40
3	368	1.00
4	483	0.70
5	525	0.30
6	575	0.10

(a) Determine the molar mass of each fraction.
(b) Determine the number-average molar mass of the sample.
(c) Another type of average molar mass of a polymer sample is called the *weight-average molar mass,* $\mathcal{M}_w$:

$$\mathcal{M}_w = \frac{\Sigma\ (\mathcal{M} \text{ of fraction} \times \text{mass of fraction})}{\text{total mass of all fractions}}$$

Calculate the weight-average molar mass of the above sample.

12.126 A greenhouse contains 256 m^3 of air at a temperature of 26°C, and a humidifier in it vaporizes 4.20 L of water. (a) What is the pressure of water vapor in the greenhouse, assuming that none escapes and that the air was originally completely dry (*d* of H_2O = 1.00 g/mL)? (b) What total volume of liquid water would have to be vaporized to saturate the air (i.e., achieve 100% relative humidity)? (See Table 5.2, p. 200.)

12.127 Like most transition metals, tantalum (Ta) exhibits several oxidation states. Give the formula of each tantalum compound whose unit cell is depicted below:

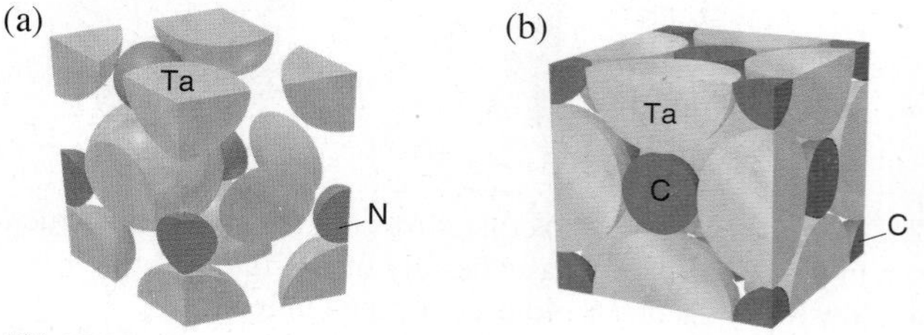

12.128 KF has the same type of crystal structure as NaCl. The unit cell of KF has an edge length of 5.39 Å. Find the density of KF.

12.129 Furfural, which is prepared from corncobs, is an important solvent in synthetic rubber manufacturing, and it is reduced to furfuryl alcohol, which is used to make polymer resins. Furfural can also be oxidized to 2-furoic acid.

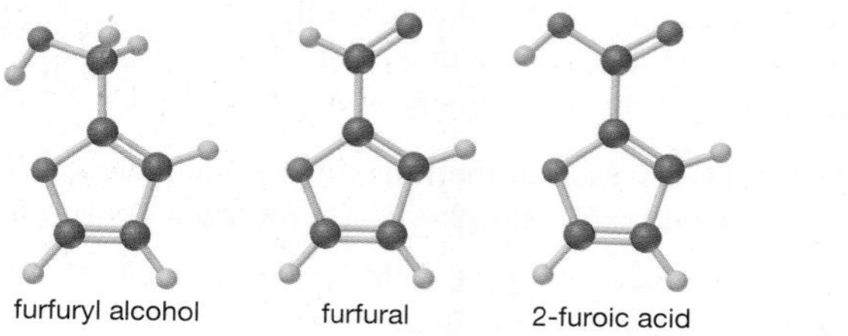

(a) Which of these compounds can form H bonds? Draw structures in each case.
(b) The molecules of some substances can form an "internal" H bond, that is, an H bond *within* a molecule. This takes the form of a polygon with atoms as corners and bonds as sides and an H bond as one of the sides. Which of these molecules is (are) likely to form a stable internal H bond? Draw the structure. (*Hint:* Structures with 5 or 6 atoms as corners are most stable.)

12.130 On a humid day in New Orleans, the temperature is 22.0°C, and the partial pressure of water vapor in the air is 31.0 torr. The 9000-ton air-conditioning system in the Louisiana Superdome maintains an inside air temperature of 22.0°C also, but a partial pressure of water vapor of 10.0 torr. The volume of air in the dome is 2.4×10^6 m^3, and the total pressure is 1.0 atm both inside and outside the dome. (a) What mass of water (in metric tons) must be removed every time the inside air is completely replaced with outside air? (*Hint:* How many moles of gas are in the dome? How many moles of water vapor? How many moles of dry air? How many moles of outside air must be added to the air in the dome to simulate the composition of outside air?) (b) Find the heat released when this mass of water condenses.

12.131 The boiling point of amphetamine, $C_9H_{13}N$, is 201°C at 760 torr and 83°C at 13 torr. What is the concentration (in g/m^3) of amphetamine when it is in contact with 20.°C air?

12.132 Diamond has a face-centered cubic unit cell, with four more C atoms in tetrahedral holes within the cell. Densities of diamonds vary from 3.01 g/cm^3 to 3.52 g/cm^3 because C atoms are missing from some holes. (a) Calculate the unit-cell edge length of the densest diamond. (b) Assuming the cell dimensions are fixed, how many C atoms are in the unit cell of the diamond with the lowest density?

12.133 Is it possible for a salt of formula AB_3 to have a face-centered cubic unit cell of anions with cations in all the eight available holes? Explain.

12.134 The density of solid gallium at its melting point is 5.9 g/cm^3, whereas that of liquid gallium is 6.1 g/cm^3. Is the temperature at the triple point higher or lower than the normal melting point? Is the slope of the solid-liquid line for gallium positive or negative?

12.135 A 4.7-L sealed bottle containing 0.33 g of liquid ethanol, C_2H_6O, is placed in a refrigerator and reaches equilibrium with its vapor at −11°C. (a) What mass of ethanol is present in the vapor? (b) When the container is removed and warmed to room temperature, 20.°C, will all the ethanol vaporize? (c) How much liquid ethanol would be present at 0.0°C? The vapor pressure of ethanol is 10. torr at −2.3°C and 40. torr at 19°C.

12.136 Substance A has the following properties.

mp at 1 atm:	−20.°C	bp at 1 atm:	85°C
ΔH_{fus}:	180. J/g	ΔH_{vap}:	500. J/g
c_{solid}:	1.0 J/g·°C	c_{liquid}:	2.5 J/g·°C
c_{gas}:	0.5 J/g·°C		

At 1 atm, a 25-g sample of A is heated from −40.°C to 100.°C at a constant rate of 450. J/min. (a) How many minutes does it take to heat the sample to its melting point? (b) How many minutes does it take to melt the sample? (c) Perform any other necessary calculations, and draw a curve of temperature vs. time for the entire heating process.

12.137 An aerospace manufacturer is building a prototype experimental aircraft that cannot be detected by radar. Boron nitride is chosen for incorporation into the body parts, and the boric acid/ammonia method is used to prepare the ceramic material. Given 85.5% and 86.8% yields for the two reaction steps, how much boron nitride can be prepared from 1.00 metric ton of boric acid and 12.5 m^3 of ammonia at 275 K and 3.07×10^3 kPa? Assume that ammonia does not behave ideally under these conditions and is recycled completely in the reaction process.

12.138 The ball-and-stick models below represent three compounds with the same molecular formula, $C_4H_8O_2$:

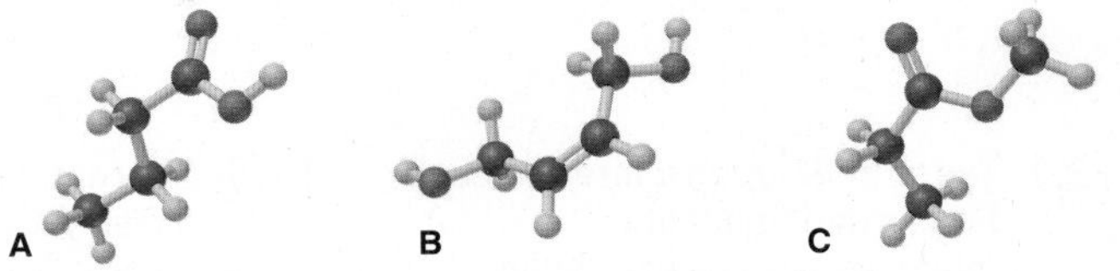

(a) Which compound(s) can form intermolecular H bonds?
(b) Which has the highest viscosity?

12.139 The ΔH°_f of gaseous dimethyl ether (CH_3OCH_3) is −185.4 kJ/mol; the vapor pressure is 1.00 atm at −23.7°C and 0.526 atm at −37.8°C. (a) Calculate ΔH°_{vap} of dimethyl ether. (b) Calculate ΔH°_f of liquid dimethyl ether.

12.140 The crystal structure of sodium is based on the body-centered cubic unit cell. What is the mass of one unit cell of Na?

12.141 The *intrinsic viscosity* of a solute in a solvent, $[\eta]_{solvent}$, is the portion of the total viscosity due to the solute and is related to solute shape. In polymer science, it relates as well to intermolecular interactions between solvent and polymer: higher $[\eta]_{solvent}$ means stronger interaction. The $[\eta]_{solvent}$ values of polymers in solution are given by the Mark-Houwink equation, $[\eta]_{solvent} = K\mathcal{M}^a$, where $\mathcal{M}$ is the molar mass of the polymer, and K and a are constants specific to the polymer and solvent. Use the data below for 25°C to answer the following questions:

Polymer	Solvent	K (mL/g)	a
Polystyrene	Benzene	9.5×10^{-3}	0.74
	Cyclohexane	8.1×10^{-2}	0.50
Polyisobutylene	Benzene	8.3×10^{-2}	0.50
	Cyclohexane	2.6×10^{-1}	0.70

(a) A polystyrene sample has a molar mass of 104,160 g/mol. Calculate the intrinsic viscosity in benzene and in cyclohexane. Which solvent has stronger interactions with the polymer?
(b) A different polystyrene sample has a molar mass of 52,000 g/mol. Calculate its $[\eta]_{benzene}$. Given a polymer standard of known $\mathcal{M}$, how could you use its measured $[\eta]$ in a given solvent to determine the molar mass of any sample of that polymer?
(c) Compare $[\eta]$ of a polyisobutylene sample [repeat unit $(CH_3)_2CCH_2$] with a molar mass of 104,160 g/mol with that of the polystyrene in part (a). What does this suggest about the solvent-polymer interactions of the two samples?

12.142 One way of purifying gaseous H_2 is to pass it under high pressure through the holes of a metal's crystal structure. Palladium, which adopts a cubic closest packed structure, absorbs more H_2 than any other element and is one of the metals used for this purpose. How the metal and H_2 interact is unclear, but it is estimated that the density of absorbed H_2 approaches that of liquid hydrogen (70.8 g/L). What volume (in L) of gaseous H_2 (at STP) can be packed into the spaces of 1 dm^3 of palladium metal?

The Properties of Mixtures: Solutions and Colloids

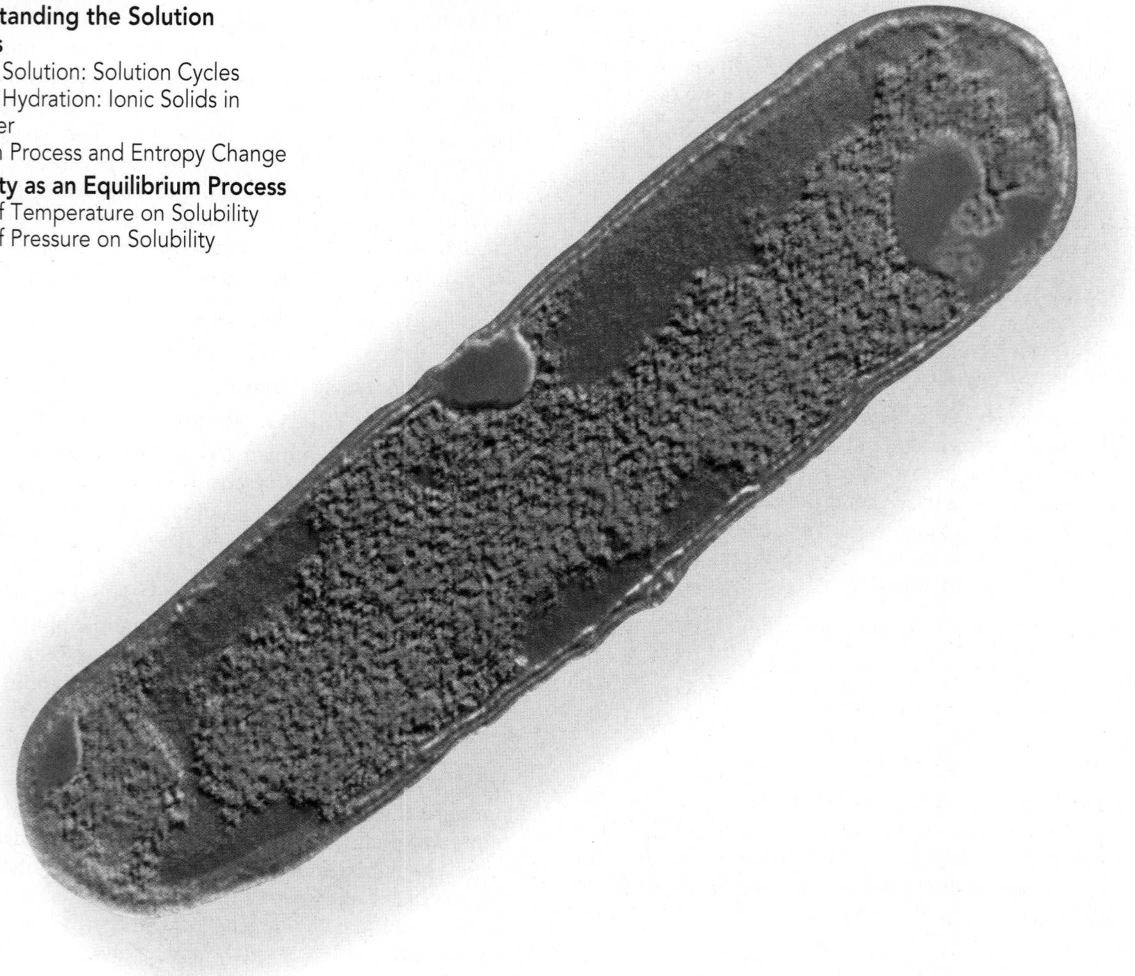

13

Concepts and skills to review before you study this chapter

- separation of mixtures (Section 2.9)
- calculations involving mass percent (Section 3.1) and molarity (Section 3.5)
- electrolytes; water as solvent (Sections 4.1 and 12.5)
- mole fraction and Dalton's law (Section 5.4)
- intermolecular forces and polarizability (Section 12.3)
- monomers and polymers (Section 12.7)
- vapor pressure of liquids (Section 12.2)

Virtually all the gases, liquids, and solids in the real world are *mixtures*—two or more substances mixed together physically, not combined chemically. Synthetic mixtures, such as glass and soap, usually contain only a dozen or so components, but natural mixtures, such as seawater and soil, often contain over 50. Living mixtures, such as trees and students, are the most complex—even a simple bacterial cell (*photo*) contains well over 5000 different compounds (Table 13.1).

Recall from Chapter 2 that a mixture has two defining characteristics: *its composition is variable,* and *it retains some properties of its components.* We focus here on two common types of mixtures—solutions and colloids—whose main differences relate to particle size and number of phases:

- A *solution* is a *homogeneous* mixture; thus, it exists as one phase. In a solution, the particles are individual atoms, ions, or small molecules.
- A *colloid* is a type of *heterogeneous* mixture. A heterogeneous mixture has two or more phases. They may be visibly distinct, like pebbles in concrete, or not, like the much smaller particles in the colloids smoke and milk. In a colloid, the particles are typically macromolecules or aggregations of small molecules that are dispersed so finely they don't settle out.

Table 13.1 Approximate Composition of a Bacterium

Substance	Mass % of Cell	Number of Types	Number of Molecules
Water	~70	1	5×10^{10}
Ions	1	20	?
Sugars*	3	200	3×10^{8}
Amino acids*	0.4	100	5×10^{7}
Lipids*	2	50	3×10^{7}
Nucleotides*	0.4	200	1×10^{7}
Other small molecules	0.2	~200	?
Macromolecules (proteins, nucleic acids, polysaccharides)	23	~5000	6×10^{6}

*Includes precursors and metabolites.

IN THIS CHAPTER . . . We focus on how intermolecular forces and other energy considerations affect a solute dissolving in a solvent, how we calculate concentrations, and how solutions differ from pure substances. We also briefly consider the behavior and applications of colloids.

- We survey intermolecular forces between solute and solvent and find that substances with similar types of forces form a solution.
- We see how the dual polarity of organic molecules gives rise to these same intermolecular forces, which determine the structures and functions of soaps, antibiotics, biological macromolecules, and cell membranes.
- We use a stepwise cycle to see why a substance dissolves and examine the roles of the heat of solution and the dispersal of matter. To understand the latter factor, we introduce the concept of entropy.
- We examine the equilibrium nature of solubility and see how temperature and pressure affect it.
- We define various solution concentration units and see how to interconvert them mathematically.
- We see why the physical properties of solutions are different from those of pure substances and how we apply those differences.
- We investigate colloids and apply solution and colloid chemistry to the purification of water.

13.1 • TYPES OF SOLUTIONS: INTERMOLECULAR FORCES AND SOLUBILITY

A **solute** dissolves in a **solvent** to form a solution. In general, *the solvent is the most abundant component,* but in some cases, the substances are **miscible**—soluble in each other in any proportion—so the terms "solute" and "solvent" lose their meaning. *The physical state of the solvent usually determines the physical state of the solution.* Solutions can be gaseous, liquid, or solid, but we focus mostly on liquid solutions because they are by far the most important.

The **solubility (*S*)** of a solute is the maximum amount that dissolves in a fixed quantity of a given solvent at a given temperature, where an excess of the solute is present. Different solutes have different solubilities:

- Sodium chloride (NaCl), $S = 39.12$ g/100. mL water at 100.°C.
- Silver chloride (AgCl), $S = 0.0021$ g/100. mL water at 100.°C.

Solubility is a *quantitative* term, but *dilute* and *concentrated* are qualitative, referring to the *relative* amounts of dissolved solute; the NaCl solution above is concentrated, and the AgCl solution is dilute.

A given solute may dissolve in one solvent and not another. The explanation lies in the relative strengths of the intermolecular forces within both solute and solvent and between them. The useful rule-of-thumb **"like dissolves like"** says that *substances with similar types of intermolecular forces dissolve in each other.* Thus, by knowing the forces, we can often predict whether a solute will dissolve in a solvent.

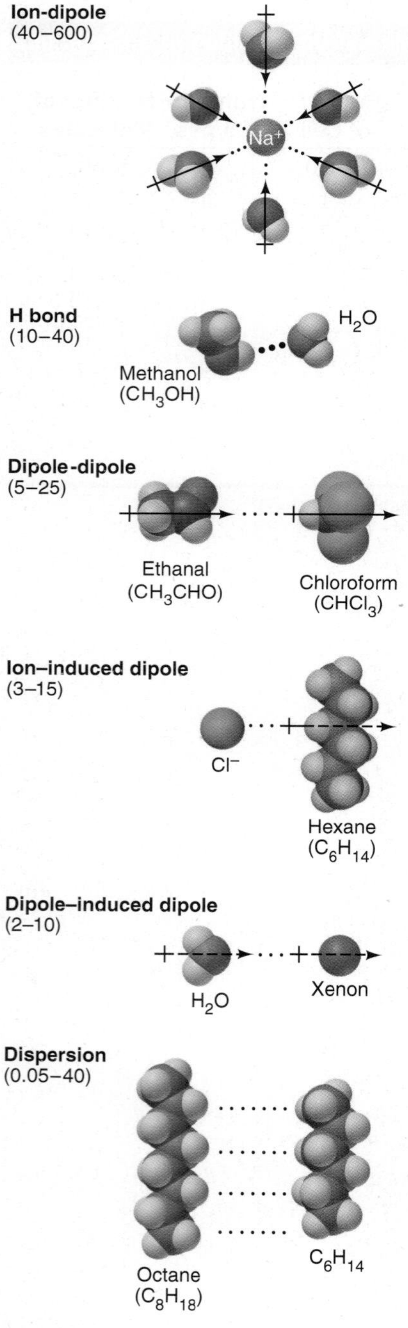

Figure 13.1 Types of intermolecular forces in solutions. Forces are listed in order of decreasing strength (values are in kJ/mol), with an example of each.

Intermolecular Forces in Solution

All the intermolecular forces we discussed for pure substances also occur in solutions (Figure 13.1; also see Section 12.3):

1. *Ion-dipole forces* are the principal force involved when an ionic compound dissolves in water. Two events occur simultaneously:
   - *Forces compete.* When a salt is added to water, an ion and the oppositely charged pole of a water molecule attract each other. These attractions compete with and overcome attractions between the ions, and the crystal structure breaks down.
   - *Hydration shells form.* As an ion separates, water molecules cluster around it in **hydration shells.** The number of water molecules in the closest shell depends on the ion's size: four fit tetrahedrally around small ions like Li^+, while the larger Na^+ and F^- have six water molecules surrounding them octahedrally (Figure 13.2). In the innermost shell, normal H bonding is disrupted to form the ion-dipole forces. But these water molecules are H bonded to others in the next shell, and those are H bonded to others still farther away.
2. *Hydrogen bonding* is the principal force in solutions of polar, O- and N-containing organic and biological compounds, such as alcohols, amines, and amino acids.
3. *Dipole-dipole forces,* in the absence of H bonding, allow polar molecules like propanal (CH_3CH_2CHO) to dissolve in polar solvents like dichloromethane (CH_2Cl_2).
4. **Ion–induced dipole forces,** one type of *charge-induced dipole force,* rely on polarizability. They arise when an ion's charge distorts the electron cloud of a nearby nonpolar molecule. This type of force initiates the binding of the Fe^{2+} ion in hemoglobin to an O_2 molecule entering a red blood cell.
5. **Dipole–induced dipole forces,** also based on polarizability, arise when a polar molecule distorts the electron cloud of a nonpolar molecule. They are weaker than ion–induced dipole forces because the charge of each pole is less than an ion's (Coulomb's law). The solubility in water of atmospheric O_2, N_2, and noble gases, while limited, is due in part to these forces. Paint thinners and grease solvents also use them.
6. *Dispersion forces* contribute to the solubility of all solutes in all solvents, but they are the *principal* intermolecular force in solutions of nonpolar substances, such as those in petroleum or gasoline.

The same forces keep biological macromolecules in their active shapes (Section 13.2).

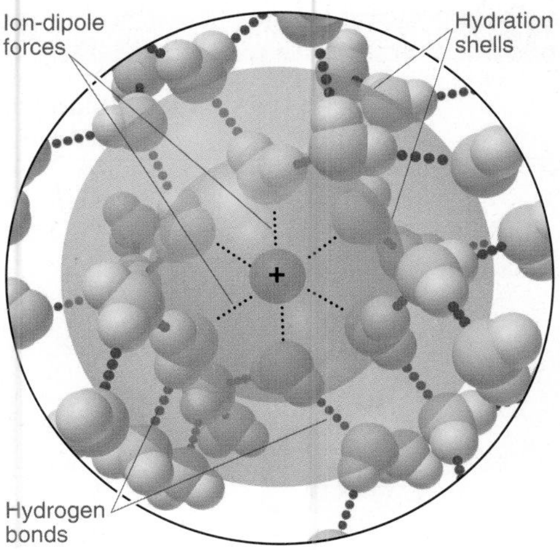

Figure 13.2 Hydration shells around an Na^+ ion. Ion-dipole forces orient water molecules around an ion. In the innermost shell here, six water molecules surround the cation octahedrally.

Liquid Solutions and the Role of Molecular Polarity

From cytoplasm to tree sap, gasoline to cleaning fluid, iced tea to urine, liquid solutions are very familiar. Water is the most prominent solvent, but there are many other liquid solvents, with polarities from very polar to nonpolar.

Applying the Like-Dissolves-Like Rule The like-dissolves-like rule says that when the forces *within* the solute are *similar* to those *within* the solvent, the forces *replace* each other and a solution forms. Thus,

- *Salts are soluble in water* because the strong ion-dipole attractions between ion and water are so similar to the strong attractions between the ions and the strong H bonds between water molecules that they *can* replace each other.
- *Salts are insoluble in hexane (C_6H_{14})* because the weak ion–induced dipole forces between ion and nonpolar hexane *cannot* replace attractions between the ions.
- *Oil is insoluble in water* because the weak dipole–induced dipole forces between oil and water molecules cannot replace the strong H bonds within water molecules and the extensive dispersion forces within the oil.
- *Oil is soluble in hexane* because dispersion forces in one readily replace dispersion forces in the other.

Dual Polarity and Effects on Solubility To examine these ideas further, let's compare the solubilities of a series of alcohols in water and hexane, solvents with very different intermolecular forces. Alcohols are organic compounds that have a dual polarity, a polar hydroxyl (—OH) group bonded to a nonpolar hydrocarbon group:

- The —OH portion interacts through strong H bonds with water and through weak dipole–induced dipole forces with hexane.
- The hydrocarbon portion interacts through many dispersion forces with hexane and through weak dipole–induced dipole forces with water.

The general formula for an alcohol is $CH_3(CH_2)_nOH$, and we'll look at straight-chain examples with one to six carbons ($n = 0$ to 5):

1. *Solubility in water is high for smaller alcohols.* From the models in Table 13.2 *(next page)*, we see that the —OH group is a relatively large portion of the alcohols with one to three carbons ($n = 0$ to 2). These molecules interact with each other through H bonding, just as water molecules do. When they mix with water, H bonding in solute and in solvent is replaced by H bonding *between* solute and solvent (Figure 13.3, *next page*). As a result, these smaller alcohols are miscible with water.

Table 13.2 Solubility* of a Series of Alcohols in Water and in Hexane

Alcohol	Model	Solubility in Water	Solubility in Hexane
CH_3OH (methanol)		∞	1.2
CH_3CH_2OH (ethanol)		∞	∞
$CH_3(CH_2)_2OH$ (1-propanol)		∞	∞
$CH_3(CH_2)_3OH$ (1-butanol)		1.1	∞
$CH_3(CH_2)_4OH$ (1-pentanol)		0.30	∞
$CH_3(CH_2)_5OH$ (1-hexanol)		0.058	∞

*Expressed in mol alcohol/1000 g solvent at 20°C.

2. *Solubility in water is low for larger alcohols.* Solubility decreases dramatically for alcohols larger than three carbons ($n > 2$); in fact, those with chains longer than six carbons are insoluble in water. For larger alcohols to dissolve, the nonpolar chains have to move among the water molecules, replacing weak attractions with water for strong H bonds between water molecules. While the —OH portion of such an alcohol forms H bonds to water, these cannot make up for all the other H bonds between water molecules that have to break to make room for the hydrocarbon portion.

Table 13.2 shows that the opposite trend occurs with hexane:

1. *Solubility in hexane is low for smaller alcohols.* For alcohols in hexane, in addition to dispersion forces, weak dipole–induced dipole forces exist between the —OH of methanol (CH_3OH) and hexane. These cannot replace the strong H bonding between CH_3OH molecules, so solubility is low.

2. *Solubility in hexane is high for larger alcohols.* In any larger alcohol ($n > 0$), dispersion forces between the hydrocarbon portion and hexane *can* replace dispersion forces between hexane molecules. With only weak forces within the solvent to be replaced, even ethanol, with a two-carbon chain, has enough dispersion forces between it and hexane to be miscible.

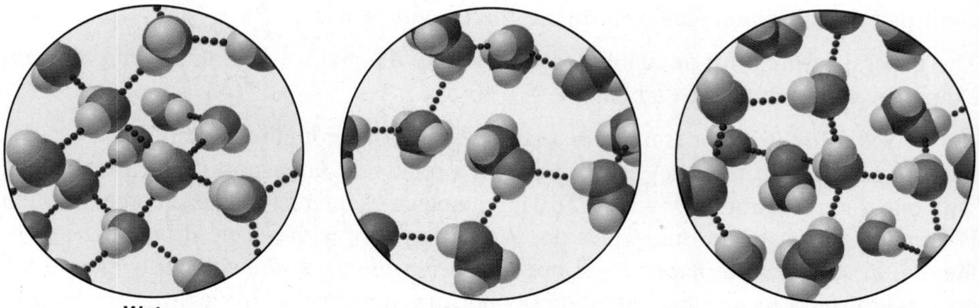

Figure 13.3 Like dissolves like: solubility of methanol in water. H bonds in water and in methanol replace one another when the two substances form a solution.

Many organic molecules have polar and nonpolar portions, which determine their solubility. For example, carboxylic acids and amines behave like alcohols: methanoic acid (HCOOH, formic acid) and methanamine (CH_3NH_2) are miscible with water and slightly soluble in hexane, whereas hexanoic acid [$CH_3(CH_2)_4COOH$] and 1-hexanamine [$CH_3(CH_2)_5NH_2$] are slightly soluble in water and very soluble in hexane.

Sample Problem 13.1 Predicting Relative Solubilities

Problem Predict which solvent will dissolve more of the given solute:
(a) Sodium chloride in methanol (CH_3OH) or in 1-propanol ($CH_3CH_2CH_2OH$)
(b) Ethylene glycol ($HOCH_2CH_2OH$) in hexane ($CH_3CH_2CH_2CH_2CH_2CH_3$) or in water
(c) Diethyl ether ($CH_3CH_2OCH_2CH_3$) in water or in ethanol (CH_3CH_2OH)

Plan We examine the formulas of solute and solvent to determine the forces in and between solute and solvent. A solute is more soluble in a solvent whose intermolecular forces are similar to, and therefore can replace, its own.

Solution (a) Methanol. NaCl is ionic, so it dissolves through ion-dipole forces. Both methanol and 1-propanol have a polar —OH group, but the hydrocarbon portion of each alcohol interacts only weakly with the ions and 1-propanol has a longer hydrocarbon portion than methanol.
(b) Water. Ethylene glycol molecules have two —OH groups, so they interact with each other through H bonding. H bonds formed with H_2O can replace these H bonds between solute molecules better than dipole–induced dipole forces with hexane can.
(c) Ethanol. Diethyl ether molecules interact through dipole-dipole and dispersion forces. They can form H bonds to H_2O or to ethanol. But ethanol can also interact with the ether effectively through dispersion forces because it has a hydrocarbon chain.

Follow-Up Problem 13.1 Which solute is more soluble in the given solvent:
(a) 1-butanol ($CH_3CH_2CH_2CH_2OH$) or 1,4-butanediol ($HOCH_2CH_2CH_2CH_2OH$) in water; **(b)** chloroform ($CHCl_3$) or carbon tetrachloride (CCl_4) in water?

Gas-Liquid Solutions A substance with very weak intermolecular attractions has a low boiling point and is a gas under ordinary conditions. Likewise, it is not very soluble in water because solute-solvent forces are weak. Thus, for nonpolar or slightly polar gases, boiling point generally correlates with solubility in water (Table 13.3).

The small amount of a nonpolar gas that *does* dissolve may be vital. At 25°C and 1 atm, the solubility of O_2 is only 3.2 mL/100. mL of water, but aquatic animal life requires it. At times, the solubility of a nonpolar gas may *seem* high because it is also *reacting* with solvent. Oxygen seems more soluble in blood than in water because it bonds to hemoglobin in red blood cells. Carbon dioxide, which is essential for aquatic plants and coral-reef growth, seems very soluble in water (~81 mL of CO_2/100. mL of H_2O at 25°C and 1 atm) because it is dissolving *and* reacting:

$$CO_2(g) + H_2O(l) \longrightarrow H^+(aq) + HCO_3^-(aq)$$

Table 13.3 Correlation Between Boiling Point and Solubility in Water

Gas	Solubility (*M*)*	bp (K)
He	4.2×10^{-4}	4.2
Ne	6.6×10^{-4}	27.1
N_2	10.4×10^{-4}	77.4
CO	15.6×10^{-4}	81.6
O_2	21.8×10^{-4}	90.2
NO	32.7×10^{-4}	121.4

*At 273 K and 1 atm.

Gas Solutions and Solid Solutions

Gas solutions and solid solutions also have vital importance and numerous applications.

Gas-Gas Solutions *All gases are miscible with each other.* Air is the classic example of a gaseous solution, consisting of about 18 gases in widely differing proportions. Anesthetic gas proportions are finely adjusted to the needs of the patient and the length of the surgical procedure. The proportions of many industrial gas mixtures, such as CO/H_2 in syngas production or N_2/H_2 in ammonia production, are controlled to optimize product yield under varying conditions of temperature and pressure.

Gas-Solid Solutions *When a gas dissolves in a solid, it occupies the spaces between the closely packed particles.* Hydrogen gas can be purified by passing an impure sample through palladium. Only H_2 molecules are small enough to fit between the

Pd atoms, where they form Pd—H bonds. The H atoms move from one Pd atom to another and emerge from the metal as H_2 molecules (see Figure 14.2, p. 525).

The ability of gases to dissolve in a solid also has disadvantages. The electrical conductivity of copper is greatly reduced by the presence of O_2, which dissolves into the crystal structure and reacts to form copper(I) oxide. High-conductivity copper is prepared by melting and recasting the metal in an O_2-free atmosphere.

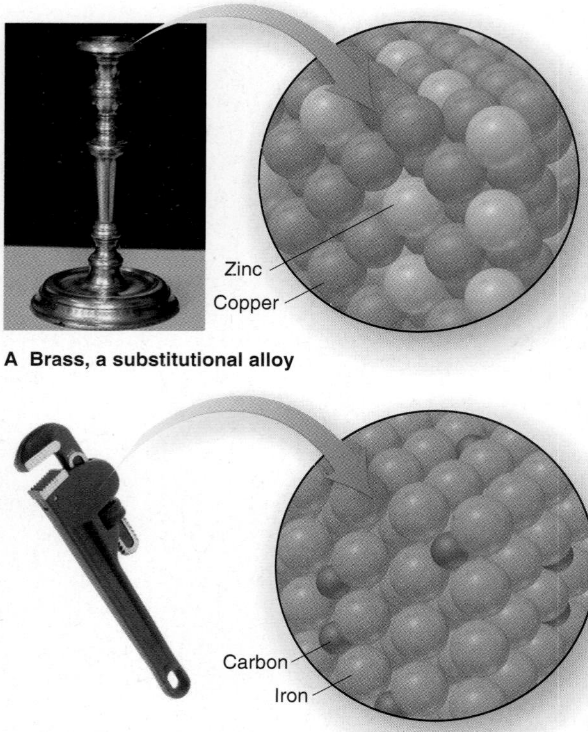

Figure 13.4 The arrangement of atoms in two types of alloys.

Solid-Solid Solutions Solids diffuse so little that their mixtures are usually heterogeneous. Some solid-solid solutions can be formed by melting the solids and then mixing them and allowing them to freeze. Many **alloys,** mixtures of elements that have a metallic character, are solid-solid solutions (although several have microscopic heterogeneous regions). In a *substitutional alloy* like brass (Figure 13.4A), atoms of zinc replace atoms of the main element, copper, at some sites in the cubic-closest packing array. In an *interstitial alloy* like carbon steel (Figure 13.4B), atoms of carbon (a nonmetal is typical in this type of alloy) fill some of the spaces (*interstices*) between atoms of the main element, iron, in the body-centered array.

Waxes are also solid-solid solutions. Most are amorphous solids with some small regions of crystalline regularity. A natural *wax* is defined as a solid of biological origin that is insoluble in water and soluble in nonpolar solvents. Beeswax, which bees secrete to build their combs, is a homogeneous mixture of fatty acids, long-chain carboxylic acids, and hydrocarbons in which some of the molecules contain chains more than 40 carbon atoms long. Carnauba wax, from a South American palm, is a mixture of compounds, each consisting of a fatty acid bound to a long-chain alcohol. It is hard but forms a thick gel in nonpolar solvents, so it is perfect for waxing cars.

Summary of Section 13.1

- A solution is a homogeneous mixture of a solute dissolved in a solvent through the action of intermolecular forces.
- Ion-dipole, ion–induced dipole, and dipole–induced dipole forces occur in solutions, in addition to all the intermolecular forces that also occur in pure substances.
- If similar intermolecular forces occur in solute and solvent, they replace each other when the substances mix and a solution is likely to form ("like dissolves like").
- When ionic compounds dissolve in water, the ions become surrounded by hydration shells of H-bonded water molecules.
- Solubility of organic molecules in various solvents depends on the relative sizes of their polar and nonpolar portions.
- The solubility of nonpolar gases in water is low because of weak intermolecular forces. Gases are miscible with one another and dissolve in solids by fitting into spaces in the crystal structure.
- Solid-solid solutions include alloys and waxes, and some are formed by mixing molten components.

13.2 • INTERMOLECULAR FORCES AND BIOLOGICAL MACROMOLECULES

The three-dimensional shapes of proteins, nucleic acids, and cell membranes and the functions of soaps and antibiotics depend on intermolecular forces and are explained by two ideas:

- Polar and ionic groups attract water, but nonpolar groups do not.
- Just as separate molecules attract each other, so do distant groups on the same molecule.

The Structures of Proteins

Proteins are unbranched polymers formed from about 20 different monomers called **amino acids.** They range in size from about 50 amino acids ($\mathcal{M} \approx 5\times10^3$ g/mol) to several thousand ($\mathcal{M} \approx 5\times10^5$ g/mol). Proteins with a few types of amino acids in repeating patterns have extended helical or sheetlike shapes and give structure to hair, skin, and so forth. Proteins with many types of amino acids have complex, globular shapes and function as antibodies, enzymes and so forth. Let's see how intermolecular forces among amino acids influence the shapes of globular proteins.

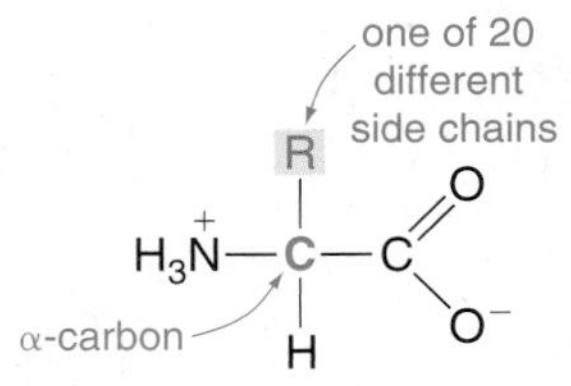

Figure 13.5 The charged form of an amino acid under physiological conditions.

The Polarity of Amino-Acid Side Chains In the cell, a free amino acid has four groups bonded to its α-carbon (Figure 13.5): charged carboxyl ($—COO^-$) and amine ($—NH_3^+$) groups, an H atom, and a *side chain,* which ranges from an H atom to a two-ringed C_9H_8N group. Amino acids can be classified by the polarity or charge of their side chains: nonpolar, polar, and ionic. A few examples are

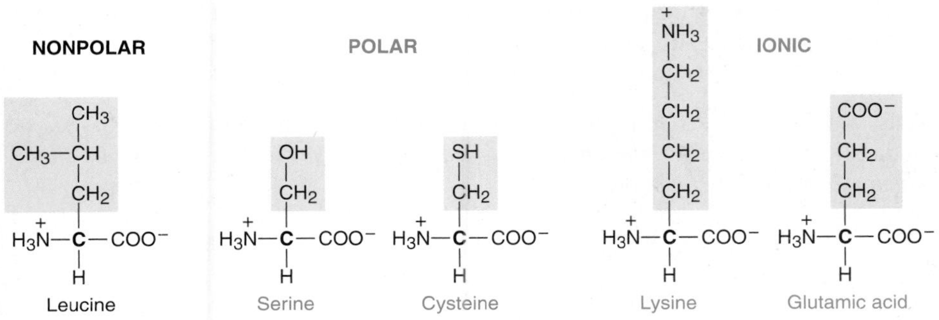

In a protein, the carboxyl group of one amino acid is linked covalently to the amine group of the next by a *peptide* bond. (We discuss amino acid structures and peptide bond formation in Chapter 15.) Thus, as Figure 13.6 shows, the *backbone* of a protein is a polypeptide chain: an α-*carbon connected through a peptide bond (orange screen) to the next* α-*carbon,* and so forth. The various side chains (*gray screens*) dangle off the α-carbons on alternate sides of the chain.

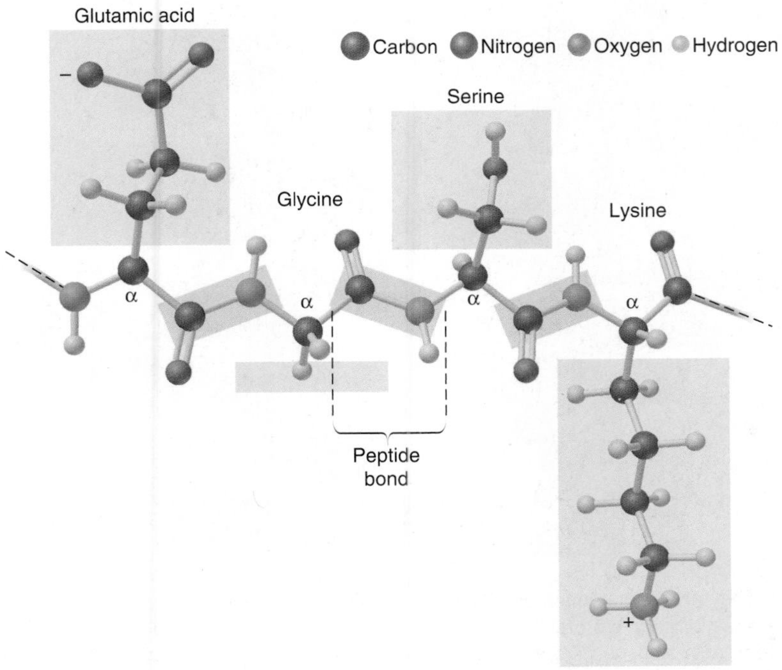

Figure 13.6 A portion of a polypeptide chain. Three peptide bonds (*orange screens*) join four amino acids in this chain portion.

Intermolecular Forces and Protein Shape The same forces that act between separate molecules are responsible for a protein's shape, because *distant groups on the protein chain end up near each other as the chain bends.* Figure 13.7 depicts the forces within the protein and between the protein and the aqueous medium of the cell. In general order of importance, they are

- Covalent peptide bonds create the backbone (polypeptide chain).
- Helical and sheetlike segments arise from *H bonds between the C═O of one peptide bond and the N—H of another.*
- Polar and ionic side chains protrude into the surrounding cell fluid, interacting with water through ion-dipole forces and H bonds.
- Nonpolar side chains interact through dispersion forces within the nonaqueous protein interior.
- The —SH ends of two cysteine side chains form a covalent —S—S— bond, a *disulfide bridge,* between distant parts of the chain that fixes a bend.
- Oppositely charged ends of ionic side chains, $—COO^-$ and $—NH_3^+$ groups, that lie near each other form an electrostatic *salt link* (or *ion pair*) that creates bend in the protein chain.
- Other H bonds between side chains keep distant chain portions near each other.

Thus, *soluble proteins have polar-ionic exteriors and nonpolar interiors.* As we emphasize in Chapter 15, *the amino acid sequence of a protein determines its shape, which determines its function.*

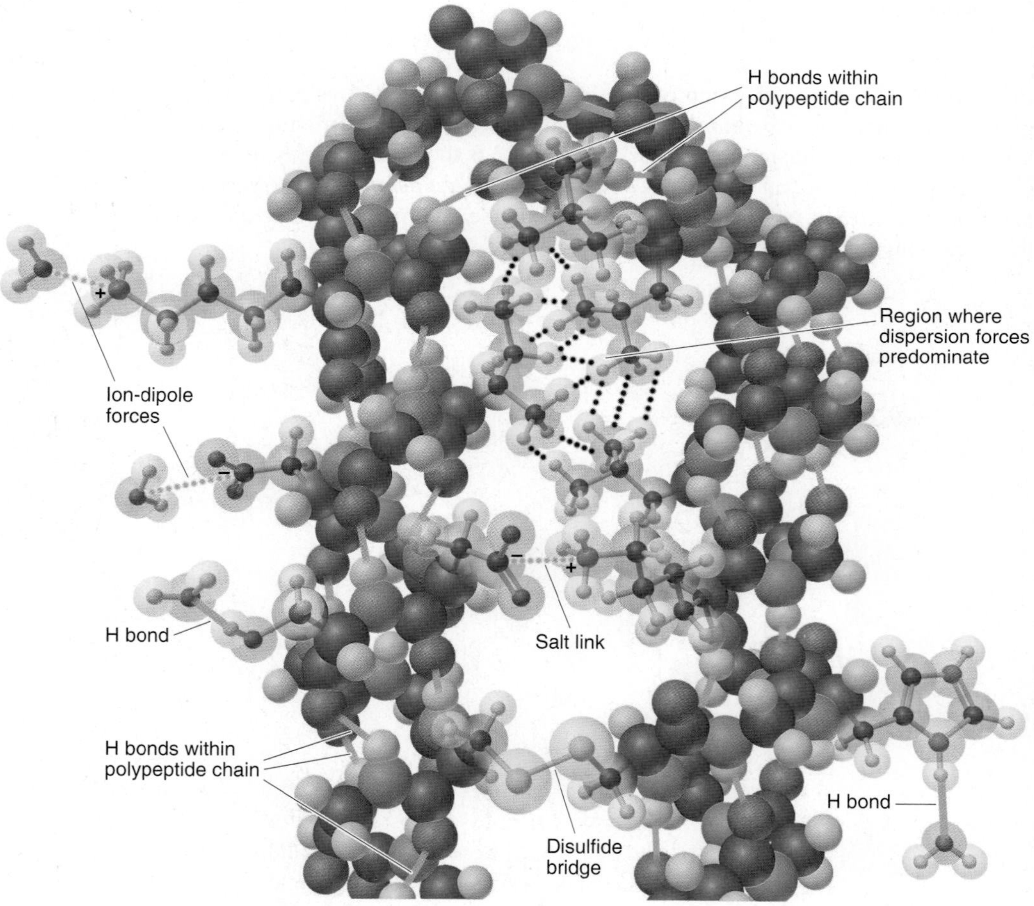

Figure 13.7 The forces that maintain protein structure. Covalent, ionic, and intermolecular forces act between parts of a protein and between the protein and surrounding H_2O molecules to determine the protein's shape. (Water molecules and some amino-acid side chains are shown as ball-and-stick models within space-filling contours.)

Dual Polarity in Soaps, Membranes, and Antibiotics

Dual polarity, which we discussed in regard to the solubility of alcohols, also helps explain how soaps, cell membranes, and antibiotics function.

Action of Soaps A **soap** is the salt formed when a strong base (metal hydroxide) reacts with a *fatty acid,* a carboxylic acid with a long hydrocarbon chain. A typical soap molecule is made up of a nonpolar "tail" 15–19 carbons long and a polar-ionic "head" consisting of a $—COO^-$ group and the cation of the strong base. The cation greatly influences a soap's properties. Lithium soaps are hard and high melting and used in car lubricants. Potassium soaps are low melting and used in liquid form. Softer, more water-soluble sodium soaps, including sodium stearate, $CH_3(CH_2)_{16}COONa$, are components of common bar soaps:

Sodium stearate, $C_{17}H_{35}COONa$

When grease on your hands or clothes is immersed in soapy water, the soap molecule's nonpolar tails interact with the nonpolar grease molecules through dispersion forces, while the polar-ionic heads attract water molecules through ion-dipole forces and H bonds. Tiny aggregates of grease molecules, embedded with soap molecules whose polar-ionic heads stick into the water, are flushed away by added water (Figure 13.8).

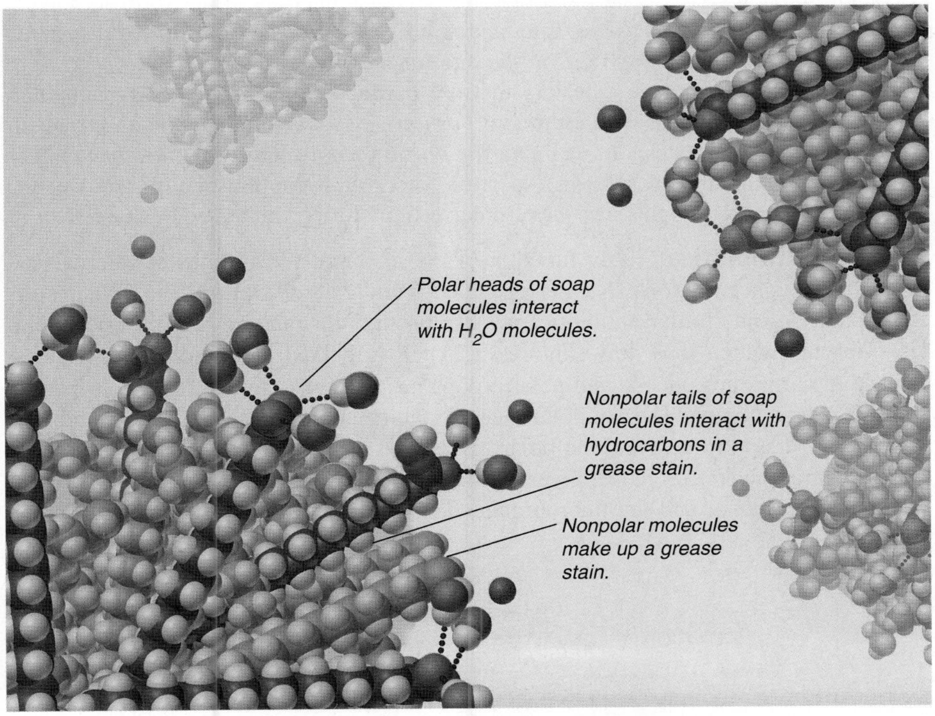

Figure 13.8 The cleaning ability of a soap depends on the dual polarity of its molecules.

Lipid Bilayers and the Structure of the Cell Membrane The most abundant molecules in cell membranes are *phospholipids.* Like soaps, they have a dual polarity—a nonpolar tail consists of two fatty acid chains, and an organophosphate group is the polar-ionic head (Figure 13.9). Remarkably, phospholipids self-assemble in water into a sheetlike double layer called a **lipid bilayer,** with the tails of the two layers touching and the heads in the water. In the laboratory, bilayers form spherical vesicles that trap water inside. These structures are favored energetically because of their intermolecular forces:

- Ion-dipole forces occur between polar heads and water inside and outside.
- Dispersion forces occur between nonpolar tails within the bilayer interior.
- Minimal contact exists between nonpolar tails and water.

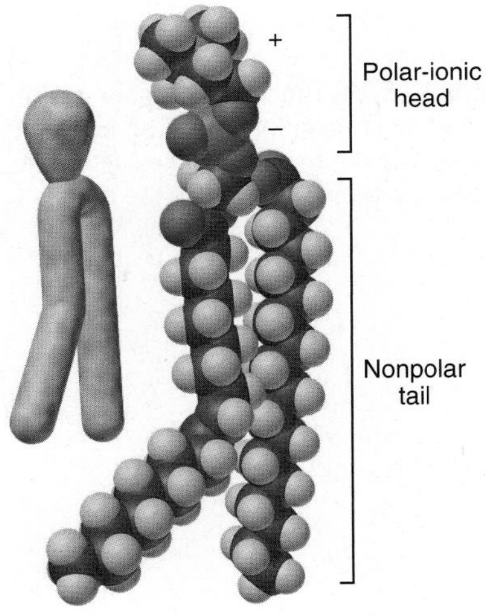

Figure 13.9 A membrane phospholipid. Lecithin (phosphatidylcholine), a phospholipid, is shown as a space-filling model and as a simplified purple-and-gray shape.

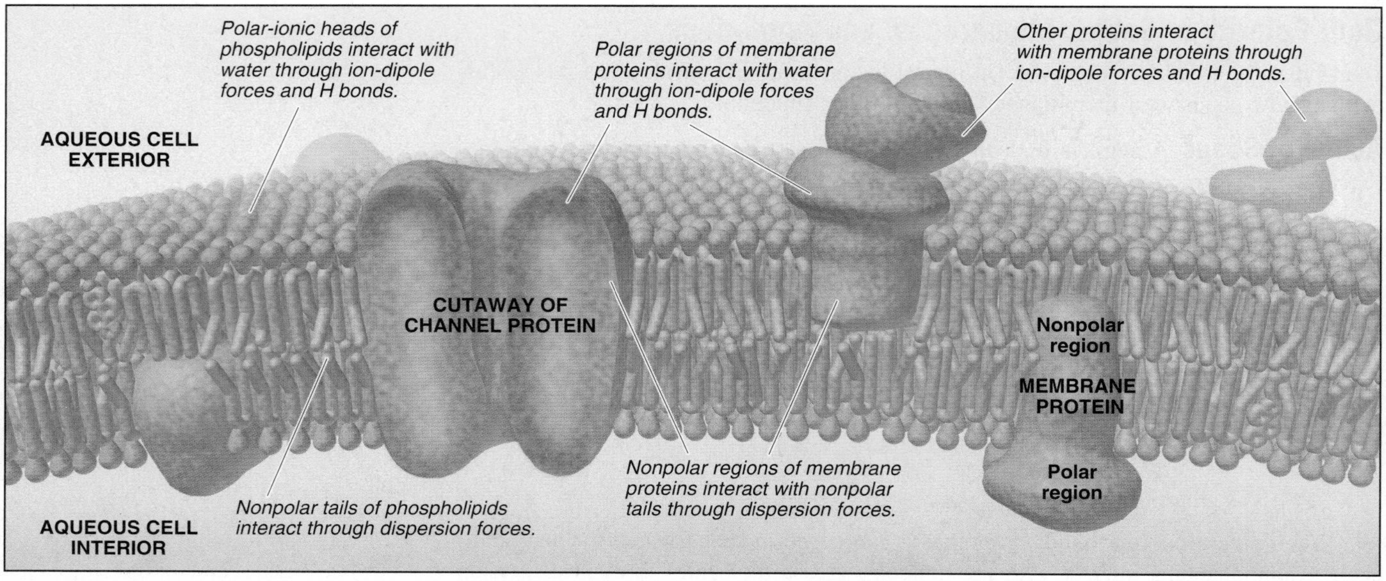

Figure 13.10 Intermolecular forces and cell membrane structure.

A typical animal cell membrane consists of a phospholipid bilayer with proteins partially embedded in it (Figure 13.10). Membrane proteins, which play countless essential roles, differ fundamentally from soluble proteins in terms of their dual polarity:

- Soluble proteins have polar exteriors and nonpolar interiors. They form ion-dipole and H-bonding forces between water and *polar groups on the exterior* and dispersion forces between *nonpolar groups in the interior* (see Figure 13.7).
- Membrane proteins have exteriors that are partially polar and partially nonpolar. They have polar groups on the *exterior portion that juts into the aqueous surroundings* and nonpolar groups on *the exterior portion embedded in the membrane*. The nonpolar groups thus can form dispersion forces with the phospholipid tails of the bilayer. Channel proteins also have polar groups lining the aqueous channel.

Action of Antibiotics A key function of the membrane is to balance internal and external ion concentrations: Na^+ is excluded from the cell, and K^+ is kept inside. Gramicidin A and similar antibiotics act by forming channels in the bacterial membrane through which ions flow (Figure 13.11). Two helical gramicidin A molecules, their nonpolar groups outside and polar groups inside, lie end to end to form a channel through the membrane. The nonpolar outside stabilizes the molecule in the membrane through dispersion forces, and the polar inside passes the ions along using ion-dipole forces, like a "bucket brigade." Over 10^7 ions pass in and out through each of these channels per second, and the microorganism soon dies.

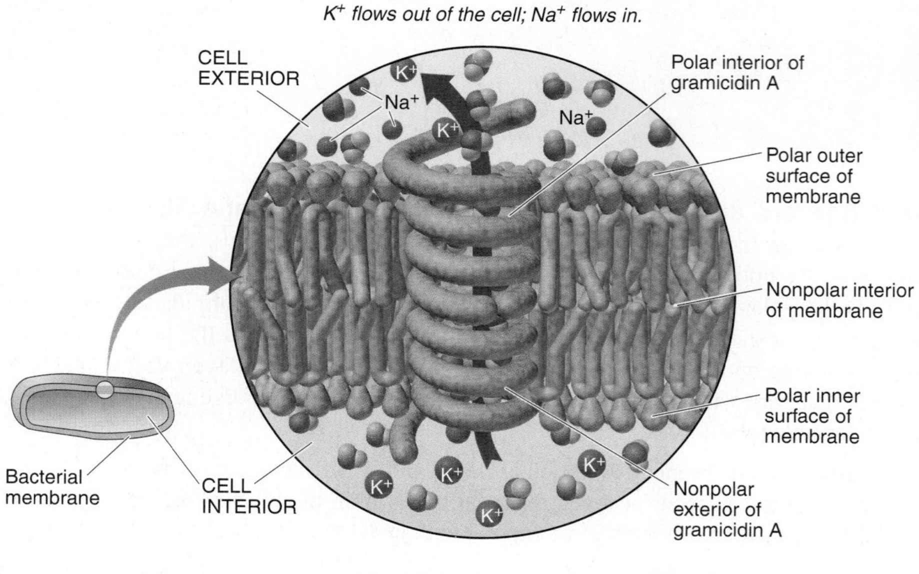

Figure 13.11 The mode of action of the antibiotic gramicidin A. The K^+ ions are shown leaving the cell. At the same time (not shown), Na^+ ions enter the cell.

The Structure of DNA

The chemical information that guides the design and construction, and therefore the function, of all proteins is contained in **nucleic acids,** unbranched polymers made up of monomers called **mononucleotides.** Each mononucleotide consists of an N-containing base, a sugar, and a phosphate group (Figure 13.12). In DNA (*deoxyribonucleic acid*), the sugar is *2-deoxyribose,* in which —H substitutes for —OH on the second C atom of the five-C sugar ribose.

The repeating pattern of the DNA chain is *sugar linked to phosphate linked to sugar linked to phosphate,* and so on. Attached to each sugar is one of four N-containing bases, flat ring structures that dangle off the polynucleotide chain, similar to the way amino-acid side chains dangle off the polypeptide chain.

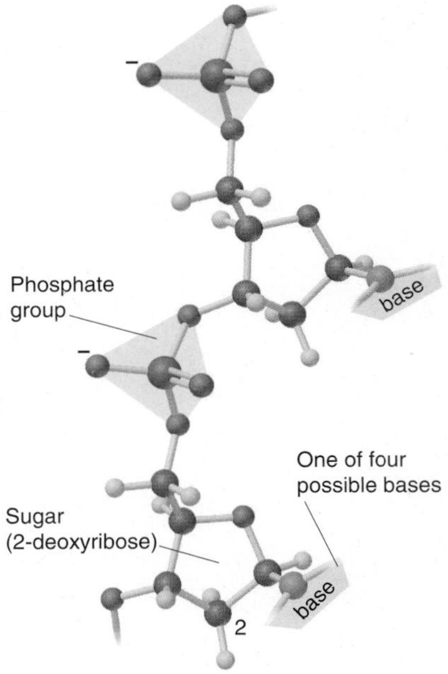

Figure 13.12 A short portion of the polynucleotide chain of DNA.

Intermolecular Forces and the Double Helix DNA exists as two chains wrapped around each other in a **double helix** stabilized by intermolecular forces (Figure 13.13):

- *On the more polar exterior,* negatively charged sugar-phosphate groups interact with the aqueous surroundings via ion-dipole forces and H bonds.
- *In the less polar interior,* flat, N-containing bases stack above each other and interact by dispersion forces.
- *Bases form specific interchain H bonds;* that is, each base in one chain is always H bonded with its complementary base in the other chain. Thus, *the base sequence of one chain is the H-bonded complement of the base sequence of the other.*

A DNA molecule contains millions of H bonds linking bases in these prescribed pairs. The *total* energy of the H bonds keeps the chains together, but each H bond is weak enough (around 5% of a typical covalent single bond) that a few at a time can break as the chains separate during crucial cellular processes. (In Chapter 15, we'll see how H-bonded base pairs are essential for protein synthesis and DNA replication.)

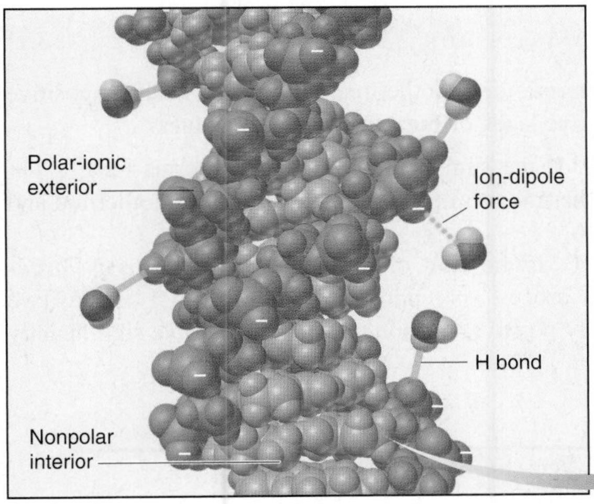

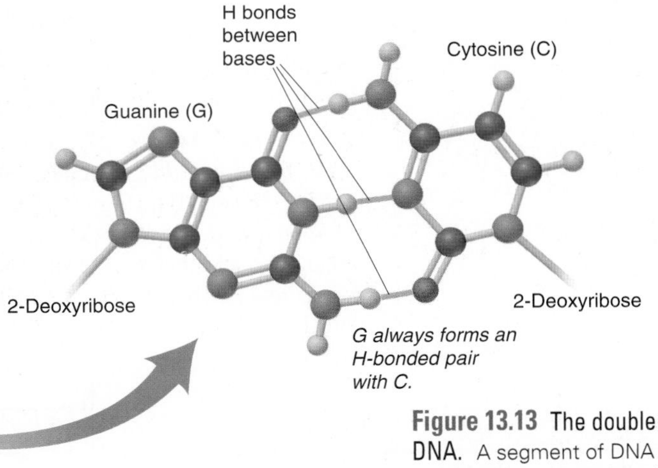

Figure 13.13 The double helix of DNA. A segment of DNA (*left*) has its polar-ionic sugar-phosphate portion (*pink*) facing the water and the nonpolar bases (*gray*) stacking in the interior. The expanded portion (*right*) shows an H-bonded pair of the bases guanine and cytosine.

Summary of Section 13.2

- In soluble proteins, polar and ionic amino-acid side chains on the exterior interact with surrounding water, and nonpolar side chains in the interior interact with each other.
- With polar-ionic heads *and* nonpolar tails, a soap dissolves grease *and* interacts with water.
- Like soaps, phospholipids also have dual polarity. They assemble into a water-impermeable lipid bilayer. In a cell membrane, the embedded portion of membrane proteins has exterior nonpolar side chains that face the nonpolar tails in the lipid bilayer. Some antibiotics form channels with nonpolar exteriors and polar interiors that shuttle ions through the cell membrane.
- DNA forms a double helix with a sugar-phosphate, polar-ionic exterior. In the interior, N-containing bases H bond in specific pairs and stack through dispersion forces.

13.3 • WHY SUBSTANCES DISSOLVE: UNDERSTANDING THE SOLUTION PROCESS

The qualitative *macroscopic* rule "like dissolves like" is based on *molecular* interactions between solute and solvent. To see *why* like dissolves like, we'll break down the solution process conceptually into steps and examine them quantitatively.

Heat of Solution: Solution Cycles

Before a solution forms, solute particles are attracting each other, as are solvent particles. For one to dissolve in the other, three steps must take place, each accompanied by an enthalpy change:

Step 1. Solute particles separate from each other. This step involves overcoming intermolecular attractions, so it is *endothermic:*

$$\text{Solute (aggregated)} + heat \longrightarrow \text{solute (separated)} \qquad \Delta H_{solute} > 0$$

Step 2. Solvent particles separate from each other. This step also involves overcoming attractions, so it is *endothermic,* too:

$$\text{Solvent (aggregated)} + heat \longrightarrow \text{solvent (separated)} \qquad \Delta H_{solvent} > 0$$

Step 3. Solute and solvent particles mix and form a solution. The different particles attract each other and come together, so this step is *exothermic:*

$$\text{Solute (separated)} + \text{solvent (separated)} \longrightarrow \text{solution} + heat \qquad \Delta H_{mix} < 0$$

The overall process is called a *thermochemical solution cycle,* and in yet another application of Hess's law, we combine the three individual enthalpy changes to find the **heat of solution (ΔH_{soln}),** the total enthalpy change that occurs when solute and solvent form a solution:

$$\Delta H_{soln} = \Delta H_{solute} + \Delta H_{solvent} + \Delta H_{mix} \qquad (13.1)$$

Overall solution formation is exothermic or endothermic, and ΔH_{soln} is either positive or negative, depending on the relative sizes of the individual ΔH values:

- *Exothermic process:* $\Delta H_{soln} < 0$. If the sum of the endothermic terms ($\Delta H_{solute} + \Delta H_{solvent}$) is *smaller* than the exothermic term (ΔH_{mix}), the process is exothermic and ΔH_{soln} is negative (Figure 13.14A).
- *Endothermic process:* $\Delta H_{soln} > 0$. If the sum of the endothermic terms is *larger* than the exothermic term, the process is endothermic and ΔH_{soln} is positive (Figure 13.14B). If ΔH_{soln} is highly positive, the solute may not dissolve significantly in that solvent.

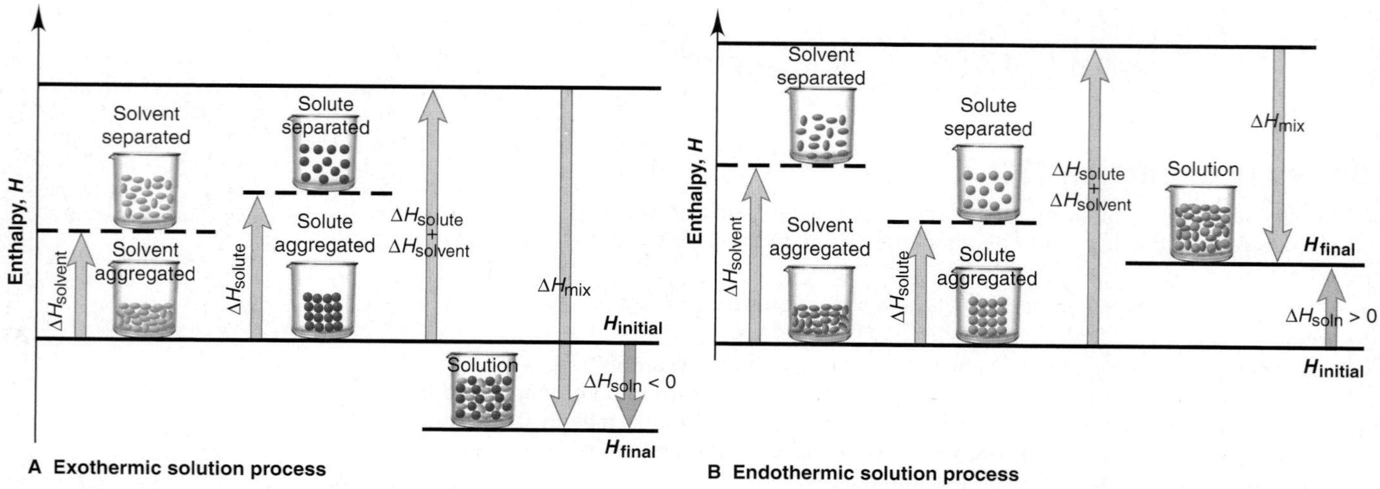

Figure 13.14 Enthalpy components of the heat of solution. **A,** ΔH_{mix} is larger than the sum of ΔH_{solute} and $\Delta H_{solvent}$, so ΔH_{soln} is negative. **B,** ΔH_{mix} is smaller than the sum of ΔH_{solute} and $\Delta H_{solvent}$, so ΔH_{soln} is positive.

Heat of Hydration: Ionic Solids in Water

The $\Delta H_{solvent}$ and ΔH_{mix} components of the solution cycle are difficult to measure individually. Combined, they equal the enthalpy change for **solvation,** the process of surrounding a solute particle with solvent particles:

$$\Delta H_{solvation} = \Delta H_{solvent} + \Delta H_{mix}$$

Solvation in water is called **hydration.** Thus, enthalpy changes for separating the water molecules ($\Delta H_{solvent}$) and mixing the separated solute with them (ΔH_{mix}) are combined into the **heat of hydration (ΔH_{hydr}).** In water, Equation 13.1 becomes

$$\Delta H_{soln} = \Delta H_{solute} + \Delta H_{hydr}$$

The heat of hydration is a key factor in dissolving an ionic solid. Breaking H bonds in water is more than compensated for by forming the stronger ion-dipole forces, so hydration of an ion is *always* exothermic. The ΔH_{hydr} of an ion is defined as the enthalpy change for the hydration of 1 mol of separated (gaseous) ions:

$$M^+(g) \text{ [or } X^-(g)] \xrightarrow{H_2O} M^+(aq) \text{ [or } X^-(aq)] \qquad \Delta H_{\text{hydr of the ion}} \text{ (always } <0)$$

Importance of Charge Density Heats of hydration exhibit trends based on the ion's **charge density,** the ratio of its charge to its volume. In general, the higher the charge density, the more negative ΔH_{hydr} is. Coulomb's law explains why: the higher the charge of an ion and the smaller its radius, the closer it gets to the oppositely charged pole of an H_2O (see Figure 2.12, p. 57), and the stronger the attraction. Thus,

- A 2+ ion attracts H_2O molecules more strongly than a 1+ ion of similar size.
- A small 1+ ion attracts H_2O molecules more strongly than a large 1+ ion.

Periodic trends in ΔH_{hydr} values are based on trends in charge density (Table 13.4):

- *Down a group,* the charge stays the same and the size increases; thus, the charge densities decrease, as do the ΔH_{hydr} values.
- *Across a period,* say, from Group 1A(1) to Group 2A(2), the 2A ion has a smaller radius *and* a higher charge, so its charge density and ΔH_{hydr} are greater.

Components of Aqueous Heats of Solution To separate an ionic solute, MX, into gaseous ions (ΔH_{solute}) requires a lot of energy; recall from Chapter 9 that this is the lattice energy, and it is highly positive:

$$MX(s) \longrightarrow M^+(g) + X^-(g) \qquad \Delta H_{solute} \text{ (always } > 0) = \Delta H_{lattice}$$

Thus, for ionic compounds in water, the heat of solution is the lattice energy (always positive) plus the combined heats of hydration of the ions (always negative):

$$\Delta H_{soln} = \Delta H_{lattice} + \Delta H_{\text{hydr of the ions}} \qquad (13.2)$$

Once again, the sizes of the individual terms determine the sign of ΔH_{soln}.

Figure 13.15 (*next page*) shows enthalpy diagrams for three ionic solutes dissolving in water:

- *NaCl.* Sodium chloride has a small positive ΔH_{soln} (3.9 kJ/mol) because its lattice energy is only slightly greater than the combined ionic heats of hydration: if you dissolve NaCl in water in a flask, you don't feel any temperature change.
- *NaOH.* Sodium hydroxide has a large negative ΔH_{soln} (−44.5 kJ/mol) because its lattice energy is much *smaller* than the combined ionic heats of hydration: if you dissolve NaOH in water, the flask feels hot.
- *NH_4NO_3.* Ammonium nitrate has a large positive ΔH_{soln} (25.7 kJ/mol) because its lattice energy is much *larger* than the combined ionic heats of hydration: if you dissolve NH_4NO_3 in water, the flask feels cold.

Hot and cold packs consist of a thick outer pouch of water and a thin inner pouch of a salt. A squeeze breaks the inner pouch, and the salt dissolves. Most hot packs use anhydrous $CaCl_2$ (ΔH_{soln} = −82.8 kJ/mol), and cold packs use NH_4NO_3 (ΔH_{soln} = 25.7 kJ/mol). A cold pack can keep the solution at 0°C for about half an hour. In Japan, some soup is sold in double-walled cans with a salt in a packet immersed in water between the walls. Open the can and the packet breaks, the salt dissolves, and the soup quickly warms to about 90°C.

Table 13.4 Trends in Ionic Heats of Hydration

Ion	Ionic Radius (pm)	ΔH_{hydr} (kJ/mol)
Group 1A(1)		
Na^+	102	−410
K^+	138	−336
Rb^+	152	−315
Cs^+	167	−282
Group 2A(2)		
Mg^{2+}	72	−1903
Ca^{2+}	100	−1591
Sr^{2+}	118	−1424
Ba^{2+}	135	−1317
Group 7A(17)		
F^-	133	−431
Cl^-	181	−313
Br^-	196	−284
I^-	220	−247

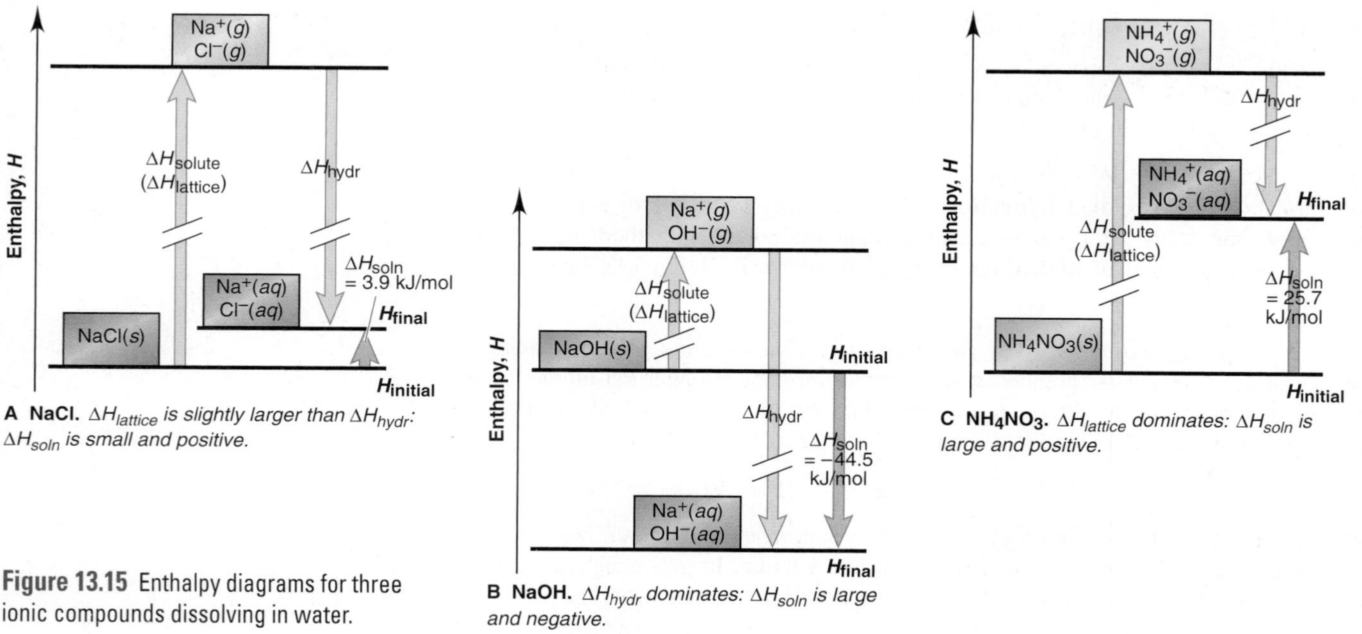

Figure 13.15 Enthalpy diagrams for three ionic compounds dissolving in water.

The Solution Process and the Change in Entropy

The heat of solution (ΔH_{soln}) is one of two factors that determine whether a solute dissolves. The other factor is the natural tendency of a system of particles to spread out and the system's kinetic energy to become more dispersed or distributed. A thermodynamic variable called **entropy (S)** is directly related to the number of ways a system can disperse its energy, which is closely related to the freedom of motion of the particles.

Let's see what it means for a system to "distribute its energy." We'll first compare the three physical states and then compare solute and solvent with solution.

Entropy and the Three Physical States The states of matter differ significantly in their entropy.

- In a solid, the particles are fixed in their positions with little freedom of motion. In a liquid, they can move around each other and so have greater freedom of motion. And in a gas, the particles have little restriction and much more freedom of motion.
- The more freedom of motion the particles have, the more ways they can distribute their kinetic energy; thus, a liquid has higher entropy than a solid, and a gas has higher entropy than a liquid:

$$S_{gas} > S_{liquid} > S_{solid}$$

- We can also look at the *change* in entropy (ΔS) of a phase change. Thus, for example, the change in entropy when a liquid vaporizes ($\Delta S_{vap} = S_{gas} - S_{liquid}$) is positive ($\Delta S_{vap} > 0$), the change in entropy when a liquid freezes (fusion) ($\Delta S_{fus} = S_{solid} - S_{liquid}$) is negative ($\Delta S_{fus} < 0$), and so forth.

Entropy and the Formation of Solutions The formation of solutions also involves a change in entropy. *A solution usually has higher entropy than the pure solute and pure solvent* because the number of ways to distribute the energy is related to the number of interactions between different molecules. There are far more interactions possible when solute and solvent are mixed than when they are pure; thus,

$$S_{soln} > (S_{solute} + S_{solvent}) \qquad \text{or} \qquad \Delta S_{soln} > 0$$

You know from everyday experience that solutions form naturally, but pure solutes and solvents don't: you've seen sugar dissolve in water, but you've never seen a sugar solution separate into pure sugar and water. In Chapter 20, we'll see that energy is needed to reverse the natural tendency of systems to distribute their energy—to get "mixed up." Water treatment plants, oil refineries, steel mills, and many other industrial facilities expend a lot of energy to separate mixtures into pure components.

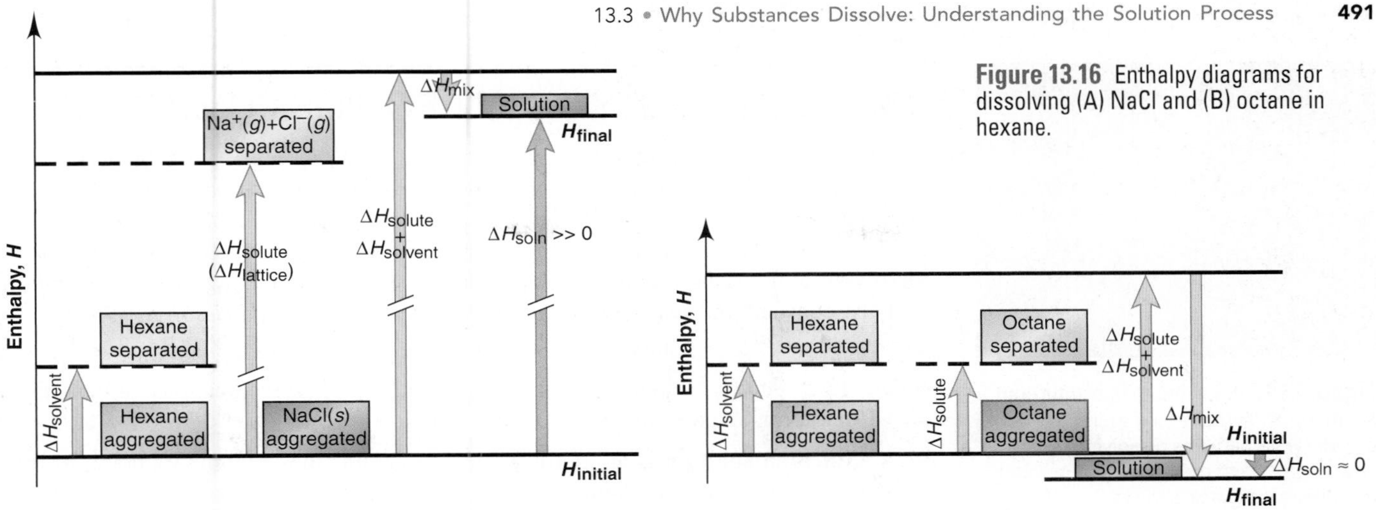

Figure 13.16 Enthalpy diagrams for dissolving (A) NaCl and (B) octane in hexane.

A NaCl. *ΔH_{mix} is* ***much*** *smaller than ΔH_{solute}; ΔH_{soln} is so much larger than the entropy increase due to mixing that NaCl does* ***not*** *dissolve.*

B Octane. *ΔH_{soln} is very small, but the entropy increase due to mixing is large, so octane dissolves.*

Enthalpy vs. Entropy Changes in Solution Formation Solution formation involves the interplay of two factors: systems change toward a state of *lower enthalpy* and *higher entropy,* so the relative sizes of ΔH_{soln} and ΔS_{soln} determine whether a solution forms. Let's consider three solute-solvent pairs to see which factor dominates:

1. *NaCl in hexane.* Given their very different intermolecular forces, we predict that sodium chloride does *not* dissolve in hexane (C_6H_{14}) (Figure 13.16A). Separating the solvent is easy because the dispersion forces are weak ($\Delta H_{solvent} \geq 0$), but separating the solute requires supplying the very large $\Delta H_{lattice}$ ($\Delta H_{solute} >> 0$). Mixing releases little heat because ion–induced dipole forces between Na^+ (or Cl^-) and hexane are weak ($\Delta H_{mix} \leq 0$). Because the sum of the endothermic terms is *much* larger than the exothermic term, $\Delta H_{soln} >> 0$. *A solution does not form because the entropy increase from mixing solute and solvent would be much smaller than the enthalpy increase required to separate the solute: $\Delta S_{mix} << \Delta H_{solute}$.*

2. *Octane in hexane.* We predict that octane (C_8H_{18}) is soluble in hexane because both are held together by dispersion forces of similar strength; in fact, they are miscible. That is, both ΔH_{solute} and $\Delta H_{solvent}$ are around zero. The similar forces mean that ΔH_{mix} is around zero also. And a lot of heat is not released; in fact, ΔH_{soln} is around zero (Figure 13.16B). So why does a solution form so readily? *With no enthalpy change driving the process, octane dissolves in hexane because the entropy increases greatly when the pure substances mix: $\Delta S_{mix} >> \Delta H_{soln}$.*

3. *NH_4NO_3 in water.* A large enough increase in entropy can sometimes cause a solution to form even when the enthalpy increase is large ($\Delta H_{soln} >> 0$). As we saw in Figure 13.15C, when ammonium nitrate (NH_4NO_3) dissolves in water, the process is highly endothermic; that is, $\Delta H_{lattice} >> \Delta H_{\text{hydr of the ions}}$. Nevertheless, *the increase in entropy that occurs when the crystal breaks down and the ions mix with water molecules is greater than the increase in enthalpy: $\Delta S_{soln} > \Delta H_{soln}$.*

In Chapter 20, we'll return in depth to the relation between enthalpy and entropy to understand physical and chemical systems.

Summary of Section 13.3

- In a thermochemical solution cycle, the heat of solution is the sum of the endothermic separations of solute and of solvent and the exothermic mixing of their particles.
- In water, the combination of solvent separation and mixing with solute particles is hydration. For ions, heats of hydration depend on the ion's charge density but are always negative because ion-dipole forces are strong.
- Systems naturally increase their entropy (distribute their energy in more ways). A gas has higher entropy than a liquid, which has higher entropy than a solid, and a solution has higher entropy than the pure solute and solvent.
- Relative sizes of the enthalpy and entropy changes determine solution formation. A substance with a positive ΔH_{soln} dissolves *only* if ΔS_{soln} is larger than ΔH_{soln}.

Figure 13.17 **Equilibrium in a saturated solution.** At some temperature, the number of solute particles dissolving (*white arrows*) per unit time equals the number recrystallizing (*black arrows*).

13.4 • SOLUBILITY AS AN EQUILIBRIUM PROCESS

When an excess amount of solid is added to a solvent, particles leave the crystal, are surrounded by solvent, and move away. Some dissolved solute particles collide with undissolved solute and recrystallize, but, as long as the rate of dissolving is greater than the rate of recrystallizing, the concentration rises. At a given temperature, when solid is dissolving at the same rate as dissolved particles are recrystallizing, the concentration remains constant and *undissolved solute is in equilibrium with dissolved solute:*

$$\text{Solute (undissolved)} \rightleftharpoons \text{solute (dissolved)}$$

Figure 13.17 shows an ionic solid in equilibrium with dissolved cations and anions.

Three terms express the extent of this solution process:

- A **saturated solution** is at equilibrium and contains the maximum amount of dissolved solute at a given temperature in the presence of undissolved solute. Therefore, if you filter off the solution and add more solute, it doesn't dissolve.
- An **unsaturated solution** contains *less* than the equilibrium concentration of dissolved solute; add more solute, and more dissolves until the solution is saturated.
- A **supersaturated solution** contains *more* than the equilibrium concentration and is unstable relative to the saturated solution; add a "seed" crystal of solute or tap the container, and the excess solute crystallizes immediately, leaving a saturated solution (Figure 13.18). You can often prepare a supersaturated solution if the solute is more soluble at higher temperature. While heating, dissolve more than the amount required for saturation at some lower temperature, and then slowly cool the solution. If the excess solute remains dissolved, the solution is supersaturated.

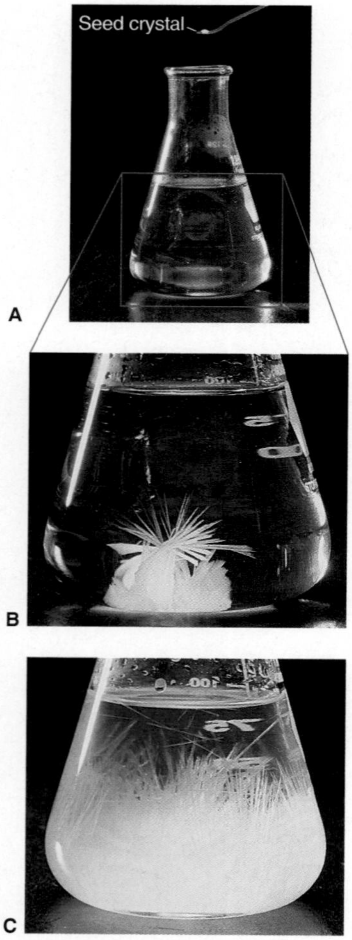

Figure 13.18 **Sodium acetate crystallizing from a supersaturated solution.** When a seed crystal of sodium acetate is added to a supersaturated solution of it **(A)**, solute begins to crystallize **(B)** and continues until the remaining solution is saturated **(C)**.

Effect of Temperature on Solubility

You know that more sugar dissolves in hot tea than in iced tea; in fact, temperature affects the solubility of most substances. Let's examine the effects of temperature on the solubility of solids and gases.

Temperature and the Solubility of Solids in Water Like sugar, *most solids are more soluble at higher temperatures* (Figure 13.19). Note that cerium sulfate is one of several exceptions, mostly other sulfates. Some salts have higher solubility up to a certain temperature and then lower solubility at still higher temperatures.

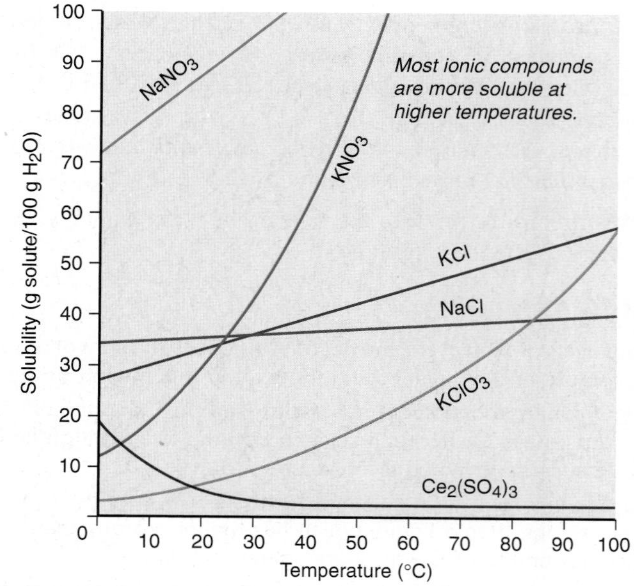

Figure 13.19 Relation between solubility and temperature for several ionic compounds.

Unfortunately, the effect of temperature on solubility is a complex phenomenon, and the sign of ΔH_{soln} does not reflect that complexity. Tabulated ΔH_{soln} values give the enthalpy change for making a solution at the standard state of 1 *M*; but in order to understand the effect of temperature, we need to know the sign of the enthalpy change very close to the point of saturation, which may differ from the sign of the tabulated value. For example, tables give a negative ΔH_{soln} for NaOH and a positive one for NH_4NO_3, yet both compounds are more soluble at higher temperatures. The point is that, although the effect of temperature reflects the equilibrium nature of solubility, no single measure can predict the effect for a given solute.

Temperature and the Solubility of Gases in Water The effect of temperature on *gas* solubility is much more predictable. When a solid dissolves in a liquid, the solute particles must separate, so $\Delta H_{solute} > 0$. In contrast, gas particles are already separated, so $\Delta H_{solute} \approx 0$. Because hydration is exothermic ($\Delta H_{hydr} < 0$), the sum of these two terms is negative. Thus, $\Delta H_{soln} < 0$ for all gases in water:

$$\text{Solute}(g) + \text{water}(l) \rightleftharpoons \text{saturated solution}(aq) + \text{heat}$$

Thus, *gas solubility in water* ***decreases*** *with rising temperature (addition of heat).* Gases have weak intermolecular forces with water. When the temperature rises, the average kinetic energy increases, allowing the gas particles to easily overcome these forces and re-enter the gas phase.

This behavior leads to *thermal pollution.* Many electric power plants use large amounts of water from a nearby river or lake for cooling, and the warmed water is returned to the source. The metabolic rates of fish and other aquatic animals increase in this warmer water, increasing their need for O_2. But the concentration of dissolved O_2 is lower in warm water, so they become "oxygen deprived." Also, the less dense warm water floats and prevents O_2 from reaching the cooler water below. Thus, even creatures at deeper levels become oxygen deprived. Farther from the plant, the water temperature and O_2 solubility return to normal. To mitigate the problem, cooling towers lower the temperature of the water before it exits the plant (Figure 13.20); nuclear power plants use a similar approach (Section 24.7).

Figure 13.20 Preventing thermal pollution with cooling towers.

Effect of Pressure on Solubility

Pressure has little effect on the solubility of liquids and solids because they are almost incompressible. But it has a *major* effect on the solubility of gases. Consider a piston-cylinder assembly with a gas above a saturated aqueous solution of the gas (Figure 13.21A). At equilibrium, at a given pressure, the same number of gas molecules enter and leave the solution per unit time:

$$\text{Gas} + \text{solvent} \rightleftharpoons \text{saturated solution}$$

Push down on the piston, and you disturb the equilibrium: gas volume decreases, so gas pressure (and concentration) increases, and gas particles collide with the liquid surface more often. Thus, more particles enter than leave the solution per unit time (Figure 13.21B). More gas dissolves to reduce this disturbance (a shift to the right in the preceding equation) until the system re-establishes equilibrium (Figure 13.21C).

The relation between gas pressure and solubility has many familiar applications. In a closed can of cola, dissolved CO_2 is in equilibrium with 4 atm of CO_2 in the small

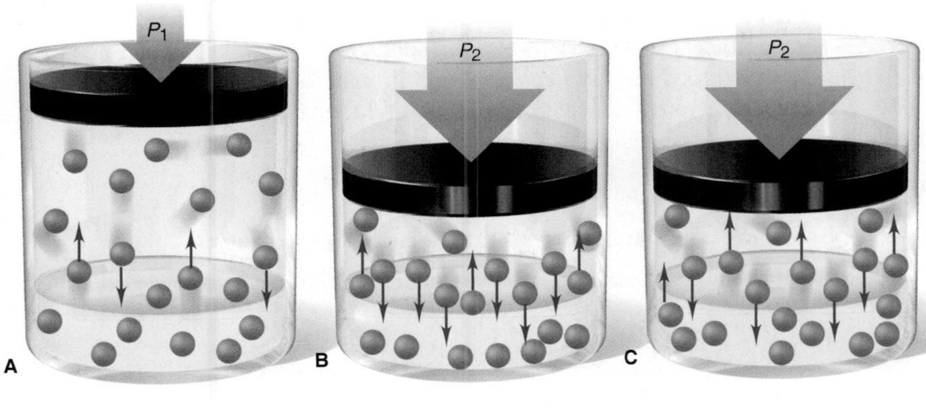

Figure 13.21 The effect of pressure on gas solubility.

What happens to gases dissolved in the blood of a scuba diver?

volume above the solution. Open the can and the dissolved CO_2 bubbles out of solution until the drink goes "flat" because it reaches equilibrium with CO_2 in air ($P_{CO_2} = 3\times10^{-4}$ atm). In a different situation (*see photo*), scuba divers who breathe compressed air have a high concentration of N_2 dissolved in their blood. If they ascend too quickly, they may suffer decompression sickness (the "bends"), in which lower external pressure allows the dissolved N_2 to form bubbles in the blood that block capillaries.

Henry's law expresses the quantitative relationship between gas pressure and solubility: *the solubility of a gas (S_{gas}) is directly proportional to the partial pressure of the gas (P_{gas}) above the solution:*

$$S_{gas} = k_H \times P_{gas} \quad (13.3)$$

where k_H is the *Henry's law constant* and is specific for a given gas-solvent combination at a given temperature. With S_{gas} in mol/L and P_{gas} in atm, the units of k_H are mol/L·atm.

Sample Problem 13.2 Using Henry's Law to Calculate Gas Solubility

Problem The partial pressure of carbon dioxide gas inside a bottle of cola is 4 atm at 25°C. What is the solubility of CO_2? The Henry's law constant for CO_2 in water is 3.3×10^{-2} mol/L·atm at 25°C.

Plan We know P_{CO_2} (4 atm) and the value of k_H (3.3×10^{-2} mol/L·atm), so we substitute them into Equation 13.3 to find S_{CO_2}.

Solution $S_{CO_2} = k_H \times P_{CO_2} = (3.3\times10^{-2}\ \text{mol/L·atm})(4\ \text{atm}) = 0.1\ \text{mol/L}$

Check The units are correct. We rounded to one significant figure because there is one in the pressure value. A 0.5-L bottle of cola has about 0.2 g of dissolved CO_2.

Follow-Up Problem 13.2 If air contains 78% N_2 by volume, what is the solubility of N_2 in water at 25°C and 1 atm (k_H for N_2 in H_2O at 25°C = 7×10^{-4} mol/L·atm)?

Summary of Section 13.4

- A solution that contains the maximum amount of dissolved solute in the presence of excess undissolved solute is saturated. A saturated solution is in equilibrium with excess solute, because solute particles are entering and leaving the solution at the same rate.
- Most solids are more soluble at higher temperatures.
- All gases have a negative ΔH_{soln} in water, so heating lowers gas solubility in water.
- Henry's law says that the solubility of a gas is directly proportional to its partial pressure above the solution.

13.5 • CONCENTRATION TERMS

Concentration is the *proportion* of a substance in a mixture, so it is an *intensive* property (like density and temperature), one that does not depend on the quantity of mixture: 1.0 L or 1.0 mL of 0.1 *M* NaCl have the same concentration. Concentration is a ratio of quantities (Table 13.5), most often solute to *solution,* but sometimes solute to *solvent.* Both parts of the ratio can be given in units of mass, volume, or amount (mol), and chemists express concentration by several terms, including molarity, molality, and various expressions of "parts of solute per part by solution."

Molarity and Molality

Two very common concentration terms are molarity and molality:

1. Molarity (*M*) is the *number of moles of solute dissolved in 1 L of solution:*

$$\text{Molarity } (M) = \frac{\text{amount (mol) of solute}}{\text{volume (L) of solution}} \quad (13.4)$$

Table 13.5 Concentration Definitions

Concentration Term	Ratio
Molarity (M)	$\dfrac{\text{amount (mol) of solute}}{\text{volume (L) of solution}}$
Molality (m)	$\dfrac{\text{amount (mol) of solute}}{\text{mass (kg) of solvent}}$
Parts by mass	$\dfrac{\text{mass of solute}}{\text{mass of solution}}$
Parts by volume	$\dfrac{\text{volume of solute}}{\text{volume of solution}}$
Mole fraction (X)	$\dfrac{\text{amount (mol) of solute}}{\text{amount (mol) of solute + amount (mol) of solvent}}$

In Chapter 3, we used molarity to convert liters of solution into amount of dissolved solute. Molarity has two drawbacks that affect its use in precise work:

- *Effect of temperature.* A liquid expands when heated, so a unit volume of hot solution contains less solute than one of cold solution; thus, the molarity is different.
- *Effect of mixing.* Because of solute-solvent interactions that are difficult to predict, *volumes may not be additive:* adding 500. mL of one solution to 500. mL of another may not give 1000. mL of final solution.

2. **Molality (m)** does not contain volume in its ratio; it is *the number of moles of solute dissolved in 1000 g (1 kg) of solvent:*

$$\text{Molality } (m) = \frac{\text{amount (mol) of solute}}{\text{mass (kg) of solvent}} \tag{13.5}$$

Note that molality includes the quantity of *solvent,* not solution. Molality has two advantages over molarity for precise work:

- *Effect of temperature.* Molal solutions are based on *masses* of components, not *volume.* And since mass does not change with temperature, neither does molality.
- *Effect of mixing.* Unlike volumes, masses *are* additive: adding 500. g of one solution to 500. g of another *does* give 1000. g of final solution.

For these reasons, molality is the preferred term when temperature, and hence density, may change, as in a study of physical properties. Note that, in the case of water, 1 L has a mass of 1 kg, so *molality and molarity are nearly the same for dilute aqueous solutions.*

Sample Problem 13.3 Calculating Molality

Problem What is the molality of a solution prepared by dissolving 32.0 g of $CaCl_2$ in 271 g of water?

Plan To use Equation 13.5, we convert mass of $CaCl_2$ (32.0 g) to amount (mol) with the molar mass (g/mol) and then divide by the mass of water (271 g), being sure to convert from grams to kilograms (see the road map).

Solution Converting from grams of solute to moles:

$$\text{Amount (mol) of } CaCl_2 = 32.0 \text{ g } CaCl_2 \times \frac{1 \text{ mol } CaCl_2}{110.98 \text{ g } CaCl_2} = 0.288 \text{ mol } CaCl_2$$

Finding molality:

$$\text{Molality} = \frac{\text{mol solute}}{\text{kg solvent}} = \frac{0.288 \text{ mol } CaCl_2}{271 \text{ g} \times \dfrac{1 \text{ kg}}{10^3 \text{ g}}} = 1.06\ m\ CaCl_2$$

Road Map

Mass (g) of $CaCl_2$

↓ divide by $\mathcal{M}$ (g/mol)

Amount (mol) of $CaCl_2$

↓ divide by kg of water

Molality (m) of $CaCl_2$ solution

Check The answer seems reasonable: the given amount (mol) of $CaCl_2$ and mass (kg) of H_2O are about the same, so their ratio is about 1.

Follow-Up Problem 13.3 How many grams of glucose ($C_6H_{12}O_6$) must be dissolved in 563 g of ethanol (C_2H_5OH) to prepare a 2.40×10^{-2} *m* solution?

Parts of Solute by Parts of Solution

Several concentration terms relate the number of solute (or solvent) parts to a number of *solution* parts. Both can be expressed in units of mass, volume, or amount (mol).

Parts by Mass The most common of these terms is **mass percent, % (w/w),** which you encountered in Chapter 3. The word *percent* means "per hundred," so mass percent means mass of solute dissolved in 100. parts by mass of solution:

$$\text{Mass percent} = \frac{\text{mass of solute}}{\text{mass of solute} + \text{mass of solvent}} \times 100 = \frac{\text{mass of solute}}{\text{mass of solution}} \times 100 \quad (13.6)$$

Mass percent values appear on jars of solid chemicals to indicate impurities.

Two very similar terms are parts per million (ppm) by mass and parts per billion (ppb) by mass, or grams of solute per million or per billion grams of solution: in Equation 13.6, you multiply by 10^6 or by 10^9, respectively, instead of by 100. Environmental toxicologists use these units to measure pollutants. For example, TCDD (*t*etra*c*hloro*d*ibenzo*d*ioxin) (*see margin*), a byproduct of paper bleaching, is unsafe at soil levels above 1 ppb. From normal contact with air, water, and soil, North Americans have an average of 0.01 ppb TCDD in their tissues.

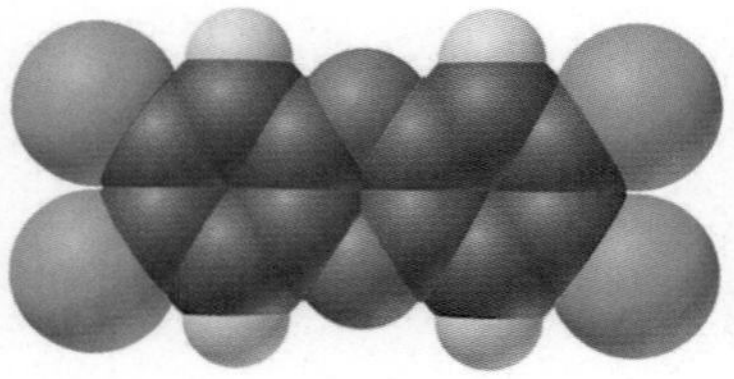

Is this deadly toxin in your body?

Parts by Volume The most common parts-by-volume term is **volume percent, % (v/v),** the volume of solute in 100. volumes of solution:

$$\text{Volume percent} = \frac{\text{volume of solute}}{\text{volume of solution}} \times 100 \quad (13.7)$$

For example, rubbing alcohol is an aqueous solution of isopropanol (a three-carbon alcohol) that contains 70 volumes of alcohol in 100. volumes of solution, or 70% (v/v).

Parts by volume is often used to express tiny concentrations of liquids or gases. Minor atmospheric components occur in parts per million by volume (ppmv). For example, about 0.05 ppmv of the toxic gas carbon monoxide (CO) is in clean air, 1000 times as much (50 ppmv of CO) in air over urban traffic, and 10,000 times as much (500 ppmv of CO) in cigarette smoke. *Pheromones* are compounds secreted by members of a species to signal food, danger, sexual readiness, and so forth. Many organisms, including dogs and monkeys, release pheromones, and researchers suspect that humans do as well. Some insect pheromones, such as the sexual attractant of the gypsy moth, are active at a few hundred molecules per milliliter of air, 100 parts per quadrillion by volume.

A concentration term often used in health-related facilities for aqueous solutions is % (w/v), a ratio of solute *weight* (actually mass) to solution *volume.* Thus, a 1.5% (w/v) NaCl solution contains 1.5 g of NaCl per 100. mL of *solution.*

Mole Fraction The **mole fraction (*X*)** of a solute is the ratio of number of moles of solute to the total number of moles (solute plus solvent), that is, parts by mole:

$$\text{Mole fraction } (X) = \frac{\text{amount (mol) of solute}}{\text{amount (mol) of solute} + \text{amount (mol) of solvent}} \quad (13.8)$$

Put another way, the mole fraction gives the proportion of solute (or solvent) particles in solution. The *mole percent* is the mole fraction expressed as a percentage:

$$\text{Mole percent (mol \%)} = \text{mole fraction} \times 100$$

Sample Problem 13.4 Expressing Concentrations in Parts by Mass, Parts by Volume, and Mole Fraction

Problem **(a)** Find the concentration of calcium ion (in ppm) in a 3.50-g pill that contains 40.5 mg of Ca^{2+}.
(b) The label on a 0.750-L bottle of Italian chianti indicates "11.5% alcohol by volume." How many liters of alcohol does the wine contain?
(c) A sample of rubbing alcohol contains 142 g of isopropyl alcohol (C_3H_7OH) and 58.0 g of water. What are the mole fractions of alcohol and water?

Plan **(a)** We know the mass of Ca^{2+} (40.5 mg) and the mass of the pill (3.50 g). We convert the mass of Ca^{2+} from mg to g, find the mass ratio of Ca^{2+} to pill, and multiply by 10^6 to obtain ppm. **(b)** We know the volume % (11.5%, or 11.5 parts by volume of alcohol to 100. parts of chianti) and the total volume (0.750 L), so we use Equation 13.7 to find liters of alcohol. **(c)** We know the mass and formula of each component, so we convert masses to amounts (mol) and apply Equation 13.8 to find the mole fractions.

Solution **(a)** Finding parts per million by mass of Ca^{2+}. Combining the steps, we have

$$\text{ppm } Ca^{2+} = \frac{\text{mass of } Ca^{2+}}{\text{mass of pill}} \times 10^6 = \frac{40.5 \text{ mg } Ca^{2+} \times \dfrac{1 \text{ g}}{10^3 \text{ mg}}}{3.50 \text{ g}} \times 10^6$$

$$= \boxed{1.16\times10^4 \text{ ppm } Ca^{2+}}$$

(b) Finding volume (L) of alcohol:

$$\text{Volume (L) of alcohol} = 0.750 \text{ L chianti} \times \frac{11.5 \text{ L alcohol}}{100. \text{ L chianti}}$$

$$= \boxed{0.0862 \text{ L}}$$

(c) Finding mole fractions. Converting from mass (g) to amount (mol):

$$\text{Amount (mol) of } C_3H_7OH = 142 \text{ g } C_3H_7OH \times \frac{1 \text{ mol } C_3H_7OH}{60.09 \text{ g } C_3H_7OH} = 2.36 \text{ mol } C_3H_7OH$$

$$\text{Amount (mol) of } H_2O = 58.0 \text{ g } H_2O \times \frac{1 \text{ mol } H_2O}{18.02 \text{ g } H_2O} = 3.22 \text{ mol } H_2O$$

Calculating mole fractions:

$$X_{C_3H_7OH} = \frac{\text{moles of } C_3H_7OH}{\text{total moles}} = \frac{2.36 \text{ mol}}{2.36 \text{ mol} + 3.22 \text{ mol}} = \boxed{0.423}$$

$$X_{H_2O} = \frac{\text{moles of } H_2O}{\text{total moles}} = \frac{3.22 \text{ mol}}{2.36 \text{ mol} + 3.22 \text{ mol}} = \boxed{0.577}$$

Check **(a)** The mass ratio is about 0.04 g/4 g $= 10^{-2}$, and $10^{-2}\times10^6 = 10^4$ ppm, so it seems correct. **(b)** The volume % is a bit more than 10%, so the volume of alcohol should be a bit more than 75 mL (0.075 L). **(c)** Always check that the *mole fractions add up to 1:* 0.423 + 0.577 = 1.000.

Follow-Up Problem 13.4 An alcohol solution contains 35.0 g of 1-propanol (C_3H_7OH) and 150. g of ethanol (C_2H_5OH). Calculate the mass percent and the mole fraction of each alcohol.

Interconverting Concentration Terms

All the terms we just discussed represent different ways of expressing concentration, so they are interconvertible. Keep these points in mind:

- To convert a term based on amount to one based on mass, you need the molar mass. These conversions are similar to the mass-mole conversions you've done earlier.
- To convert a term based on mass to one based on volume, you need the solution *density.* Given the mass of solution, the density (mass/volume) gives the volume, or vice versa.
- Molality includes quantity of *solvent;* the other terms include quantity of *solution.*

Sample Problem 13.5 Interconverting Concentration Terms

Problem Hydrogen peroxide is a powerful oxidizing agent; it is used in concentrated solution in rocket fuel, but in dilute solution in hair bleach. An aqueous solution of H_2O_2 is 30.0% by mass and has a density of 1.11 g/mL. Calculate the **(a)** molality, **(b)** mole fraction of H_2O_2, and **(c)** molarity.

Plan We know the mass % (30.0) and the density (1.11 g/mL). **(a)** For molality, we need the amount (mol) of solute and the mass (kg) of *solvent.* If we assume 100.0 g of solution, the mass % equals the grams of H_2O_2, which we subtract to obtain the grams of solvent. To find molality, we convert grams of H_2O_2 to moles and divide by mass of solvent (converting g to kg). **(b)** To find the mole fraction, we use the moles of H_2O_2 [from part (a)] and convert the grams of H_2O to moles. Then we divide the moles of H_2O_2 by the total moles. **(c)** To find molarity, we assume 100.0 g of solution and use the solution density to find the volume. Then we divide the moles of H_2O_2 [from part (a)] by *solution* volume (in L).

Solution **(a)** From mass % to molality. Finding mass of solvent (assuming 100.0 g of solution):

$$\text{Mass (g) of } H_2O = 100.0 \text{ g solution} - 30.0 \text{ g } H_2O_2 = 70.0 \text{ g } H_2O$$

Converting from grams of H_2O_2 to moles:

$$\text{Amount (mol) of } H_2O_2 = 30.0 \text{ g } H_2O_2 \times \frac{1 \text{ mol } H_2O_2}{34.02 \text{ g } H_2O_2} = 0.882 \text{ mol } H_2O_2$$

Calculating molality:

$$\text{Molality of } H_2O_2 = \frac{0.882 \text{ mol } H_2O_2}{70.0 \text{ g} \times \dfrac{1 \text{ kg}}{10^3 \text{ g}}} = 12.6\ m\ H_2O_2$$

(b) From mass % to mole fraction:

$$\text{Amount (mol) of } H_2O_2 = 0.882 \text{ mol } H_2O_2 \text{ [from part (a)]}$$

$$\text{Amount (mol) of } H_2O = 70.0 \text{ g } H_2O \times \frac{1 \text{ mol } H_2O}{18.02 \text{ g } H_2O} = 3.88 \text{ mol } H_2O$$

$$X_{H_2O_2} = \frac{0.882 \text{ mol}}{0.882 \text{ mol} + 3.88 \text{ mol}} = 0.185$$

(c) From mass % and density to molarity. Converting from solution mass to volume:

$$\text{Volume (mL) of solution} = 100.0 \text{ g} \times \frac{1 \text{ mL}}{1.11 \text{ g}} = 90.1 \text{ mL}$$

Calculating molarity:

$$\text{Molarity} = \frac{\text{mol } H_2O_2}{\text{L soln}} = \frac{0.882 \text{ mol } H_2O_2}{90.1 \text{ mL} \times \dfrac{1 \text{ L soln}}{10^3 \text{ mL}}} = 9.79\ M\ H_2O_2$$

Check Rounding shows the answers to be reasonable: **(a)** The ratio of ~0.9 mol/0.07 kg is greater than 10. **(b)** ~0.9 mol H_2O_2/(1 mol + 4 mol) ≈ 0.2. **(c)** The ratio of moles to liters (0.9/0.09) is around 10.

Follow-Up Problem 13.5 Concentrated hydrochloric acid is 11.8 *M* HCl and has a density of 1.190 g/mL. Calculate the mass %, molality, and mole fraction of HCl.

Summary of Section 13.5

- The concentration of a solution is independent of the quantity of solution and can be expressed as molarity (mol solute/L solution), molality (mol solute/kg solvent), parts by mass (mass solute/mass solution), parts by volume (volume solute/volume solution), or mole fraction [mol solute/(mol solute + mol solvent)] (Table 13.5).
- Molality is based on mass, so it is independent of temperature; the mole fraction gives the proportion of dissolved particles.
- If, in addition to the quantities of solute and solution, the solution density is known, the various ways of expressing concentration are interconvertible.

13.6 • COLLIGATIVE PROPERTIES OF SOLUTIONS

The presence of solute gives a solution different physical properties than the pure solvent. But, in the case of four important properties, it is the *number* of solute particles, *not* their chemical identity, that makes the difference. These **colligative properties** (*colligative* means "collective") are vapor pressure lowering, boiling point elevation, freezing point depression, and osmotic pressure. Most of the effects are small, but they have many applications, including some vital to organisms.

We predict the magnitude of a colligative property from the solute formula, which shows the number of particles in solution and is closely related to our classification of solutes (Chapter 4) by their ability to conduct an electric current (Figure 13.22):

1. *Electrolytes.* An aqueous solution of an **electrolyte** conducts because the solute separates into ions as it dissolves.
   - *Strong electrolytes*—soluble salts, strong acids, and strong bases—dissociate completely, so their solutions conduct well.
   - *Weak electrolytes*—weak acids and weak bases—dissociate very little, so their solutions conduct poorly.
2. *Nonelectrolytes.* Compounds such as sugar and alcohol do not dissociate into ions at all. They are **nonelectrolytes** because their solutions do not conduct a current.

Thus we can predict that

- *For nonelectrolytes,* 1 mol of compound yields 1 mol of particles in solution. For example, 0.35 *M* glucose contains 0.35 mol of solute particles per liter.
- *For strong electrolytes,* 1 mol of compound yields the amount (mol) of ions in the formula unit: 0.4 *M* Na_2SO_4 has 0.8 mol of Na^+ ions and 0.4 mol of SO_4^{2-} ions, or 1.2 mol of particles, per liter (see Sample Problem 4.1, p. 138).
- *For weak electrolytes,* the calculation is complicated because the solution reaches equilibrium; we examine these systems in Chapters 18 and 19.

In this section, we discuss colligative properties of three types of solute—nonvolatile nonelectrolytes, volatile nonelectrolytes, and strong electrolytes.

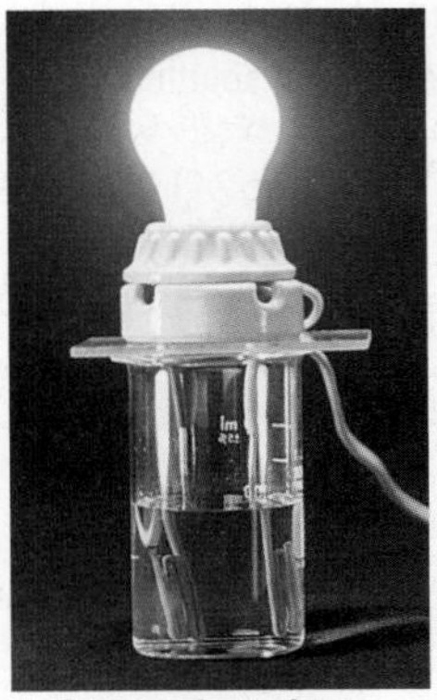

A Strong electrolyte

B Weak electrolyte

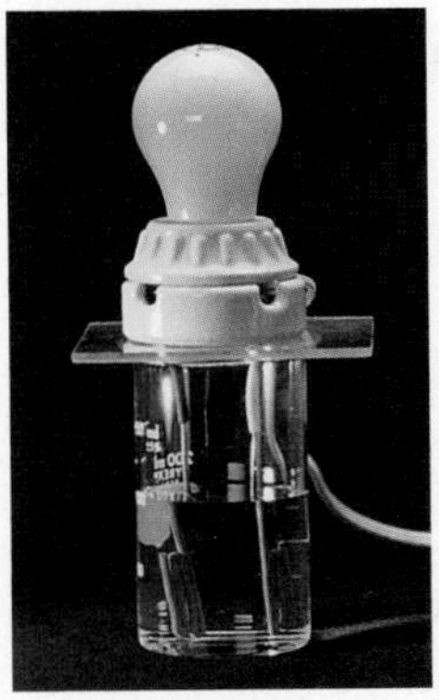

C Nonelectrolyte

Figure 13.22 Conductivity of three types of electrolyte solutions. **A,** For strong electrolytes, the number of particles equals the number of ions in a formula unit. **B,** Weak electrolytes form few ions. **C,** For nonelectrolytes, the number of particles equals the number of molecules.

Nonvolatile Nonelectrolyte Solutions

We start with solutions of *nonvolatile nonelectrolytes,* because they provide the clearest examples of the colligative properties. These solutes do not dissociate and have negligible vapor pressure at the boiling point of the solvent; sucrose (table sugar) dissolved in water is an example.

Vapor Pressure Lowering *The vapor pressure of a nonvolatile nonelectrolyte solution is always lower than the vapor pressure of the pure solvent.* The difference in vapor pressures is the **vapor pressure lowering (ΔP).**

1. *Why the vapor pressure of a solution is lower.* We can explain this lowering in terms of maintaining equilibrium or increasing entropy (Figure 13.23, *next page*):

- *Maintaining equilibrium.* In pure solvent, the opposing rates of vaporization (molecules leaving the liquid) and of condensation (molecules entering the liquid) are equal at equilibrium. In a solution, some solute molecules are on the surface, so the number of solvent molecules on the surface is lower; therefore, fewer vaporize per unit time. To maintain equilibrium, fewer gas molecules must enter the liquid, which happens if the vapor pressure is lower.
- *Increasing entropy.* A solvent vaporizes because the gaseous state has higher entropy than the liquid. But, with dissolved particles present, the solution already has higher entropy, so the solvent has less tendency to vaporize.

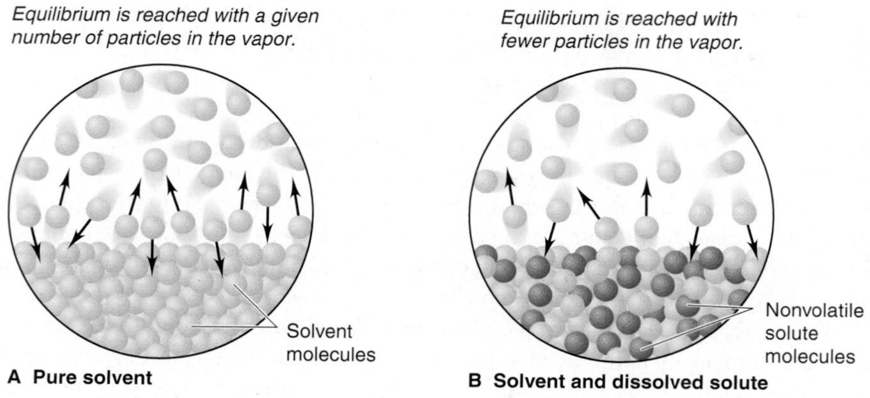

Figure 13.23 Effect of solute on the vapor pressure of solution. **A,** Equilibrium between a liquid and its vapor occurs when equal numbers of molecules vaporize and condense in a given time. **B,** Solute molecules decrease the number of solvent molecules at the surface *and* increase the entropy, so equilibrium occurs at a lower vapor pressure.

2. *Quantifying vapor pressure lowering.* **Raoult's law** says that the vapor pressure of solvent above a solution ($P_{solvent}$) equals the mole fraction of solvent ($X_{solvent}$) times the vapor pressure of the pure solvent ($P^\circ_{solvent}$):

$$P_{solvent} = X_{solvent} \times P^\circ_{solvent} \qquad (13.9)$$

Since $X_{solvent}$ is less than 1 in a solution, $P_{solvent}$ is less than $P^\circ_{solvent}$. An **ideal solution** is one that follows Raoult's law at any concentration. However, just as real gases deviate from ideality, so do real solutions. In practice, Raoult's law works reasonably well for *dilute* solutions and becomes exact at infinite dilution.

Let's see how the *amount* of dissolved solute affects ΔP. The solution consists of solvent and solute, so the sum of their mole fractions equals 1:

$$X_{solvent} + X_{solute} = 1; \quad \text{thus,} \quad X_{solvent} = 1 - X_{solute}$$

From Raoult's law, we have

$$P_{solvent} = X_{solvent} \times P^\circ_{solvent} = (1 - X_{solute}) \times P^\circ_{solvent}$$

Multiplying through on the right side gives

$$P_{solvent} = P^\circ_{solvent} - (X_{solute} \times P^\circ_{solvent})$$

Rearranging and introducing ΔP gives

$$P^\circ_{solvent} - P_{solvent} = \Delta P = X_{solute} \times P^\circ_{solvent} \qquad (13.10)$$

Thus, ΔP equals the mole fraction of solute times the vapor pressure of the pure solvent—a relationship applied in the next sample problem.

Sample Problem 13.6 Using Raoult's Law to Find ΔP

Road Map

Volume (mL) of glycerol (or H_2O)
↓ multiply by density (g/mL)
Mass (g) of glycerol (or H_2O)
↓ divide by $\mathcal{M}$ (g/mol)
Amount (mol) of glycerol (or H_2O)
↓ divide by total number of moles
Mole fraction (X) of glycerol
↓ multiply by $P^\circ_{H_2O}$
Vapor pressure lowering (ΔP)

Problem Find the vapor pressure lowering, ΔP, when 10.0 mL of glycerol ($C_3H_8O_3$) is added to 500. mL of water at 50.°C. At this temperature, the vapor pressure of pure water is 92.5 torr and its density is 0.988 g/mL. The density of glycerol is 1.26 g/mL.

Plan To calculate ΔP, we use Equation 13.10. We are given the vapor pressure of pure water ($P^\circ_{H_2O}$ = 92.5 torr), so we just need the mole fraction of glycerol, $X_{glycerol}$. We convert the given volume of glycerol (10.0 mL) to mass using the given density (1.26 g/L), find the molar mass from the formula, and convert mass (g) to amount (mol). The same procedure gives amount of H_2O. From these amounts, we find $X_{glycerol}$ and ΔP.

Solution Calculating the amount (mol) of glycerol and of water:

$$\text{Amount (mol) of glycerol} = 10.0 \text{ mL glycerol} \times \frac{1.26 \text{ g glycerol}}{1 \text{ mL glycerol}} \times \frac{1 \text{ mol glycerol}}{92.09 \text{ g glycerol}}$$
$$= 0.137 \text{ mol glycerol}$$

$$\text{Amount (mol) of } H_2O = 500. \text{ mL } H_2O \times \frac{0.988 \text{ g } H_2O}{1 \text{ mL } H_2O} \times \frac{1 \text{ mol } H_2O}{18.02 \text{ g } H_2O} = 27.4 \text{ mol } H_2O$$

Calculating the mole fraction of glycerol:

$$X_{glycerol} = \frac{0.137 \text{ mol}}{0.137 \text{ mol} + 27.4 \text{ mol}} = 0.00498$$

Finding the vapor pressure lowering:

$$\Delta P = X_{glycerol} \times P^\circ_{H_2O} = 0.00498 \times 92.5 \text{ torr} = 0.461 \text{ torr}$$

Check The amount of each component seems correct: for glycerol, ~10 mL × 1.25 g/mL ÷ 100 g/mol = 0.125 mol; for H_2O, ~500 mL × 1 g/mL ÷ 20 g/mol = 25 mol. The small ΔP is reasonable because the mole fraction of solute is small.

Comment 1. The calculation assumes that glycerol is nonvolatile. At 1 atm, glycerol boils at 290.0°C, so the vapor pressure of glycerol at 50°C is negligible. **2.** To introduce the calculation, we assume the solution is close to ideal and Raoult's law holds.

Follow-Up Problem 13.6 Calculate the vapor pressure lowering of a solution of 2.00 g of aspirin ($\mathcal{M}$ = 180.15 g/mol) in 50.0 g of methanol (CH_3OH) at 21.2°C. Pure methanol has a vapor pressure of 101 torr at this temperature.

Boiling Point Elevation *A solution boils at a higher temperature than the pure solvent.* This colligative property results from the previous vapor pressure lowering:

1. *Why a solution boils at a higher T.* Recall that the boiling point, T_b, of a liquid is the temperature at which its vapor pressure equals the external pressure, P_{ext}. But, the vapor pressure of a solution is always lower than that of the pure solvent. Therefore, it is lower than P_{ext} at T_b of the solvent, so the solution doesn't boil. Thus, the **boiling point elevation (ΔT_b)** results because a higher temperature is needed to raise the solution's vapor pressure to equal P_{ext}.

We superimpose a phase diagram for the solution on one for the solvent to see ΔT_b (Figure 13.24): the gas-liquid line for the solution lies *below* the line for the solvent at any T and to the right of it at any P, and the line crosses 1 atm (P_{ext}, or P_{atm}) at a higher T.

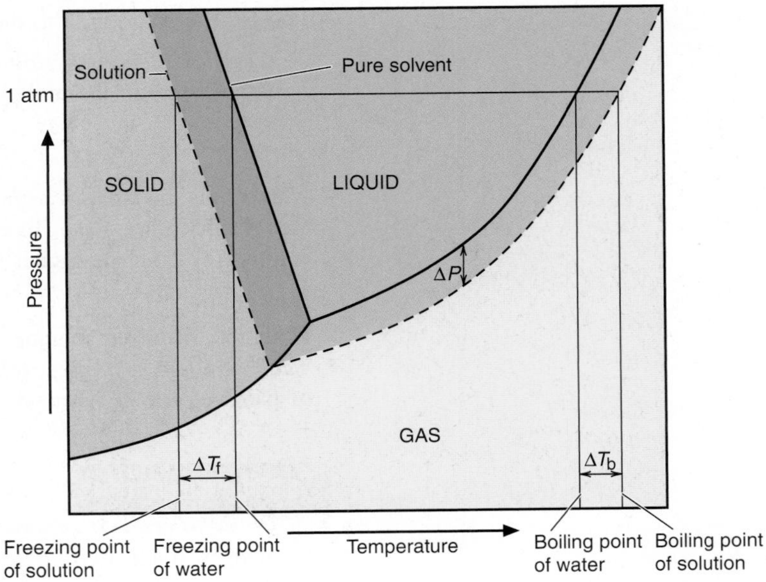

Figure 13.24 Boiling and freezing points of solvent and solution. Phase diagrams of an aqueous solution (*dashed lines*) and of pure water (*solid lines*) show that, by lowering the vapor pressure (ΔP), a solute elevates the boiling point (ΔT_b) and depresses the freezing point (ΔT_f). (The slope of the solid-liquid line is exaggerated.)

2. *Quantifying boiling point elevation.* Like vapor pressure lowering, boiling point elevation is proportional to the concentration of solute:

$$\Delta T_b \propto m \quad \text{or} \quad \Delta T_b = K_b m \qquad (13.11)$$

where m is the solution molality and K_b is the *molal boiling point elevation constant.* Since $\Delta T_b > 0$, we subtract the lower solvent T_b from the higher solution T_b:

$$\Delta T_b = T_{b(solution)} - T_{b(solvent)}$$

Molality is used because it relates to mole fraction and, thus, to particles of solute, and it is not affected by temperature.

The constant K_b has units of degrees Celsius per molal unit (°C/m) and is specific for a given solvent (Table 13.6). The K_b for water is 0.512°C/m, so ΔT_b for aqueous

Table 13.6 Molal Boiling Point Elevation and Freezing Point Depression Constants of Several Solvents

Solvent	Boiling Point (°C)*	K_b (°C/m)	Melting Point (°C)	K_f (°C/m)
Acetic acid	117.9	3.07	16.6	3.90
Benzene	80.1	2.53	5.5	4.90
Carbon disulfide	46.2	2.34	−111.5	3.83
Carbon tetrachloride	76.5	5.03	−23	30.
Chloroform	61.7	3.63	−63.5	4.70
Diethyl ether	34.5	2.02	−116.2	1.79
Ethanol	78.5	1.22	−117.3	1.99
Water	100.0	0.512	0.0	1.86

*At 1 atm.

solutions is quite small. For example, if you dissolve 1.00 mol of glucose (180. g; 1.00 mol of particles) or 0.500 mol of NaCl (29.2 g; also 1.00 mol of particles) in 1.00 kg of water at 1 atm, the solutions will boil at 100.512°C instead of 100.000°C.

Freezing Point Depression *A solution freezes at a lower temperature than the pure solvent,* and this colligative property also results from vapor pressure lowering:

1. *Why a solution freezes at a lower T.* Only solvent vaporizes from solution, so solute molecules are left behind. Similarly, *only solvent freezes,* again leaving solute molecules behind. The freezing point of a solution is the temperature at which its vapor pressure equals that of the pure solvent, that is, when solid solvent and liquid solution are in equilibrium. The **freezing point depression (ΔT_f)** occurs because the vapor pressure of the solution is always lower than that of the solvent, so the solution freezes at a lower temperature; that is, only at a lower temperature will solvent particles leave and enter the solid at the same rate. In Figure 13.24, the solid-liquid line for the solution is to the left of the pure solvent line at 1 atm, or any pressure.

2. *Quantifying freezing point depression.* Like ΔT_b, the freezing point depression is proportional to the molal concentration of solute:

$$\Delta T_f \propto m \qquad \text{or} \qquad \Delta T_f = K_f m \tag{13.12}$$

where K_f is the *molal freezing point depression constant,* which also has units of °C/m (see Table 13.6). Also, like ΔT_b, $\Delta T_f > 0$, but in this case, we subtract the lower solution T_f from the higher solvent T_f:

$$\Delta T_f = T_{f(solvent)} - T_{f(solution)}$$

Here, too, the effect in aqueous solution is small because K_f for water is just 1.86°C/m. Thus, at 1 atm, 1 m glucose, 0.5 m NaCl, and 0.33 m K_2SO_4, all solutions with 1 mol of particles per kilogram of water, freeze at −1.86°C instead of at 0.00°C.

Sample Problem 13.7 Determining Boiling and Freezing Points of a Solution

Problem You add 1.00 kg of ethylene glycol ($C_2H_6O_2$) antifreeze to 4450 g of water in your car's radiator. What are the boiling and freezing points of the solution?

Plan To find the boiling and freezing points, we need ΔT_b and ΔT_f. We first find the molality by converting mass of solute (1.00 kg) to amount (mol) and dividing by mass of solvent (4450 g, converted to kg). Then we calculate ΔT_b and ΔT_f from Equations 13.11 and 13.12 (using constants from Table 13.6). We add ΔT_b to the solvent boiling point and subtract ΔT_f from its freezing point. The road map shows the steps.

Road Map

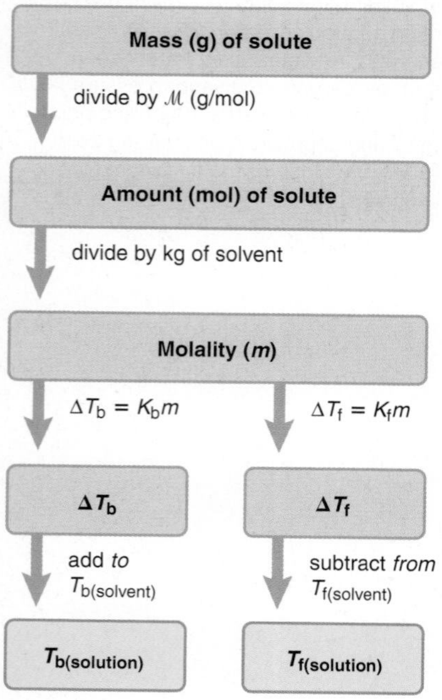

Solution Calculating the molality:

$$\text{Amount (mol) of } C_2H_6O_2 = 1.00 \text{ kg } C_2H_6O_2 \times \frac{10^3 \text{ g}}{1 \text{ kg}} \times \frac{1 \text{ mol } C_2H_6O_2}{62.07 \text{ g } C_2H_6O_2}$$
$$= 16.1 \text{ mol } C_2H_6O_2$$

$$\text{Molality} = \frac{\text{mol solute}}{\text{kg solvent}} = \frac{16.1 \text{ mol } C_2H_6O_2}{4450 \text{ g } H_2O \times \frac{1 \text{ kg}}{10^3 \text{ g}}} = 3.62\ m\ C_2H_6O_2$$

Finding the boiling point elevation and $T_{b(solution)}$, with $K_b = 0.512$°C/m:

$$\Delta T_b = \frac{0.512°\text{C}}{m} \times 3.62\ m = 1.85°\text{C}$$

$$T_{b(solution)} = T_{b(solvent)} + \Delta T_b = 100.00°\text{C} + 1.85°\text{C} = 101.85°\text{C}$$

Finding the freezing point depression and $T_{f(solution)}$, with $K_f = 1.86$°C/m:

$$\Delta T_f = \frac{1.86°\text{C}}{m} \times 3.62\ m = 6.73°\text{C}$$

$$T_{f(solution)} = T_{f(solvent)} - \Delta T_f = 0.00°\text{C} - 6.73°\text{C} = -6.73°\text{C}$$

Check The changes in boiling and freezing points should be in the same proportion as the constants used. That is, $\Delta T_b/\Delta T_f$ should equal K_b/K_f: 1.85/6.73 = 0.275 = 0.512/1.86.

Comment These answers are approximate because the concentration far exceeds that of a *dilute* solution, for which Raoult's law is most accurate.

Follow-Up Problem 13.7 What is the lowest molality of ethylene glycol solution that will protect your car's coolant from freezing at 0.00°F? (Assume the solution is ideal.)

Osmotic Pressure This colligative property occurs when solutions of higher and lower concentrations are separated by a **semipermeable membrane,** one that allows solvent, but *not* solute, to pass through. The phenomenon is called **osmosis:** a net flow of solvent into the more concentrated solution causes a pressure difference known as *osmotic pressure*. Many organisms regulate internal concentrations by osmosis.

1. *Why osmotic pressure arises*. Consider a simple apparatus in which a semipermeable membrane lies at the curve of a U tube and separates an aqueous sugar solution from pure water. Water molecules pass in *either* direction, but the larger sugar molecules do not. Because sugar molecules are on the solution side of the membrane, fewer water molecules touch that side, so fewer leave the solution than enter it in a given time (Figure 13.25A). The *net flow of water into the solution* increases its volume and thus decreases its concentration.

As the height of the solution rises and the height of the water falls, a pressure difference forms that resists more water entering and pushes some water back through the membrane. When water is being pushed out of the solution at the same rate it is entering, the system is at equilibrium (Figure 13.25B). The pressure difference at this point is the **osmotic pressure (Π),** which is the same as the pressure that must be applied to *prevent* net movement of water from solvent to solution (or from lower to higher concentration, Figure 13.25C).

2. *Quantifying osmotic pressure*. The osmotic pressure is proportional to the number of solute particles in a given solution *volume*, that is, to the molarity (M):

$$\Pi \propto \frac{n_{\text{solute}}}{V_{\text{soln}}} \qquad \text{or} \qquad \Pi \propto M$$

The proportionality constant is R times the absolute temperature T. Thus,

$$\Pi = \frac{n_{\text{solute}}}{V_{\text{soln}}} RT = MRT \tag{13.13}$$

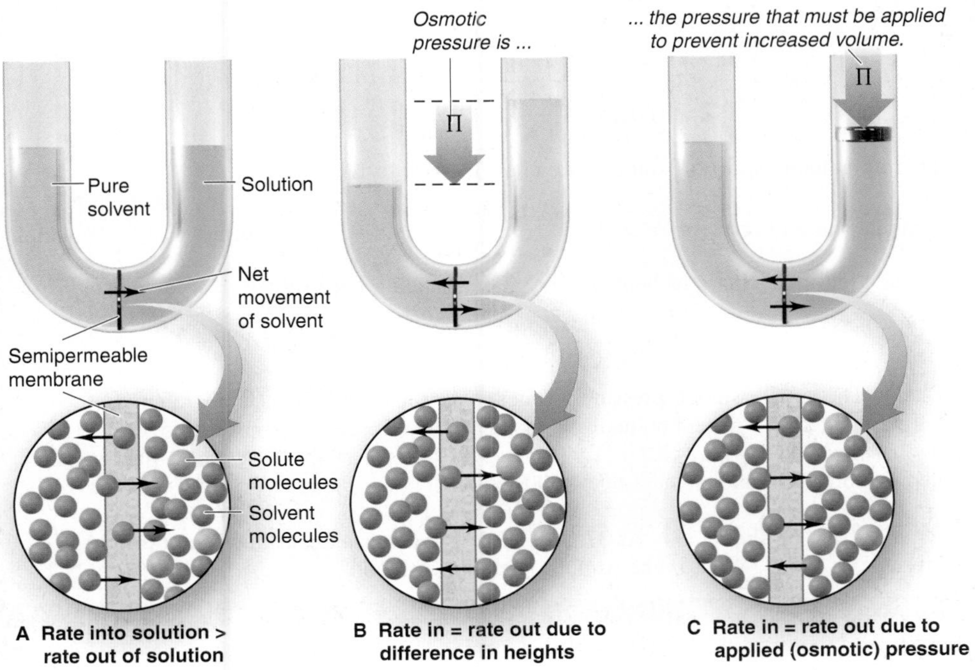

Figure 13.25 The development of osmotic pressure. A, In a given time, more solvent enters the solution through the membrane than leaves. **B,** At equilibrium, solvent flow is equalized. **C,** The *osmotic pressure* (Π) *prevents* the volume change.

The similarity of Equation 13.13 to the ideal gas law ($P = nRT/V$) is not surprising, because both relate the pressure of a system to its concentration and temperature.

The Underlying Theme of Colligative Properties A common theme runs through our explanations of the four colligative properties of nonvolatile solutes. Each property arises because solute particles cannot move between two phases:

- They cannot enter the gas phase, which leads to *vapor pressure lowering* and *boiling point elevation.*
- They cannot enter the solid phase, which leads to *freezing point depression.*
- They cannot cross a semipermeable membrane, which leads to *osmotic pressure.*

In each situation, the presence of solute decreases the mole fraction of solvent, which lowers the number of solvent particles leaving the solution per unit time. This lowering requires a new balance in numbers of particles moving between two phases per unit time, and this new balance results in the measured colligative property.

Using Colligative Properties to Find Solute Molar Mass

Each colligative property is proportional to solute concentration. Thus, by measuring the property—lower freezing point, higher boiling point, and so forth—we determine the amount (mol) of solute particles and, given the mass of solute, the molar mass.

In principle, any of the colligative properties can be used but, of the four, osmotic pressure creates the largest changes and, thus, the most precise measurements. Polymer chemists and biochemists estimate molar masses as great as 10^5 g/mol by measuring osmotic pressure. Because only a tiny fraction of a mole of a macromolecular solute dissolves, the change in the other colligative properties would be too small.

Sample Problem 13.8 Determining Molar Mass from Osmotic Pressure

Problem Biochemists have discovered more than 400 mutant varieties of hemoglobin, the blood protein that carries O_2. A physician dissolves 21.5 mg of one variety in water to make 1.50 mL of solution at 5.0°C. She measures an osmotic pressure of 3.61 torr. What is the molar mass of the protein?

Road Map

Π (atm)

↓ $M = \Pi/RT$

M (mol/L)

↓ multiply by volume (L) of solution

Amount (mol) of solute

↓ divide *into* mass (g) of solute

$\mathcal{M}$ (g/mol)

Plan We know the osmotic pressure (Π = 3.61 torr), R, and T (5.0°C). We convert Π from torr to atm, and T from °C to K, and then use Equation 13.13 to solve for molarity (M). Then we calculate the amount (mol) of hemoglobin from the known volume (1.50 mL) and use the known mass (21.5 mg) to find $\mathcal{M}$.

Solution Combining unit conversion steps and solving for molarity:

$$M = \frac{\Pi}{RT} = \frac{\dfrac{3.61\ \text{torr}}{760\ \text{torr}/1\ \text{atm}}}{\left(0.0821\ \dfrac{\text{atm}\cdot\text{L}}{\text{mol}\cdot\text{K}}\right)(273.15\ \text{K} + 5.0)} = 2.08\times10^{-4}\ M$$

Finding amount (mol) of solute (after changing mL to L):

$$\text{Amount (mol) of solute} = M \times V = \frac{2.08\times10^{-4}\ \text{mol}}{1\ \text{L soln}} \times 0.00150\ L\ \text{soln} = 3.12\times10^{-7}\ \text{mol}$$

Calculating molar mass of hemoglobin (after changing mg to g):

$$\mathcal{M} = \frac{0.0215\ \text{g}}{3.12\times10^{-7}\ \text{mol}} = 6.89\times10^4\ \text{g/mol}$$

Check The small osmotic pressure implies a very low molarity. Hemoglobin is a biopolymer, so we expect a small number of moles [$(\sim2\times10^{-4}$ mol/L$)(1.5\times10^{-3}$ L$) = 3\times10^{-7}$ mol] and a high $\mathcal{M}$ ($\sim21\times10^{-3}$ g/3×10^{-7} mol $= 7\times10^4$ g/mol). Mammalian hemoglobin has a molar mass of 64,500 g/mol.

Follow-Up Problem 13.8 At 37°C, 0.30 M sucrose has about the same osmotic pressure as blood. What is the osmotic pressure of blood?

Volatile Nonelectrolyte Solutions

What is the effect on vapor pressure when the solute *is* volatile, that is, when the vapor consists of solute *and* solvent molecules? From Raoult's law (Equation 13.9),

$$P_{\text{solvent}} = X_{\text{solvent}} \times P^{\circ}_{\text{solvent}} \quad \text{and} \quad P_{\text{solute}} = X_{\text{solute}} \times P^{\circ}_{\text{solute}}$$

where X_{solvent} and X_{solute} are the mole fractions in the *liquid* phase. According to Dalton's law (p. 99), the total vapor pressure is the sum of the partial vapor pressures:

$$P_{\text{total}} = P_{\text{solvent}} + P_{\text{solute}} = (X_{\text{solvent}} \times P^{\circ}_{\text{solvent}}) + (X_{\text{solute}} \times P^{\circ}_{\text{solute}})$$

Thus, just as a nonvolatile solute lowers the vapor pressure of the solvent by making the solvent's mole fraction less than 1, *the presence of each volatile component lowers the vapor pressure of the other* by making each mole fraction less than 1.

Let's examine this idea with a solution of benzene (C_6H_6) and toluene (C_7H_8), which are miscible, in which the mole fractions in the liquid are equal: $X_{\text{ben}} = X_{\text{tol}} = 0.500$. At 25°C, the vapor pressures of the pure substances are 95.1 torr for benzene (P°_{ben}) and 28.4 torr for toluene (P°_{tol}). Note that benzene is *more volatile* than toluene. We find the partial pressures from Raoult's law:

$$P_{\text{ben}} = X_{\text{ben}} \times P^{\circ}_{\text{ben}} = 0.500 \times 95.1 \text{ torr} = 47.6 \text{ torr}$$
$$P_{\text{tol}} = X_{\text{tol}} \times P^{\circ}_{\text{tol}} = 0.500 \times 28.4 \text{ torr} = 14.2 \text{ torr}$$

Thus, the presence of benzene in the liquid lowers the vapor pressure of toluene, and vice versa.

Now let's calculate the mole fraction of each substance *in the vapor* by applying Dalton's law. Recall from Section 5.4 that $X_A = P_A/P_{\text{total}}$. Therefore, for benzene and toluene in the vapor,

$$X_{\text{ben}} = \frac{P_{\text{ben}}}{P_{\text{total}}} = \frac{47.6 \text{ torr}}{47.6 \text{ torr} + 14.2 \text{ torr}} = 0.770$$
$$X_{\text{tol}} = \frac{P_{\text{tol}}}{P_{\text{total}}} = \frac{14.2 \text{ torr}}{47.6 \text{ torr} + 14.2 \text{ torr}} = 0.230$$

The key point is that *the vapor has a higher mole fraction of the* ***more*** *volatile component.* Through a single vaporization-condensation step, a 50/50 *liquid* ratio of benzene-to-toluene created a 77/23 *vapor* ratio. Condense this vapor into a separate container, and the new *liquid* would have this 77/23 composition, and the new *vapor* above it would be enriched still further in the more volatile benzene.

In the laboratory method of **fractional distillation,** a solution of two or more volatile components is attached to a *fractionating column* packed with glass beads (or ceramic chunks) and connected to a condenser and collection flask. As the solution is heated and the vapor mixture meets the beads, numerous vaporization-condensation steps enrich the mixture until the vapor leaving the column, and thus the liquid finally collected, consists only of the most volatile component (see Figure 13.28).

Strong Electrolyte Solutions

For colligative properties of strong electrolyte solutions, the solute formula tells us the number of particles. For instance, the boiling point elevation (ΔT_b) of 0.050 *m* NaCl should be $2 \times \Delta T_b$ of 0.050 *m* glucose ($C_6H_{12}O_6$), because NaCl dissociates into two particles per formula unit. Thus, we use a multiplying factor called the *van't Hoff factor (i),* named after the Dutch chemist Jacobus van't Hoff (1852–1911):

$$i = \frac{\text{measured value for electrolyte solution}}{\text{expected value for nonelectrolyte solution}}$$

To calculate colligative properties for strong electrolyte solutions, we include i:

For vapor pressure lowering:	$\Delta P = i(X_{\text{solute}} \times P^{\circ}_{\text{solvent}})$
For boiling point elevation:	$\Delta T_b = i(K_b m)$
For freezing point depression:	$\Delta T_f = i(K_f m)$
For osmotic pressure:	$\Pi = i(MRT)$

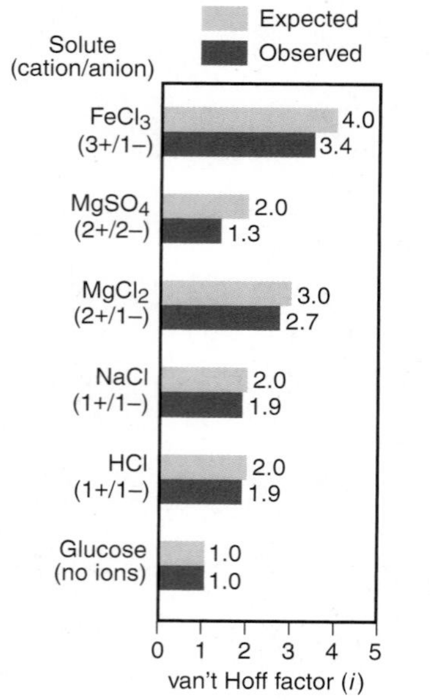

Figure 13.26 **Nonideal behavior of strong electrolyte solutions.** Van't Hoff factors (i) for 0.050 m solutions show the largest deviation for salts with multiply-charged ions. Glucose (a nonelectrolyte) behaves as expected.

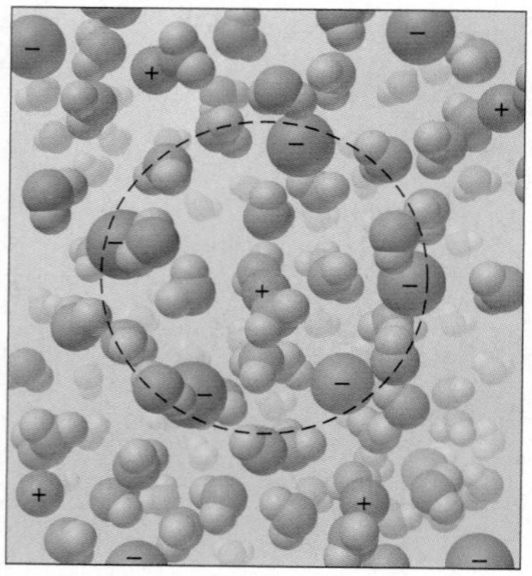

Figure 13.27 **An ionic atmosphere model for nonideal behavior of electrolyte solutions.**

Nonideal Solutions and Ionic Atmospheres *If* strong electrolyte solutions behaved ideally, the factor i would be the amount (mol) of particles in solution divided by the amount (mol) of dissolved solute; that is, i would be 2 for KBr, 3 for $Mg(NO_3)_2$, and so forth. However, *most strong electrolyte solutions are* ***not*** *ideal,* and the measured value of i is typically *lower* than the value expected from the formula. For example, for the boiling point elevation of 0.050 m NaCl, the expected value is 2.0, but, from experiment, we have

$$i = \frac{\Delta T_b \text{ of } 0.050\ m \text{ NaCl}}{\Delta T_b \text{ of } 0.050\ m \text{ glucose}} = \frac{0.049°C}{0.026°C} = 1.9$$

It seems as though the ions are not behaving independently, even though other evidence indicates that soluble salts dissociate completely. One clue to understanding the results is that multiply-charged ions cause a larger deviation (Figure 13.26).

To explain this nonideal behavior, we picture positive ions clustered, on average, near negative ions, and vice versa, to form an **ionic atmosphere** of net opposite charge (Figure 13.27). In effect, each type of ion acts "tied up," so its actual concentration seems *lower*. The *effective* concentration is the *stoichiometric* concentration, which is based on the formula multiplied by i. The greater the charge, the stronger the attractions, which explains the larger deviation for salts with multiply-charged ions.

Comparing Real Solutions and Real Gases At ordinary conditions and concentrations, particles are *much* closer together in liquids than in gases. And, as a result, nonideal behavior is much more common, and the deviations much larger. Nevertheless, the two systems have similarities:

- Gases display nearly ideal behavior at low pressures because the distances between particles are large. Similarly, the van't Hoff factor (i) approaches the ideal value as the solution becomes more dilute, that is, as the distance between ions increases.
- Attractions between particles cause deviations from the expected pressure in gases and from the expected size of a colligative property in ionic solutions.
- For both real gases and real solutions, we use empirically determined numbers (van der Waals constants or van't Hoff factors) to transform theories (the ideal gas law or Raoult's law) into more useful relations.

Sample Problem 13.9 Depicting Strong Electrolyte Solutions

Problem A 0.952-g sample of magnesium chloride dissolves in 100. g of water in a flask.

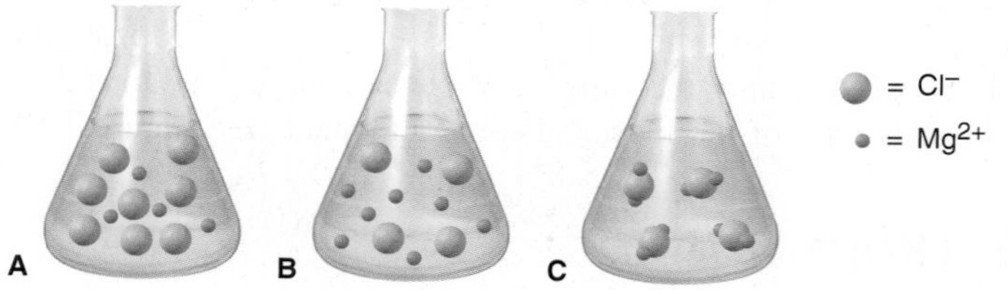

(a) Which scene depicts the solution best?
(b) What is the amount (mol) represented by each green sphere?
(c) Assuming the solution is ideal, what is its freezing point (at 1 atm)?

Plan **(a)** We find the numbers of cations and anions per formula unit from the name and compare it with the three scenes. **(b)** We convert the given mass to amount (mol), use the answer from part (a) to find moles of chloride ions (*green spheres*), and divide by the number of green spheres to get moles/sphere. **(c)** We find the molality (m) from amount (mol) of solute divided by the given mass of water (changed to kg). We multiply K_f for water (Table 13.6) by m to get ΔT_f, and then subtract that from 0.000°C to get the solution freezing point.

Solution **(a)** The formula is $MgCl_2$; only scene A has 1 Mg^{2+} for every 2 Cl^-.

(b)
$$\text{Amount (mol) of } MgCl_2 = \frac{0.952 \text{ g } MgCl_2}{95.21 \text{ g/mol } MgCl_2} = 0.0100 \text{ mol } MgCl_2$$

Therefore, Amount (mol) of Cl^- $= 0.0100 \text{ mol } MgCl_2 \times \frac{2\ Cl^-}{1\ MgCl_2} = 0.0200 \text{ mol } Cl^-$

$$\text{Moles/sphere} = \frac{0.0200 \text{ mol } Cl^-}{8 \text{ spheres}} = 2.50\times10^{-3} \text{ mol/sphere}$$

(c) $$\text{Molality } (m) = \frac{\text{mol of solute}}{\text{kg of solvent}} = \frac{0.0100 \text{ mol } MgCl_2}{100.\ g \times \frac{1\ kg}{1000\ g}} = 0.100\ m\ MgCl_2$$

Assuming an ideal solution, $i = 3$ for $MgCl_2$ (3 ions per formula unit), so we have

$$\Delta T_f = i(K_f m) = 3(1.86°C/m \times 0.100\ m) = 0.558°C$$

and $$T_f = 0.000°C - 0.558°C = -0.558°C$$

Check Let's quickly check the ΔT_f in part (c): We have 0.01 mol dissolved in 0.1 kg, or 0.1 m. Then, rounding K_f, we have about $3(2°C/m \times 0.1\ m) = 0.6°C$.

Follow-Up Problem 13.9 The $MgCl_2$ solution in the sample problem has a density of 1.006 g/mL at 20.0°C. **(a)** What is the osmotic pressure of the solution? **(b)** A U tube, with semipermeable membrane, is filled with the solution in the left arm and a glucose solution of equal molarity in the right. After time, which scene depicts the U tube best?

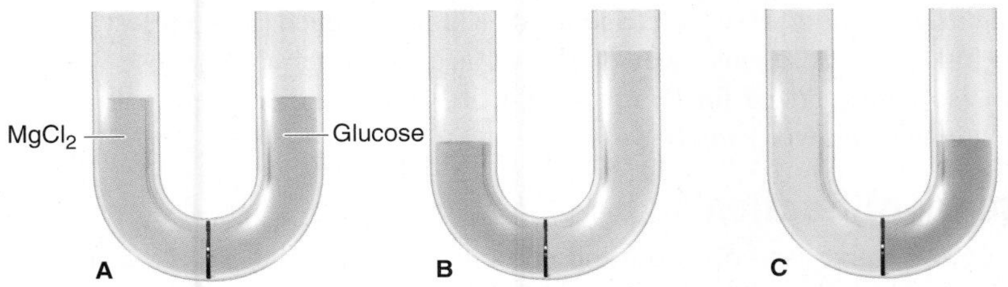

Applications of Colligative Properties

Two colligative properties in particular, freezing point depression and osmotic pressure, have key applications that involve all three types of solutes we've discussed, nonvolatile and volatile nonelectrolytes and strong electrolytes.

Uses of Freezing Point Depression Applications of this property appear in everyday life, nature, and industry:

- *Plane de-icer and car antifreeze.* The main ingredient in plane de-icer and car antifreeze, ethylene glycol ($C_2H_6O_2$), lowers the freezing point of water in winter and raises its boiling point in summer. Due to extensive H bonding, ethylene glycol is miscible with water and nonvolatile at 100°C.

- *Biological antifreeze.* Structurally similar to ethylene glycol and also miscible with water, glycerol ($C_3H_8O_3$) is produced by some fish and insects, including the common housefly, to lower the freezing point of their blood and thus allow them to survive winters.

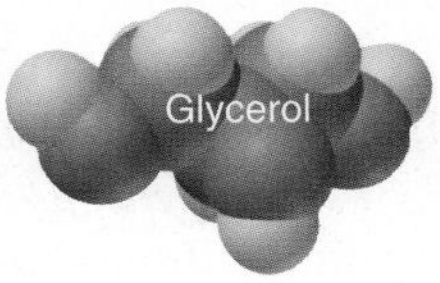

- *De-icing sidewalks and roads.* NaCl, or a mixture of it with $CaCl_2$, is used to melt ice on roads. A small amount dissolves in the ice by lowering its freezing point and melting it. More salt dissolves, more ice melts, and so forth. An advantage of $CaCl_2$ is that it has a highly negative ΔH_{soln}, so heat is released when it dissolves, which melts more ice.
- *Refining petroleum and silicon.* Countless vaporization-condensation steps within a 30-m fractionating tower separate the hundreds of volatile compounds in crude oil into a few "fractions" based on boiling point range (Figure 13.28). Impure silicon is refined by continuous melting and refreezing into a sample pure enough for use in computer chips (Chapter 22).

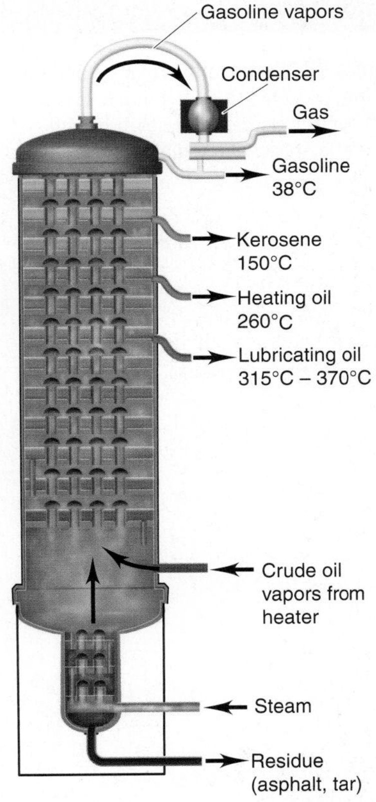

Figure 13.28 Fractional distillation in petroleum refining.

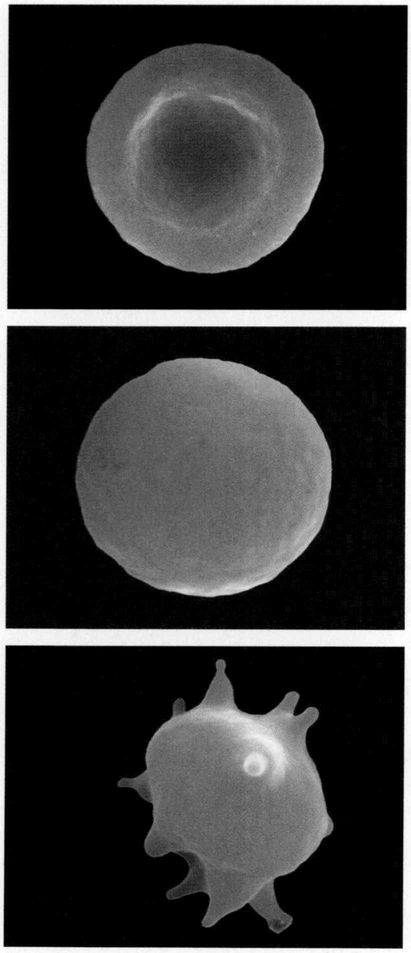

Figure 13.29 Osmotic pressure and cell shape. Isotonic (*top*), hypotonic (*middle*), and hypertonic (*bottom*) solutions influence the shape of a red blood cell.

Uses of Osmotic Pressure Of the four colligative properties, this one has the most applications vital to organisms.

- *Tonicity and cell shape.* The term *tonicity* refers to the tone, or firmness, of a cell. Placing the cell in an *isotonic* solution, one that has the same concentration of particles as the cell fluid, maintains the cell's normal shape because water enters and leaves the cell at the same rate (Figure 13.29, *top*). A *hypotonic* solution has a lower concentration of particles, so water enters the cell faster than it leaves, causing the cell to burst (*middle*). In contrast, a *hypertonic* solution has a higher concentration, so the cell shrinks because water leaves faster than it enters (*bottom*). To maintain cell shape, contact-lens rinse is isotonic saline (0.15 *M* NaCl), as are solutions used to deliver nutrients or drugs intravenously.
- *Absorption of water by trees.* Tree sap is a more concentrated solution than surrounding groundwater, so water passes through root membranes into the tree, creating an osmotic pressure that can exceed 20 atm in the tallest trees.
- *Regulation of water volume in the body.* Of the four major biological cations—Na^+, K^+, Mg^{2+}, and Ca^{2+}—sodium ion has the primary role of regulating water volume. It accounts for over 90 mol % of cations *outside* a cell: high Na^+ draws water out of the cell and low Na^+ leaves more inside. And the primary role of the kidneys is to regulate Na^+ concentration.
- *Food preservation.* Before refrigeration, salt was valued as a preservative. Packed onto food, salt causes microbes on the surface to shrivel as they lose water. In fact, it was so highly prized for this purpose that Roman soldiers were paid in salt, from which comes the word *salary*.

Summary of Section 13.6

- Colligative properties arise from the number, not type, of dissolved solute particles.
- Compared to pure solvent, a solution has lower vapor pressure (Raoult's law), elevated boiling point, and depressed freezing point, and it gives rise to osmotic pressure.
- Colligative properties are used to determine solute molar mass; osmotic pressure gives the most precise measurements.
- When solute *and* solvent are volatile, each lowers the vapor pressure of the other, with the vapor pressure of the more volatile component greater. When the vapor is condensed, the new solution is richer in that component than the original solution.
- Calculating colligative properties of electrolyte solutions requires a factor (i) that adjusts for the number of ions per formula unit. These solutions exhibit nonideal behavior because charge attractions effectively reduce the concentration of ions.

13.7 • THE STRUCTURE AND PROPERTIES OF COLLOIDS

Particle size plays a defining role in three types of mixtures:

- *Suspensions.* Stir a handful of fine sand into a glass of water, and the particles are suspended at first but gradually settle to the bottom. Sand in water is a **suspension,** a *heterogeneous* mixture containing particles large enough (>1000 nm) to be visibly distinct from the surrounding fluid.
- *Solutions.* In contrast, stirring sugar into water forms a solution, a *homogeneous* mixture in which the particles are invisible, individual sugar molecules (around 1 nm) distributed evenly throughout the surrounding fluid.
- *Colloids.* Between these extremes is a large group of mixtures called *colloidal dispersions,* or **colloids,** in which a dispersed (solute-like) substance is distributed throughout a dispersing (solvent-like) substance. The particles are larger than simple molecules but too small to settle out.

In this section, we examine the classification and key features of colliods.

1. *Particle size and surface area.* Colloidal particles range in diameter from 1 to 1000 nm (10^{-9} to 10^{-6} m). It may be a single macromolecule (natural or synthetic) or an aggregate of many atoms, ions, or molecules. As a result of the small particle size, a

colloid has a *very large total surface area*. A cube with 1-cm sides has a total surface area of 6 cm^2. If it's divided equally into 10^{12} cubes, the cubes are the size of large colloidal particles and have a total surface area of 60,000 cm^2, or 6 m^2. The enormous surface area of a colloid attracts other particles through various intermolecular forces.

2. *Classification of colloids.* Colloids are commonly classified by the physical state of the dispersed and dispersing substances (Table 13.7). Many familiar commercial products and natural objects are colloids. Whipped cream and shaving cream are *foams,* a gas dispersed in a liquid. Styrofoam is a *solid foam,* a gas dispersed in a solid. Most biological fluids are aqueous *sols,* solids dispersed in water: proteins and nucleic acids are the colloidal-size particles dispersed in an aqueous fluid of ions and small molecules within a cell. Soaps and detergents work by forming an *emulsion,* a liquid dispersed in another liquid. Other emulsions are mayonnaise and hand cream. Bile salts convert fats to an emulsion in the watery fluid of the small intestine.

Table 13.7 Types of Colloids

Colloid Type	Dispersed Substance	Dispersing Medium	Example(s)
Aerosol	Liquid	Gas	Fog
Aerosol	Solid	Gas	Smoke
Foam	Gas	Liquid	Whipped cream
Solid foam	Gas	Solid	Marshmallow
Emulsion	Liquid	Liquid	Milk
Solid emulsion	Liquid	Solid	Butter
Sol	Solid	Liquid	Paint, cell fluid
Solid sol	Solid	Solid	Opal

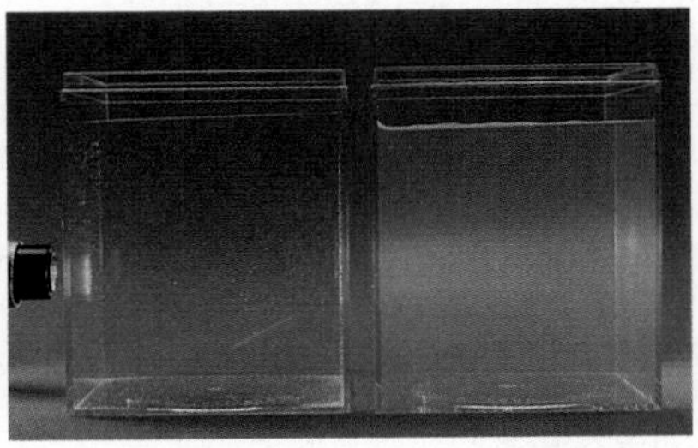

A

B

Figure 13.30 Light scattering and the Tyndall effect. **A,** The narrow, barely visible light beam that passes through a solution (*left*), is scattered and broadened by passing through a colloid (*right*). **B,** Sunlight is scattered by dust in air.

3. *Tyndall effect and Brownian motion.* Light passing through a colloid is scattered randomly because the dispersed particles have sizes similar to wavelengths of visible light (400 to 750 nm). The scattered light beam appears broader than one passing through a solution, an example of the **Tyndall effect** (Figure 13.30). Dust scatters sunlight shining through it, as does mist pierced by headlights.

Under low magnification, colloidal particles exhibit *Brownian motion,* an erratic change of speed and direction. Brownian motion results from collisions with molecules of the dispersing medium, and Einstein's explanation of it in 1905 led many to accept the molecular nature of matter.

4. *Stabilizing and destabilizing colloids.* Why don't colloidal particles aggregate and settle out? Colloidal particles dispersed in water have charged surfaces that stabilize the colloid through ion-dipole forces. Molecules with dual polarities, like lipids and soaps, form spherical *micelles,* with the charged heads on the exterior and hydrocarbon tails in the interior (Section 13.2). Aqueous proteins mimic this arrangement, with charged amino acid groups facing the water and nonpolar groups buried within the molecule. Oily particles can be dispersed in water by adding ions, which are adsorbed onto their surfaces. Repulsions between the ions on the oil and partial charges on water molecules prevent the particles from aggregating.

Despite these forces, various methods that coagulate the particles destabilize the colloid. Heating makes the particles collide more often and with enough force to coalesce and settle out. Addition of an electrolyte solution containing oppositely charged ions neutralizes the surface charges, so the particles coagulate and settle. In smokestack gases from a coal-burning power plant, ions become adsorbed onto uncharged colloidal particles, which are then attracted to the charged plates of a device called a *Cotrell precipitator* installed in the stack. At the mouths of rivers, where salt concentrations increase near an ocean or sea, colloidal clay particles coalesce into muddy deltas, like those of the Mississippi and the Nile (Figure 13.31). Thus, the city of New Orleans and the ancient Egyptian empire were made possible by such large-scale colloid chemistry.

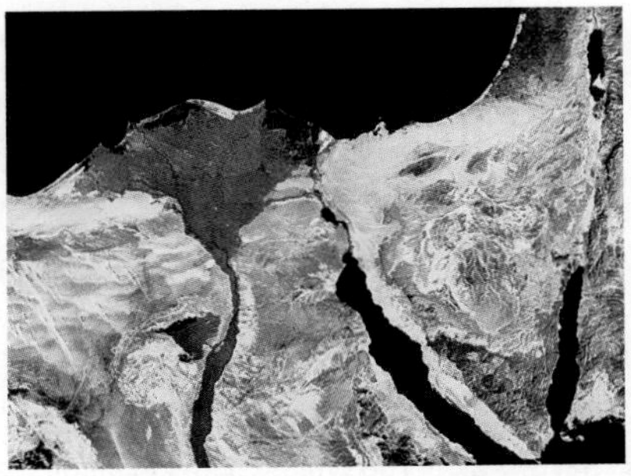

Figure 13.31 The Nile delta (reddish-brown area).

The upcoming Chemical Connections essay applies solution and colloid chemistry to the purification of water for residential and industrial use.

CHEMICAL CONNECTIONS TO ENVIRONMENTAL ENGINEERING | Solutions and Colloids in Water Purification

Most water destined for human use comes from lakes, rivers, reservoirs, or groundwater. Present in this essential resource may be soluble toxic organic compounds and high concentrations of NO_3^- and Fe^{3+}, colloidal clay and microbes, and suspended debris. Let's see how water is treated to remove these dissolved, dispersed, and suspended particles.

Water Treatment Plants

Treating water involves several steps (Figure B13.1):

Step 1. Screening and settling. As water enters the facility, screens remove debris, and settling removes particles such as sand.

Step 2. Coagulating. This step and the next two remove colloids. These particles have negative surfaces that repel each other. Added aluminum sulfate [cake alum; $Al_2(SO_4)_3$] or iron(III) chloride ($FeCl_3$), which supply Al^{3+} or Fe^{3+} that neutralize the charges, coagulates the particles through intermolecular forces.

Step 3. Flocculating and sedimenting. Mixing water and flocculating agents in large basins causes a fluffy *floc* to form. Added cationic polymers form long-chain bridges between floc particles, which grow bigger and heavier and flow into other basins, where they form a sediment and are removed. Some plants use *dissolved air flotation* (DAF) instead: bubbles forced through the water attach to the floc, and the floating mass is skimmed.

Step 4. Filtering. Various filters remove remaining particles. In *slow sand filters,* the water passes through sand and/or gravel of increasing particle size. In *rapid sand filters,* the sand is backwashed with water, and the colloidal mass is removed. Membrane filters (*not shown*) with pore sizes of 0.1–10 μm are thin tubes bundled together inside a vessel. The water is forced into these tubes, and the colloid-free filtrate is collected from a large central tube. Filtration is very effective at removing microorganisms resistant to disinfecting.

Step 5. Disinfecting. Water sources often contain harmful microorganisms that are killed by one of three agents:

- Chlorine, as aqueous bleach (ClO^-) or Cl_2, is most common, but carcinogenic chlorinated organic compounds can form.
- UV light emitted by high-intensity fluorescent tubes disinfects by disrupting microorganisms' DNA.
- Ozone (O_3) gas is a powerful oxidizing agent.

Sodium fluoride (NaF) to prevent tooth decay and phosphate salts to prevent leaching of lead from pipes may then be added.

Step 6 (not shown). Adsorbing onto granular activated carbon (GAC). Petroleum and other organic contaminants are removed by adsorption. GAC is a highly porous agent formed by "activating" wood, coal, or coconut shells with steam: 1 kg of GAC has a surface area of 275 acres!

Water Softening via Ion Exchange

Water with large amounts of 2+ ions, such as Ca^{2+} and Mg^{2+}, is called **hard water.** Combined with fatty-acid anions in soap, these cations form solid deposits on clothes, washing machines, and sinks:

$$\underset{}{Ca^{2+}(aq)} + \underset{\text{soap}}{2C_{17}H_{35}COONa(aq)} \longrightarrow \underset{\text{insoluble deposit}}{(C_{17}H_{35}COO)_2Ca(s)} + 2Na^+(aq)$$

When a large amount of HCO_3^- is present, the cations form *scale,* a carbonate deposit in boilers and hot-water pipes that interferes with the transfer of heat:

$$Ca^{2+}(aq) + 2HCO_3^-(aq) \longrightarrow CaCO_3(s) + CO_2(g) + H_2O(l)$$

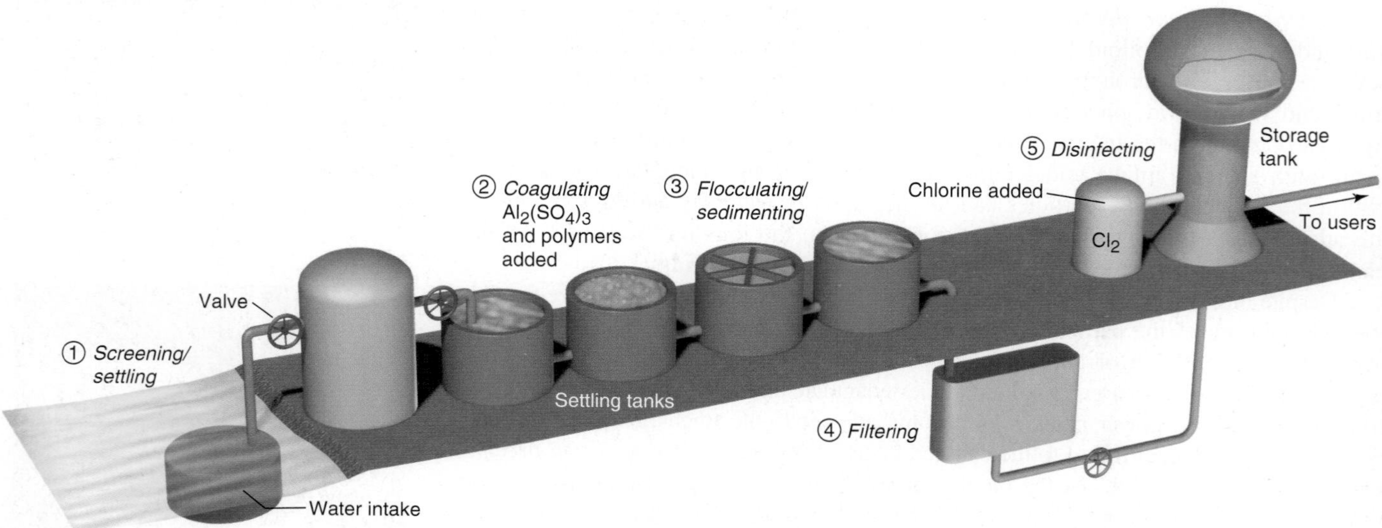

Figure B13.1 The typical steps in municipal water treatment.

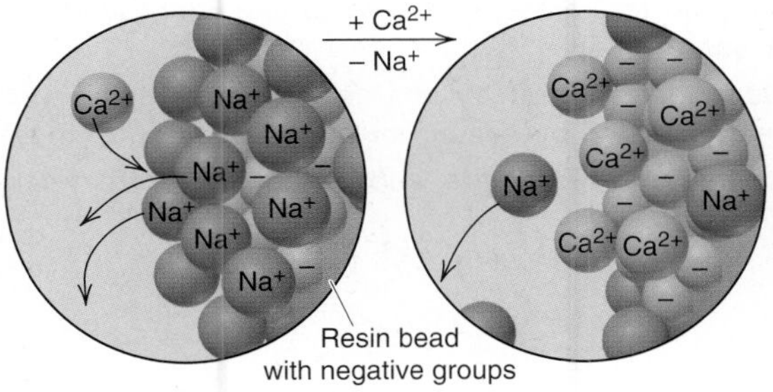

Figure B13.2 Ion exchange to remove hard-water cations.

Removing hard-water cations, called **water softening,** is done by exchanging Na^+ ions for Ca^{2+} and Mg^{2+} ions. A domestic **ion exchange** system contains an insoluble polymer *resin* with bonded anionic groups, such as $—SO_3^-$ or $—COO^-$, and Na^+ ions for charge balance (Figure B13.2). The hard-water cations displace the Na^+ ions and bind to the anionic groups. When the resin sites are occupied, the resin is regenerated with concentrated Na^+ solution that exchanges Na^+ ions for bound Ca^{2+} and Mg^{2+}.

Membrane Processes and Reverse Osmosis

Membranes with 0.0001–0.01 μm pores can remove unwanted ions from water. Recall that solutions of different concentrations separated by a semipermeable membrane create osmotic pressure. In **reverse osmosis,** a pressure *greater* than the osmotic pressure is *applied* to the more concentrated solution to force water back through the membrane and filter out ions. In homes, toxic *heavy-metal ions,* such as Pb^{2+}, Cd^{2+}, and Hg^{2+}, are removed this way. On a large scale, reverse osmosis is used for **desalination,** which can convert seawater (40,000 ppm of ions) to drinking water (400 ppm) (Figure B13.3).

Wastewater Treatment

Wastewater, used domestic or industrial water, is treated in several ways before being returned to a natural source:

- In *primary* treatment, the water enters a settling basin to remove particles.
- In *biological* treatment, bacteria metabolize organic compounds and are then removed by settling.
- In *advanced* treatment, a process is tailored to remove a specific pollutant. For example, ammonia, which causes excessive growth of plants and algae, is removed in two steps:
  1. *Nitrification.* Certain bacteria oxidize ammonia (electron donor) with O_2 (electron acceptor) to form nitrate ion:

$$NH_4^+ + 2O_2 \longrightarrow NO_3^- + 2H^+ + H_2O$$

  2. *Denitrification.* Other bacteria oxidize an added compound like methanol (CH_3OH) using the NO_3^-:

$$5CH_3OH + 6NO_3^- \longrightarrow 3N_2 + 5CO_2 + 7H_2O + 6OH^-$$

  Thus, the process converts NH_3 in wastewater to N_2, which is released to the atmosphere.

Problems

B13.1 Briefly answer each of the following:
(a) Why is cake alum [$Al_2(SO_4)_3$] added during water purification?
(b) Why is water that contains large amounts of Ca^{2+} and Mg^{2+} difficult to use for cleaning?
(c) What is the meaning of "reverse" in reverse osmosis?
(d) Why might a water treatment plant use ozone as a disinfectant instead of chlorine?
(e) How does passing a saturated NaCl solution through a "spent" ion-exchange resin regenerate the resin?

B13.2 Wastewater discharged into a stream by a sugar refinery contains 3.55 g of sucrose ($C_{12}H_{22}O_{11}$) per liter. A government-sponsored study is testing the feasibility of removing the sugar by reverse osmosis. What pressure must be applied to the apparatus at 20.°C to produce pure water?

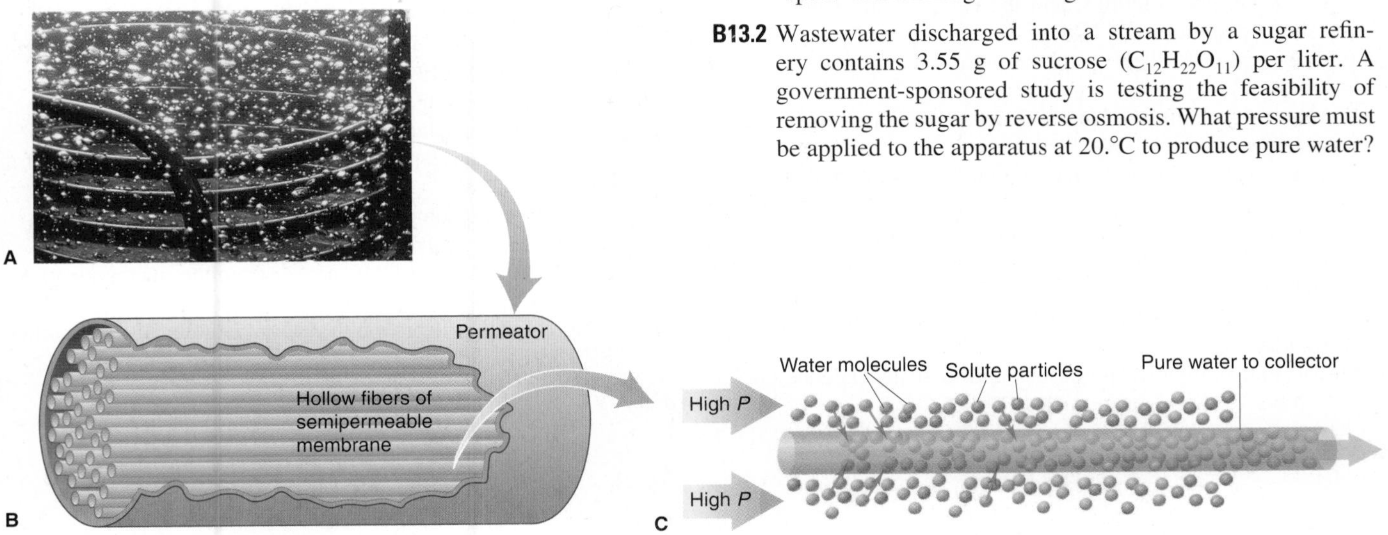

Figure B13.3 Reverse osmosis to remove ions. **A,** Part of a reverse-osmosis permeator. **B,** Each permeator contains a bundle of hollow fibers of semipermeable membrane. **C,** Pumping seawater at high pressure removes ions and purer water enters the fibers and is collected.

Summary of Section 13.7

- Particles in a colloid are smaller than those in a suspension and larger than those in a solution.
- Colloids are classified by the physical states of the dispersed and dispersing substances and involve many combinations of gas, liquid, and/or solid.
- Colloids have extremely large surface areas, scatter incoming light (Tyndall effect), and exhibit random (Brownian) motion.
- Colloidal particles in water are stabilized by charged surfaces that keep them dispersed, but they can be coagulated by heating or by the addition of ions.
- Solution behavior and colloid chemistry are applied to water treatment and purification.

CHAPTER REVIEW GUIDE

Learning Objectives

Relevant section (§) and/or sample problem (SP) numbers appear in parentheses.

Understand These Concepts

1. The quantitative meaning of solubility (§13.1)
2. The major types of intermolecular forces in solution and their relative strengths (§13.1)
3. How the like-dissolves-like rule depends on intermolecular forces (§13.1)
4. Why gases have relatively low solubilities in water (§13.1)
5. General characteristics of solutions formed by various combinations of gases, liquids, and solids (§13.1)
6. How intermolecular forces stabilize the structures of proteins, the cell membrane, and DNA (§13.2)
7. The enthalpy components of a solution cycle and their effect on ΔH_{soln} (§13.3)
8. The dependence of ΔH_{hydr} on ionic charge density and the factors that determine whether ionic solution processes are exothermic or endothermic (§13.3)
9. The meaning of entropy and how the balance between the change in enthalpy and the change in entropy governs the solution process (§13.3)
10. The distinctions among saturated, unsaturated, and supersaturated solutions, and the equilibrium nature of a saturated solution (§13.4)
11. The relation between temperature and the solubility of solids (§13.4)
12. Why the solubility of gases in water decreases with a rise in temperature (§13.4)
13. The effect of gas pressure on solubility and its quantitative expression as Henry's law (§13.4)
14. The meaning of molarity, molality, mole fraction, and parts by mass or by volume of a solution, and how to convert among them (§13.5)
15. The distinction between electrolytes and nonelectrolytes in solution (§13.6)
16. The four colligative properties and their dependence on number of dissolved particles (§13.6)
17. Ideal solutions and the importance of Raoult's law (§13.6)
18. How the phase diagram of a solution differs from that of the pure solvent (§13.6)
19. Why the vapor over a solution of volatile nonelectrolyte is richer in the more volatile component (§13.6)
20. Why electrolyte solutions are not ideal and the meanings of the van't Hoff factor and ionic atmosphere (§13.6)
21. How particle size distinguishes suspensions, colloids, and solutions (§13.7)
22. How colloidal behavior is demonstrated by the Tyndall effect and Brownian motion (§13.7)

Master These Skills

1. Predicting relative solubilities from intermolecular forces (SP 13.1)
2. Using Henry's law to calculate the solubility of a gas (SP 13.2)
3. Expressing concentration in terms of molality, parts by mass, parts by volume, and mole fraction (SPs 13.3, 13.4)
4. Interconverting among the various terms for expressing concentration (SP 13.5)
5. Using Raoult's law to calculate the vapor pressure lowering of a solution (SP 13.6)
6. Determining boiling point elevation and freezing point depression of a solution (SP 13.7)
7. Using a colligative property to calculate the molar mass of a solute (SP 13.8)
8. Calculating the composition of vapor over a solution of volatile nonelectrolyte (§13.6)
9. Calculating the van't Hoff factor i from the magnitude of a colligative property (§13.6)
10. Using a solution depiction to determine colligative properties (SP 13.9)

Key Terms

Page numbers appear in parentheses.

Section 13.1
solute (478)
solvent (478)
miscible (478)
solubility (S) (478)
like-dissolves-like rule (478)
hydration shell (478)
ion–induced dipole force (478)
dipole–induced dipole force (478)
alloy (482)

Section 13.2
protein (483)
amino acid (483)
soap (485)
lipid bilayer (485)
nucleic acid (487)
mononucleotide (487)
double helix (487)

Section 13.3
heat of solution (ΔH_{soln}) (488)
solvation (489)
hydration (489)
heat of hydration (ΔH_{hydr}) (489)
charge density (489)
entropy (S) (490)

Section 13.4
saturated solution (492)
unsaturated solution (492)
supersaturated solution (492)
Henry's law (494)

Section 13.5
molality (m) (495)
mass percent [% (w/w)] (496)
volume percent [% (v/v)] (496)
mole fraction (X) (496)

Section 13.6
colligative property (499)
electrolyte (499)
nonelectrolyte (499)
vapor pressure lowering (ΔP) (499)
Raoult's law (500)
ideal solution (500)
boiling point elevation (ΔT_b) (501)
freezing point depression (ΔT_f) (502)
semipermeable membrane (503)
osmosis (503)
osmotic pressure (Π) (503)
fractional distillation (505)
ionic atmosphere (506)

Section 13.7
suspension (508)
colloid (508)
Tyndall effect (509)
hard water (510)
water softening (511)
ion exchange (511)
reverse osmosis (511)
desalination (511)
wastewater (511)

Key Equations and Relationships

Page numbers appear in parentheses.

13.1 Dividing the general heat of solution into component enthalpies (488):

$$\Delta H_{soln} = \Delta H_{solute} + \Delta H_{solvent} + \Delta H_{mix}$$

13.2 Dividing the heat of solution of an ionic compound in water into component enthalpies (489):

$$\Delta H_{soln} = \Delta H_{lattice} + \Delta H_{hydr\ of\ the\ ions}$$

13.3 Relating gas solubility to its partial pressure (Henry's law) (494):

$$S_{gas} = k_H \times P_{gas}$$

13.4 Defining concentration in terms of molarity (494):

$$\text{Molarity } (M) = \frac{\text{amount (mol) of solute}}{\text{volume (L) of solution}}$$

13.5 Defining concentration in terms of molality (495):

$$\text{Molality } (m) = \frac{\text{amount (mol) of solute}}{\text{mass (kg) of solvent}}$$

13.6 Defining concentration in terms of mass percent (496):

$$\text{Mass percent } [\%\ (w/w)] = \frac{\text{mass of solute}}{\text{mass of solution}} \times 100$$

13.7 Defining concentration in terms of volume percent (496):

$$\text{Volume percent } [\%\ (v/v)] = \frac{\text{volume of solute}}{\text{volume of solution}} \times 100$$

13.8 Defining concentration in terms of mole fraction (496):

Mole fraction (X)

$$= \frac{\text{amount (mol) of solute}}{\text{amount (mol) of solute} + \text{amount (mol) of solvent}}$$

13.9 Expressing the relationship between the vapor pressure of solvent above a solution and its mole fraction in the solution (Raoult's law) (500):

$$P_{solvent} = X_{solvent} \times P^{\circ}_{solvent}$$

13.10 Calculating the vapor pressure lowering due to solute (500):

$$\Delta P = X_{solute} \times P^{\circ}_{solvent}$$

13.11 Calculating the boiling point elevation of a solution (501):

$$\Delta T_b = K_b m$$

13.12 Calculating the freezing point depression of a solution (502):

$$\Delta T_f = K_f m$$

13.13 Calculating the osmotic pressure of a solution (503):

$$\Pi = \frac{n_{solute}}{V_{soln}} RT = MRT$$

Brief Solutions to Follow-Up Problems

13.1 (a) 1,4-Butanediol is more soluble in water because it can form more H bonds.
(b) Chloroform is more soluble in water because of dipole-dipole forces.

13.2 $S_{N_2} = (7\times10^{-4}\ \text{mol/L·atm})(0.78\ \text{atm})$
$= 5\times10^{-4}\ \text{mol/L}$

13.3 Mass (g) of glucose

$$= 563\ \text{g ethanol} \times \frac{1\ \text{kg}}{10^3\ \text{g}} \times \frac{2.40\times10^{-2}\ \text{mol glucose}}{1\ \text{kg ethanol}} \times \frac{180.16\ \text{g glucose}}{1\ \text{mol glucose}}$$
$$= 2.43\ \text{g glucose}$$

13.4 $$\text{Mass \% } C_3H_7OH = \frac{35.0\ \text{g}}{35.0\ \text{g} + 150.\ \text{g}} \times 100 = 18.9\ \text{mass \%}$$

$$\text{Mass \% } C_2H_5OH = 100.0 - 18.9 = 81.1\ \text{mass \%}$$

$$X_{C_3H_7OH} = \frac{35.0\ \text{g } C_3H_7OH \times \dfrac{1\ \text{mol } C_3H_7OH}{60.09\ \text{g } C_3H_7OH}}{\left(35.0\ \text{g } C_3H_7OH \times \dfrac{1\ \text{mol } C_3H_7OH}{60.09\ \text{g } C_3H_7OH}\right) + \left(150.\ \text{g } C_2H_5OH \times \dfrac{1\ \text{mol } C_2H_5OH}{46.07\ \text{g } C_2H_5OH}\right)} = 0.152$$

$$X_{C_2H_5OH} = 1.000 - 0.152 = 0.848$$

13.5 $$\text{Mass \% HCl} = \frac{\text{mass of HCl}}{\text{mass of soln}} \times 100 = \frac{\dfrac{11.8\ \text{mol HCl}}{1\ \text{L soln}} \times \dfrac{36.46\ \text{g HCl}}{1\ \text{mol HCl}}}{\dfrac{1.190\ \text{g}}{1\ \text{mL soln}} \times \dfrac{10^3\ \text{mL}}{1\ \text{L}}} \times 100$$
$$= 36.2\ \text{mass \% HCl}$$

$$\text{Mass (kg) of soln} = 1\ \text{L soln} \times \frac{1.190\times10^{-3}\ \text{kg soln}}{1\times10^{-3}\ \text{L soln}} = 1.190\ \text{kg soln}$$

$$\text{Mass (kg) of HCl} = 11.8\ \text{mol HCl} \times \frac{36.46\ \text{g HCl}}{1\ \text{mol HCl}} \times \frac{1\ \text{kg}}{10^3\ \text{g}} = 0.430\ \text{kg HCl}$$

$$\text{Molality of HCl} = \frac{\text{mol HCl}}{\text{kg water}} = \frac{\text{mol HCl}}{\text{kg soln} - \text{kg HCl}} = \frac{11.8\ \text{mol HCl}}{0.760\ \text{kg } H_2O} = 15.5\ m\ \text{HCl}$$

$$X_{HCl} = \frac{\text{mol HCl}}{\text{mol HCl} + \text{mol } H_2O} = \frac{11.8\ \text{mol}}{11.8\ \text{mol} + \left(760\ \text{g } H_2O \times \dfrac{1\ \text{mol}}{18.02\ \text{g } H_2O}\right)} = 0.219$$

13.6 $$\Delta P = X_{aspirin} \times P^{\circ}_{methanol} = \frac{\dfrac{2.00\ \text{g}}{180.15\ \text{g/mol}}}{\dfrac{2.00\ \text{g}}{180.15\ \text{g/mol}} + \dfrac{50.0\ \text{g}}{32.04\ \text{g/mol}}} \times 101\ \text{torr}$$
$$= 0.713\ \text{torr}$$

13.7 $$\text{Molality of } C_2H_6O_2 = \frac{(32°\text{F} - 0.00°\text{F})\left(\dfrac{5°\text{C}}{9°\text{F}}\right)}{1.86°\text{C}/m} = 9.56\ m$$

13.8 $$\Pi = MRT = (0.30\ \text{mol/L})\left(0.0821\ \frac{\text{atm·L}}{\text{mol·K}}\right)(37°\text{C} + 273.15)$$
$$= 7.6\ \text{atm}$$

13.9 (a) Mass of 0.100 m solution
$$= 1\ \text{kg water} + 0.100\ \text{mol } MgCl_2 = 1000\ \text{g} + 9.52\ \text{g} = 1009.52\ \text{g}$$

$$\text{Volume of solution} = 1009.52\ \text{g} \times \frac{1\ \text{mL}}{1.006\ \text{g}} = 1003\ \text{mL}$$

$$\text{Molarity} = \frac{9.52\ \text{g } MgCl_2}{1003\ \text{mL soln}} \times \frac{1\ \text{mol}}{95.21\ \text{g } MgCl_2} \times \frac{10^3\ \text{mL}}{1\ \text{L}} = 9.97\times10^{-2}\ M$$

Osmotic pressure (Π)
$$= i(MRT) = 3(9.97\times10^{-2}\ \text{mol/L})\left(0.0821\ \frac{\text{atm·L}}{\text{mol·K}}\right)(293\ \text{K}) = 7.19\ \text{atm}$$

(b) Scene C

PROBLEMS

Problems with **colored** numbers are answered in Appendix E and worked in detail in the Student Solutions Manual. Problem sections match those in the text and provide the numbers of relevant sample problems. Most offer Concept Review Questions, Skill-Building Exercises (grouped in pairs covering the same concept), and Problems in Context. The Comprehensive Problems are based on material from any section or previous chapter.

Types of Solutions: Intermolecular Forces and Solubility

(Sample Problem 13.1)

Concept Review Questions

13.1 Describe how properties of seawater illustrate the two characteristics that define mixtures.

13.2 What types of intermolecular forces give rise to hydration shells in an aqueous solution of sodium chloride?

13.3 Acetic acid is miscible with water. Would you expect carboxylic acids with general formula $CH_3(CH_2)_nCOOH$ to become more or less water soluble as n increases? Explain.

13.4 Which would you expect to be more effective as a soap, sodium acetate or sodium stearate? Explain.

13.5 Hexane and methanol are miscible as gases but only slightly soluble in each other as liquids. Explain.

13.6 Hydrogen chloride (HCl) gas is much more soluble than propane gas (C_3H_8) in water, even though HCl has a lower boiling point. Explain.

Skill-Building Exercises (grouped in similar pairs)

13.7 Which gives the more concentrated solution, (a) KNO_3 in H_2O or (b) KNO_3 in carbon tetrachloride (CCl_4)? Explain.

13.8 Which gives the more concentrated solution, stearic acid [$CH_3(CH_2)_{16}COOH$] in (a) H_2O or (b) CCl_4? Explain.

13.9 What is the strongest type of intermolecular force between solute and solvent in each solution?

(a) $CsCl(s)$ in $H_2O(l)$ (b) $CH_3\overset{\overset{\displaystyle O}{\|}}{C}CH_3(l)$ in $H_2O(l)$
(c) $CH_3OH(l)$ in $CCl_4(l)$

13.10 What is the strongest type of intermolecular force between solute and solvent in each solution?

(a) $Cu(s)$ in $Ag(s)$ (b) $CH_3Cl(g)$ in $CH_3OCH_3(g)$
(c) $CH_3CH_3(g)$ in $CH_3CH_2CH_2NH_2(l)$

13.11 What is the strongest type of intermolecular force between solute and solvent in each solution?

(a) $CH_3OCH_3(g)$ in $H_2O(l)$ (b) $Ne(g)$ in $H_2O(l)$
(c) $N_2(g)$ in $C_4H_{10}(g)$

13.12 What is the strongest type of intermolecular force between solute and solvent in each solution?

(a) $C_6H_{14}(l)$ in $C_8H_{18}(l)$ (b) $H_2C{=}O(g)$ in $CH_3OH(l)$
(c) $Br_2(l)$ in $CCl_4(l)$

13.13 Which member of each pair is more soluble in diethyl ether? Why?

(a) $NaCl(s)$ or $HCl(g)$ (b) $H_2O(l)$ or $CH_3\overset{\overset{\displaystyle O}{\|}}{C}H(l)$
(c) $MgBr_2(s)$ or $CH_3CH_2MgBr(s)$

13.14 Which member of each pair is more soluble in water? Why?

(a) $CH_3CH_2OCH_2CH_3(l)$ or $CH_3CH_2OCH_3(g)$
(b) $CH_2Cl_2(l)$ or $CCl_4(l)$
(c)

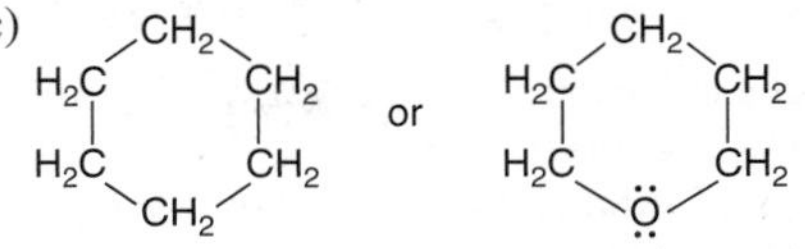

cyclohexane tetrahydropyran

Problems in Context

13.15 The dictionary defines *homogeneous* as "uniform in composition throughout." River water is a mixture of dissolved compounds, such as calcium bicarbonate, and suspended soil particles. Is river water homogeneous? Explain.

13.16 Gluconic acid is a derivative of glucose used in cleaners and in the dairy and brewing industries. Caproic acid is a carboxylic acid used in the flavoring industry. Although both are six-carbon acids (*see structures below*), gluconic acid is soluble in water and nearly insoluble in hexane, whereas caproic acid has the opposite solubility behavior. Explain.

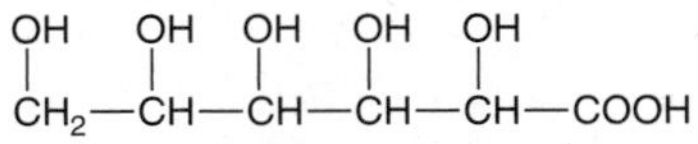

gluconic acid

$CH_3{-}CH_2{-}CH_2{-}CH_2{-}CH_2{-}COOH$

caproic acid

Intermolecular Forces and Biological Macromolecules

Concept Review Questions

13.17 Name three intermolecular forces that stabilize the shape of a soluble, globular protein, and explain how they act.

13.18 Name three intermolecular forces that stabilize the structure of DNA, and explain how they act.

13.19 How can relatively weak H bonds hold the double helix together yet allow DNA to function?

13.20 Is the sodium salt of propanoic acid as effective a soap as sodium stearate? Explain.

13.21 What intermolecular forces stabilize a lipid bilayer?

13.22 In what way do proteins embedded in a membrane differ structurally from soluble proteins?

13.23 Histones are proteins that control gene function by attaching through salt links to exterior regions of DNA. Name an amino acid whose side chain is often found on the exterior of histones.

Why Substances Dissolve: Understanding the Solution Process

Concept Review Questions

13.24 What is the relationship between solvation and hydration?

13.25 For a general solvent, which enthalpy terms in the thermochemical solution cycle are combined to obtain $\Delta H_{solvation}$?

13.26 (a) What is the charge density of an ion, and what two properties of an ion affect it?
(b) Arrange the following in order of increasing charge density:

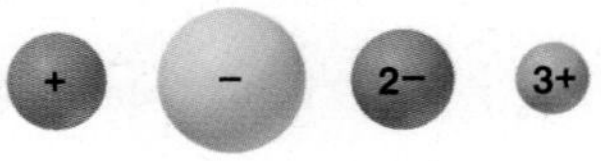

(c) How do the two properties in part (a) affect the ionic heat of hydration, ΔH_{hydr}?

13.27 For ΔH_{soln} to be very small, what quantities must be nearly equal in magnitude? Will their signs be the same or opposite?

13.28 Water is added to a flask containing solid NH_4Cl. As the salt dissolves, the solution becomes colder.
(a) Is the dissolving of NH_4Cl exothermic or endothermic?
(b) Is the magnitude of $\Delta H_{lattice}$ of NH_4Cl larger or smaller than the combined ΔH_{hydr} of the ions? Explain.
(c) Given the answer to (a), why does NH_4Cl dissolve in water?

13.29 An ionic compound has a highly negative ΔH_{soln} in water. Would you expect it to be very soluble or nearly insoluble in water? Explain in terms of enthalpy and entropy changes.

Skill-Building Exercises (grouped in similar pairs)

13.30 Sketch an enthalpy diagram for the process of dissolving KCl(*s*) in H_2O (endothermic).

13.31 Sketch an enthalpy diagram for the process of dissolving NaI(*s*) in H_2O (exothermic).

13.32 Which ion in each pair has greater charge density? Explain.
(a) Na^+ or Cs^+ (b) Sr^{2+} or Rb^+ (c) Na^+ or Cl^-
(d) O^{2-} or F^- (e) OH^- or SH^- (f) Mg^{2+} or Ba^{2+}
(g) Mg^{2+} or Na^+ (h) NO_3^- or CO_3^{2-}

13.33 Which ion has the lower ratio of charge to volume? Explain.
(a) Br^- or I^- (b) Sc^{3+} or Ca^{2+} (c) Br^- or K^+
(d) S^{2-} or Cl^- (e) Sc^{3+} or Al^{3+} (f) SO_4^{2-} or ClO_4^-
(g) Fe^{3+} or Fe^{2+} (h) Ca^{2+} or K^+

13.34 Which has the *larger* ΔH_{hydr} in each pair of Problem 13.32?

13.35 Which has the *smaller* ΔH_{hydr} in each pair of Problem 13.33?

13.36 (a) Use the following data to calculate the combined heat of hydration for the ions in potassium bromate ($KBrO_3$):

$\Delta H_{lattice} = 745$ kJ/mol $\quad \Delta H_{soln} = 41.1$ kJ/mol

(b) Which ion contributes more to the answer to part (a)? Why?

13.37 (a) Use the following data to calculate the combined heat of hydration for the ions in sodium acetate ($NaC_2H_3O_2$):

$\Delta H_{lattice} = 763$ kJ/mol $\quad \Delta H_{soln} = 17.3$ kJ/mol

(b) Which ion contributes more to the answer to part (a)? Why?

13.38 State whether the entropy of the system increases or decreases in each of the following processes:
(a) Gasoline burns in a car engine.
(b) Gold is extracted and purified from its ore.
(c) Ethanol (CH_3CH_2OH) dissolves in 1-propanol ($CH_3CH_2CH_2OH$).

13.39 State whether the entropy of the system increases or decreases in each of the following processes:
(a) Pure gases are mixed to prepare an anesthetic.
(b) Electronic-grade silicon is prepared from sand.
(c) Dry ice (solid CO_2) sublimes.

Problems in Context

13.40 Besides its use in making black-and-white film, silver nitrate ($AgNO_3$) is used similarly in forensic science. The NaCl left behind in the sweat of a fingerprint is treated with $AgNO_3$ solution to form AgCl. This precipitate is developed to show the black-and-white fingerprint pattern. Given $\Delta H_{lattice}$ of $AgNO_3$ = 822 kJ/mol and $\Delta H_{hydr} = -799$ kJ/mol, calculate its ΔH_{soln}.

Solubility as an Equilibrium Process

(Sample Problem 13.2)

Concept Review Questions

13.41 You are given a bottle of solid X and three aqueous solutions of X—one saturated, one unsaturated, and one supersaturated. How would you determine which solution is which?

13.42 Potassium permanganate ($KMnO_4$) has a solubility of 6.4 g/100 g of H_2O at 20°C and a curve of solubility vs. temperature that slopes upward to the right. How would you prepare a supersaturated solution of $KMnO_4$?

13.43 Why does the solubility of any gas in water decrease with rising temperature?

Skill-Building Exercises (grouped in similar pairs)

13.44 For a saturated aqueous solution of each of the following at 20°C and 1 atm, will the solubility increase, decrease, or stay the same when the indicated change occurs?
(a) $O_2(g)$, increase *P* (b) $N_2(g)$, increase *V*

13.45 For a saturated aqueous solution of each of the following at 20°C and 1 atm, will the solubility increase, decrease, or stay the same when the indicated change occurs?
(a) He(*g*), decrease *T* (b) RbI(*s*), increase *P*

13.46 The Henry's law constant (k_H) for O_2 in water at 20°C is 1.28×10^{-3} mol/L·atm. (a) How many grams of O_2 will dissolve in 2.50 L of H_2O that is in contact with pure O_2 at 1.00 atm? (b) How many grams of O_2 will dissolve in 2.50 L of H_2O that is in contact with air, where the partial pressure of O_2 is 0.209 atm?

13.47 Argon makes up 0.93% by volume of air. Calculate its solubility (mol/L) in water at 20°C and 1.0 atm. The Henry's law constant for Ar under these conditions is 1.5×10^{-3} mol/L·atm.

Problems in Context

13.48 Caffeine is about 10 times as soluble in hot water as in cold water. A chemist puts a hot-water extract of caffeine into an ice bath, and some caffeine crystallizes. Is the remaining solution saturated, unsaturated, or supersaturated?

13.49 The partial pressure of CO_2 gas above the liquid in a bottle of champagne at 20°C is 5.5 atm. What is the solubility of CO_2 in champagne? Assume Henry's law constant is the same for champagne as for water: at 20°C, $k_H = 3.7\times10^{-2}$ mol/L·atm.

13.50 Respiratory problems are treated with devices that deliver air with a higher partial pressure of O_2 than normal air. Why?

Concentration Terms

(Sample Problems 13.3 to 13.5)

Concept Review Questions

13.51 Explain the difference between molarity and molality. Under what circumstances would molality be a more accurate measure of the concentration of a prepared solution than molarity? Why?

13.52 Which way of expressing concentration includes (a) volume of solution; (b) mass of solution; (c) mass of solvent?

13.53 A solute has a solubility in water of 21 g/kg solvent. Is this value the same as 21 g/kg solution? Explain.

13.54 You want to convert among molarity, molality, and mole fraction of a solution. You know the masses of solute and solvent and the volume of solution. Is this enough information to carry out all the conversions? Explain.

13.55 When a solution is heated, which ways of expressing concentration change in value? Which remain unchanged? Explain.

Skill-Building Exercises (grouped in similar pairs)

13.56 Calculate the molarity of each aqueous solution:
(a) 32.3 g of table sugar ($C_{12}H_{22}O_{11}$) in 100. mL of solution
(b) 5.80 g of $LiNO_3$ in 505 mL of solution

13.57 Calculate the molarity of each aqueous solution:
(a) 0.82 g of ethanol (C_2H_5OH) in 10.5 mL of solution
(b) 1.27 g of gaseous NH_3 in 33.5 mL of solution

13.58 Calculate the molarity of each aqueous solution:
(a) 78.0 mL of 0.240 *M* NaOH diluted to 0.250 L with water
(b) 38.5 mL of 1.2 *M* HNO_3 diluted to 0.130 L with water

13.59 Calculate the molarity of each aqueous solution:
(a) 25.5 mL of 6.25 *M* HCl diluted to 0.500 L with water
(b) 8.25 mL of 2.00×10^{-2} *M* KI diluted to 12.0 mL with water

13.60 How would you prepare the following aqueous solutions?
(a) 365 mL of 8.55×10^{-2} *M* KH_2PO_4 from solid KH_2PO_4
(b) 465 mL of 0.335 *M* NaOH from 1.25 *M* NaOH

13.61 How would you prepare the following aqueous solutions?
(a) 2.5 L of 0.65 *M* NaCl from solid NaCl
(b) 15.5 L of 0.3 *M* urea $[(NH_2)_2C{=}O]$ from 2.1 *M* urea

13.62 How would you prepare the following aqueous solutions?
(a) 1.40 L of 0.288 *M* KBr from solid KBr
(b) 255 mL of 0.0856 *M* $LiNO_3$ from 0.264 *M* $LiNO_3$

13.63 How would you prepare the following aqueous solutions?
(a) 57.5 mL of 1.53×10^{-3} *M* $Cr(NO_3)_3$ from solid $Cr(NO_3)_3$
(b) 5.8×10^3 m^3 of 1.45 *M* NH_4NO_3 from 2.50 *M* NH_4NO_3

13.64 Calculate the molality of the following:
(a) A solution containing 85.4 g of glycine (NH_2CH_2COOH) dissolved in 1.270 kg of H_2O
(b) A solution containing 8.59 g of glycerol ($C_3H_8O_3$) in 77.0 g of ethanol (C_2H_5OH)

13.65 Calculate the molality of the following:
(a) A solution containing 174 g of HCl in 757 g of H_2O
(b) A solution containing 16.5 g of naphthalene ($C_{10}H_8$) in 53.3 g of benzene (C_6H_6)

13.66 What is the molality of a solution consisting of 44.0 mL of benzene (C_6H_6; $d = 0.877$ g/mL) in 167 mL of hexane (C_6H_{14}; $d = 0.660$ g/mL)?

13.67 What is the molality of a solution consisting of 2.66 mL of carbon tetrachloride (CCl_4; $d = 1.59$ g/mL) in 76.5 mL of methylene chloride (CH_2Cl_2; $d = 1.33$ g/mL)?

13.68 How would you prepare the following aqueous solutions?
(a) 3.10×10^2 g of 0.125 *m* ethylene glycol ($C_2H_6O_2$) from ethylene glycol and water
(b) 1.20 kg of 2.20 mass % HNO_3 from 52.0 mass % HNO_3

13.69 How would you prepare the following aqueous solutions?
(a) 1.50 kg of 0.0355 *m* ethanol (C_2H_5OH) from ethanol and water
(b) 445 g of 13.0 mass % HCl from 34.1 mass % HCl

13.70 A solution contains 0.35 mol of isopropanol (C_3H_7OH) dissolved in 0.85 mol of water. (a) What is the mole fraction of isopropanol? (b) The mass percent? (c) The molality?

13.71 A solution contains 0.100 mol of NaCl dissolved in 8.60 mol of water. (a) What is the mole fraction of NaCl? (b) The mass percent? (c) The molality?

13.72 What mass of cesium bromide must be added to 0.500 L of water ($d = 1.00$ g/mL) to produce a 0.400 *m* solution? What are the mole fraction and the mass percent of CsBr?

13.73 What are the mole fraction and the mass percent of a solution made by dissolving 0.30 g of KI in 0.400 L of water ($d = 1.00$ g/mL)?

13.74 Calculate the molality, molarity, and mole fraction of NH_3 in an 8.00 mass % aqueous solution ($d = 0.9651$ g/mL).

13.75 Calculate the molality, molarity, and mole fraction of $FeCl_3$ in a 28.8 mass % aqueous solution ($d = 1.280$ g/mL).

Problems in Context

13.76 Wastewater from a cement factory contains 0.25 g of Ca^{2+} ion and 0.056 g of Mg^{2+} ion per 100.0 L of solution. The solution density is 1.001 g/mL. Calculate the Ca^{2+} and Mg^{2+} concentrations in ppm (by mass).

13.77 An automobile antifreeze mixture is made by mixing equal volumes of ethylene glycol ($d = 1.114$ g/mL; $\mathcal{M} = 62.07$ g/mol) and water ($d = 1.00$ g/mL) at 20°C. The density of the mixture is 1.070 g/mL. Express the concentration of ethylene glycol as:
(a) Volume percent (b) Mass percent (c) Molarity
(d) Molality (e) Mole fraction

Colligative Properties of Solutions

(Sample Problems 13.6 to 13.9)

Concept Review Questions

13.78 The chemical formula of a solute does *not* affect the extent of the solution's colligative properties. What characteristic of a solute *does* affect these properties? Name a physical property of a solution that *is* affected by the chemical formula of the solute.

13.79 What is a nonvolatile nonelectrolyte? Why is this type of solute the simplest case for examining colligative properties?

13.80 In what sense is a strong electrolyte "strong"? What property of the substance makes it a strong electrolyte?

13.81 Express Raoult's law in words. Is Raoult's law valid for a solution of a volatile solute? Explain.

13.82 What are the most important differences between the phase diagram of a pure solvent and the phase diagram of a solution of that solvent?

13.83 Is the composition of the vapor at the top of a fractionating column different from the composition at the bottom? Explain.

13.84 Is the boiling point of 0.01 *m* KF(*aq*) higher or lower than that of 0.01 *m* glucose(*aq*)? Explain.

13.85 Which aqueous solution has a boiling point closer to its predicted value, 0.050 *m* NaF or 0.50 *m* KCl? Explain.

13.86 Which aqueous solution has a freezing point closer to its predicted value, 0.01 *m* NaBr or 0.01 *m* $MgCl_2$? Explain.

13.87 The freezing point depression constants of the solvents cyclohexane and naphthalene are 20.1°C/*m* and 6.94°C/*m*, respectively. Which solvent would give a more accurate result if you are using freezing point depression to determine the molar mass of a substance that is soluble in either one? Why?

Skill-Building Exercises (grouped in similar pairs)

13.88 Classify the following substances as strong electrolytes, weak electrolytes, or nonelectrolytes:
(a) Hydrogen chloride (HCl) (b) Potassium nitrate (KNO_3)
(c) Glucose ($C_6H_{12}O_6$) (d) Ammonia (NH_3)

13.89 Classify the following substances as strong electrolytes, weak electrolytes, or nonelectrolytes:
(a) Sodium permanganate ($NaMnO_4$)
(b) Acetic acid (CH_3COOH)
(c) Methanol (CH_3OH)
(d) Calcium acetate [$Ca(C_2H_3O_2)_2$]

13.90 How many moles of solute particles are present in 1 L of each of the following aqueous solutions?
(a) 0.3 *M* KBr (b) 0.065 *M* HNO_3
(c) 10^{-4} *M* $KHSO_4$ (d) 0.06 *M* ethanol (C_2H_5OH)

13.91 How many moles of solute particles are present in 1 mL of each of the following aqueous solutions?
(a) 0.02 *M* $CuSO_4$ (b) 0.004 *M* $Ba(OH)_2$
(c) 0.08 *M* pyridine (C_5H_5N) (d) 0.05 *M* $(NH_4)_2CO_3$

13.92 Which solution has the lower freezing point?
(a) 11.0 g of CH_3OH in 100. g of H_2O *or*
22.0 g of CH_3CH_2OH in 200. g of H_2O
(b) 20.0 g of H_2O in 1.00 kg of CH_3OH *or*
20.0 g of CH_3CH_2OH in 1.00 kg of CH_3OH

13.93 Which solution has the higher boiling point?
(a) 38.0 g of $C_3H_8O_3$ in 250. g of ethanol *or*
38.0 g of $C_2H_6O_2$ in 250. g of ethanol
(b) 15 g of $C_2H_6O_2$ in 0.50 kg of H_2O *or*
15 g of NaCl in 0.50 kg of H_2O

13.94 Rank the following aqueous solutions in order of increasing (a) osmotic pressure; (b) boiling point; (c) freezing point; (d) vapor pressure at 50°C:
(I) 0.100 *m* $NaNO_3$
(II) 0.100 *m* glucose
(III) 0.100 *m* $CaCl_2$

13.95 Rank the following aqueous solutions in order of decreasing (a) osmotic pressure; (b) boiling point; (c) freezing point; (d) vapor pressure at 298 K:
(I) 0.04 *m* urea [$(NH_2)_2C{=}O$]
(II) 0.01 *m* $AgNO_3$
(III) 0.03 *m* $CuSO_4$

13.96 Calculate the vapor pressure of a solution of 34.0 g of glycerol ($C_3H_8O_3$) in 500.0 g of water at 25°C. The vapor pressure of water at 25°C is 23.76 torr. (Assume ideal behavior.)

13.97 Calculate the vapor pressure of a solution of 0.39 mol of cholesterol in 5.4 mol of toluene at 32°C. Pure toluene has a vapor pressure of 41 torr at 32°C. (Assume ideal behavior.)

13.98 What is the freezing point of 0.251 *m* urea in water?

13.99 What is the boiling point of 0.200 *m* lactose in water?

13.100 The boiling point of ethanol (C_2H_5OH) is 78.5°C. What is the boiling point of a solution of 6.4 g of vanillin ($\mathcal{M}$ = 152.14 g/mol) in 50.0 g of ethanol (K_b of ethanol = 1.22°C/*m*)?

13.101 The freezing point of benzene is 5.5°C. What is the freezing point of a solution of 5.00 g of naphthalene ($C_{10}H_8$) in 444 g of benzene (K_f of benzene = 4.90°C/*m*)?

13.102 What is the minimum mass of ethylene glycol ($C_2H_6O_2$) that must be dissolved in 14.5 kg of water to prevent the solution from freezing at −12.0°F? (Assume ideal behavior.)

13.103 What is the minimum mass of glycerol ($C_3H_8O_3$) that must be dissolved in 11.0 mg of water to prevent the solution from freezing at −15°C? (Assume ideal behavior.)

13.104 Calculate the molality and van't Hoff factor (*i*) for the following aqueous solutions:
(a) 1.00 mass % NaCl, freezing point = −0.593°C
(b) 0.500 mass % CH_3COOH, freezing point = −0.159°C

13.105 Calculate the molality and van't Hoff factor (*i*) for the following aqueous solutions:
(a) 0.500 mass % KCl, freezing point = −0.234°C
(b) 1.00 mass % H_2SO_4, freezing point = −0.423°C

Problems in Context

13.106 In a study designed to prepare new gasoline-resistant coatings, a polymer chemist dissolves 6.053 g of poly(vinyl alcohol) in enough water to make 100.0 mL of solution. At 25°C, the osmotic pressure of this solution is 0.272 atm. What is the molar mass of the polymer sample?

13.107 The U.S. Food and Drug Administration lists dichloromethane (CH_2Cl_2) and carbon tetrachloride (CCl_4) among the many cancer-causing chlorinated organic compounds. What are the partial pressures of these substances in the vapor above a solution of 1.60 mol of CH_2Cl_2 and 1.10 mol of CCl_4 at 23.5°C? The vapor pressures of pure CH_2Cl_2 and CCl_4 at 23.5°C are 352 torr and 118 torr, respectively. (Assume ideal behavior.)

The Structure and Properties of Colloids

Concept Review Questions

13.108 Is the fluid inside a bacterial cell considered a solution, a colloid, or both? Explain.

13.109 What type of colloid is each of the following?
(a) Milk (b) Fog (c) Shaving cream

13.110 What is Brownian motion, and what causes it?

13.111 In a movie theater, you can see the beam of projected light. What phenomenon does this exemplify? Why does it occur?

13.112 Why don't soap micelles coagulate and form large globules? Is soap more effective in freshwater or in seawater? Why?

Comprehensive Problems

13.113 The three aqueous ionic solutions below have total volumes of 25. mL for A, 50. mL for B, and 100. mL for C. If each sphere represents 0.010 mol of ions, calculate: (a) the total molarity of ions for each solution; (b) the highest molarity of solute; (c) the lowest molality of solute (assuming the solution densities are equal); (d) the highest osmotic pressure (assuming ideal behavior).

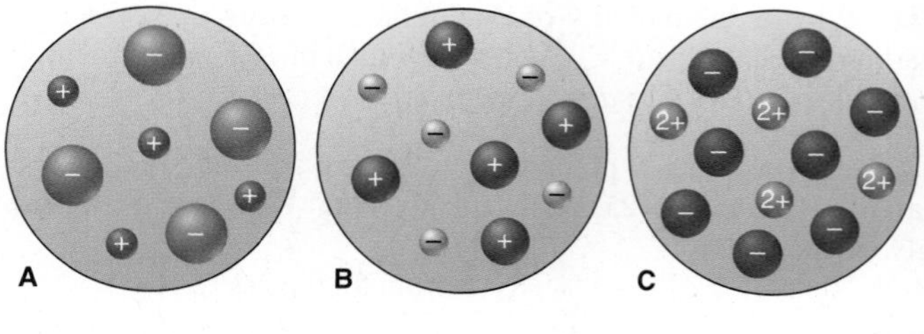

13.114 An aqueous solution is 10.% glucose by mass (*d* = 1.039 g/mL at 20°C). Calculate its freezing point, boiling point at 1 atm, and osmotic pressure.

13.115 Because zinc has nearly the same atomic radius as copper (*d* = 8.95 g/cm³), zinc atoms substitute for some copper atoms in the many types of brass. Calculate the density of the brass with (a) 10.0 atom % Zn and (b) 38.0 atom % Zn.

13.116 Gold occurs in seawater at an average concentration of 1.1×10^{-2} ppb. How many liters of seawater must be processed to recover 1 troy ounce of gold, assuming 81.5% efficiency (*d* of seawater = 1.025 g/mL; 1 troy ounce = 31.1 g)?

13.117 Use atomic properties to explain why xenon is 11 times as soluble as helium in water at 0°C on a mole basis.

13.118 Which of the following best represents a molecular-scale view of an ionic compound in aqueous solution? Explain.

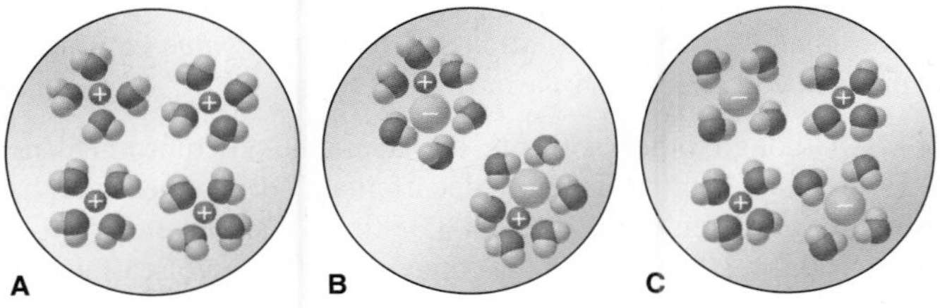

13.119 Four 0.50 *m* aqueous solutions are depicted below. Assume the solutions behave ideally: (a) Which has the highest boiling point? (b) Which has the lowest freezing point? (c) Can you determine which one has the highest osmotic pressure? Explain.

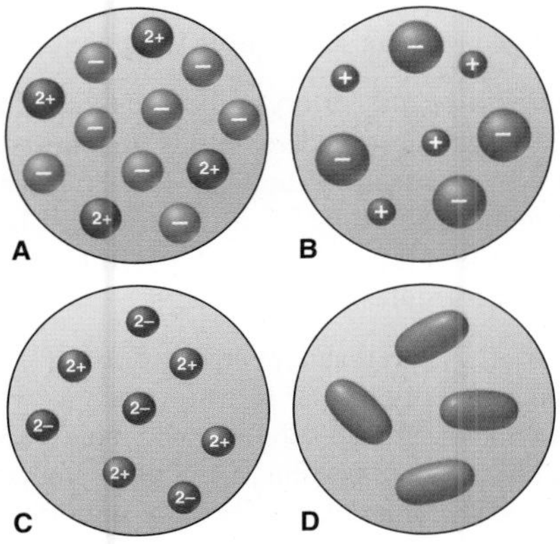

13.120 Thermal pollution from industrial wastewater causes the temperature of river or lake water to increase, which can affect fish survival as the concentration of dissolved O_2 decreases. Use the following data to find the molarity of O_2 at each temperature (assume the solution density is the same as water):

Temperature (°C)	Solubility of O_2 (mg/kg H_2O)	Density of H_2O (g/mL)
0.0	14.5	0.99987
20.0	9.07	0.99823
40.0	6.44	0.99224

13.121 Pyridine (*right*) is an essential portion of many biologically active compounds, such as nicotine and vitamin B_6. Like ammonia, it has a nitrogen with a lone pair, which makes it act as a weak base. Because it is miscible in a wide range of solvents, from water to benzene, pyridine is one of the most important bases and solvents in organic syntheses. Account for its solubility behavior in terms of intermolecular forces.

13.122 A chemist is studying small organic compounds for their potential use as an antifreeze. When 0.243 g of a compound is dissolved in 25.0 mL of water, the freezing point of the solution is −0.201°C. (a) Calculate the molar mass of the compound (*d* of water = 1.00 g/mL). (b) Analysis shows that the compound is 53.31 mass % C and 11.18 mass % H, the remainder being O. Calculate the empirical and molecular formulas of the compound. (c) Draw a Lewis structure for a compound with this formula that forms H bonds and another for one that does not.

13.123 Air in a smoky bar contains 4.0×10^{-6} mol/L of CO. What mass of CO is inhaled by a bartender who respires at a rate of 11 L/min during an 8.0-h shift?

13.124 Is 50% by mass of methanol dissolved in ethanol different from 50% by mass of ethanol dissolved in methanol? Explain.

13.125 Three gaseous mixtures of N_2 (blue), Cl_2 (green), and Ne (purple) are depicted below. (a) Which has the smallest mole fraction of N_2? (b) Which have the same mole fraction of Ne? (c) Rank all three in order of increasing mole fraction of Cl_2.

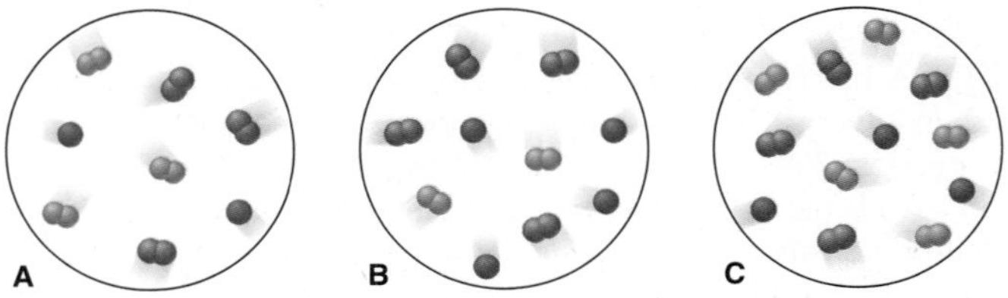

13.126 A water treatment plant needs to attain a fluoride concentration of 4.50×10^{-5} *M*. (a) What mass of NaF must be added to a 5000.-L blending tank of water? (b) What mass per day of fluoride is ingested by a person who drinks 2.0 L of this water?

13.127 Four U tubes each have distilled water in the right arm, a solution in the left arm, and a semipermeable membrane between arms. (a) If the solute is KCl, which solution is most concentrated? (b) If each solute is different but all the solutions have the same molarity, which contains the smallest number of dissolved ions?

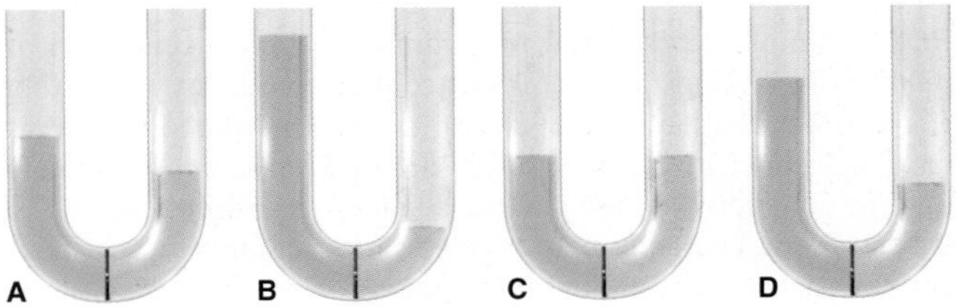

13.128 β-Pinene ($C_{10}H_{16}$) and α-terpineol ($C_{10}H_{18}O$) are used in cosmetics to provide a "fresh pine" scent. At 367 K, the pure substances have vapor pressures of 100.3 torr and 9.8 torr, respectively. What is the composition of the vapor (in terms of mole fractions) above a solution containing equal masses of these compounds at 367 K? (Assume ideal behavior.)

13.129 A solution of 1.50 g of solute dissolved in 25.0 mL of H_2O at 25°C has a boiling point of 100.45°C. (a) What is the molar mass of the solute if it is a nonvolatile nonelectrolyte and the solution behaves ideally (*d* of H_2O at 25°C = 0.997 g/mL)? (b) Conductivity measurements show the solute to be ionic of general formula AB_2 or A_2B. What is the molar mass if the solution behaves ideally? (c) Analysis indicates an empirical formula of CaN_2O_6. Explain the difference between the actual formula mass and that calculated from the boiling point elevation. (d) Find the van't Hoff factor (*i*) for this solution.

13.130 A pharmaceutical preparation made with ethanol (C_2H_5OH) is contaminated with methanol (CH_3OH). A sample of vapor above the liquid mixture contains a 97/1 mass ratio of C_2H_5OH to CH_3OH. What is the mass ratio of these alcohols in the liquid? At the temperature of the liquid, the vapor pressures of C_2H_5OH and CH_3OH are 60.5 torr and 126.0 torr, respectively.

13.131 Water treatment plants commonly use chlorination to destroy bacteria. A byproduct is chloroform ($CHCl_3$), a suspected carcinogen, produced when HOCl, formed by reaction of Cl_2 and water, reacts with dissolved organic matter. The United States, Canada, and the World Health Organization have set a limit of 100. ppb of

$CHCl_3$ in drinking water. Convert this concentration into molarity, molality, mole fraction, and mass percent.

13.132 A saturated Na_2CO_3 solution is prepared, and a small excess of solid is present (white pile in beaker). A seed crystal of $Na_2{}^{14}CO_3$ (^{14}C is a radioactive isotope of ^{12}C) is added (small red piece), and the radioactivity is measured over time. (a) Would you expect radioactivity in the solution? Explain. (b) Would you expect radioactivity in all the solid or just in the seed crystal? Explain.

13.133 A biochemical engineer isolates a bacterial gene fragment and dissolves a 10.0-mg sample in enough water to make 30.0 mL of solution. The osmotic pressure of the solution is 0.340 torr at 25°C. (a) What is the molar mass of the gene fragment? (b) If the solution density is 0.997 g/mL, how large is the freezing point depression for this solution (K_f of water = 1.86°C/*m*)?

13.134 A river is contaminated with 0.65 mg/L of dichloroethylene ($C_2H_2Cl_2$). What is the concentration (in ng/L) of dichloroethylene at 21°C in the air breathed by a person swimming in the river (k_H for $C_2H_2Cl_2$ in water is 0.033 mol/L·atm)?

13.135 At an air-water interface, fatty acids such as oleic acid lie in a one-molecule-thick layer (*monolayer*), with the heads in the water and the tails perpendicular in the air. When 2.50 mg of oleic acid is placed on a water surface, it forms a circular monolayer 38.6 cm in diameter. Find the surface area (in cm^2) occupied by one molecule ($\mathcal{M}$ of oleic acid = 283 g/mol).

13.136 A simple device used for estimating the concentration of total dissolved solids in an aqueous solution works by measuring the electrical conductivity of the solution. The method assumes that equal concentrations of different solids give approximately the same conductivity, and that the conductivity is proportional to concentration. The table below gives some actual electrical conductivities (in arbitrary units) for solutions of selected solids at the indicated concentrations (in ppm by mass):

	Conductivity		
Sample	**0 ppm**	**5.00×10³ ppm**	**10.00×10³ ppm**
$CaCl_2$	0.0	8.0	16.0
K_2CO_3	0.0	7.0	14.0
Na_2SO_4	0.0	6.0	11.0
Seawater (dil)	0.0	8.0	15.0
Sucrose ($C_{12}H_{22}O_{11}$)	0.0	0.0	0.0
Urea [$(NH_2)_2C{=}O$]	0.0	0.0	0.0

(a) How reliable are these measurements for estimating concentrations of dissolved solids? (b) For what types of substances might this method have a large error? Why? (c) Based on this method, an aqueous $CaCl_2$ solution has a conductivity of 14.0 units. Calculate its mole fraction and molality.

13.137 Two beakers are placed in a closed container (*left*). One beaker contains water, the other a concentrated aqueous sugar solution. With time, the solution volume increases and the water volume decreases (*right*). Explain on the molecular level.

13.138 The release of volatile organic compounds into the atmosphere is regulated to limit ozone formation. In a laboratory simulation, 5% of the ethanol in a liquid detergent is released. Thus, a "down-the-drain" factor of 0.05 is used to estimate ethanol emissions from the detergent. The k_H values for ethanol and 2-butoxyethanol ($C_4H_9OCH_2CH_2OH$) are 5×10^{-6} atm·m^3/mol and 1.6×10^{-6} atm·m^3/mol, respectively. (a) Estimate a "down-the-drain" factor for 2-butoxyethanol in the detergent. (b) What is the k_H for ethanol in units of L·atm/mol? (c) Is this value consistent with a value given as 0.64 Pa·m^3/mol?

13.139 Although other solvents are available, dichloromethane (CH_2Cl_2) is still often used to "decaffeinate" drinks because the solubility of caffeine in CH_2Cl_2 is 8.35 times that in water.
(a) A 100.0-mL sample of cola containing 10.0 mg of caffeine is extracted with 60.0 mL of CH_2Cl_2. What mass of caffeine remains in the aqueous phase?
(b) A second identical cola sample is extracted with two successive 30.0-mL portions of CH_2Cl_2. What mass of caffeine remains in the aqueous phase after each extraction?
(c) Which approach extracts more caffeine?

13.140 How do you prepare 250. g of 0.150 *m* aqueous $NaHCO_3$?

13.141 Tartaric acid occurs in crystalline residues found in wine vats. It is used in baking powders and as an additive in foods. It contains 32.3% by mass carbon and 3.97% by mass hydrogen; the balance is oxygen. When 0.981 g of tartaric acid is dissolved in 11.23 g of water, the solution freezes at −1.26°C. Find the empirical and molecular formulas of tartaric acid.

13.142 Methanol (CH_3OH) and ethanol (C_2H_5OH) are miscible because the major intermolecular force for each is hydrogen bonding. In some methanol-ethanol solutions, the mole fraction of methanol is higher, but the mass percent of ethanol is higher. What is the range of mole fraction of methanol for these solutions?

13.143 A solution of 5.0 g of benzoic acid (C_6H_5COOH) in 100.0 g of carbon tetrachloride has a boiling point of 77.5°C.
(a) Calculate the molar mass of benzoic acid in the solution.
(b) Suggest a reason for the difference between the molar mass based on the formula and that found in part (a).

13.144 Derive a general equation that expresses the relationship between the molarity and the molality of a solution. Why are the numerical values of these two terms approximately equal for very dilute aqueous solutions?

13.145 A florist prepares a solution of nitrogen-phosphorus fertilizer by dissolving 5.66 g of NH_4NO_3 and 4.42 g of $(NH_4)_3PO_4$ in enough water to make 20.0 L of solution. What are the molarities of NH_4^+ and of PO_4^{3-} in the solution?

13.146 Suppose coal-fired power plants used water in scrubbers to remove SO_2 from smokestack gases (see Chemical Connections, p. 249). (a) If the partial pressure of SO_2 in the stack gases is 2.0×10^{-3} atm, what is the solubility of SO_2 in the scrubber liquid (k_H for SO_2 in water is 1.23 mol/L·atm at 200.°C)? (b) From your answer to part (a), why are basic solutions, such as limewater slurries [$Ca(OH)_2$], used in scrubbers?

13.147 Urea is a white crystalline solid used as a fertilizer, in the pharmaceutical industry, and in the manufacture of certain polymer resins. Analysis of urea reveals that, by mass, it is 20.1% carbon, 6.7% hydrogen, 46.5% nitrogen and the balance oxygen.
(a) Find the empirical formula of urea.
(b) A 5.0 g/L solution of urea in water has an osmotic pressure of 2.04 atm, measured at 25°C. What is the molar mass and molecular formula of urea?

13.148 The total concentration of dissolved particles in blood is 0.30 *M*. An intravenous (IV) solution must be isotonic with blood, which means it must have the same concentration.
(a) To relieve dehydration, a patient is given 100. mL/h of IV glucose ($C_6H_{12}O_6$) for 2.5 h. What mass (g) of glucose did she receive? (b) If isotonic saline (NaCl) is used, what is the molarity of the solution? (c) If the patient is given 150. mL/h of IV saline for 1.5 h, how many grams of NaCl did she receive?

13.149 Deviations from Raoult's law lead to the formation of *azeotropes,* constant boiling mixtures that cannot be separated by distillation, making industrial separations difficult. For components A and B, there is a positive deviation if the A-B attraction is less than A-A and B-B attractions (A and B reject each other), and a negative deviation if the A-B attraction is greater than A-A and B-B attractions. If the A-B attraction is nearly equal to the A-A and B-B attractions, the solution obeys Raoult's law. Explain whether the behavior of each pair will be nearly ideal, have a positive deviation, or a negative deviation:
(a) Benzene (C_6H_6) and methanol
(b) Water and ethyl acetate
(c) Hexane and heptane
(d) Methanol and water
(e) Water and hydrochloric acid

13.150 Acrylic acid ($CH_2{=}CHCOOH$) is a monomer used to make superabsorbent polymers and various compounds for paint and adhesive production. At 1 atm, it boils at 141.5°C but is prone to polymerization. Its vapor pressure at 25°C is 4.1 mbar. What pressure (in mmHg) is needed to distill the pure acid at 65°C?

13.151 To effectively stop polymerization, certain inhibitors require the presence of a small amount of O_2. At equilibrium with 1 atm of air, the concentration of O_2 dissolved in the monomer acrylic acid ($CH_2{=}CHCOOH$) is 1.64×10^{-3} *M*. (a) What is the k_H (mol/L·atm) for O_2 in acrylic acid? (b) If 0.005 atm of O_2 is sufficient to stop polymerization, what is the molarity of O_2? (c) What is the mole fraction? (d) What is the concentration in ppm? (Pure acrylic acid is 14.6 *M*; P_{O_2} in air is 0.2095 atm.)

13.152 Volatile organic solvents have been implicated in adverse health effects in industrial workers. Greener methods are phasing these solvents out. Rank the solvents in Table 13.6 (p. 501) in terms of increasing volatility.

13.153 At ordinary temperatures, water is a poor solvent for organic substances. But at high pressure and above 200°C, water develops many properties of organic solvents. Find the minimum pressure needed to maintain water as a liquid at 200.°C (ΔH_{vap} = 40.7 kJ/mol at 100°C and 1.00 atm; assume it remains constant with temperature).

13.154 In ice-cream making, the ingredients are kept below 0.0°C in an ice-salt bath. (a) Assuming that NaCl dissolves completely and forms an ideal solution, what mass of it is needed to lower the melting point of 5.5 kg of ice to −5.0°C? (b) Given the same assumptions as in part (a), what mass of $CaCl_2$ is needed?

13.155 Perfluorocarbons (PFCs), hydrocarbons with all H atoms replaced by F atoms, have very weak cohesive forces. One unusual application has a live mouse submerged in O_2-saturated PFCs.
(a) At 298 K, perfluorohexane (C_6F_{14}, $\mathcal{M}$ = 338 g/mol, d = 1.674 g/mL) in equilibrium with 101,325 Pa of O_2 has a mole fraction of O_2 of 4.28×10^{-3}. What is the k_H in mol/L·atm?
(b) According to one source, the k_H for O_2 in water at 25°C is 756.7 L·atm/mol. What is the solubility of O_2 in water at 25°C in ppm? (c) Rank the k_H values in descending order for O_2 in water, ethanol, C_6F_{14}, and C_6H_{14}. Explain your ranking.

13.156 The solubility of N_2 in blood is a serious problem for divers breathing compressed air (78% N_2 by volume) at depths greater than 50 ft.
(a) What is the molarity of N_2 in blood at 1.00 atm?
(b) What is the molarity of N_2 in blood at a depth of 50. ft?
(c) Find the volume (in mL) of N_2, measured at 25°C and 1.00 atm, released per liter of blood when a diver at a depth of 50. ft rises to the surface (k_H for N_2 in water at 25°C is 7.0×10^{-4} mol/L·atm and at 37°C is 6.2×10^{-4} mol/L·atm; assume d of water is 1.00 g/mL).

13.157 Figure 12.11 (p. 430) shows the phase changes of pure water. Consider how the diagram would change if air were present at 1 atm and dissolved in the water. (a) Would the three phases of water still attain equilibrium at some temperature? Explain. (b) In principle, would that temperature be higher, lower, or the same as the triple point for pure water? Explain. (c) Would ice sublime at a few degrees below the freezing point under this pressure? Explain. (d) Would the liquid have the same vapor pressure as that shown in Figure 12.9B at 100°C? At 120°C?

13.158 KNO_3, $KClO_3$, KCl, and NaCl are recrystallized as follows:
Step 1. A saturated aqueous solution of the compound is prepared at 50°C.
Step 2. The mixture is filtered to remove undissolved compound.
Step 3. The filtrate is cooled to 0°C.
Step 4. The crystals that form are filtered, dried, and weighed.
(a) Which compound has the highest percent recovery and which the lowest (see Figure 13.19, p. 492)?
(b) Starting with 100. g of each compound, how many grams of each can be recovered?

13.159 Eighty proof whiskey is 40% ethanol (C_2H_5OH) by volume. A man has 7.0 L of blood and drinks 28 mL of the whiskey, of which 22% of the ethanol goes into his blood.
(a) What concentration (in g/mL) of ethanol is in his blood (d of ethanol = 0.789 g/mL)?
(b) What volume (in mL) of whiskey would raise his blood alcohol level to 8.0×10^{-4} g/mL, the level at which a person is considered intoxicated?

13.160 Soft drinks are canned under 4 atm of CO_2 and release CO_2 when opened.
(a) How many moles of CO_2 are dissolved in a 355-mL can of soda before it is opened?
(b) After it has gone flat?
(c) What volume (in L) would the released CO_2 occupy at 1.00 atm and 25°C (k_H for CO_2 at 25°C is 3.3×10^{-2} mol/L·atm; P_{CO_2} in air is 3×10^{-4} atm)?

13.161 Gaseous O_2 in equilibrium with O_2 dissolved in water at 283 K is depicted at right. (a) Which scene below represents the system at 298 K? (b) Which scene represents the system when the pressure of O_2 is increased by half?

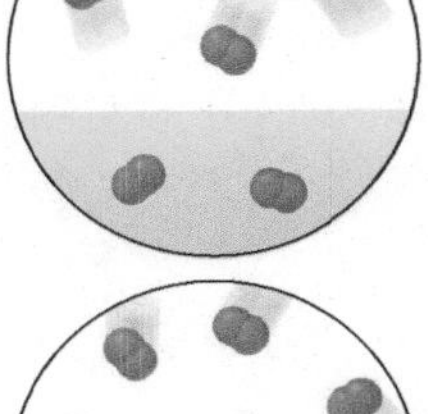

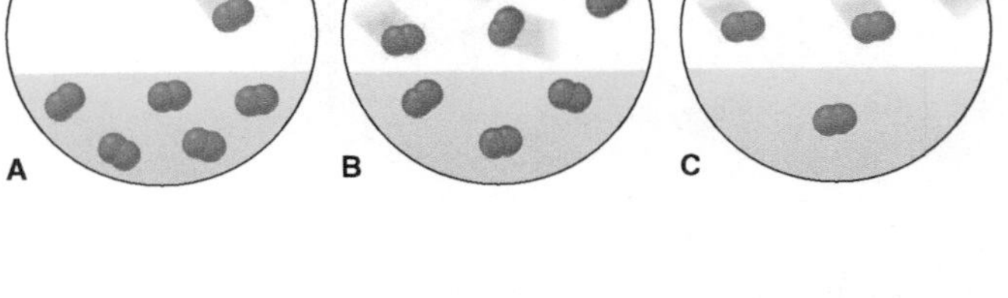

A B C

Common Mathematical Operations in Chemistry

In addition to basic arithmetic and algebra, four mathematical operations are used frequently in general chemistry: manipulating logarithms, using exponential notation, solving quadratic equations, and graphing data. Each is discussed briefly below.

MANIPULATING LOGARITHMS

Meaning and Properties of Logarithms

A *logarithm* is an exponent. Specifically, if $x^n = A$, we can say that the logarithm to the base x of the number A is n, and we can denote it as

$$\log_x A = n$$

Because logarithms are exponents, they have the following properties:

$$\log_x 1 = 0$$

$$\log_x (A \times B) = \log_x A + \log_x B$$

$$\log_x \frac{A}{B} = \log_x A - \log_x B$$

$$\log_x A^y = y \log_x A$$

Types of Logarithms

Common and natural logarithms are used in chemistry and the other sciences.

1. For *common* logarithms, the base (x in the examples above) is 10, but they are written without specifying the base; that is, $\log_{10} A$ is written more simply as $\log A$; thus, the notation *log* means base 10. The common logarithm of 1000 is 3; in other words, you must raise 10 to the 3rd power to obtain 1000:

$$\log 1000 = 3 \qquad \text{or} \qquad 10^3 = 1000$$

Similarly, we have

$$\log 10 = 1 \qquad \text{or} \qquad 10^1 = 10$$

$$\log 1{,}000{,}000 = 6 \qquad \text{or} \qquad 10^6 = 1{,}000{,}000$$

$$\log 0.001 = -3 \qquad \text{or} \qquad 10^{-3} = 0.001$$

$$\log 853 = 2.931 \qquad \text{or} \qquad 10^{2.931} = 853$$

The last example illustrates an important point about significant figures with all logarithms: *the number of significant figures in the number equals the number of digits to the right of the decimal point in the logarithm.* That is, the number 853 has three significant figures, and the logarithm 2.931 has three digits to the right of the decimal point.

To find a common logarithm with an electronic calculator, enter the number and press the LOG button.

2. For *natural* logarithms, the base is the number e, which is 2.71828 . . . , and $\log_e A$ is written $\ln A$; thus, the notation *ln* means base e. The relationship between the common and natural logarithms is easily obtained:

$$\log 10 = 1 \qquad \text{and} \qquad \ln 10 = 2.303$$

Therefore, we have

$$\ln A = 2.303 \log A$$

To find a natural logarithm with an electronic calculator, enter the number and press the LN button. If your calculator does not have an LN button, enter the number, press the LOG button, and multiply by 2.303.

Antilogarithms

The *antilogarithm* is the base raised to the logarithm:

$$\text{antilogarithm (antilog) of } n \text{ is } 10^n$$

Using two of the earlier examples, the antilog of 3 is 1000, and the antilog of 2.931 is 853. To obtain the antilog with a calculator, enter the number and press the 10^x button. Similarly, to obtain the natural antilogarithm, enter the number and press the e^x button. [On some calculators, enter the number and first press INV and then the LOG (or LN) button.]

USING EXPONENTIAL (SCIENTIFIC) NOTATION

Many quantities in chemistry are very large or very small. For example, in the conventional way of writing numbers, the number of gold atoms in 1 gram of gold is

59,060,000,000,000,000,000,000 atoms (to four significant figures)

As another example, the mass in grams of one gold atom is

0.0000000000000000000003272 g (to four significant figures)

Exponential (scientific) notation provides a much more practical way of writing such numbers. In exponential notation, we express numbers in the form

$$A \times 10^n$$

where A (the coefficient) is greater than or equal to 1 and less than 10 (that is, $1 \leq A < 10$), and n (the exponent) is an integer.

If the number we want to express in exponential notation is larger than 1, the exponent is positive ($n > 0$); if the number is smaller than 1, the exponent is negative ($n < 0$). The size of n tells the number of places the decimal point (in conventional notation) must be moved to obtain a coefficient A greater than or equal to 1 and less than 10 (in exponential notation). In exponential notation, 1 gram of gold contains 5.906×10^{22} atoms, and each gold atom has a mass of 3.272×10^{-22} g.

Changing Between Conventional and Exponential Notation

In order to use exponential notation, you must be able to convert to it from conventional notation, and vice versa.

1. To change a number from conventional to exponential notation, move the decimal point to the left for numbers equal to or greater than 10 and to the right for numbers between 0 and 1:

   75,000,000 changes to 7.5×10^7 (decimal point 7 places to the left)
   0.006042 changes to 6.042×10^{-3} (decimal point 3 places to the right)

2. To change a number from exponential to conventional notation, move the decimal point the number of places indicated by the exponent to the right for numbers with positive exponents and to the left for numbers with negative exponents:

   1.38×10^5 changes to 138,000 (decimal point 5 places to the right)
   8.41×10^{-6} changes to 0.00000841 (decimal point 6 places to the left)

3. An exponential number with a coefficient greater than 10 or less than 1 can be changed to the standard exponential form by converting the coefficient to the standard form and adding the exponents:

$$582.3\times10^6 \text{ changes to } 5.823 \times 10^2 \times 10^6 = 5.823\times10^{(2+6)} = 5.823\times10^8$$
$$0.0043\times10^{-4} \text{ changes to } 4.3 \times 10^{-3} \times 10^{-4} = 4.3\times10^{[(-3)+(-4)]} = 4.3\times10^{-7}$$

Using Exponential Notation in Calculations

In calculations, you can treat the coefficient and exponents separately and apply the properties of exponents (see earlier section on logarithms).

1. To multiply exponential numbers, multiply the coefficients, add the exponents, and reconstruct the number in standard exponential notation:

$$(5.5\times10^3)(3.1\times10^5) = (5.5 \times 3.1)\times10^{(3+5)} = 17\times10^8 = 1.7\times10^9$$
$$(9.7\times10^{14})(4.3\times10^{-20}) = (9.7 \times 4.3)\times10^{[14+(-20)]} = 42\times10^{-6} = 4.2\times10^{-5}$$

2. To divide exponential numbers, divide the coefficients, subtract the exponents, and reconstruct the number in standard exponential notation:

$$\frac{2.6\times10^6}{5.8\times10^2} = \frac{2.6}{5.8} \times 10^{(6-2)} = 0.45\times10^4 = 4.5\times10^3$$
$$\frac{1.7\times10^{-5}}{8.2\times10^{-8}} = \frac{1.7}{8.2} \times 10^{[(-5)-(-8)]} = 0.21\times10^3 = 2.1\times10^2$$

3. To add or subtract exponential numbers, change all numbers so that they have the same exponent, then add or subtract the coefficients:

$$(1.45\times10^4) + (3.2\times10^3) = (1.45\times10^4) + (0.32\times10^4) = 1.77\times10^4$$
$$(3.22\times10^5) - (9.02\times10^4) = (3.22\times10^5) - (0.902\times10^5) = 2.32\times10^5$$

SOLVING QUADRATIC EQUATIONS

A *quadratic equation* is one in which the highest power of x is 2. The general form of a quadratic equation is

$$ax^2 + bx + c = 0$$

where a, b, and c are numbers. For given values of a, b, and c, the values of x that satisfy the equation are called *solutions* of the equation. We calculate x with the quadratic formula:

$$x = \frac{-b \pm \sqrt{b^2 - 4ac}}{2a}$$

We commonly require the quadratic formula when solving for some concentration in an equilibrium problem. For example, we might have an expression that is rearranged into the quadratic equation

$$\underset{\text{a}}{4.3x^2} + \underset{\text{b}}{0.65x} - \underset{\text{c}}{8.7} = 0$$

Applying the quadratic formula, with $a = 4.3$, $b = 0.65$, and $c = -8.7$, gives

$$x = \frac{-0.65 \pm \sqrt{(0.65)^2 - 4(4.3)(-8.7)}}{2(4.3)}$$

The "plus or minus" sign ($\pm$) indicates that there are always two possible values for x. In this case, they are

$$x = 1.3 \quad \text{and} \quad x = -1.5$$

In any real physical system, however, only one of the values will have any meaning. For example, if x were $[H_3O^+]$, the negative value would give a negative concentration, which has no physical meaning.

GRAPHING DATA IN THE FORM OF A STRAIGHT LINE

Visualizing changes in variables by means of a graph is used throughout science. In many cases, it is most useful if the data can be graphed in the form of a straight line. Any equation will appear as a straight line if it has, or can be rearranged to have, the following general form:

$$y = mx + b$$

where y is the dependent variable (typically plotted along the vertical axis), x is the independent variable (typically plotted along the horizontal axis), m is the slope of the line, and b is the intercept of the line on the y axis. The intercept is the value of y when $x = 0$:

$$y = m(0) + b = b$$

The slope of the line is the change in y for a given change in x:

$$\text{Slope } (m) = \frac{y_2 - y_1}{x_2 - x_1} = \frac{\Delta y}{\Delta x}$$

The *sign* of the slope tells the *direction* of the line. If y increases as x increases, m is positive, and the line slopes upward with higher values of x; if y decreases as x increases, m is negative, and the line slopes downward with higher values of x. The *magnitude* of the slope indicates the *steepness* of the line. A line with $m = 3$ is three times as steep (y changes three times as much for a given change in x) as a line with $m = 1$.

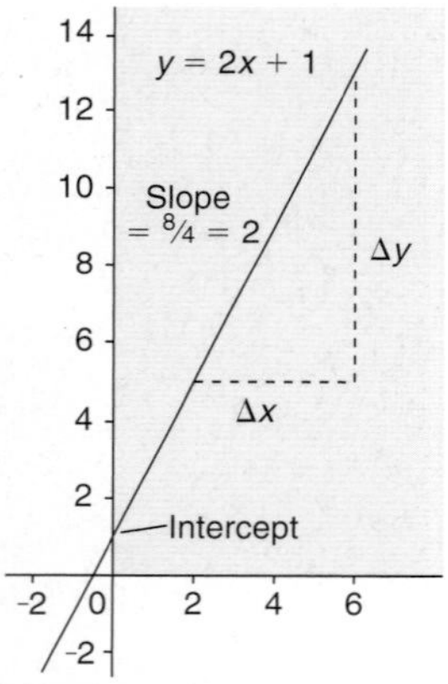

Figure A.1

Consider the linear equation $y = 2x + 1$. A graph of this equation is shown in Figure A.1. In practice, you can find the slope by drawing a right triangle to the line, using the line as the hypotenuse. Then, one leg gives Δy, and the other gives Δx. In the figure, $\Delta y = 8$ and $\Delta x = 4$.

At several places in the text, an equation is rearranged into the form of a straight line in order to determine information from the slope and/or the intercept. For example, in Chapter 16, we obtained the following expression:

$$\ln \frac{[A]_0}{[A]_t} = kt$$

Based on the properties of logarithms, we have

$$\ln [A]_0 - \ln [A]_t = kt$$

Rearranging into the form of an equation for a straight line gives

$$\begin{aligned} \ln [A]_t &= -kt + \ln [A]_0 \\ y &= mx + b \end{aligned}$$

Thus, a plot of $\ln [A]_t$ vs. t is a straight line, from which you can see that the slope is $-k$ (the negative of the rate constant) and the intercept is $\ln [A]_0$ (the natural logarithm of the initial concentration of A).

At many other places in the text, linear relationships occur that were not shown in graphical terms. For example, the conversion of temperature scales in Chapter 1 can also be expressed in the form of a straight line:

$$\begin{aligned} {}^\circ\text{F} &= \tfrac{9}{5}{}^\circ\text{C} + 32 \\ y &= mx + b \end{aligned}$$

Standard Thermodynamic Values for Selected Substances*

Substance or Ion	ΔH°_f (kJ/mol)	ΔG°_f (kJ/mol)	S° (J/mol·K)
$e^-(g)$	0	0	20.87
Aluminum			
$Al(s)$	0	0	28.3
$Al^{3+}(aq)$	−524.7	−481.2	−313
$AlCl_3(s)$	−704.2	−628.9	110.7
$Al_2O_3(s)$	−1676	−1582	50.94
Barium			
$Ba(s)$	0	0	62.5
$Ba(g)$	175.6	144.8	170.28
$Ba^{2+}(g)$	1649.9	—	—
$Ba^{2+}(aq)$	−538.36	−560.7	13
$BaCl_2(s)$	−806.06	−810.9	126
$BaCO_3(s)$	−1219	−1139	112
$BaO(s)$	−548.1	−520.4	72.07
$BaSO_4(s)$	−1465	−1353	132
Boron			
B(β-rhombohedral)	0	0	5.87
$BF_3(g)$	−1137.0	−1120.3	254.0
$BCl_3(g)$	−403.8	−388.7	290.0
$B_2H_6(g)$	35	86.6	232.0
$B_2O_3(s)$	−1272	−1193	53.8
$H_3BO_3(s)$	−1094.3	−969.01	88.83
Bromine			
$Br_2(l)$	0	0	152.23
$Br_2(g)$	30.91	3.13	245.38
$Br(g)$	111.9	82.40	174.90
$Br^-(g)$	−218.9	—	—
$Br^-(aq)$	−120.9	−102.82	80.71
$HBr(g)$	−36.3	−53.5	198.59
Cadmium			
$Cd(s)$	0	0	51.5
$Cd(g)$	112.8	78.20	167.64
$Cd^{2+}(aq)$	−72.38	−77.74	−61.1
$CdS(s)$	−144	−141	71
Calcium			
$Ca(s)$	0	0	41.6
$Ca(g)$	192.6	158.9	154.78
$Ca^{2+}(g)$	1934.1	—	—
$Ca^{2+}(aq)$	−542.96	−553.04	−55.2
$CaF_2(s)$	−1215	−1162	68.87
$CaCl_2(s)$	−795.0	−750.2	114
$CaCO_3(s)$	−1206.9	−1128.8	92.9
$CaO(s)$	−635.1	−603.5	38.2
$Ca(OH)_2(s)$	−986.09	−898.56	83.39
$Ca_3(PO_4)_2(s)$	−4138	−3899	263
$CaSO_4(s)$	−1432.7	−1320.3	107
Carbon			
C(graphite)	0	0	5.686
C(diamond)	1.896	2.866	2.439
$C(g)$	715.0	669.6	158.0
$CO(g)$	−110.5	−137.2	197.5
$CO_2(g)$	−393.5	−394.4	213.7
$CO_2(aq)$	−412.9	−386.2	121
$CO_3^{2-}(aq)$	−676.26	−528.10	−53.1
$HCO_3^-(aq)$	−691.11	587.06	95.0
$H_2CO_3(aq)$	−698.7	−623.42	191
$CH_4(g)$	−74.87	−50.81	186.1
$C_2H_2(g)$	227	209	200.85
$C_2H_4(g)$	52.47	68.36	219.22
$C_2H_6(g)$	−84.667	−32.89	229.5
$C_3H_8(g)$	−105	−24.5	269.9
$C_4H_{10}(g)$	−126	−16.7	310
$C_6H_6(l)$	49.0	124.5	172.8
$CH_3OH(g)$	−201.2	−161.9	238
$CH_3OH(l)$	−238.6	−166.2	127
$HCHO(g)$	−116	−110	219
$HCOO^-(aq)$	−410	−335	91.6
$HCOOH(l)$	−409	−346	129.0
$HCOOH(aq)$	−410	−356	164
$C_2H_5OH(g)$	−235.1	−168.6	282.6
$C_2H_5OH(l)$	−277.63	−174.8	161
$CH_3CHO(g)$	−166	−133.7	266
$CH_3COOH(l)$	−487.0	−392	160
$C_6H_{12}O_6(s)$	−1273.3	−910.56	212.1
$C_{12}H_{22}O_{11}(s)$	−2221.7	−1544.3	360.24
$CN^-(aq)$	151	166	118
$HCN(g)$	135	125	201.7
$HCN(l)$	105	121	112.8
$HCN(aq)$	105	112	129
$CS_2(g)$	117	66.9	237.79
$CS_2(l)$	87.9	63.6	151.0
$CH_3Cl(g)$	−83.7	−60.2	234
$CH_2Cl_2(l)$	−117	−63.2	179

*All values at 298 K.

(continued)

Substance or Ion	ΔH°_f (kJ/mol)	ΔG°_f (kJ/mol)	S° (J/mol·K)
$CHCl_3(l)$	−132	−71.5	203
$CCl_4(g)$	−96.0	−53.7	309.7
$CCl_4(l)$	−139	−68.6	214.4
$COCl_2(g)$	−220	−206	283.74
Cesium			
$Cs(s)$	0	0	85.15
$Cs(g)$	76.7	49.7	175.5
$Cs^+(g)$	458.5	427.1	169.72
$Cs^+(aq)$	−248	−282.0	133
$CsF(s)$	−554.7	−525.4	88
$CsCl(s)$	−442.8	−414	101.18
$CsBr(s)$	−395	−383	121
$CsI(s)$	−337	−333	130
Chlorine			
$Cl_2(g)$	0	0	223.0
$Cl(g)$	121.0	105.0	165.1
$Cl^-(g)$	−234	−240	153.25
$Cl^-(aq)$	−167.46	−131.17	55.10
$HCl(g)$	−92.31	−95.30	186.79
$HCl(aq)$	−167.46	−131.17	55.06
$ClO_2(g)$	102	120	256.7
$Cl_2O(g)$	80.3	97.9	266.1
Chromium			
$Cr(s)$	0	0	23.8
$Cr^{3+}(aq)$	−1971	—	—
$CrO_4^{2-}(aq)$	−863.2	−706.3	38
$Cr_2O_7^{2-}(aq)$	−1461	−1257	214
Copper			
$Cu(s)$	0	0	33.1
$Cu(g)$	341.1	301.4	166.29
$Cu^+(aq)$	51.9	50.2	−26
$Cu^{2+}(aq)$	64.39	64.98	−98.7
$Cu_2O(s)$	−168.6	−146.0	93.1
$CuO(s)$	−157.3	−130	42.63
$Cu_2S(s)$	−79.5	−86.2	120.9
$CuS(s)$	−53.1	−53.6	66.5
Fluorine			
$F_2(g)$	0	0	202.7
$F(g)$	78.9	61.8	158.64
$F^-(g)$	−255.6	−262.5	145.47
$F^-(aq)$	−329.1	−276.5	−9.6
$HF(g)$	−273	−275	173.67
Hydrogen			
$H_2(g)$	0	0	130.6
$H(g)$	218.0	203.30	114.60
$H^+(aq)$	0	0	0
$H^+(g)$	1536.3	1517.1	108.83
Iodine			
$I_2(s)$	0	0	116.14
$I_2(g)$	62.442	19.38	260.58
$I(g)$	106.8	70.21	180.67
$I^-(g)$	−194.7	—	—
$I^-(aq)$	−55.94	−51.67	109.4
$HI(g)$	25.9	1.3	206.33
Iron			
$Fe(s)$	0	0	27.3
$Fe^{3+}(aq)$	−47.7	−10.5	−293

Substance or Ion	ΔH°_f (kJ/mol)	ΔG°_f (kJ/mol)	S° (J/mol·K)
$Fe^{2+}(aq)$	−87.9	−84.94	113
$FeCl_2(s)$	−341.8	−302.3	117.9
$FeCl_3(s)$	−399.5	−334.1	142
$FeO(s)$	−272.0	−251.4	60.75
$Fe_2O_3(s)$	−825.5	−743.6	87.400
$Fe_3O_4(s)$	−1121	−1018	145.3
Lead			
$Pb(s)$	0	0	64.785
$Pb^{2+}(aq)$	1.6	−24.3	21
$PbCl_2(s)$	−359	−314	136
$PbO(s)$	−218	−198	68.70
$PbO_2(s)$	−276.6	−219.0	76.6
$PbS(s)$	−98.3	−96.7	91.3
$PbSO_4(s)$	−918.39	−811.24	147
Lithium			
$Li(s)$	0	0	29.10
$Li(g)$	161	128	138.67
$Li^+(g)$	687.163	649.989	132.91
$Li^+(aq)$	−278.46	−293.8	14
$LiF(s)$	−616.9	−588.7	35.66
$LiCl(s)$	−408	−384	59.30
$LiBr(s)$	−351	−342	74.1
$LiI(s)$	−270	−270	85.8
Magnesium			
$Mg(s)$	0	0	32.69
$Mg(g)$	150	115	148.55
$Mg^{2+}(g)$	2351	—	—
$Mg^{2+}(aq)$	−461.96	−456.01	118
$MgCl_2(s)$	−641.6	−592.1	89.630
$MgCO_3(s)$	−1112	−1028	65.86
$MgO(s)$	−601.2	−569.0	26.9
$Mg_3N_2(s)$	−461	−401	88
Manganese			
$Mn(s, \alpha)$	0	0	31.8
$Mn^{2+}(aq)$	−219	−223	−84
$MnO_2(s)$	−520.9	−466.1	53.1
$MnO_4^-(aq)$	−518.4	−425.1	190
Mercury			
$Hg(l)$	0	0	76.027
$Hg(g)$	61.30	31.8	174.87
$Hg^{2+}(aq)$	171	164.4	−32
$Hg_2^{2+}(aq)$	172	153.6	84.5
$HgCl_2(s)$	−230	−184	144
$Hg_2Cl_2(s)$	−264.9	−210.66	196
$HgO(s)$	−90.79	−58.50	70.27
Nitrogen			
$N_2(g)$	0	0	191.5
$N(g)$	473	456	153.2
$N_2O(g)$	82.05	104.2	219.7
$NO(g)$	90.29	86.60	210.65
$NO_2(g)$	33.2	51	239.9
$N_2O_4(g)$	9.16	97.7	304.3
$N_2O_5(g)$	11	118	346
$N_2O_5(s)$	−43.1	114	178
$NH_3(g)$	−45.9	−16	193
$NH_3(aq)$	−80.83	26.7	110
$N_2H_4(l)$	50.63	149.2	121.2

(continued)

Substance or Ion	ΔH_f° (kJ/mol)	ΔG_f° (kJ/mol)	S° (J/mol·K)
$NO_3^-(aq)$	−206.57	−110.5	146
$HNO_3(l)$	−173.23	−79.914	155.6
$HNO_3(aq)$	−206.57	−110.5	146
$NF_3(g)$	−125	−83.3	260.6
$NOCl(g)$	51.71	66.07	261.6
$NH_4Cl(s)$	−314.4	−203.0	94.6
Oxygen			
$O_2(g)$	0	0	205.0
$O(g)$	249.2	231.7	160.95
$O_3(g)$	143	163	238.82
$OH^-(aq)$	−229.94	−157.30	−10.54
$H_2O(g)$	−241.826	−228.60	188.72
$H_2O(l)$	−285.840	−237.192	69.940
$H_2O_2(l)$	−187.8	−120.4	110
$H_2O_2(aq)$	−191.2	−134.1	144
Phosphorus			
$P_4(s$, white)	0	0	41.1
$P(g)$	314.6	278.3	163.1
$P(s$, red)	−17.6	−12.1	22.8
$P_2(g)$	144	104	218
$P_4(g)$	58.9	24.5	280
$PCl_3(g)$	−287	−268	312
$PCl_3(l)$	−320	−272	217
$PCl_5(g)$	−402	−323	353
$PCl_5(s)$	−443.5	—	—
$P_4O_{10}(s)$	−2984	−2698	229
$PO_4^{3-}(aq)$	−1266	−1013	−218
$HPO_4^{2-}(aq)$	−1281	−1082	−36
$H_2PO_4^-(aq)$	−1285	−1135	89.1
$H_3PO_4(aq)$	−1277	−1019	228
Potassium			
$K(s)$	0	0	64.672
$K(g)$	89.2	60.7	160.23
$K^+(g)$	514.197	481.202	154.47
$K^+(aq)$	−251.2	−282.28	103
$KF(s)$	−568.6	−538.9	66.55
$KCl(s)$	−436.7	−409.2	82.59
$KBr(s)$	−394	−380	95.94
$KI(s)$	−328	−323	106.39
$KOH(s)$	−424.8	−379.1	78.87
$KClO_3(s)$	−397.7	−296.3	143.1
$KClO_4(s)$	−432.75	−303.2	151.0
Rubidium			
$Rb(s)$	0	0	69.5
$Rb(g)$	85.81	55.86	169.99
$Rb^+(g)$	495.04	—	—
$Rb^+(aq)$	−246	−282.2	124
$RbF(s)$	−549.28	—	—
$RbCl(s)$	−435.35	−407.8	95.90
$RbBr(s)$	−389.2	−378.1	108.3
$RbI(s)$	−328	−326	118.0
Silicon			
$Si(s)$	0	0	18.0
$SiF_4(g)$	−1614.9	−1572.7	282.4
$SiO_2(s)$	−910.9	−856.5	41.5
Silver			
$Ag(s)$	0	0	42.702
$Ag(g)$	289.2	250.4	172.892
$Ag^+(aq)$	105.9	77.111	73.93
$AgF(s)$	−203	−185	84
$AgCl(s)$	−127.03	−109.72	96.11
$AgBr(s)$	−99.51	−95.939	107.1
$AgI(s)$	−62.38	−66.32	114
$AgNO_3(s)$	−45.06	19.1	128.2
$Ag_2S(s)$	−31.8	−40.3	146
Sodium			
$Na(s)$	0	0	51.446
$Na(g)$	107.76	77.299	153.61
$Na^+(g)$	609.839	574.877	147.85
$Na^+(aq)$	−239.66	−261.87	60.2
$NaF(s)$	−575.4	−545.1	51.21
$NaCl(s)$	−411.1	−384.0	72.12
$NaBr(s)$	−361	−349	86.82
$NaOH(s)$	−425.609	−379.53	64.454
$Na_2CO_3(s)$	−1130.8	−1048.1	139
$NaHCO_3(s)$	−947.7	−851.9	102
$NaI(s)$	−288	−285	98.5
Strontium			
$Sr(s)$	0	0	54.4
$Sr(g)$	164	110	164.54
$Sr^{2+}(g)$	1784	—	—
$Sr^{2+}(aq)$	−545.51	−557.3	−39
$SrCl_2(s)$	−828.4	−781.2	117
$SrCO_3(s)$	−1218	−1138	97.1
$SrO(s)$	−592.0	−562.4	55.5
$SrSO_4(s)$	−1445	−1334	122
Sulfur			
S(rhombic)	0	0	31.9
S(monoclinic)	0.3	0.096	32.6
$S(g)$	279	239	168
$S_2(g)$	129	80.1	228.1
$S_8(g)$	101	49.1	430.211
$S^{2-}(aq)$	41.8	83.7	22
$HS^-(aq)$	−17.7	12.6	61.1
$H_2S(g)$	−20.2	−33	205.6
$H_2S(aq)$	−39	−27.4	122
$SO_2(g)$	−296.8	−300.2	248.1
$SO_3(g)$	−396	−371	256.66
$SO_4^{2-}(aq)$	−907.51	−741.99	17
$HSO_4^-(aq)$	−885.75	−752.87	126.9
$H_2SO_4(l)$	−813.989	−690.059	156.90
$H_2SO_4(aq)$	−907.51	−741.99	17
Tin			
Sn(white)	0	0	51.5
Sn(gray)	3	4.6	44.8
$SnCl_4(l)$	−545.2	−474.0	259
$SnO_2(s)$	−580.7	−519.7	52.3
Titanium			
$Ti(s)$	0	0	30.7
$TiCl_4(l)$	−804.2	−737.2	252.3
$TiO_2(s)$	−944.0	−888.8	50.6
Zinc			
$Zn(s)$	0	0	41.6
$Zn(g)$	130.5	94.93	160.9
$Zn^{2+}(aq)$	−152.4	−147.21	−106.5
$ZnO(s)$	−348.0	−318.2	43.9
$ZnS(s$, zinc blende)	−203	−198	57.7

Appendix C

Equilibrium Constants for Selected Substances*

Dissociation (Ionization) Constants (K_a) of Selected Acids

Name and Formula	Lewis Structure†	K_{a1}	K_{a2}	K_{a3}
Acetic acid CH_3COOH	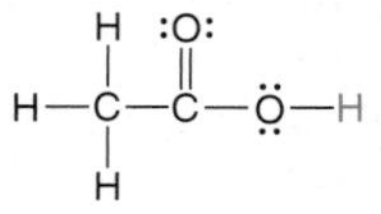	1.8×10^{-5}		
Acetylsalicylic acid $CH_3COOC_6H_4COOH$	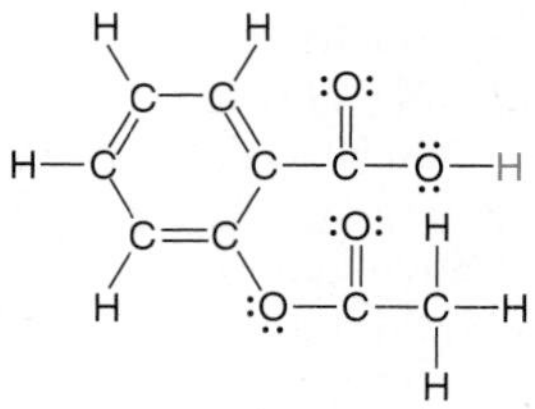	3.6×10^{-4}		
Adipic acid $HOOC(CH_2)_4COOH$	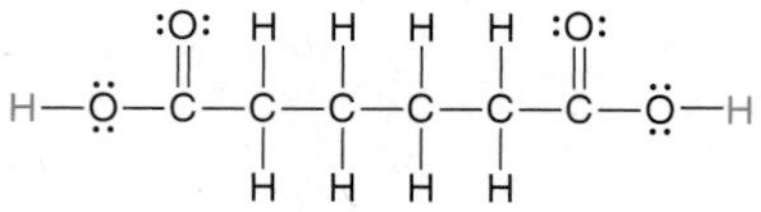	3.8×10^{-5}	3.8×10^{-6}	
Arsenic acid H_3AsO_4	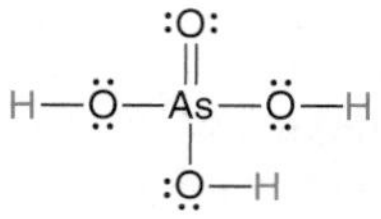	6×10^{-3}	1.1×10^{-7}	3×10^{-12}
Ascorbic acid $H_2C_6H_6O_6$	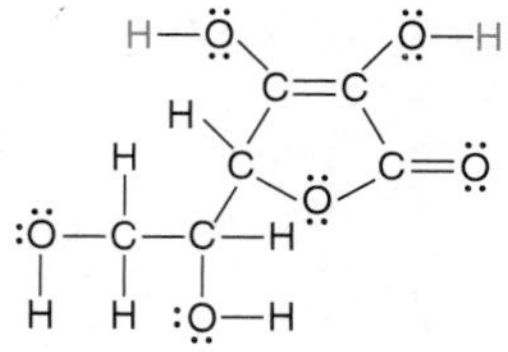	1.0×10^{-5}	5×10^{-12}	
Benzoic acid C_6H_5COOH	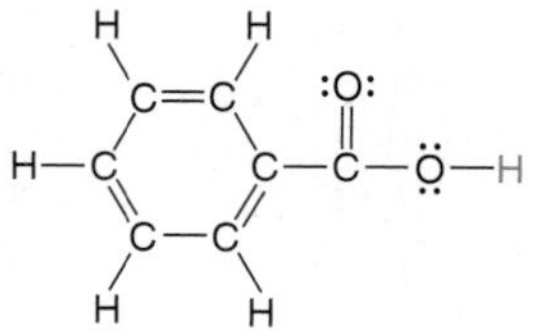	6.3×10^{-5}		
Carbonic acid H_2CO_3	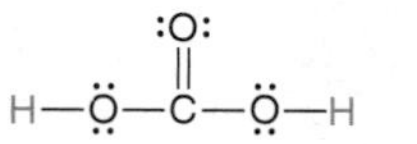	4.5×10^{-7}	4.7×10^{-11}	
Chloroacetic acid $ClCH_2COOH$	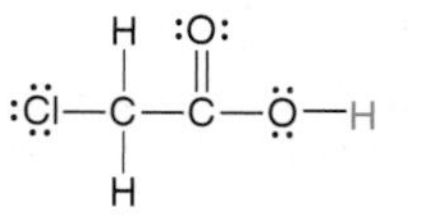	1.4×10^{-3}		
Chlorous acid $HClO_2$	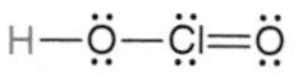	1.1×10^{-2}		

*All values at 298 K, except for acetylsalicylic acid, which is at 37°C (310 K) in 0.15 *M* NaCl.

†Acidic (ionizable) proton(s) shown in red. Structures have lowest formal charges. Benzene rings show one resonance form.

(continued)

Dissociation (Ionization) Constants (K_a) of Selected Acids

Name and Formula	Lewis Structure†	K_{a1}	K_{a2}	K_{a3}
Citric acid $HOOCCH_2C(OH)(COOH)CH_2COOH$	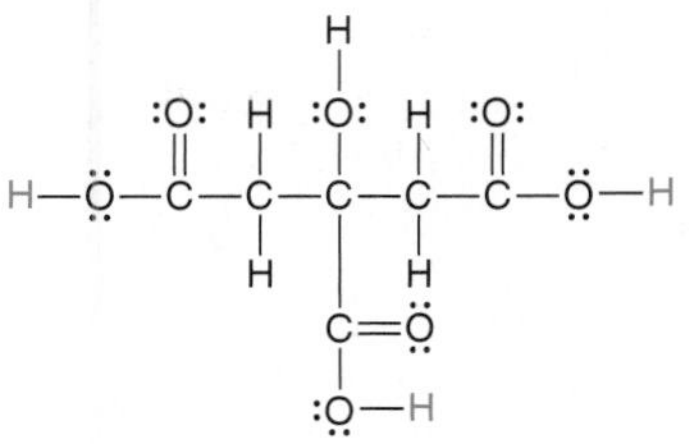	7.4×10^{-4}	1.7×10^{-5}	4.0×10^{-7}
Formic acid $HCOOH$	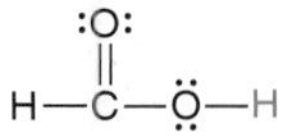	1.8×10^{-4}		
Glyceric acid $HOCH_2CH(OH)COOH$	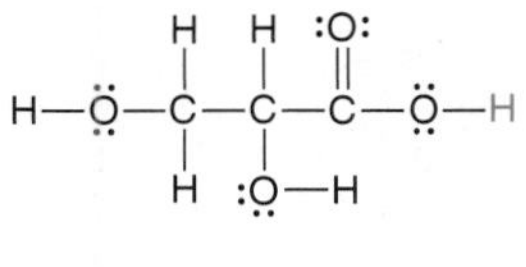	2.9×10^{-4}		
Glycolic acid $HOCH_2COOH$	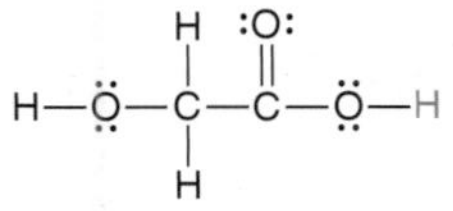	1.5×10^{-4}		
Glyoxylic acid $HC(O)COOH$	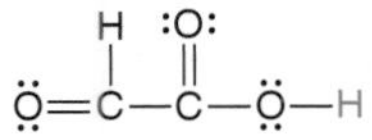	3.5×10^{-4}		
Hydrocyanic acid HCN	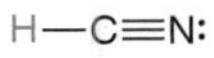	6.2×10^{-10}		
Hydrofluoric acid HF	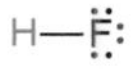	6.8×10^{-4}		
Hydrosulfuric acid H_2S	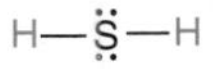	9×10^{-8}	1×10^{-17}	
Hypobromous acid $HBrO$	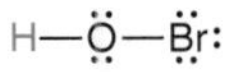	2.3×10^{-9}		
Hypochlorous acid $HClO$	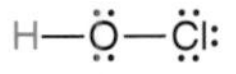	2.9×10^{-8}		
Hypoiodous acid HIO	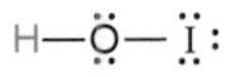	2.3×10^{-11}		
Iodic acid HIO_3	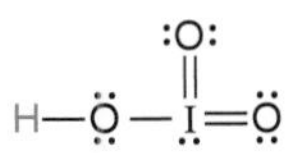	1.6×10^{-1}		
Lactic acid $CH_3CH(OH)COOH$	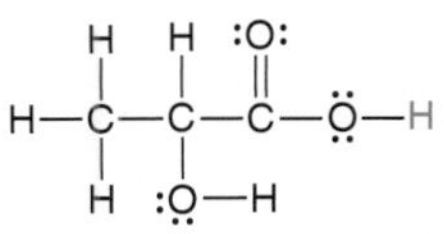	1.4×10^{-4}		
Maleic acid $HOOCCH{=}CHCOOH$	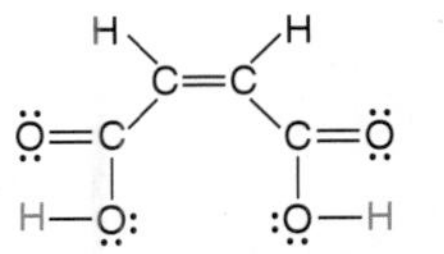	1.2×10^{-2}	4.7×10^{-7}	

(continued)

Dissociation (Ionization) Constants (K_a) of Selected Acids (*continued*)

Name and Formula	Lewis Structure†	K_{a1}	K_{a2}	K_{a3}
Malonic acid $HOOCCH_2COOH$	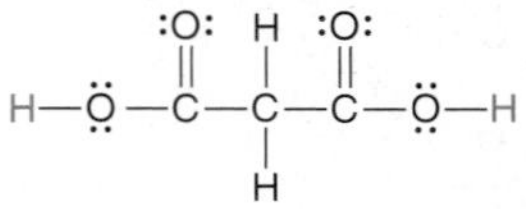	1.4×10^{-3}	2.0×10^{-6}	
Nitrous acid HNO_2	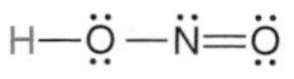	7.1×10^{-4}		
Oxalic acid HOOCCOOH	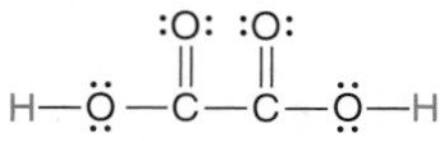	5.6×10^{-2}	5.4×10^{-5}	
Phenol C_6H_5OH	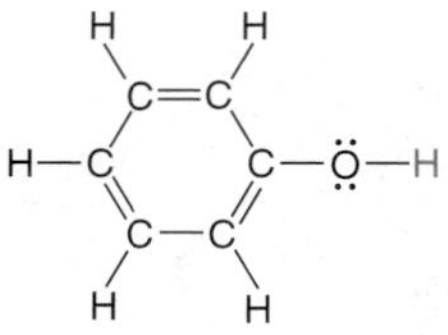	1.0×10^{-10}		
Phenylacetic acid $C_6H_5CH_2COOH$	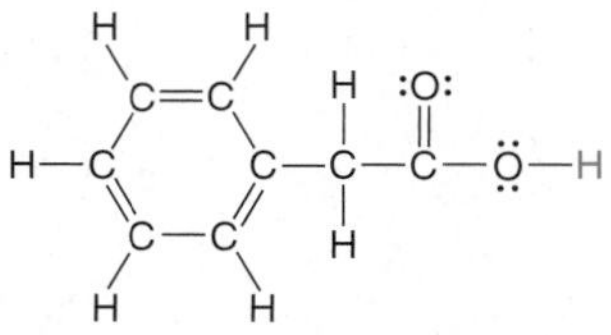	4.9×10^{-5}		
Phosphoric acid H_3PO_4	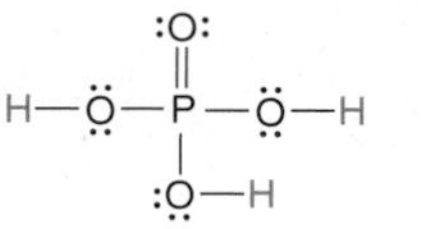	7.2×10^{-3}	6.3×10^{-8}	4.2×10^{-13}
Phosphorous acid $HPO(OH)_2$	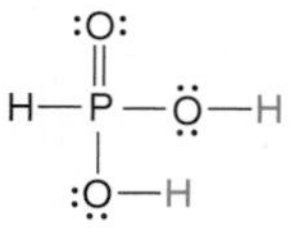	3×10^{-2}	1.7×10^{-7}	
Propanoic acid CH_3CH_2COOH	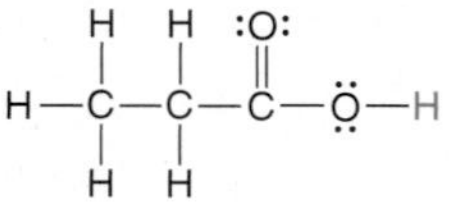	1.3×10^{-5}		
Pyruvic acid $CH_3C(O)COOH$	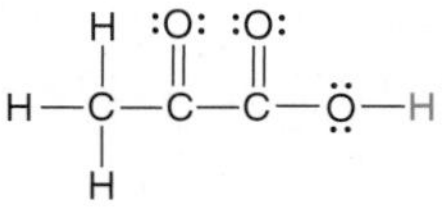	2.8×10^{-3}		
Succinic acid $HOOCCH_2CH_2COOH$	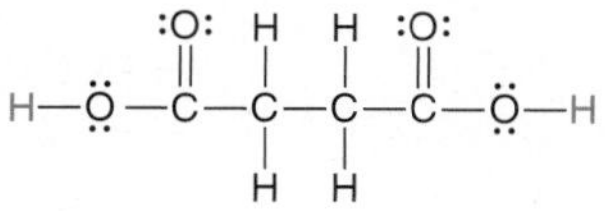	6.2×10^{-5}	2.3×10^{-6}	
Sulfuric acid H_2SO_4	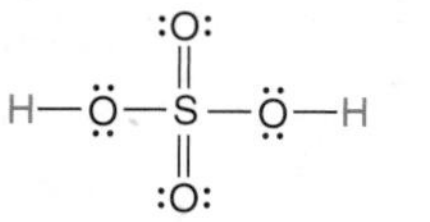	Very large	1.0×10^{-2}	
Sulfurous acid H_2SO_3	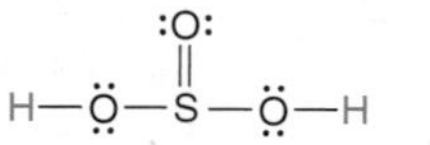	1.4×10^{-2}	6.5×10^{-8}	

(*continued*)

Dissociation (Ionization) Constants (K_b) of Selected Amine Bases

Name and Formula	Lewis Structure†	K_{b1}	K_{b2}
Ammonia NH_3	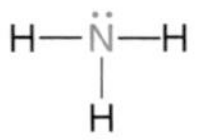	1.76×10^{-5}	
Aniline $C_6H_5NH_2$	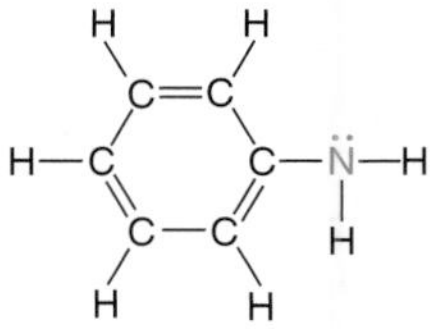	4.0×10^{-10}	
Diethylamine $(CH_3CH_2)_2NH$	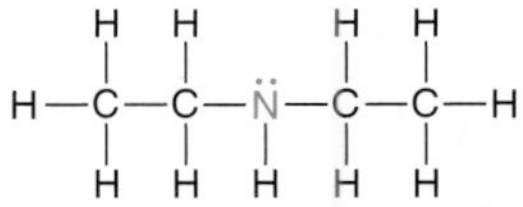	8.6×10^{-4}	
Dimethylamine $(CH_3)_2NH$	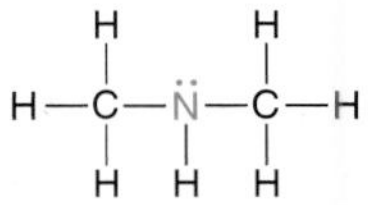	5.9×10^{-4}	
Ethanolamine $HOCH_2CH_2NH_2$	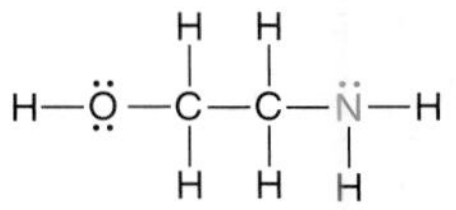	3.2×10^{-5}	
Ethylamine $CH_3CH_2NH_2$	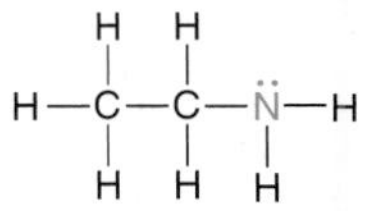	4.3×10^{-4}	
Ethylenediamine $H_2NCH_2CH_2NH_2$	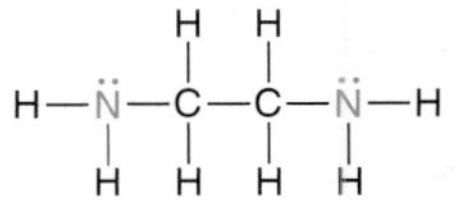	8.5×10^{-5}	7.1×10^{-8}
Methylamine CH_3NH_2	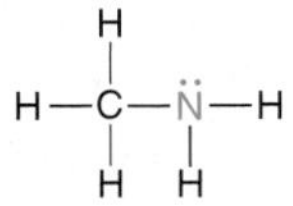	4.4×10^{-4}	
tert-Butylamine $(CH_3)_3CNH_2$	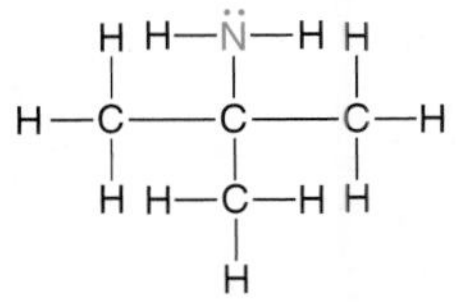	4.8×10^{-4}	
Piperidine $C_5H_{10}NH$	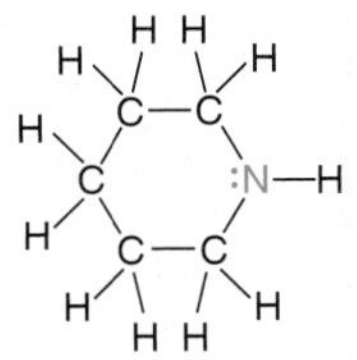	1.3×10^{-3}	
n-Propylamine $CH_3CH_2CH_2NH_2$	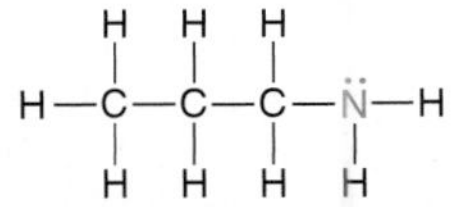	3.5×10^{-4}	

†Blue type indicates the basic nitrogen and its lone pair.

(continued)

Dissociation (Ionization) Constants (K_b) of Selected Amine Bases (*continued*)

Name and Formula	Lewis Structure†	K_{b1}	K_{b2}
Isopropylamine $(CH_3)_2CHNH_2$	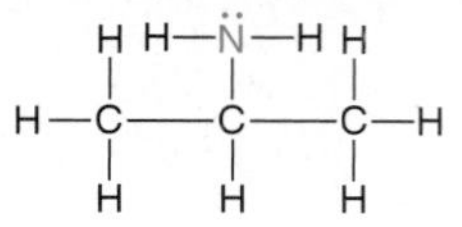	4.7×10^{-4}	
1,3-Propylenediamine $H_2NCH_2CH_2CH_2NH_2$	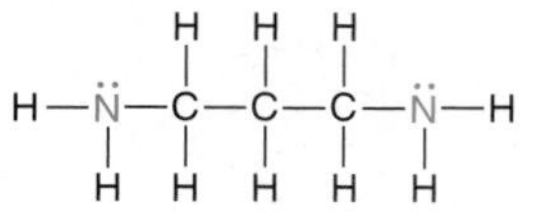	3.1×10^{-4}	3.0×10^{-6}
Pyridine C_5H_5N	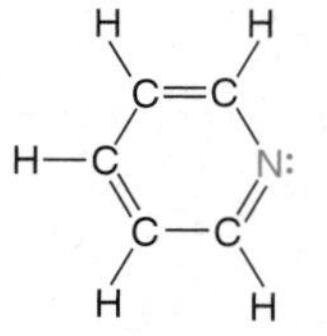	1.7×10^{-9}	
Triethylamine $(CH_3CH_2)_3N$	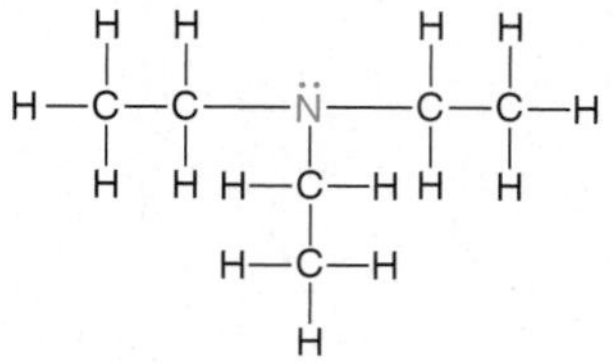	5.2×10^{-4}	
Trimethylamine $(CH_3)_3N$	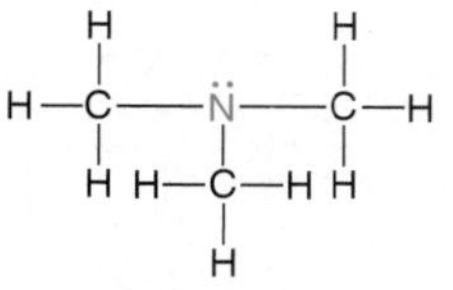	6.3×10^{-5}	

Dissociation (Ionization) Constants (K_a) of Some Hydrated Metal Ions

Free Ion	Hydrated Ion	K_a
Fe^{3+}	$Fe(H_2O)_6^{3+}(aq)$	6×10^{-3}
Sn^{2+}	$Sn(H_2O)_6^{2+}(aq)$	4×10^{-4}
Cr^{3+}	$Cr(H_2O)_6^{3+}(aq)$	1×10^{-4}
Al^{3+}	$Al(H_2O)_6^{3+}(aq)$	1×10^{-5}
Cu^{2+}	$Cu(H_2O)_6^{2+}(aq)$	3×10^{-8}
Pb^{2+}	$Pb(H_2O)_6^{2+}(aq)$	3×10^{-8}
Zn^{2+}	$Zn(H_2O)_6^{2+}(aq)$	1×10^{-9}
Co^{2+}	$Co(H_2O)_6^{2+}(aq)$	2×10^{-10}
Ni^{2+}	$Ni(H_2O)_6^{2+}(aq)$	1×10^{-10}

Formation Constants (K_f) of Some Complex Ions

Complex Ion	K_f
$Ag(CN)_2^-$	3.0×10^{20}
$Ag(NH_3)_2^+$	1.7×10^{7}
$Ag(S_2O_3)_2^{3-}$	4.7×10^{13}
AlF_6^{3-}	$4\ \times10^{19}$
$Al(OH)_4^-$	$3\ \times10^{33}$
$Be(OH)_4^{2-}$	$4\ \times10^{18}$
CdI_4^{2-}	$1\ \times10^{6}$
$Co(OH)_4^{2-}$	$5\ \times10^{9}$
$Cr(OH)_4^-$	8.0×10^{29}
$Cu(NH_3)_4^{2+}$	5.6×10^{11}
$Fe(CN)_6^{4-}$	$3\ \times10^{35}$
$Fe(CN)_6^{3-}$	4.0×10^{43}
$Hg(CN)_4^{2-}$	9.3×10^{38}
$Ni(NH_3)_6^{2+}$	2.0×10^{8}
$Pb(OH)_3^-$	$8\ \times10^{13}$
$Sn(OH)_3^-$	$3\ \times10^{25}$
$Zn(CN)_4^{2-}$	4.2×10^{19}
$Zn(NH_3)_4^{2+}$	7.8×10^{8}
$Zn(OH)_4^{2-}$	$3\ \times10^{15}$

Solubility-Product Constants (K_{sp}) of Slightly Soluble Ionic Compounds

Name, Formula	K_{sp}
Carbonates	
Barium carbonate, $BaCO_3$	2.0×10^{-9}
Cadmium carbonate, $CdCO_3$	1.8×10^{-14}
Calcium carbonate, $CaCO_3$	3.3×10^{-9}
Cobalt(II) carbonate, $CoCO_3$	1.0×10^{-10}
Copper(II) carbonate, $CuCO_3$	3×10^{-12}
Lead(II) carbonate, $PbCO_3$	7.4×10^{-14}
Magnesium carbonate, $MgCO_3$	3.5×10^{-8}
Mercury(I) carbonate, Hg_2CO_3	8.9×10^{-17}
Nickel(II) carbonate, $NiCO_3$	1.3×10^{-7}
Strontium carbonate, $SrCO_3$	5.4×10^{-10}
Zinc carbonate, $ZnCO_3$	1.0×10^{-10}
Chromates	
Barium chromate, $BaCrO_4$	2.1×10^{-10}
Calcium chromate, $CaCrO_4$	1×10^{-8}
Lead(II) chromate, $PbCrO_4$	2.3×10^{-13}
Silver chromate, Ag_2CrO_4	2.6×10^{-12}
Cyanides	
Mercury(I) cyanide, $Hg_2(CN)_2$	5×10^{-40}
Silver cyanide, $AgCN$	2.2×10^{-16}
Halides	
Fluorides	
Barium fluoride, BaF_2	1.5×10^{-6}
Calcium fluoride, CaF_2	3.2×10^{-11}
Lead(II) fluoride, PbF_2	3.6×10^{-8}
Magnesium fluoride, MgF_2	7.4×10^{-9}
Strontium fluoride, SrF_2	2.6×10^{-9}
Chlorides	
Copper(I) chloride, $CuCl$	1.9×10^{-7}
Lead(II) chloride, $PbCl_2$	1.7×10^{-5}
Silver chloride, $AgCl$	1.8×10^{-10}
Bromides	
Copper(I) bromide, $CuBr$	5×10^{-9}
Silver bromide, $AgBr$	5.0×10^{-13}
Iodides	
Copper(I) iodide, CuI	1×10^{-12}
Lead(II) iodide, PbI_2	7.9×10^{-9}
Mercury(I) iodide, Hg_2I_2	4.7×10^{-29}
Silver iodide, AgI	8.3×10^{-17}
Hydroxides	
Aluminum hydroxide, $Al(OH)_3$	3×10^{-34}
Cadmium hydroxide, $Cd(OH)_2$	7.2×10^{-15}
Calcium hydroxide, $Ca(OH)_2$	6.5×10^{-6}
Cobalt(II) hydroxide, $Co(OH)_2$	1.3×10^{-15}
Copper(II) hydroxide, $Cu(OH)_2$	2.2×10^{-20}
Iron(II) hydroxide, $Fe(OH)_2$	4.1×10^{-15}
Iron(III) hydroxide, $Fe(OH)_3$	1.6×10^{-39}
Magnesium hydroxide, $Mg(OH)_2$	6.3×10^{-10}
Manganese(II) hydroxide, $Mn(OH)_2$	1.6×10^{-13}
Nickel(II) hydroxide, $Ni(OH)_2$	6×10^{-16}
Zinc hydroxide, $Zn(OH)_2$	3×10^{-16}
Iodates	
Barium iodate, $Ba(IO_3)_2$	1.5×10^{-9}
Calcium iodate, $Ca(IO_3)_2$	7.1×10^{-7}
Lead(II) iodate, $Pb(IO_3)_2$	2.5×10^{-13}
Silver iodate, $AgIO_3$	3.1×10^{-8}
Strontium iodate, $Sr(IO_3)_2$	3.3×10^{-7}
Zinc iodate, $Zn(IO_3)_2$	3.9×10^{-6}
Oxalates	
Barium oxalate dihydrate, $BaC_2O_4\cdot2H_2O$	1.1×10^{-7}
Calcium oxalate monohydrate, $CaC_2O_4\cdot H_2O$	2.3×10^{-9}
Strontium oxalate monohydrate, $SrC_2O_4\cdot H_2O$	5.6×10^{-8}
Phosphates	
Calcium phosphate, $Ca_3(PO_4)_2$	1.2×10^{-29}
Magnesium phosphate, $Mg_3(PO_4)_2$	5.2×10^{-24}
Silver phosphate, Ag_3PO_4	2.6×10^{-18}
Sulfates	
Barium sulfate, $BaSO_4$	1.1×10^{-10}
Calcium sulfate, $CaSO_4$	2.4×10^{-5}
Lead(II) sulfate, $PbSO_4$	1.6×10^{-8}
Radium sulfate, $RaSO_4$	2×10^{-11}
Silver sulfate, Ag_2SO_4	1.5×10^{-5}
Strontium sulfate, $SrSO_4$	3.2×10^{-7}
Sulfides	
Cadmium sulfide, CdS	1.0×10^{-24}
Copper(II) sulfide, CuS	8×10^{-34}
Iron(II) sulfide, FeS	8×10^{-16}
Lead(II) sulfide, PbS	3×10^{-25}
Manganese(II) sulfide, MnS	3×10^{-11}
Mercury(II) sulfide, HgS	2×10^{-50}
Nickel(II) sulfide, NiS	3×10^{-16}
Silver sulfide, Ag_2S	8×10^{-48}
Tin(II) sulfide, SnS	1.3×10^{-23}
Zinc sulfide, ZnS	2.0×10^{-22}

Standard Electrode (Half-Cell) Potentials*

Half-Reaction	$E°$ (V)
$F_2(g) + 2e^- \rightleftharpoons 2F^-(aq)$	+2.87
$O_3(g) + 2H^+(aq) + 2e^- \rightleftharpoons O_2(g) + H_2O(l)$	+2.07
$Co^{3+}(aq) + e^- \rightleftharpoons Co^{2+}(aq)$	+1.82
$H_2O_2(aq) + 2H^+(aq) + 2e^- \rightleftharpoons 2H_2O(l)$	+1.77
$PbO_2(s) + 3H^+(aq) + HSO_4^-(aq) + 2e^- \rightleftharpoons PbSO_4(s) + 2H_2O(l)$	+1.70
$Ce^{4+}(aq) + e^- \rightleftharpoons Ce^{3+}(aq)$	+1.61
$MnO_4^-(aq) + 8H^+(aq) + 5e^- \rightleftharpoons Mn^{2+}(aq) + 4H_2O(l)$	+1.51
$Au^{3+}(aq) + 3e^- \rightleftharpoons Au(s)$	+1.50
$Cl_2(g) + 2e^- \rightleftharpoons 2Cl^-(aq)$	+1.36
$Cr_2O_7^{2-}(aq) + 14H^+(aq) + 6e^- \rightleftharpoons 2Cr^{3+}(aq) + 7H_2O(l)$	+1.33
$MnO_2(s) + 4H^+(aq) + 2e^- \rightleftharpoons Mn^{2+}(aq) + 2H_2O(l)$	+1.23
$O_2(g) + 4H^+(aq) + 4e^- \rightleftharpoons 2H_2O(l)$	+1.23
$Br_2(l) + 2e^- \rightleftharpoons 2Br^-(aq)$	+1.07
$NO_3^-(aq) + 4H^+(aq) + 3e^- \rightleftharpoons NO(g) + 2H_2O(l)$	+0.96
$2Hg^{2+}(aq) + 2e^- \rightleftharpoons Hg_2^{2+}(aq)$	+0.92
$Hg_2^{2+}(aq) + 2e^- \rightleftharpoons 2Hg(l)$	+0.85
$Ag^+(aq) + e^- \rightleftharpoons Ag(s)$	+0.80
$Fe^{3+}(aq) + e^- \rightleftharpoons Fe^{2+}(aq)$	+0.77
$O_2(g) + 2H^+(aq) + 2e^- \rightleftharpoons H_2O_2(aq)$	+0.68
$MnO_4^-(aq) + 2H_2O(l) + 3e^- \rightleftharpoons MnO_2(s) + 4OH^-(aq)$	+0.59
$I_2(s) + 2e^- \rightleftharpoons 2I^-(aq)$	+0.53
$O_2(g) + 2H_2O(l) + 4e^- \rightleftharpoons 4OH^-(aq)$	+0.40
$Cu^{2+}(aq) + 2e^- \rightleftharpoons Cu(s)$	+0.34
$AgCl(s) + e^- \rightleftharpoons Ag(s) + Cl^-(aq)$	+0.22
$SO_4^{2-}(aq) + 4H^+(aq) + 2e^- \rightleftharpoons SO_2(g) + 2H_2O(l)$	+0.20
$Cu^{2+}(aq) + e^- \rightleftharpoons Cu^+(aq)$	+0.15
$Sn^{4+}(aq) + 2e^- \rightleftharpoons Sn^{2+}(aq)$	+0.13
$2H^+(aq) + 2e^- \rightleftharpoons H_2(g)$	0.00
$Pb^{2+}(aq) + 2e^- \rightleftharpoons Pb(s)$	−0.13
$Sn^{2+}(aq) + 2e^- \rightleftharpoons Sn(s)$	−0.14
$N_2(g) + 5H^+(aq) + 4e^- \rightleftharpoons N_2H_5^+(aq)$	−0.23
$Ni^{2+}(aq) + 2e^- \rightleftharpoons Ni(s)$	−0.25
$Co^{2+}(aq) + 2e^- \rightleftharpoons Co(s)$	−0.28
$PbSO_4(s) + H^+(aq) + 2e^- \rightleftharpoons Pb(s) + HSO_4^-(aq)$	−0.31
$Cd^{2+}(aq) + 2e^- \rightleftharpoons Cd(s)$	−0.40
$Fe^{2+}(aq) + 2e^- \rightleftharpoons Fe(s)$	−0.44
$Cr^{3+}(aq) + 3e^- \rightleftharpoons Cr(s)$	−0.74
$Zn^{2+}(aq) + 2e^- \rightleftharpoons Zn(s)$	−0.76
$2H_2O(l) + 2e^- \rightleftharpoons H_2(g) + 2OH^-(aq)$	−0.83
$Mn^{2+}(aq) + 2e^- \rightleftharpoons Mn(s)$	−1.18
$Al^{3+}(aq) + 3e^- \rightleftharpoons Al(s)$	−1.66
$Mg^{2+}(aq) + 2e^- \rightleftharpoons Mg(s)$	−2.37
$Na^+(aq) + e^- \rightleftharpoons Na(s)$	−2.71
$Ca^{2+}(aq) + 2e^- \rightleftharpoons Ca(s)$	−2.87
$Sr^{2+}(aq) + 2e^- \rightleftharpoons Sr(s)$	−2.89
$Ba^{2+}(aq) + 2e^- \rightleftharpoons Ba(s)$	−2.90
$K^+(aq) + e^- \rightleftharpoons K(s)$	−2.93
$Li^+(aq) + e^- \rightleftharpoons Li(s)$	−3.05

*All values at 298 K. Written as reductions; $E°$ value refers to all components in their standard states: 1 *M* for dissolved species; 1 atm pressure for the gas behaving ideally; the pure substance for solids and liquids.

Answers to Selected Problems

Chapter 1

1.2 Gas molecules fill the entire container; the volume of a gas is the volume of the container. Solids and liquids have a definite volume. The volume of the container does not affect the volume of a solid or liquid. (a) gas (b) liquid (c) liquid **1.4** Physical property: a characteristic shown by a substance itself, without any interaction with or change into other substances. Chemical property: a characteristic of a substance that appears as it interacts with, or transforms into, other substances. (a) Color (yellow-green and silvery to white) and physical state (gas and metal to crystals) are physical properties. The interaction between chlorine gas and sodium metal is a chemical property. (b) Color and magnetism are physical properties. No chemical changes. **1.6**(a) Physical change; there is only a temperature change. (b) Chemical change; the change in appearance indicates an irreversible chemical change. (c) Physical change; there is only a change in size, not composition. (d) Chemical change; the wood (and air) become different substances with different compositions. **1.8**(a) fuel (b) wood **1.13** Lavoisier measured the total mass of the reactants and products, not just the mass of the solids. The total mass of the reactants and products remained constant. His measurements showed that a gas was involved in the reaction. He called this gas *oxygen* (one of his key discoveries). **1.16** A well-designed experiment must have the following essential features: (1) There must be at least two variables that are expected to be related; (2) there must be a way to control all the variables, so that only one at a time may be changed; (3) the results must be reproducible. **1.19**(a) $(2.54\ cm)^2/(1\ in)^2$ and $(1\ m)^2/(100\ cm)^2$ (b) $(1000\ m)^2/(1\ km)^2$ and $(100\ cm)^2/(1\ m)^2$ (c) $(1.609\times10^3\ m/mi)$ and $(1\ h/3600\ s)$ (d) $(1000\ g/2.205\ lb)$ and $(3.531\times10^{-5}\ ft^3/cm^3)$ **1.21** An extensive property depends on the amount of material present. An intensive property is the same regardless of how much material is present. (a) extensive property (b) intensive property (c) extensive property (d) intensive property **1.23**(a) increases (b) remains the same (c) decreases (d) increases (e) remains the same **1.26** 1.43 nm **1.28** 3.94×10^3 in **1.30**(a) $2.07\times10^{-9}\ km^2$ (b) \$10.43 **1.32** Answers will vary, depending on the person's mass. **1.34**(a) $5.52\times10^3\ kg/m^3$ (b) $345\ lb/ft^3$ **1.36**(a) $2.56\times10^{-9}\ mm^3$ (b) 10^{-10} L **1.38**(a) $9.626\ cm^3$ (b) 64.92 g **1.40** $2.70\ g/cm^3$ **1.42**(a) 20.°C; 293 K (b) 109 K; −263°F (c) −273°C; −460.°F **1.45**(a) 2.47×10^{-7} m (b) 67.6 Å **1.52**(a) none (b) none (c) $0.041\underline{0}$ (d) $4.\underline{0100}\times10^4$ **1.54**(a) 0.00036 (b) 35.83 (c) 22.5 **1.56** 6×10^2 **1.58**(a) 1.34 m (b) 21,621 mm^3 (c) 443 cm **1.60**(a) 1.310000×10^5 (b) 4.7×10^{-4} (c) 2.10006×10^5 (d) 2.1605×10^3 **1.62**(a) 5550 (b) 10,070. (c) 0.000000885 (d) 0.003004 **1.64**(a) 8.025×10^4 (b) 1.0098×10^{-3} (c) 7.7×10^{-11}

1.66(a) 4.06×10^{-19} J (b) 1.61×10^{24} molecules (c) 1.82×10^5 J/mol **1.68**(a) Height measured, not exact. (b) Planets counted, exact. (c) Number of grams in a pound is not a unit definition, not exact. (d) Definition of "millimeter," exact. **1.70** 7.50 ± 0.05 cm **1.72**(a) I_{avg} = 8.72 g; II_{avg} = 8.72 g; III_{avg} = 8.50 g; IV_{avg} = 8.56 g; sets I and II are most accurate. (b) Set III is the most precise, but is the least accurate. (c) Set I has the best combination of high accuracy and high precision. (d) Set IV has both low accuracy and low precision. **1.74**(a)

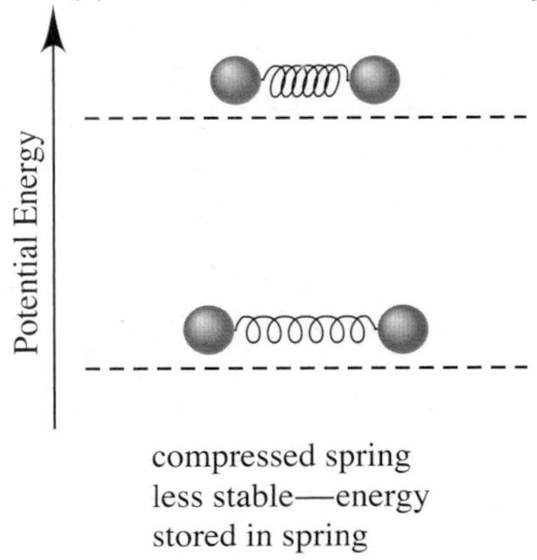

(b)

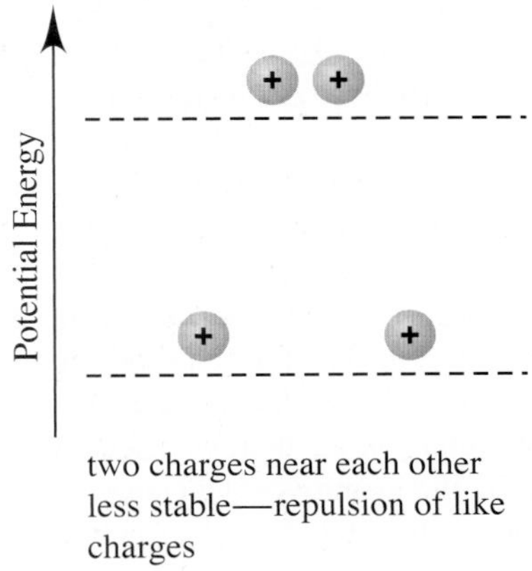

1.76 7.7/1 **1.78**(a) density = 0.21 g/L, will float (b) CO_2 is denser than air, will sink (c) density = 0.30 g/L, will float (d) O_2 is denser than air, will sink (e) density = 1.38 g/L, will sink (f) 0.55 g for empty ball; 0.50 g for ball filled with hydrogen **1.80**(a) 8.0×10^{12} g (b) $4.1\times10^5\ m^3$ (c) 9.5×10^{13} dollars **1.82**(a) −195.79°C (b) −320.42°F (c) 5.05 L **1.83**(a) 2.6 m/s (b) 16 km (c) 12:45 pm **1.85** freezing point = −3.7°X; boiling point = 63.3°X **1.86** 2.3×10^{25} g oxygen; 1.4×10^{25} g silicon; 5×10^{15} g ruthenium and rhodium

Chapter 2

Answers to Boxed Reading Problems: B2.1 (a) 5 peaks (b) *m/e* ratio of heaviest particle = 74; *m/e* ratio of lightest particle = 35 **B2.3** (a) Since salt dissolves in water and pepper does not, add water to mixture and filter to remove solid pepper. Evaporate water to recover solid salt. (d) Heat the mixture; the ethanol will boil off (distill), while the sugar will remain behind.

• **2.1** Compounds contain different types of atoms; there is only one type of atom in an element. **2.4**(a) The presence of more than one element makes pure calcium chloride a compound. (b) There is only one kind of atom, so sulfur is an element. (c) The presence of more than one compound makes baking powder a mixture. (d) The presence of more than one type of atom means cytosine cannot be an element. The specific, not variable, arrangement means it is a compound. **2.12**(a) elements, compounds, and mixtures (b) compounds (c) compounds **2.14**(a) Law of definite composition: the composition is the same regardless of its source. (b) Law of mass conservation: the total quantity of matter does not change. (c) Law of multiple proportions: two elements can combine to form two different compounds that have different proportions of those elements. **2.16**(a) No, the percent by mass of each element in a compound is fixed. (b) Yes, the *mass* of each element in a compound depends on the amount of compound. **2.18** The two experiments demonstrate the law of definite composition. The unknown compound decomposes the same way both times. The experiments also demonstrate the law of conservation of mass since the total mass before reaction equals the total mass after reaction. **2.20**(a) 1.34 g F (b) 0.514 Ca; 0.486 F (c) 51.4 mass % Ca; 48.6 mass % F **2.22**(a) 0.603 (b) 322 g Mg **2.24** 3.498×10^6 g Cu; 1.766×10^6 g S **2.26** compound 1: 0.905 S/Cl; compound 2: 0.451 S/Cl; ratio: 2.00/1.00 **2.29** Coal A **2.31** Dalton postulated that atoms of an element are identical and that compounds result from the chemical combination of specific ratios of different elements. **2.32** If you know the ratio of any two quantities and the value of one of them, the other can always be calculated; in this case, the charge and the mass/charge ratio were known. **2.36** The atomic number is the number of protons in an atom's nucleus. When the atomic number changes, the identity of the element changes. The mass number is the total number of protons and neutrons in the nucleus. The identity of an element is based on the number of protons, not the number of neutrons. The mass number can vary (by a change in number of neutrons) without changing the identity of the element. **2.39** All three isotopes have 18 protons and 18 electrons. Their respective mass numbers are 36, 38, and 40, with the respective numbers of neutrons being 18, 20, and 22. **2.41**(a) These have the same number of protons and electrons, but different numbers of neutrons; same *Z*. (b) These have the same number of neutrons, but different numbers of protons and electrons; same *N*. (c) These have different numbers of protons, neutrons, and electrons; same *A*.

2.43(a) ${}^{38}_{18}Ar$ (b) ${}^{55}_{25}Mn$ (c) ${}^{109}_{47}Ag$
2.45(a) ${}^{48}_{22}Ti$ (b) ${}^{79}_{34}Se$ (c) ${}^{11}_{5}B$

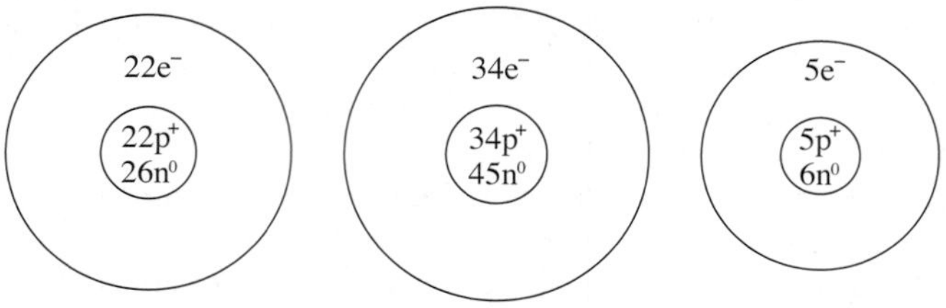

2.47 69.72 amu **2.49** ${}^{35}Cl$ = 75.774%, ${}^{37}Cl$ = 24.226% **2.52**(a) In the modern periodic table, the elements are arranged in order of increasing atomic number. (b) Elements in a group (or family) have similar chemical properties. (c) Elements can be classified as metals, metalloids, or nonmetals. **2.55** The alkali metals [Group 1A(1)] are metals and readily lose one electron to form cations; the halogens [Group 7A(17)] are nonmetals and readily gain one electron to form anions. **2.56**(a) germanium; Ge; 4A(14); metalloid (b) phosphorus; P; 5A(15); nonmetal (c) helium; He; 8A(18); nonmetal (d) lithium; Li; 1A(1); metal (e) molybdenum; Mo; 6B(6); metal **2.58**(a) Ra; 88 (b) Si; 14 (c) Cu; 63.55 amu (d) Br; 79.90 amu **2.60** Atoms of these two kinds of substances will form ionic bonds, in which one or more electrons are transferred from the metal atom to the nonmetal atom to form a cation and an anion, respectively. **2.63** Coulomb's law states the energy of attraction in an ionic bond is directly proportional to the product of charges and inversely proportional to the distance between charges. The product of charges in MgO [(2+) (2−)] is greater than that in LiF [(1+) (1−)]. Thus, MgO has stronger ionic bonding. **2.66** The Group 1A(1) elements form cations, and the Group 7A(17) elements form anions. **2.68** Each potassium atom loses one electron to form an ion with a 1+ charge. Each sulfur atom gains two electrons to form an ion with a 2− charge. Two potassiums, losing one electron each, are required for each sulfur, which gains two electrons. The oppositely charged ions attract each other to form an ionic solid, K_2S. **2.70** K^+; I^- **2.72**(a) oxygen; 17; 6A(16); 2 (b) fluorine; 19; 7A(17); 2 (c) calcium; 40; 2A(2); 4 **2.74** Lithium forms the Li^+ ion; oxygen forms the O^{2-} ion. Number of O^{2-} ions = 4.2×10^{21} O^{2-} ions. **2.76** NaCl **2.78** The subscripts in a formula give the numbers of ions in a formula unit of the compound. The subscripts indicate that there are two F^- ions for each Mg^{2+} ion. Using this information and the mass of each element, we can calculate percent mass of each element in the compound. **2.80** The two samples are similar in that both contain 20 billion oxygen atoms and 20 billion hydrogen atoms. They differ in that they contain different types of molecules: H_2O_2 molecules in the hydrogen peroxide sample, and H_2 and O_2 molecules in the mixture. In addition, the mixture contains 20 billion molecules (10 billion H_2 and 10 billion O_2), while the hydrogen peroxide sample contains 10 billion molecules. **2.84**(a) Na_3N, sodium nitride (b) SrO, strontium oxide (c) $AlCl_3$, aluminum chloride **2.86**(a) MgF_2, magnesium fluoride (b) ZnS, zinc sulfide (c) $SrCl_2$, strontium chloride **2.88**(a) $SnCl_4$ (b) iron(III) bromide

(c) CuBr (d) manganese(III) oxide **2.90**(a) cobalt(II) oxide (b) Hg_2Cl_2 (c) lead(II) acetate trihydrate (d) Cr_2O_3 **2.92**(a) BaO (b) $Fe(NO_3)_2$ (c) MgS **2.94**(a) H_2SO_4; sulfuric acid (b) HIO_3; iodic acid (c) HCN; hydrocyanic acid (d) H_2S; hydrosulfuric acid **2.96**(a) ammonium ion, NH_4^+; ammonia, NH_3 (b) magnesium sulfide, MgS; magnesium sulfite, $MgSO_3$; magnesium sulfate, $MgSO_4$ (c) hydrochloric acid, HCl; chloric acid, $HClO_3$; chlorous acid, $HClO_2$ (d) cuprous bromide, CuBr; cupric bromide, $CuBr_2$ **2.98** Disulfur tetrafluoride, S_2F_4 **2.100**(a) calcium chloride (b) copper(I) oxide (c) stannic fluoride (d) hydrochloric acid **2.102**(a) 12 oxygen atoms; 342.2 amu (b) 9 hydrogen atoms; 132.06 amu (c) 8 oxygen atoms; 344.6 amu **2.104**(a) $(NH_4)_2SO_4$; 132.15 amu (b) NaH_2PO_4; 119.98 amu (c) $KHCO_3$; 100.12 amu **2.106**(a) 108.02 amu (b) 331.2 amu (c) 72.08 amu **2.108**(a) SO_3; sulfur trioxide; 80.07 amu (b) C_3H_8; propane; 44.09 amu **2.112** Separating the components of a mixture requires physical methods only; that is, no chemical changes (no changes in composition) take place, and the components maintain their chemical identities and properties throughout. Separating the components of a compound requires a chemical change (change in composition). **2.115**(a) compound (b) homogeneous mixture (c) heterogeneous mixture (d) homogeneous mixture (e) homogeneous mixture **2.117**(a) filtration (b) chromatography **2.119**(a) fraction of volume $= 5.2\times10^{-13}$ (b) mass of nucleus $= 6.64466\times10^{-24}$ g; fraction of mass $=$ 0.999726 **2.120** strongest ionic bonding: MgO; weakest ionic bonding: RbI **2.124**(a) I = NO; II = N_2O_3; III = N_2O_5 (b) I has 1.14 g O per 1.00 g N; II, 1.71 g O; III, 2.86 g O **2.128**(a) Cl^-, 1.898 mass %; Na^+, 1.056 mass %; SO_4^{2-}, 0.265 mass %; Mg^{2+}, 0.127 mass %; Ca^{2+}, 0.04 mass %; K^+, 0.038 mass %; HCO_3^-, 0.014 mass % (b) 30.72% (c) Alkaline earth metal ions, total mass % = 0.17%; alkali metal ions, total mass % = 1.094% (d) Anions (2.177 mass %) make up a larger mass fraction than cations (1.26 mass %). **2.131** Molecular formula, $C_4H_6O_4$; molecular mass, 118.09 amu; 40.68% by mass C; 5.122% by mass H; 54.20% by mass O **2.134**(a) Formulas and masses in amu: $^{15}N_2{}^{18}O$, 48; $^{15}N_2{}^{16}O$, 46; $^{14}N_2{}^{18}O$, 46; $^{14}N_2{}^{16}O$, 44; $^{15}N^{14}N^{18}O$, 47; $^{15}N^{14}N^{16}O$, 45 (b) $^{15}N_2{}^{18}O$, least common; $^{14}N_2{}^{16}O$, most common **2.136** 58.091 amu **2.138** nitroglycerin, 39.64 mass % NO; isoamyl nitrate, 22.54 mass % NO **2.139** 0.370 lb C; 0.0222 lb H; 0.423 lb O; 0.185 lb N **2.144**(1) chemical change (2) physical change (3) chemical change (4) chemical change (5) physical change

Chapter 3

3.2(a) 12 mol C atoms (b) 1.445×10^{25} C atoms **3.7**(a) left (b) left (c) left (d) neither **3.8**(a) 121.64 g/mol (b) 76.02 g/mol (c) 106.44 g/mol (d) 152.00 g/mol **3.10**(a) 134.7 g/mol (b) 175.3 g/mol (c) 342.17 g/mol (d) 125.84 g/mol **3.12**(a) 1.1×10^2 g $KMnO_4$ (b) 0.188 mol O atoms (c) 1.5×10^{20} O atoms **3.14**(a) 9.73 g $MnSO_4$ (b) 44.6 mol $Fe(ClO_4)_3$ (c) 1.74×10^{21} N atoms **3.16**(a) 1.56×10^3 g Cu_2CO_3 (b) 0.0725 g N_2O_5 (c) 0.644 mol $NaClO_4$; 3.88×10^{23} formula units $NaClO_4$ (d) 3.88×10^{23} Na^+ ions; 3.88×10^{23} ClO_4^- ions; 3.88×10^{23} Cl atoms; 1.55×10^{24} O atoms **3.18**(a) 6.375 mass % H (b) 71.52 mass % O **3.20**(a) 0.1252 mass fraction C (b) 0.3428 mass fraction O **3.23**(a) 0.9507 mol cisplatin (b) 3.5×10^{24} H atoms **3.25**(a) 195 mol rust (b) 195 mol Fe_2O_3 (c) 2.18×10^4 g Fe **3.27** $CO(NH_2)_2$ > NH_4NO_3 > $(NH_4)_2SO_4$ > KNO_3 **3.28**(a) 883 mol PbS (b) 1.88×10^{25} Pb atoms **3.32**(b) From the mass percent, determine the empirical formula. Add up the total number of atoms in the empirical formula, and divide that number into the total number of atoms in the molecule. The result is the multiplier that converts the empirical formula into the molecular formula.

Road Map

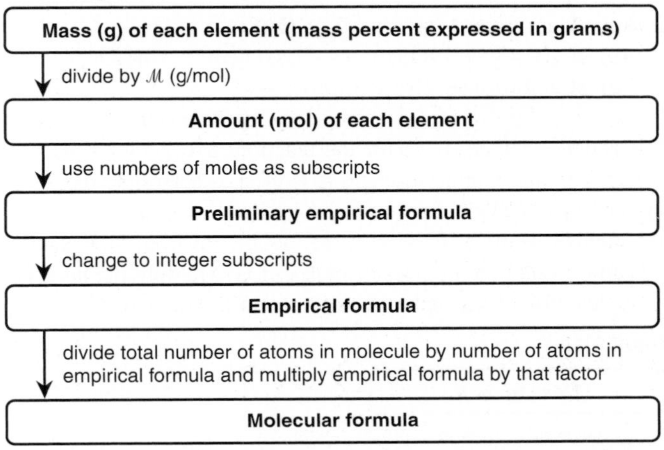

(c) Find the empirical formula from the mass percents. Compare the number of atoms given for the one element to the number in the empirical formula. Multiply the empirical formula by the factor that is needed to obtain the given number of atoms for that element.

Road Map

First three steps are the same as in road map for part (b).

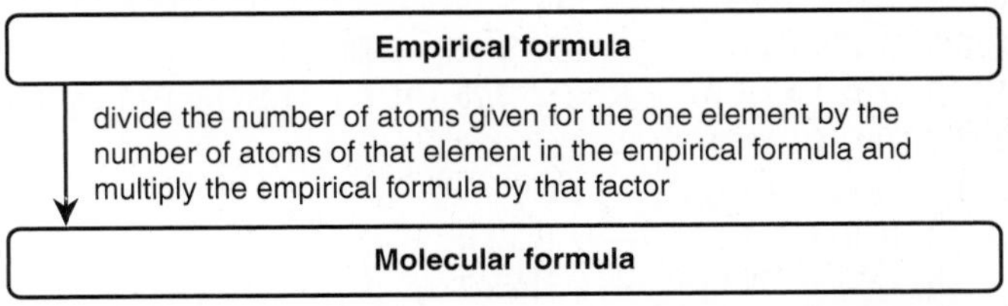

(e) Count the numbers of the various types of atoms in the structural formula and put these into a molecular formula.

Road Map

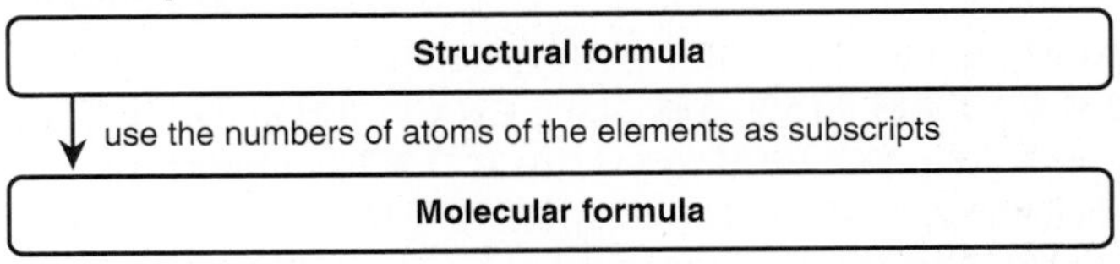

3.34(a) CH_2; 14.03 g/mol (b) CH_3O; 31.03 g/mol (c) N_2O_5; 108.02 g/mol (d) $Ba_3(PO_4)_2$; 601.8 g/mol (e) TeI_4; 635.2 g/mol **3.36** Disulfur dichloride; SCl; 135.04 g/mol **3.38**(a) C_3H_6 (b) N_2H_4 (c) N_2O_4 (d) $C_5H_5N_5$ **3.40**(a) Cl_2O_7 (b) $SiCl_4$ (c) CO_2 **3.42**(a) NO_2 (b) N_2O_4 **3.44**(a) 1.20 mol F (b) 24.0 g M

(c) calcium **3.47** $C_{21}H_{30}O_5$ **3.49** $C_{10}H_{20}O$ **3.50** A balanced equation provides information on the identities of reactants and products, the physical states of reactants and products, and the molar ratios by which reactants form products. **3.53** b
3.54(a) $16Cu(s) + S_8(s) \longrightarrow 8Cu_2S(s)$
(b) $P_4O_{10}(s) + 6H_2O(l) \longrightarrow 4H_3PO_4(l)$
(c) $B_2O_3(s) + 6NaOH(aq) \longrightarrow 2Na_3BO_3(aq) + 3H_2O(l)$
(d) $4CH_3NH_2(g) + 9O_2(g) \longrightarrow 4CO_2(g) + 10H_2O(g) + 2N_2(g)$
3.56(a) $2SO_2(g) + O_2(g) \longrightarrow 2SO_3(g)$
(b) $Sc_2O_3(s) + 3H_2O(l) \longrightarrow 2Sc(OH)_3(s)$
(c) $H_3PO_4(aq) + 2NaOH(aq) \longrightarrow Na_2HPO_4(aq) + 2H_2O(l)$
(d) $C_6H_{10}O_5(s) + 6O_2(g) \longrightarrow 6CO_2(g) + 5H_2O(g)$
3.58(a) $4Ga(s) + 3O_2(g) \longrightarrow 2Ga_2O_3(s)$
(b) $2C_6H_{14}(l) + 19O_2(g) \longrightarrow 12CO_2(g) + 14H_2O(g)$
(c) $3CaCl_2(aq) + 2Na_3PO_4(aq) \longrightarrow Ca_3(PO_4)_2(s) + 6NaCl(aq)$
3.64 Balance the equation for the reaction: $aA + bB \longrightarrow cC$. Since A is the limiting reactant, A is used to determine the amount of C. Divide the mass of A by its molar mass to obtain the number of moles of A. Use the molar ratio from the balanced equation to find the number of moles of C. Multiply the number of moles of C by its molar mass to obtain the mass of C.

Road Map

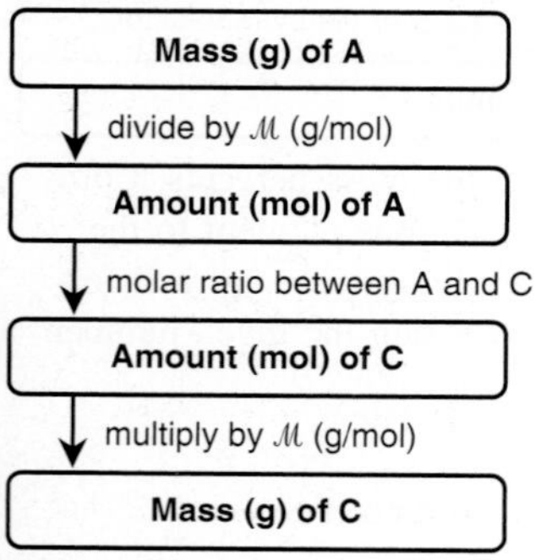

3.66(a) 0.455 mol Cl_2 (b) 32.3 g Cl_2 **3.68**(a) 1.42×10^3 mol KNO_3 (b) 1.43×10^5 g KNO_3 **3.70** 195.8 g H_3BO_3; 19.16 g H_2 **3.72** 2.60×10^3 g Cl_2
3.74(a) $I_2(s) + Cl_2(g) \longrightarrow 2ICl(s)$
$ICl(s) + Cl_2(g) \longrightarrow ICl_3(s)$
(b) $I_2(s) + 3Cl_2(g) \longrightarrow 2ICl_3(s)$
(c) 1.33×10^3 g I_2
3.76(a) 0.105 mol CaO (b) 0.175 mol CaO (c) calcium (d) 5.88 g CaO **3.78** 1.36 mol HIO_3, 239 g HIO_3; 44.9 g H_2O in excess **3.80** 4.40 g CO_2; 4.80 g O_2 in excess **3.82** 12.2 g $Al(NO_2)_3$, no NH_4Cl, 48.7 g $AlCl_3$, 30.7 g N_2, 39.5 g H_2O **3.84** 50.% **3.86** 90.5% **3.88** 24.0 g CH_3Cl **3.90**(a) 39.7 g CF_4 **3.91** A **3.95**(a) C (b) B (c) C (d) B **3.98** No, instructions should read: "Take 100.0 mL of the 10.0 *M* solution and, with stirring, add water until the total volume is 1000. mL."
3.99(a) 7.85 g $Ca(C_2H_3O_2)_2$ (b) 0.254 *M* KI (c) 124 mol NaCN **3.101**(a) 4.65 g K_2SO_4 (b) 0.0653 *M* $CaCl_2$ (c) 1.11×10^{20} Mg^{2+} ions **3.103**(a) 0.0617 *M* KCl (b) 0.00363 *M* $(NH_4)_2SO_4$ (c) 0.138 *M* Na^+ **3.105**(a) 987 g HNO_3/L (b) 15.7 *M* HNO_3 **3.107** 845 mL **3.109** 0.88 g $BaSO_4$ **3.112**(a) Instructions: Be sure to wear goggles to protect your eyes! Pour approximately 2.0 gal of water into the container. Add to the water, slowly and with mixing, 0.90 gal of concentrated HCl. Dilute to 3.0 gal with more water.
(b) 22.6 mL **3.117** $x = 3$ **3.118** ethane > propane > cetyl palmitate > ethanol > benzene **3.123**(a) $Fe_2O_3(s) + 3CO(g) \longrightarrow 2Fe(s) + 3CO_2(g)$ (b) 3.39×10^7 g CO **3.125** 89.8%
3.127(a) $2AB_2 + B_2 \longrightarrow 2AB_3$ (b) AB_2 (c) 5.0 mol AB_3 (d) 0.5 mol B_2 **3.129** B, C, and D have the same empirical formula, C_2H_4O; 44.05 g/mol **3.130** 44.3% **3.133**(a) C (b) B (c) D **3.140**(a) 586 g CO_2 (b) 10.5% CH_4 by mass **3.142** 10/0.66/1.0 **3.147**(a) 192.12 g/mol; $C_6H_8O_7$ (b) 0.549 mol
3.148(a) $N_2(g) + O_2(g) \longrightarrow 2NO(g)$
$2NO(g) + O_2(g) \longrightarrow 2NO_2(g)$
$3NO_2(g) + H_2O(g) \longrightarrow 2HNO_3(aq) + NO(g)$
(b) $2N_2(g) + 5O_2(g) + 2H_2O(g) \longrightarrow 4HNO_3(aq)$
(c) 6.07×10^3 t HNO_3
3.149 A **3.151**(a) 0.039 g heme (b) 6.3×10^{-5} mol heme (c) 3.5×10^{-3} g Fe (d) 4.1×10^{-2} g hemin **3.153**(a) 46.65 mass % N in urea; 31.98 mass % N in arginine; 21.04 mass % N in ornithine (b) 28.45 g N **3.155** 29.54% **3.157**(a) 89.3% (b) 1.47 g ethylene **3.159**(a) 125 g salt (b) 65.6 L H_2O

Chapter 4

4.2 Ionic or polar covalent compounds **4.3** Ions must be present, and they come from ionic compounds or from electrolytes such as acids and bases. **4.6** B **4.10**(a) Benzene is likely to be insoluble in water because it is nonpolar and water is polar. (b) Sodium hydroxide, an ionic compound, is likely to be very soluble in water. (c) Ethanol (CH_3CH_2OH) is likely to be soluble in water because the alcohol group (—OH) is very polar, like the water molecule. (d) Potassium acetate, an ionic compound, is likely to be very soluble in water.
4.12(a) Yes, CsBr is a soluble salt. (b) Yes, HI is a strong acid.
4.14(a) 0.64 mol (b) 0.242 mol (c) 1.18×10^{-4} mol
4.16(a) 3.0 mol (b) 7.57×10^{-5} mol (c) 0.148 mol
4.18(a) 0.058 mol Al^{3+}; 3.5×10^{22} Al^{3+} ions; 0.18 mol Cl^-; 1.1×10^{23} Cl^- ions (b) 4.62×10^{-4} mol Li^+; 2.78×10^{20} Li^+ ions; 2.31×10^{-4} mol SO_4^{2-}; 1.39×10^{20} SO_4^{2-} ions (c) 1.50×10^{-2} mol K^+; 9.02×10^{21} K^+ ions; 1.50×10^{-2} mol Br^-; 9.02×10^{21} Br^- ions **4.20**(a) 0.35 mol H^+ (b) 6.3×10^{-3} mol H^+ (c) 0.22 mol H^+ **4.24** Spectator ions do not appear in a net ionic equation because they are not involved in the reaction and serve only to balance charges. **4.28** Assuming that the left beaker contains $AgNO_3$ (because it has gray Ag^+ ions), the right must contain NaCl. Then, NO_3^- is blue, Na^+ is brown, and Cl^- is green.
Molecular equation: $AgNO_3(aq) + NaCl(aq) \longrightarrow AgCl(s) + NaNO_3(aq)$
Total ionic equation: $Ag^+(aq) + NO_3^-(aq) + Na^+(aq) + Cl^-(aq) \longrightarrow AgCl(s) + Na^+(aq) + NO_3^-(aq)$
Net ionic equation: $Ag^+(aq) + Cl^-(aq) \longrightarrow AgCl(s)$
4.29(a) Molecular: $Hg_2(NO_3)_2(aq) + 2KI(aq) \longrightarrow Hg_2I_2(s) + 2KNO_3(aq)$

Total ionic: $Hg_2^{2+}(aq) + 2NO_3^-(aq) + 2K^+(aq) + 2I^-(aq) \longrightarrow Hg_2I_2(s) + 2K^+(aq) + 2NO_3^-(aq)$
Net ionic: $Hg_2^{2+}(aq) + 2I^-(aq) \longrightarrow Hg_2I_2(s)$
Spectator ions are K^+ and NO_3^-.
(b) Molecular: $FeSO_4(aq) + Sr(OH)_2(aq) \longrightarrow Fe(OH)_2(s) + SrSO_4(s)$
Total ionic: $Fe^{2+}(aq) + SO_4^{2-}(aq) + Sr^{2+}(aq) + 2OH^-(aq) \longrightarrow Fe(OH)_2(s) + SrSO_4(s)$
Net ionic: This is the same as the total ionic equation, because there are no spectator ions.

4.31(a) No precipitate will form. (b) A precipitate will form because silver ions, Ag^+, and bromide ions, Br^-, will combine to form a solid salt, silver bromide, AgBr. The ammonium and nitrate ions do not form a precipitate.
Molecular: $NH_4Br(aq) + AgNO_3(aq) \longrightarrow AgBr(s) + NH_4NO_3(aq)$
Total ionic: $NH_4^+(aq) + Br^-(aq) + Ag^+(aq) + NO_3^-(aq) \longrightarrow AgBr(s) + NH_4^+(aq) + NO_3^-(aq)$
Net ionic: $Ag^+(aq) + Br^-(aq) \longrightarrow AgBr(s)$

4.33(a) No precipitate will form.
(b) $BaSO_4$ will precipitate.
Molecular: $(NH_4)_2SO_4(aq) + BaCl_2(aq) \longrightarrow BaSO_4(s) + 2NH_4Cl(aq)$
Total ionic: $2NH_4^+(aq) + SO_4^{2-}(aq) + Ba^{2+}(aq) + 2Cl^-(aq) \longrightarrow BaSO_4(s) + 2NH_4^+(aq) + 2Cl^-(aq)$
Net ionic: $SO_4^{2-}(aq) + Ba^{2+}(aq) \longrightarrow BaSO_4(s)$

4.35 0.0354 M Pb^{2+} **4.37**(a) $PbSO_4$ (b) $Pb^{2+}(aq) + SO_4^{2-}(aq) \longrightarrow PbSO_4(s)$ (c) 1.5 g $PbSO_4$ **4.39** Potassium carbonate, K_2CO_3 **4.41** 2.206 mass % Cl^- **4.47**(a) Formation of a gas, $SO_2(g)$, and of a nonelectrolyte (water) will cause the reaction to go to completion. (b) Formation of a precipitate $Ba_3(PO_4)_2(s)$, and of a nonelectrolyte (water) will cause the reaction to go to completion.

4.49(a) Molecular equation: $KOH(aq) + HBr(aq) \longrightarrow KBr(aq) + H_2O(l)$
Total ionic equation: $K^+(aq) + OH^-(aq) + H^+(aq) + Br^-(aq) \longrightarrow K^+(aq) + Br^-(aq) + H_2O(l)$
Net ionic equation: $OH^-(aq) + H^+(aq) \longrightarrow H_2O(l)$
The spectator ions are $K^+(aq)$ and $Br^-(aq)$.
(b) Molecular equation: $NH_3(aq) + HCl(aq) \longrightarrow NH_4Cl(aq)$
Total ionic equation: $NH_3(aq) + H^+(aq) + Cl^-(aq) \longrightarrow NH_4^+(aq) + Cl^-(aq)$
NH_3, a weak base, is written in the molecular (undissociated) form. HCl, a strong acid, is written as dissociated ions. NH_4Cl is a soluble compound because all ammonium compounds are soluble.
Net ionic equation: $NH_3(aq) + H^+(aq) \longrightarrow NH_4^+(aq)$
Cl^- is the only spectator ion.

4.51 Total ionic equation: $CaCO_3(s) + 2H^+(aq) + 2Cl^-(aq) \longrightarrow Ca^{2+}(aq) + 2Cl^-(aq) + H_2O(l) + CO_2(g)$
Net ionic equation: $CaCO_3(s) + 2H^+(aq) \longrightarrow Ca^{2+}(aq) + H_2O(l) + CO_2(g)$

4.53 0.05839 M CH_3COOH **4.64**(a) S has O.N. = +6 in SO_4^{2-} (i.e., H_2SO_4) and O.N. = +4 in SO_2, so S has been reduced (and I^- oxidized); H_2SO_4 acts as an oxidizing agent. (b) The oxidation numbers remain constant throughout; H_2SO_4 transfers an H^+ to F^- to produce HF, so it acts as an acid. **4.66**(a) +4 (b) +3 (c) +4 (d) −3 **4.68**(a) −1 (b) +2 (c) −3 (d) +3 **4.70**(a) −3 (b) +5 (c) +3 **4.72**(a) +6 (b) +3 (c) +7 **4.74**(a) MnO_4^- is the oxidizing agent; $H_2C_2O_4$ is the reducing agent. (b) Cu is the reducing agent; NO_3^- is the oxidizing agent. **4.76**(a) Oxidizing agent is NO_3^-; reducing agent is Sn. (b) Oxidizing agent is MnO_4^-; reducing agent is Cl^-.

4.78(a) $8HNO_3(aq) + K_2CrO_4(aq) + 3Fe(NO_3)_2(aq) \longrightarrow 2KNO_3(aq) + 3Fe(NO_3)_3(aq) + Cr(NO_3)_3(aq) + 4H_2O(l)$
Oxidizing agent is K_2CrO_4; reducing agent is $Fe(NO_3)_2$.
(b) $8HNO_3(aq) + 3C_2H_6O(l) + K_2Cr_2O_7(aq) \longrightarrow 2KNO_3(aq) + 3C_2H_4O(l) + 7H_2O(l) + 2Cr(NO_3)_3(aq)$
Oxidizing agent is $K_2Cr_2O_7$; reducing agent is C_2H_6O.
(c) $6HCl(aq) + 2NH_4Cl(aq) + K_2Cr_2O_7(aq) \longrightarrow 2KCl(aq) + 2CrCl_3(aq) + N_2(g) + 7H_2O(l)$
Oxidizing agent is $K_2Cr_2O_7$; reducing agent is NH_4Cl.
(d) $KClO_3(aq) + 6HBr(aq) \longrightarrow 3Br_2(l) + 3H_2O(l) + KCl(aq)$
Oxidizing agent is $KClO_3$; reducing agent is HBr.

4.80(a) 4.54×10^{-3} mol MnO_4^- (b) 0.0113 mol H_2O_2 (c) 0.386 g H_2O_2 (d) 2.61 mass % H_2O_2 (e) H_2O_2
4.86 A combination reaction that is also a redox reaction is $2Mg(s) + O_2(g) \longrightarrow 2MgO(s)$. A combination reaction that is not a redox reaction is $CaO(s) + H_2O(l) \longrightarrow Ca(OH)_2(aq)$.
4.87(a) $Ca(s) + 2H_2O(l) \longrightarrow Ca(OH)_2(aq) + H_2(g)$; displacement
(b) $2NaNO_3(s) \longrightarrow 2NaNO_2(s) + O_2(g)$; decomposition
(c) $C_2H_2(g) + 2H_2(g) \longrightarrow C_2H_6(g)$; combination
4.89(a) $2Sb(s) + 3Cl_2(g) \longrightarrow 2SbCl_3(s)$; combination
(b) $2AsH_3(g) \longrightarrow 2As(s) + 3H_2(g)$; decomposition
(c) $Zn(s) + Fe(NO_3)_2(aq) \longrightarrow Zn(NO_3)_2(aq) + Fe(s)$; displacement
4.91(a) $Sr(s) + Br_2(l) \longrightarrow SrBr_2(s)$
(b) $2Ag_2O(s) \xrightarrow{\Delta} 4Ag(s) + O_2(g)$
(c) $Mn(s) + Cu(NO_3)_2(aq) \longrightarrow Mn(NO_3)_2(aq) + Cu(s)$
4.93(a) $N_2(g) + 3H_2(g) \longrightarrow 2NH_3(g)$
(b) $2NaClO_3(s) \xrightarrow{\Delta} 2NaCl(s) + 3O_2(g)$
(c) $Ba(s) + 2H_2O(l) \longrightarrow Ba(OH)_2(aq) + H_2(g)$
4.95(a) $2Cs(s) + I_2(s) \longrightarrow 2CsI(s)$
(b) $2Al(s) + 3MnSO_4(aq) \longrightarrow Al_2(SO_4)_3(aq) + 3Mn(s)$
(c) $2SO_2(g) + O_2(g) \longrightarrow 2SO_3(g)$
(d) $2C_4H_{10}(g) + 13O_2(g) \longrightarrow 8CO_2(g) + 10H_2O(g)$
(e) $2Al(s) + 3Mn^{2+}(aq) \longrightarrow 2Al^{3+}(aq) + 3Mn(s)$
4.97 315 g O_2; 3.95 kg Hg **4.99**(a) O_2 is in excess. (b) 0.117 mol Li_2O (c) 0 g Li, 3.49 g Li_2O, and 4.63 g O_2 **4.101** 67.2 mass % $KClO_3$ **4.103** 2.79 kg Fe **4.104** 99.9 g compound B, which is $FeCl_2$ **4.108** The reaction is $2NO + Br_2 \rightleftharpoons 2NOBr$, which can proceed in either direction. If NO and Br_2 are placed in a container, they will react to form NOBr, and NOBr will decompose to form NO and Br_2. Eventually, the concentrations of NO, Br_2, and NOBr

adjust so that the rates of the forward and reverse reactions become equal, and equilibrium is reached.
4.110(a) $Fe(s) + 2H^+(aq) \longrightarrow Fe^{2+}(aq) + H_2(g)$
O.N.: 0 +1 +2 0
(b) 3.1×10^{21} Fe^{2+} ions
4.112 5.11 g C_2H_5OH; 24.9 L CO_2
4.114(a) $Ca^{2+}(aq) + C_2O_4^{2-}(aq) \longrightarrow CaC_2O_4(s)$
(b) $5H_2C_2O_4(aq) + 2MnO_4^-(aq) + 6H^+(aq) \longrightarrow 10CO_2(g) + 2Mn^{2+}(aq) + 8H_2O(l)$
(c) $KMnO_4$ (d) $H_2C_2O_4$ (e) 55.06 mass % $CaCl_2$
4.117 2.809 mass % $CaMg(CO_3)_2$ **4.119**(a) Step 1: oxidizing agent is O_2; reducing agent is NH_3. Step 2: oxidizing agent is O_2; reducing agent is NO. Step 3: oxidizing agent is NO_2; reducing agent is NO_2. (b) 1.2×10^4 kg NH_3 **4.123** 627 L air **4.125** 0.75 kg SiO_2; 0.26 kg Na_2CO_3; 0.18 kg $CaCO_3$ **4.128**(a) 4 mol IO_3^- (b) 12 mol I_2; IO_3^- is oxidizing agent and I^- is reducing agent. (c) 12.87 mass % thyroxine **4.131** 3.0×10^{-3} mol CO_2 (b) 0.11 L CO_2 **4.133**(a) $C_7H_5O_4Bi$ (b) $C_{21}H_{15}O_{12}Bi_3$ (c) $Bi(OH)_3(s) + 3HC_7H_5O_3(aq) \longrightarrow Bi(C_7H_5O_3)_3(s) + 3H_2O(l)$ (d) 0.490 mg $Bi(OH)_3$
4.135(a) Ethanol: $C_2H_5OH(l) + 3O_2(g) \longrightarrow 2CO_2(g) + 3H_2O(l)$
Gasoline: $2C_8H_{18}(l) + 25O_2(g) \longrightarrow 16CO_2(g) + 18H_2O(g)$
(b) 2.50×10^3 g O_2 (c) 1.75×10^3 L O_2 (d) 8.38×10^3 L air
4.137 yes

Chapter 5

Answers to Boxed Reading Problems: B5.1 The density of the atmosphere decreases with increasing altitude. High density causes more drag on the aircraft. At high altitudes, low density means that there are relatively few gas particles present to collide with the aircraft. **B5.3** 0.934 %, 7.10 torr

• **5.1**(a) The volume of the liquid remains constant, but the volume of the gas increases to the volume of the larger container. (b) The volume of the container holding the gas sample increases when heated, but the volume of the container holding the liquid sample remains essentially constant when heated. (c) The volume of the liquid remains essentially constant, but the volume of the gas is reduced. **5.6** 990 cmH_2O **5.8**(a) 566 mmHg (b) 1.32 bar (c) 3.60 atm (d) 107 kPa **5.10** 0.9408 atm **5.12** 0.966 atm **5.18** At constant temperature and volume, the pressure of a gas is directly proportional to number of moles of the gas. **5.20**(a) Volume decreases to one-third of the original volume. (b) Volume increases by a factor of 3.0. (c) Volume increases by a factor of 4. **5.22**(a) Volume decreases by a factor of 2. (b) Volume increases by a factor of 1.48. (c) Volume decreases by a factor of 3. **5.24** −144°C **5.26** 35.3 L **5.28** 0.085 mol Cl_2 **5.30** 1.16 g ClF_3 **5.33** yes **5.35** Beaker is inverted for H_2 and upright for CO_2. The molar mass of CO_2 is greater than the molar mass of air, which, in turn, has a greater molar mass than H_2. **5.39** 5.86 g/L **5.41** 1.78×10^{-3} mol AsH_3; 3.48 g/L **5.43** 51.1 g/mol **5.45** 1.33 atm **5.47** 39.2 g P_4 **5.49** 41.2 g PH_3 **5.51** 0.0249 g Al **5.55** C_5H_{12} **5.57**(a) 0.90 mol (b) 6.76 torr **5.58** 286 mL SO_2 **5.60** 0.0997 atm SiF_4 **5.65** At STP, the volume occupied by a mole of any gas is the same. At the same temperature, all gases have the same average kinetic energy, resulting in the same pressure. **5.68**(a) $P_A > P_B > P_C$ (b) $E_A = E_B = E_C$ (c) $rate_A > rate_B > rate_C$ (d) total $E_A >$ total $E_B >$ total E_C (e) $d_A = d_B = d_C$ (f) collision frequency in A > collision frequency in B > collision frequency in C **5.69** 13.21 **5.71**(a) curve 1 (b) curve 1 (c) curve 1; fluorine and argon have about the same molar mass **5.73** 14.9 min **5.75** 4 atoms per molecule **5.78** negative deviations; $N_2 < Kr < CO_2$ **5.80** At 1 atm; at lower pressures, the gas molecules are farther apart and intermolecular forces are less important. **5.83** 6.81×10^4 g/mol **5.86**(a) 22.1 atm (b) 20.9 atm **5.90**(a) 597 torr N_2; 159 torr O_2; 0.3 torr CO_2; 3.5 torr H_2O (b) 74.9 mol % N_2; 13.7 mol % O_2; 5.3 mol % CO_2; 6.2 mol % H_2O (c) 1.6×10^{21} molecules O_2 **5.92**(a) 4×10^2 mL (b) 0.013 mol N_2 **5.93** 35.7 L NO_2 **5.98** Al_2Cl_6 **5.100** 1.52×10^{-2} mol SO_3 **5.104**(a) 1.95×10^3 g Ni (b) 3.5×10^4 g Ni (c) 63 m^3 CO **5.106**(a) 9 volumes of $O_2(g)$ (b) CH_5N **5.109** The lungs would expand by a factor of 4.86; the diver can safely ascend 52.5 ft to a depth of 73 ft. **5.111** 6.07 g H_2O_2 **5.116** 6.53×10^{-3} g N_2 **5.120**(a) xenon (b) water vapor (c) mercury vapor (d) water vapor **5.124** 17.2 g CO_2; 17.8 g Kr **5.130** Ne, 676 m/s; Ar, 481 m/s; He, 1.52×10^3 m/s **5.132**(a) 0.052 g (b) 1.1 mL **5.139**(a) 16.5 L CO_2 (b) $P_{H_2O} = 48.8$ torr; $P_{O_2} = P_{CO_2} = 3.7\times10^2$ torr **5.144** 332 steps **5.146** 1.4 **5.150** $P_{total} = 245$ torr; $P_{I_2} = 25.2$ torr

Chapter 6

Answers to Boxed Reading Problem: B6.2 (a) $2C(coal) + 2H_2O(g) \longrightarrow CH_4(g) + CO_2(g)$ (b) 12 kJ (c) -3.30×10^4 kJ

• **6.4** Increase: eating food, lying in the sun, taking a hot bath. Decrease: exercising, taking a cold bath, going outside on a cold day. **6.6** The amount of the change in internal energy is the same for heater and air conditioner. Since both devices consume the same amount of electrical energy, the change in energy of the heater equals that of the air conditioner. **6.8** 0 J **6.10** 1.54×10^3 J **6.12**(a) 6.6×10^7 kJ (b) 1.6×10^7 kcal (c) 6.3×10^7 Btu **6.15** 8.8 h **6.17** Measuring the heat transfer at constant pressure is more convenient than measuring at constant volume. **6.19**(a) exothermic (b) endothermic (c) exothermic (d) exothermic (e) endothermic (f) endothermic (g) exothermic
6.22

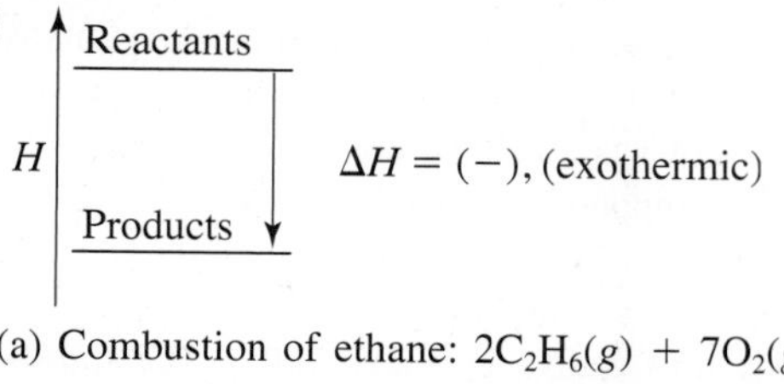

6.24(a) Combustion of ethane: $2C_2H_6(g) + 7O_2(g) \longrightarrow 4CO_2(g) + 6H_2O(g) + \text{heat}$

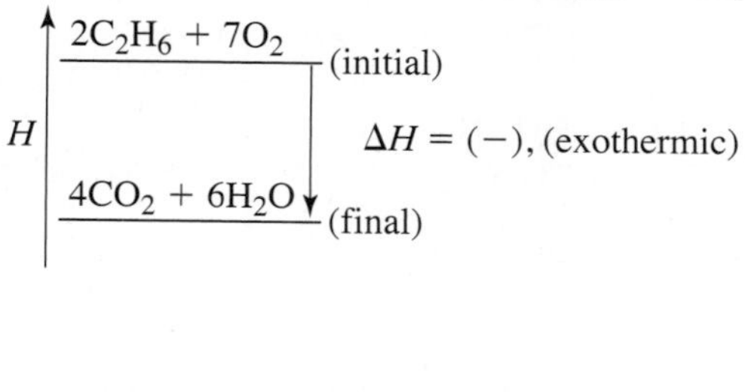

(b) Freezing of water: $H_2O(l) \longrightarrow H_2O(s)$ + heat

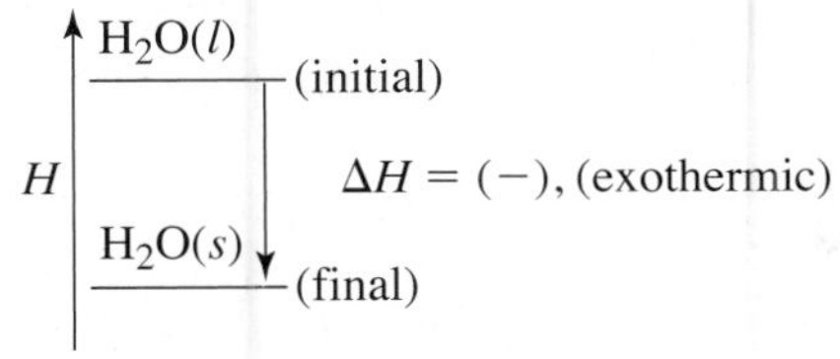

6.26(a) $2CH_3OH(l) + 3O_2(g) \longrightarrow 2CO_2(g) + 4H_2O(g)$ + heat

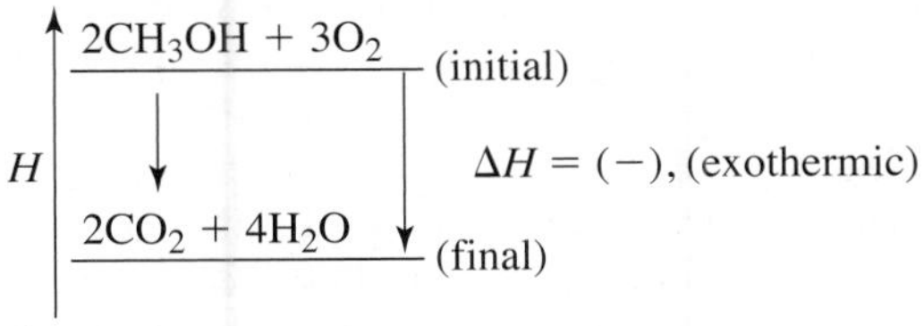

(b) $\frac{1}{2}N_2(g) + O_2(g)$ + heat $\longrightarrow NO_2(g)$

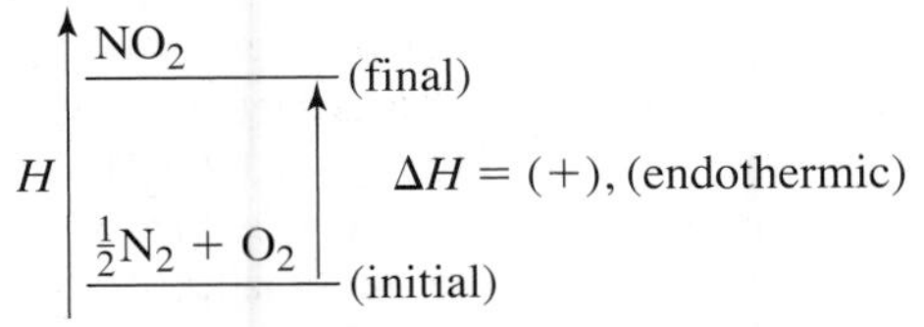

6.28(a) This is a phase change from the solid phase to the gas phase. Heat is absorbed by the system so q_{sys} is positive (+). (b) The volume of the system is expanding as more moles of gas are present after the phase change than were present before the phase change. So the system has done work of expansion, and w is negative. Since $\Delta E_{sys} = q + w$, q is positive, and w is negative, the sign of ΔE_{sys} cannot be predicted. It will be positive if $q > w$ and negative if $q < w$. (c) $\Delta E_{univ} = 0$. If the system loses energy, the surroundings gain an equal amount of energy. The sum of the energy of the system and the energy of the surroundings remains constant. **6.31** To determine the specific heat capacity of a substance, you need its mass, the heat added (or lost), and the change in temperature. **6.33** Heat capacity is the quantity of heat required to raise the temperature of an object 1 K. Specific heat capacity is the quantity of heat required to raise 1 g of a material by 1 K. Molar heat capacity is the quantity of heat required to raise the temperature of 1 mol of a substance by 1 K. **6.35** 6.9×10^3 J **6.37** 295°C **6.39** 77.5°C **6.41** 45°C **6.43** 36.6°C **6.50** The reaction has a positive ΔH, because it requires the input of energy to break the oxygen-oxygen bond. **6.51** ΔH is negative; it is opposite in sign and half of the value for the vaporization of 2 mol of H_2O. **6.52**(a) exothermic (b) 20.2 kJ (c) -4.2×10^2 kJ (d) -15.7 kJ

6.54(a) $\frac{1}{2}N_2(g) + \frac{1}{2}O_2(g) \longrightarrow NO(g)$; $\Delta H = 90.29$ kJ
(b) -10.5 kJ

6.56 -1.88×10^6 kJ

6.60(a) $C_2H_4(g) + 3O_2(g) \longrightarrow 2CO_2(g) + 2H_2O(l)$;
$\Delta H_{rxn} = -1411$ kJ
(b) 1.39 g C_2H_4

6.64 -110.5 kJ **6.65** -813.4 kJ **6.67** $N_2(g) + 2O_2(g) \longrightarrow 2NO_2(g)$; $\Delta H_{overall} = 66.4$ kJ; equation 1 is A, equation 2 is B, and equation 3 is C. **6.69** 44.0 kJ **6.72** The standard enthalpy of reaction, ΔH°_{rxn}, is the enthalpy change for a reaction where all substances are in their standard states. The standard enthalpy of formation, ΔH°_f, is the enthalpy change that accompanies the formation of one mole of a compound in its standard state from elements in their standard states.

6.74(a) $\frac{1}{2}Cl_2(g) + Na(s) \longrightarrow NaCl(s)$
(b) $H_2(g) + \frac{1}{2}O_2(g) \longrightarrow H_2O(g)$
(c) no changes

6.75(a) $Ca(s) + Cl_2(g) \longrightarrow CaCl_2(s)$
(b) $Na(s) + \frac{1}{2}H_2(g) + C(\text{graphite}) + \frac{3}{2}O_2(g) \longrightarrow NaHCO_3(s)$
(c) $C(\text{graphite}) + 2Cl_2(g) \longrightarrow CCl_4(l)$
(d) $\frac{1}{2}H_2(g) + \frac{1}{2}N_2(g) + \frac{3}{2}O_2(g) \longrightarrow HNO_3(l)$

6.77(a) -1036.9 kJ (b) -433 kJ **6.79** -157.3 kJ/mol **6.81**(a) 503.9 kJ (b) $-\Delta H_1 + 2\Delta H_2 = 504$ kJ **6.82**(a) $C_{18}H_{36}O_2(s) + 26O_2(g) \longrightarrow 18CO_2(g) + 18H_2O(g)$ (b) $-10{,}488$ kJ (c) -36.9 kJ; -8.81 kcal (d) 8.81 kcal/g $\times$ 11.0 g = 96.9 kcal **6.84**(a) initial = 23.6 L/mol; final = 24.9 L/mol (b) 187 J (c) -1.2×10^2 J (d) 3.1×10^2 J (e) 310 J (f) $\Delta H = \Delta E + P\Delta V = \Delta E - w = (q + w) - w = q_P$ **6.93**(a) 1.1×10^3 J (b) 1.1×10^8 J (c) 1.3×10^2 mol CH_4 (d) \$0.0050/mol (e) \$0.85 **6.98**(a) $\Delta H^\circ_{rxn1} = -657.0$ kJ; $\Delta H^\circ_{rxn2} = 32.9$ kJ (b) -106.6 kJ **6.99**(a) -6.81×10^3 J (b) +243°C **6.100** -22.2 kJ **6.101**(a) 34 kJ/mol (b) -757 kJ **6.103**(a) -1.25×10^3 kJ (b) 2.24×10^3°C

Chapter 7

Answers to Boxed Reading Problem: B7.1 (a) slope = $1.3\times10^4/M$; y-intercept = 0.00

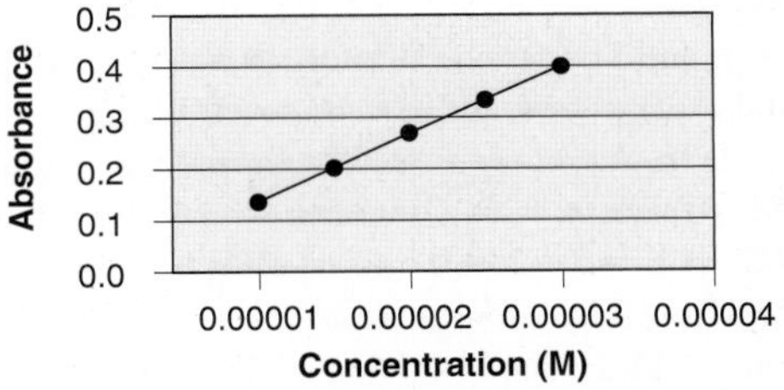

(b) diluted solution = 1.8×10^{-5} M; original solution = 1.4×10^{-4} M

7.2(a) x-ray < ultraviolet < visible < infrared < microwave < radio waves (b) radio < microwave < infrared < visible < ultraviolet < x-ray
(c) radio < microwave < infrared < visible < ultraviolet < x-ray **7.7** 316 m; 3.16×10^{11} nm; 3.16×10^{12} Å **7.9** 2.5×10^{-23} J **7.11** red < yellow < blue **7.13** 1.3483×10^7 nm; 1.3483×10^8 Å **7.16**(a) 1.24×10^{15} s^{-1}; 8.21×10^{-19} J (b) 1.4×10^{15} s^{-1}; 9.0×10^{-19} J **7.18** Bohr's key assumption was that the electron in an atom does not radiate energy while in a stationary state, and it can move to a different orbit only by absorbing or emitting a photon whose energy is equal to the difference in energy between two states. These differences in energy correspond to the wavelengths in the known line spectra for the hydrogen atom. A solar system model does not allow for the movement of electrons between levels. **7.20**(a) absorption (b) emission (c) emission (d) absorption **7.22** Yes, the predicted line spectra are accurate. The energies could be predicted from

$E_n = \dfrac{-(Z^2)(2.18\times10^{-18}\text{ J})}{n^2}$, where Z is the atomic number for

the atom or ion. The energy levels for Be^{3+} will be greater by a factor of 16 ($Z = 4$) than those for the hydrogen atom. This means that the pattern of lines will be similar, but the lines will be at different wavelengths. **7.23** 434.17 nm **7.25** 1875.6 nm **7.27** -2.76×10^5 J/mol **7.29** d < a < c < b **7.31** $n = 4$
7.37 Macroscopic objects do exhibit a wavelike motion, but the wavelength is too small for humans to perceive.
7.39(a) 7.10×10^{-37} m (b) 1×10^{-35} m **7.41** 2.2×10^{-26} m/s **7.43** 3.75×10^{-36} kg **7.47** The total probability of finding the 1*s* electron in any distance *r* from the H nucleus is greatest when the value of *r* is 0.529 Å. The probability is greater for the 1*s* orbital. **7.48**(a) principal determinant of the electron's energy or distance from the nucleus (b) determines the shape of the orbital (c) determines the orientation of the orbital in three-dimensional space **7.49**(a) one (b) five (c) three (d) nine **7.51**(a) m_l: $-2, -1, 0, +1, +2$ (b) m_l: 0 (if $n = 1$, then $l = 0$) (c) m_l: $-3, -2, -1, 0, +1, +2, +3$
7.53(a)

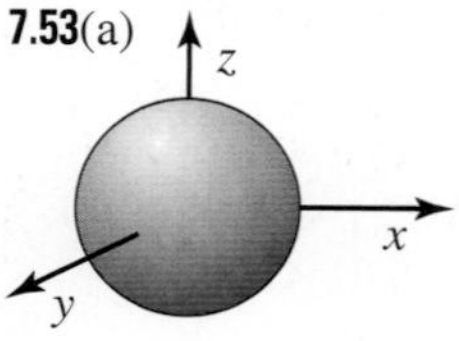

(b)

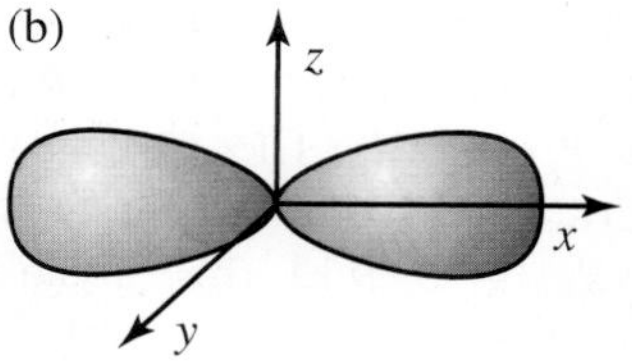

7.55

Sublevel	Allowable m_l values	No. of orbitals
(a) *d* ($l = 2$)	$-2, -1, 0, +1, +2$	5
(b) *p* ($l = 1$)	$-1, 0, +1$	3
(c) *f* ($l = 3$)	$-3, -2, -1, 0, +1, +2, +3$	7

7.57(a) $n = 5$ and $l = 0$; one orbital (b) $n = 3$ and $l = 1$; three orbitals (c) $n = 4$ and $l = 3$; seven orbitals **7.59**(a) no; $n = 2, l = 1, m_l = -1$; $n = 2, l = 0, m_l = 0$ (b) allowed (c) allowed (d) no; $n = 5, l = 3, m_l = +3$; $n = 5, l = 2, m_l = 0$ **7.62**(a) $E = -(2.180\times10^{-18}\text{ J})(1/n^2)$. This is identical to the expression from Bohr's theory. (b) 3.028×10^{-19} J (c) 656.1 nm **7.63**(a) The attraction of the nucleus for the electrons must be overcome. (b) The electrons in silver are more tightly held by the nucleus. (c) silver (d) Once the electron is freed from the atom, its energy increases in proportion to the frequency of the light. **7.66** Li^{2+} **7.68**(a) $2 \longrightarrow 1$ (b) $5 \longrightarrow 2$ (c) $4 \longrightarrow 2$ (d) $3 \longrightarrow 2$ (e) $6 \longrightarrow 3$
7.72(a) $l = 1$ or 2 (b) $l = 1$ or 2 (c) $l = 3, 4, 5,$ or 6 (d) $l = 2$ or 3
7.74(a) $\Delta E =$

$$(-2.18\times10^{-18}\text{ J})\left(\frac{1}{\infty^2} - \frac{1}{n^2_{\text{initial}}}\right)Z^2\left(\frac{6.022\times10^{23}}{1\text{ mol}}\right)$$

(b) 3.28×10^7 J/mol (c) 205 nm (d) 22.8 nm
7.76(a) 5.293×10^{-11} m (b) 5.293×10^{-9} m **7.78** 6.4×10^{27} photons **7.80**(a) no overlap (b) overlap (c) two (d) At longer wavelengths, the hydrogen spectrum begins to become a continuous band. **7.82**(a) 7.56×10^{-18} J; 2.63×10^{-8} m (b) 5.122×10^{-17} J; 3.881×10^{-9} m (c) 1.2×10^{-18} J; 1.66×10^{-7} m **7.84**(a) 1.87×10^{-19} J (b) 3.58×10^{-19} J
7.86(a) red; green (b) 5.89 kJ (Sr); 5.83 kJ (Ba) **7.88**(a) This is the wavelength of maximum absorbance, so it gives the highest sensitivity. (b) ultraviolet region (c) 1.93×10^{-2} g vitamin A/g oil **7.92** 1.0×10^{18} photons/s **7.95** $3s \longrightarrow 2p$; $3d \longrightarrow 2p$; $4s \longrightarrow 2p$; $3p \longrightarrow 2s$

Chapter 8

8.1 Elements are listed in the periodic table in an ordered, systematic way that correlates with a periodicity of their chemical and physical properties. The theoretical basis for the table in terms of atomic number and electron configuration does not allow for a "new element" between Sn and Sb. **8.3**(a) predicted atomic mass = 54.23 amu (b) predicted melting point = 6.3°C
8.6 The quantum number m_s relates to just the electron; all the others describe the orbital. **8.9** Shielding occurs when electrons protect, or shield, other electrons from the full nuclear attraction. The effective nuclear charge is the nuclear charge an electron actually experiences. As the number of electrons, especially inner electrons, increases, the effective nuclear charge decreases.
8.11(a) 6 (b) 10 (c) 2 **8.13**(a) 6 (b) 2 (c) 14 **8.16** Hund's rule states that electrons will occupy empty orbitals in a given sublevel (with parallel spins) before filling half-filled orbitals. The lowest energy arrangement has the maximum number of unpaired electrons with parallel spins.

N: $1s^22s^22p^3$ [↑↓] [↑↓] [↑ | ↑ | ↑]
1s 2s 2p

8.18 Main-group elements from the same group have similar outer electron configurations, and the (old) group number equals the number of outer electrons. Outer electron configurations vary in a periodic manner within a period, with each succeeding element having an additional electron. **8.20** The maximum number of electrons in any energy level *n* is $2n^2$, so the $n = 4$ energy level holds a maximum of $2(4^2) = 32$ electrons. **8.21**(a) $n = 5$, $l = 0$, $m_l = 0$, and $m_s = +\frac{1}{2}$ (b) $n = 3$, $l = 1$, $m_l = +1$, and $m_s = -\frac{1}{2}$ (c) $n = 5$, $l = 0$, $m_l = 0$, and $m_s = +\frac{1}{2}$ (d) $n = 2$, $l = 1$, $m_l = +1$, and $m_s = -\frac{1}{2}$
8.23(a) Rb: $1s^22s^22p^63s^23p^64s^23d^{10}4p^65s^1$
(b) Ge: $1s^22s^22p^63s^23p^64s^23d^{10}4p^2$
(c) Ar: $1s^22s^22p^63s^23p^6$
8.25(a) Cl: $1s^22s^22p^63s^23p^5$ (b) Si: $1s^22s^22p^63s^23p^2$
(c) Sr: $1s^22s^22p^63s^23p^64s^23d^{10}4p^65s^2$
8.27(a) Ti: [Ar] $4s^23d^2$

[↑↓] [↑ | ↑ | | |] [| |]
4s 3d 4p

(b) Cl: [Ne] $3s^23p^5$

[↑↓] [↑↓ | ↑↓ | ↑]
3s 3p

(c) V: [Ar] $4s^23d^3$

[↑↓] [↑ | ↑ | ↑ | |] [| |]
4s 3d 4p

8.29(a) Mn: [Ar] $4s^23d^5$

4s	3d	4p
↑↓	↑ ↑ ↑ ↑ ↑	☐ ☐ ☐

(b) P: [Ne] $3s^23p^3$

3s	3p
↑↓	↑ ↑ ↑

(c) Fe: [Ar] $4s^23d^6$

4s	3d	4p
↑↓	↑↓ ↑ ↑ ↑ ↑	☐ ☐ ☐

8.31(a) O; Group 6A(16); Period 2

2s	2p
↑↓	↑↓ ↑ ↑

(b) P; Group 5A(15); Period 3

3s	3p
↑↓	↑ ↑ ↑

8.33(a) Cl; Group 7A(17); Period 3

3s	3p
↑↓	↑↓ ↑↓ ↑

(b) As; Group 5A(15); Period 4

4s	4p
↑↓	↑ ↑ ↑

8.35(a) [Ar] $4s^23d^{10}4p^1$; Group 3A(13) (b) [He] $2s^22p^6$; Group 8A(18)

8.37

	Inner Electrons	Outer Electrons	Valence Electrons
(a) O	2	6	6
(b) Sn	46	4	4
(c) Ca	18	2	2
(d) Fe	18	2	8
(e) Se	28	6	6

8.39(a) B; Al, Ga, In, and Tl (b) S; O, Se, Te, and Po (c) La; Sc, Y, and Ac **8.41**(a) C; Si, Ge, Sn, and Pb (b) V; Nb, Ta, and Db (c) P; N, As, Sb, and Bi

8.43 Na (first excited state): $1s^22s^22p^63p^1$

1s	2s	2p	3s	3p
↑↓	↑↓	↑↓ ↑↓ ↑↓	☐	↑ ☐ ☐

8.50 A high IE_1 and a very negative EA_1 suggest that the elements are halogens, in Group 7A(17), which form 1− ions. **8.53**(a) K < Rb < Cs (b) O < C < Be (c) Cl < S < K (d) Mg < Ca < K **8.55**(a) Ba < Sr < Ca (b) B < N < Ne (c) Rb < Se < Br (d) Sn < Sb < As **8.57** $1s^22s^22p^1$ (boron, B) **8.59**(a) Na (b) Na (c) Be **8.61**(1) Metals conduct electricity; nonmetals do not. (2) Metal ions have a positive charge; nonmetal ions have a negative charge. (3) Metal oxides are mostly ionic and act as bases; nonmetal oxides are mostly covalent and act as acids. **8.62** Metallic character increases down a group and decreases to the right across a period. These trends are the same as those for atomic size and opposite those for ionization energy. **8.65** Possible ions are 2+ and 4+. The 2+ ions form by loss of the outermost two *p* electrons; the 4+ ions form by loss of these and the outermost two *s* electrons. **8.69**(a) Rb (b) Ra (c) I **8.71**(a) As (b) P (c) Be **8.73** acidic solution; $SO_2(g) + H_2O(l) \longrightarrow H_2SO_3(aq)$

8.75(a) Cl^-: $1s^22s^22p^63s^23p^6$ (b) Na^+: $1s^22s^22p^6$ (c) Ca^{2+}: $1s^22s^22p^63s^23p^6$ **8.77**(a) Al^{3+}: $1s^22s^22p^6$ (b) S^{2-}: $1s^22s^22p^63s^23p^6$ (c) Sr^{2+}: $1s^22s^22p^63s^23p^64s^2\ 3d^{10}4p^6$ **8.79**(a) 0 (b) 3 (c) 0 (d) 1 **8.81** a, b, and d **8.83**(a) V^{3+}: [Ar] $3d^2$, paramagnetic (b) Cd^{2+}: [Kr] $4d^{10}$, diamagnetic (c) Co^{3+}: [Ar] $3d^6$, paramagnetic (d) Ag^+: [Kr] $4d^{10}$, diamagnetic **8.85** For palladium to be diamagnetic, all of its electrons must be paired. (a) You might first write the condensed electron configuration for Pd as [Kr] $5s^24d^8$. However, the partial orbital diagram is not consistent with diamagnetism.

5s	4d	5p
↑↓	↑↓ ↑↓ ↑↓ ↑ ↑	☐ ☐ ☐

(b) This is the only configuration that supports diamagnetism, [Kr] $4d^{10}$.

5s	4d	5p
☐	↑↓ ↑↓ ↑↓ ↑↓ ↑↓	☐ ☐ ☐

(c) Promoting an *s* electron into the *d* sublevel still leaves two electrons unpaired.

5s	4d	5p
↑	↑↓ ↑↓ ↑↓ ↑↓ ↑	☐ ☐ ☐

8.87(a) $Li^+ < Na^+ < K^+$ (b) $Rb^+ < Br^- < Se^{2-}$ (c) $F^- < O^{2-} < N^{3-}$ **8.90** Ce: [Xe] $6s^24f^15d^1$; Ce^{4+}: [Xe]; Eu: [Xe] $6s^24f^7$; Eu^{2+}: [Xe] $4f^7$. Ce^{4+} has a noble-gas configuration; Eu^{2+} has a half-filled *f* subshell. **8.91**(a) Cl_2O, dichlorine monoxide (b) Cl_2O_3, dichlorine trioxide (c) Cl_2O_5, dichlorine pentaoxide (d) Cl_2O_7, dichlorine heptaoxide (e) SO_3, sulfur trioxide (f) SO_2, sulfur dioxide (g) N_2O_5, dinitrogen pentaoxide (h) N_2O_3, dinitrogen trioxide (i) CO_2, carbon dioxide (j) P_4O_{10}, tetraphosphorus decaoxide **8.94**(a) $SrBr_2$, strontium bromide (b) CaS, calcium sulfide (c) ZnF_2, zinc fluoride (d) LiF, lithium fluoride **8.95**(a) 2009 kJ/mol (b) −549 kJ/mol **8.97** All ions except Fe^{8+} and Fe^{14+} are paramagnetic; Fe^+ and Fe^{3+} would be most attracted.

Chapter 9

Answers to Boxed Reading Problems: B9.1 The C=C bond shows absorption of IR at shorter wavelength (higher energy) because it is a stronger bond than C—C. The C≡C bond would show absorption at a shorter wavelength (higher energy) than the C=C bond since the triple bond has a larger bond energy than the double bond. **B9.2** (a) 7460 nm (symmetric stretch), 1.50×10^4 nm (bending), 4260 nm (asymmetrical stretch) (b) 2.66×10^{-20} J (symmetric stretch), 1.33×10^{-20} J (bending), 4.67×10^{-20} J (asymmetrical stretch); bending requires the least amount of energy.

• **9.1**(a) Greater ionization energy decreases metallic character. (b) Larger atomic radius increases metallic character. (c) Higher number of outer electrons decreases metallic character. (d) Larger effective nuclear charge decreases metallic character. **9.4**(a) Cs (b) Rb (c) As **9.6**(a) ionic (b) covalent (c) metallic **9.8**(a) covalent (b) ionic (c) covalent **9.10**(a) Rb· (b) ·Ṡi· (c) :Ï· **9.12**(a) ·Sr· (b) :Ṗ· (c) :Ṡ· **9.14**(a) 6A(16); [noble gas] ns^2np^4 (b) 3(A)13; [noble gas] ns^2np^1 **9.20**(a) Ba^{2+}, [Xe]; Cl^-, [Ne] $3s^23p^6$, $:\ddot{\underset{..}{Cl}}:^-$; $BaCl_2$

(b) Sr^{2+}, [Kr]; O^{2-}, [He] $2s^22p^6$, $:\ddot{O}:^{2-}$; SrO (c) Al^{3+}, [Ne]; F^-, [He] $2s^22p^6$, $:\ddot{F}:^-$; AlF_3 (d) Rb^+, [Kr]; O^{2-}, [He] $2s^22p^6$, $:\ddot{O}:^{2-}$; Rb_2O. **9.22**(a) 2A(2) (b) 6A(16) (c) 1A(1) **9.24**(a) 3A(13) (b) 2A(2) (c) 6A(16) **9.26**(a) BaS; the charge on each ion is twice the charge on the ions in CsCl. (b) LiCl; Li^+ is smaller than Cs^+. **9.28**(a) BaS; Ba^{2+} is larger than Ca^{2+}. (b) NaF; the charge on each ion is less than the charge on Mg and O. **9.30** 788 kJ; the lattice energy for NaCl is less than that for LiF, because the Na^+ and Cl^- ions are larger than Li^+ and F^- ions. **9.33** −336 kJ **9.34** When two chlorine atoms are far apart, there is no interaction between them. As the atoms move closer together, the nucleus of each atom attracts the electrons of the other atom. The closer the atoms, the greater this attraction; however, the repulsions of the two nuclei and the electrons also increase at the same time. The final internuclear distance is the distance at which maximum attraction is achieved in spite of the repulsion. **9.35** The bond energy is the energy required to break the bond between H atoms and Cl atoms in one mole of HCl molecules in the gaseous state. Energy is needed to break bonds, so bond breaking is always endothermic and $\Delta H^\circ_{\text{bond breaking}}$ is positive. The quantity of energy needed to break the bond is released upon its formation, so $\Delta H^\circ_{\text{bond forming}}$ has the same magnitude as $\Delta H^\circ_{\text{bond breaking}}$ but is opposite in sign (always exothermic and negative). **9.39**(a) I—I < Br—Br < Cl—Cl (b) S—Br < S—Cl < S—H (c) C—N < C=N < C≡N **9.41**(a) C—O < C=O; the C=O bond (bond order = 2) is stronger than the C—O bond (bond order = 1). (b) C—H < O—H; O is smaller than C so the O—H bond is shorter and stronger than the C—H bond. **9.43** Less energy is required to break weak bonds. **9.45** Both are one-carbon molecules. Since methane contains fewer carbon-oxygen bonds, it will have the greater heat of reaction per mole for combustion. **9.47** −168 kJ **9.49** −22 kJ **9.50** −59 kJ **9.51** Electronegativity increases from left to right and increases from bottom to top within a group. Fluorine and oxygen are the two most electronegative elements. Cesium and francium are the two least electronegative elements. **9.53** The H—O bond in water is polar covalent. A nonpolar covalent bond occurs between two atoms with identical electronegativities. A polar covalent bond occurs when the atoms have differing electronegativities. Ionic bonds result from electron transfer between atoms.
9.56(a) Si < S < O (b) Mg < As < P
9.58(a) N > P > Si (b) As > Ga > Ca
9.60
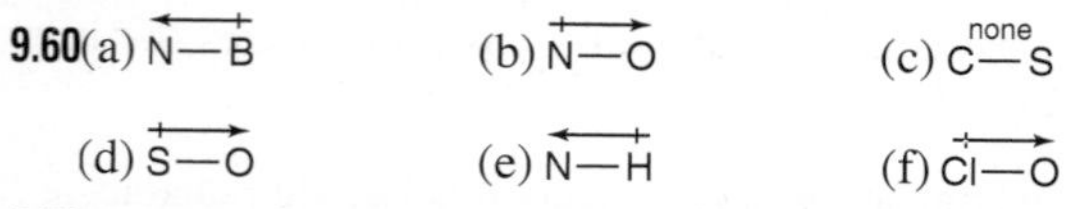

9.62 a, d, and e **9.64**(a) nonpolar covalent (b) ionic (c) polar covalent (d) polar covalent (e) nonpolar covalent (f) polar covalent; $SCl_2 < SF_2 < PF_3$
9.66
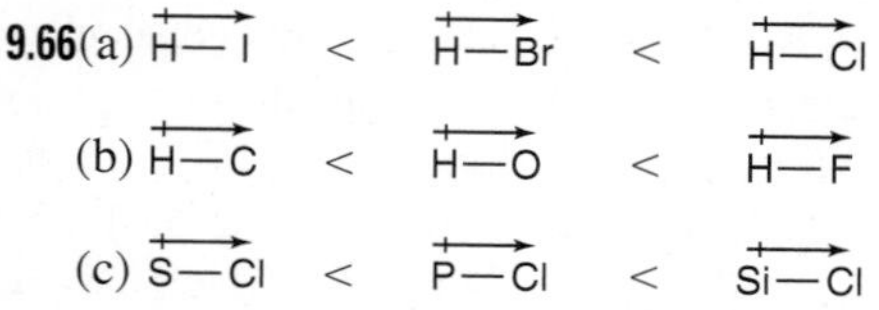

9.69(a) Shiny, conducts heat, conducts electricity, and is malleable. (b) Metals lose electrons to form positive ions, and metals form basic oxides. **9.73**(a) 800. kJ/mol, which is lower than the value in Table 9.2 (b) -2.417×10^4 kJ (c) 1690. g CO_2 (d) 65.2 L O_2 **9.75**(a) −125 kJ (b) yes, since ΔH°_f is negative (c) −392 kJ (d) No, ΔH°_f for $MgCl_2$ is much more negative than that for MgCl. **9.77**(a) 406 nm (b) 2.93×10^{-19} J (c) 1.87×10^4 m/s **9.80** C—Cl: 3.53×10^{-7} m; bond in O_2: 2.40×10^{-7} m **9.81** XeF_2: 132 kJ/mol; XeF_4: 150. kJ/mol; XeF_6: 146 kJ/mol **9.83**(a) The presence of the very electronegative fluorine atoms bonded to one of the carbons makes the C—C bond polar. This polar bond will tend to undergo heterolytic rather than homolytic cleavage. More energy is required to achieve heterolytic cleavage. (b) 1420 kJ **9.86** 13,286 kJ **9.88** 8.70×10^{14} s^{-1}; 3.45×10^{-7} m; the ultraviolet region of the electromagnetic spectrum
9.90(a) $CH_3OCH_3(g)$: −326 kJ; $CH_3CH_2OH(g)$: −369 kJ (b) The formation of gaseous ethanol is more exothermic. (c) 43 kJ

Chapter 10

Answers to Boxed Reading Problem: B10.1 resonance form on the left: trigonal planar around C, trigonal pyramidal around N; resonance form on the right: trigonal planar around both C and N.

• **10.1** He cannot serve as a central atom because it does not bond. H cannot because it forms only one bond. Fluorine cannot because it needs only one electron to complete its valence level, and it does not have *d* orbitals available to expand its valence level. Thus, it can bond to only one other atom.
10.3 All the structures obey the octet rule except c and g.
10.5
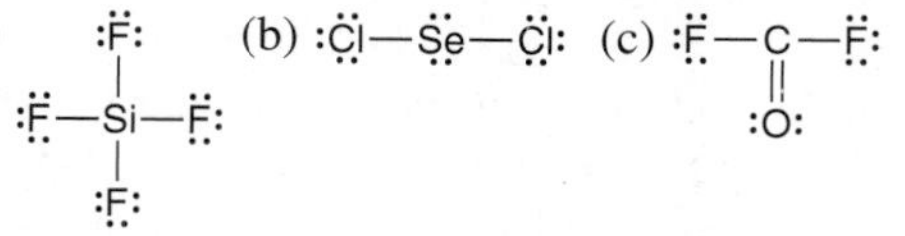

10.7
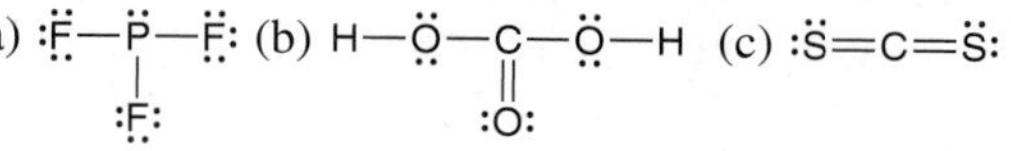

10.9
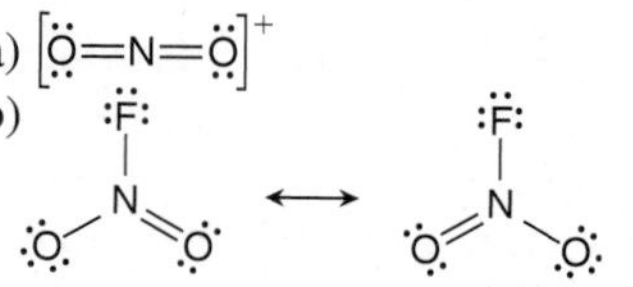

10.11
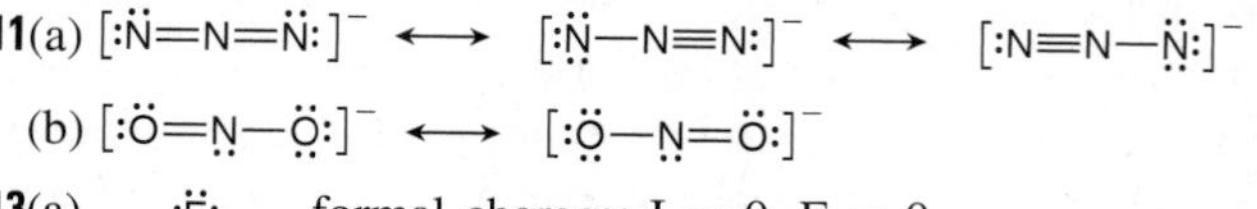

10.13(a)
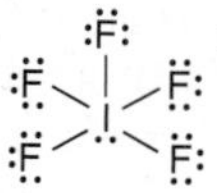
formal charges: I = 0, F = 0
(b)
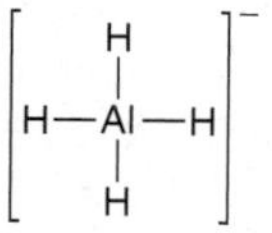
formal charges: H = 0, Al = −1
10.15
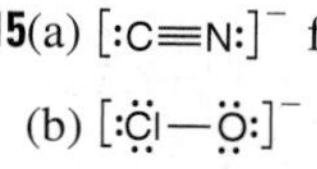

(a) formal charges: C = −1, N = 0
(b) formal charges: Cl = 0, O = −1

10.17(a) 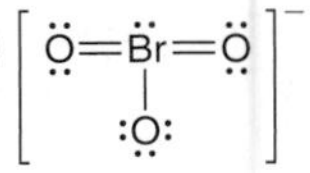 formal charges: Br = 0, doubly bonded O = 0, singly bonded O = −1 O.N.: Br = +5; O = −2

(b) 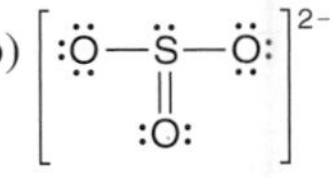 formal charges: S = 0, singly bonded O = −1, doubly bonded O = 0 O.N.: S = +4; O = −2

10.19(a) B has 6 valence electrons in BH_3, so the molecule is electron deficient. (b) As has an expanded valence level with 10 electrons. (c) Se has an expanded valence level with 10 electrons.

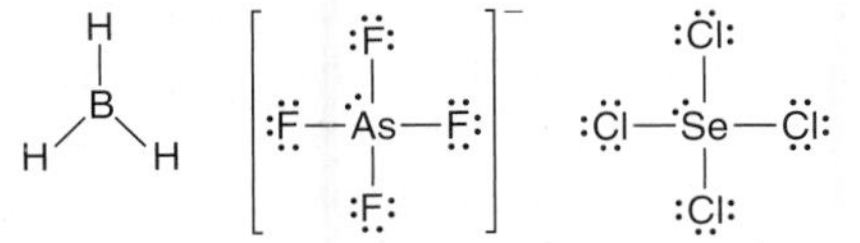

(a) (b) (c)

10.21(a) Br expands its valence level to 10 electrons. (b) I has an expanded valence level of 10 electrons. (c) Be has only 4 valence electrons in BeF_2, so the molecule is electron deficient.

(a) 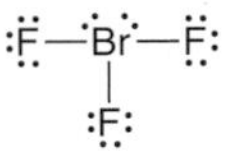 (b) 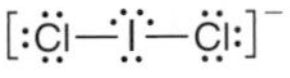 (c) 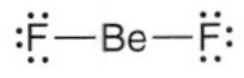

10.23

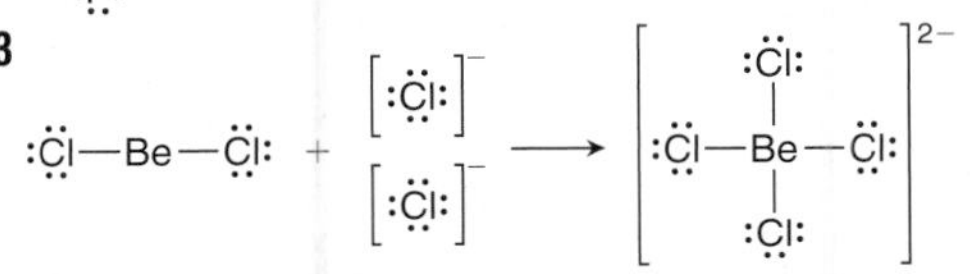

10.26 structure A **10.28** The molecular shape and the electron-group arrangement are the same when no lone pairs are present on the central atom. **10.30** tetrahedral, AX_4; trigonal pyramidal, AX_3E; bent or V shaped, AX_2E_2

10.32(a) 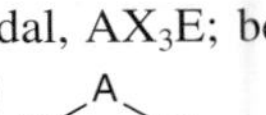 (b) 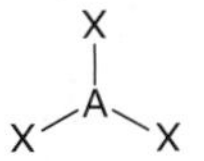

(c) 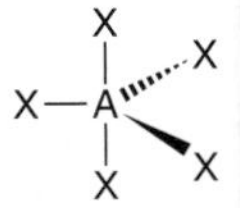 (d) 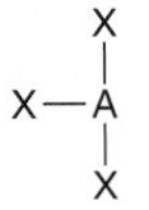

(e) 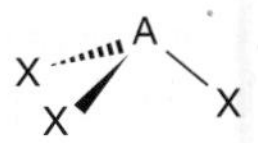 (f) 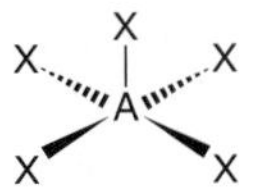

10.34(a) trigonal planar, bent, 120° (b) tetrahedral, trigonal pyramidal, 109.5° (c) tetrahedral, trigonal pyramidal, 109.5° **10.36**(a) trigonal planar, trigonal planar, 120° (b) trigonal planar, bent, 120° (c) tetrahedral, tetrahedral, 109.5° **10.38**(a) trigonal planar, AX_3, 120° (b) trigonal pyramidal, AX_3E, 109.5° (c) trigonal bipyramidal, AX_5, 90° and 120° **10.40**(a) bent, 109.5°, less than 109.5° (b) trigonal bipyramidal, 90° and 120°, angles are ideal (c) seesaw, 90° and 120°, less than ideal (d) linear, 180°, angle is ideal **10.42**(a) C: tetrahedral, 109.5°; O: bent, < 109.5° (b) N: trigonal planar, 120° **10.44**(a) C in CH_3: tetrahedral, 109.5°; C with C=O: trigonal planar, 120°; O with H: bent, < 109.5° (b) O: bent, < 109.5° **10.46** $OF_2 < NF_3 < CF_4 < BF_3 < BeF_2$ **10.48**(a) The C and N each have three groups, so the ideal angles are 120°; the O has four groups, so the ideal angle is 109.5°. The N and O have lone pairs, so the angles are less than ideal. (b) All central atoms have four pairs, so the ideal angles are 109.5°. The lone pairs on the O reduce this value. (c) The B has three groups and an ideal bond angle of 120°. All the O's have four groups (ideal bond angles of 109.5°), two of which are lone pairs that reduce the angle.

10.51

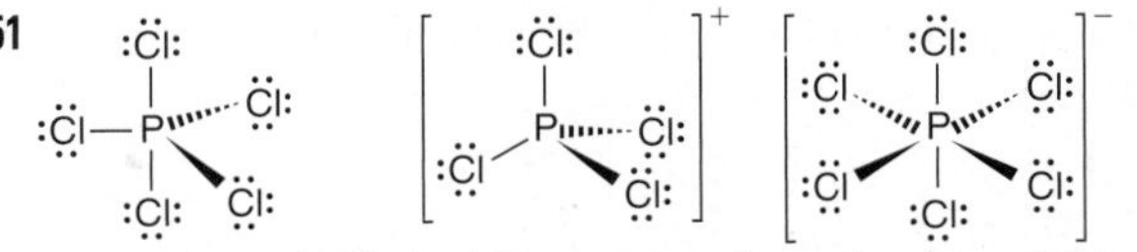

In the gas phase, PCl_5 is AX_5, so the shape is trigonal bipyramidal, and the bond angles are 120° and 90°. The PCl_4^+ ion is AX_4, so the shape is tetrahedral, and the bond angles are 109.5°. The PCl_6^- ion is AX_6, so the shape is octahedral, and the bond angles are 90°. **10.52** Molecules are polar if they have polar bonds that are not arranged to cancel each other. A polar bond is present any time there is a bond between elements with differing electronegativities. **10.55**(a) CF_4 (b) BrCl and SCl_2 **10.57**(a) SO_2, because it is polar and SO_3 is not. (b) IF has a greater electronegativity difference between its atoms. (c) SF_4, because it is polar and SiF_4 is not. (d) H_2O has a greater electronegativity difference between its atoms.

10.59

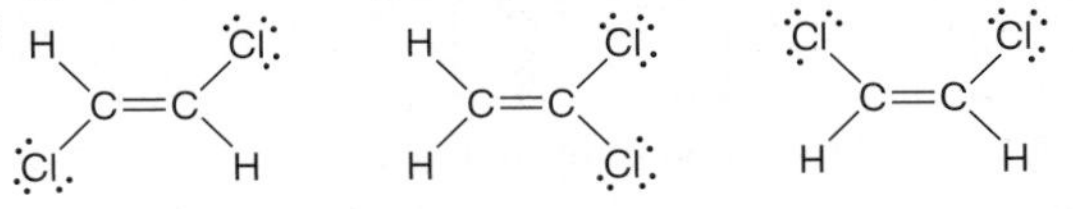

X Y Z

Yes, compound Y has a dipole moment.

10.61(a) 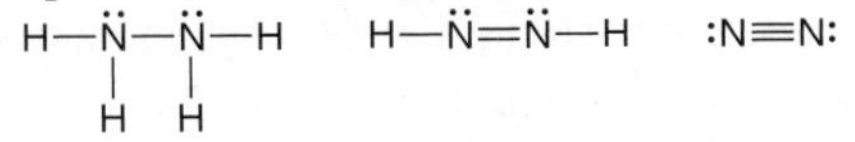

Hydrazine Diazene Nitrogen

The single N—N bond (bond order = 1) is weaker and longer than the others. The triple bond (bond order = 3) is stronger and shorter than the others. The double bond (bond order = 2) has an intermediate strength and length.

(b) $\Delta H^\circ_{rxn} = -367$ kJ

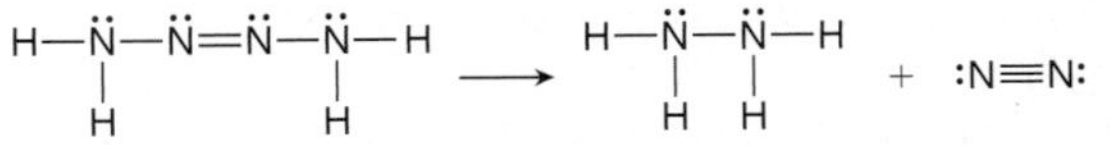

10.65(a) formal charges: Al = −1, end Cl = 0, bridging Cl = +1; I = −1, end Cl = 0, bridging Cl = +1 (b) The iodine atoms are each AX_4E_2, and the shape around each is square planar. These square planar portions are adjacent, giving a planar molecule.

10.70

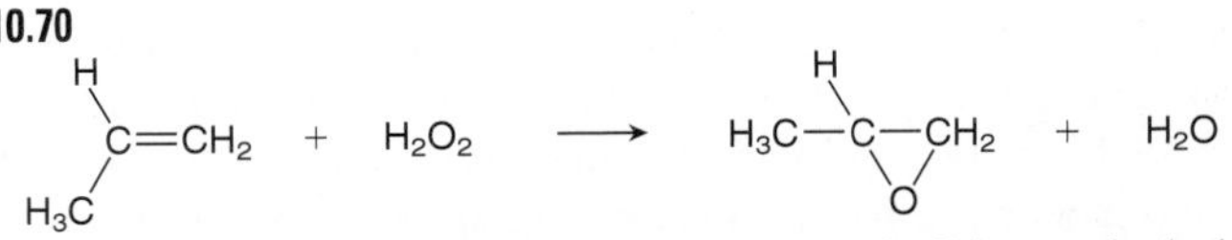

(a) In propylene oxide, the shape around each C is tetrahedral, with ideal angles of 109.5°. (b) The C that is not part of the three-membered ring should have close to the ideal angle. The atoms in the ring form an equilateral triangle, so the angles around the two C's in the ring are reduced from the ideal 109.5° to 60°. **10.75**(a) −1267 kJ/mol (b) −1226 kJ/mol (c) −1234.8 kJ/mol. The two answers differ by less than 10 kJ/mol. This is very good agreement since average bond energies were used to calculate answers a and b. (d) −37 kJ

10.77 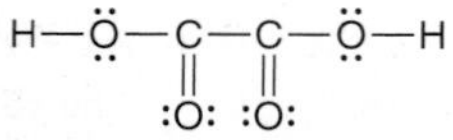

10.80 CH_4: -409 kJ/mol O_2; H_2S: -398 kJ/mol O_2 **10.82**(a) The O in the OH species has only 7 valence electrons, which is less than an octet, and 1 electron is unpaired. (b) 426 kJ (c) 508 kJ **10.84**(a) The F atoms will substitute at the axial positions first. (b) PF_5 and PCl_3F_2 **10.86** $H_2C_2O_4$:

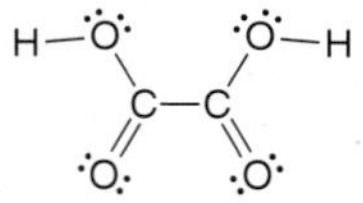

$HC_2O_4^-$:

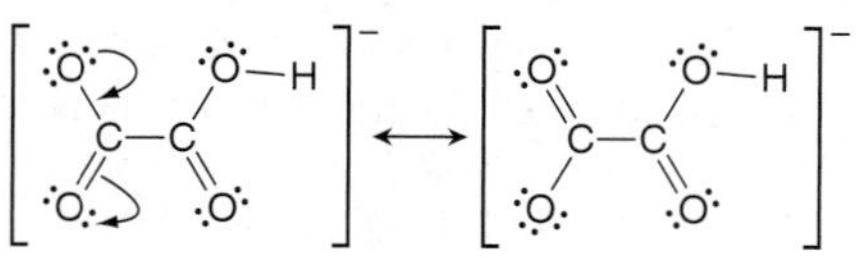

$C_2O_4^{2-}$:

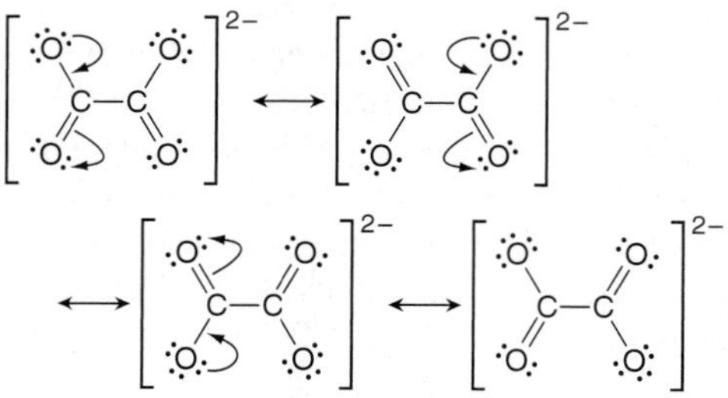

In $H_2C_2O_4$, there are two shorter and stronger C=O bonds and two longer and weaker C—O bonds. In $HC_2O_4^-$, the carbon-oxygen bonds on the side retaining the H remain as one long, weak C—O and one short, strong C=O. The carbon-oxygen bonds on the other side of the molecule have resonance forms with a bond order of 1.5, so they are intermediate in length and strength. In $C_2O_4^{2-}$, all the carbon-oxygen bonds have a bond order of 1.5. **10.90** 22 kJ **10.91** Trigonal planar molecules are nonpolar, so AY_3 cannot be that shape. Trigonal pyramidal molecules and T-shaped molecules are polar, so AY_3 could have either of these shapes. **10.95**(a) 339 pm (b) 316 pm and 223 pm (c) 270 pm

Chapter 11

11.1(a) sp^2 (b) sp^3d^2 (c) sp (d) sp^3 (e) sp^3d **11.3** C has only 2*s* and 2*p* atomic orbitals, allowing for a maximum of four hybrid orbitals. Si has 3*s*, 3*p*, and 3*d* atomic orbitals, allowing it to form more than four hybrid orbitals. **11.5**(a) six, sp^3d^2 (b) four, sp^3 **11.7**(a) sp^2 (b) sp^2 (c) sp^2 **11.9**(a) sp^3 (b) sp^3 (c) sp^3 **11.11**(a) Si: one *s* and three *p* atomic orbitals form four sp^3 hybrid orbitals. (b) C: one *s* and one *p* atomic orbital forms two *sp* hybrid orbitals. (c) S: one *s*, three *p*, and one *d* atomic orbital mix to form five sp^3d hybrid orbitals. (d) N: one *s* and three *p* atomic orbitals mix to form four sp^3 hybrid orbitals. **11.13**(a) B ($sp^3 \longrightarrow sp^3$) (b) A ($sp^2 \longrightarrow sp^3$)

11.15 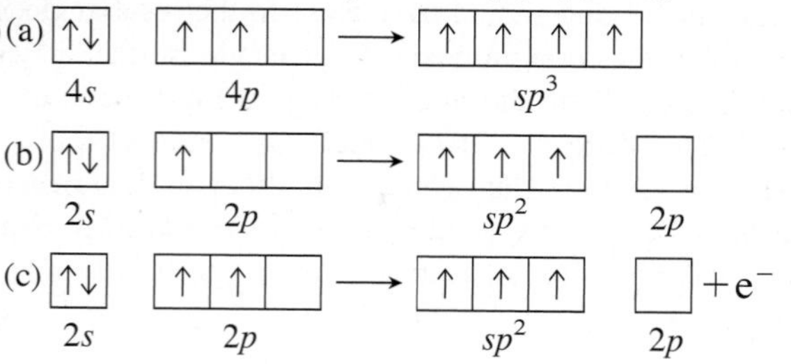

11.17 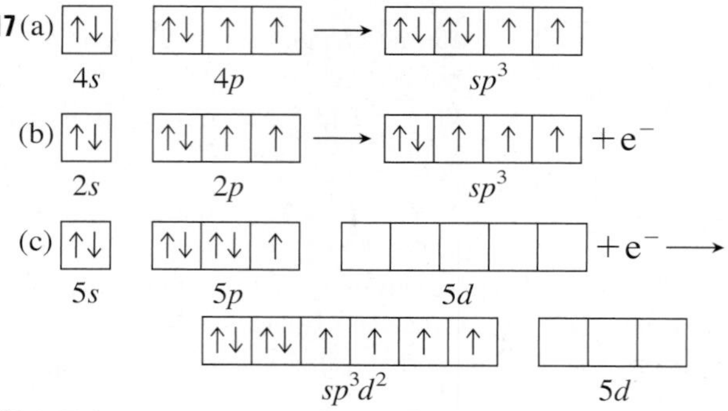

11.20(a) False. A double bond is one σ and one π bond. (b) False. A triple bond consists of one σ and two π bonds. (c) True (d) True (e) False. A π bond consists of a second pair of electrons after a σ bond has been previously formed. (f) False. End-to-end overlap results in a bond with electron density along the bond axis. **11.21**(a) Nitrogen uses sp^2 to form three σ bonds and one π bond. (b) Carbon uses *sp* to form two σ bonds and two π bonds. (c) Carbon uses sp^2 to form three σ bonds and one π bond.

11.23(a) N: sp^2, forming 2 σ bonds and 1 π bond

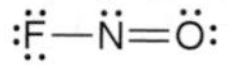

(b) C: sp^2, forming 3 σ bonds and 1 π bond

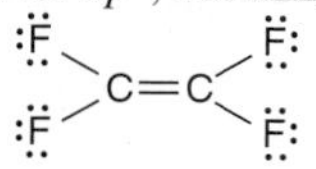

(c) C: *sp*, forming 2 σ bonds and 2 π bonds

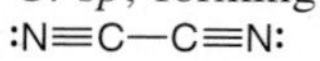

11.25 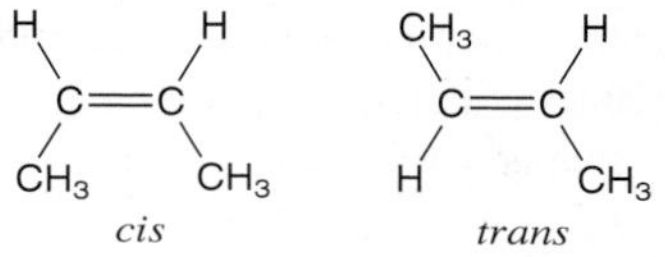

The single bonds are all σ bonds. The double bond is one σ bond and one π bond. **11.26** Four MOs form from the four *p* atomic orbitals. The total number of MOs must equal the number of atomic orbitals. **11.28**(a) Bonding MOs have lower energy than antibonding MOs. Lower energy means more stable. (b) Bonding MOs do not have a nodal plane perpendicular to the bond. (c) Bonding MOs have higher electron density between nuclei than antibonding MOs. **11.30**(a) two (b) two (c) four **11.32**(a) A is π^*_{2p}, B is σ_{2p}, C is π_{2p}, and D is σ^*_{2p}. (b) π^*_{2p} (A), σ_{2p} (B), and π_{2p} (C) have at least one electron. (c) π^*_{2p} (A) has only one electron. **11.34**(a) stable (b) paramagnetic (c) $(\sigma_{2s})^2(\sigma^*_{2s})^1$ **11.36**(a) $C_2^+ < C_2 < C_2^-$ (b) $C_2^- < C_2 < C_2^+$ **11.40**(a) C (ring): sp^2; C (all others): sp^3; O (all): sp^3; N: sp^3 (b) 26 (c) 6 **11.42**(a) 17 (b) All carbons are sp^2; the ring N is sp^2, the other N's are sp^3. **11.44**(a) B changes from sp^2 to sp^3. (b) P changes from sp^3 to sp^3d. (c) C changes from *sp* to sp^2. Two electron groups surround C in C_2H_2, and three electron groups surround C in C_2H_4. (d) Si changes from sp^3 to sp^3d^2. (e) no change for S **11.46** P: tetrahedral, sp^3; N: trigonal pyramid, sp^3; C_1 and C_2: tetrahedral, sp^3; C_3: trigonal planar, sp^2 **11.51**(a) B and D are present. (b) Yes, *sp* hybrid orbitals. (c) Two sets of *sp* orbitals, four sets of sp^2 orbitals, and three sets of sp^3 orbitals. **11.52** Through resonance, the C—N bond gains some double-bond character, which hinders rotation about that bond.

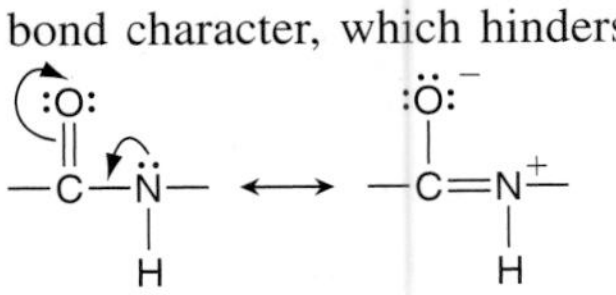

11.55(a) C in $-CH_3$: sp^3; all other C atoms: sp^2; O in two C—O bonds: sp^3; O in two C=O bonds: sp^2 (b) two (c) eight; one **11.56**(a) four (b) eight

Chapter 12

Answer to Boxed Reading Problem: B12.1 1.76×10^{-10} m

• **12.1** In a solid, the energy of attraction of the particles is greater than their energy of motion; in a gas, it is less. Gases have high compressibility and the ability to flow, while solids have neither. **12.4**(a) Because the intermolecular forces are only partially overcome when fusion occurs but need to be totally overcome in vaporization. (b) Because solids have greater intermolecular forces than liquids do. (c) $\Delta H_{vap} = -\Delta H_{cond}$ **12.5**(a) intermolecular (b) intermolecular (c) intramolecular (d) intramolecular **12.7**(a) condensation (b) fusion (c) vaporization **12.9** The gas molecules slow down as the gas is compressed. Therefore, much of the kinetic energy lost by the propane molecules is released to the surroundings. **12.13** At first, the vaporization of liquid molecules from the surface predominates, which increases the number of gas molecules and hence the vapor pressure. As more molecules enter the gas phase, more gas molecules hit the surface of the liquid and "stick" more frequently, so the condensation rate increases. When the vaporization and condensation rates become equal, the vapor pressure becomes constant. **12.14** As intermolecular forces increase, (a) critical temperature increases, (b) boiling point increases, (c) vapor pressure decreases, and (d) heat of vaporization increases. **12.18** because the condensation of the vapor supplies an additional 40.7 kJ/mol **12.19** 7.67×10^3 J **12.21** 0.777 atm **12.23** 2×10^4 J/mol

12.25

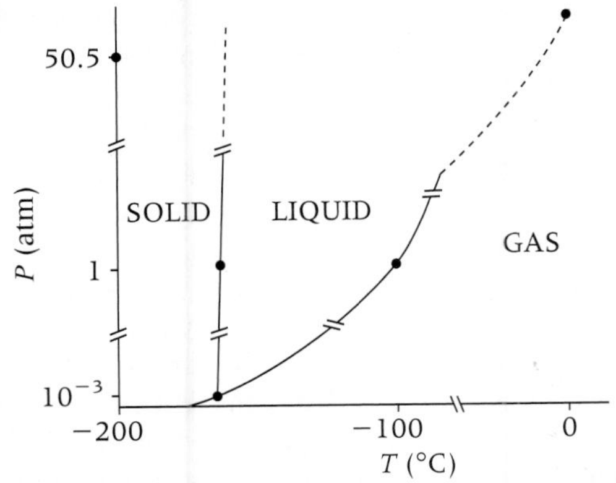

Solid ethylene is more dense than liquid ethylene. **12.28** 32 atm **12.32** O is smaller and more electronegative than Se; so the electron density on O is greater, which attracts H more strongly. **12.34** All particles (atoms and molecules) exhibit dispersion forces, but the total force is weak for small molecules. Dipole-dipole forces between small polar molecules dominate the dispersion forces. **12.37**(a) hydrogen bonding (b) dispersion forces (c) dispersion forces **12.39**(a) dipole-dipole forces (b) dispersion forces (c) hydrogen bonding **12.41**(a)

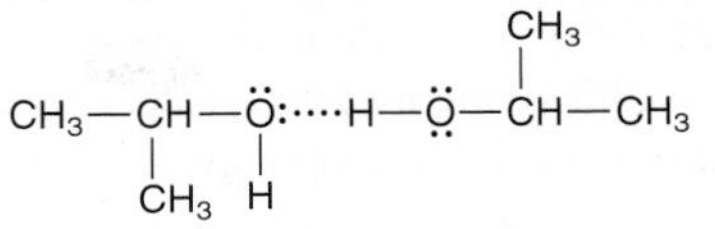

(b)

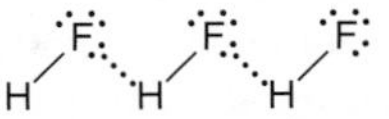

12.43(a) dispersion forces (b) hydrogen bonding (c) dispersion forces **12.45**(a) I^- (b) $CH_2{=}CH_2$ (c) H_2Se. In (a) and (c) the larger particle has the higher polarizability. In (b), the less tightly held π electron clouds are more easily distorted. **12.47**(a) C_2H_6; it is a smaller molecule exhibiting weaker dispersion forces than C_4H_{10}. (b) CH_3CH_2F; it has no H—F bonds, so it exhibits only dipole-dipole forces, which are weaker than the hydrogen bonds of CH_3CH_2OH. (c) PH_3; it has weaker intermolecular forces (dipole-dipole) than NH_3 (hydrogen bonding). **12.49**(a) HCl; it has dipole-dipole forces, and there are stronger ionic bonds in LiCl. (b) PH_3; it has dipole-dipole forces, and there is stronger hydrogen bonding in NH_3. (c) Xe; it exhibits weaker dispersion forces since its smaller size results in lower polarizability than the larger I_2 molecules. **12.51**(a) C_4H_8 (cyclobutane), because it is more compact than C_4H_{10}. (b) PBr_3; the dipole-dipole forces in PBr_3 are weaker than the ionic bonds in NaBr. (c) HBr; the dipole-dipole forces in HBr are weaker than the hydrogen bonds in water. **12.53** As atomic size decreases and electronegativity increases, the electron density of an atom increases. Thus, the attraction to an H atom on another molecule increases while its bonded H atom becomes more positive. Fluorine is the smallest of the three and the most electronegative, so the H bonds in hydrogen fluoride are the strongest. Oxygen is smaller and more electronegative than nitrogen, so H bonds in water are stronger than H bonds in ammonia. **12.57** The cohesive forces in water and mercury are stronger than the adhesive forces to the nonpolar wax on the floor. Weak adhesive forces result in spherical drops. The adhesive forces overcome the even weaker cohesive forces in the oil, and so the oil drop spreads out. **12.59** Surface tension is defined as the energy needed to increase the surface area by a given amount, so units of energy per area are appropriate. **12.61** $CH_3CH_2CH_2OH <$ $HOCH_2CH_2OH < HOCH_2CH(OH)CH_2OH$.
More hydrogen bonding means more attraction between molecules, so more energy is needed to increase surface area. **12.63** $HOCH_2CH(OH)CH_2OH > HOCH_2CH_2OH >$ $CH_3CH_2CH_2OH$. More hydrogen bonding means more attraction between molecules, so they flow less easily. **12.68** Water is a good solvent for polar and ionic substances and a poor solvent for nonpolar substances. Water is a polar molecule and dissolves polar substances because their intermolecular forces are of similar strength. **12.69** A single water molecule can form four H bonds. The two hydrogen atoms each form one H bond to oxygen atoms on neighboring water molecules. The two

lone pairs on the oxygen atom form H bonds with hydrogen atoms on two neighboring molecules. **12.72** Water exhibits strong capillary action, which allows it to be easily absorbed by the plant's roots and transported upward to the leaves. **12.78** simple cubic **12.81** The energy gap is the energy difference between the highest filled energy level (valence band) and the lowest unfilled energy level (conduction band). In conductors and superconductors, the energy gap is zero because the valence band overlaps the conduction band. In semiconductors, the energy gap is small. In insulators, the gap is large. **12.83** atomic mass and atomic radius **12.84**(a) face-centered cubic (b) body-centered cubic (c) face-centered cubic **12.86**(a) The change in unit cell is from a sodium chloride structure in CdO to a zinc blende structure in CdSe. (b) Yes, the coordination number of Cd changes from 6 in CdO to 4 in CdSe. **12.88**(a) Nickel forms a metallic solid since it is a metal whose atoms are held together by metallic bonds. (b) Fluorine forms a molecular solid since the F_2 molecules are held together by dispersion forces. (c) Methanol forms a molecular solid since the CH_3OH molecules are held together by hydrogen bonds. (d) Tin forms a metallic solid since it is a metal whose atoms are held together by metallic bonds. (e) Silicon is in the same group as carbon, so it exhibits similar bonding properties. Since diamond and graphite are both network covalent solids, it makes sense that Si forms a network covalent solid as well. (f) Xe is an atomic solid since its individual atoms are held together by dispersion forces. **12.90** four **12.92**(a) four Se^{2-} ions, four Zn^{2+} ions (b) 577.48 amu (c) 1.77×10^{-22} cm^3 (d) 5.61×10^{-8} cm **12.94**(a) insulator (b) conductor (c) semiconductor **12.96**(a) Conductivity increases. (b) Conductivity increases. (c) Conductivity decreases. **12.98** 1.68×10^{-8} cm **12.105** A substance whose properties are the same in all directions is isotropic; otherwise, the substance is anisotropic. Liquid crystals have a degree of order only in certain directions, so they are anisotropic. **12.111**(a) n-type semiconductor (b) p-type semiconductor **12.113** $n = 3.4\times10^3$ **12.115** 8.4 pm **12.118**(a) 19.8 torr (b) 0.0485 g **12.124** 259 K **12.126**(a) 2.23×10^{-2} atm (b) 6.23 L
12.129(a) furfuryl alcohol

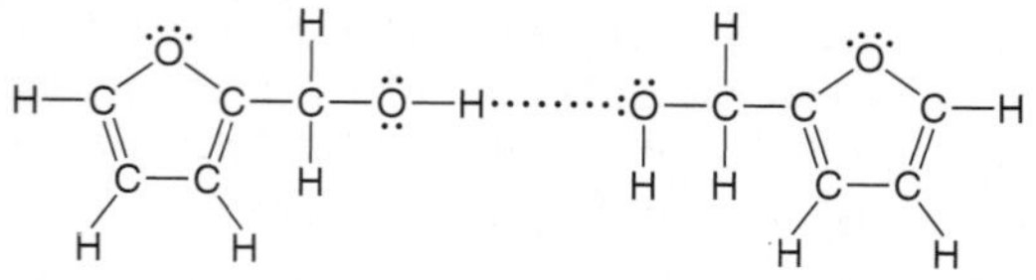

2-furoic acid

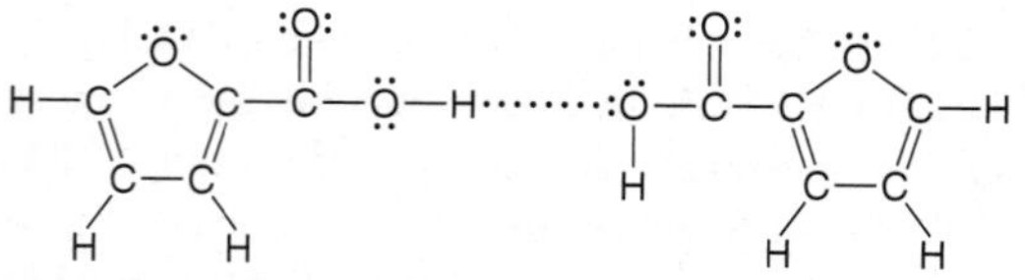

(b) furfuryl alcohol 2-furoic acid

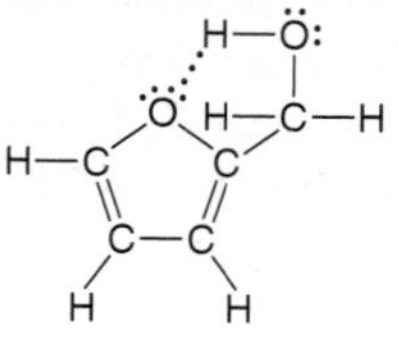

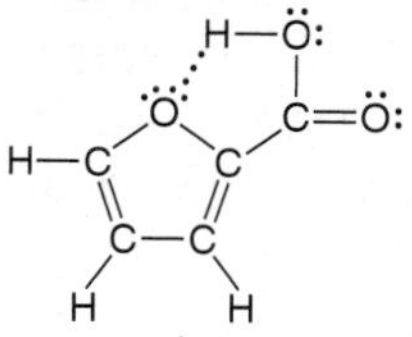

12.130(a) 49.3 metric tons H_2O (b) -1.11×10^8 kJ **12.131** 2.9 g/m^3 **12.136**(a) 1.1 min (b) 10. min (c)

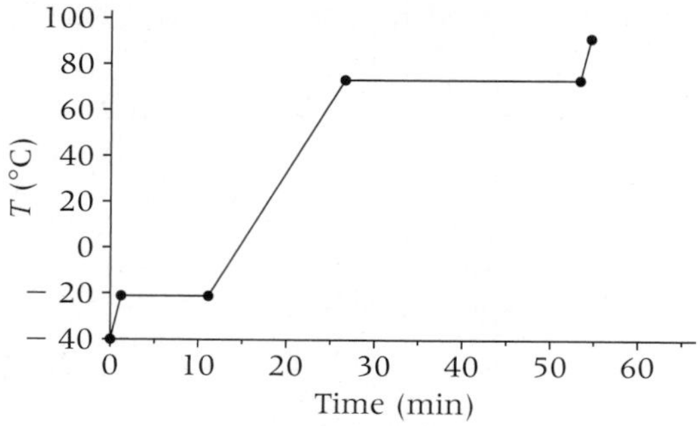

12.137 2.98×10^5 g BN **12.140** 45.98 amu

Chapter 13

Answers to Boxed Reading Problem: B13.1 (a) The colloidal particles in water generally have negatively charged surfaces and so repel each other, slowing the settling process. Cake alum, $Al_2(SO_4)_3$, is added to coagulate the colloids. The Al^{3+} ions neutralize the negative surface charges and allow the particles to aggregate and settle. (b) Water that contains large amounts of divalent cations (such as Ca^{2+}, and Mg^{2+}) is called hard water. During cleaning, these ions combine with the fatty-acid anions in soaps to produce insoluble deposits. (c) In reverse osmosis, a pressure greater than the osmotic pressure is applied to the solution, forcing the water back through the membrane, leaving the ions behind. (d) Chlorine may give the water an unpleasant odor, and can form carcinogenic chlorinated compounds. (e) The high concentration of NaCl displaces the divalent and polyvalent ions from the ion-exchange resin.

• **13.2** When a salt such as NaCl dissolves, ion-dipole forces cause the ions to separate, and many water molecules cluster around each ion in hydration shells. Ion-dipole forces bind the first shell to an ion. The water molecules in that shell form H bonds to others to create the next shell, and so on. **13.4** Sodium stearate is a more effective soap because the hydrocarbon chain in the stearate ion is longer than that in the acetate ion. The longer chain allows for more dispersion forces with grease molecules. **13.7** KNO_3 is an ionic compound and is therefore more soluble in water. **13.9**(a) ion-dipole forces (b) hydrogen bonding (c) dipole–induced dipole forces **13.11**(a) hydrogen bonding (b) dipole–induced dipole forces (c) dispersion forces **13.13**(a) HCl(*g*), because the molecular interactions (dipole-dipole forces) in ether are like those in HCl but not like the ionic bonding in NaCl. (b) $CH_3CHO(l)$, because the molecular interactions with ether (dipole-dipole) can replace those between CH_3CHO, but not the H bonds in water. (c) $CH_3CH_2MgBr(s)$, because the molecular interactions (dipole-dipole and dispersion forces) are greater than between ether and the ions in $MgBr_2$. **13.16** Gluconic acid is soluble in water due to extensive hydrogen bonding by the —OH groups attached to five of its carbons. The dispersion forces in the nonpolar tail of caproic acid are more similar to the dispersion forces in hexane; thus, caproic acid is soluble in hexane. **13.18** The nitrogen-containing bases form H bonds to their complementary bases. The flat, N-containing bases stack above each other, which allows extensive dispersion forces. The exterior negatively charged sugar-phosphate chains form ion-dipole and H bonds with water molecules in the aqueous surroundings, which also stabilizes the structure. **13.21** Dispersion forces are present between the nonpolar tails of the lipid molecules within the bilayer. The polar heads interact with the aqueous surroundings through H bonds and ion-dipole forces. **13.25** The enthalpy changes needed to separate the solvent ($\Delta H_{solvent}$) and to mix the solvent and solute (ΔH_{mix}) combine to give $\Delta H_{solvation}$. **13.29** very soluble, because a decrease in enthalpy and an increase in entropy both favor the formation of a solution

13.30

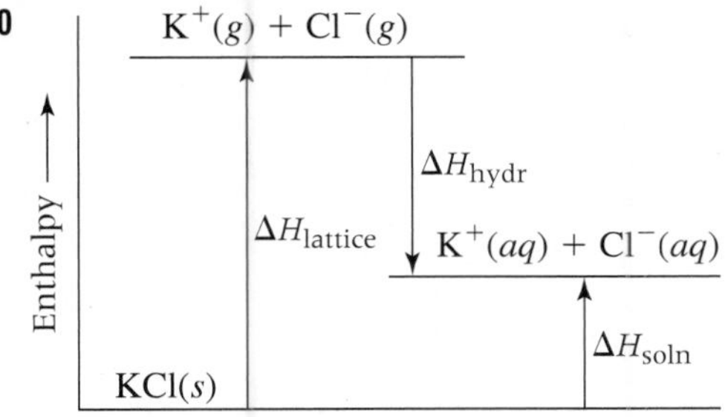

13.32(a) The volume of Na^+ is smaller. (b) Sr^{2+} has a larger ionic charge and a smaller volume. (c) Na^+ is smaller than Cl^-. (d) O^{2-} has a larger ionic charge with a similar ion volume. (e) OH^- has a smaller volume than SH^-. (f) Mg^{2+} has a smaller volume. (g) Mg^{2+} has both a smaller volume and a larger ionic charge. (h) CO_3^{2-} has both a smaller volume and a larger ionic charge. **13.34**(a) Na^+ (b) Sr^{2+} (c) Na^+ (d) O^{2-} (e) OH^- (f) Mg^{2+} (g) Mg^{2+} (h) CO_3^{2-} **13.36**(a) −704 kJ/mol (b) The K^+ ion contributes more because it is smaller and, therefore, has a greater charge density. **13.38**(a) increases (b) decreases (c) increases **13.41** Add a pinch of X to each solution. Addition of a "seed" crystal of solute to a supersaturated solution causes the excess solute to crystallize immediately, leaving behind a saturated solution. The solution in which the added X dissolves is the unsaturated solution. The solution in which the added X remains undissolved is the saturated solution. **13.44**(a) increase (b) decrease **13.46**(a) 0.102 g O_2 (b) 0.0214 g O_2 **13.49** 0.20 mol/L **13.52**(a) molarity and % w/v or % v/v (b) parts-by-mass (% w/w) (c) molality **13.54** With just this information, you can convert between molality and molarity, but you need to know the molar mass of the solvent to convert to mole fraction. **13.56**(a) 0.944 M $C_{12}H_{22}O_{11}$ (b) 0.167 M $LiNO_3$ **13.58**(a) 0.0749 M NaOH (b) 0.36 M HNO_3 **13.60**(a) Add 4.25 g KH_2PO_4 to enough water to make 365 mL of aqueous solution. (b) Add 125 mL of 1.25 M NaOH to enough water to make 465 mL of solution. **13.62**(a) Weigh out 48.0 g KBr, dissolve it in about 1 L distilled water, and then dilute to 1.40 L with distilled water. (b) Measure 82.7 mL of the 0.264 M $LiNO_3$ solution and add distilled water to make a total of 255 mL. **13.64**(a) 0.896 m glycine (b) 1.21 m glycerol **13.66** 4.48 m C_6H_6 **13.68**(a) Add 2.39 g $C_2H_6O_2$ to 308 g H_2O. (b) Add 0.0508 kg of 52.0% HNO_3 by mass to 1.15 kg H_2O to make 1.20 kg of 2.20% HNO_3 by mass. **13.70**(a) 0.29 (b) 58 mass % (c) 23 m C_3H_7OH **13.72** 42.6 g CsBr; mole fraction = 7.16×10^{-3}; 7.84% by mass **13.74** 5.11 m NH_3; 4.53 M NH_3; mole fraction = 0.0843 **13.76** 2.5 ppm Ca^{2+}; 0.56 ppm Mg^{2+} **13.80** It conducts a "strong" current. A strong electrolyte dissociates completely into ions in solution. **13.82** The boiling point is higher and the freezing point is lower for the solution than for the solvent. **13.85** A dilute solution of an electrolyte behaves more ideally than a concentrated one. With increasing concentration, the effective concentration deviates from the molar concentration because of ionic attractions. Thus, 0.050 m NaF has a boiling point closer to its predicted value. **13.88**(a) strong electrolyte (b) strong electrolyte (c) nonelectrolyte (d) weak electrolyte **13.90**(a) 0.6 mol of solute particles (b) 0.13 mol (c) 2×10^{-4} mol (d) 0.06 mol **13.92**(a) CH_3OH in H_2O (b) H_2O in CH_3OH solution **13.94**(a) $\Pi_{II} < \Pi_{I} < \Pi_{III}$ (b) $bp_{II} < bp_{I} < bp_{III}$ (c) $fp_{III} < fp_{I} < fp_{II}$ (d) $vp_{III} < vp_{I} < vp_{II}$ **13.96** 23.4 torr **13.98** −0.467°C **13.100** 79.5°C **13.102** 1.18×10^4 g $C_2H_6O_2$ **13.104**(a) NaCl: 0.173 m and i = 1.84 (b) CH_3COOH: 0.0837 m and i = 1.02 **13.107** 209 torr for CH_2Cl_2; 48.1 torr for CCl_4 **13.108** The fluid inside a bacterial cell is both a solution and a colloid. It is a solution of ions and small molecules and a colloid of large molecules (proteins and nucleic acids). **13.112** Soap micelles have nonpolar tails pointed inward and anionic heads pointed outward. The like charges on the heads of one micelle repel those on the heads of a neighboring micelle. This repulsion between micelles keeps them from coagulating. Soap is more effective in freshwater than in seawater because the divalent cations in seawater combine with the anionic heads to form a precipitate. **13.116** 3.4×10^9 L **13.120** 0.0°C: 4.53×10^{-4} M O_2; 20.0°C: 2.83×10^{-4} M O_2; 40.0°C: 2.00×10^{-4} M O_2 **13.122**(a) 89.9 g/mol (b) C_2H_5O; $C_4H_{10}O_2$ (c) Forms H bonds:

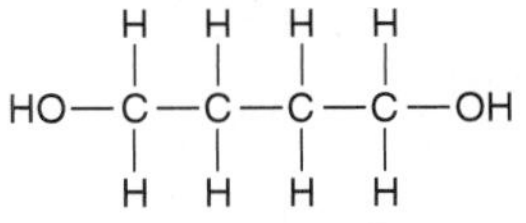

Does not form H bonds:

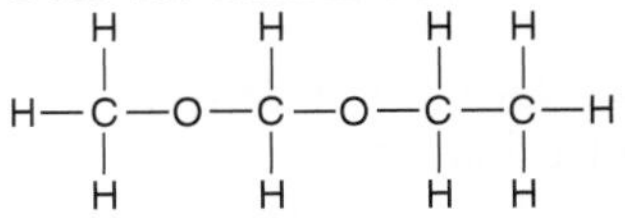

13.126(a) 9.45 g NaF (b) 0.0017 g F^- **13.129**(a) 68 g/mol (b) 2.1×10^2 g/mol (c) The molar mass of CaN_2O_6 is 164.10 g/mol. This value is less than the 2.1×10^2 g/mol calculated when the compound is assumed to be a strong electrolyte and is greater than the 68 g/mol calculated when the compound is assumed to be a nonelectrolyte. Thus, the compound forms a nonideal solution because the ions interact but do not dissociate completely in solution. (d) i = 2.4 **13.133**(a) 1.82×10^4 g/mol (b) 3.41×10^{-5}°C **13.134** 8.2×10^5 ng/L **13.138**(a) 0.02 (b) 5×10^{-3} atm·L/mol (c) yes **13.140** Weigh 3.11 g of $NaHCO_3$ and dissolve in 247 g of water. **3.144** M = m

(kg solvent/L solution) = $m \times d_{solution}$. Thus, for very dilute solutions, molality × density = molarity. For an aqueous solution, the number of liters of solution is approximately the same as the kg of solvent because the density of water is close to 1 kg/L, so $m = M$. **13.146**(a) 2.5×10^{-3} *M* SO_2 (b) The base reacts with the sulfur dioxide to produce calcium sulfite. The reaction of sulfur dioxide makes "room" for more sulfur dioxide to dissolve. **13.151**(a) 7.83×10^{-3} mol L·atm (b) 4×10^{-5} *M* (c) 3×10^{-6} (d) 1 ppm **13.155**(a) 0.0212 mol/L·atm (b) 8.86 ppm (c) k_H: $C_6F_{14} > C_6H_{14} >$ ethanol > water. To dissolve oxygen in a solvent, the solvent molecules must be moved apart to make room for the gas. The stronger the intermolecular forces in the solvent, the more difficult it is to separate solvent particles and the lower the solubility of the gas. In both C_6F_{14} and C_6H_{14} have weak dispersion forces, with C_6F_{14} having the weaker forces due to the electronegative fluorine atoms repelling each other. In both ethanol and water, the molecules are held together by strong hydrogen bonds with those bonds being stronger in water, as the boiling point indicates. **13.157**(a) Yes, the phases of water can still coexist at some temperature and can therefore establish equilibrium. (b) The triple point would occur at a lower pressure and lower temperature because the dissolved air would lower the vapor pressure of the solvent. (c) Yes, this is possible because the gas-solid phase boundary exists below the new triple point. (d) No; at both temperatures, the presence of the solute lowers the vapor pressure of the liquid. **13.159**(a) 2.8×10^{-4} g/mL (b) 81 mL

Chapter 14

14.1 The outermost electron is attracted by a smaller effective nuclear charge in Li because of shielding by the inner electrons, and it is farther from the nucleus in Li. Both of these factors lead to a lower ionization energy for Li.
14.3(a) NH_3 will hydrogen bond.

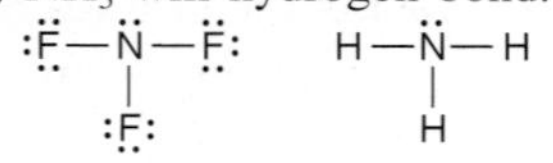

(b) CH_3CH_2OH will hydrogen bond.

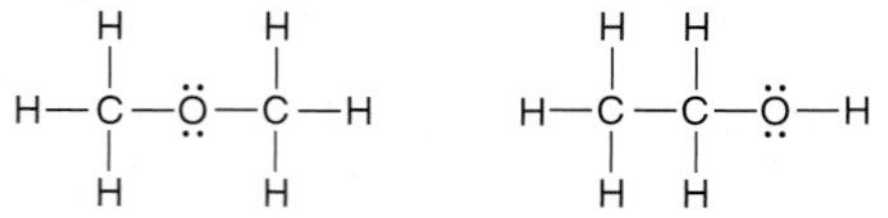

14.5(a) $2Al(s) + 6HCl(aq) \longrightarrow 2AlCl_3(aq) + 3H_2(g)$
(b) $LiH(s) + H_2O(l) \longrightarrow LiOH(aq) + H_2(g)$
14.7(a) $NaBH_4$: +1 for Na, +3 for B, −1 for H
$Al(BH_4)_3$: +3 for Al, +3 for B, −1 for H
$LiAlH_4$: +1 for Li, +3 for Al, −1 for H
(b) tetrahedral

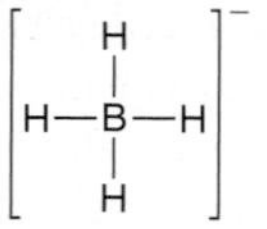

14.10 For Groups 1A(1) to 4A(14), the number of covalent bonds equals the (old) group number. For Groups 5A(15) to 7A(17), it equals 8 minus the (old) group number. There are exceptions in Period 3 to Period 6 because it is possible for the 3A(13) to 7A(17) elements to use *d* orbitals and form more bonds. **14.13**(a) Group 3A(13) or 3B(3) (b) If E is in Group 3B(3), the oxide will be more basic and the fluoride will be more ionic; if E is in Group 3A(13), the oxide will be more acidic and the fluoride will be more covalent.
14.16(a) reducing agent (b) Alkali metals have relatively low ionization energies, which means they easily lose the outermost electron.
(c) $2Na(s) + 2H_2O(l) \longrightarrow 2Na^+(aq) + 2OH^-(aq) + H_2(g)$
$2Na(s) + Cl_2(g) \longrightarrow 2NaCl(s)$
14.18 Density and ionic size increase down a group; the other three properties decrease down a group.
14.20 $2Na(s) + O_2(g) \longrightarrow Na_2O_2(s)$
14.22 $K_2CO_3(s) + 2HI(aq) \longrightarrow 2KI(aq) + H_2O(l) + CO_2(g)$
14.26 Group 2A(2) metals have an additional valence electron to increase the strength of metallic bonding, which leads to higher melting points, higher boiling points, greater hardness, and greater density.
14.27(a) $CaO(s) + H_2O(l) \longrightarrow Ca(OH)_2(s)$
(b) $2Ca(s) + O_2(g) \longrightarrow 2CaO(s)$
14.30(a) $BeO(s) + H_2O(l) \longrightarrow$ no reaction
(b) $BeCl_2(l) + 2Cl^-(\text{solvated}) \longrightarrow BeCl_4^{2-}(\text{solvated})$
Be behaves like other Group 2A(2) elements in reaction (b).
14.33 The electron removed from Group 2A(2) atoms occupies the outer *s* orbital, whereas in Group 3A(13) atoms, the electron occupies the outer *p* orbital. For example, the electron configuration for Be is $1s^22s^2$ and for B it is $1s^22s^22p^1$. It is easier to remove the *p* electron of B than an *s* electron of Be, because the energy of a *p* orbital is higher than that of the *s* orbital of the same level. Even though atomic size decreases because of increasing Z_{eff}, IE decreases from 2A(2) to 3A(13).
14.34(a) Most atoms form stable compounds when they complete their outer shell (octet). Some compounds of Group 3A(13) elements, like boron, have only six electrons around the central atom. Having fewer than eight electrons is called *electron deficiency*.
(b) $BF_3(g) + NH_3(g) \longrightarrow F_3B{-}NH_3(g)$
$B(OH)_3(aq) + OH^-(aq) \longrightarrow B(OH)_4^-(aq)$
14.36 $In_2O_3 < Ga_2O_3 < Al_2O_3$ **14.38** Apparent O.N., +3; actual O.N., +1. 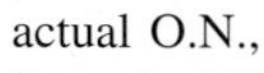 The anion I_3^- has the general formula AX_2E_3 and bond angles of 180°. $(Tl^{3+})(I^-)_3$ does not exist because of the low strength of the Tl—I bond.
14.43(a) $B_2O_3(s) + 2NH_3(g) \longrightarrow 2BN(s) + 3H_2O(g)$
(b) 1.30×10^2 kJ (c) 5.3 kg borax **14.44** Basicity in water is greater for the oxide of a metal. Tin(IV) oxide is more basic in water than carbon dioxide because tin has more metallic character than carbon. **14.46**(a) Ionization energy generally decreases down a group. (b) The deviations (increases) from the expected trend are due to the presence of the first transition series between Si and Ge and of the lanthanides between Sn and Pb. (c) Group 3A(13) **14.49** Atomic size increases down a group. As atomic size increases, ionization energy decreases and so it is easier to form a positive ion. An atom that is easier to ionize exhibits greater metallic character.

14.51(a) 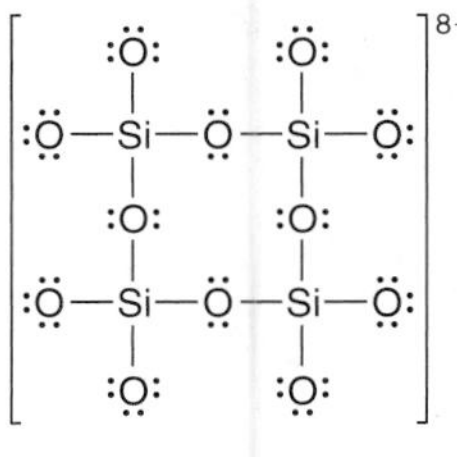 (b) 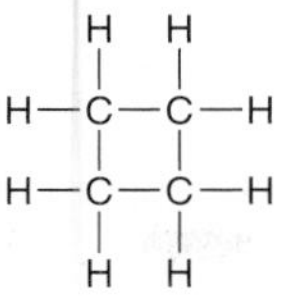

14.54(a) diamond, C (b) calcium carbonate, $CaCO_3$ (c) carbon dioxide, CO_2 (d) carbon monoxide, CO (e) silicon, Si **14.58**(a) −3 to +5 (b) For a group of nonmetals, the oxidation states range from the lowest, group number − 8, or 5 − 8 = −3 for Group 5A, to the highest, equal to the group number, or +5 for Group 5A. **14.61** $H_3AsO_4 < H_3PO_4 < HNO_3$
14.63(a) $4As(s) + 5O_2(g) \longrightarrow 2As_2O_5(s)$
(b) $2Bi(s) + 3F_2(g) \longrightarrow 2BiF_3(s)$
(c) $Ca_3As_2(s) + 6H_2O(l) \longrightarrow 3Ca(OH)_2(s) + 2AsH_3(g)$
14.65(a) $N_2(g) + 2Al(s) \xrightarrow{\Delta} 2AlN(s)$
(b) $PF_5(g) + 4H_2O(l) \longrightarrow H_3PO_4(aq) + 5HF(g)$
14.67 trigonal bipyramidal, with axial F atoms and equatorial Cl atoms; 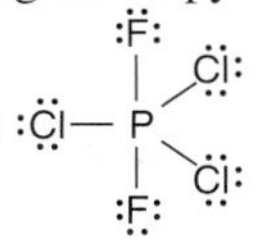

14.71(a) 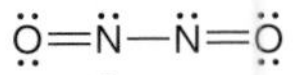 (b) 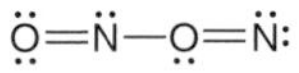
(c) 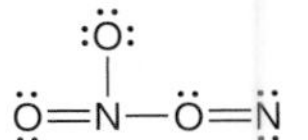 (d) 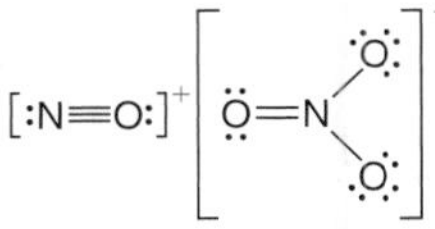

14.73(a) $2KNO_3(s) \xrightarrow{\Delta} 2KNO_2(s) + O_2(g)$ (b) $4KNO_3(s) \xrightarrow{\Delta} 2K_2O(s) + 2N_2(g) + 5O_2(g)$ **14.75**(a) Boiling point and conductivity vary in similar ways down both groups. (b) Degree of metallic character and types of bonding vary in similar ways down both groups. (c) Both P and S have allotropes, and both bond covalently with almost every other nonmetal. (d) Both N and O are diatomic gases at normal temperatures and pressures. (e) O_2 is a reactive gas, whereas N_2 is not. Nitrogen can have any of six oxidation states, whereas oxygen has two.
14.77(a) $NaHSO_4(aq) + NaOH(aq) \longrightarrow Na_2SO_4(aq) + H_2O(l)$
(b) $S_8(s) + 24F_2(g) \longrightarrow 8SF_6(g)$
(c) $FeS(s) + 2HCl(aq) \longrightarrow H_2S(g) + FeCl_2(aq)$
(d) $Te(s) + 2I_2(s) \longrightarrow TeI_4(s)$
14.79(a) acidic (b) acidic (c) basic (d) amphoteric (e) basic **14.81** $H_2O < H_2S < H_2Te$ **14.84**(a) O_3, ozone (b) SO_3, sulfur trioxide (c) SO_2, sulfur dioxide (d) H_2SO_4, sulfuric acid (e) $Na_2S_2O_3{\cdot}5H_2O$, sodium thiosulfate pentahydrate
14.86 $S_2F_{10}(g) \longrightarrow SF_4(g) + SF_6(g)$; O.N. of S in S_2F_{10} is +5; O.N. of S in SF_4 is +4; O.N. of S in SF_6 is +6. **14.88**(a) −1, +1, +3, +5, +7 (b) The electron configuration for Cl is [Ne] $3s^23p^5$. By gaining one electron, Cl achieves an octet. By forming covalent bonds, Cl completes or expands its valence level by maintaining electron pairs in bonds or as lone pairs. (c) Fluorine has only the −1 oxidation state because its small size and absence of *d* orbitals prevent it from forming more than one covalent bond. **14.90**(a) Cl—Cl bond is stronger than Br—Br bond. (b) Br—Br bond is stronger than I—I bond. (c) Cl—Cl bond is stronger than F—F bond. The fluorine atoms are so small that electron-electron repulsion of the lone pairs decreases the strength of the bond.
14.92(a) $3Br_2(l) + 6OH^-(aq) \longrightarrow 5Br^-(aq) + BrO_3^-(aq) + 3H_2O(l)$
(b) $ClF_5(l) + 6OH^-(aq) \longrightarrow 5F^-(aq) + ClO_3^-(aq) + 3H_2O(l)$
14.93(a) $2Rb(s) + Br_2(l) \longrightarrow 2RbBr(s)$
(b) $I_2(s) + H_2O(l) \longrightarrow HI(aq) + HIO(aq)$
(c) $Br_2(l) + 2I^-(aq) \longrightarrow I_2(s) + 2Br^-(aq)$
(d) $CaF_2(s) + H_2SO_4(l) \longrightarrow CaSO_4(s) + 2HF(g)$
14.95 HIO < HBrO < HClO < $HClO_2$ **14.99** $I_2 < Br_2 < Cl_2$, because Cl_2 is able to oxidize Re to the +6 oxidation state, Br_2 only to +5, and I_2 only to +4 **14.100** helium; argon **14.102** Only dispersion forces hold atoms of noble gases together. **14.106** $\Delta H_{soln} = -411$ kJ **14.110**(a) Second ionization energies for alkali metals are so high because the electron being removed is from the next lower energy level and these are very tightly held by the nucleus. Also, the alkali metal would lose its noble gas electron configuration.
(b) $2CsF_2(s) \longrightarrow 2CsF(s) + F_2(g)$; −405 kJ/mol
14.112(a) hyponitrous acid, $H_2N_2O_2$; nitroxyl, HNO
(b) 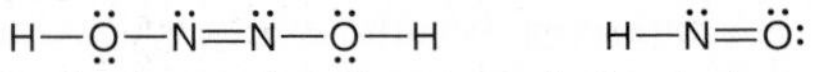
(c) In both species the shape is bent about the N atoms.
(d) 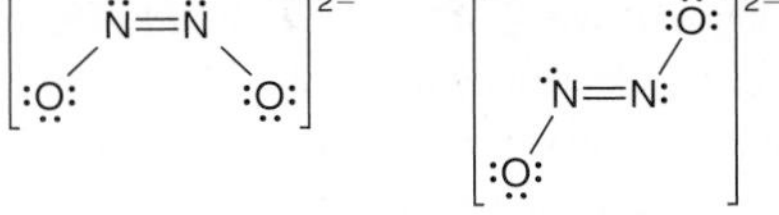
cis *trans*

14.116 13 t **14.118** In a disproportionation reaction, a substance acts as both a reducing agent and an oxidizing agent because atoms of an element within the substance attain both higher and lower oxidation states in the products. The disproportionation reactions are b, c, d, e, and f. **14.120**(a) Group 5A(15) (b) Group 7A(17) (c) Group 6A(16) (d) Group 1A(1) (e) Group 3A(13) (f) Group 8A(18)
14.122 117.2 kJ
14.127 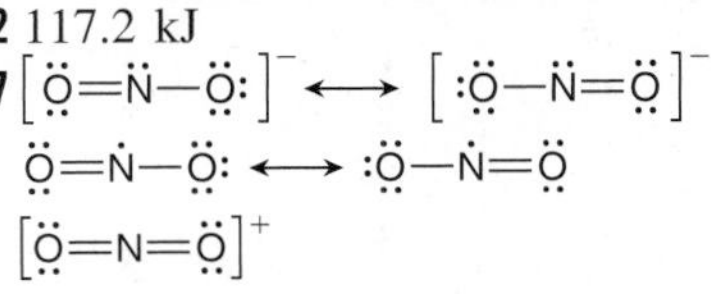

The nitronium ion (NO_2^+) has a linear shape because the central N atom has two surrounding electron groups, which achieve maximum repulsion at 180°. The nitrite ion (NO_2^-) bond angle is more compressed than the nitrogen dioxide (NO_2) bond angle because the lone pair of electrons takes up more space than the lone electron. **14.129** 2.29×10^4 g UF_6 **14.133** O^+, O^-, and O^{2+} **14.134**(a) 39.96 mass % in $CuHAsO_3$; As, 62.42 mass % in $(CH_3)_3As$ (b) 0.35 g $CuHAsO_3$

Chapter 15

Answers to Boxed Reading Problems: B15.1 butane, 2 peaks; 2-methylpropane, 2 peaks; pentane, 3 peaks; 2-methylbutane, 4 peaks; 2,2-dimethylpropane, 1 peak **B15.2** 0.08 J/mol **B15.4** ddATP: four complementary chain pieces; ddCTP: three complementary chain pieces

• **15.2**(a) Carbon's electronegativity is midway between the most metallic and most nonmetallic elements of Period 2. To attain a filled outer shell, carbon forms covalent bonds to other atoms in molecules, network covalent solids, and polyatomic ions. (b) Since carbon has four valence shell electrons, it forms four covalent bonds to attain an octet. (c) To reach the He electron configuration, a carbon atom must lose four electrons, requiring too much energy to form the C^{4+} cation. To reach the Ne electron configuration, the carbon atom must gain four electrons, also requiring too much energy to form the C^{4-} anion. (d) Carbon is able to bond to itself extensively because its small size allows for close approach and great orbital overlap. The extensive orbital overlap results in a strong, stable bond. (e) The C—C σ bond is short enough to allow sideways overlap of unhybridized *p* orbitals of neighboring C atoms. The sideways overlap of *p* orbitals results in the π bonds that are part of double and triple bonds. **15.3**(a) H, O, N, P, S, and halogens (b) Heteroatoms are atoms of any element other than carbon and hydrogen. (c) More electronegative than C: N, O, F, Cl, and Br; less electronegative than C: H and P. Sulfur and iodine have the same electronegativity as carbon. (d) Since carbon can bond to a wide variety of heteroatoms and to carbon atoms, it can form many different compounds. **15.6** The C—H and C—C bonds are unreactive because electronegativities are close and the bonds are short. The C—I bond is somewhat reactive because it is long and weak. The C=O bond is reactive because oxygen is more electronegative than carbon and the electron-rich π bond makes it attract electron-poor atoms. The C—Li bond is also reactive because the bond polarity results in an electron-rich region around carbon and an electron-poor region around lithium. **15.7**(a) An alkane and a cycloalkane are organic compounds that consist of carbon and hydrogen and have only single bonds. A cycloalkane has a ring of carbon atoms. An alkene is a hydrocarbon with at least one double bond. An alkyne is a hydrocarbon with at least one triple bond. (b) alkane = C_nH_{2n+2}, cycloalkane = C_nH_{2n}, alkene = C_nH_{2n}, alkyne = C_nH_{2n-2} (c) Alkanes and cycloalkanes are saturated hydrocarbons. **15.10** a, c, and f

15.13(a)

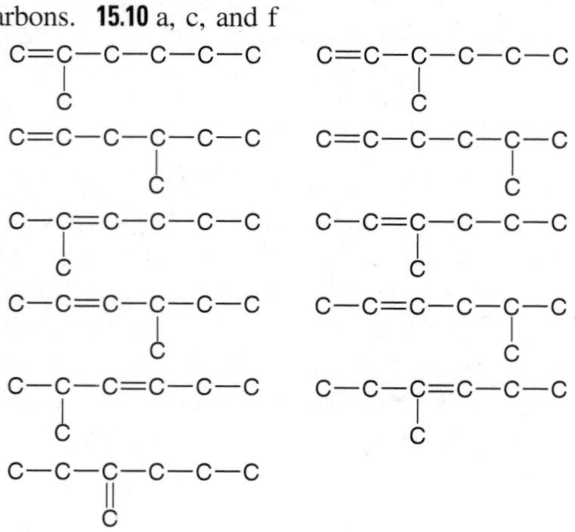

(b)

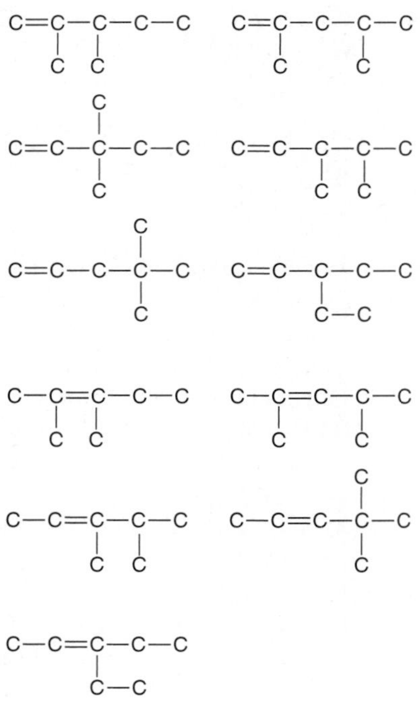

(c)

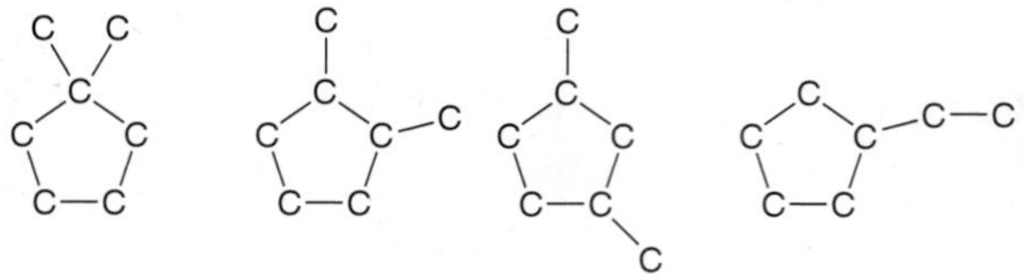

15.15(a)

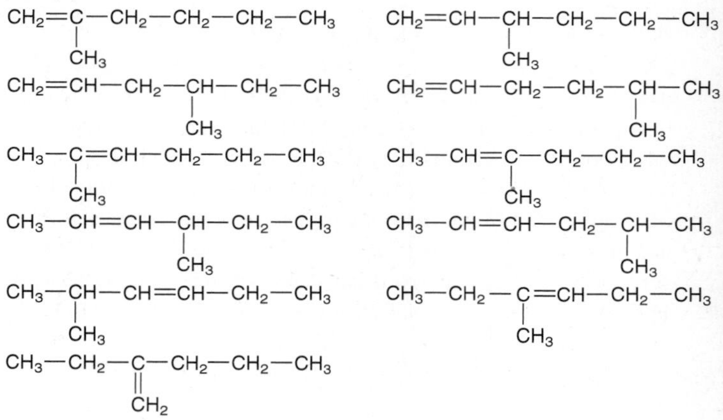

(b) 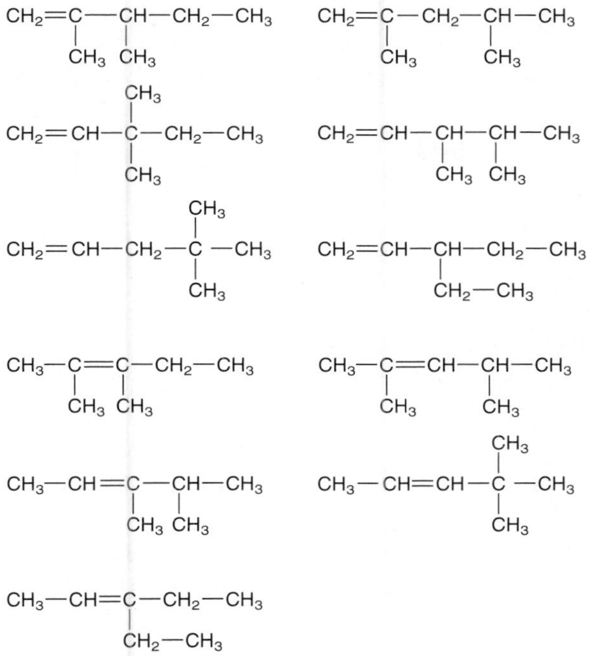

(c) 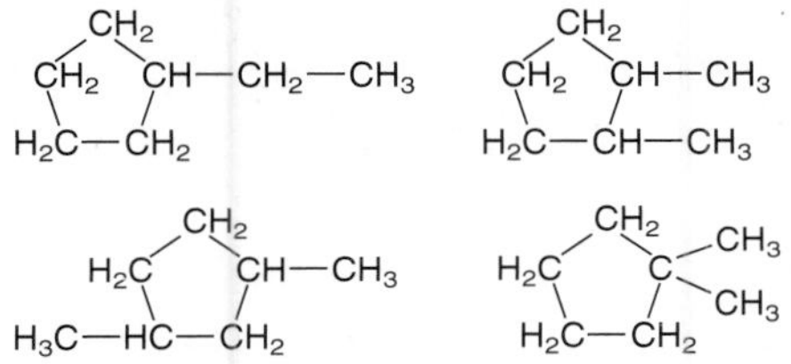

15.17(a) 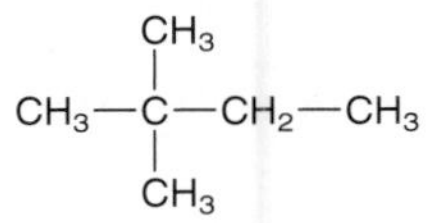

(b) $H_2C{=}CH{-}CH_2{-}CH_3$

(c) 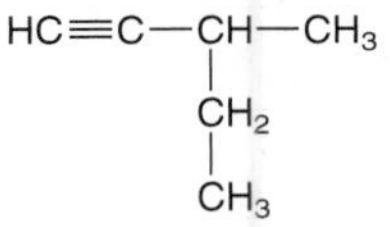

(d) Structure is correct.

15.19(a) 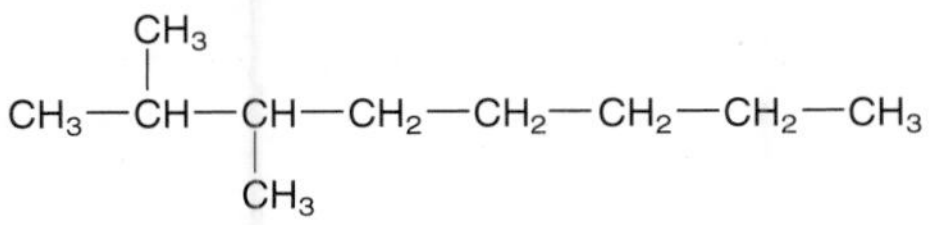

(b) 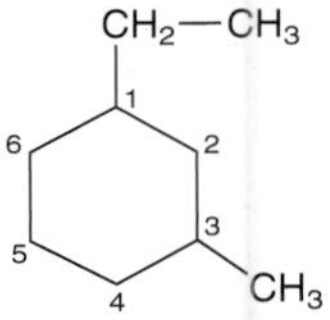

(c) 3,4-dimethylheptane (d) 2,2-dimethylbutane

15.21(a) 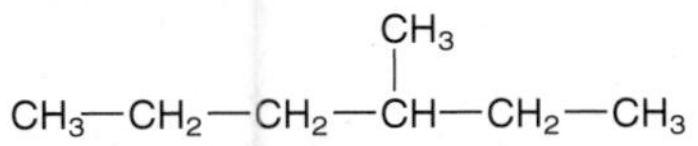

Correct name is 3-methylhexane.

(b) 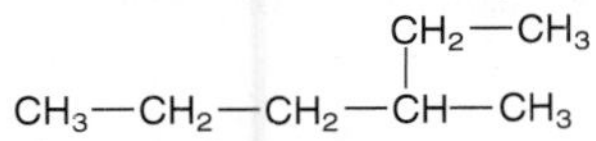

Correct name is 3-methylhexane.

(c) 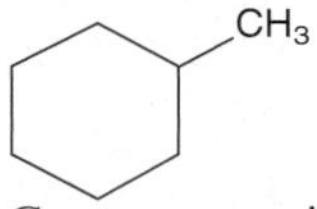

Correct name is methylcyclohexane.

(d) 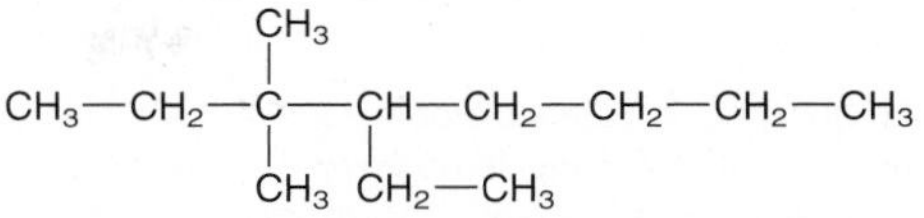

Correct name is 4-ethyl-3,3-dimethyloctane.

15.23(a) 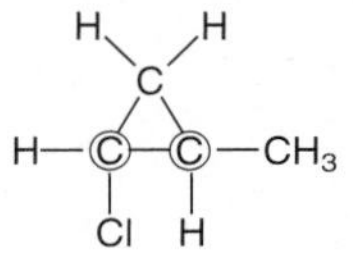

(b) 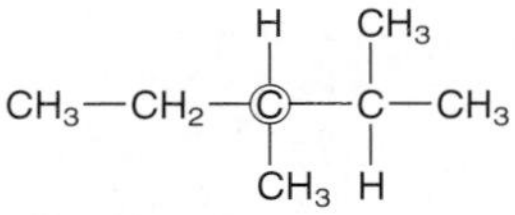

15.25(a) 3-Bromohexane is optically active.

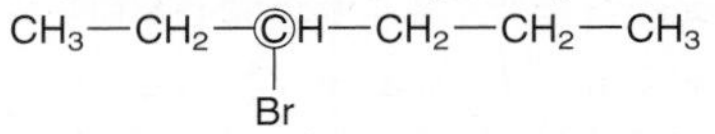

(b) 3-Chloro-3-methylpentane is not optically active.

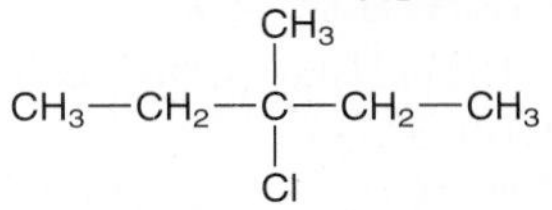

(c) 1,2-Dibromo-2-methylbutane is optically active.

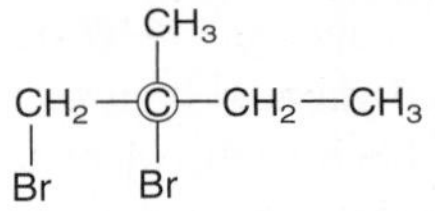

15.27(a) 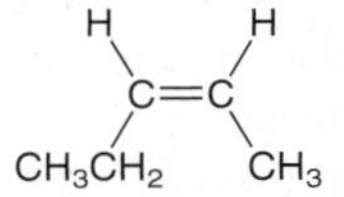

cis-2-pentene

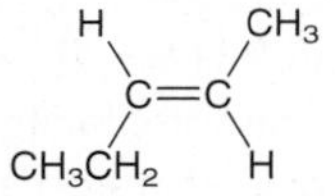

trans-2-pentene

(b) 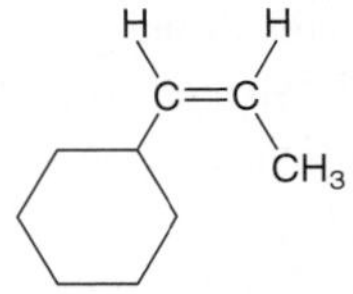

cis-1-cyclohexylpropene

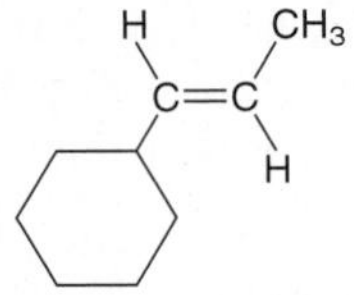

trans-1-cyclohexylpropene

(c) no geometric isomers

15.29(a) no geometric isomers

(b) 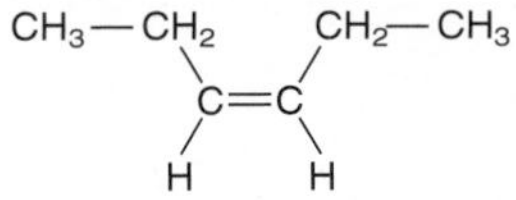

cis-3-hexene

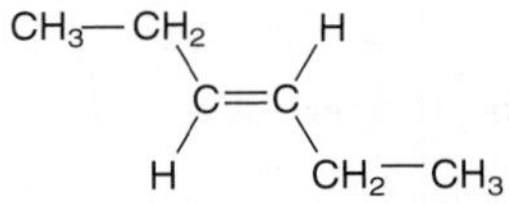

trans-3-hexene

(c) no geometric isomers

(d) 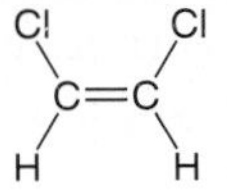

cis-1,2-dichloroethene

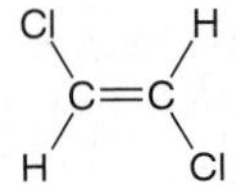

trans-1,2-dichloroethene

15.31

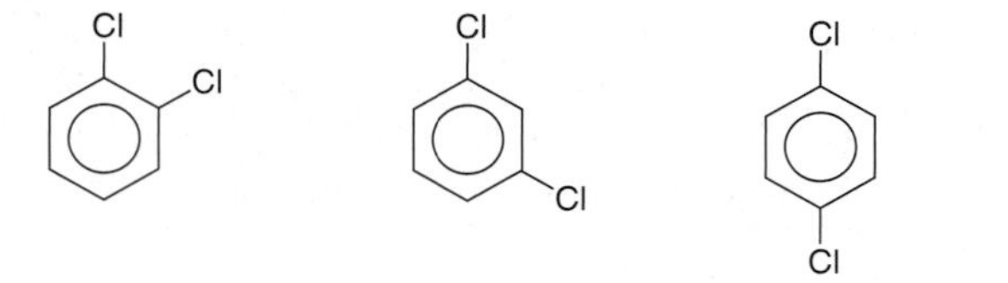

1,2-dichlorobenzene (*o*-dichlorobenzene) 1,3-dichlorobenzene (*m*-dichlorobenzene) 1,4-dichlorobenzene (*p*-dichlorobenzene)

15.33

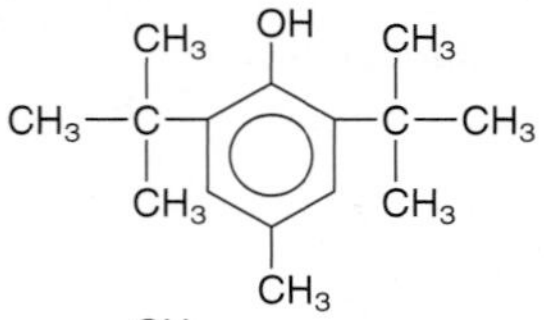

15.34

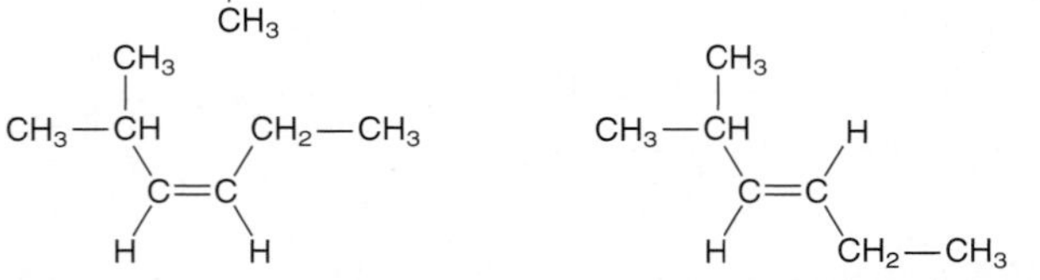

cis-2-methyl-3-hexene *trans*-2-methyl-3-hexene

The compound 2-methyl-2-hexene does not have *cis-trans* isomers. **15.38** π bond **15.40**(a) elimination (b) addition **15.42**(a) $CH_3CH_2CH{=}CHCH_2CH_3 + H_2O \xrightarrow{H^+} CH_3CH_2CH_2CH(OH)CH_2CH_3$

(b) $CH_3CHBrCH_3 + CH_3CH_2OK \longrightarrow CH_3CH{=}CH_2 + CH_3CH_2OH + KBr$

(c) $CH_3CH_3 + 2Cl_2 \xrightarrow{hv} CHCl_2CH_3 + 2HCl$

15.44(a) oxidation (b) reduction (c) reduction **15.46**(a) oxidized (b) oxidized **15.49**(a) Methylethylamine is more soluble because it has the ability to form H bonds with water molecules. (b) 1-Butanol has a higher melting point because it can form intermolecular H bonds. (c) Propylamine has a higher boiling point because it contains N—H bonds that allow H bonding, and trimethylamine cannot form H bonds. **15.52** Both groups react by addition to the π bond. The very polar C=O bond attracts the electron-rich O of water to the partially positive C. There is no such polarity in the alkene, so either C atom can be attacked, and two products result.

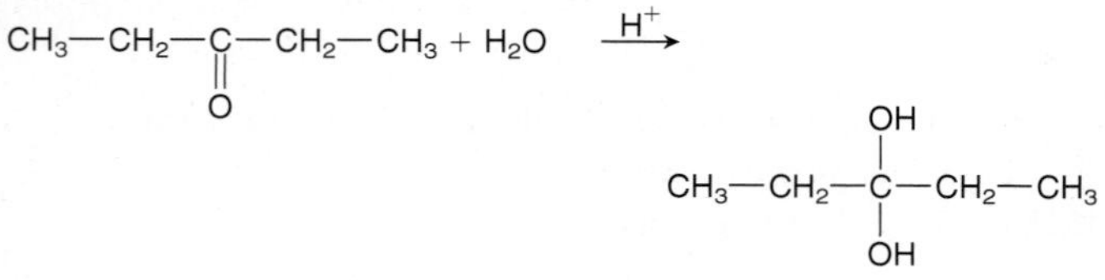

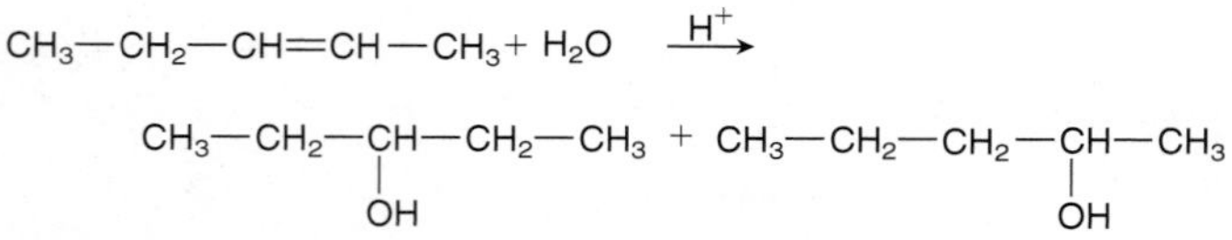

15.55 Esters and acid anhydrides form through dehydration-condensation reactions, and water is the other product. **15.57**(a) alkyl halide (b) nitrile (c) carboxylic acid (d) aldehyde

15.59(a)

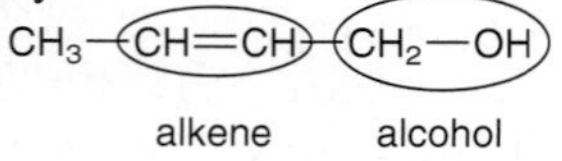

(b)

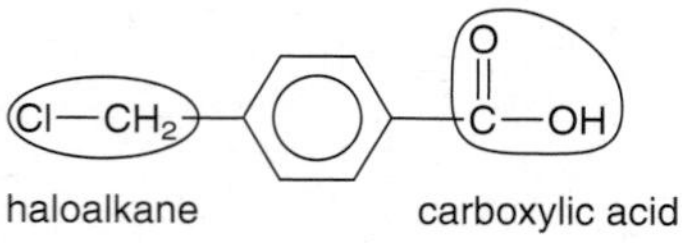

(c)

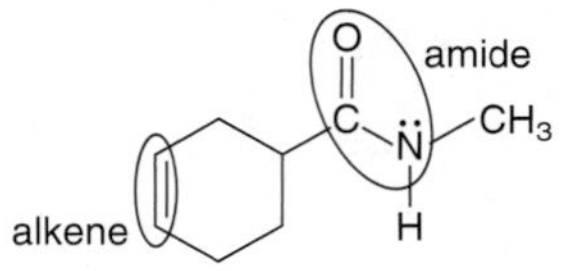

(d)

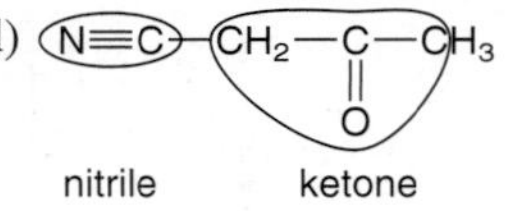

(e)

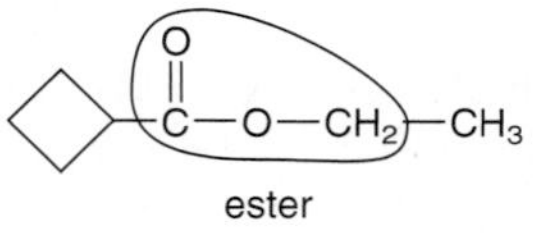

15.61

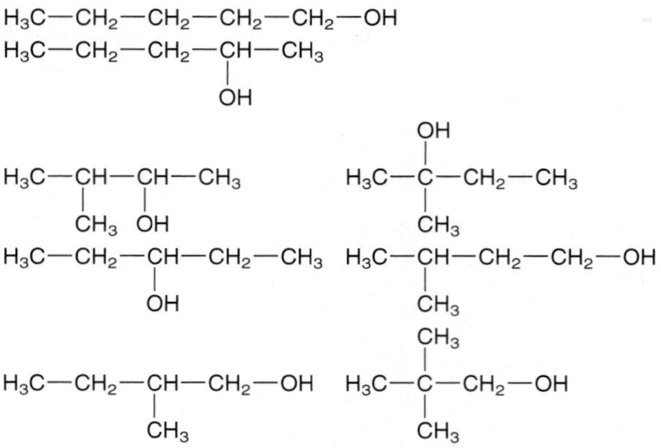

15.63

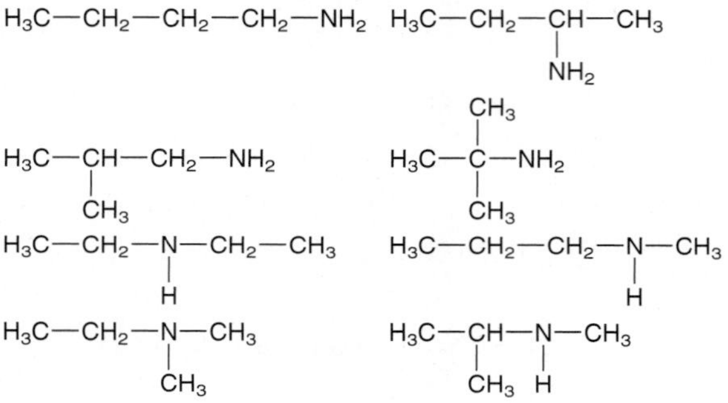

15.65(a)

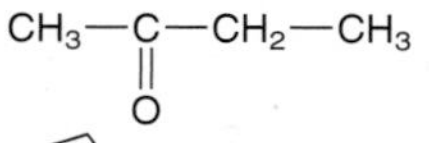

(b)

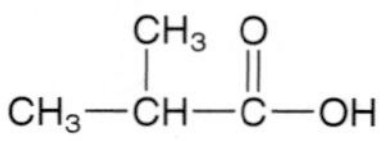

(c)

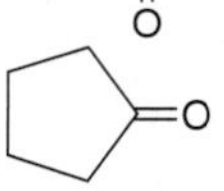

15.67(a)

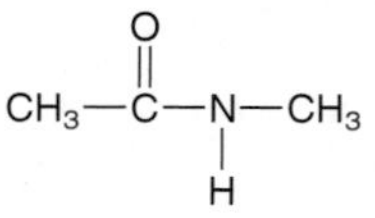

(b)

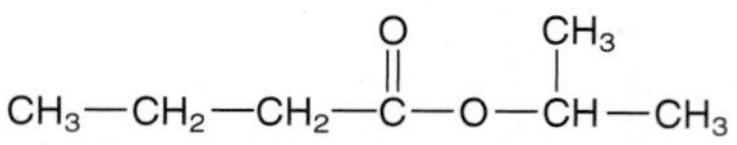

(c)

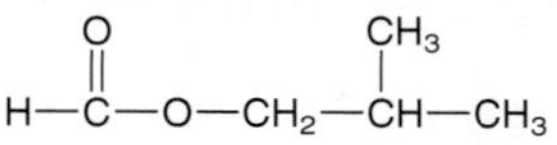

15.69(a)

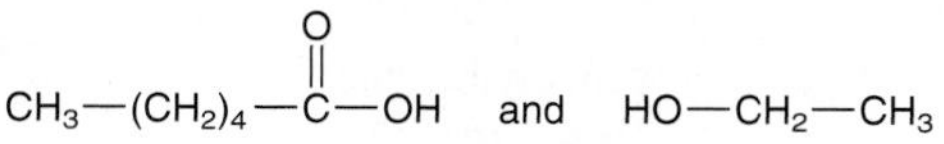

(b)

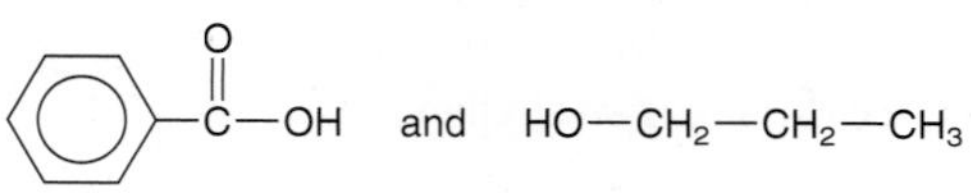

(c)

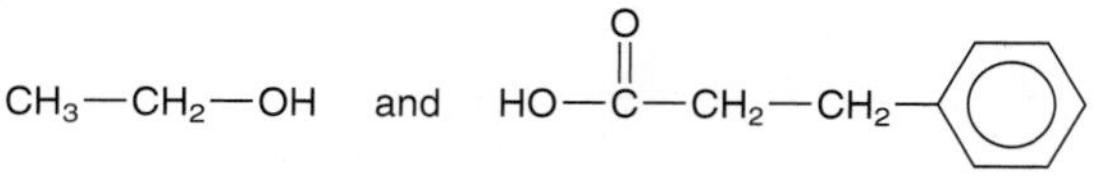

15.71(a) $CH_3—CH_2—OH$

(b)

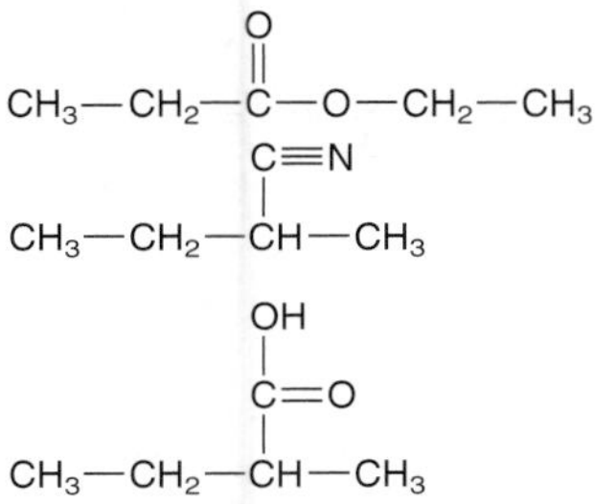

15.73(a) propanoic acid (b) ethylamine **15.77** addition reactions and condensation reactions **15.80** Dispersion forces strongly attract the long, unbranched chains of high-density polyethylene (HDPE). Low-density polyethylene (LDPE) has branching in the chains that prevents packing and weakens the attractions. **15.82** An amine and a carboxylic acid react to form nylon; a carboxylic acid and an alcohol form a polyester.

15.83(a) (b)

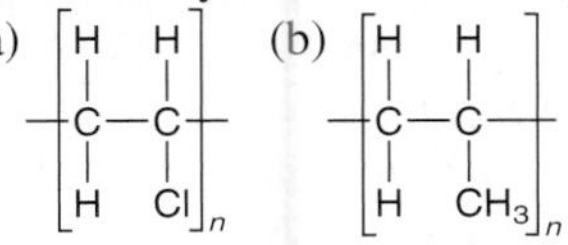

15.87(a) condensation (b) addition (c) condensation (d) condensation **15.89** The amino acid sequence in a protein determines its shape and structure, which determine its function. **15.92** The DNA base sequence determines the RNA base sequence, which determines the protein amino acid sequence.

15.93(a) (b) (c)

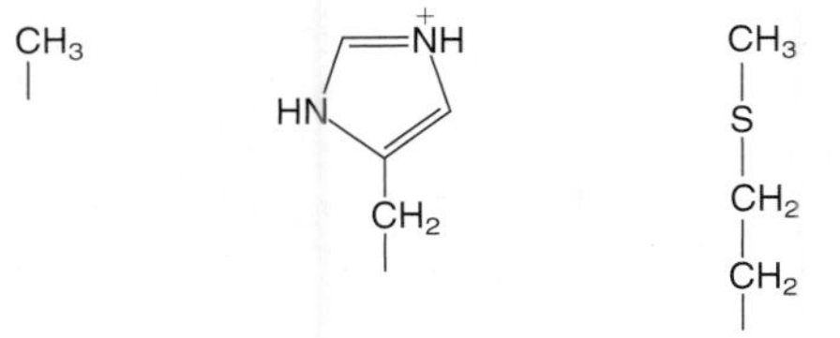

15.95(a)

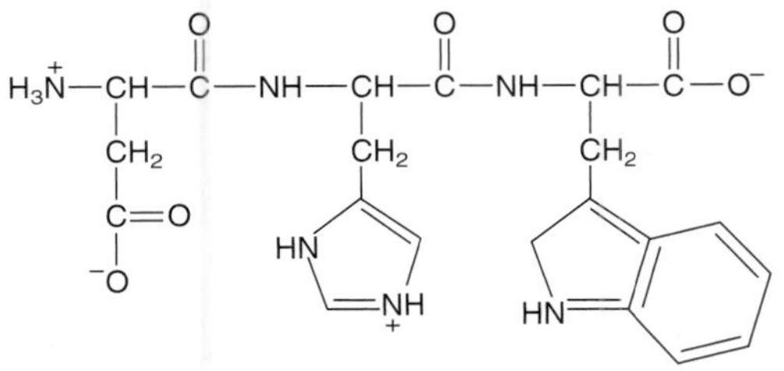

(b)

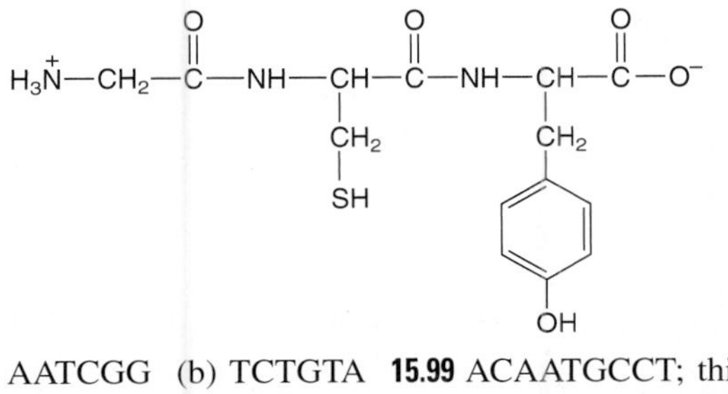

15.97(a) AATCGG (b) TCTGTA **15.99** ACAATGCCT; this sequence codes for three amino acids. **15.101**(a) Both R groups are from cysteine, which can form a disulfide bond (covalent bond). (b) Lysine and aspartic acid give a salt link. (c) Asparagine and serine will hydrogen bond. (d) Valine and phenylalanine interact through dispersion forces.

15.106(a) Perform an acid-catalyzed dehydration of the alcohol followed by addition of Br_2. (b) Oxidize 1 mol of ethanol to acetic acid, then react 1 mol of acetic acid with 1 mol of ethanol to form the ester.

15.108

$H_2N—CH_2—CH_2—CH_2—CH_2—CH_2—NH_2$
cadaverine

$H_2N—CH_2—CH_2—CH_2—CH_2—NH_2$
putrescine

$Br—CH_2CH_2—Br + 2CN^- \longrightarrow N{\equiv}C—CH_2CH_2—C{\equiv}N + 2Br^-$

$N{\equiv}C—CH_2CH_2—C{\equiv}N \xrightarrow{\text{reduction}} H_2N—CH_2CH_2CH_2CH_2—NH_2$

15.109(a)

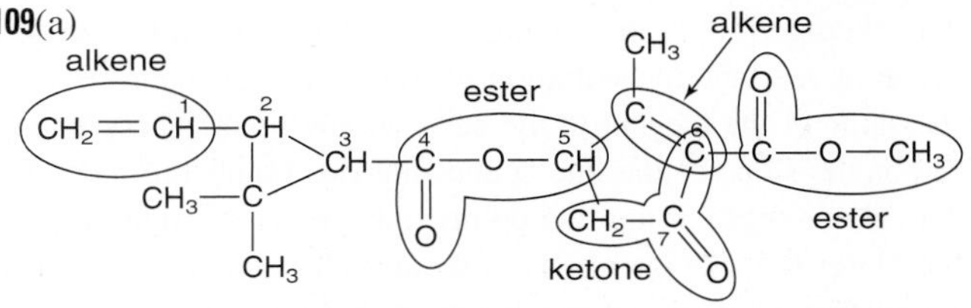

(b) Carbon 1 is sp^2 hybridized. Carbon 2 is sp^3 hybridized. Carbon 3 is sp^3 hybridized. Carbon 4 is sp^2 hybridized. Carbon 5 is sp^3 hybridized. Carbons 6 and 7 are sp^2 hybridized.

(c) Carbons 2, 3, and 5 are chiral centers, as they are each bonded to four different groups.

15.113 The resonance structures show that the bond between carbon and nitrogen will have some double bond character that restricts rotation around the bond.

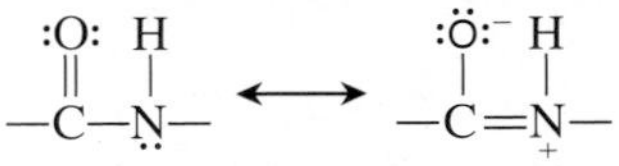

15.116(a) Hydrolysis requires the addition of water to break the peptide bonds. (b) glycine, 4; alanine, 1; valine, 3; proline, 6; serine, 7; arginine, 49 (c) 10,700 g/mol **15.117** When 2-butanone is reduced, equal amounts of both isomers are produced because the reaction does not favor the production of one over the other. The mixture is not optically active since the rotation of light to the right by one isomer cancels the rotation of light to the left by the other isomer.

Chapter 16

Answers to Boxed Reading Problems:

B16.2 (a)

Step 1	~~$NO(g)$~~ $+ O_3(g)$	$\longrightarrow$ ~~$NO_2(g)$~~ $+ O_2(g)$
Step 2	~~$NO_2(g)$~~ $+ O(g)$	$\longrightarrow$ ~~$NO(g)$~~ $+ O_2(g)$
Overall	$O_3(g) + O(g)$	$\longrightarrow 2O_2(g)$

(b) rate $= 3{\times}10^7$ molecule/s

B16.3 (a) Step 1 with Cl will have the higher value for the p factor. Since Cl is a single atom, no matter how it collides with the ozone molecule, the two particles should react, if the collision has enough energy. NO is a molecule. If the O_3 molecule collides with the N atom in the NO molecule, reaction can occur as a bond can form between N and O; if the O_3

molecule collides with the O atom in the NO molecule, reaction will not occur as the bond between N and O cannot form. The probability of a successful collision is smaller with NO.

(b) 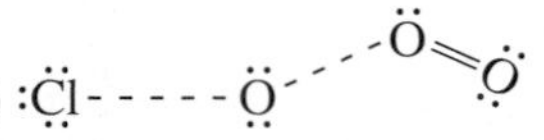

• **16.2** Reaction rate is proportional to concentration. An increase in pressure will increase the concentration, resulting in an increased rate. **16.3** The addition of water will lower the concentrations of all dissolved solutes, and the rate will decrease. **16.5** An increase in temperature increases the rate by increasing the number of collisions between particles, but more importantly, it increases the energy of collisions. **16.8**(a) The instantaneous rate is the rate at one point in time during the reaction. The average rate is the average over a period of time. On a graph of reactant concentration vs. time, the instantaneous rate is the slope of the tangent to the curve at any point. The average rate is the slope of the line connecting two points on the curve. The closer together the two points (the shorter the time interval), the closer the average rate is to the instantaneous rate. (b) The initial rate is the instantaneous rate at the point on the graph where $t = 0$, that is, when reactants are mixed.

16.10

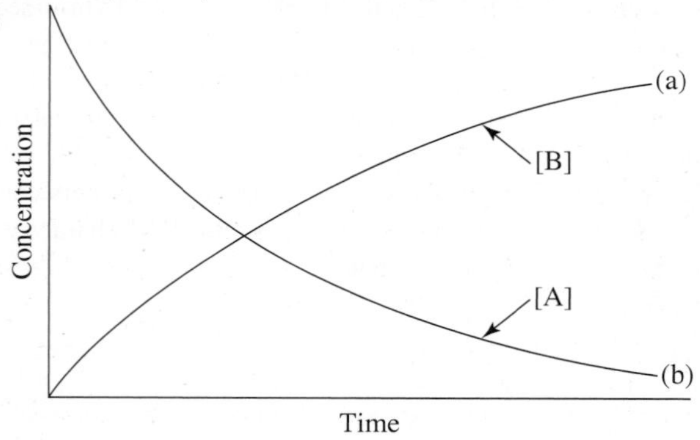

16.12(a) $\text{rate} = -\left(\frac{1}{2}\right)\frac{\Delta AX_2}{\Delta t}$

$= -\left(\frac{1}{2}\right)\frac{(0.0088\ M - 0.0500\ M)}{(20.0\text{ s} - 0\text{ s})}$

$= 0.0010\ M/\text{s}$

(b) 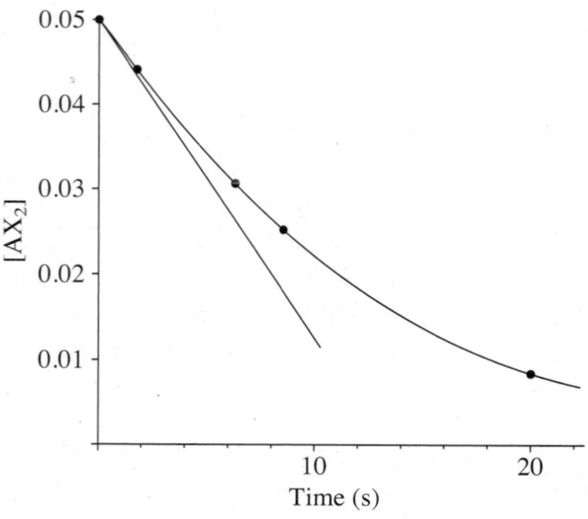

The initial rate is higher than the average rate because the rate decreases as reactant concentration decreases.

16.14 $\text{rate} = -\frac{1}{2}\frac{\Delta[\text{A}]}{\Delta t} = \frac{\Delta[\text{B}]}{\Delta t} = \frac{\Delta[\text{C}]}{\Delta t}$; 4 mol/L·s

16.16 $\text{rate} = -\frac{\Delta[\text{A}]}{\Delta t} = -\frac{1}{2}\frac{\Delta[\text{B}]}{\Delta t} = \frac{\Delta[\text{C}]}{\Delta t}$; 0.2 mol/L·s

16.18 $2N_2O_5(g) \longrightarrow 4NO_2(g) + O_2(g)$

16.21 $\text{rate} = -\frac{\Delta[N_2]}{\Delta t} = -\frac{1}{3}\frac{\Delta[H_2]}{\Delta t} = \frac{1}{2}\frac{\Delta[NH_3]}{\Delta t}$

16.22(a) $\text{rate} = -\frac{1}{3}\frac{\Delta[O_2]}{\Delta t} = \frac{1}{2}\frac{[\Delta O_3]}{\Delta t}$

(b) 1.45×10^{-5} mol/L·s

16.23(a) k is the rate constant, the proportionality constant in the rate law; it is reaction and temperature specific. (b) m represents the order of the reaction with respect to [A], and n represents the order of the reaction with respect to [B]. The order of a reactant does not necessarily equal its stoichiometric coefficient in the balanced equation. (c) $L^2/\text{mol}^2{\cdot}\text{min}$ **16.25**(a) Rate doubles. (b) Rate decreases by a factor of 4. (c) Rate increases by a factor of 9. **16.26** first order in BrO_3^-; first order in Br^-; second order in H^+; fourth order overall **16.28**(a) Rate doubles. (b) Rate is halved. (c) The rate increases by a factor of 16. **16.30** second order in NO_2; first order in Cl; third order overall **16.32**(a) Rate increases by a factor of 9. (b) Rate increases by a factor of 8. (c) Rate is halved. **16.34**(a) second order in A; first order in B (b) $\text{rate} = k[\text{A}]^2[\text{B}]$ (c) $5.00\times10^3\ L^2/\text{mol}^2{\cdot}\text{min}$ **16.36**(a) time^{-1} (b) L/mol·time (c) $L^2/\text{mol}^2{\cdot}\text{time}$ (d) $L^{3/2}/\text{mol}^{3/2}{\cdot}\text{time}$ **16.39**(a) first order (b) second order (c) zero order **16.41** 7 s **16.43**(a) $k = 0.0660\ \text{min}^{-1}$ (b) 21.0 min

16.45(a)

***x*-axis (time, s)**	**[NH_3]**	***y*-axis (ln [NH_3])**
0	4.000 M	1.38629
1.000	3.986 M	1.38279
2.000	3.974 M	1.37977

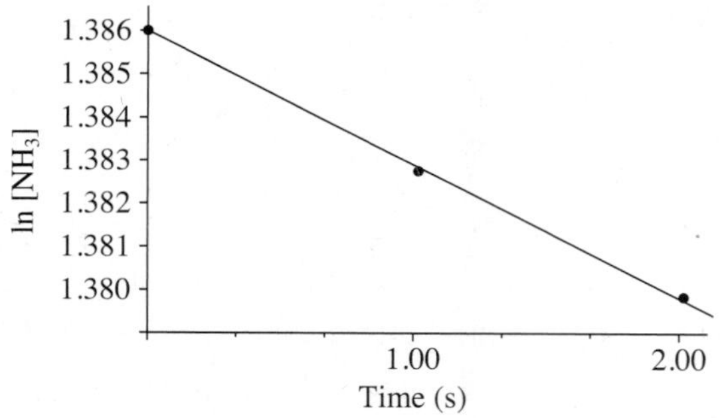

$k = 3\times10^{-3}\ \text{s}^{-1}$

(b) $t_{1/2} = 2\times10^2$ s

16.47 No, other factors that affect the rate are the energy and orientation of the collisions. **16.50** Measure the rate constant at a series of temperatures and plot ln k versus $1/T$. The slope of the line equals $-E_a/R$. **16.53** No, reaction is reversible and will eventually reach a state where the forward and reverse rates are equal. When this occurs, there are no concentrations equal to zero. Since some reactants are reformed from EF, the amount of EF will be less than 4×10^{-5} mol. **16.54** At the same temperature, both reaction mixtures have the same average kinetic energy, but the reactant molecules do not have the same average velocity. The trimethylamine molecule has greater mass than the ammonia molecule, so trimethylamine molecules will collide less often with HCl. Moreover, the bulky groups bonded to nitrogen in trimethylamine mean that collisions with HCl having the correct orientation occur less frequently. Therefore, the rate of the reaction between NH_3 and HCl is higher. **16.55** 12 unique collisions **16.57** 2.96×10^{-18} **16.59** 0.033 s^{-1}

16.61(a)

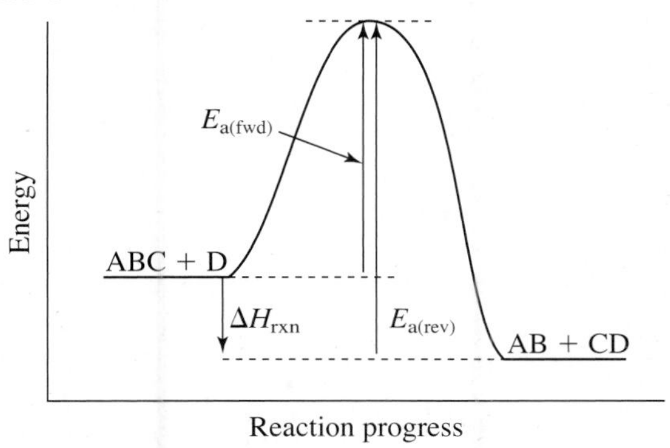

(b) 2.70×10^2 kJ/mol

(c)

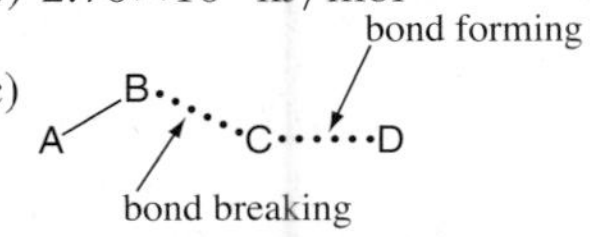

16.64(a) Because the enthalpy change is positive, the reaction is endothermic.

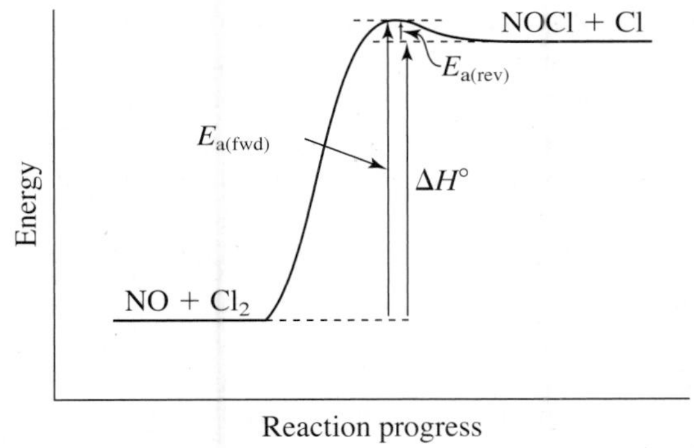

(b) 3 kJ (c)

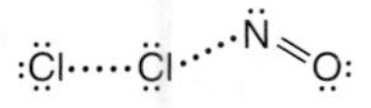

16.65 The rate of an overall reaction depends on the rate of the slowest step. The rate of the overall reaction will be lower than the average of the individual rates because the average includes higher rates as well. **16.69** The probability of three particles colliding with one another with the proper energy and orientation is much less than the probability for two particles.

16.70 No, the overall rate law must contain only reactants (no intermediates), and the overall rate is determined by the slow step.

16.72(a) $A(g) + B(g) + C(g) \longrightarrow D(g)$

(b) X and Y are intermediates.

(c)

Step	Molecularity	Rate Law
$A(g) + B(g) \rightleftharpoons X(g)$	bimolecular	$rate_1 = k_1[A][B]$
$X(g) + C(g) \longrightarrow Y(g)$	bimolecular	$rate_2 = k_2[X][C]$
$Y(g) \longrightarrow D(g)$	unimolecular	$rate_3 = k_3[Y]$

(d) yes (e) yes **16.74** The proposed mechanism is valid because the individual steps are chemically reasonable, they add to give the overall equation, and the rate law for the mechanism matches the observed rate law. **16.77** No. A catalyst changes the mechanism of a reaction to one with lower activation energy. Lower activation energy means a faster reaction. An increase in temperature does not influence the activation energy, but increases the fraction of collisions with sufficient energy to equal or exceed the activation energy. **16.78**(a) No. The spark provides energy that is absorbed by the H_2 and O_2 molecules to achieve the activation energy. (b) Yes. The powdered metal acts as a heterogeneous catalyst, providing a surface on which the oxygen-hydrogen reaction can proceed with a lower activation energy.

16.83(a) Water does not appear as a reactant in the rate-determining step.

(b) Step 1: $rate_1 = k_1[(CH_3)_3CBr]$
Step 2: $rate_2 = k_2[(CH_3)_3C^+]$
Step 3: $rate_3 = k_3[(CH_3)_3COH_2{}^+]$

(c) $(CH_3)_3C^+$ and $(CH_3)_3COH_2{}^+$

(d) The rate-determining step is step 1. The rate law for this step agrees with the rate law observed with $k = k_1$.

16.85 4.61×10^4 J/mol **16.89**(a) Rate increases 2.5 times. (b) Rate is halved. (c) Rate decreases by a factor of 0.01. (d) Rate does not change. **16.90** second order **16.93** 57 yr **16.96**(a) 0.21 h^{-1}; 3.3 h (b) 6.6 h (c) If the concentration of sucrose is relatively low, the concentration of water remains nearly constant even with small changes in the amount of water. This gives an apparent zero-order reaction with respect to water. Thus, the reaction is first order overall because the rate does not change with changes in the amount of water. **16.99**(a) 0.68 M (b) 0.57 **16.102** 71 kPa **16.106** 7.3×10^3 J/mol **16.108**(a) 2.4×10^{-15} M (b) 2.4×10^{-11} mol/L·s **16.111**(a) 2.8 days (b) 7.4 days (c) 4.5 mol/m^3 **6.114**(a) $rate_1 = 1.7\times10^{-5}$ M s^{-1}; $rate_2 = 3.4\times10^{-5}$ M s^{-1}; $rate_3 = 3.4\times10^{-5}$ M s^{-1} (b) zero order with respect to $S_2O_8{}^{2-}$; first order with respect to I^- (c) 4.3×10^{-4} s^{-1} (d) rate = $(4.3\times10^{-4}$ $s^{-1})$[KI] **16.117**(a) 7×10^4 cells/L (b) 2.0×10^1 min **16.120**(a) Use the Monod equation.

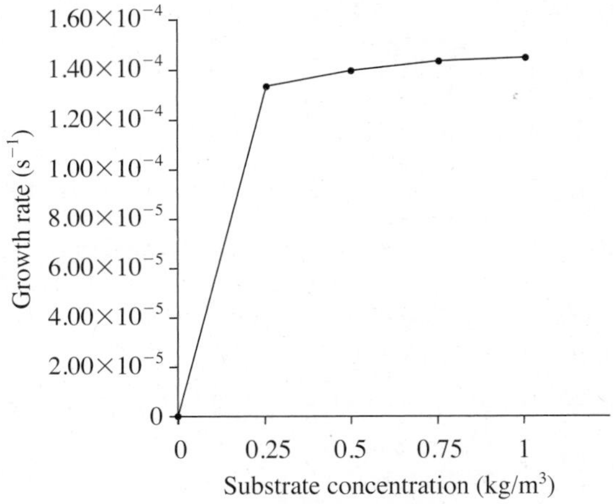

(b) 8.2×10^3 cells/m^3 (c) 8.4×10^3 cells/m^3

16.125(a) 8.0×10^1 s (b) 59 s (c) 2.6×10^2 s

Chapter 17

Answers to Boxed Reading Problem: B17.1 (a) Enzyme 3 (d) If F inhibited enzyme 6, then the second branch would not take place when enough F was made.

• **17.1** If the change is one of concentrations, it results temporarily in more products and less reactants. After equilibrium is re-established, K_c remains unchanged because the ratio of products and reactants remains the same. **17.7** The equilibrium constant expression is $K = [O_2]$. If the temperature remains constant, K remains constant. If the initial amount of Li_2O_2 present is sufficient to reach equilibrium, the amount of O_2 obtained will be constant.

17.8(a) $Q = \dfrac{[HI]^2}{[H_2][I_2]}$

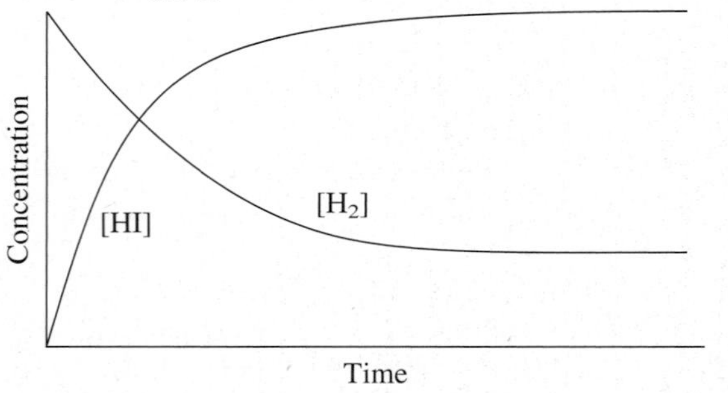

The value of Q increases as a function of time until it reaches the value of K. (b) no **17.11** Yes. If Q_1 is for the formation of 1 mol NH_3 from H_2 and N_2, and Q_2 is for the formation of NH_3 from H_2 and 1 mol of N_2, then $Q_2 = Q_1^2$.

17.12(a) $4NO(g) + O_2(g) \rightleftharpoons 2N_2O_3(g)$;

$$Q_c = \frac{[N_2O_3]^2}{[NO]^4[O_2]}$$

(b) $SF_6(g) + 2SO_3(g) \rightleftharpoons 3SO_2F_2(g)$;

$$Q_c = \frac{[SO_2F_2]^3}{[SF_6][SO_3]^2}$$

(c) $2SClF_5(g) + H_2(g) \rightleftharpoons S_2F_{10}(g) + 2HCl(g)$;

$$Q_c = \frac{[S_2F_{10}][HCl]^2}{[SClF_5]^2[H_2]}$$

17.14(a) $2NO_2Cl(g) \rightleftharpoons 2NO_2(g) + Cl_2(g)$;

$$Q_c = \frac{[NO_2]^2[Cl_2]}{[NO_2Cl]^2}$$

(b) $2POCl_3(g) \rightleftharpoons 2PCl_3(g) + O_2(g)$;

$$Q_c = \frac{[PCl_3]^2[O_2]}{[POCl_3]^2}$$

(c) $4NH_3(g) + 3O_2(g) \rightleftharpoons 2N_2(g) + 6H_2O(g)$;

$$Q_c = \frac{[N_2]^2[H_2O]^6}{[NH_3]^4[O_2]^3}$$

17.16(a) 7.9 (b) 3.2×10^{-5}

17.18(a) $2Na_2O_2(s) + 2CO_2(g) \rightleftharpoons 2Na_2CO_3(s) + O_2(g)$;

$$Q_c = \frac{[O_2]}{[CO_2]^2}$$

(b) $H_2O(l) \rightleftharpoons H_2O(g)$; $Q_c = [H_2O(g)]$

(c) $NH_4Cl(s) \rightleftharpoons NH_3(g) + HCl(g)$; $Q_c = [NH_3][HCl]$

17.20(a) $2NaHCO_3(s) \rightleftharpoons Na_2CO_3(s) + CO_2(g) + H_2O(g)$;

$Q_c = [CO_2][H_2O]$

(b) $SnO_2(s) + 2H_2(g) \rightleftharpoons Sn(s) + 2H_2O(g)$;

$$Q_c = \frac{[H_2O]^2}{[H_2]^2}$$

(c) $H_2SO_4(l) + SO_3(g) \rightleftharpoons H_2S_2O_7(l)$;

$$Q_c = \frac{1}{[SO_3]}$$

17.23(a)

(1)	$Cl_2(g) + F_2(g) \rightleftharpoons 2ClF(g)$
(2)	$2ClF(g) + 2F_2(g) \rightleftharpoons 2ClF_3(g)$
overall:	$Cl_2(g) + 3F_2(g) \rightleftharpoons 2ClF_3(g)$

(b) $$Q_{overall} = Q_1Q_2 = \frac{\cancel{[ClF]^2}}{[Cl_2][F_2]} \times \frac{[ClF_3]^2}{\cancel{[ClF]^2}[F_2]^2} = \frac{[ClF_3]^2}{[Cl_2][F_2]^3}$$

17.25 K_c and K_p are equal when $\Delta n_{gas} = 0$. **17.26**(a) smaller (b) Assuming that $RT > 1$ ($T > 12.2$ K), $K_p > K_c$ if there are more moles of products than reactants at equilibrium, and $K_p < K_c$ if there are more moles of reactants than products. **17.27**(a) 3 (b) −1 (c) 3 **17.29**(a) 3.2 (b) 28.5 **17.31**(a) 0.15 (b) 3.6×10^{-7} **17.33** The reaction quotient (Q) and equilibrium constant (K) are determined by the ratio [products]/[reactants]. When $Q < K$, the reaction proceeds to the right to form more products. **17.35** no; to the left **17.38** At equilibrium, equal concentrations of $CFCl_3$ and HCl exist, regardless of starting reactant concentrations, because the product coefficients are equal. **17.40**(a) The approximation applies when the change in concentration from initial concentration to equilibrium concentration is so small that it is insignificant; this occurs when K is small and initial concentration is large. (b) This approximation should not be used when the change in concentration is greater than 5%. This can occur when $[reactant]_{initial}$ is very small or when change in [reactant] is relatively large due to a large K. **17.41** 50.8

17.43 Concentration (*M*)	$PCl_5(g)$	$\rightleftharpoons$	$PCl_3(g)$	+ $Cl_2(g)$
Initial	0.075		0	0
Change	$-x$		$+x$	$+x$
Equilibrium	$0.075 - x$		x	x

17.45 28 atm **17.47** 0.33 atm **17.49** 3.5×10^{-3} M **17.51** [HI] = 0.0152 M; $[I_2]$ = 0.00328 M **17.53** $[I_2]_{eq} = [Cl_2]_{eq}$ = 0.0199 M; $[ICl]_{eq}$ = 0.0601 M **17.55** 6.01×10^{-6} **17.58** Equilibrium position refers to the specific concentrations or pressures of reactants and products that exist at equilibrium, whereas equilibrium constant is the overall ratio of equilibrium concentrations or pressures. Equilibrium position changes as a result of a change in reactant and product concentrations. **17.59**(a) B, because the amount of product increases with temperature (b) A, because the lowest temperature will give the least product **17.63**(a) shifts toward products (b) shifts toward products (c) does not shift (d) shifts toward reactants **17.65**(a) more F and less F_2 (b) more C_2H_2 and H_2 and less CH_4 **17.67**(a) no effect (b) less H_2 and O_2 and more H_2O **17.69**(a) no change (b) increase volume **17.71**(a) amount decreases (b) amounts increase (c) amounts increase (d) amount decreases **17.73** 2.0 **17.76**(a) lower temperature, higher pressure (b) Q decreases; no change in K (c) Reaction rates are lower at lower temperatures, so a catalyst is used to speed up the reaction. **17.78**(a) $P_{N_2} = 31$ atm; $P_{H_2} = 93$ atm; $P_{total} = 174$ atm (b) $P_{N_2} = 18$ atm; $P_{H_2} = 111$ atm; $P_{total} = 179$ atm; not a valid argument **17.81** 0.204 atm **17.84**(a) 3×10^{-3} atm (b) high pressure; low temperature (c) 2×10^5 (d) No, because water condenses at a higher temperature. **17.87**(a) 0.016 atm (b) $K_c = 5.6\times10^2$; $P_{O_2} = 0.16$ atm **17.89** 12.5 g $CaCO_3$ **17.93** Both concentrations increased by a factor of 2.2. **17.95**(a) 3.0×10^{-14} atm (b) 0.013 pg CO/L **17.97**(a) 98.0% (b) 99.0% (c) 2.60×10^5 J/mol **17.99**(a) $2CH_4(g) + O_2(g) + 2H_2O(g) \rightleftharpoons 2CO_2(g) + 6H_2(g)$ (b) 1.76×10^{29} (c) 3.19×10^{23} (d) 48 atm **17.100**(a) 4.0×10^{-21} atm (b) 5.5×10^{-8} atm (c) 29 N atoms/L; 4.0×10^{14} H atoms/L (d) The more reasonable step is $N_2(g) + H(g) \longrightarrow NH(g) + N(g)$. With only 29 N atoms in 1.0 L, the first reaction would produce virtually no $NH(g)$ molecules. There are orders of magnitude more N_2 molecules than N atoms, so the second reaction is the more reasonable step. **17.103**(a) $P_{N_2} = 0.780$ atm; $P_{O_2} = 0.210$ atm; $P_{NO} = 2.67\times10^{-16}$ atm (b) 0.990 atm (c) $K_c = K_p = 4.35\times10^{-31}$ **17.105**(a) 1.26×10^{-3} (b) 794 (c) −51.8 kJ (d) 1.2×10^4 J/mol **17.109**(a) 1.52 (b) 0.9626 atm (c) 0.2000 mol CO (d) 0.01097 M

Chapter 18

18.2 All Arrhenius acids have H in their formula and produce hydronium ion (H_3O^+) in aqueous solution. All Arrhenius bases have OH in their formula and produce hydroxide ion (OH^-) in aqueous solution. Neutralization occurs when each H_3O^+ ion combines with an OH^- ion to form two molecules of H_2O. Chemists found the reaction of any strong base with any strong acid always had a ΔH of −56 kJ/mol H_2O produced.
18.4 Strong acids and bases dissociate completely into ions when dissolved in water. Weak acids and bases dissociate only partially. The characteristic property of all weak acids is that a great majority of the acid molecules are undissociated.
18.5 a, c, and d
18.7 b and d

18.9(a) $K_a = \dfrac{[CN^-][H_3O^+]}{[HCN]}$

(b) $K_a = \dfrac{[CO_3^{2-}][H_3O^+]}{[HCO_3^-]}$

(c) $K_a = \dfrac{[HCOO^-][H_3O^+]}{[HCOOH]}$

18.11(a) $K_a = \dfrac{[NO_2^-][H_3O^+]}{[HNO_2]}$

(b) $K_a = \dfrac{[CH_3COO^-][H_3O^+]}{[CH_3COOH]}$

(c) $K_a = \dfrac{[BrO_2^-][H_3O^+]}{[HBrO_2]}$

18.13 $CH_3COOH < HF < HIO_3 < HI$ **18.15**(a) weak acid (b) strong base (c) weak acid (d) strong acid **18.17**(a) strong base (b) strong acid (c) weak acid (d) weak acid
18.22(a) The acid with the smaller K_a (4×10^{-5}) has the higher pH, because less dissociation yields fewer hydronium ions. (b) The acid with the larger pK_a (3.5) has the higher pH, because it has a smaller K_a and, thus, lower $[H_3O^+]$. (c) Lower concentration (0.01 M) contains fewer hydronium ions. (d) A 0.1 M weak acid solution contains fewer hydronium ions. (e) The 0.01 M base solution contains more hydroxide ions, so fewer hydronium ions. (f) The solution that has pOH = 6.0 has the higher pH: pH = 14.0 − 6.0 = 8.0.
18.23(a) 12.05; basic (b) 11.13; acidic **18.25**(a) 2.212; acidic (b) −0.708; basic
18.27(a) $[H_3O^+] = 1.4\times10^{-10}$ M, $[OH^-] = 7.1\times10^{-5}$ M, pOH = 4.15
(b) $[H_3O^+] = 2.7\times10^{-5}$ M, $[OH^-] = 3.7\times10^{-10}$ M, pH = 4.57
18.29(a) $[H_3O^+] = 1.7\times10^{-5}$ M, $[OH^-] = 5.9\times10^{-10}$ M, pOH = 9.23
(b) $[H_3O^+] = 4.5\times10^{-9}$ M, $[OH^-] = 2.2\times10^{-6}$ M, pH = 8.36
18.31 4.8×10^{-4} mol OH^-/L **18.33** 1.4×10^{-4} mol OH^-
18.36(a) Rising temperature increases the value of K_w. (b) $K_w = 2.5\times10^{-14}$; pOH = 6.80; $[OH^-] = 1.6\times10^{-7}$ M
18.37 The Brønsted-Lowry theory defines acids as proton donors and bases as proton acceptors, while the Arrhenius definition looks at acids as containing ionizable hydrogen atoms and at bases as containing hydroxide ions. In both definitions, an acid produces H_3O^+ ions and a base produces OH^- ions when added to water. Ammonia and carbonate ion are two Brønsted-Lowry bases that are not Arrhenius bases because they do not contain OH^- ions. Brønsted-Lowry acids must contain an ionizable hydrogen atom in order to be proton donors, so a Brønsted-Lowry acid is also an Arrhenius acid. **18.40** An amphiprotic species is one that can lose a proton to act as an acid or gain a proton to act as a base. The dihydrogen phosphate ion, $H_2PO_4^-$, is an example.
$H_2PO_4^-(aq) + OH^-(aq) \longrightarrow H_2O(l) + HPO_4^{2-}(aq)$
$H_2PO_4^-(aq) + HCl(aq) \longrightarrow H_3PO_4(aq) + Cl^-(aq)$
18.41(a) $H_3PO_4(aq) + H_2O(l) \rightleftharpoons H_2PO_4^-(aq) + H_3O^+(aq)$

$K_a = \dfrac{[H_3O^+][H_2PO_4^-]}{[H_3PO_4]}$

(b) $C_6H_5COOH(aq) + H_2O(l) \rightleftharpoons C_6H_5COO^-(aq) + H_3O^+(aq)$

$K_a = \dfrac{[H_3O^+][C_6H_5COO^-]}{[C_6H_5COOH]}$

(c) $HSO_4^-(aq) + H_2O(l) \rightleftharpoons SO_4^{2-}(aq) + H_3O^+(aq)$

$K_a = \dfrac{[H_3O^+][SO_4^{2-}]}{[HSO_4^-]}$

18.43(a) Cl^- (b) HCO_3^- (c) OH^- **18.45**(a) NH_4^+ (b) NH_3 (c) $C_{10}H_{14}N_2H^+$

18.47(a) $HCl + H_2O \rightleftharpoons Cl^- + H_3O^+$
acid base base acid
Conjugate acid-base pairs: HCl/Cl^- and H_3O^+/H_2O
(b) $HClO_4 + H_2SO_4 \rightleftharpoons ClO_4^- + H_3SO_4^+$
acid base base acid
Conjugate acid-base pairs: $HClO_4/ClO_4^-$ and $H_3SO_4^+/H_2SO_4$
(c) $HPO_4^{2-} + H_2SO_4 \rightleftharpoons H_2PO_4^- + HSO_4^-$
base acid acid base
Conjugate acid-base pairs: H_2SO_4/HSO_4^- and $H_2PO_4^-/HPO_4^{2-}$
18.49(a) $NH_3 + H_3PO_4 \rightleftharpoons NH_4^+ + H_2PO_4^-$
base acid acid base
Conjugate acid-base pairs: $H_3PO_4/H_2PO_4^-$ and NH_4^+/NH_3
(b) $CH_3O^- + NH_3 \rightleftharpoons CH_3OH + NH_2^-$
base acid acid base
Conjugate acid-base pairs: NH_3/NH_2^- and CH_3OH/CH_3O^-
(c) $HPO_4^{2-} + HSO_4^- \rightleftharpoons H_2PO_4^- + SO_4^{2-}$
base acid acid base
Conjugate acid-base pairs: HSO_4^-/SO_4^{2-} and $H_2PO_4^-/HPO_4^{2-}$
18.51(a) $OH^-(aq) + H_2PO_4^-(aq) \rightleftharpoons H_2O(l) + HPO_4^{2-}(aq)$
Conjugate acid-base pairs: $H_2PO_4^-/HPO_4^{2-}$ and H_2O/OH^-
(b) $HSO_4^-(aq) + CO_3^{2-}(aq) \rightleftharpoons SO_4^{2-}(aq) + HCO_3^-(aq)$
Conjugate acid-base pairs: HSO_4^-/SO_4^{2-} and HCO_3^-/CO_3^{2-}
18.53 $K_c > 1$: $HS^- + HCl \rightleftharpoons H_2S + Cl^-$
$K_c < 1$: $H_2S + Cl^- \rightleftharpoons HS^- + HCl$
18.55 $K_c > 1$ for both a and b **18.57** $K_c < 1$ for both a and b **18.59**(a) A strong acid is 100% dissociated, so the acid concentration will be very different after dissociation. (b) A weak acid dissociates to a very small extent, so the acid concentration before and after dissociation is nearly the same. (c) same as b, but with the extent of dissociation greater (d) same as a **18.60** No. HCl is a strong acid and dissociates to a greater extent than the weak acid CH_3COOH. The K_a of the acid, not the concentration of H_3O^+, determines the strength of the acid. **18.63** 1.5×10^{-5} **18.65** $[H_3O^+] = [NO_2^-] = 2.1\times10^{-2}$ M; $[OH^-] = 4.8\times10^{-13}$ M **18.67** $[H_3O^+] = [ClCH_2COO^-] = 0.041$ M; $[ClCH_2COOH] = 1.21$ M; pH = 1.39 **18.69**(a) $[H_3O^+] = 6.0\times10^{-3}$ M; pH = 2.22; $[OH^-] = 1.7\times10^{-12}$ M; pOH = 11.78 (b) 1.9×10^{-4} **18.71** 2.2×10^{-7} **18.73**(a) 2.37 (b) 11.53 **18.75**(a) 2.290 (b) 12.699 **18.77** 1.1% **18.79** $[H_3O^+] = [HS^-] = 9\times10^{-5}$ M; pH = 4.0; $[OH^-] = 1\times10^{-10}$ M; pOH = 10.0; $[H_2S] = 0.10$ M; $[S^{2-}] = 1\times10^{-17}$ M **18.82** 1.5% **18.83** All Brønsted-Lowry bases contain at least one lone pair of electrons, which binds an H^+ and allows the base to act as a proton acceptor.
18.86(a) $C_5H_5N(aq) + H_2O(l) \rightleftharpoons OH^-(aq) + C_5H_5NH^+(aq)$
$$K_b = \frac{[C_5H_5NH^+][OH^-]}{[C_5H_5N]}$$
(b) $CO_3^{2-}(aq) + H_2O(l) \rightleftharpoons OH^-(aq) + HCO_3^-(aq)$
$$K_b = \frac{[HCO_3^-][OH^-]}{[CO_3^{2-}]}$$
18.88(a) $HONH_2(aq) + H_2O(l) \rightleftharpoons OH^-(aq) + HONH_3^+(aq)$
$$K_b = \frac{[HONH_3^+][OH^-]}{[HONH_2]}$$
(b) $HPO_4^{2-}(aq) + H_2O(l) \rightleftharpoons H_2PO_4^-(aq) + OH^-(aq)$
$$K_b = \frac{[H_2PO_4^-][OH^-]}{[HPO_4^{2-}]}$$
18.90 11.79 **18.92** 11.45 **18.94**(a) 5.6×10^{-10} (b) 2.5×10^{-5} **18.96**(a) 12.04 (b) 10.77 **18.98**(a) 11.19 (b) 5.56 **18.100**(a) 8.78 (b) 4.66 **18.102** $[OH^-] = 5.5\times10^{-4}$ M; pH = 10.74 **18.104** As a nonmetal becomes more electronegative, the acidity of its binary hydride increases. The electronegative nonmetal attracts the electrons more strongly in the polar bond, shifting the electron density away from H, thus making H^+ more easily transferred to a water molecule to form H_3O^+. **18.107** Chlorine is more electronegative than iodine, and $HClO_4$ has more oxygen atoms than HIO. **18.108**(a) H_2SeO_4 (b) H_3PO_4 (c) H_2Te **18.110**(a) H_2Se (b) $B(OH)_3$ (c) $HBrO_2$ **18.112**(a) 0.5 M $AlBr_3$ (b) 0.3 M $SnCl_2$ **18.114**(a) 0.2 M $Ni(NO_3)_2$ (b) 0.35 M $Al(NO_3)_3$ **18.117** NaF contains the anion of the weak acid HF, so F^- acts as a base. NaCl contains the anion of the strong acid HCl.
18.119(a) $KBr(s) \xrightarrow{H_2O} K^+(aq) + Br^-(aq)$; neutral
(b) $NH_4I(s) \xrightarrow{H_2O} NH_4^+(aq) + I^-(aq)$
$NH_4^+(aq) + H_2O(l) \rightleftharpoons NH_3(aq) + H_3O^+(aq)$; acidic
(c) $KCN(s) \xrightarrow{H_2O} K^+(aq) + CN^-(aq)$
$CN^-(aq) + H_2O(l) \rightleftharpoons HCN(aq) + OH^-(aq)$; basic
18.121(a) $Na_2CO_3(s) \xrightarrow{H_2O} 2Na^+(aq) + CO_3^{2-}(aq)$
$CO_3^{2-}(aq) + H_2O(l) \rightleftharpoons HCO_3^-(aq) + OH^-(aq)$; basic
(b) $CaCl_2(s) \xrightarrow{H_2O} Ca^{2+}(aq) + 2Cl^-(aq)$; neutral
(c) $Cu(NO_3)_2(s) \xrightarrow{H_2O} Cu^{2+}(aq) + 2NO_3^-(aq)$
$Cu(H_2O)_6^{2+}(aq) + H_2O(l) \rightleftharpoons Cu(H_2O)_5OH^+(aq) + H_3O^+(aq)$; acidic
18.123(a) $SrBr_2(s) \xrightarrow{H_2O} Sr^{2+}(aq) + 2Br^-(aq)$; neutral
(b) $Ba(CH_3COO)_2(s) \xrightarrow{H_2O} Ba^{2+}(aq) + 2CH_3COO^-(aq)$
$CH_3COO^-(aq) + H_2O(l) \rightleftharpoons CH_3COOH(aq) + OH^-(aq)$; basic
(c) $(CH_3)_2NH_2Br(s) \xrightarrow{H_2O} (CH_3)_2NH_2^+(aq) + Br^-(aq)$
$(CH_3)_2NH_2^+(aq) + H_2O(l) \rightleftharpoons (CH_3)_2NH(aq) + H_3O^+(aq)$; acidic
18.125(a) $NH_4^+(aq) + H_2O(l) \rightleftharpoons NH_3(aq) + H_3O^+(aq)$
$PO_4^{3-}(aq) + H_2O(l) \rightleftharpoons HPO_4^{2-}(aq) + OH^-(aq)$;
$K_b > K_a$; basic
(b) $SO_4^{2-}(aq) + H_2O(l) \rightleftharpoons HSO_4^-(aq) + OH^-(aq)$;
Na^+ gives no reaction; basic
(c) $ClO^-(aq) + H_2O(l) \rightleftharpoons HClO(aq) + OH^-(aq)$;
Li^+ gives no reaction; basic

18.127(a) $Fe(NO_3)_2 < KNO_3 < K_2SO_3 < K_2S$
(b) $NaHSO_4 < NH_4NO_3 < NaHCO_3 < Na_2CO_3$
18.129 Since both bases produce OH^- ions in water, both bases appear equally strong. $CH_3O^-(aq) + H_2O(l) \longrightarrow OH^-(aq) + CH_3OH(aq)$ and $NH_2^-(aq) + H_2O(l) \longrightarrow OH^-(aq) + NH_3(aq)$. **18.131** Ammonia, NH_3, is a more basic solvent than H_2O. In a more basic solvent, weak acids such as HF act like strong acids and are 100% dissociated. **18.133** A Lewis acid is an electron-pair acceptor while a Brønsted-Lowry acid is a proton donor. The proton of a Brønsted-Lowry acid is a Lewis acid because it accepts an electron pair when it bonds with a base. All Lewis acids are not Brønsted-Lowry acids. A Lewis base is an electron-pair donor and a Brønsted-Lowry base is a proton acceptor. All Brønsted-Lowry bases are Lewis bases, and vice versa. **18.134**(a) No, $Zn(H_2O)_6^{2+}(aq) + 6NH_3(aq) \rightleftharpoons Zn(NH_3)_6^{2+} + 6H_2O(l)$; NH_3 is a weak Brønsted-Lowry base, but a strong Lewis base. (b) cyanide ion and water (c) cyanide ion **18.137**(a) Lewis acid (b) Lewis base (c) Lewis acid (d) Lewis base **18.139**(a) Lewis acid (b) Lewis base (c) Lewis base (d) Lewis acid **18.141**(a) Lewis acid: Na^+; Lewis base: H_2O (b) Lewis acid: CO_2; Lewis base: H_2O (c) Lewis acid: BF_3; Lewis base: F^- **18.143**(a) Lewis (b) Brønsted-Lowry and Lewis (c) none (d) Lewis **18.146** 3.5×10^{-8} to 4.5×10^{-8} M H_3O^+; 5.2×10^{-7} to 6.6×10^{-7} M OH^- **18.147**(a) Acids vary in the extent of dissociation depending on the acid-base character of the solvent. (b) Methanol is a weaker base than water since phenol dissociates less in methanol than in water.
(c) $C_6H_5OH(\text{solvated}) + CH_3OH(l) \rightleftharpoons CH_3OH_2^+(\text{solvated}) + C_6H_5O^-(\text{solvated})$
(d) $CH_3OH(l) + CH_3OH(l) \rightleftharpoons CH_3O^-(\text{solvated}) + CH_3OH_2^+(\text{solvated})$; $K = [CH_3O^-][CH_3OH_2^+]$
18.120(a) $SnCl_4$ is the Lewis acid; $(CH_3)_3N$ is the Lewis base (b) $5d$ **18.151** pH = 5.00, 6.00, 6.79, 6.98, 7.00 **18.157** 3×10^{18} **18.160** 10.48 **18.162** 2.41 **18.164** amylase, 2×10^{-7} M; pepsin, 1×10^{-2} M; trypsin, 3×10^{-10} M **18.168** 1.47×10^{-3} **18.170**(a) Ca^{2+} does not react with water; $CH_3CH_2COO^-(aq) + H_2O(l) \rightleftharpoons CH_3CH_2COOH(aq) + OH^-(aq)$; basic (b) 9.08 **18.176** 4.5×10^{-5} **18.179**(a) The concentration of oxygen is higher in the lungs, so the equilibrium shifts to the right. (b) In an oxygen-deficient environment, the equilibrium shifts to the left to release oxygen. (c) A decrease in $[H_3O^+]$ shifts the equilibrium to the right. More oxygen is absorbed, but it will be more difficult to remove the O_2. (d) An increase in $[H_3O^+]$ shifts the equilibrium to the left. Less oxygen is bound to Hb, but it will be easier to remove it. **18.181**(a) 1.012 M (b) 0.004 M (c) 0.4% **18.182**(a) 10.0 (b) The pK_b for the 3° amine group is much smaller than that for the aromatic ring, thus the K_b is significantly larger (yielding a much greater amount of OH^-). (c) 4.7 (d) 5.1

Chapter 19

Answers to Boxed Reading Problem: B19.2 (a) 65 mol (b) 6.28 (c) 4.0×10^3 g HCO_3^-

• **19.2** The acid component neutralizes added base, and the base component neutralizes added acid, so the pH of the buffer solution remains relatively constant. The components of a buffer do not neutralize one another because they are a conjugate acid-base pair. **19.7** The buffer range, the pH over which the buffer acts effectively, is greatest when the buffer-component concentration ratio is 1; the range decreases as this ratio deviates from 1. **19.9**(a) Ratio and pH increase; added OH^- reacts with HA. (b) Ratio and pH decrease; added H^+ reacts with A^-. (c) Ratio and pH increase; added A^- increases $[A^-]$. (d) Ratio and pH decrease; added HA increases [HA]. **19.11** $[H_3O^+] = 5.6\times10^{-6}$ M; pH = 5.25 **19.13** $[H_3O^+] = 5.2\times10^{-4}$ M; pH = 3.28 **19.15** 3.89 **19.17** 10.03 **19.19** 9.47 **19.21**(a) K_{a2} (b) 10.55 **19.23** 3.6 **19.25** 0.20 **19.27** 3.37 **19.29** 8.82 **19.31**(a) 4.81 (b) 0.66 g KOH **19.33**(a) $HOOC(CH_2)_4COOH/HOOC(CH_2)_4COO^-$ or $C_6H_5NH_3^+/C_6H_5NH_2$ (b) $H_2PO_4^-/HPO_4^{2-}$ or $H_2AsO_4^-/HAsO_4^{2-}$ **19.35**(a) $HOCH_2CH(OH)COOH/HOCH_2CH(OH)COO^-$ or $CH_3COOC_6H_4COOH/CH_3COOC_6H_4COO^-$ (b) $C_5H_5NH^+/C_5H_5N$ **19.38** 1.6 **19.40** To see a distinct color in a mixture of two colors, you need one to have about 10 times the intensity of the other. For this to be the case, the concentration ratio $[HIn]/[In^-]$ has to be greater than 10/1 or less than 1/10. This occurs when $pH = pK_a - 1$ or $pH = pK_a + 1$, respectively, giving a pH range of about 2 units. **19.42** The equivalence point in a titration is the point at which the number of moles of base is stoichiometrically equivalent to the number of moles of acid. The endpoint is the point at which the added indicator changes color. If an appropriate indicator is selected, the endpoint is close to the equivalence point, but they are not usually the same. The pH at the endpoint, or color change, may precede or follow the pH at the equivalence point, depending on the indicator chosen. **19.44**(a) initial pH: *strong acid*–strong base < *weak acid*–strong base < *weak base*–strong acid (b) pH at equivalence point: *weak base*–strong acid < *strong acid*–strong base < *weak acid*–strong base **19.46** At the center of the buffer region, the concentrations of weak acid and conjugate base are equal, so the pH = pK_a of the acid. **19.48** pH range from 7.5 to 9.5 **19.50**(a) bromthymol blue (b) thymol blue or phenolphthalein **19.52**(a) methyl red (b) bromthymol blue **19.54**(a) 1.0000 (b) 1.6368 (c) 2.898 (d) 3.903 (e) 7.00 (f) 10.10 (g) 12.05 **19.56**(a) 2.91 (b) 4.81 (c) 5.29 (d) 6.09 (e) 7.41 (f) 8.76 (g) 10.10 (h) 12.05 **19.58**(a) 59.0 mL and 8.54 (b) 66.0 mL and 7.13, total 132.1 mL and 9.69 **19.60**(a) 123 mL and 5.17 (b) 194 mL and 5.80 **19.63** Fluoride ion is the conjugate base of a weak acid and reacts with H_2O: $F^-(aq) + H_2O(l) \rightleftharpoons HF(aq) + OH^-(aq)$. As the pH increases, the equilibrium shifts to the left and $[F^-]$ increases. As the pH decreases, the equilibrium shifts to the right and $[F^-]$ decreases. The changes in $[F^-]$ influence the solubility of BaF_2. Chloride ion is the conjugate base of a strong acid, so it does not react with water and its concentration is not influenced by pH. **19.65** The compound precipitates. **19.66**(a) $K_{sp} = [Ag^+]^2[CO_3^{2-}]$ (b) $K_{sp} = [Ba^{2+}][F^-]^2$ (c) $K_{sp} = [Cu^{2+}][HS^-][OH^-]$

19.68(a) $K_{sp} = [Ca^{2+}][CrO_4^{2-}]$ (b) $K_{sp} = [Ag^+][CN^-]$ (c) $K_{sp} = [Ni^{2+}][HS^-][OH^-]$ **19.70** 1.3×10^{-4} **19.72** 2.8×10^{-11} **19.74**(a) 2.3×10^{-5} *M* (b) 4.2×10^{-9} *M* **19.76**(a) 1.7×10^{-3} *M* (b) 2.0×10^{-4} *M* **19.78**(a) $Mg(OH)_2$ (b) PbS (c) Ag_2SO_4 **19.80**(a) $CaSO_4$ (b) $Mg_3(PO_4)_2$ (c) $PbSO_4$ **19.82**(a) $AgCl(s) \rightleftharpoons Ag^+(aq) + Cl^-(aq)$. The chloride ion is the anion of a strong acid, so it does not react with H_3O^+. No change with pH.
(b) $SrCO_3(s) \rightleftharpoons Sr^{2+}(aq) + CO_3^{2-}(aq)$. The strontium ion is the cation of a strong base, so pH will not affect its solubility. The carbonate ion acts as a base:
$CO_3^{2-}(aq) + H_2O(l) \rightleftharpoons HCO_3^-(aq) + OH^-(aq)$; also $CO_2(g)$ forms and escapes: $CO_3^{2-}(aq) + 2H_3O^+(aq) \longrightarrow CO_2(g) + 3H_2O(l)$. Therefore, the solubility of $SrCO_3$ will increase with addition of H_3O^+ (decreasing pH).
19.84(a) $Fe(OH)_2(s) \rightleftharpoons Fe^{2+}(aq) + 2OH^-(aq)$. The OH^- ion reacts with added H_3O^+: $OH^-(aq) + H_3O^+(aq) \longrightarrow 2H_2O(l)$. The added H_3O^+ consumes the OH^-, driving the equilibrium toward the right to dissolve more $Fe(OH)_2$. Solubility increases with addition of H_3O^+ (decreasing pH).
(b) $CuS(s) + H_2O(l) \rightleftharpoons Cu^{2+}(aq) + HS^-(aq) + OH^-(aq)$. Both HS^- and OH^- are anions of weak acids, so both ions react with added H_3O^+. Solubility increases with addition of H_3O^+ (decreasing pH). **19.86** yes **19.88** yes **19.91**(a) $Fe(OH)_3$ (b) The two metal ions are separated by adding just enough NaOH to precipitate iron(III) hydroxide. (c) 2.0×10^{-7} *M* **19.94** No, because it indicates that a complex ion forms between the lead ion and hydroxide ions:

$$Pb^{2+}(aq) + nOH^-(aq) \rightleftharpoons Pb(OH)_n^{2-n}(aq)$$

19.95 $Hg(H_2O)_4^{2+}(aq) + 4CN^-(aq) \rightleftharpoons Hg(CN)_4^{2-}(aq) + 4H_2O(l)$
19.97 $Ag(H_2O)_2^+(aq) + 2S_2O_3^{2-}(aq) \rightleftharpoons Ag(S_2O_3)_2^{3-}(aq) + 2H_2O(l)$
19.99 8.1×10^{-15} *M* **19.101** 0.05 *M* **19.103** 1.0×10^{-16} *M* Zn^{2+}; 0.025 *M* $Zn(CN)_4^{2-}$; 0.049 *M* CN^- **19.105** 0.035 L of 2.00 *M* NaOH and 0.465 L of 0.200 *M* HCOOH **19.107**(a) 0.99 (b) assuming the volumes are additive: 0.468 L of 1.0 *M* HCOOH and 0.232 L of 1.0 *M* NaOH (c) 0.34 *M* **19.110** 1.3×10^{-4} *M* **19.113**(a) 14 (b) 1 g from the second beaker **19.116**(a) 0.088 (b) 0.14 **19.117** 0.260 *M* TRIS; pH = 8.53 **19.119** Lower the pH below 6.6 **19.123** 8×10^{-5}
19.125(a)

V (mL)	pH	$\Delta pH/\Delta V$	V_{avg} (mL)
0.00	1.00		
10.00	1.22	0.022	5.00
20.00	1.48	0.026	15.00
30.00	1.85	0.037	25.00
35.00	2.18	0.066	32.50
39.00	2.89	0.18	37.00
39.50	3.20	0.62	39.25
39.75	3.50	1.2	39.63
39.90	3.90	2.7	39.83
39.95	4.20	6	39.93
39.99	4.90	18	39.97
40.00	7.00	200	40.00
40.01	9.40	200	40.01
40.05	9.80	10	40.03
40.10	10.40	10	40.08
40.25	10.50	0.67	40.18
40.50	10.79	1.2	40.38
41.00	11.09	0.60	40.75
45.00	11.76	0.17	43.00
50.00	12.05	0.058	47.50
60.00	12.30	0.025	55.00
70.00	12.43	0.013	65.00
80.00	12.52	0.009	75.00

(b)
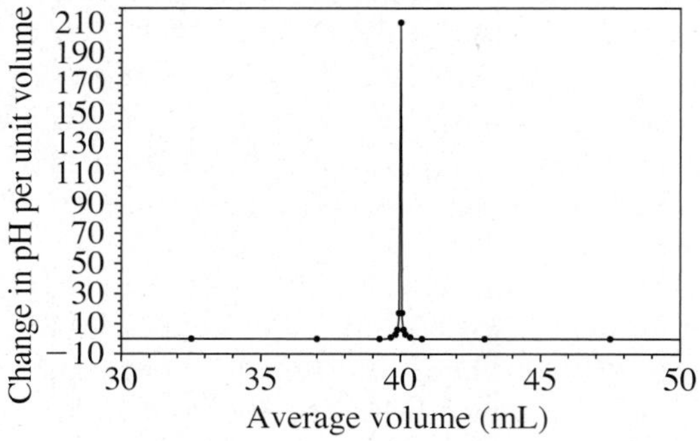

Maximum slope (equivalence point) is at V_{avg} = 40.00 mL. **19.127** 4.05 **19.133** H_2CO_3/HCO_3^- and $H_2PO_4^-/HPO_4^{2-}$; $[HPO_4^{2-}]/[H_2PO_4^-] = 5.8$ **19.134** 3.8 **19.136**(a) 58.2 mL (b) 7.85 mL (c) 6.30 **19.138** 170 mL **19.142** 5.68 **19.144** 3.9×10^{-9} μg Pb^{2+}/100 mL blood **19.146** No NaCl will precipitate. **19.147**(a) A and D (b) $pH_A = 4.35$; $pH_B = 8.67$; $pH_C = 2.67$; $pH_D = 4.57$ (c) C, A, D, B (d) B

Chapter 20

Answer to Boxed Reading Problem: B20.2 −12.6 kJ/mol

• **20.2** A spontaneous process occurs by itself, whereas a nonspontaneous process requires a continuous input of energy to make it happen. It is possible to cause a nonspontaneous process to occur, but the process stops once the energy source is removed. A reaction that is nonspontaneous under one set of conditions may be spontaneous under a different set of conditions. **20.5** The transition from liquid to gas involves a greater increase in dispersal of energy and freedom of motion than does the transition from solid to liquid. **20.6** In an exothermic reaction, $\Delta S_{surr} > 0$. In an endothermic reaction, $\Delta S_{surr} < 0$. A chemical cold pack for injuries is an example of an application using a spontaneous endothermic process. **20.8** a, b, and c **20.10** a and b **20.12**(a) positive (b) negative (c) negative **20.14**(a) positive (b) positive (c) positive **20.16**(a) negative (b) negative (c) positive **20.18**(a) positive (b) negative (c) positive **20.20**(a) positive (b) negative (c) positive **20.22**(a) Butane. The double bond in 2-butene restricts freedom of rotation. (b) $Xe(g)$. It has the greater molar mass. (c) $CH_4(g)$. Gases have greater entropy than liquids. **20.24**(a) $C_2H_5OH(l)$. It is a more complex molecule.

(b) $KClO_3(aq)$. Ions in solution have their energy more dispersed than those in a solid. (c) $K(s)$. It has a greater molar mass. **20.26**(a) Diamond < graphite < charcoal. Freedom of motion is least in the network solid; more freedom between graphite sheets; most freedom in amorphous solid. (b) Ice < liquid water < water vapor. Entropy increases as a substance changes from solid to liquid to gas. (c) O atoms < O_2 < O_3. Entropy increases with molecular complexity. **20.28**(a) $ClO_4^-(aq) > ClO_3^-(aq) > ClO_2^-(aq)$; decreasing molecular complexity (b) $NO_2(g) > NO(g) > N_2(g)$. N_2 has lower standard molar entropy because it consists of two of the same atoms; the other species have two different types of atoms. NO_2 is more complex than NO. (c) $Fe_3O_4(s) > Fe_2O_3(s) > Al_2O_3(s)$. Fe_3O_4 is more complex and more massive. Fe_2O_3 is more massive than Al_2O_3. **20.31** For a system at equilibrium, $\Delta S_{univ} = \Delta S_{sys} + \Delta S_{surr} = 0$. For a system moving to equilibrium, $\Delta S_{univ} > 0$. **20.32** $S^\circ_{Cl_2O(g)} = 2S^\circ_{HClO(g)} - S^\circ_{H_2O(g)} - \Delta S^\circ_{rxn}$ **20.33**(a) negative; $\Delta S^\circ = -172.4$ J/K (b) positive; $\Delta S^\circ = 141.6$ J/K (c) negative; $\Delta S^\circ = -837$ J/K **20.35** $\Delta S^\circ = 93.1$ J/K; yes, the positive sign of ΔS is expected because there is a net increase in the number of gas molecules. **20.37** $\Delta S^\circ = -311$ J/K; yes, the negative entropy change matches the decrease in moles of gas. **20.39** -75.6 J/K **20.41** -242 J/K **20.44** -97.2 J/K **20.46** A spontaneous process has $\Delta S_{univ} > 0$. Since the absolute temperature is always positive, ΔG_{sys} must be negative ($\Delta G_{sys} < 0$) for a spontaneous process. **20.48** ΔH° is positive and ΔS° is positive. Melting is an example. **20.49** The entropy changes little within a phase. As long as the substance does not change phase, the value of ΔS° is relatively unaffected by temperature. **20.50**(a) -1138.0 kJ (b) -1379.4 kJ (c) -224 kJ **20.52**(a) -1138 kJ (b) -1379 kJ (c) -226 kJ **20.54**(a) Entropy decreases (ΔS° is negative) because the number of moles of gas decreases. The combustion of CO releases energy (ΔH° is negative). (b) -257.2 kJ or -257.3 kJ, depending on the method **20.56**(a) -0.409 kJ/mol·K (b) -197 kJ/mol **20.58**(a) $\Delta H^\circ_{rxn} = 90.7$ kJ; $\Delta S^\circ_{rxn} = 221$ J/K (b) At 28°C, $\Delta G^\circ = 24.3$ kJ; at 128°C, $\Delta G^\circ = 2.2$ kJ; at 228°C, $\Delta G^\circ = -19.9$ kJ (c) For the substances in their standard states, the reaction is nonspontaneous at 28°C, near equilibrium at 128°C, and spontaneous at 228°C. **20.60** $\Delta H^\circ = 30910$ J, $\Delta S^\circ = 93.15$ J/K, $T = 331.8$ K **20.62**(a) $\Delta H^\circ_{rxn} = -241.826$ kJ, $\Delta S^\circ_{rxn} = -44.4$ J/K, $\Delta G^\circ_{rxn} = -228.60$ kJ (b) Yes. The reaction will become nonspontaneous at higher temperatures. (c) The reaction is spontaneous below 5.45×10^3 K. **20.64**(a) ΔG° is a relatively large positive value. (b) $K >> 1$. Q depends on initial conditions, not equilibrium conditions. **20.67** The standard free energy change, ΔG°, applies when all components of the system are in their standard states; $\Delta G^\circ = \Delta G$ when all concentrations equal 1 M and all partial pressures equal 1 atm. **20.68**(a) 1.7×10^6 (b) 3.89×10^{-34} (c) 1.26×10^{48} **20.70**(a) 6.57×10^{173} (b) 4.46×10^{-15} (c) 3.46×10^4 **20.72** 4.89×10^{-51} **20.74** 3.36×10^5 **20.76** 2.7×10^4 J/mol; no **20.78**(a) 2.9×10^4 J/mol (b) The reverse direction, formation of reactants, is spontaneous, so the reaction proceeds to the left. (c) 7.0×10^3 J/mol; the reaction proceeds to the left to reach equilibrium. **20.80**(a) no T (b) 163 kJ (c) 1×10^2 kJ/mol **20.83**(a) spontaneous (b) + (c) + (d) − (e) −, not spontaneous (f) − **20.87**(a) 2.3×10^2 (b) The treatment is to administer oxygen-rich air; increasing the concentration of oxygen shifts the equilibrium to the left, in the direction of $Hb\cdot O_2$. **20.89** $-370.$ kJ **20.91**(a) $2N_2O_5(g) + 6F_2(g) \longrightarrow 4NF_3(g) + 5O_2(g)$ (b) $\Delta G^\circ_{rxn} = -569$ kJ (c) $\Delta G_{rxn} = -5.60\times10^2$ kJ/mol **20.93** $\Delta H^\circ_{rxn} = -137.14$ kJ; $\Delta S^\circ_{rxn} = -120.3$ J/K; $\Delta G^\circ_{rxn} = -101.25$ kJ **20.101**(a) 1.67×10^3 J/mol (b) 7.37×10^3 J/mol (c) -4.04×10^3 J/mol (d) 0.19 **20.105**(a) 465 K (b) 6.59×10^{-4} (c) The reaction rate is higher at the higher temperature. The shorter time required (kinetics) overshadows the lower yield (thermodynamics).

Chapter 21

Answers to Boxed Reading Problem: B21.1 (a) reduction: $Fe^{3+} + e^- \longrightarrow Fe^{2+}$; oxidation: $Cu^+ \longrightarrow Cu^{2+} + e^-$ (b) Overall: $Fe^{3+} + Cu^+ \longrightarrow Fe^{2+} + Cu^{2+}$

• **21.1** Oxidation is the loss of electrons and results in a higher oxidation number; reduction is the gain of electrons and results in a lower oxidation number. **21.3** No, one half-reaction cannot take place independently because there is a transfer of electrons from one substance to another. If one substance loses electrons, another substance must gain them. **21.6** To remove H^+ ions from an equation, add an equal number of OH^- ions to both sides to neutralize the H^+ ions and produce water. **21.8** Spontaneous reactions, for which $\Delta G_{sys} < 0$, take place in voltaic cells (also called galvanic cells). Nonspontaneous reactions, for which $\Delta G_{sys} > 0$, take place in electrolytic cells. **21.10**(a) Cl^- (b) MnO_4^- (c) MnO_4^- (d) Cl^- (e) from Cl^- to MnO_4^- (f) $8H_2SO_4(aq) + 2KMnO_4(aq) + 10KCl(aq) \longrightarrow 2MnSO_4(aq) + 5Cl_2(g) + 8H_2O(l) + 6K_2SO_4(aq)$

21.12(a) $ClO_3^-(aq) + 6H^+(aq) + 6I^-(aq) \longrightarrow Cl^-(aq) + 3H_2O(l) + 3I_2(s)$
Oxidizing agent is ClO_3^- and reducing agent is I^-.
(b) $2MnO_4^-(aq) + H_2O(l) + 3SO_3^{2-}(aq) \longrightarrow 2MnO_2(s) + 3SO_4^{2-}(aq) + 2OH^-(aq)$
Oxidizing agent is MnO_4^- and reducing agent is SO_3^{2-}.
(c) $2MnO_4^-(aq) + 6H^+(aq) + 5H_2O_2(aq) \longrightarrow 2Mn^{2+}(aq) + 8H_2O(l) + 5O_2(g)$
Oxidizing agent is MnO_4^- and reducing agent is H_2O_2.

21.14(a) $Cr_2O_7^{2-}(aq) + 14H^+(aq) + 3Zn(s) \longrightarrow 2Cr^{3+}(aq) + 7H_2O(l) + 3Zn^{2+}(aq)$
Oxidizing agent is $Cr_2O_7^{2-}$ and reducing agent is Zn.
(b) $MnO_4^-(aq) + 3Fe(OH)_2(s) + 2H_2O(l) \longrightarrow MnO_2(s) + 3Fe(OH)_3(s) + OH^-(aq)$
Oxidizing agent is MnO_4^- and reducing agent is $Fe(OH)_2$.
(c) $2NO_3^-(aq) + 12H^+(aq) + 5Zn(s) \longrightarrow N_2(g) + 6H_2O(l) + 5Zn^{2+}(aq)$
Oxidizing agent is NO_3^- and reducing agent is Zn.

21.16(a) $4NO_3^-(aq) + 4H^+(aq) + 4Sb(s) \longrightarrow 4NO(g) + 2H_2O(l) + Sb_4O_6(s)$
Oxidizing agent is NO_3^- and reducing agent is Sb.

(b) $5BiO_3^-(aq) + 14H^+(aq) + 2Mn^{2+}(aq) \longrightarrow 5Bi^{3+}(aq) + 7H_2O(l) + 2MnO_4^-(aq)$
Oxidizing agent is BiO_3^- and reducing agent is Mn^{2+}.
(c) $Pb(OH)_3^-(aq) + 2Fe(OH)_2(s) \longrightarrow Pb(s) + 2Fe(OH)_3(s) + OH^-(aq)$
Oxidizing agent is $Pb(OH)_3^-$ and reducing agent is $Fe(OH)_2$.

21.18(a) $5As_4O_6(s) + 8MnO_4^-(aq) + 18H_2O(l) \longrightarrow 20AsO_4^{3-}(aq) + 8Mn^{2+}(aq) + 36H^+(aq)$
Oxidizing agent is MnO_4^- and reducing agent is As_4O_6.
(b) $P_4(s) + 6H_2O(l) \longrightarrow 2HPO_3^{2-}(aq) + 2PH_3(g) + 4H^+(aq)$
P_4 is both the oxidizing agent and the reducing agent.
(c) $2MnO_4^-(aq) + 3CN^-(aq) + H_2O(l) \longrightarrow 2MnO_2(s) + 3CNO^-(aq) + 2OH^-(aq)$
Oxidizing agent is MnO_4^- and reducing agent is CN^-.

21.21(a) $Au(s) + 3NO_3^-(aq) + 4Cl^-(aq) + 6H^+(aq) \longrightarrow AuCl_4^-(aq) + 3NO_2(g) + 3H_2O(l)$ (b) Oxidizing agent is NO_3^- and reducing agent is Au. (c) HCl provides chloride ions that combine with the gold(III) ion to form the stable $AuCl_4^-$ ion. **21.22**(a) A (b) E (c) C (d) A (e) E (f) E **21.25** An active electrode is a reactant or product in the cell reaction. An inactive electrode does not take part in the reaction and is present only to conduct a current. Platinum and graphite are commonly used as inactive electrodes. **21.26**(a) A (b) B (c) A (d) Hydrogen bubbles will form when metal A is placed in acid. Metal A is a better reducing agent than metal B, so if metal B reduces H^+ in acid, then metal A will also.

21.27(a) Oxidation: $Zn(s) \longrightarrow Zn^{2+}(aq) + 2e^-$
Reduction: $Sn^{2+}(aq) + 2e^- \longrightarrow Sn(s)$
Overall: $Zn(s) + Sn^{2+}(aq) \longrightarrow Zn^{2+}(aq) + Sn(s)$
(b)

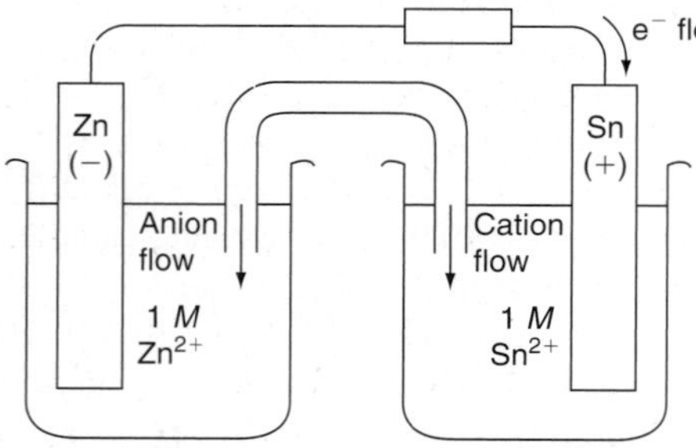

21.29(a) left to right (b) left (c) right (d) Ni (e) Fe (f) Fe (g) 1 M $NiSO_4$ (h) K^+ and NO_3^- (i) neither (j) from right to left
(k) Oxidation: $Fe(s) \longrightarrow Fe^{2+}(aq) + 2e^-$
Reduction: $Ni^{2+}(aq) + 2e^- \longrightarrow Ni(s)$
Overall: $Fe(s) + Ni^{2+}(aq) \longrightarrow Fe^{2+}(aq) + Ni(s)$

21.31(a) Reduction: $Fe^{2+}(aq) + 2e^- \longrightarrow Fe(s)$
Oxidation: $Mn(s) \longrightarrow Mn^{2+}(aq) + 2e^-$
Overall: $Fe^{2+}(aq) + Mn(s) \longrightarrow Fe(s) + Mn^{2+}(aq)$
(b)

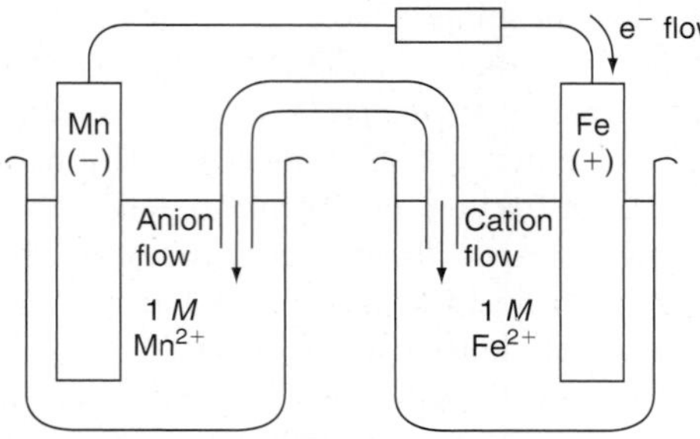

21.33(a) $Al(s) \mid Al^{3+}(aq) \parallel Cr^{3+}(aq) \mid Cr(s)$
(b) $Pt(s) \mid SO_2(g) \mid SO_4^{2-}(aq), H^+(aq) \parallel Cu^{2+}(aq) \mid Cu(s)$
21.36 A negative E°_{cell} indicates that the redox reaction is not spontaneous at the standard state, that is, $\Delta G^\circ > 0$. The reverse reaction is spontaneous with $E^\circ_{cell} > 0$. **21.37** Similar to other state functions, E° changes sign when a reaction is reversed. Unlike ΔG°, ΔH°, and S°, E° (the ratio of energy to charge) is an intensive property. When the coefficients in a reaction are multiplied by a factor, the values of ΔG°, ΔH°, and S° are multiplied by that factor. However, E° does not change because both the energy and charge are multiplied by the factor and thus their ratio remains unchanged.

21.38(a) Oxidation: $Se^{2-}(aq) \longrightarrow Se(s) + 2e^-$
Reduction: $2SO_3^{2-}(aq) + 3H_2O(l) + 4e^- \longrightarrow S_2O_3^{2-}(aq) + 6OH^-(aq)$
(b) $E^\circ_{anode} = E^\circ_{cathode} - E^\circ_{cell} = -0.57\ V - 0.35\ V = -0.92\ V$

21.40(a) $Br_2 > Fe^{3+} > Cu^{2+}$ (b) $Ca^{2+} < Ag^+ < Cr_2O_7^{2-}$

21.42(a) $Co(s) + 2H^+(aq) \longrightarrow Co^{2+}(aq) + H_2(g)$
$E^\circ_{cell} = 0.28$ V; spontaneous
(b) $2Mn^{2+}(aq) + 5Br_2(l) + 8H_2O(l) \longrightarrow 2MnO_4^-(aq) + 10Br^-(aq) + 16H^+(aq)$
$E^\circ_{cell} = -0.44$ V; not spontaneous
(c) $Hg_2^{2+}(aq) \longrightarrow Hg^{2+}(aq) + Hg(l)$
$E^\circ_{cell} = -0.07$ V; not spontaneous

21.44(a) $2Ag(s) + Cu^{2+}(aq) \longrightarrow 2Ag^+(aq) + Cu(s)$
$E^\circ_{cell} = -0.46$ V; not spontaneous
(b) $Cr_2O_7^{2-}(aq) + 3Cd(s) + 14H^+(aq) \longrightarrow 2Cr^{3+}(aq) + 3Cd^{2+}(aq) + 7H_2O(l)$
$E^\circ_{cell} = 1.73$ V; spontaneous
(c) $Pb(s) + Ni^{2+}(aq) \longrightarrow Pb^{2+}(aq) + Ni(s)$
$E^\circ_{cell} = -0.12$ V; not spontaneous

21.46 $3N_2O_4(g) + 2Al(s) \longrightarrow 6NO_2^-(aq) + 2Al^{3+}(aq)$
$E^\circ_{cell} = 0.867\ V - (-1.66\ V) = 2.53\ V$
$2Al(s) + 3SO_4^{2-}(aq) + 3H_2O(l) \longrightarrow 2Al^{3+}(aq) + 3SO_3^{2-}(aq) + 6OH^-(aq)$
$E^\circ_{cell} = 2.59$ V
$SO_4^{2-}(aq) + 2NO_2^-(aq) + H_2O(l) \longrightarrow SO_3^{2-}(aq) + N_2O_4(g) + 2OH^-(aq)$
$E^\circ_{cell} = 0.06$ V
Oxidizing agents: $Al^{3+} < N_2O_4 < SO_4^{2-}$
Reducing agents: $SO_3^{2-} < NO_2^- < Al$

21.48 $2HClO(aq) + Pt(s) + 2H^+(aq) \longrightarrow Cl_2(g) + Pt^{2+}(aq) + 2H_2O(l)$

$E^\circ_{cell} = 0.43$ V

$2HClO(aq) + Pb(s) + SO_4^{2-}(aq) + 2H^+(aq) \longrightarrow Cl_2(g) + PbSO_4(s) + 2H_2O(l)$

$E^\circ_{cell} = 1.94$ V

$Pt^{2+}(aq) + Pb(s) + SO_4^{2-}(aq) \longrightarrow Pt(s) + PbSO_4(s)$

$E^\circ_{cell} = 1.51$ V

Oxidizing agents: $PbSO_4 < Pt^{2+} < HClO$

Reducing agents: $Cl_2 < Pt < Pb$

21.50 yes; C > A > B **21.53** $A(s) + B^+(aq) \longrightarrow A^+(aq) + B(s)$ with $Q = [A^+]/[B^+]$. (a) $[A^+]$ increases and $[B^+]$ decreases. (b) E_{cell} decreases. (c) $E_{cell} = E^\circ_{cell} - (RT/nF) \ln([A^+]/[B^+])$; $E_{cell} = E^\circ_{cell}$ when $(RT/nF)\ln([A^+]/[B^+]) = 0$. This occurs when $\ln([A^+]/[B^+]) = 0$, that is, $[A^+]$ equals $[B^+]$. (d) Yes, when $[A^+] > [B^+]$. **21.55** In a concentration cell, the overall reaction decreases the concentration of the more concentrated electrolyte because it is reduced in the cathode compartment. **21.56**(a) 3×10^{35} (b) 4×10^{-31} **21.58**(a) 1×10^{-67} (b) 6×10^9 **21.60**(a) -2.03×10^5 J (b) 1.74×10^5 J **21.62**(a) 3.82×10^5 J (b) -5.6×10^4 J **21.64** $E^\circ = 0.28$ V; $\Delta G^\circ = -2.7\times10^4$ J **21.66** $E^\circ_{cell} = 0.054$ V; $\Delta G^\circ = -1.0\times10^4$ J **21.68** 8.8×10^{-5} *M* **21.70**(a) 0.05 V (b) 0.50 *M* (c) $[Co^{2+}] = 0.91$ *M*; $[Ni^{2+}] = 0.09$ *M* **21.72** A; 0.083 V **21.74** Electrons flow from the anode, where oxidation occurs, to the cathode, where reduction occurs. The electrons always flow from the anode to the cathode no matter what type of battery. **21.76** A D-sized alkaline battery is larger than an AAA-sized one, so it contains greater amounts of the cell components. The cell potential is an intensive property and does not depend on the amounts of the cell components. The total charge, however, does depend on the amount of cell components, so the D-sized battery produces more charge. **21.78** The Teflon spacers keep the two metals separated so that the copper cannot conduct electrons that would promote the corrosion (rusting) of the iron skeleton. **21.81** Sacrificial anodes are made of metals with E° less than that of iron, -0.44 V, so they are more easily oxidized than iron. Only b, f, and g will work for iron: a will form an oxide coating that prevents further oxidation; c will react with groundwater quickly; d and e are less easily oxidized than iron. **21.83** To reverse the reaction requires 0.34 V with the cell in its standard state. A 1.5 V cell supplies more than enough potential, so the Cd metal is oxidized to Cd^{2+} and Cr metal plates out. **21.85** The oxidation number of N in NO_3^- is +5, the maximum O.N. for N. In the nitrite ion, NO_2^-, the O.N. of N is +3, so nitrogen can be further oxidized. **21.87**(a) Br_2 (b) Na **21.89** I_2 gas forms at the anode; magnesium (liquid) forms at the cathode. **21.91** Bromine gas forms at the anode; calcium metal forms at the cathode. **21.93** copper and bromine **21.95** iodine, zinc, and silver

21.97(a) Anode: $2H_2O(l) \longrightarrow O_2(g) + 4H^+(aq) + 4e^-$

Cathode: $2H_2O(l) + 2e^- \longrightarrow H_2(g) + 2OH^-(aq)$

(b) Anode: $2H_2O(l) \longrightarrow O_2(g) + 4H^+(aq) + 4e^-$

Cathode: $Sn^{2+}(aq) + 2e^- \longrightarrow Sn(s)$

21.99(a) Anode: $2H_2O(l) \longrightarrow O_2(g) + 4H^+(aq) + 4e^-$

Cathode: $NO_3^-(aq) + 4H^+(aq) + 3e^- \longrightarrow NO(g) + 2H_2O(l)$

(b) Anode: $2Cl^-(aq) \longrightarrow Cl_2(g) + 2e^-$

Cathode: $2H_2O(l) + 2e^- \longrightarrow H_2(g) + 2OH^-(aq)$

21.101(a) 3.75 mol e^- (b) 3.62×10^5 C (c) 28.7 A **21.103** 0.275 g Ra **21.105** 9.20×10^3 s **21.107**(a) The sodium and sulfate ions conduct a current, facilitating electrolysis. Pure water, which contains very low (10^{-7} *M*) concentrations of H^+ and OH^-, conducts electricity very poorly. (b) The reduction of H_2O has a more positive half-potential than does the reduction of Na^+; the oxidation of H_2O is the only reaction possible because SO_4^{2-} cannot be oxidized. Thus, it is easier to reduce H_2O than Na^+ and easier to oxidize H_2O than SO_4^{2-}. **21.109** 62.6 g Zn **21.111**(a) 3.3×10^{11} C (b) 4.8×10^{11} J (c) 1.2×10^4 kg **21.114** 64.3 mass % Cu **21.115**(a) 8 days (b) 32 days (c) \$940 **21.118** (a) 2.4×10^4 days (b) 2.1 g (c) 6.1×10^{-5} dollars **21.121**(a) Pb/Pb^{2+}: $E^\circ_{cell} = 0.13$ V; Cu/Cu^{2+}: $E^\circ_{cell} = 0.34$ V (b) The anode (negative electrode) is Pb. The anode in the other cell is platinum in the standard hydrogen electrode. (c) The precipitation of PbS decreases $[Pb^{2+}]$, which increases the potential. (d) -0.13 V **21.124** The three steps equivalent to the overall reaction $M^+(aq) + e^- \longrightarrow M(s)$ are

(1) $M^+(aq) \longrightarrow M^+(g)$ $\quad \Delta H$ is $-\Delta H_{hydration}$

(2) $M^+(g) + e^- \longrightarrow M(g)$ $\quad \Delta H$ is $-$IE

(3) $M(g) \longrightarrow M(s)$ $\quad \Delta H$ is $-\Delta H_{atomization}$

The energy for step 3 is similar for all three elements, so the difference in energy for the overall reaction depends on the values for $\Delta H_{hydration}$ and IE. The Li^+ ion has a much greater hydration energy than Na^+ and K^+ because it is smaller, with a larger charge density that holds the water molecules more tightly. The energy required to remove the waters surrounding Li^+ offsets the lower ionization energy, making the overall energy for the reduction of lithium larger than expected. **21.125** The very high and very low standard electrode potentials involve extremely reactive substances, such as F_2 (a powerful oxidizer) and Li (a powerful reducer). These substances react directly with water because any aqueous cell with a voltage of more than 1.23 V has the ability to electrolyze water into hydrogen and oxygen. **21.127**(a) 1.073×10^5 s (b) 1.5×10^4 kW·h (c) 0.92¢ **21.129** If metal E and a salt of metal F are mixed, the salt is reduced, producing metal F because E has the greatest reducing strength of the three metals; F < D < E.

21.131(a) Cell I: 4 mol electrons; $\Delta G = -4.75\times10^5$ J

Cell II: 2 mol electrons; $\Delta G = -3.94\times10^5$ J

Cell III: 2 mol electrons; $\Delta G = -4.53\times10^5$ J

(b) Cell I: -13.2 kJ/g

Cell II: -0.613 kJ/g

Cell III: -2.63 kJ/g

Cell I has the highest ratio (most energy released per gram) because the reactants have very low mass, while Cell II has the lowest ratio because the reactants have large masses.

21.135(a) 9.7 g Cu (b) 0.56 *M* Cu^{2+}

21.137 $Sn^{2+}(aq) + 2e^- \longrightarrow Sn(s)$
$Cr^{3+}(aq) + e^- \longrightarrow Cr^{2+}(aq)$
$Fe^{2+}(aq) + 2e^- \longrightarrow Fe(s)$
$U^{4+}(aq) + e^- \longrightarrow U^{3+}(aq)$
21.141(a) $3.6\times10^{-9}\ M$ (b) 0.3 M
21.143(a) Nonstandard cell:
$E_{\text{waste}} = E^\circ_{\text{cell}} - (0.0592\text{ V}/1)\log[\text{Ag}^+]_{\text{waste}}$
Standard cell:
$E_{\text{standard}} = E^\circ_{\text{cell}} - (0.0592\text{ V}/1)\log[\text{Ag}^+]_{\text{standard}}$

$$\text{(b) } [\text{Ag}^+]_{\text{waste}} = \text{antilog}\left(\frac{E_{\text{standard}} - E_{\text{waste}}}{0.0592}\right)[\text{Ag}^+]_{\text{standard}}$$

$$\text{(c) } C_{\text{Ag}^+,\text{ waste}} = \text{antilog}\left(\frac{E_{\text{standard}} - E_{\text{waste}}}{0.0592}\right)C_{\text{Ag}^+,\text{ standard}},$$

where C is concentration in ng/L
(d) 900 ng/L
(e) $[\text{Ag}^+]_{\text{waste}} =$

$$\text{antilog}\left[\frac{(E_{\text{standard}} - E_{\text{waste}})\dfrac{nF}{2.303R} + T_{\text{standard}}\log[\text{Ag}^+]_{\text{standard}}}{T_{\text{waste}}}\right]$$

21.145 (a) 1.08×10^3 C (b) 0.629 g Cd, 1.03 g NiO(OH), 0.202 g H_2O; total mass of reactants = 1.86 g (c) 10.1% **21.147** Li > Ba > Na > Al > Mn > Zn > Cr > Fe > Ni > Sn > Pb > Cu > Ag > Hg > Au. Metals with potentials lower than that of water (−0.83 V) can displace H_2 from water: Li, Ba, Na, Al, and Mn. Metals with potentials lower than that of hydrogen (0.00 V) can displace H_2 from acid: Li, Ba, Na, Al, Mn, Zn, Cr, Fe, Ni, Sn, and Pb. Metals with potentials greater than that of hydrogen (0.00 V) cannot displace H_2: Cu, Ag, Hg, and Au. **21.150**(a) 5.3×10^{-11} (b) 0.20 V (c) 0.43 V (d) 8.2×10^{-4} M NaOH **21.153**(a) -1.18×10^5 kJ (b) 1.20×10^4 L (c) 9.43×10^4 s (d) 157 kW·h (e) 22.0¢ **21.154** 2.94

Chapter 22

22.2 Fe from Fe_2O_3; Ca from $CaCO_3$; Na from NaCl; Zn from ZnS **22.3**(a) Differentiation refers to the processes involved in the formation of Earth into regions (core, mantle, and crust) of differing composition. Substances separated according to their densities, with the more dense material in the core and the less dense in the crust. (b) O, Si, Al, and Fe (c) O **22.7** Plants produced O_2, slowly increasing the oxygen concentration in the atmosphere and creating an environment for oxidizing metals. The oxygen-free decay of plant and animal material created large fossil fuel deposits. **22.9** Fixation refers to the process of converting a substance in the atmosphere into a form more readily usable by organisms. Carbon and nitrogen; fixation of carbon dioxide gas by plants and fixation of nitrogen gas by nitrogen-fixing bacteria. **22.12** Atmospheric nitrogen is fixed by three pathways: atmospheric, industrial, and biological. Atmospheric fixation requires high-temperature reactions (e.g., initiated by lightning) to convert N_2 into NO and other oxidized species. Industrial fixation involves mainly the formation of ammonia, NH_3, from N_2 and H_2. Biological fixation occurs in nitrogen-fixing bacteria that live on the roots of legumes. Human activity is an example of industrial fixation. It contributes about 17% of the fixed nitrogen. **22.14**(a) the atmosphere (b) Plants excrete acid from their roots to convert PO_4^{3-} ions into more soluble $H_2PO_4^-$ ions, which the plant can absorb. Through excretion and decay, organisms return soluble phosphate compounds to the cycle. **22.17**(a) 1.1×10^3 L (b) 4.2×10^2 m^3 **22.18**(a) The iron(II) ions form an insoluble salt, $Fe_3(PO_4)_2$, that decreases the yield of phosphorus. (b) 8.8 t **22.20**(a) Roasting consists of heating the mineral in air at high temperatures to convert the mineral to the oxide. (b) Smelting is the reduction of the metal oxide to the free metal using heat and a reducing agent such as coke. (c) Flotation is a separation process in which the ore is removed from the gangue by exploiting the difference in density in the presence of detergent. The gangue sinks to the bottom and the lighter ore-detergent mix is skimmed off the top. (d) Refining is the final step in the purification process to yield the pure metal. **22.25**(a) Slag is a byproduct of steel-making and contains the impurity SiO_2. (b) Pig iron is the impure product of iron metallurgy (containing 3–4% C and other impurities). (c) Steel refers to iron alloyed with other elements to attain desirable properties. (d) The basic-oxygen process is used to purify pig iron and obtain carbon steel. **22.27** Iron and nickel are more easily oxidized and less easily reduced than copper. They are separated from copper in the roasting step and converted to slag. In the electrorefining process, all three metals are in solution, but only Cu^{2+} ions are reduced at the cathode to form Cu(s). **22.30** Le Châtelier's principle says that the system shifts toward formation of K as the gaseous metal leaves the cell. **22.31**(a) $E^\circ_{\text{half-cell}} = -3.05$ V, -2.93 V, and -2.71 V for Li^+, K^+, and Na^+, respectively. In all of these cases, it is energetically more favorable to reduce H_2O to H_2 than to reduce M^+ to M. (b) $2RbX + Ca \longrightarrow CaX_2 + 2Rb$, where $\Delta H = \text{IE}_1(\text{Ca}) + \text{IE}_2(\text{Ca}) - 2\text{IE}_1(\text{Rb}) = 929$ kJ/mol. Based on the IEs and positive ΔH for the forward reaction, it seems more reasonable that Rb metal will reduce Ca^{2+} than the reverse. (c) If the reaction is carried out at a temperature greater than the boiling point of Rb, the product mixture will contain gaseous Rb, which can be removed from the reaction vessel; this would cause a shift in equilibrium to form more Rb as product. (d) $2CsX + Ca \longrightarrow CaX_2 + 2Cs$, where $\Delta H = \text{IE}_1(\text{Ca}) + \text{IE}_2(\text{Ca}) - 2\text{IE}_1(\text{Cs}) = 983$ kJ/mol. This reaction is more unfavorable than for Rb, but Cs has a lower boiling point. **22.32**(a) 4.5×10^4 L (b) 1.30×10^8 C (c) 1.69×10^6 s **22.35**(a) Mg^{2+} is more difficult to reduce than H_2O, so $H_2(g)$ would be produced instead of Mg metal. $Cl_2(g)$ forms at the anode due to overvoltage. (b) The ΔH°_f of $MgCl_2(s)$ is −641.6 kJ/mol. High temperature favors the reverse (endothermic) reaction, the formation of magnesium metal and chlorine gas. **22.37**(a) Sulfur dioxide is the reducing agent and is oxidized to the +6 state (SO_4^{2-}). (b) $HSO_4^-(aq)$ (c) $H_2SeO_3(aq) + 2SO_2(g) + H_2O(l) \longrightarrow Se(s) + 2HSO_4^-(aq) + 2H^+(aq)$ **22.42**(a) O.N. for Cu: in Cu_2S, +1; in Cu_2O, +1; in Cu, 0 (b) Cu_2S is the reducing agent, and Cu_2O is the oxidizing agent. **22.44**(a) 1.3×10^6 C (b) 1.2×10^3 A

22.47 $2ZnS(s) + C(graphite) \longrightarrow 2Zn(s) + CS_2(g)$; $\Delta G^\circ_{rxn} = 463$ kJ. Since ΔG°_{rxn} is positive, this reaction is not spontaneous at standard-state conditions. $2ZnO(s) + C(s) \longrightarrow 2Zn(s) + CO_2(g)$; $\Delta G^\circ_{rxn} = 242.0$ kJ. This reaction is also not spontaneous, but is less unfavorable. **22.48** The formation of sulfur trioxide is very slow at ordinary temperatures. Increasing the temperature can speed up the reaction, but because the reaction is exothermic, increasing the temperature decreases the yield. Adding a catalyst increases the rate of the reaction, allowing a lower temperature to be used to enhance the yield. **22.51**(a) Cl_2, H_2, and NaOH (b) The mercury-cell method yields higher purity NaOH, but releases some Hg, which is released into the environment. **22.52**(a) $\Delta G^\circ = -142$ kJ; yes (b) The rate of the reaction is very low at 25°C. (c) $\Delta G^\circ_{500} = -53$ kJ, so the reaction is spontaneous. (d) $K_{25} = 7.8\times10^{24} > K_{500} = 3.8\times10^{3}$ (e) 1.05×10^3 K **22.53** 7×10^2 lb Cl_2 **22.56**(a) $P_4O_{10}(s) + 6H_2O(l) \longrightarrow 4H_3PO_4(l)$ (b) 1.52 **22.58**(a) 9.006×10^9 g CO_2 (b) The 4.3×10^{10} g CO_2 produced by automobiles is much greater than that from the blast furnace. **22.60**(a) If $[OH^-] > 1.1\times10^{-4}$ *M* (i.e., if pH > 10.04), $Mg(OH)_2$ will precipitate. (b) 1 (To the correct number of significant figures, all the magnesium precipitates.) **22.61**(a) K_{25}(step 1) $= 1\times10^{168}$; K_{25}(side rxn) $= 7\times10^{228}$ (b) K_{900}(step 1) $= 4.5\times10^{49}$; K_{900}(side rxn) $= 1.4\times10^{63}$ (c) 8.8×10^7 dollars (d) 6.4×10^7 dollars

22.64(1) $2H_2O(l) + 2FeS_2(s) + 7O_2(g) \longrightarrow 2Fe^{2+}(aq) + 4SO_4^{2-}(aq) + 4H^+(aq)$ increases acidity

(2) $4H^+(aq) + 4Fe^{2+}(aq) + O_2(g) \longrightarrow 4Fe^{3+}(aq) + 2H_2O(l)$

(3) $Fe^{3+}(aq) + 3H_2O(l) \longrightarrow Fe(OH)_3(s) + 3H^+(aq)$ increases acidity

(4) $8H_2O(l) + FeS_2(s) + 14Fe^{3+}(aq) \longrightarrow 15Fe^{2+}(aq) + 2SO_4^{2-}(aq) + 16H^+(aq)$ increases acidity

22.65 density of ferrite: 7.86 g/cm³; density of austenite: 7.55 g/cm³

22.67(a) Cathode: $Na^+(l) + e^- \longrightarrow Na(l)$

Anode: $4OH^-(l) \longrightarrow O_2(g) + 2H_2O(g) + 4e^-$

(b) 50%

22.70(a) $nCO_2(g) + nH_2O(l) \longrightarrow (CH_2O)_n(s) + nO_2(g)$ (b) 27 L (c) 7.6×10^4 L **22.71** 73 mg/L **22.72** 891 kg Na_3AlF_6 **22.73**(a) 23.2 min (b) 14 effusion steps

22.75(a) 1.890 t Al_2O_3 (b) 0.3339 t C (c) 100% (d) 74% (e) 2.813×10^3 m³ **22.80** Acid rain increases the leaching of phosphate into the groundwater, due to the protonation of PO_4^{3-} to form HPO_4^{2-} and $H_2PO_4^-$. As shown in calculations for parts (a) and (b), solubility of $Ca_3(PO_4)_2$ increases from 6.4×10^{-7} *M* (in pure water) to 1.1×10^{-2} *M* (in acidic rainwater). (a) 6.4×10^{-7} *M* (b) 1.1×10^{-2} *M* **22.81**(a) 1.00 mol % (b) 238.9 g/mol **22.83** density of silver = 10.51 g/cm³; density of sterling silver = 10.2 g/cm³

Chapter 23

Answer to Boxed Reading Problem: B23.2 Zinc ions prefer a tetrahedral environment. The other ions listed prefer other environments (Ni^{2+} forms square planar complex ions while Fe^{2+} and Mn^{2+} form octahedral complex ions). If these ions are placed in a tetrahedral environment in place of the zinc, they cannot function as well as zinc since the enzyme catalyst would have a different shape.

• **23.2**(a) $1s^22s^22p^63s^23p^64s^23d^{10}4p^65s^24d^x$ (b) $1s^22s^22p^63s^23p^64s^23d^{10}4p^65s^24d^{10}5p^66s^24f^{14}5d^x$ **23.4** Five; examples are Mn, [Ar] $4s^23d^5$, and Fe^{3+}, [Ar] $3d^5$. **23.6**(a) The elements should increase in size as they increase in mass from Period 5 to Period 6. Because there are 14 inner transition elements in Period 6, the effective nuclear charge increases significantly; so the atomic size decreases, or "contracts." This effect is significant enough that Zr^{4+} and Hf^{4+} are almost the same size but differ greatly in atomic mass. (b) The atomic size increases from Period 4 to Period 5, but stays fairly constant from Period 5 to Period 6. (c) Atomic mass increases significantly from Period 5 to Period 6, but atomic radius (and thus volume) increases slightly, so Period 6 elements are very dense. **23.9**(a) A paramagnetic substance is attracted to a magnetic field, while a diamagnetic substance is slightly repelled by one. (b) Ions of transition elements often have half-filled *d* orbitals whose unpaired electrons make the ions paramagnetic. Ions of main-group elements usually have a noble-gas configuration with no partially filled levels. (c) Some *d* orbitals in the transition element ions are empty, which allows an electron from one *d* orbital to move to a slightly higher energy one. The energy required for this transition is small and falls in the visible wavelength range. All orbitals are filled in ions of main-group elements, so enough energy would have to be added to move an electron to the next principal energy level, not just another orbital within the same energy level. This amount of energy is very large and much greater than the visible range of wavelengths.

23.10(a) $1s^22s^22p^63s^23p^64s^23d^3$ (b) $1s^22s^22p^63s^23p^64s^23d^{10}4p^65s^24d^1$ (c) [Xe] $6s^24f^{14}5d^{10}$

23.12(a) [Xe] $6s^24f^{14}5d^6$ (b) [Ar] $4s^23d^7$ (c) [Kr] $5s^14d^{10}$

23.14(a) [Ar], no unpaired electrons (b) [Ar] $3d^9$, one unpaired electron (c) [Ar] $3d^5$, five unpaired electrons (d) [Kr] $4d^2$, two unpaired electrons **23.16**(a) +5 (b) +4 (c) +7 **23.18** Cr, Mo, and W **23.20** in CrF_2, because the chromium is in a lower oxidation state **23.22** Atomic size increases slightly down a group of transition elements, but nuclear charge increases much more, so the first ionization energy generally increases. The reduction potential for Mo is lower, so it is more difficult to oxidize Mo than Cr. In addition, the ionization energy of Mo is higher than that of Cr, so it is more difficult to remove electrons from Mo. **23.24** CrO_3, with Cr in a higher oxidation state, yields a more acidic aqueous solution. **23.28**(a) seven (b) This corresponds to a half-filled *f* subshell. **23.30**(a) [Xe] $6s^25d^1$ (b) [Xe] $4f^1$ (c) [Rn] $7s^25f^{11}$ (d) [Rn] $5f^2$

23.32(a) Eu^{2+}: [Xe] $4f^7$; Eu^{3+}: [Xe] $4f^6$; Eu^{4+}: [Xe] $4f^5$. The stability of the half-filled *f* subshell makes Eu^{2+} most stable. (b) Tb^{2+}: [Xe] $4f^9$; Tb^{3+}: [Xe] $4f^8$; Tb^{4+}: [Xe] $4f^7$. Tb should show a +4 oxidation state because that gives a half-filled subshell. **23.34** Gd has the electron configuration [Xe] $6s^24f^75d^1$ with eight unpaired electrons. Gd^{3+} has seven unpaired electrons: [Xe] $4f^7$. **23.37** The coordination number indicates the number of ligand atoms bonded to the metal ion. The oxidation number represents the number of electrons lost to form the ion. The coordination number is unrelated to the oxidation number. **23.39** 2, linear; 4, tetrahedral or square planar; 6, octahedral **23.42** The complex ion has a negative charge. **23.45**(a) hexaaquanickel(II) chloride (b) tris(ethylenediamine)chromium(III) perchlorate (c) potassium hexacyanomanganate(II) **23.47**(a) 2+, 6 (b) 3+, 6 (c) 2+, 6 **23.49**(a) potassium dicyanoargentate(I) (b) sodium tetrachlorocadmate(II) (c) tetraammineaquabromocobalt(III) bromide **23.51**(a) 1+, 2 (b) 2+, 4 (c) 3+, 6 **23.53**(a) $[Zn(NH_3)_4]SO_4$ (b) $[Cr(NH_3)_5Cl]Cl_2$ (c) $Na_3[Ag(S_2O_3)_2]$ **23.55**(a) 4, two ions (b) 6, three ions (c) 2, four ions **23.57**(a) $[Cr(H_2O)_6]_2(SO_4)_3$ (b) $Ba[FeBr_4]_2$ (c) $[Pt(en)_2]CO_3$ **23.59**(a) 6, five ions (b) 4, three ions (c) 4, two ions **23.61**(a) The nitrite ion forms linkage isomers because it can bind to the metal ion through the lone pair on the N atom or any lone pair on either O atom.

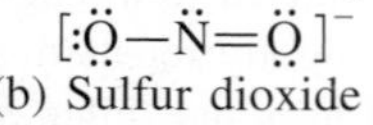

(b) Sulfur dioxide molecules form linkage isomers because the lone pair on the S atom or any lone pair on either O atom can bind the central metal ion.

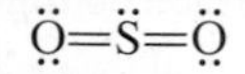

(c) Nitrate ions have an N atom with no lone pair and three O atoms, all with lone pairs that can bind to the metal ion. But all of the O atoms are equivalent, so these ions do not form linkage isomers.

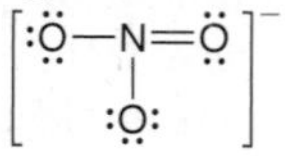

23.63(a) geometric isomerism

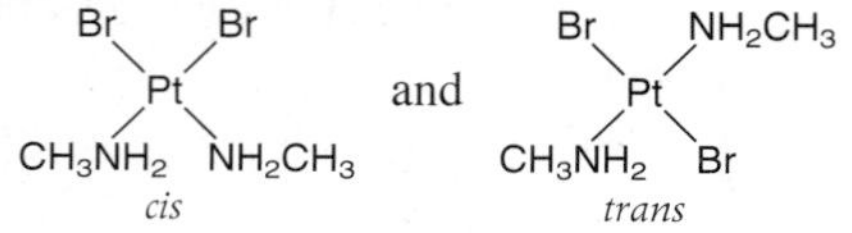

(b) geometric isomerism

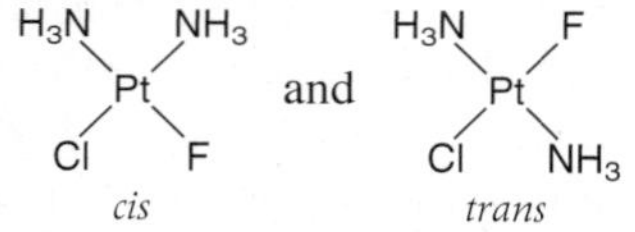

(c) geometric isomerism

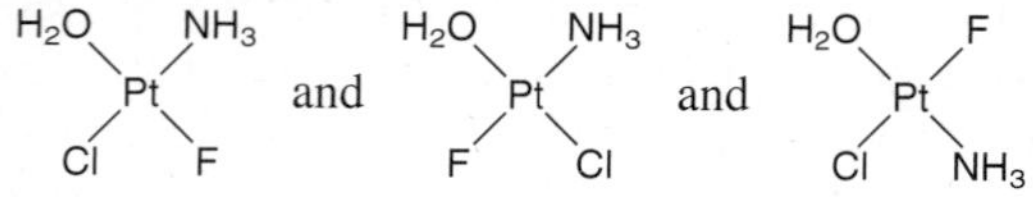

23.65(a) geometric isomerism

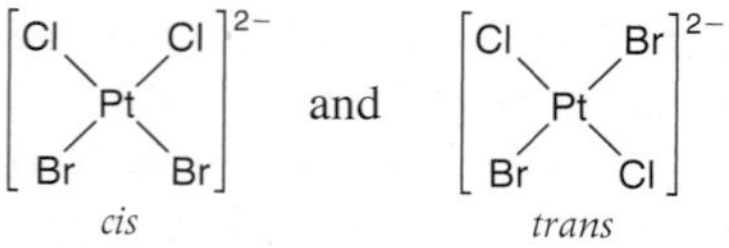

(b) linkage isomerism

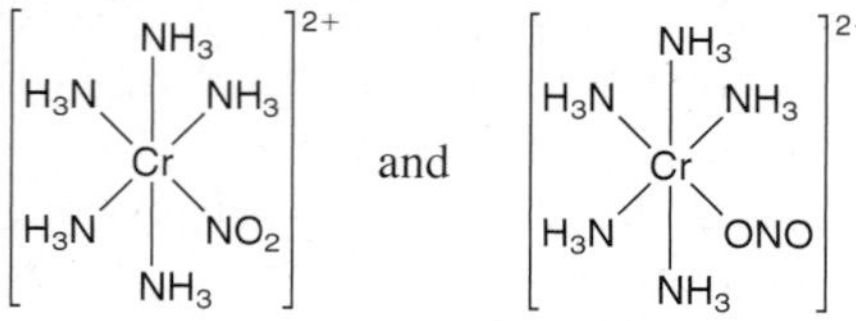

(c) geometric isomerism

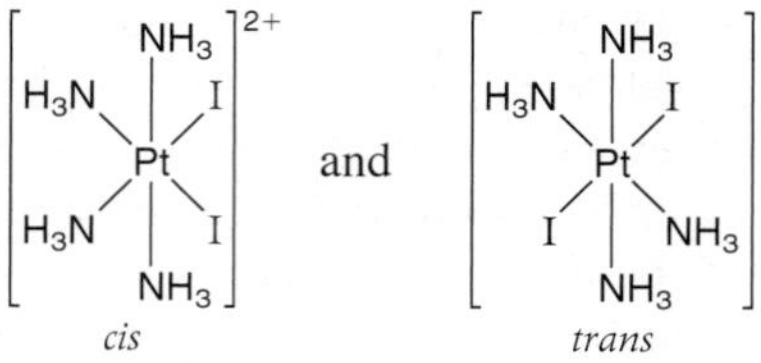

23.67 The compound with the traditional formula is $CrCl_3 \cdot 4NH_3$; the actual formula is $[Cr(NH_3)_4Cl_2]Cl$. **23.69**(a) $K[Pd(NH_3)Cl_3]$ (b) $[PdCl_2(NH_3)_2]$ (c) $K_2[PdCl_6]$ (d) $[Pd(NH_3)_4Cl_2]Cl_2$ **23.71**(a) dsp^2 (b) sp^3 **23.74** absorption of orange or yellow light **23.75**(a) The crystal field splitting energy (Δ) is the energy difference between the two sets of *d* orbitals that result from electrostatic effects of ligands on a central transition metal atom. (b) In an octahedral field of ligands, the ligands approach along the *x*, *y*, and *z* axes. The $d_{x^2-y^2}$ and d_{z^2} orbitals are located *along* the *x*, *y*, and *z* axes, so ligand interaction is higher in energy. The other orbital-ligand interactions are lower in energy because the d_{xy}, d_{yz}, and d_{xz} orbitals are located *between* the *x*, *y*, and *z* axes. (c) In a tetrahedral field of ligands, the ligands do not approach along the *x*, *y*, and *z* axes. The ligand interaction is greater for the d_{xy}, d_{yz}, and d_{xz} orbitals and lesser for the $d_{x^2-y^2}$ and d_{z^2} orbitals. Therefore, the crystal field splitting is reversed, and the d_{xy}, d_{yz}, and d_{xz} orbitals are higher in energy than the $d_{x^2-y^2}$ and d_{z^2} orbitals. **23.78** If Δ is greater than $E_{pairing}$, electrons will pair their spins in the lower energy set of *d* orbitals before entering the higher energy set of *d* orbitals as unpaired electrons. If Δ is less than $E_{pairing}$, electrons will occupy the higher energy set of *d* orbitals as unpaired electrons before pairing in the lower energy set of *d* orbitals. **23.80**(a) no *d* electrons (b) eight *d* electrons (c) six *d* electrons **23.82**(a) five (b) ten (c) seven

23.84

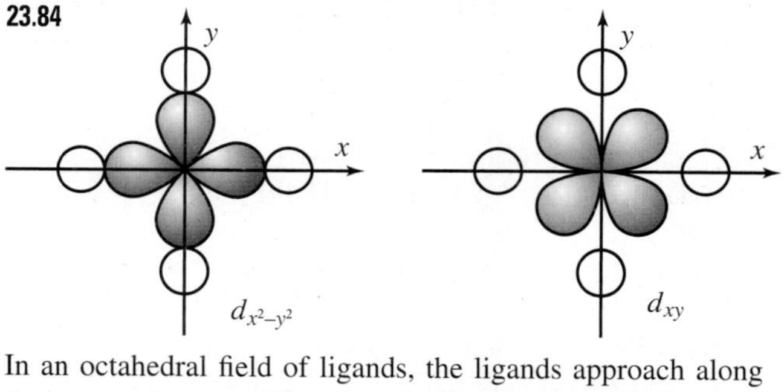

In an octahedral field of ligands, the ligands approach along the *x*, *y*, and *z* axes. The $d_{x^2-y^2}$ orbital is located along the *x* and *y* axes, so ligand interaction is greater. The d_{xy} orbital is offset from the *x* and *y* axes by 90°, so ligand interaction is less. The greater interaction of the $d_{x^2-y^2}$ orbital results in its higher energy.

23.86 a and d

23.88

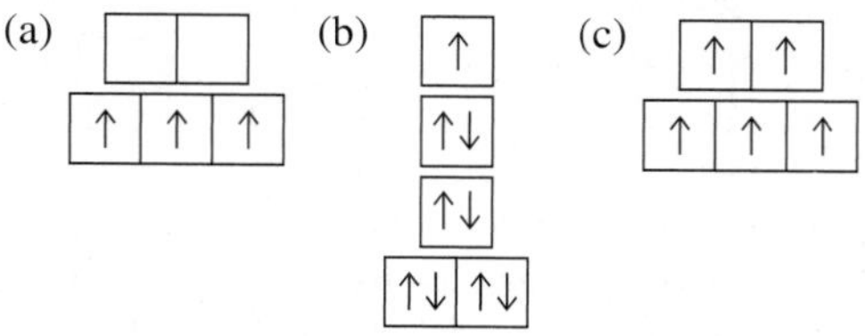

23.90

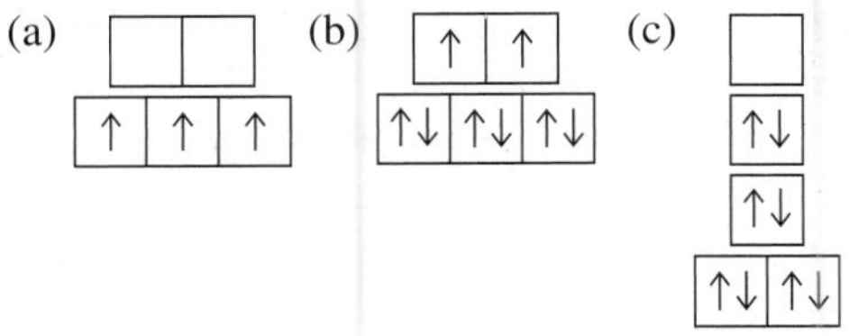

23.92 $[Cr(H_2O)_6]^{3+} < [Cr(NH_3)_6]^{3+} < [Cr(NO_2)_6]^{3-}$
23.94 A violet complex absorbs yellow-green light. The light absorbed by a complex with a weaker field ligand would be at a lower energy and higher wavelength. Light of lower energy than yellow-green light is yellow, orange, or red. The color observed would be blue or green. **23.97** The H_2O ligand is weaker than the NH_3 ligand. The weaker field ligand results in a lower splitting energy and absorbs visible light of lower energy. The hexaaqua complex appears green because it absorbs red light. The hexaammine complex appears violet because it absorbs yellow light, which has higher energy (shorter λ) than red light. **23.101** Hg^+ is [Xe] $6s^14f^{14}5d^{10}$ and Cu^+ is [Ar] $3d^{10}$. The mercury(I) ion has one electron in the 6*s* orbital that can form a covalent bond with the electron in the 6*s* orbital of another mercury(I) ion. In the copper(I) ion there are no electrons in the *s* orbital, so these ions cannot bond with one another. **23.102**(a) 6 (b) +3 (c) two (d) 1 mol
23.109 geometric (*cis-trans*) and linkage isomerism

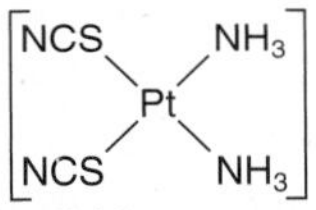

cis-diamminedithiocyanatoplatinum(II)

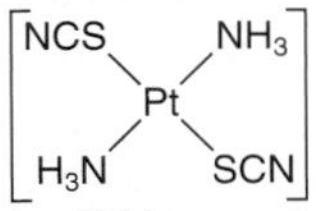

trans-diamminedithiocyanatoplatinum(II)

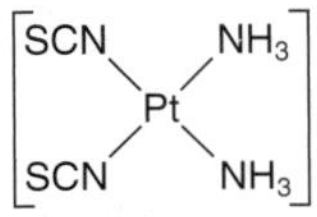

cis-diamminediisothiocyanatoplatinum(II)

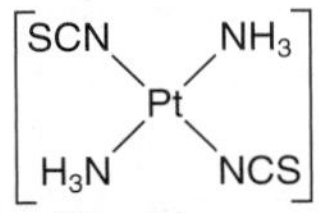

trans-diamminediisothiocyanatoplatinum(II)

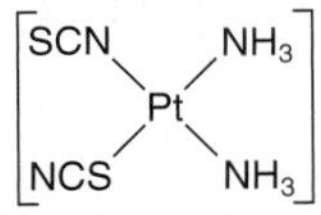

cis-diammineisothiocyanatothiocyanatoplatinum(II)

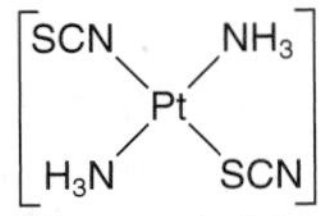

trans-diammineisothiocyanatothiocyanatoplatinum(II)

23.110 $[Co(NH_3)_4(H_2O)Cl]^{2+}$
tetraammineaquachlorocobalt(III) ion
2 geometric isomers

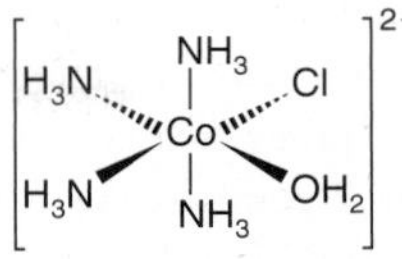

cis

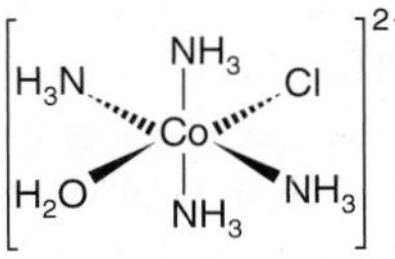

trans

$[Cr(H_2O)_3Br_2Cl]$
triaquadibromochlorochromium(III)
3 geometric isomers

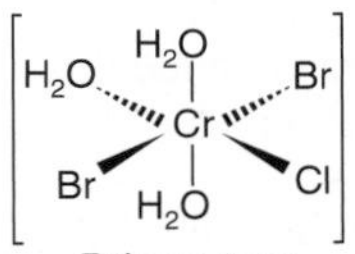

Br's are *trans*

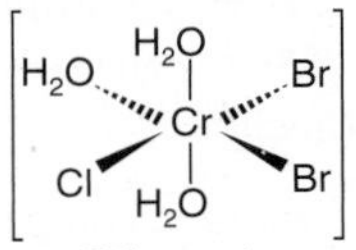

Br's are *cis*
H_2O's are *cis* and *trans*

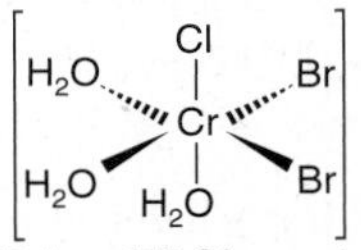

Br's and H_2O's are *cis*

$[Cr(NH_3)_2(H_2O)_2Br_2]^+$
diamminediaquadibromochromium(III) ion
6 isomers (5 geometric)

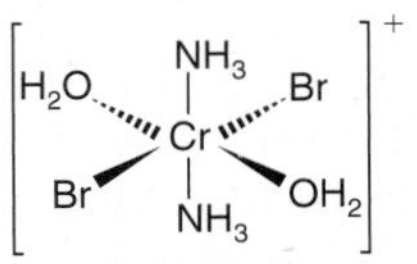

all ligands are *trans*

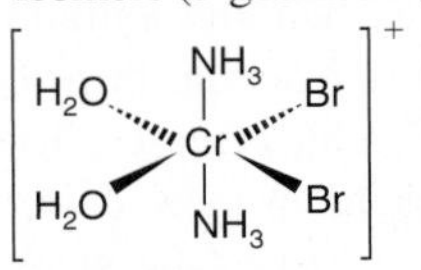

only NH_3 is *trans*

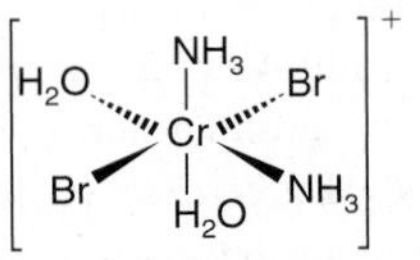

only Br is *trans*

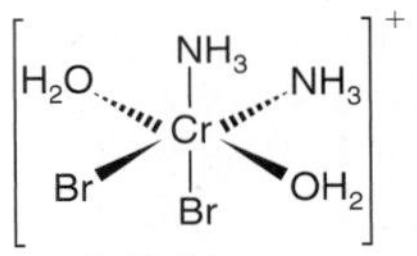

only H_2O is *trans*

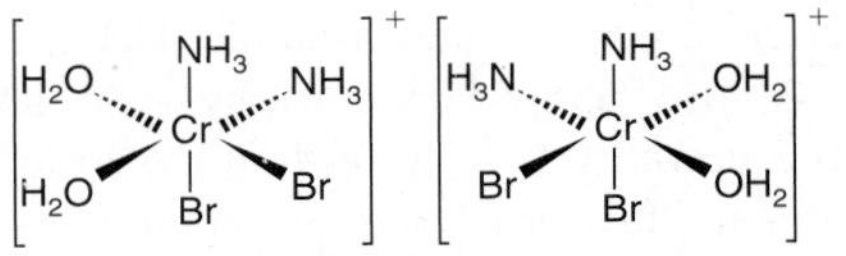

optical isomers
all three ligands are *cis*

23.115(a) no optical isomers (b) no optical isomers (c) no optical isomers (d) no optical isomers (e) optical isomers
23.116 $Pt[P(C_2H_5)_3]_2Cl_2$

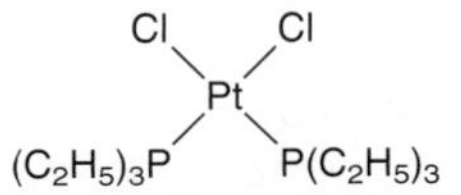

cis-dichlorobis(triethylphosphine)platinum(II)

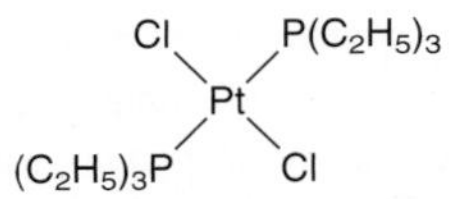

trans-dichlorobis(triethylphosphine)platinum(II)

23.118(a) The first reaction shows no change in the number of particles. In the second reaction, the number of reactant particles is greater than the number of product particles. A decrease in the number of particles means a decrease in entropy. Based on entropy change only, the first reaction is favored. (b) The ethylenediamine complex will be more stable with respect to ligand exchange in water because the entropy change for that exchange is unfavorable (negative).

Chapter 24

Answers to Boxed Reading Problems: B24.1 In the *s*-process, a nucleus captures a neutron sometime over a long period of time. Then the nucleus emits a beta particle to form another element. The stable isotopes of most heavy elements up to ^{209}Bi form by the *s*-process. The *r*-process very quickly forms less stable isotopes and those with *A* greater than 230 by multiple neutron captures, followed by multiple beta decays. **B24.3** The simultaneous fusion of three nuclei is a termolecular process. Termolecular processes have a very low probability of occurring. The bimolecular fusion of ^{8}Be with ^{4}He is more likely. **B24.4** $^{210}_{83}\text{Bi} \longrightarrow {}^{0}_{-1}\beta + {}^{210}_{84}\text{Po}$ (nuclide A); $^{210}_{84}\text{Po} \longrightarrow {}^{4}_{2}\alpha + {}^{206}_{82}\text{Pb}$ (nuclide B); $^{206}_{82}\text{Pb} + 3{}^{1}_{0}\text{n} \longrightarrow {}^{209}_{82}\text{Pb}$ (nuclide C); $^{209}_{82}\text{Pb} \longrightarrow {}^{0}_{-1}\beta + {}^{209}_{83}\text{Bi}$ (nuclide D)

• **24.1**(a) Chemical reactions are accompanied by relatively small changes in energy; nuclear reactions are accompanied by relatively large changes in energy. (b) Increasing temperature increases the rate of a chemical reaction but has no effect on a nuclear reaction. (c) Both chemical and nuclear reaction rates increase with higher reactant concentrations. (d) If the reactant is limiting in a chemical reaction, then more reactant produces more product and the yield increases. The presence of more radioactive reactant results in more decay product, so a higher reactant concentration increases the yield. **24.2**(a) 95.02% (b) The atomic mass is larger than the isotopic mass of ^{32}S. Sulfur-32 is the lightest isotope. **24.4**(a) *Z* down by 2, *N* down by 2 (b) *Z* up by 1, *N* down by 1 (c) no change in *Z* or *N* (d) *Z* down by 1, *N* up by 1 (e) *Z* down by 1, *N* up by 1 A different element is produced in all cases except c. **24.6** A neutron-rich nuclide decays by beta (minus) decay. A neutron-poor nuclide undergoes positron decay or electron capture. **24.8**(a) $^{234}_{92}\text{U} \longrightarrow {}^{4}_{2}\alpha + {}^{230}_{90}\text{Th}$ (b) $^{232}_{93}\text{Np} + {}^{0}_{-1}\text{e} \longrightarrow {}^{232}_{92}\text{U}$ (c) $^{12}_{7}\text{N} \longrightarrow {}^{0}_{1}\beta + {}^{12}_{6}\text{C}$ **24.10**(a) $^{27}_{12}\text{Mg} \longrightarrow {}^{0}_{-1}\beta + {}^{27}_{13}\text{Al}$ (b) $^{23}_{12}\text{Mg} \longrightarrow {}^{0}_{1}\beta + {}^{23}_{11}\text{Na}$ (c) $^{103}_{46}\text{Pd} + {}^{0}_{-1}\text{e} \longrightarrow {}^{103}_{45}\text{Rh}$ **24.12**(a) $^{48}_{23}\text{V} \longrightarrow {}^{48}_{22}\text{Ti} + {}^{0}_{1}\beta$ (b) $^{107}_{48}\text{Cd} + {}^{0}_{-1}\text{e} \longrightarrow {}^{107}_{47}\text{Ag}$ (c) $^{210}_{86}\text{Rn} \longrightarrow {}^{206}_{84}\text{Po} + {}^{4}_{2}\alpha$ **24.14**(a) $^{186}_{78}\text{Pt} + {}^{0}_{-1}\text{e} \longrightarrow {}^{186}_{77}\text{Ir}$ (b) $^{225}_{89}\text{Ac} \longrightarrow {}^{221}_{87}\text{Fr} + {}^{4}_{2}\alpha$ (c) $^{129}_{52}\text{Te} \longrightarrow {}^{129}_{53}\text{I} + {}^{0}_{-1}\beta$ **24.16**(a) Appears stable because its *N* and *Z* values are both magic numbers, but its *N*/*Z* ratio (1.50) is too high; it is unstable. (b) Appears unstable because its *Z* value is an odd number, but its *N*/*Z* ratio (1.19) is in the band of stability, so it is stable. (c) Unstable because its *N*/*Z* ratio is too high. **24.18**(a) The *N*/*Z* ratio for ^{127}I is 1.4; it is stable. (b) The *N*/*Z* ratio for ^{106}Sn is 1.1; it is unstable because this ratio is too low. (c) The *N*/*Z* ratio is 1.1 for ^{68}As. The ratio is within the range of stability, but the nuclide is most likely unstable because there are odd numbers of both protons and neutrons. **24.20**(a) alpha decay (b) positron decay or electron capture (c) positron decay or electron capture **24.22**(a) beta (minus) decay (b) positron decay or electron capture (c) alpha decay **24.24** Stability results from a favorable *N*/*Z* ratio, even numbered *N* and/or *Z*, and the occurrence of magic numbers. The *N*/*Z* ratio of ^{52}Cr is 1.17, which is within the band of stability. The fact that *Z* is even does not account for the variation in stability because all isotopes of chromium have the same *Z*. However, ^{52}Cr has 28 neutrons, so *N* is both an even number and a magic number for this isotope only. **24.28** seven α emissions and four β^- emissions **24.31** No, it is not valid to conclude that $t_{1/2}$ equals 1 min because the number of nuclei is so small. Decay rate is an average rate and is only meaningful when the sample is macroscopic and contains a large number of nuclei. For the sample containing 6×10^{12} nuclei, the conclusion is valid. **24.33** 2.56×10^{-2} Ci/g **24.35** 1.4×10^{8} Bq/g **24.37** 1×10^{-12} day^{-1} **24.39** 2.31×10^{-7} yr^{-1} **24.41** 1.49 mg **24.43** 2.2×10^{9} yr **24.45** 30 dpm **24.47** 1.0×10^{6} yr **24.50** Neither γ radiation nor neutron beams have charge, so neither is deflected by a magnetic or electric field. Neutron beams differ from γ radiation in that a neutron has a mass approximately equal to that of a proton. It was observed that a neutron beam induces the emission of protons from a substance; γ radiation does not cause such emission. **24.52** Protons are repelled from the target nuclei due to interaction with like (positive) charges. Higher energy is required to overcome the repulsion. **24.53**(a) $^{10}_{5}\text{B} + {}^{4}_{2}\alpha \longrightarrow {}^{1}_{0}\text{n} + {}^{13}_{7}\text{N}$ (b) $^{28}_{14}\text{Si} + {}^{2}_{1}\text{H} \longrightarrow {}^{1}_{0}\text{n} + {}^{29}_{15}\text{P}$ (c) $^{242}_{96}\text{Cm} + {}^{4}_{2}\alpha \longrightarrow 2{}^{1}_{0}\text{n} + {}^{244}_{98}\text{Cf}$ **24.58** Ionizing radiation is more dangerous to children because their rapidly dividing cells are more susceptible to radiation than adults' slowly dividing cells. **24.60**(a) 5.4×10^{-7} rad (b) 5.4×10^{-9} Gy **24.62**(a) 7.5×10^{-10} Gy (b) 7.5×10^{-5} mrem (c) 7.5×10^{-10} Sv **24.65** 1.86×10^{-3} rad **24.67** NAA does not destroy the sample, while chemical analyses do. Neutrons bombard a nonradioactive sample, inducing some atoms within the sample to be radioactive. The radioisotopes decay by emitting radiation characteristic of each isotope. **24.73** Energy is released when a nucleus forms from nucleons. The nuclear binding energy is the quantity of energy holding 1 mol of nuclei together. This energy must be absorbed to break up the nucleus into nucleons and is released when nucleons come together. **24.75**(a) 1.861×10^{4} eV (b) 2.981×10^{-15} J **24.77** 7.6×10^{11} J **24.79**(a) 7.976 MeV/nucleon (b) 127.6 MeV/atom (c) 1.231×10^{10} kJ/mol **24.81**(a) 8.768 MeV/nucleon (b) 517.3 MeV/atom (c) 4.99×10^{10} kJ/mol **24.85** Radioactive decay is a spontaneous process in which unstable nuclei emit radioactive particles and energy. Fission occurs as the result of high-energy bombardment of nuclei with small particles that cause the nuclei to break into smaller nuclides, radioactive particles, and energy. All fission events are not the same. The nuclei split in a number of ways to produce several different products. **24.88** The water serves to slow the neutrons so that they are better able to cause a fission reaction. Heavy water is a better moderator because it does not absorb neutrons as well as light water does; thus, more neutrons are available to initiate the fission process. However, D_2O does not occur naturally in great abundance, so its production adds to the cost of a heavy-water reactor. **24.93**(a) 1.1×10^{-29} kg (b) 9.9×10^{-13} J (c) 5.9×10^{8} kJ/mol; this is approximately 1 million times larger than a typical enthalpy of reaction. **24.95** 8.0×10^{3} yr **24.98** 1.35×10^{-5} *M* **24.100** 6.2×10^{-2} **24.102**(a) 5.99 h (b) 21% **24.104**(a) 0.999 (b) 0.298 (c) 5.58×10^{-6}

(d) Radiocarbon dating is more reliable for the fraction in part (b) because a significant amount of ^{14}C has decayed and a significant amount remains. Therefore, a change in the amount of ^{14}C will be noticeable. For the fraction in part (a), very little ^{14}C has decayed, and for (c) very little ^{14}C remains. In either case, it will be more difficult to measure the change, so the error will be relatively large. **24.106** 6.58 h **24.110** 4.904×10^{-9} L/h **24.113** 81 yr **24.115**(a) 0.15 Bq/L (b) 0.27 Bq/L (c) 3.3 d; a total of 12.8 d **24.118** 7.4 s **24.121** 1926

24.124 6.27×10^{5} eV/reaction, 6.05×10^{7} kJ/mol reaction **24.127**(a) 2.07×10^{-17} J (b) 1.45×10^{7} H atoms (c) 1.4960×10^{-5} J (d) 1.4959×10^{-5} J (e) No, the captain should continue using the current technology. **24.130**(a) 0.043 MeV, 2.9×10^{-11} m (b) 4.713 MeV **24.134**(a) 3.26×10^{3} d (b) 3.2×10^{-3} s (c) 2.78×10^{11} yr **24.136**(a) 1.80×10^{17} J (b) 6.15×10^{16} kJ (c) The procedure in part (b) produces more energy per kilogram of antihydrogen. **24.137** 9.316×10^{2} MeV **24.141** 7.81 d

Glossary

Numbers in parentheses refer to the page(s) on which a term is introduced and/or discussed.

A

absolute scale (also *Kelvin scale*) The preferred temperature scale in scientific work, which has absolute zero (0 K, or −273.15°C) as the lowest temperature. (23) [See also *kelvin (K)*.]

absorption spectrum The spectrum produced when atoms absorb specific wavelengths of incoming light and become excited from lower to higher energy levels. (273)

abundance The amount of an element in a particular region of the natural world. (905)

accuracy The closeness of a measurement to the actual value. (29)

acid In common laboratory terms, any species that produces H^+ ions when dissolved in water. (145) [See also *Arrhenius, Brønsted-Lowry,* and *Lewis acid-base definitions.*]

acid anhydride A compound, usually formed by a dehydration-condensation reaction of an oxoacid, that yields two molecules of the acid when it reacts with water. (600)

acid-base buffer (also *buffer*) A solution that resists changes in pH when a small amount of either strong acid or strong base is added. (765)

acid-base indicator An organic molecule whose color is different in acid and in base and is used to monitor the equivalence point of a titration or the pH of a solution. (728)

acid-base reaction Any reaction between an acid and a base. (145) (See also *neutralization reaction.*)

acid-base titration curve A plot of the pH of a solution of acid (or base) versus the volume of base (or acid) added to the solution. (774)

acid-dissociation (acid-ionization) constant (K_a) An equilibrium constant for the dissociation of an acid (HA) in H_2O to yield the conjugate base (A^-) and H_3O^+:

$$K_a = \frac{[H_3O^+][A^-]}{[HA]} \qquad (722)$$

actinides The Period 7 elements that constitute the second inner transition series (5*f* block), which includes thorium (Th; $Z = 90$) through lawrencium (Lr; $Z = 103$). (306, 952)

activated complex (See *transition state.*)

activation energy (E_a) The minimum energy with which molecules must collide to react. (649)

active site The region of an enzyme formed by specific amino acid side chains at which catalysis occurs. (662)

activity ($\mathcal{A}$) (also *decay rate*) The change in number of nuclei ($\mathcal{N}$) of a radioactive sample divided by the change in time (t). (988)

activity series of the metals A listing of metals arranged in order of decreasing strength of the metal as a reducing agent in aqueous reactions. (165)

actual yield The amount of product actually obtained in a chemical reaction. (112)

addition polymer (also *chain-reaction,* or *chain-growth, polymer*) A polymer formed when monomers (usually containing C=C) combine through an addition reaction. (604)

addition reaction A type of organic reaction in which atoms linked by a multiple bond become bonded to more atoms. (588)

adduct The product of a Lewis acid-base reaction characterized by the formation of a new covalent bond. (751)

adenosine triphosphate (ATP) A high-energy molecule that serves most commonly as a store and source of energy in organisms. (836)

alcohol An organic compound (ending, *-ol*) that contains a —C—Ö—H functional group. (591)

aldehyde An organic compound (ending, *-al*) that contains the carbonyl functional group (C=Ö) in which the carbonyl C is also bonded to H. (597)

alkane A hydrocarbon that contains only single bonds and no rings (general formula, C_nH_{2n+2}). (576)

alkene A hydrocarbon that contains at least one C=C bond (general formula, C_nH_{2n}). (582)

alkyl group A saturated hydrocarbon chain with one bond available. (588)

alkyl halide (See *haloalkane.*)

alkyne A hydrocarbon that contains at least one C≡C bond (general formula, C_nH_{2n-2}). (583)

allotrope One of two or more crystalline or molecular forms of an element. In general, one allotrope is more stable than another at a particular pressure and temperature. (539)

alloy A mixture with metallic properties that consists of solid phases of two or more pure elements, a solid-solid solution, or distinct intermediate phases. (354, 482, 921)

alpha (α) decay A radioactive process in which an alpha particle is emitted from a nucleus. (981)

alpha particle (α or ${}^4_2He^{2+}$) A positively charged particle, identical to a helium-4 nucleus, that is one of the common types of radioactive emissions. (979)

amide An organic compound that contains the —C(=:O:)—N̈— functional group. (599)

amine An organic compound (general formula, —C—N̈—) derived structurally by replacing one or more H atoms of ammonia with organic groups; a weak organic base. (594, 754)

amino acid An organic compound [general formula, H_2N—CH(R)—COOH] with at least one carboxyl and one amine group on the same molecule; the monomer unit of a protein. (483, 608)

amorphous solid A solid that has a poorly defined shape because it lacks extensive molecular-level ordering of its particles. (441)

ampere (A) The SI unit of electric current; 1 ampere of current results when 1 coulomb flows through a conductor in 1 second. (890)

amphoteric Able to act as either an acid or a base. (316)

amplitude The height of the crest (or depth of the trough) of a wave; related to the intensity of the energy (brightness of the light). (262)

angular momentum quantum number (l) An integer from 0 to $n - 1$ that is related to the shape of an atomic orbital. (281)

anion A negatively charged ion. (55)
anode The electrode at which oxidation occurs in an electrochemical cell. Electrons are given up by the reducing agent and leave the cell at the anode. (856)
antibonding MO A molecular orbital formed when wave functions are subtracted from each other, which decreases electron density between the nuclei and leaves a node. Electrons occupying such an orbital destabilize the molecule. (406)
apatite A compound of general formula $Ca_5(PO_4)_3X$, where X is generally F, Cl, or OH; a source of phosphorus. (914)
aqueous solution A solution in which water is the solvent. (70)
aromatic hydrocarbon A compound of C and H with one or more rings of C atoms (often drawn with alternating C—C and C=C bonds), in which there is extensive delocalization of π electrons. (584)
Arrhenius acid-base definition A model of acid-base behavior in which an acid is a substance that has H in its formula and dissociates in water to yield H_3O^+, and a base is a substance that has OH in its formula and produces OH^- in water. (720)
Arrhenius equation An equation that expresses the exponential relationship between temperature and the rate constant: $k = Ae^{-E_a/RT}$. (649)
atmosphere The mixture of gases that extends from a planet's surface and eventually merges with outer space; the gaseous portion of Earth's crust. (212, 908) (For the unit, see *standard atmosphere.*)
atom The smallest particle of an element that retains the chemical nature of the element. A neutral, spherical entity composed of a positively charged central nucleus surrounded by one or more negatively charged electrons. (43)
atomic mass (also *atomic weight*) The average of the masses of the naturally occurring isotopes of an element weighted according to their abundances. (50)
atomic mass unit (amu) (also *dalton, Da*) A mass exactly equal to $\frac{1}{12}$ the mass of a carbon-12 atom. (50)
atomic number (*Z*) The unique number of protons in the nucleus of each atom of an element (equal to the number of electrons in the neutral atom). An integer that expresses the positive charge of a nucleus or subatomic particle in multiples of the electronic charge. (48)
atomic orbital (also *wave function*) A mathematical expression that describes the motion of the electron's matter-wave in terms of time and position in the region of the nucleus. The term is used qualitatively to mean the region of space in which there is a high probability of finding the electron. (279)
atomic solid A solid consisting of individual atoms held together by dispersion forces; the frozen noble gases are the only examples. (449)
atomic symbol (also *element symbol*) A one- or two-letter abbreviation for the English, Latin, or Greek name of an element. (49)
atomic weight (See *atomic mass.*)
aufbau principle The conceptual approach for building up atoms by adding one proton at a time to the nucleus and one electron around it to obtain the ground-state electron configurations of the elements. (299)
autoionization (also *self-ionization*) A reaction in which two molecules of a substance react to give ions. The most important example is for water:

$$2H_2O(l) \rightleftharpoons H_3O^+(aq) + OH^-(aq) \qquad (724)$$

average rate The change in concentration of reactants (or products) divided by a finite time period. (630)
Avogadro's law The gas law stating that, at fixed temperature and pressure, equal volumes of any ideal gas contain equal numbers of particles, and, therefore, the volume of a gas is directly proportional to its amount (mol): $V \propto n$. (190)
Avogadro's number A number (6.022×10^{23} to four significant figures) equal to the number of atoms in exactly 12 g of carbon-12; the number of atoms, molecules, or formula units in one mole of an element or compound. (83)
axial group An atom (or group) that lies above or below the trigonal plane of a trigonal bipyramidal molecule, or a similar structural feature in a molecule. (377)

B

background radiation Natural ionizing radiation, the most important form of which is cosmic radiation. (997)
balancing coefficient (also *stoichiometric coefficient*) A numerical multiplier of all the atoms in the formula immediately following it in a balanced chemical equation. (99)
band of stability The band of stable nuclides that appears on a plot of number of neutrons versus number of protons for all nuclides. (983)
band theory An extension of molecular orbital (MO) theory that explains many properties of metals and other solids, in particular, the differences in electrical conductivity of conductors, semiconductors, and insulators. (452)
barometer A device used to measure atmospheric pressure. Most commonly, a tube open at one end, which is filled with mercury and inverted into a dish of mercury. (183)
base In common laboratory terms, any species that produces OH^- ions when dissolved in water. (146) [See also *Arrhenius, Brønsted-Lowry,* and *Lewis acid-base definitions.*]
base-dissociation (base-ionization) constant (K_b) An equilibrium constant for the reaction of a base (B) with H_2O to yield the conjugate acid (BH^+) and OH^-:

$$K_b = \frac{[BH^+][OH^-]}{[B]} \qquad (740)$$

base pair Two complementary mononucleotide bases that are H bonded to each other; guanine (G) always pairs with cytosine (C), and adenine (A) always pairs with thymine (T) (or uracil, U). (613)
base unit (also *fundamental unit*) A unit that defines the standard for one of the seven physical quantities in the International System of Units (SI). (17)
basic-oxygen process The method used to convert pig iron to steel, in which O_2 is blown over and through molten pig iron to oxidize impurities and decrease the content of carbon. (925)
battery A group of voltaic cells arranged in series; primary and secondary types are self-contained, but flow batteries are not. (878)
becquerel (Bq) The SI unit of radioactivity; 1 Bq = 1 d/s (disintegration per second). (988)
bent shape (also *V shape*) A molecular shape that arises when a central atom is bonded to two other atoms and has one or two lone pairs; occurs as the AX_2E shape class (bond angle $< 120°$) in the trigonal planar arrangement and as the AX_2E_2 shape class (bond angle $< 109.5°$) in the tetrahedral arrangement. (375)
beta (β) decay A radioactive change that encompasses any of three specific processes— β^- decay, β^+ emission, and e^- capture. (981)

beta (β^-) decay A radioactive process in which a beta particle is emitted from a nucleus. (981)
beta particle (β, β^-, or $_{-1}^{0}\beta$) A negatively charged particle, identified as a high-speed electron, that is one of the common types of radioactive emissions. (979)
bimolecular reaction An elementary reaction involving the collision of two reactant species. (655)
binary covalent compound A compound that consists of atoms of two elements in which bonding occurs primarily through electron sharing. (65)
binary ionic compound A compound that consists of the oppositely charged ions of two elements. (55)
biomass conversion The process of applying chemical and biological methods to convert plant or animal matter into fuels. (249)
biosphere The living systems that inhabit Earth. (908)
blast furnace A tower-shaped furnace made of brick material in which intense heat and blasts of air are used to convert iron ore and coke to iron metal and carbon dioxide. (924)
body-centered cubic unit cell A unit cell in which a particle lies at each corner and in the center of a cube. (442)
boiling point (bp or T_b) The temperature at which the vapor pressure of a gas equals the external (atmospheric) pressure. (428)
boiling point elevation (ΔT_b) The increase in the boiling point of a solvent caused by the presence of dissolved solute. (501)
bond angle The angle formed by the nuclei of two surrounding atoms with the nucleus of the central atom at the vertex. (374)
bond energy (BE) (also *bond enthalpy* or *bond strength*) The enthalpy change (always >0) accompanying the breakage of a given bond in 1 mol of gaseous molecules. (339)
bond length The distance between the nuclei of two bonded atoms. (340)
bond order The number of electron pairs shared by two bonded atoms. (339)
bonding MO A molecular orbital formed when wave functions are added to each other, which increases electron density between the nuclei. Electrons occupying such an orbital stabilize the molecule. (406)
bonding pair (also *shared pair*) An electron pair shared by two nuclei; the mutual attraction between the nuclei and the electron pair forms a covalent bond. (339)
Born-Haber cycle A series of hypothetical steps and their enthalpy changes that convert elements to an ionic compound; it is used to calculate the lattice energy. (333)
Boyle's law The gas law stating that, at constant temperature and amount of gas, the volume occupied by a gas is inversely proportional to the applied (external) pressure: $V \propto 1/P$. (187)
branch A side chain appended to a polymer backbone or longest sequence of atoms in an organic compound. (465)
bridge bond (also *three-center, two-electron bond*) A covalent bond in which three atoms are held together by two electrons. (536)
Brønsted-Lowry acid-base definition A model of acid-base behavior based on proton transfer, in which an acid and a base are defined, respectively, as species that donate and accept a proton. (729)
buffer (See *acid-base buffer*.)
buffer capacity A measure of the ability of a buffer to resist a change in pH; related to the total concentrations and relative proportions of buffer components. (770)
buffer range The pH range over which a buffer acts effectively. (771)

C

calibration The process of correcting for systematic error of a measuring device by comparing it to a known standard. (29)
calorie (cal) A unit of energy defined as exactly 4.184 joules; originally defined as the heat needed to raise the temperature of 1 g of water 1°C (from 14.5°C to 15.5°C). (233)
calorimeter A device used to measure the heat released or absorbed by a physical or chemical process taking place within it. (239)
capillarity (or *capillary action*) A property that results in a liquid rising through a narrow space against the pull of gravity. (438)
carbon steel The steel that is produced by the basic-oxygen process, contains about 1% to 1.5% C and other impurities, and is alloyed with metals that prevent corrosion and increase strength. (925)
carbonyl group The C=O grouping of atoms. (597)
carboxylic acid An organic compound (ending, *-oic acid*) that contains the $-\overset{\overset{:O:}{\|}}{C}-\ddot{\underset{..}{O}}H$ group. (599)
catalyst A substance or mixture that increases the rate of a reaction without being used up in the process. (660)
catenation The process by which atoms of an element bond to each other in chains; most common with carbon in organic compounds but also occurs with boron, silicon, sulfur, and several other elements. (572)
cathode The electrode at which reduction occurs in an electrochemical cell. Electrons enter the cell and are acquired by the oxidizing agent at the cathode. (856)
cathode ray The ray of light emitted by the cathode (negative electrode) in a gas discharge tube; travels in straight lines, unless deflected by magnetic or electric fields. (45)
cation A positively charged ion. (55)
cell potential (E_{cell}) (also *electromotive force,* or *emf; cell voltage*) The potential difference between the electrodes of an electrochemical cell when no current flows. (861)
Celsius scale (formerly *centigrade scale*) A temperature scale in which the freezing and boiling points of water are defined as 0°C and 100°C, respectively. (23)
ceramic A nonmetallic, nonpolymeric solid that is hardened by heating it to high temperatures and, in most cases, consists of silicate microcrystals suspended in a glassy cementing medium. (459)
chain reaction In nuclear fission, a self-sustaining process in which neutrons released by splitting of one nucleus cause other nuclei to split, which releases more neutrons, and so on. (1006)
change in enthalpy (ΔH) The change in internal energy plus the product of the constant pressure and the change in volume: $\Delta H = \Delta E + P\Delta V$; the heat lost or gained at constant pressure: $\Delta H = q_P$. (235)
charge density The ratio of the charge of an ion to its volume. (489)
Charles's law The gas law stating that at constant pressure, the volume occupied by a fixed amount of gas is directly proportional to its absolute temperature: $V \propto T$. (188)
chelate A complex ion in which the metal ion is bonded to a bidentate or polydentate ligand. (955)

chemical bond The force that holds two atoms together in a molecule (or formula unit). (55)

chemical change (also *chemical reaction*) A change in which one or more substances are converted into one or more substances with different composition and properties. (4)

chemical equation A statement that uses chemical formulas to express the identities and quantities of the substances involved in a chemical or physical change. (98)

chemical formula A notation of atomic symbols and numerical subscripts that shows the type and number of each atom in a molecule or formula unit of a substance. (59)

chemical kinetics The study of the rates and mechanisms of reactions. (627)

chemical property A characteristic of a substance that appears as it interacts with, or transforms into, other substances. (4)

chemical reaction (See *chemical change.*)

chemistry The scientific study of matter and its properties, the changes it undergoes, and the energy associated with those changes. (4)

chiral molecule One that is not superimposable on its mirror image; an optically active molecule. In organic compounds, a chiral molecule typically contains a C atom bonded to four different groups (asymmetric C). (580)

chlor-alkali process An industrial method that electrolyzes concentrated aqueous NaCl and produces Cl_2, H_2, and NaOH. (936)

chromatography A separation technique in which a mixture is dissolved in a fluid (gas or liquid), and the components are separated through differences in adsorption to (or solubility in) a solid surface (or viscous liquid). (72)

***cis-trans* isomers** (See *geometric isomers.*)

Clausius-Clapeyron equation An equation that expresses the linear relationship between vapor pressure P of a liquid and temperature T; in two-point form, it is

$$\ln \frac{P_2}{P_1} = \frac{-\Delta H_{\text{vap}}}{R}\left(\frac{1}{T_2} - \frac{1}{T_1}\right) \qquad (427)$$

coal gasification An industrial process for altering the large molecules in coal to sulfur-free gaseous fuels. (249)

colligative property A property of a solution that depends on the number, not the identity, of solute particles. (499) (See also *boiling point elevation, freezing point depression, osmotic pressure,* and *vapor pressure lowering.*)

collision frequency The average number of collisions per second that a particle undergoes. (211)

collision theory A model that explains reaction rate as based on the number, energy, and orientation of colliding particles. (648)

colloid A heterogeneous mixture in which a solute-like phase is dispersed throughout a solvent-like phase. (508)

combustion The process of burning in air, often with release of heat and light. (10)

combustion analysis A method for determining the formula of a compound from the amounts of its combustion products; used commonly for organic compounds. (95)

common-ion effect The shift in the position of an ionic equilibrium away from an ion involved in the process that is caused by the addition or presence of that ion. (766)

complex (See *coordination compound.*)

complex ion An ion consisting of a central metal ion bonded covalently to molecules and/or anions called ligands (792, 953)

composition The types and amounts of simpler substances that make up a sample of matter. (4)

compound A substance composed of two or more elements that are chemically combined in fixed proportions. (38)

concentration A measure of the quantity of solute dissolved in a given quantity of solution (or solvent). (114)

concentration cell A voltaic cell in which both compartments contain the same components but at different concentrations. (874)

condensation The process of a gas changing into a liquid. (420)

condensation polymer A polymer formed by monomers with two functional groups that are linked together in a dehydration-condensation reaction. (606)

conduction band In band theory, the empty, higher energy portion of the band of molecular orbitals into which electrons move when conducting heat and electricity. (453)

conductor A substance (usually a metal) that conducts an electric current well. (453)

conjugate acid-base pair Two species related to each other through the gain or loss of a proton; the acid has one more proton than its conjugate base. (729)

constitutional isomers (also *structural isomers*) Compounds with the same molecular formula but different arrangements of atoms. (579, 957)

contact process An industrial process for the manufacture of sulfuric acid based on the catalyzed oxidation of SO_2. (934)

controlled experiment An experiment that measures the effect of one variable at a time by keeping other variables constant. (12)

conversion factor A ratio of equivalent quantities that is equal to 1 and used to convert the units of a quantity. (13)

coordinate covalent bond A covalent bond formed when one atom donates both electrons to provide the shared pair and, once formed, is identical to any covalent single bond. (961)

coordination compound (also *complex*) A substance containing at least one complex ion and counter ion(s). (953)

coordination isomers Two or more coordination compounds with the same composition in which the complex ions have different ligand arrangements. (957)

coordination number In a crystal, the number of nearest neighbors surrounding a particle. (442) In a complex, the number of ligand atoms bonded to the central metal ion. (953)

copolymer A polymer that consists of two or more types of monomer. (465)

core The dense, innermost region of Earth. (906)

core electrons (See *inner electrons.*)

corrosion The natural redox process that results in unwanted oxidation of a metal. (882)

coulomb (C) The SI unit of electric charge. One coulomb is the charge of 6.242×10^{18} electrons; one electron possesses a charge of 1.602×10^{-19} C. (862)

Coulomb's law A law stating that the electrostatic energy between particles A and B is directly proportional to the product of their charges and inversely proportional to the distance between them:

$$\text{electrostatic energy} \propto \frac{\text{charge A} \times \text{charge B}}{\text{distance}} \qquad (335)$$

counter ion A simple ion associated with a complex ion in a coordination compound. (953)

coupling of reactions The pairing of reactions of which one releases enough free energy for the other to occur. (834)
covalent bond A type of bond in which atoms are bonded through the sharing of electrons; the mutual attraction of the nuclei and an electron pair that holds atoms together in a molecule. (58, 338)
covalent bonding The idealized bonding type that is based on localized electron-pair sharing between two atoms with little difference in their tendencies to lose or gain electrons (most commonly nonmetals). (330)
covalent compound A compound that consists of atoms bonded together by shared electron pairs. (55)
covalent radius One-half the shortest distance between nuclei of identical covalently bonded atoms. (308)
critical mass The minimum mass needed to achieve a chain reaction. (1007)
critical point The point on a phase diagram above which the vapor cannot be condensed to a liquid; the end of the liquid-gas curve. (429)
crosslink A branch that covalently joins one polymer chain to another. (465)
crust The thin, light, heterogeneous outer layer of Earth, which consists of gasous, liquid, and solid regions. (906)
crystal defect Any of a variety of disruptions in the regularity of a crystal structure. (455)
crystal field splitting energy (Δ) The difference in energy between two sets of metal-ion *d* orbitals that results from electrostatic interactions with the surrounding ligands. (964)
crystal field theory A model that explains the color and magnetism of coordination compounds based on the effects of ligands on metal-ion *d*-orbital energies. (962)
crystalline solid Solid with a well-defined shape because of the orderly arrangement of the atoms, molecules, or ions. (441)
crystallization A technique used to separate and purify the components of a mixture through differences in solubility in which a component comes out of solution as crystals. (72)
cubic closest packing A crystal structure based on the face-centered cubic unit cell in which the layers have an *abcabc* . . . pattern. (444)
cubic meter (m^3) The SI-derived unit of volume. (18)
curie (Ci) The most common unit of radioactivity, defined as the number of nuclei disintegrating each second in 1 g of radium-226; 1 Ci = 3.70×10^{10} d/s (disintegrations per second). (988)
cyclic hydrocarbon A hydrocarbon with one or more rings in its structure. (578)

D

***d* orbital** An atomic orbital with $l = 2$. (286)
dalton (Da) A unit of mass identical to *atomic mass unit.* (50)
Dalton's law of partial pressures A gas law stating that, in a mixture of unreacting gases, the total pressure is the sum of the partial pressures of the individual gases: $P_{total} = P_1 + P_2 + \cdots$. (199)
data Pieces of quantitative information obtained by observation. (12)
de Broglie wavelength The wavelength of a moving particle obtained from the de Broglie equation: $\lambda = h/mu$. (276)
decay constant The rate constant *k* for radioactive decay. (988)
decay series (also *disintegration series*) The succession of steps a parent nucleus undergoes as it decays into a stable daughter nucleus. (986)
degree of polymerization (*n*) The number of monomer repeat units in a polymer chain. (461)
dehydration-condensation reaction A reaction in which an H_2O molecule is lost for every pair of OH groups that join. (550)
delocalization (See *electron-pair delocalization.*)
density (*d*) An intensive physical property of a substance at a given temperature and pressure, defined as the ratio of the mass to the volume: $d = m/V$. (22)
deposition The process of changing directly from gas to solid. (421)
derived unit Any of various combinations of the seven SI base units. (17)
desalination A process used to remove large amounts of ions from seawater, usually by reverse osmosis. (511)
deuterons Nuclei of the stable hydrogen isotope deuterium, ^2H. (993)
diagonal relationship Physical and chemical similarities between a Period 2 element and one located diagonally down and to the right in Period 3. (533)
diamagnetism The tendency of a species not to be attracted (or to be slightly repelled) by a magnetic field as a result of its electrons being paired. (319)
diastereomers (See *geometric isomers.*)
differentiation The geochemical process of forming regions in Earth based on differences in composition and density. (906)
diffraction The phenomenon in which a wave striking the edge of an object bends around it. A wave passing through a slit as wide as its wavelength forms a circular wave. (264)
diffusion The movement of one fluid through another. (210)
dimensional analysis (also *factor-label method*) A calculation method in which arithmetic steps are accompanied by canceling units that represent physical dimensions. (15)
dipole-dipole force The intermolecular attraction between oppositely charged poles of nearby polar molecules. (432)
dipole–induced dipole force The intermolecular attraction between a polar molecule and the oppositely charged pole it induces in a nearby molecule. (478)
dipole moment (μ) A measure of molecular polarity; the magnitude of the partial charges on the ends of a molecule (in coulombs) times the distance between them (in meters). (383)
disaccharide An organic compound formed by a dehydration-condensation reaction between two simple sugars (monosaccharides). (607)
disintegration series (See *decay series.*)
dispersion force (also *London force*) The intermolecular attraction between all particles as a result of instantaneous polarizations of their electron clouds; the intermolecular force primarily responsible for the condensed states of nonpolar substances. (435)
disproportionation A reaction in which a given substance is both oxidized and reduced. (547)
distillation A separation technique in which a more volatile component of a mixture vaporizes and condenses separately from the less volatile components. (72)
donor atom An atom that donates a lone pair of electrons to form a covalent bond, usually from ligand to metal ion in a complex. (954)
doping Adding small amounts of other elements into the crystal structure of a semiconductor to enhance a specific property, usually conductivity. (455)

double bond A covalent bond that consists of two bonding pairs; two atoms sharing four electrons in the form of one σ and one π bond. (339)
double helix The two intertwined polynucleotide strands held together by H bonds that form the structure of DNA (deoxyribonucleic acid). (487, 612)
Downs cell An industrial apparatus that electrolyzes molten NaCl to produce sodium and chlorine. (923)
dynamic equilibrium The condition at which the forward and reverse reactions are taking place at the same rate, so there is no net change in the amounts of reactants or products. (167)

E

e_g orbitals The set of orbitals (composed of $d_{x^2-y^2}$ and d_{z^2}) that results when the energies of the metal-ion *d* orbitals are split by a ligand field. This set is higher in energy than the other (t_{2g}) set in an octahedral field of ligands and lower in energy in a tetrahedral field. (964)
effective collision A collision in which the particles meet with sufficient energy and an orientation that allows them to react. (651)
effective nuclear charge (Z_{eff}) The nuclear charge an electron actually experiences as a result of shielding effects due to the presence of other electrons. (297)
effusion The process by which a gas escapes from its container through a tiny hole into an evacuated space. (209)
elastomer A polymeric material that can be stretched and springs back to its original shape when released. (465)
electrochemical cell A system that incorporates a redox reaction to produce or use electrical energy. (851)
electrochemistry The study of the relationship between chemical change and electrical work. (851)
electrode The part of an electrochemical cell that conducts the electricity between the cell and the surroundings. (855)
electrolysis The nonspontaneous lysing (splitting) of a substance, often to its component elements, by supplying electrical energy. (886)
electrolyte A substance that conducts a current when it dissolves in water. (137, 499) A mixture of ions, in which the electrodes of an electrochemical cell are immersed, that conducts a current. (855)
electrolytic cell An electrochemical system that uses electrical energy to drive a nonspontaneous chemical reaction ($\Delta G > 0$). (855)
electromagnetic radiation (also *electromagnetic energy* or *radiant energy*) Oscillating, perpendicular electric and magnetic fields moving simultaneously through space as waves and manifested as visible light, x-rays, microwaves, radio waves, and so on. (261)
electromagnetic spectrum The continuum of wavelengths of radiant energy. (262)
electromotive force (emf) (See *cell potential.*)
electron (e^-) A subatomic particle that possesses a unit negative charge (-1.60218×10^{-19} C) and occupies the space around the atomic nucleus. (48)
electron affinity (EA) The energy change (in kJ) accompanying the addition of one mole of electrons to one mole of gaseous atoms or ions. (314)
electron capture (EC) A type of radioactive decay in which a nucleus draws in an orbital electron, usually one from the lowest energy level, and releases energy. (981)
electron cloud depiction An imaginary representation of an electron's rapidly changing position around the nucleus over time. (280)
electron configuration The distribution of electrons within the orbitals of the atoms of an element; also the notation for such a distribution. (295)
electron deficient Referring to a bonded atom, such as Be or B, that has fewer than eight valence electrons. (369)
electron density diagram (also *electron probability density diagram*) The pictorial representation for a given energy sublevel of the quantity ψ^2 (the probability density of the electron lying within a particular tiny volume) as a function of *r* (distance from the nucleus). (280)
electron-pair delocalization (also *delocalization*) The process by which electron density is spread over several atoms rather than remaining between two. (367)
electron-sea model A qualitative description of metallic bonding proposing that metal atoms pool their valence electrons into a delocalized "sea" of electrons in which the metal cores (metal ions) are submerged in an orderly array. (354)
electron volt (eV) The energy (in joules, J) that an electron acquires when it moves through a potential difference of 1 volt; 1 eV = 1.602×10^{-19} J. (1004)
electronegativity (EN) The relative ability of a bonded atom to attract shared electrons. (349)
electronegativity difference (ΔEN) The difference in electronegativities between the atoms in a bond. (351)
electrorefining An industrial, electrolytic purification process in which a sample of impure metal acts as the anode and a sample of the pure metal acts as the cathode. (921)
element The simplest type of substance with unique physical and chemical properties. An element consists of only one kind of atom, so it cannot be broken down into simpler substances. (38)
element symbol (See *atomic symbol.*)
elementary reaction (also *elementary step*) A simple reaction that describes a single molecular event in a proposed reaction mechanism. (655)
elimination reaction A type of organic reaction in which C atoms are bonded to fewer atoms in the product than in the reactant, which leads to multiple bonding. (589)
emission spectrum The line spectrum produced when excited atoms return to lower energy levels and emit photons characteristic of the element. (273)
empirical formula A chemical formula that shows the lowest relative number of atoms of each element in a compound. (92)
enantiomers (See *optical isomers.*)
end point The point in a titration at which the indicator changes color. (152, 776)
endothermic process A process that occurs with an absorption of heat from the surroundings and therefore an increase in the enthalpy of the system ($\Delta H > 0$). (237)
energy The capacity to do work, that is, to move matter. (8) [See also *kinetic energy* (E_k) and *potential energy* (E_p).]
enthalpy (H) A thermodynamic quantity that is the sum of the internal energy plus the product of the pressure and volume. (235)
enthalpy diagram A graphic depiction of the enthalpy change of a system. (237)

enthalpy of formation (ΔH_f) (also *heat of formation*) The enthalpy change occurring when 1 mol of a compound forms from its elements. When all components are in their standard states, this is called the *standard enthalpy of formation* (ΔH°_f). (246)
enthalpy of fusion (See *heat of fusion.*)
enthalpy of hydration (See *heat of hydration.*)
enthalpy of reaction (ΔH_{rxn}) (also *heat of reaction*) The enthalpy change that occurs during a reaction. When all components are in their standard states, this is called the *standard enthalpy of reaction* (ΔH°_{rxn}). (246)
enthalpy of solution (See *heat of solution.*)
enthalpy of sublimation (See *heat of sublimation.*)
enthalpy of vaporization (See *heat of vaporization.*)
entropy (S) A thermodynamic quantity related to the number of ways the energy of a system can be dispersed through the motions of its particles. (490, 814)
environmental cycle The physical, chemical, and biological paths through which the atoms of an element move within Earth's crust. (911)
enzyme A biological macromolecule (usually a protein) that acts as a catalyst. (662)
enzyme-substrate complex (ES) The intermediate in an enzyme-catalyzed reaction, which consists of enzyme and substrate(s) and whose concentration determines the rate of product formation. (663)
equatorial group An atom (or group) that lies in the trigonal plane of a trigonal bipyramidal molecule, or a similar structural feature in a molecule. (377)
equilibrium constant (K) The value obtained when equilibrium concentrations are substituted into the reaction quotient. (679)
equilibrium vapor pressure (See *vapor pressure.*)
equivalence point The point in a titration when the number of moles of the added species is stoichiometrically equivalent to the original number of moles of the other species. (152, 775)
ester An organic compound that contains the 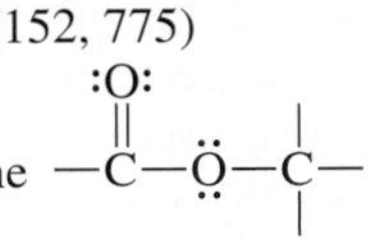 group. (599)
exact number A quantity, usually obtained by counting or based on a unit definition, that has no uncertainty associated with it and, therefore, contains as many significant figures as a calculation requires. (28)
exchange reaction (See *metathesis reaction.*)
excited state Any electron configuration of an atom or molecule other than the lowest energy (ground) state. (269)
exclusion principle A principle developed by Wolfgang Pauli stating that no two electrons in an atom can have the same set of four quantum numbers. The principle arises from the fact that an orbital has a maximum occupancy of two electrons and their spins are paired. (297)
exothermic process A process that occurs with a release of heat to the surroundings and therefore a decrease in the enthalpy of the system ($\Delta H < 0$). (236)
expanded valence shell A valence level that can accommodate more than eight electrons by using available *d* orbitals; occurs only with central nonmetal atoms from Period 3 or higher. (370)
experiment A set of procedural steps that tests a hypothesis. (12)
extensive property A property, such as mass, that depends on the quantity of substance present. (25)

F

face-centered cubic unit cell A unit cell in which a particle occurs at each corner and in the center of each face of a cube. (442)
Faraday constant (F) The physical constant representing the charge of 1 mol of electrons: $F = 96{,}485$ C/mol e^-. (870)
fatty acid A carboxylic acid that has a long hydrocarbon chain and is derived from a natural source. (599)
filtration A method of separating the components of a mixture on the basis of differences in particle size. (72)
first law of thermodynamics (See *law of conservation of energy.*)
fission The process by which a heavier nucleus splits into lighter nuclei with the release of energy. (1003)
fixation A chemical/biochemical process that converts a gaseous substance in the environment into a condensed form that can be used by organisms. (911)
flame test A procedure for identifying the presence of metal ions in which a granule of a compound or a drop of its solution is placed in a flame to observe a characteristic color. (273)
flotation A metallurgical process in which oil and detergent are mixed with pulverized ore in water to create a slurry that separates the mineral from the gangue. (917)
formal charge The hypothetical charge on an atom in a molecule or ion, equal to the number of valence electrons minus the sum of all the unshared and half the shared valence electrons. (368)
formation constant (K_f) An equilibrium constant for the formation of a complex ion from the hydrated metal ion and ligands. (794)
formation equation An equation in which 1 mole of a compound forms from its elements. (246)
formula mass The sum (in amu) of the atomic masses of a formula unit of a (usually ionic) compound. (66)
formula unit The chemical unit of a compound that contains the relative numbers of the types of atoms or ions expressed in the chemical formula. (60)
fossil fuel Any fuel, including coal, petroleum, and natural gas, derived from the products of the decay of dead organisms. (249)
fraction by mass (also *mass fraction*) The portion of a compound's mass contributed by an element; the mass of an element in a compound divided by the mass of the compound. (41)
fractional distillation A physical process involving numerous vaporization-condensation steps used to separate two or more volatile components. (505)
free energy (G) A thermodynamic quantity that is the difference between the enthalpy and the product of the absolute temperature and the entropy: $G = H - TS$. (827)
free energy change (ΔG) The change in free energy that occurs during a reaction. (827)
free radical A molecular or atomic species with one or more unpaired electrons, which typically make it very reactive. (370, 996)
freezing The process of cooling a liquid until it solidifies. (420)
freezing point depression (ΔT_f) The lowering of the freezing point of a solvent caused by the presence of dissolved solute particles. (502)
frequency (ν) The number of cycles a wave undergoes per second, expressed in units of 1/second, or s^{-1} [also called *hertz* (Hz)]; related inversely to wavelength. (261)

frequency factor (A) The product of the collision frequency Z and an orientation probability factor p that is specific for a reaction. (651)

fuel cell (also *flow battery*) A battery that is not self-contained and in which electricity is generated by the controlled oxidation of a fuel. (881)

functional group A specific combination of atoms, typically containing a carbon-carbon multiple bond and/or carbon-heteroatom bond, that reacts in a characteristic way no matter what molecule it occurs in. (573)

fundamental unit (See *base unit.*)

fusion (See *melting.*)

fusion (nuclear) The process by which light nuclei combine to form a heavier nucleus with the release of energy. (1003)

G

galvanic cell (See *voltaic cell.*)

gamma emission The type of radioactive decay in which gamma rays are emitted from an excited nucleus. (981)

gamma (γ) ray A very high-energy photon. (979)

gangue In an ore, the debris, such as sand, rock, and clay, attached to the mineral. (917)

gas One of the three states of matter. A gas fills its container regardless of the shape because its particles are far apart. (6)

Geiger-Müller counter An ionization counter that detects radioactive emissions through their ionization of gas atoms within the instrument. (987)

genetic code The set of three-base sequences that is translated into specific amino acids during the process of protein synthesis. (613)

geometric isomers (also *cis-trans isomers* or *diastereomers*) Stereoisomers in which the molecules have the same connections between atoms but differ in the spatial arrangements of the atoms. The *cis* isomer has similar groups on the same side of a double bond; the *trans* isomer has them on opposite sides. (582, 958)

Graham's law of effusion A gas law stating that the rate of effusion of a gas is inversely proportional to the square root of its density (or molar mass):

$$\text{rate} \propto \frac{1}{\sqrt{\mathcal{M}}} \qquad (209)$$

gray (Gy) The SI unit of absorbed radiation dose; 1 Gy = 1 J/kg tissue. (996)

green chemistry Field that is focused on developing methods to synthesize compounds efficiently and reduce or prevent the release of harmful products into the environment. (113)

ground state The electron configuration of an atom or ion that is lowest in energy. (269)

group A vertical column in the periodic table; elements in a group usually have the same outer electron configuration and, thus, similar chemical behavior. (53)

H

H bond (See *hydrogen bond.*)

Haber process An industrial process used to form ammonia from its elements. (706)

half-cell A portion of an electrochemical cell in which a half-reaction takes place. (857)

half-life ($t_{1/2}$) In chemical processes, the time required for half the initial reactant concentration to be consumed. (644) In nuclear processes, the time required for half the initial number of nuclei in a sample to decay. (988)

half-reaction method A method of balancing redox reactions by treating the oxidation and reduction half-reactions separately. (852)

haloalkane (also *alkyl halide*) A hydrocarbon with one or more halogen atoms (X) in place of H; contains a $-\overset{|}{\underset{|}{C}}-\ddot{\underset{..}{X}}:$ group. (593)

hard water Water that contains large amounts of divalent cations, especially Ca^{2+} and Mg^{2+}. (510)

heat (q) (also *thermal energy*) The energy transferred between objects because of a difference in their temperatures only. (23, 230)

heat capacity The quantity of heat required to change the temperature of an object by 1 K. (238)

heat of formation (See *enthalpy of formation.*)

heat of fusion (ΔH_{fus}) (also *enthalpy of fusion*) The enthalpy change occurring when 1 mol of a solid substance melts; designated ΔH°_{fus} at the standard state. (421)

heat of hydration (ΔH_{hydr}) (also *enthalpy of hydration*) The enthalpy change occurring when 1 mol of a gaseous species (often an ion) is hydrated. The sum of the enthalpies from separating water molecules and mixing the gaseous species with them; designated ΔH°_{hydr} at the standard state. (489)

heat of reaction (ΔH_{rxn}) (See *enthalpy of reaction.*)

heat of solution (ΔH_{soln}) (also *enthalpy of solution*) The enthalpy change occurring when a solution forms from solute and solvent. The sum of the enthalpies from separating solute and solvent substances and mixing them; designated ΔH°_{soln} at the standard state. (488)

heat of sublimation (ΔH_{subl}) (also *enthalpy of sublimation*) The enthalpy change occurring when 1 mol of a solid substance changes directly to a gas. The sum of the heats of fusion and vaporization; designated ΔH°_{subl} at the standard state. (421)

heat of vaporization (ΔH_{vap}) (also *enthalpy of vaporization*) The enthalpy change occurring when 1 mol of a liquid substance vaporizes; designated ΔH°_{vap} at the standard state. (421)

heating-cooling curve A plot of temperature vs. time for a substance when heat is absorbed or released by the system at a constant rate. (422)

Henderson-Hasselbalch equation An equation for calculating the pH of a buffer system:

$$\text{pH} = \text{p}K_a + \log\left(\frac{[\text{base}]}{[\text{acid}]}\right) \qquad (770)$$

Henry's law A law stating that the solubility of a gas in a liquid is directly proportional to the partial pressure of the gas above the liquid: $S_{gas} = k_H \times P_{gas}$. (494)

Hess's law A law stating that the enthalpy change of an overall process is the sum of the enthalpy changes of the individual steps. (244)

heteroatom Any atom in an organic compound other than C or H. (573)

heterogeneous catalyst A catalyst that occurs in a different phase from the reactants, usually a solid interacting with gaseous or liquid reactants. (661)

heterogeneous mixture A mixture that has one or more visible boundaries among its components. (70)

hexagonal closest packing A crystal structure based on the hexagonal unit cell in which the layers have an *abab* . . . pattern. (444)
high-spin complex Complex ion that has the same number of unpaired electrons as in the isolated metal ion; contains weak-field ligands. (966)
homogeneous catalyst A catalyst (gas, liquid, or soluble solid) that exists in the same phase as the reactants. (660)
homogeneous mixture (also *solution*) A mixture that has no visible boundaries among its components. (70)
homologous series A series of organic compounds in which each member differs from the next by a $—CH_2—$ (methylene) group. (576)
homonuclear diatomic molecule A molecule composed of two identical atoms. (408)
Hund's rule A principle stating that when orbitals of equal energy are available, the electron configuration of lowest energy has the maximum number of unpaired electrons with parallel spins. (300)
hybrid orbital An atomic orbital postulated to form during bonding by the mathematical mixing of specific combinations of nonequivalent orbitals in a given atom. (396)
hybridization A postulated process of orbital mixing to form hybrid orbitals. (396)
hydrate A compound in which a specific number of water molecules are associated with each formula unit. (63)
hydration Solvation in water. (489)
hydration shell The oriented cluster of water molecules that surrounds an ion in aqueous solution. (478)
hydrocarbon An organic compound that contains only H and C atoms. (574)
hydrogen bond (H bond) A type of dipole-dipole force that arises between molecules that have an H atom bonded to a small, highly electronegative atom with lone pairs, usually N, O, or F. (432)
hydrogenation The addition of hydrogen to a carbon-carbon multiple bond to form a carbon-carbon single bond. (662)
hydrolysis Cleaving a molecule by reaction with water, in which one part of the molecule bonds to the water —OH and the other to the water H. (600)
hydronium ion (H_3O^+) A proton covalently bonded to a water molecule. (720)
hydrosphere The liquid portion of Earth's crust. (908)
hypothesis A testable proposal made to explain an observation. If inconsistent with experimental results, a hypothesis is revised or discarded. (12)

I

ideal gas A hypothetical gas that exhibits linear relationships among volume, pressure, temperature, and amount (mol) at all conditions; approximated by simple gases at ordinary conditions. (186)
ideal gas law (also *ideal gas equation*) An equation that expresses the relationships among volume, pressure, temperature, and amount (mol) of an ideal gas: $PV = nRT$. (191)
ideal solution A solution whose vapor pressure equals the mole fraction of the solvent times the vapor pressure of the pure solvent; approximated only by very dilute solutions. (500) (See also *Raoult's law*.)
indicator (See *acid-base indicator*.)
induced-fit model A model of enzyme action that pictures the binding of the substrate as inducing the active site to change its shape and become catalytically active. (663)
infrared (IR) The region of the electromagnetic spectrum between the microwave and visible regions. (262)
infrared (IR) spectroscopy An instrumental technique for determining the types of bonds in a covalent molecule by measuring the absorption of IR radiation. (343)
initial rate The instantaneous rate occurring as soon as the reactants are mixed, that is, at $t = 0$. (631)
inner electrons (also *core electrons*) Electrons that fill all the energy levels of an atom except the valence level; electrons also present in atoms of the previous noble gas and any completed transition series. (306)
inner transition elements The elements of the periodic table in which *f* orbitals are being filled; the lanthanides and actinides. (306, 952)
instantaneous rate The reaction rate at a particular time, given by the slope of a tangent to a plot of reactant concentration vs. time. (631)
insulator A substance (usually a nonmetal) that does not conduct an electric current. (453)
integrated rate law A mathematical expression for reactant concentration as a function of time. (642)
intensive property A property, such as density, that does not depend on the quantity of substance present. (25)
interhalogen compound A compound consisting entirely of halogens. (558)
intermolecular forces (also *interparticle forces*) The attractive and repulsive forces among the particles—molecules, atoms, or ions—in a sample of matter. (419)
internal energy (E) The sum of the kinetic and potential energies of all the particles in a system. (230)
ion A charged particle that forms from an atom (or covalently bonded group of atoms) when it gains or loses one or more electrons. (55)
ion-dipole force The intermolecular attractive force between an ion and a polar molecule (dipole). (432)
ion exchange A process of softening water by exchanging one type of ion (usually Ca^{2+}) for another (usually Na^+) by binding the ions on a specially designed resin. (511)
ion–induced dipole force The attractive force between an ion and the dipole it induces in the electron cloud of a nearby nonpolar molecule. (478)
ion pair A pair of ions that form a gaseous ionic molecule; sometimes formed when a salt boils. (337)
ion-product constant for water (K_w) The equilibrium constant for the autoionization of water; equal to 1.0×10^{-14} at 298 K.

$$K_w = [H_3O^+][OH^-] \quad (724)$$

ionic atmosphere A cluster of ions of net opposite charge surrounding a given ion in solution. (506)
ionic bonding The idealized type of bonding based on the attraction of oppositely charged ions that arise through electron transfer between atoms with large differences in their tendencies to lose or gain electrons (typically metals and nonmetals). (330)
ionic compound A compound that consists of oppositely charged ions. (55)
ionic radius The size of an ion as measured by the distance between the nuclei of adjacent ions in a crystalline ionic compound. (320)

ionic solid A solid whose unit cell contains cations and anions. (449)
ionization In nuclear chemistry, the process by which a substance absorbs energy from high-energy radioactive particles and loses an electron to become ionized. (995)
ionization energy (IE) The energy (in kJ) required to remove completely one mole of electrons from one mole of gaseous atoms or ions. (311)
ionizing radiation The high-energy radiation from natural and artificial sources that forms ions in a substance by causing electron loss. (995)
isoelectronic Having the same number and configuration of electrons as another species. (317)
isomer One of two or more compounds with the same molecular formula but different properties, often as a result of different arrangements of atoms. (97, 579, 957)
isotopes Atoms of a given atomic number (that is, of a specific element) that have different numbers of neutrons and therefore different mass numbers. (49, 978)
isotopic mass The mass (in amu) of an isotope relative to the mass of carbon-12. (50)

J

joule (J) The SI unit of energy; $1\ J = 1\ kg\cdot m^2/s^2$. (233)

K

kelvin (K) The SI base unit of temperature. The kelvin is the same size as the Celsius degree. (23)
Kelvin scale (See *absolute scale.*)
ketone An organic compound (ending, *-one*) that contains a carbonyl group bonded to two other C atoms, 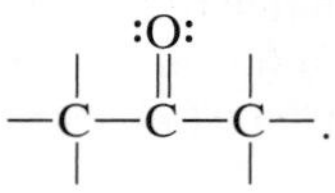. (597)
kilogram (kg) The SI base unit of mass. (20)
kinetic energy (E_k) The energy an object has because of its motion. (8)
kinetic-molecular theory The model that explains gas behavior in terms of particles in random motion whose volumes and interactions are negligible. (204)

L

lanthanide contraction The additional decrease in atomic and ionic size, beyond the expected trend, caused by the poor shielding of the increasing nuclear charge by *f* electrons in the elements following the lanthanides. (949)
lanthanides (also *rare earths*) The Period 6 (4*f*) series of inner transition elements, which includes cerium (Ce; $Z = 58$) through lutetium (Lu; $Z = 71$). (306, 952)
lattice The three-dimensional arrangement of points created by choosing each point to be at the same location within each particle of a crystal; thus, the lattice consists of all points with identical surroundings. (442)
lattice energy ($\Delta H^\circ_{lattice}$) The enthalpy change (always positive) that accompanies the separation of 1 mol of a solid ionic compound into gaseous ions. (333)
law (See *natural law.*)
law of chemical equilibrium (also *law of mass action*) The law stating that when a system reaches equilibrium at a given temperature, the ratio of quantities that make up the reaction quotient has a constant numerical value. (680)
law of conservation of energy (also *first law of thermodynamics*) A basic observation that the total energy of the universe is constant; thus, $\Delta E_{universe} = \Delta E_{system} + \Delta E_{surroundings} = 0$. (233)
law of definite (or constant) composition A mass law stating that, no matter what its source, a particular compound is composed of the same elements in the same parts (fractions) by mass. (41)
law of mass action (See *law of chemical equilibrium.*)
law of mass conservation A mass law stating that the total mass of substances does not change during a chemical reaction. (40)
law of multiple proportions A mass law stating that if elements A and B react to form two or more compounds, the different masses of B that combine with a fixed mass of A can be expressed as a ratio of small whole numbers. (42)
Le Châtelier's principle A principle stating that if a system in a state of equilibrium is disturbed, it will undergo a change that shifts its equilibrium position in a direction that reduces the effect of the disturbance. (698)
leaching A hydrometallurgical process that extracts a metal selectively, usually through formation of a complex ion. (918)
level (also *shell*) A specific energy state of an atom given by the principal quantum number *n*. (282)
leveling effect The inability of a solvent to distinguish the strength of an acid (or base) that is stronger than the conjugate acid (or conjugate base) of the solvent. (750)
Lewis acid-base definition A model of acid-base behavior in which acids and bases are defined, respectively, as species that accept and donate an electron pair. (751)
Lewis electron-dot symbol A notation in which the element symbol represents the nucleus and inner electrons, and surrounding dots represent the valence electrons. (331)
Lewis structure (also *Lewis formula*) A structural formula consisting of electron-dot symbols, with lines as bonding pairs and dots as lone pairs. (363)
ligand A molecule or anion bonded to a central metal ion in a complex ion. (792, 953)
like-dissolves-like rule An empirical observation stating that substances having similar kinds of intermolecular forces dissolve in each other. (478)
limiting reactant (also *limiting reagent*) The reactant that is consumed when a reaction occurs and, therefore, the one that determines the maximum amount of product that can form. (107)
line spectrum A series of separated lines of different colors representing photons whose wavelengths are characteristic of an element. (267) (See also *emission spectrum.*)
linear arrangement The geometric arrangement obtained when two electron groups maximize their separation around a central atom. (374)
linear shape A molecular shape formed by three atoms lying in a straight line, with a bond angle of 180° (shape class AX_2 or AX_2E_3). (374)
linkage isomers Coordination compounds with the same composition but with different ligand donor atoms linked to the central metal ion. (957)
lipid Any of a class of biomolecules, including fats, that are soluble in nonpolar solvents and not soluble in water. (600)
lipid bilayer An extended sheetlike double layer of phospholipid molecules that forms in water and has the charged heads of the molecules on the surfaces of the bilayer and the nonpolar tails within the interior. (485)

liquid One of the three states of matter. A liquid fills a container to the extent of its own volume and thus forms a surface. (5)
liquid crystal A substance that flows like a liquid but packs like a crystalline solid at the molecular level. (456)
liter (L) A non-SI unit of volume equivalent to 1 cubic decimeter (0.001 m^3). (18)
lithosphere The solid portion of Earth's crust. (908)
lock-and-key model A model of enzyme function that pictures the enzyme active site and the substrate as rigid shapes that fit together as a lock and key, respectively. (663)
London force (See *dispersion force.*)
lone pair (also *unshared pair*) An electron pair that is part of an atom's valence level but not involved in covalent bonding. (339)
low-spin complex Complex ion that has fewer unpaired electrons than in the free metal ion because of the presence of strong-field ligands. (966)

M

macromolecule (See *polymer.*)
magnetic quantum number (m_l) An integer from $-l$ through 0 to $+l$ that specifies the orientation of an atomic orbital in the three-dimensional space about the nucleus. (281)
manometer A device used to measure the pressure of a gas in a laboratory experiment. (184)
mantle A thick homogeneous layer of Earth's internal structure that lies between the core and the crust. (906)
mass The quantity of matter an object contains. Balances are designed to measure mass. (20)
mass-action expression (See *reaction quotient.*)
mass fraction (See *fraction by mass.*)
mass number (A) The total number of protons and neutrons in the nucleus of an atom. (49)
mass percent (also *mass % or percent by mass*) The fraction by mass expressed as a percentage. (41) A concentration term [% (w/w)] expressed as the mass of solute dissolved in 100. parts by mass of solution. (496)
mass spectrometry An instrumental method for measuring the relative masses of particles in a sample by creating charged particles and separating them according to their mass-charge ratio. (50)
matter Anything that possesses mass and occupies volume. (4)
mean free path The average distance a molecule travels between collisions at a given temperature and pressure. (211)
melting (also *fusion*) The change of a substance from a solid to a liquid. (420)
melting point (mp or T_f) The temperature at which the solid and liquid forms of a substance are at equilibrium. (429)
metabolic pathway A biochemical reaction sequence that flows in one direction and has each reaction enzyme catalyzed. (708)
metal A substance or mixture that is relatively shiny and malleable and is a good conductor of heat and electricity. In reactions, metals tend to transfer electrons to nonmetals and form ionic compounds. (54)
metallic bonding An idealized type of bonding based on the attraction between metal ions and their delocalized valence electrons. (331) (See also *electron-sea model.*)
metallic radius One-half the shortest distance between the nuclei of adjacent individual atoms in a crystal of an element. (308)
metallic solid A solid whose individual atoms are held together by metallic bonding. (451)
metalloid (also *semimetal*) An element with properties between those of metals and nonmetals. (54)
metallurgy The branch of materials science concerned with the extraction and utilization of metals. (917)
metathesis reaction (also *double-displacement reaction*) A reaction in which atoms or ions of two compounds exchange bonding partners. (143)
meter (m) The SI base unit of length. The distance light travels in a vacuum in 1/299,792,458 second. (18)
methanogenesis The process of producing methane by anaerobic biodegradation of plant and animal waste. (249)
milliliter (mL) A volume (0.001 L) equivalent to 1 cm^3. (18)
millimeter of mercury (mmHg) A unit of pressure based on the difference in the heights of mercury in a barometer or manometer. Renamed the *torr* in honor of Torricelli. (185)
mineral The portion of an ore that contains the element of interest, a mineral is a naturally occurring, homogeneous, crystalline inorganic solid, with a well-defined composition. (917)
miscible Soluble in any proportion. (478)
mixture A group of two or more elements and/or compounds that are physically intermingled. (39)
MO bond order One-half the difference between the number of electrons in bonding and antibonding MOs. (407)
model (also *theory*) A simplified conceptual picture based on experiment that explains how a natural phenomenon occurs. (12)
molality (m) A concentration term expressed as number of moles of solute dissolved in 1000 g (1 kg) of solvent. (495)
molar heat capacity (C) The quantity of heat required to change the temperature of 1 mol of a substance by 1 K. (238)
molar mass ($\mathcal{M}$) The mass of 1 mol of entities (atoms, molecules, or formula units) of a substance, in units of g/mol. (84)
molarity (M) A concentration term expressed as the moles of solute dissolved in 1 L of solution. (114)
mole (mol) The SI base unit for amount of a substance. The amount that contains a number of objects equal to the number of atoms in exactly 12 g of carbon-12 (which is 6.022×10^{23}). (83)
mole fraction (X) A concentration term expressed as the ratio of moles of one component of a mixture to the total moles present. (200, 496)
molecular equation A chemical equation showing a reaction in solution in which reactants and products appear as intact, undissociated compounds. (140)
molecular formula A formula that shows the actual number of atoms of each element in a molecule of a compound. (68, 92)
molecular mass (also *molecular weight*) The sum (in amu) of the atomic masses of the elements in a molecule (or formula unit) of a compound. (66)
molecular orbital (MO) An orbital of given energy and shape that extends over a molecule and can be occupied by no more than two paired electrons. (405)
molecular orbital (MO) diagram A depiction of the relative energy and number of electrons in each MO, as well as the atomic orbitals from which the MOs form. (406)
molecular orbital (MO) theory A model that describes a molecule as a collection of nuclei and electrons in which the electrons occupy orbitals that extend over the entire molecule. (405)
molecular polarity The overall distribution of electronic charge in a molecule, determined by its shape and bond polarities. (383)

molecular shape The three-dimensional structure defined by the relative positions of the atomic nuclei in a molecule. (373)
molecular solid A solid held together by intermolecular forces between individual molecules. (449)
molecular weight (See *molecular mass.*)
molecularity The number of reactant particles involved in an elementary step. (655)
molecule A structure consisting of two or more atoms that are bound chemically and behave as an independent unit. (38)
monatomic ion An ion derived from a single atom. (55)
monomer A small molecule, linked covalently to others of the same or similar type to form a polymer; the repeat unit of the polymer. (461)
mononucleotide A monomer unit of a nucleic acid, consisting of an N-containing base, a sugar, and a phosphate group. (487, 611)
monosaccharide A simple sugar; a polyhydroxy ketone or aldehyde with three to nine C atoms. (607)

N

nanotechnology The science and engineering of nanoscale (1–100 nm) systems. (466)
natural law (also *law*) A summary, often in mathematical form, of a universal observation. (12)
Nernst equation An equation stating that the voltage of an electrochemical cell under any conditions depends on the standard cell voltage and the concentrations of the cell components:

$$E_{\text{cell}} = E^{\circ}_{\text{cell}} = \frac{RT}{nF}\ln Q \qquad (872)$$

net ionic equation A chemical equation of a reaction in solution in which spectator ions have been eliminated to show the actual chemical change. (141)
network covalent solid A solid in which all the atoms are bonded covalently so that individual molecules are not present. (451)
neutralization Process that occurs when an H^+ ion from an acid combines with an OH^- ion from a base to form H_2O. (720)
neutralization reaction An acid-base reaction that yields water and a solution of a salt; when the H^+ ions of a strong acid react with an equivalent amount of the OH^- ions of a strong base, the solution is neutral. (145)
neutron (n^0) An uncharged subatomic particle found in the nucleus, with a mass slightly greater than that of a proton. (48)
nitrile An organic compound containing the $-C{\equiv}N$: group. (603)
node A region of an orbital where the probability of finding the electron is zero. (285)
nonbonding MO A molecular orbital that is not involved in bonding. (412)
nonelectrolyte A substance whose aqueous solution does not conduct an electric current. (139, 499)
nonmetal An element that lacks metallic properties. In reactions, nonmetals tend to share electrons with each other to form covalent compounds or accept electrons from metals to form ionic compounds. (54)
nonpolar covalent bond A covalent bond between identical atoms such that the bonding pair is shared equally. (351)
nuclear binding energy The energy required to break 1 mole of nuclei of an element into individual nucleons. (1004)
nuclear magnetic resonance (NMR) spectroscopy An instrumental technique used to determine the molecular environment of a given type of nucleus, most often ^1H, from its absorption of radio waves in a magnetic field. (586)
nuclear transmutation The induced conversion of one nucleus into another by bombardment with a particle. (992)
nucleic acid An unbranched polymer consisting of mononucleotides that occurs as two types, DNA and RNA (deoxyribonucleic and ribonucleic acids), which differ chemically in the nature of the sugar portion of the mononucleotides. (487, 611)
nucleon A subatomic particle found in the nucleus; a proton or neutron. (978)
nucleus The tiny central region of the atom that contains all the positive charge and essentially all the mass. (47)
nuclide A nuclear species with specified numbers of protons and neutrons. (978)

O

observation A fact obtained with the senses, often with the aid of instruments. Quantitative observations provide data that can be compared. (12)
occurrence (also *source*) The form(s) in which an element exists in nature. (909)
octahedral arrangement The geometric arrangement obtained when six electron groups maximize their space around a central atom; when all six groups are bonding groups, the molecular shape is octahedral (AX_6; ideal bond angle = 90°). (378)
octet rule The observation that when atoms bond, they often lose, gain, or share electrons to attain a filled outer level of eight electrons (or two for H and Li). (331)
optical isomers (also *enantiomers*) A pair of stereoisomers consisting of a molecule and its mirror image that cannot be superimposed on each other. (580, 959)
optically active Able to rotate the plane of polarized light. (581)
orbital diagram A depiction of orbital occupancy in terms of electron number and spin shown by means of arrows in a series of small boxes, lines, or circles. (299)
ore A naturally occurring compound or mixture of compounds from which an element can be profitably extracted. (909)
organic compound A compound in which carbon is nearly always bonded to itself and to hydrogen, and often to other elements. (571)
organometallic compound An organic compound in which carbon has a polar covalent bond to a metal atom. (598)
osmosis The process by which solvent flows through a semipermeable membrane from a dilute to a concentrated solution. (503)
osmotic pressure (Π) The pressure that results from the ability of solvent, but not solute, particles to cross a semipermeable membrane. The pressure required to prevent the net movement of solvent across the membrane. (503)
outer electrons Electrons that occupy the highest energy level (highest n value) and are, on average, farthest from the nucleus. (306)
overall (net) equation A chemical equation that is the sum of two or more balanced sequential equations in which a product of one becomes a reactant for the next. (106)
overvoltage The additional voltage, usually associated with gaseous products forming at an electrode, that is required above the standard cell voltage to accomplish electrolysis. (888)
oxidation The loss of electrons by a species, accompanied by an increase in oxidation number. (154)

oxidation number (O.N.) (also *oxidation state*) A number equal to the magnitude of the charge an atom would have if its shared electrons were held completely by the atom that attracts them more strongly. (155)
oxidation number method A method for balancing redox reactions in which the change in oxidation numbers is used to determine balancing coefficients. (158)
oxidation-reduction reaction (also *redox reaction*) A process in which there is a net movement of electrons from one reactant (reducing agent) to another (oxidizing agent). (153)
oxidation state (See *oxidation number.*)
oxidizing agent The substance that accepts electrons in a reaction and undergoes a decrease in oxidation number. (154)
oxoanion An anion in which an element is bonded to one or more oxygen atoms. (63)

P

***p* orbital** An atomic orbital with $l = 1$. (285)
packing efficiency The percentage of the available volume occupied by atoms, ions, or molecules in a unit cell. (444)
paramagnetism The tendency of a species with unpaired electrons to be attracted by an external magnetic field. (319)
partial ionic character An estimate of the actual charge separation in a bond (caused by the electronegativity difference of the bonded atoms) relative to complete separation. (351)
partial pressure The portion of the total pressure contributed by a gas in a mixture of gases. (199)
particle accelerator A device used to impart high kinetic energies to nuclear particles. (993)
pascal (Pa) The SI unit of pressure; $1\ Pa = 1\ N/m^2$. (185)
penetration The process by which an outer electron moves through the region occupied by the core electrons to spend part of its time closer to the nucleus; penetration increases the average effective nuclear charge for that electron. (298)
percent by mass (mass %) (See *mass percent.*)
percent yield (% yield) The actual yield of a reaction expressed as a percentage of the theoretical yield. (112)
period A horizontal row of the periodic table. (53)
periodic law A law stating that when the elements are arranged by atomic number, they exhibit a periodic recurrence of properties. (295)
periodic table of the elements A table in which the elements are arranged by atomic number into columns (groups) and rows (periods). (53)
pH The negative common logarithm of $[H_3O^+]$. (726)
phase A physically distinct and homogeneous part of a system. (419)
phase change A physical change from one phase to another, usually referring to a change in physical state. (420)
phase diagram A diagram used to describe the stable phases and phase changes of a substance as a function of temperature and pressure. (429)
photoelectric effect The observation that when monochromatic light of sufficient frequency shines on a metal, an electric current is produced. (266)
photon A quantum of electromagnetic radiation. (266)
photovoltaic cell A device capable of converting light directly into electricity. (251)
physical change A change in which the physical form (or state) of a substance, but not its composition, is altered. (4)
physical property A characteristic shown by a substance itself, without interacting with or changing into other substances. (4)
pi (π) bond A covalent bond formed by sideways overlap of two atomic orbitals that has two regions of electron density, one above and one below the internuclear axis. (403)
pi (π) MO A molecular orbital formed by combination of two atomic (usually *p*) orbitals whose orientations are perpendicular to the internuclear axis. (408)
Planck's constant (*h*) A proportionality constant relating the energy and frequency of a photon, equal to 6.626×10^{-34} J·s. (266)
plastic A material that, when deformed, retains its new shape. (465)
polar covalent bond A covalent bond in which the electron pair is shared unequally, so the bond has partially negative and partially positive poles. (351)
polar molecule A molecule with an unequal distribution of charge as a result of its polar bonds and shape. (136)
polarimeter A device used to measure the rotation of plane-polarized light by an optically active compound. (581)
polarizability The ease with which a particle's electron cloud can be distorted. (434)
polyatomic ion An ion in which two or more atoms are bonded covalently. (59)
polymer (also *macromolecule*) An extremely large molecule that results from the covalent linking of many simpler molecular units (monomers). (461)
polyprotic acid An acid with more than one ionizable proton. (737)
polysaccharide A macromolecule composed of many simple sugars linked covalently. (607)
positron (β^+) The antiparticle of an electron. (981)
positron emission A type of radioactive decay in which a positron is emitted from a nucleus. (981)
potential energy (E_p) The energy an object has as a result of its position relative to other objects or because of its composition. (8)
precipitate The insoluble product of a precipitation reaction. (141)
precipitation reaction A reaction in which two soluble ionic compounds form an insoluble product, a precipitate. (141)
precision (also *reproducibility*) The closeness of a measurement to other measurements of the same phenomenon in a series of experiments. (28)
pressure (*P*) The force exerted per unit of surface area. (183)
pressure-volume work (*PV* work) A type of work in which a volume change occurs against an external pressure. (235)
principal quantum number (*n*) A positive integer that specifies the energy and relative size of an atomic orbital; a number that specifies an energy level in an atom. (281)
probability contour A shape that defines the volume around an atomic nucleus within which an electron spends a given percentage of its time. (281)
product A substance formed in a chemical reaction. (99)
property A characteristic that gives a substance its unique identity. (4)
protein A natural, linear polymer composed of any of about 20 types of amino acid monomers linked together by peptide bonds. (483, 608)

proton (p^+) A subatomic particle found in the nucleus that has a unit positive charge (1.60218×10^{-19} C). (48)
proton acceptor A substance that accepts an H^+ ion; a Brønsted-Lowry base. (729)
proton donor A substance that donates an H^+ ion; a Brønsted-Lowry acid. (729)
pseudo–noble gas configuration The $(n-1)d^{10}$ configuration of a *p*-block metal ion that has an empty outer energy level. (317)

Q

quantum A packet of energy equal to $h\nu$. The smallest quantity of energy that can be emitted or absorbed. (266)
quantum mechanics The branch of physics that examines the wave motion of objects on the atomic scale. (279)
quantum number A number that specifies a property of an orbital or an electron. (266)

R

rad (*r*adiation-*a*bsorbed *d*ose) The quantity of radiation that results in 0.01 J of energy being absorbed per kilogram of tissue; 1 rad = 0.01 J/kg tissue = 10^{-2} Gy. (996)
radial probability distribution plot The graphic depiction of the total probability distribution (sum of ψ^2) of an electron in the region near the nucleus. (280)
radioactivity The emissions resulting from the spontaneous disintegration of an unstable nucleus. (977)
radioisotope An isotope with an unstable nucleus that decays through radioactive emissions. (990)
radioisotopic dating A method for determining the age of an object based on the rate of decay of a particular radioactive nuclide relative to a stable nuclide. (990)
radius of gyration (R_g) A measure of the size of a coiled polymer chain, expressed as the average distance from the center of mass of the chain to its outside edge. (463)
random coil The shape adopted by most polymer chains and caused by random rotation about the bonds joining the repeat units. (462)
random error Error that occurs in all measurements (with its size depending on the measurer's skill and the instrument's precision) and results in values *both* higher and lower than the actual value. (29)
Raoult's law A law stating that the vapor pressure of solvent above a solution equals the mole fraction of solvent times the vapor pressure of pure solvent: $P_{solvent} = X_{solvent} \times P^\circ_{solvent}$. (500)
rare earths (See *lanthanides.*)
rate constant (k) The proportionality constant that relates reaction rate to reactant (and product) concentrations. (634)
rate-determining step (also *rate-limiting step*) The slowest step in a reaction mechanism and therefore the step that limits the overall rate. (656)
rate law (also *rate equation*) An equation that expresses the rate of a reaction as a function of reactant (and product) concentrations. (634)
reactant A starting substance in a chemical reaction. (99)
reaction energy diagram A graph that shows the potential energy of a reacting system as it progresses from reactants to products. (652)
reaction intermediate A substance that is formed and used up during the overall reaction and therefore does not appear in the overall equation. (657)
reaction mechanism A series of elementary steps that sum to the overall reaction and is consistent with the rate law. (655)
reaction order The exponent of a reactant concentration in a rate law that shows how the rate is affected by changes in that concentration. (634)
reaction quotient (Q) (also *mass-action expression*) A ratio of terms for a given reaction consisting of product concentrations multiplied together and divided by reactant concentrations multiplied together, each raised to the power of their balancing coefficient. The value of Q changes until the system reaches equilibrium, at which point it equals K. (680)
reaction rate The change in the concentrations of reactants (or products) with time. (627)
reactor core The part of a nuclear reactor that contains the fuel rods and generates heat from fission. (1008)
redox reaction (See *oxidation-reduction reaction.*)
reducing agent The substance that donates electrons in a redox reaction and undergoes an increase in oxidation number. (154)
reduction The gain of electrons by a species, accompanied by a decrease in oxidation number. (154)
refraction A phenomenon in which a wave changes its speed and therefore its direction as it passes through a phase boundary into a different medium. (263)
rem (*r*oentgen *e*quivalent for *m*an) The unit of radiation dosage for a human based on the product of the number of rads and a factor related to the biological tissue; 1 rem = 10^{-2} Sv. (996)
reproducibility (See *precision.*)
resonance hybrid The weighted average of the resonance structures of a molecule. (367)
resonance structure (also *resonance form*) One of two or more Lewis structures for a molecule that cannot be adequately depicted by a single structure. Resonance structures differ only in the position of bonding and lone electron pairs. (367)
reverse osmosis A process for preparing drinkable water that uses an applied pressure greater than the osmotic pressure to remove ions from an aqueous solution, typically seawater. (511)
rms (root-mean-square) speed (u_{rms}) The speed of a molecule having the average kinetic energy; very close to the most probable speed. (209)
roasting A pyrometallurgical process in which metal sulfides are converted to oxides. (918)
round off The process of removing digits based on a series of rules to obtain an answer with the proper number of significant figures (or decimal places). (27)

S

***s* orbital** An atomic orbital with $l = 0$. (284)
salt An ionic compound that results from an Arrhenius acid-base reaction after solvent is removed. (148)
salt bridge An inverted U tube containing a solution of a nonreacting electrolyte that connects the compartments of a voltaic cell and maintains neutrality by allowing ions to flow between compartments. (859)
saturated hydrocarbon A hydrocarbon in which each C is bonded to four other atoms. (576)
saturated solution A solution that contains the maximum amount of dissolved solute at a given temperature (prepared with undissolved solute present). (492)

scanning tunneling microscopy An instrumental technique that uses electrons moving across a minute gap to observe the topography of a surface on the atomic scale. (447)
Schrödinger equation An equation that describes how the electron matter-wave changes in space around the nucleus. Solutions of the equation provide allowable energy levels of the atom. (279)
scientific method A process of creative thinking and testing aimed at objective, verifiable discoveries of the causes of natural events. (12)
scintillation counter A device used to measure radioactivity through its excitation of atoms and their subsequent emission of light. (987)
screening (See *shielding.*)
second (s) The SI base unit of time. (25)
second law of thermodynamics A law stating that a process occurs spontaneously in the direction that increases the entropy of the universe. (817)
seesaw shape A molecular shape caused by the presence of one equatorial lone pair in a trigonal bipyramidal arrangement (AX_4E). (377)
selective precipitation The process of separating ions through differences in the solubility of their compounds with a given precipitating ion. (791)
self-ionization (See *autoionization.*)
semiconductor A substance whose electrical conductivity is poor at room temperature but increases significantly with rising temperature. (453)
semimetal (See *metalloid.*)
semipermeable membrane A membrane that allows solvent, but not solute, to pass through. (503)
shared pair (See *bonding pair.*)
shell (See *level.*)
shielding (also *screening*) The ability of other electrons, especially those occupying inner orbitals, to lessen the nuclear attraction for an outer electron. (297)
SI unit A unit composed of one or more of the base units of the Système International d'Unités, a revised metric system. (17)
side reaction An undesired chemical reaction that consumes some of the reactant and reduces the overall yield of the desired product. (112)
sievert (Sv) The SI unit of human radiation dosage; 1 Sv = 100 rem. (996)
sigma (σ) bond A type of covalent bond that arises through end-to-end orbital overlap and has most of its electron density along an imaginary line joining the nuclei. (403)
sigma (σ) MO A molecular orbital that is cylindrically symmetrical about an imaginary line that runs through the nuclei of the component atoms. (406)
significant figures The digits obtained in a measurement. The greater the number of significant figures, the greater the certainty of the measurement. (25)
silicate A type of compound found throughout rocks and soil and consisting of repeating —Si—O groupings and, in most cases, metal cations. (542)
silicone A type of synthetic polymer containing —Si—O repeat units, with organic groups and crosslinks. (542)
simple cubic unit cell A unit cell in which a particle occupies each corner of a cube. (442)
single bond A bond that consists of one electron pair. (339)
slag A molten waste product formed in a blast furnace by the reaction of acidic silica with a basic metal oxide. (925)
smelting Heating a mineral with a reducing agent, such as coke, to obtain a metal. (919)
soap The salt formed in a reaction between a fatty acid and a strong base, usually a Group 1A(1) or 2A(2) hydroxide. (485)
solid One of the three states of matter. A solid has a fixed shape that does not conform to the container shape. (5)
solubility (*S*) The maximum amount of solute that dissolves in a fixed quantity of a particular solvent at a specified temperature. (478)
solubility-product constant (K_{sp}) An equilibrium constant for a slightly soluble ionic compound dissolving in water. (783)
solute The substance that dissolves in the solvent. (114, 478)
solution (See *homogeneous mixture.*)
solvated Surrounded closely by solvent molecules. (136)
solvation The process of surrounding a solute particle with solvent particles. (489)
solvent The substance in which the solute(s) dissolve. (114, 478)
source (See *occurrence.*)
***sp* hybrid orbital** An orbital formed by the mixing of one *s* and one *p* orbital of a central atom. (396)
sp^2 hybrid orbital An orbital formed by the mixing of one *s* and two *p* orbitals of a central atom. (398)
sp^3 hybrid orbital An orbital formed by the mixing of one *s* and three *p* orbitals of a central atom. (398)
sp^3d hybrid orbital An orbital formed by the mixing of one *s*, three *p*, and one *d* orbital of a central atom. (399)
sp^3d^2 hybrid orbital An orbital formed by the mixing of one *s*, three *p*, and two *d* orbitals of a central atom. (400)
specific heat capacity (*c*) The quantity of heat required to change the temperature of 1 gram of a material by 1 K. (238)
spectator ion An ion that is present as part of a reactant but is not involved in the chemical change. (141)
spectrochemical series A ranking of ligands in terms of their ability to split *d*-orbital energies. (965)
spectrometry Any instrumental technique that uses a portion of the electromagnetic spectrum to measure the atomic and molecular energy levels of a substance. (273)
speed of light (*c*) A fundamental constant giving the speed at which electromagnetic radiation travels in a vacuum: $c = 2.99792458 \times 10^8$ m/s. (262)
spin quantum number (m_s) A number, either $+\frac{1}{2}$ or $-\frac{1}{2}$, that indicates the direction of electron spin. (296)
spontaneous change A change that occurs by itself, that is, without an ongoing input of external energy. (811)
square planar shape A molecular shape (AX_4E_2) caused by the presence of two lone pairs at opposite vertices in an octahedral arrangement. (378)
square pyramidal shape A molecular shape (AX_5E) caused by the presence of one lone pair in an octahedral arrangement. (378)
standard atmosphere (atm) The average atmospheric pressure measured at sea level and 0°C, defined as 1.01325×10^5 Pa. (185)
standard cell potential (E°_{cell}) The potential of a cell measured with all components in their standard states and no current flowing. (862)

standard electrode potential ($E^\circ_{half\text{-}cell}$) (also *standard half-cell potential*) The standard potential of a half-cell, with the half-reaction written as a reduction. (862)
standard enthalpy of formation (ΔH°_f) (also *standard heat of formation*) The enthalpy change occurring when 1 mol of a compound forms from its elements with all components in their standard states. (246)
standard enthalpy of reaction (ΔH°_{rxn}) (also *standard heat of reaction*) The enthalpy change that occurs during a reaction when all components are in their standard states. (246)
standard entropy of reaction (ΔS°_{rxn}) The entropy change that occurs when all components are in their standard states. (822)
standard free energy change (ΔG°) The free energy change that occurs when all components are in their standard states. (828)
standard free energy of formation (ΔG°_f) The standard free energy change that occurs when 1 mol of a compound is made from its elements with all components in their standard states. (829)
standard half-cell potential (See *standard electrode potential.*)
standard heat of formation (See *standard enthalpy of formation.*)
standard heat of reaction (See *standard enthalpy of reaction.*)
standard hydrogen electrode (See *standard reference half-cell.*)
standard molar entropy (S°) The entropy of 1 mol of a substance in its standard state. (817)
standard molar volume The volume of 1 mol of an ideal gas at standard temperature and pressure: 22.4141 L. (190)
standard reference half-cell (also *standard hydrogen electrode*) A specially prepared platinum electrode immersed in 1 M $H^+(aq)$ through which H_2 gas at 1 atm is bubbled. $E^\circ_{half\text{-}cell}$ is defined as 0 V. (863)
standard state A set of specifications used to compare thermodynamic data: 1 atm for gases behaving ideally, 1 M for dissolved species, or the pure substance for liquids and solids. (246)
standard temperature and pressure (STP) The reference conditions for a gas:

0°C (273.15 K) and 1 atm (760 torr) (190)

state function A property of the system determined by its current state, regardless of how it arrived at that state. (234)
state of matter One of the three physical forms of matter: solid, liquid, or gas. (5)
stationary state In the Bohr model, one of the allowable energy levels of the atom in which it does not release or absorb energy. (269)
steel An alloy of iron with small amounts of carbon and usually other metals. (924)
stellar nucleosynthesis The process by which elements are formed in the stars through nuclear fusion. (1012)
stereoisomers Molecules with the same connections of atoms but different orientations of groups in space. (580, 958) (See also *geometric isomers* and *optical isomers.*)
stoichiometric coefficient (See *balancing coefficient.*)
stoichiometry The study of the mass-mole-number relationships of chemical formulas and reactions. (83)
strong-field ligand A ligand that causes larger crystal field splitting energy and therefore is part of a low-spin complex. (964)
strong force An attractive force that exists between all nucleons and is many times stronger than the electrostatic repulsive force. (984)
structural formula A formula that shows the actual number of atoms, their relative placement, and the bonds between them. (68, 92)
structural isomers (See *constitutional isomers.*)
sublevel (also *subshell*) An energy substate of an atom within a level. Given by the n and l values, the sublevel designates the size and shape of the atomic orbitals. (282)
sublimation The process by which a solid changes directly into a gas. (421)
substance A type of matter, either an element or a compound, that has a fixed composition. (38)
substitution reaction An organic reaction that occurs when an atom (or group) from one reactant substitutes for one in another reactant. (589)
substrate A reactant that binds to the active site in an enzyme-catalyzed reaction. (662)
superconductivity The ability to conduct a current with no loss of energy to resistive heating. (454)
supersaturated solution An unstable solution in which more solute is dissolved than in a saturated solution. (492)
surface tension The energy required to increase the surface area of a liquid by a given amount. (437)
surroundings All parts of the universe other than the system being considered. (230)
suspension A heterogeneous mixture containing particles that are distinct from the surrounding medium. (508)
synthetic natural gas (SNG) A gaseous fuel mixture, mostly methane, formed from coal. (249)
system The defined part of the universe under study. (230)
systematic error A type of error producing values that are all either higher or lower than the actual value, often caused by faulty equipment or a consistent flaw in technique. (29)

T

t_{2g} orbitals The set of orbitals (composed of d_{xy}, d_{yz}, and d_{xz}) that results when the energies of the metal-ion d orbitals are split by a ligand field. This set is lower in energy than the other (e_g) set in an octahedral field and higher in energy in a tetrahedral field. (964)
T shape A molecular shape caused by the presence of two equatorial lone pairs in a trigonal bipyramidal arrangement (AX_3E_2). (377)
temperature (T) A measure of how hot or cold a substance is relative to another substance. (23) A measure of the average kinetic energy of the particles in a sample. (208)
tetrahedral arrangement The geometric arrangement formed when four electron groups maximize their separation around a central atom; when all four groups are bonding groups, the molecular shape is tetrahedral (AX_4; ideal bond angle 109.5°). (375)
theoretical yield The amount of product predicted by the stoichiometrically equivalent molar ratio in the balanced equation. (112)
theory (See *model.*)
thermochemical equation A chemical equation that shows the heat involved for the amounts of substances specified. (242)
thermochemistry The branch of thermodynamics that focuses on the heat involved in chemical and physical change. (229)
thermodynamics The study of heat (thermal energy) and its interconversions. (229)
thermometer A device for measuring temperature that contains a fluid that expands or contracts within a graduated tube. (23)
third law of thermodynamics A law stating that the entropy of a perfect crystal is zero at 0 K. (817)

titration A method of determining the concentration of a solution by monitoring relative amounts during its reaction with a solution of known concentration. (152)
torr A unit of pressure identical to 1 mmHg. (185)
total ionic equation An equation for an aqueous reaction that shows all the soluble ionic substances dissociated into ions. (141)
tracer A radioisotope that signals the presence of the species of interest by radioactive emissions. (1000)
transcription The process of producing messenger RNA from DNA. (614)
transition element An element that occupies the *d* block of the periodic table; one whose *d* orbitals are being filled. (303, 945)
transition state (also *activated complex*) An unstable species formed in an effective collision of reactants that exists momentarily when the system is highest in energy and that can either form products or re-form reactants. (652)
transition state theory A model that explains how the energy of reactant collisions is used to form a high-energy transitional species that can change to reactant or product. (652)
translation The process by which messenger RNA specifies the sequence of amino acids and synthesizes proteins. (614)
transuranium element An element with atomic number higher than that of uranium ($Z = 92$). (994)
trigonal bipyramidal arrangement The geometric arrangement formed when five electron groups maximize their separation around a central atom. When all five groups are bonding groups, the molecular shape is trigonal bipyramidal (AX_5; ideal bond angles, axial-center-equatorial 90° and equatorial-center-equatorial 120°). (376)
trigonal planar arrangement The geometric arrangement formed when three electron groups maximize their separation around a central atom. When all three groups are bonding groups, the molecular shape is trigonal planar (AX_3; ideal bond angle 120°). (374)
trigonal pyramidal shape A molecular shape (AX_3E) caused by the presence of one lone pair in a tetrahedral arrangement. (376)
triple bond A covalent bond that consists of three bonding pairs, two atoms sharing six electrons; one σ and two π bonds. (339)
triple point The pressure and temperature at which three phases of a substance are in equilibrium. In a phase diagram, the point at which three phase-transition curves meet. (429)
Tyndall effect The scattering of light by a colloid. (509)

U

ultraviolet (UV) Radiation in the region of the electromagnetic spectrum between the visible and the x-ray regions. (262)
uncertainty A characteristic of every measurement that results from the inexactness of the measuring device and the need to estimate when taking a reading. (25)
uncertainty principle The principle stated by Werner Heisenberg that it is impossible to know simultaneously the exact position and velocity of a particle; the principle becomes important only for particles of very small mass. (278)
unimolecular reaction An elementary reaction that involves the decomposition or rearrangement of a single particle. (655)
unit cell The smallest portion of a crystal that, if repeated in all three directions, gives the crystal. (442)
universal gas constant (*R*) A proportionality constant that relates the energy, amount of substance, and temperature of a system; $R = 0.0820578$ atm·L/mol·K = 8.31447 J/mol·K. (191)
unsaturated hydrocarbon A hydrocarbon with at least one carbon-carbon multiple bond; one in which at least two C atoms are bonded to fewer than four atoms. (582)
unsaturated solution A solution in which more solute can be dissolved at a given temperature. (492)
unshared pair (See *lone pair.*)

V

V shape (See *bent shape.*)
valence band In band theory, the lower energy portion of the band of molecular orbitals, which is filled with valence electrons. (453)
valence bond (VB) theory A model that attempts to reconcile the shapes of molecules with those of atomic orbitals through the concepts of orbital overlap and hybridization. (395)
valence electrons The electrons involved in compound formation; in main-group elements, the electrons in the valence (outer) level. (306)
valence-shell electron-pair repulsion (VSEPR) theory A model explaining that the shapes of molecules and ions result from minimizing electron-pair repulsions around a central atom. (373)
van der Waals constants Experimentally determined positive numbers used in the van der Waals equation to account for the intermolecular attractions and molecular volume of real gases. (216)
van der Waals equation An equation that accounts for the behavior of real gases. (216)
van der Waals radius One-half of the shortest distance between the nuclei of identical nonbonded atoms. (431)
vapor pressure (also *equilibrium vapor pressure*) The pressure exerted by a vapor at equilibrium with its liquid in a closed system. (426)
vapor pressure lowering (ΔP) The lowering of the vapor pressure of a solvent caused by the presence of dissolved solute particles. (499)
vaporization The process of changing from a liquid to a gas. (420)
variable A quantity that can have more than a single value. (12) (See also *controlled experiment.*)
viscosity A measure of the resistance of a liquid to flow. (439)
volatility The tendency of a substance to become a gas. (72)
volt (V) The SI unit of electric potential: 1 V = 1 J/C. (862)
voltage (See *cell potential.*)
voltaic cell (also *galvanic cell*) An electrochemical cell that uses a spontaneous redox reaction to generate electric energy. (855)
volume (*V*) The space occupied by a sample of matter. (18)
volume percent [% (v/v)] A concentration term defined as the volume of solute in 100. volumes of solution. (496)

W

wastewater Used water, usually containing industrial and/or residential waste, that is treated before being returned to the environment. (511)
water softening The process of replacing the hard-water ions Ca^{2+} and Mg^{2+} with Na^+ ions. (510)

wave function (See *atomic orbital.*)
wave-particle duality The principle stating that both matter and energy have wavelike and particle-like properties. (277)
wavelength (λ) The distance between any point on a wave and the corresponding point on the next wave, that is, the distance a wave travels during one cycle. (262)
weak-field ligand A ligand that causes smaller crystal field splitting energy and therefore is part of a high-spin complex. (964)
weight The force exerted by a gravitational field on an object that is directly proportional to its mass. (20)
work (w) The energy transferred when an object is moved by a force. (231)

X

x-ray diffraction analysis An instrumental technique used to determine dimensions of a crystal structure by measuring the diffraction patterns caused by x-rays impinging on the crystal. (447)

Z

zone refining A process used to purify metals and metalloids in which impurities are removed from a bar of the element by concentrating them in a thin molten zone. (921)

Chapter 1

Opener: © The McGraw-Hill Companies, Inc./John Thoeming Photographer; 1.1A: © Paul Morrell/Stone/Getty Images; 1.1B: © The McGraw-Hill Companies, Inc./Stephen Frisch Photographer; Table 1.1A: © The McGraw-Hill Companies, Inc./Stephen Frisch Photographer; Table 1.1B: © Ruth Melnick; Table 1.1C-E: © The McGraw-Hill Companies, Inc./Stephen Frisch Photographer; p. 7: Gallileo Project, SSI, University of Arizona; 1.4: © SSPL/The Image Works; 1.5A: © George Haling/Photo Researchers, Inc.; 1.5B: © Javier Soriano/AFP/Getty Images; 1.5C: © Kiselev Andrey Velerevich/Shutterstock.com; 1.5D: © ayazad/Shutterstock.com; 1.8A: © The McGraw-Hill Companies, Inc./Stephen Frisch Photographer; 1.8B: © BrandTech Scientific, Inc.; 1.13A-B: © The McGraw-Hill Companies, Inc./Stephen Frisch Photographer.

Chapter 2

Opener: © Mark Schneider/Visuals Unlimited; Table 2.1(all), 2.2A-B: © The McGraw-Hill Companies, Inc./Stephen Frisch Photographer; 2.3(top): © Punchstock RF; 2.3(bottom): © Alexander Cherednichenko/Shutterstock.com; p. 45: © Roman Crochuk/Shutterstock.com; 2.10(all), 2.11A(both), 2.11E: © The McGraw-Hill Companies, Inc./Stephen Frisch Photographer; 2.16: © Mark Schneider/Visuals Unlimited; 2.19A-B: © The McGraw-Hill Companies, Inc./Stephen Frisch Photographer.

Chapter 3

Opener: © Stepan Jezek/Shutterstock.com; 3.1, 3.7(all): © The McGraw-Hill Companies, Inc./Charles Winters Photographer; p. 104: © The McGraw-Hill Companies, Inc./Stephen Frisch Photographer; p. 105: © Richard Megna/Fundamental Photographs, NYC; 3.14A-D, 3.15(both): © The McGraw-Hill Companies, Inc./Stephen Frisch Photographer.

Chapter 4

Opener: © Paul Avis/Stone Getty Images; 4.3A-C, 4.4(both): © The McGraw-Hill Companies, Inc./Stephen Frisch Photographer; 4.5: © The McGraw-Hill Companies, Inc./Richard Megna, Photographer; 4.6, 4.8A-B: © The McGraw-Hill Companies, Inc./Stephen Frisch Photographer; 4.10: © The McGraw-Hill Companies, Inc./Charles Winters Photographer; 4.11A-C, p. 158, 4.14(both), 4.15(all), 4.16(all), 4.17(all), 4.18, 4.19(both): © The McGraw-Hill Companies, Inc./Stephen Frisch Photographer.

Chapter 5

Opener: © The McGraw-Hill Companies, Inc./John Thoeming Photographer; 5.1A-C, 5.2A-B: © The McGraw-Hill Companies, Inc./Stephen Frisch Photographer; 5.10: © The McGraw-Hill Companies, Inc./Charles Winters Photographer; p. 198: © Charles F. McCarthy/Shutterstock.com; p. 203: © The McGraw-Hill Companies, Inc./Stephen Frisch Photographer.

Chapter 6

Opener: © The McGraw-Hill Companies, Inc./Charles Winters Photographer; 6.1: © The McGraw-Hill Companies, Inc./Stephen Frisch Photographer.

Chapter 7

Opener: © Orla/Shutterstock.com; p. 264: © Anthony McAulay/Shutterstock.com; 7.5A: © Richard Megna/Fundamental Photographs, NYC; 7.6A: © Ravi/Shutterstock.com; 7.6B: © The McGraw-Hill Companies, Inc./Charles Winters Photographer; 7.6C: © Feng Yu/Shutterstock.com; B7.1A(both): © The McGraw-Hill Companies, Inc./Stephen Frisch Photographer; B7.1B: Washington DC Convention & Visitors Association; 7.13A-B: PSSC Physics © 1965, Education Development Center, Inc.; D.C. Heath & Company/Education Development Center, Inc.; 7.14: © Dennis Kunkel/Phototake.com.

Chapter 8

CO8: © bbostjan/Shutterstock.com; 8.9A-B, 8.21(all), 8.23: © The McGraw-Hill Companies, Inc./Stephen Frisch Photographer.

Chapter 9

Opener(crystal): © E. R. Degginger/Photo Researchers, Inc.; Opener(candle): © Dolgisch/Shutterstock.com; Opener(copper): © The McGraw-Hill Companies, Inc./Stephen Frisch Photographer; 9.6A-B, 9.9A, 9.10(all), 9.15, 9.26, 9.29: © The McGraw-Hill Companies, Inc./Stephen Frisch Photographer; p. 355: © Diane Hirsch/Fundamental Photographs, NYC.

Chapter 10

Opener: © Jill Braaten; 10.2A(all), 10.6(both): © The McGraw-Hill Companies, Inc./Stephen Frisch Photographer.

Chapter 11

11.23: © The McGraw-Hill Companies, Inc./Charles Winters Photographer.

Chapter 12

Opener: © Cathleen Howland/Shutterstock.com; p. 420: © Christopher Meder Photography/Shutterstock.com; 12.1A: © dinadesign/Shutterstock.com; 12.1B: © Jill Birschbach Photo Services; 12.9: © The McGraw-Hill Companies, Inc./Richard Megna Photographer; p. 438(strider): © Nuridsany & Perennou /Photo Researchers, Inc.; p. 438(dew): © Rod Planck/Photo Researchers, Inc.; 12.21A-B: © The McGraw-Hill Companies, Inc./Stephen Frisch Photographer; 12.23B: © Scott Camazine/Photo Researchers, Inc.; 12.25A: © Jeffrey A. Scovil Photography (Wayne Thompson Minerals); 12.25B: © Mark Schneider/Visuals Unlimited; 12.25C: © Jeffrey A. Scovil Photography; 12.25D: © Jeffrey A. Scovil Photography (Francis Benjamin Collection); Page 444: © Bryan Busovicki/Shutterstock.com; B12.3: Courtesy National Institute of Standards and Technology; 12.43A: © J. R. Factor/Photo Researchers, Inc.; 12.43B: © James Dennis/Phototake.com; p. 465: © Ingram Publishing/Alamy; 12.49: Courtesy of Benoit Dubertret; 12.50: © & by permission from Ferrotec (USA) Corporation. May not be reproduced without written permission; 12.51: T. Sasaki/Rice University (Image courtesy of Rice University Office of Media Relations and Information).

Chapter 13

Opener: © CNRI/Photo Researchers, Inc.; 13.4A: © Ruth Melnick; 13.4B: © Ingram Publishing/AGE Fotostock RF; 13.18A-C: © The McGraw-Hill Companies, Inc./Stephen Frisch Photographer; 13.20: © Photodisc/Getty RF; p. 494: © Peter Scoones/Photo Researchers, Inc.; 13.22A-C: © The McGraw-Hill Companies, Inc./Stephen Frisch Photographer; 13.29A-C: © David M. Phillips/Photo Researchers, Inc.; 13.30A: © Ed Degginger/Color-Pic; 13.30B: © Corbis RF; 13.31: © Earth Satellite Corporation/SPL/Photo Researchers, Inc.; B13.3A: © Robert Essel/Corbis.

Chapter 14

Opener(left): © Joseph T. & Suzanne L. Collins/Photo Researchers, Inc.; Opener(right): © Joel Sartore/National Geographic Stock; Table 14.1, p. 529,

530(top & bottom), 532, 534, 536, 538: © The McGraw-Hill Companies, Inc./Stephen Frisch Photographer; 14.10A: © Gordon Vrdoljak, UC Berkeley Electron Microscope Lab; 14.11A-B: © The McGraw-Hill Companies, Inc./Stephen Frisch Photographer; 14.15 © Gontar/Shutterstock.com; Page 544: © The McGraw-Hill Companies, Inc./Stephen Frisch Photographer; p. 547: © Daniel Stein/iStockphoto.com; p. 551, 14.21: © The McGraw-Hill Companies, Inc./Stephen Frisch Photographer; p. 555(right): © Steve Cole/Getty RF; p. 556, 14.23B, p. 562: © The McGraw-Hill Companies, Inc./Stephen Frisch Photographer; 14.26: © Ed Degginger/Color-Pic.

Chapter 15

Opener: © Georgy Markov/Shutterstock.com; 15.8: © Martin Bough/Fundamental Photographs, NYC; B15.4A: © Zephyr/Photo Researchers, Inc.; 15.14A-B: © The McGraw-Hill Companies, Inc./Richard Megna Photographer; p. 600: © Jill Braaten; 15.28: © The McGraw-Hill Companies, Inc./Charles Winters Photographer; Page 608: © The McGraw-Hill Companies, Inc./Pat Watson Photographer; 15.32A: © J. Gross/SPL/Photo Researchers, Inc.; 15.32B: © Ed Degginger/Color-Pic; B15.7: © Courtesy of Orchid Cellmark.

Chapter 16

Opener: © avatra images/Alamy; 16.2(explosion): © Crown Copyright/Health & Safety Lab./Photo Researchers, Inc.; 16.2(fruit, baby): © Ruth Melnick; 16.2(landscape): © Publiphoto/Photo Researchers, Inc.; 16.3A-B: © The McGraw-Hill Companies, Inc./Stephen Frisch Photographer; Page 629: © Roberta Schmidt/AFP/Getty Images; p. 649: © Sipa via AP Images; 16.24A-B: © 2009 Richard Megna, Fundamental Photographs, NYC; B16.1: NASA.

Chapter 17

Opener: © Richard Megna, Fundamental Photographs, NYC; 17.1A-D: © The McGraw-Hill Companies, Inc./Stephen Frisch Photographer; Page 698: © AfriPics.com/Alamy.

Chapter 18

Opener: © Jill Braaten; Table 18.1(acids, bases), 18.2, 18.6A-B: © The McGraw-Hill Companies, Inc./Stephen Frisch Photographer.

Chapter 19

Opener: © Michael J. Thompson/Shutterstock.com; 19.1A-B, 19.2A-B, 19.6: © The McGraw-Hill Companies, Inc./Stephen Frisch Photographer; 19.11: © Jackie Lewin, Royal Free Hospital/Photo Researchers, Inc.; p. 785: © Jeffrey A. Scovil Photography; 19.12A-B: © The McGraw-Hill Companies, Inc./Stephen Frisch Photographer; p. 787: © CNRI/Science Source/Photo Researchers, Inc.; 19.13: © The McGraw-Hill Companies, Inc./Stephen Frisch Photographer; 19.14: © Ruth Melnick; p. 790: © The McGraw-Hill Companies, Inc./Stephen Frisch Photographer; p. 797: © Phil Degginger/Color-Pic; 19.17: © The McGraw-Hill Companies, Inc./Stephen Frisch Photographer.

Chapter 20

Opener: © Ian Clark/Image State/Photolibrary.com; 20.1A-B: © The McGraw-Hill Companies, Inc./Stephen Frisch Photographer; 20.12: © Vanderbilt University-Clinical Nutrition Research; p. 828: © PhotoDisc RF.

Chapter 21

Opener: © ifong/Shutterstock.com; 21.1, 21.2, 21.3, 21.4B: © The McGraw-Hill Companies, Inc./Stephen Frisch Photographer; 21.6: © Richard Megna/Fundamental Photographs, NYC; 21.8: © The McGraw-Hill Companies, Inc./Stephen Frisch Photographer; 21.14: Photo © F. W. Goro; 21.15: © Jill Braaten; 21.16: © The McGraw-Hill Companies, Inc./Pat Watson Photographer; 21.17: Courtesy of the Guidant Corporation; 21.19: © The McGraw-Hill Companies, Inc./Stephen Frisch Photographer; 21.20: © AP/Wide World Photos; 21.22A: © Alfred Dias/Photo Researchers, Inc.; 21.23: © David Weintraub/Photo Researchers, Inc.; 21.27: © Jill Braaten; 21.28, p. 889: © The McGraw-Hill Companies, Inc./Stephen Frisch Photographer.

Chapter 22

Opener: © Cooper-Hewitt, National Design Museum, Smithsonian Institution/Art Resource, NY; 22.3A: © Doug Sherman/Geofile; 22.3B: © University of Cambridge, Department of Earth Sciences; p. 908: © Ruth Melnick; p. 909: © Robert Holmes/Corbis; p. 917: © Patrick W. Grace/Photo Researchers, Inc.; 22.12: © Richard Megna/Fundamental Photographs, NYC; p. 922: © Christine L. Case/Visuals Unlimited; p. 924: © Remi Benali; 22.18: Courtesy Bethlehem Steel Corporation; p. 926: © Lee Prince/Shutterstock.com; 22.19: © Tom Hollyman/Photo Researchers, Inc.; p. 927: © James L. Amos/Peter Arnold, Inc./Photolibrary.com; p. 929: © Hank Morgan/Rainbow; p. 931: © Ken Whitmore/Getty Images; 22.23c: © Nathan Benn/Woodfin Camp & Associates.

Chapter 23

Opener: © VanHart/Shutterstock.com; 23.2, 23.5A-B, 23.6: © The McGraw-Hill Companies, Inc./Stephen Frisch Photographer; 23.8: © Richard Megna/Fundamental Photographs, NYC; p. 963: © Pete Turner/The Image Bank/Getty Images; 23.19A: © The McGraw-Hill Companies, Inc./Pat Watson Photographer; 23.20A-B: © The McGraw-Hill Companies, Inc./Stephen Frisch Photographer.

Chapter 24

Opener(bananas): © Goncharuk/Shutterstock.com; Opener(pellet): © Mitsubishi Nuclear Fuel Co., Ltd.; 24.4: © Hank Morgan/Rainbow; 24.5: © Meridian Biotechnologies Ltd.; p. 991: © Copyright 1978 by Vernon Miller. For use by permission for Business Wire via Getty Images; p. 993: © Hulton Archive/Getty Images; p. 994: © Maximilien Brice/CERN; 24.13A: © Scott Camazine/Photo Researchers, Inc.; 24.13B: © T. Youssef/Custom Medical Stock Photo; 24.14: © Dr. Robert Friedland/SPL/Photo Researchers, Inc.; 24.15: © Dr. Dennis Olson/Meat Lab, Iowa State University, Ames, IA; 24.20: © Albert Copley/Visuals Unlimited; 24.21: © Dietmar Krause/Princeton Plasma Physics Lab.

Index

Page numbers followed by *f* indicate figures; *mn,* marginal notes; *n,* footnotes; and *t,* tables. Page numbers preceded by "A-" indicate pages in the *Appendix*. Page numbers preceded by "G-" indicate pages in the *Glossary.*

A

B

N

O

X

Y

Z

Periodic Table of the Elements

Metals (main-group)
Metals (transition)
Metals (inner transition)
Metalloids
Nonmetals

MAIN–GROUP ELEMENTS | TRANSITION ELEMENTS | MAIN–GROUP ELEMENTS

Period	1A (1)	2A (2)	3B (3)	4B (4)	5B (5)	6B (6)	7B (7)	8B (8)	8B (9)	8B (10)	1B (11)	2B (12)	3A (13)	4A (14)	5A (15)	6A (16)	7A (17)	8A (18)
1	1 **H** 1.008																	2 **He** 4.003
2	3 **Li** 6.941	4 **Be** 9.012											5 **B** 10.81	6 **C** 12.01	7 **N** 14.01	8 **O** 16.00	9 **F** 19.00	10 **Ne** 20.18
3	11 **Na** 22.99	12 **Mg** 24.31											13 **Al** 26.98	14 **Si** 28.09	15 **P** 30.97	16 **S** 32.07	17 **Cl** 35.45	18 **Ar** 39.95
4	19 **K** 39.10	20 **Ca** 40.08	21 **Sc** 44.96	22 **Ti** 47.88	23 **V** 50.94	24 **Cr** 52.00	25 **Mn** 54.94	26 **Fe** 55.85	27 **Co** 58.93	28 **Ni** 58.69	29 **Cu** 63.55	30 **Zn** 65.41	31 **Ga** 69.72	32 **Ge** 72.61	33 **As** 74.92	34 **Se** 78.96	35 **Br** 79.90	36 **Kr** 83.80
5	37 **Rb** 85.47	38 **Sr** 87.62	39 **Y** 88.91	40 **Zr** 91.22	41 **Nb** 92.91	42 **Mo** 95.94	43 **Tc** (98)	44 **Ru** 101.1	45 **Rh** 102.9	46 **Pd** 106.4	47 **Ag** 107.9	48 **Cd** 112.4	49 **In** 114.8	50 **Sn** 118.7	51 **Sb** 121.8	52 **Te** 127.6	53 **I** 126.9	54 **Xe** 131.3
6	55 **Cs** 132.9	56 **Ba** 137.3	57 **La** 138.9	72 **Hf** 178.5	73 **Ta** 180.9	74 **W** 183.9	75 **Re** 186.2	76 **Os** 190.2	77 **Ir** 192.2	78 **Pt** 195.1	79 **Au** 197.0	80 **Hg** 200.6	81 **Tl** 204.4	82 **Pb** 207.2	83 **Bi** 209.0	84 **Po** (209)	85 **At** (210)	86 **Rn** (222)
7	87 **Fr** (223)	88 **Ra** (226)	89 **Ac** (227)	104 **Rf** (263)	105 **Db** (262)	106 **Sg** (266)	107 **Bh** (267)	108 **Hs** (277)	109 **Mt** (268)	110 **Ds** (281)	111 **Rg** (272)	112 **Cn** (285)	113 (284)	114 (289)	115 (288)	116 (292)		118 (294)

As of late 2010, elements 113 through 116 and 118 had not been named.

INNER TRANSITION ELEMENTS

6	Lanthanides	58 **Ce** 140.1	59 **Pr** 140.9	60 **Nd** 144.2	61 **Pm** (145)	62 **Sm** 150.4	63 **Eu** 152.0	64 **Gd** 157.3	65 **Tb** 158.9	66 **Dy** 162.5	67 **Ho** 164.9	68 **Er** 167.3	69 **Tm** 168.9	70 **Yb** 173.0	71 **Lu** 175.0
7	Actinides	90 **Th** 232.0	91 **Pa** (231)	92 **U** 238.0	93 **Np** (237)	94 **Pu** (242)	95 **Am** (243)	96 **Cm** (247)	97 **Bk** (247)	98 **Cf** (251)	99 **Es** (252)	100 **Fm** (257)	101 **Md** (258)	102 **No** (259)	103 **Lr** (260)

The Elements

Name	Symbol	Atomic Number	Atomic Mass*
Actinium	Ac	89	(227)
Aluminum	Al	13	26.98
Americium	Am	95	(243)
Antimony	Sb	51	121.8
Argon	Ar	18	39.95
Arsenic	As	33	74.92
Astatine	At	85	(210)
Barium	Ba	56	137.3
Berkelium	Bk	97	(247)
Beryllium	Be	4	9.012
Bismuth	Bi	83	209.0
Bohrium	Bh	107	(267)
Boron	B	5	10.81
Bromine	Br	35	79.90
Cadmium	Cd	48	112.4
Calcium	Ca	20	40.08
Californium	Cf	98	(249)
Carbon	C	6	12.01
Cerium	Ce	58	140.1
Cesium	Cs	55	132.9
Chlorine	Cl	17	35.45
Chromium	Cr	24	52.00
Cobalt	Co	27	58.93
Copernicium	Cn	112	(285)
Copper	Cu	29	63.55
Curium	Cm	96	(247)
Darmstadtium	Ds	110	(281)
Dubnium	Db	105	(262)
Dysprosium	Dy	66	162.5
Einsteinium	Es	99	(254)
Erbium	Er	68	167.3
Europium	Eu	63	152.0
Fermium	Fm	100	(253)
Fluorine	F	9	19.00
Francium	Fr	87	(223)
Gadolinium	Gd	64	157.3
Gallium	Ga	31	69.72
Germanium	Ge	32	72.61
Gold	Au	79	197.0
Hafnium	Hf	72	178.5
Hassium	Hs	108	(277)
Helium	He	2	4.003
Holmium	Ho	67	164.9
Hydrogen	H	1	1.008
Indium	In	49	114.8
Iodine	I	53	126.9
Iridium	Ir	77	192.2
Iron	Fe	26	55.85
Krypton	Kr	36	83.80
Lanthanum	La	57	138.9
Lawrencium	Lr	103	(257)
Lead	Pb	82	207.2
Lithium	Li	3	6.941
Lutetium	Lu	71	175.0
Magnesium	Mg	12	24.31
Manganese	Mn	25	54.94
Meitnerium	Mt	109	(268)
Mendelevium	Md	101	(256)
Mercury	Hg	80	200.6
Molybdenum	Mo	42	95.94
Neodymium	Nd	60	144.2
Neon	Ne	10	20.18
Neptunium	Np	93	(244)
Nickel	Ni	28	58.70
Niobium	Nb	41	92.91
Nitrogen	N	7	14.01
Nobelium	No	102	(253)
Osmium	Os	76	190.2
Oxygen	O	8	16.00
Palladium	Pd	46	106.4
Phosphorus	P	15	30.97
Platinum	Pt	78	195.1
Plutonium	Pu	94	(242)
Polonium	Po	84	(209)
Potassium	K	19	39.10
Praseodymium	Pr	59	140.9
Promethium	Pm	61	(145)
Protactinium	Pa	91	(231)
Radium	Ra	88	(226)
Radon	Rn	86	(222)
Rhenium	Re	75	186.2
Rhodium	Rh	45	102.9
Roentgenium	Rg	111	(272)
Rubidium	Rb	37	85.47
Ruthenium	Ru	44	101.1
Rutherfordium	Rf	104	(263)
Samarium	Sm	62	150.4
Scandium	Sc	21	44.96
Seaborgium	Sg	106	(266)
Selenium	Se	34	78.96
Silicon	Si	14	28.09
Silver	Ag	47	107.9
Sodium	Na	11	22.99
Strontium	Sr	38	87.62
Sulfur	S	16	32.07
Tantalum	Ta	73	180.9
Technetium	Tc	43	(98)
Tellurium	Te	52	127.6
Terbium	Tb	65	158.9
Thallium	Tl	81	204.4
Thorium	Th	90	232.0
Thulium	Tm	69	168.9
Tin	Sn	50	118.7
Titanium	Ti	22	47.88
Tungsten	W	74	183.9
Uranium	U	92	238.0
Vanadium	V	23	50.94
Xenon	Xe	54	131.3
Ytterbium	Yb	70	173.0
Yttrium	Y	39	88.91
Zinc	Zn	30	65.41
Zirconium	Zr	40	91.22
		113**	(284)
		114	(289)
		115	(288)
		116	(292)
		118	(294)

*All atomic masses are given to four significant figures. Values in parentheses represent the mass number of the most stable isotope.
**The names and symbols for elements 113 through 116 and 118 have not yet been chosen.

Fundamental Physical Constants (six significant figures)

Avogadro's number	N_A	$= 6.02214\times10^{23}$/mol
atomic mass unit	amu	$= 1.66054\times10^{-27}$ kg
charge of the electron (or proton)	e	$= 1.60218\times10^{-19}$ C
Faraday constant	F	$= 9.64853\times10^{4}$ C/mol
mass of the electron	m_e	$= 9.10939\times10^{-31}$ kg
mass of the neutron	m_n	$= 1.67493\times10^{-27}$ kg
mass of the proton	m_p	$= 1.67262\times10^{-27}$ kg
Planck's constant	h	$= 6.62607\times10^{-34}$ J·s
speed of light in a vacuum	c	$= 2.99792\times10^{8}$ m/s
standard acceleration of gravity	g	$= 9.80665$ m/s^2
universal gas constant	R	$= 8.31447$ J/(mol·K)
		$= 8.20578\times10^{-2}$ (atm·L)/(mol·K)

SI Unit Prefixes

p	n	μ	m	c	d	k	M	G
pico-	nano-	micro-	milli-	centi-	deci-	kilo-	mega-	giga-
10^{-12}	10^{-9}	10^{-6}	10^{-3}	10^{-2}	10^{-1}	10^{3}	10^{6}	10^{9}

Conversions and Relationships

Length

SI unit: meter, m

1 km	= 1000 m
	= 0.62 mile (mi)
1 inch (in)	= 2.54 cm
1 m	= 1.094 yards (yd)
1 pm	$= 10^{-12}$ m = 0.01 Å

Volume

SI unit: cubic meter, m^3

1 dm^3	$= 10^{-3}$ m^3
	= 1 liter (L)
	= 1.057 quarts (qt)
1 cm^3	= 1 mL
1 m^3	= 35.3 ft^3

Pressure

SI unit: pascal, Pa

1 Pa	= 1 N/m^2
	= 1 kg/m·s^2
1 atm	$= 1.01325\times10^{5}$ Pa
	= 760 torr
1 bar	$= 1\times10^{5}$ Pa

Mass

SI unit: kilogram, kg

1 kg	$= 10^3$ g
	= 2.205 lb
1 metric ton (t)	$= 10^3$ kg

Energy

SI unit: joule, J

1 J	= 1 kg·m^2/s^2
	= 1 coulomb·volt (1 C·V)
1 cal	= 4.184 J
1 eV	$= 1.602\times10^{-19}$ J

Math relationships

$\pi = 3.1416$

volume of sphere $= \frac{4}{3}\pi r^3$

volume of cylinder $= \pi r^2 h$

Temperature

SI unit: kelvin, K

0 K	= −273.15°C
mp of H_2O	= 0°C (273.15 K)
bp of H_2O	= 100°C (373.15 K)
T (K)	$= T$ (°C) + 273.15
T (°C)	$= [T$ (°F) − 32]$\frac{5}{9}$
T (°F)	$= \frac{9}{5}T$ (°C) + 32

Useful Data and Information

Atomic and Molecular Properties

Atomic radii	Figure 8.13, p. 309
Bond energies	Table 9.2, p. 340
Bond lengths	Table 9.2, p. 340
Ground-state electron configurations	Figure 8.10, p. 305
Electronegativity values	Figure 9.21, p. 349
Ionic radii	Figure 8.29, p. 321
First ionization energies	Figure 8.16, p. 312
Molecular shapes	Figure 10.10, p. 379

Equilibrium Constants and Thermodynamic Data

K_a of hydrated metal ions	Appendix C, p. A-12
K_a of selected acids	Appendix C, pp. A-8 to A-10
Strengths of conjugate acid-base pairs	Figure 18.8, p. 731
K_b of amine bases	Appendix C, p. A-11
K_f of complex ions	Table 19.4, p. 796, and Appendix C, p. A-12
K_{sp} of slightly soluble ionic compounds	Appendix C, p. A-13
Standard electrode potentials, $E^\circ_{\text{half-cell}}$	Appendix D, p. A-14
Standard free energies of formation, ΔG°_f	Appendix B, pp. A-5 to A-7
Standard heats of formation, ΔH°_f	Appendix B, pp. A-5 to A-7
Standard molar entropies, S°	Appendix B, pp. A-5 to A-7

Names and Formulas

Ligands	Table 23.7, p. 956
Metals in complex anions	Table 23.8, p. 956
Metals with more than one monatomic ion	Table 2.4, p. 62
Monatomic ions	Table 2.3, p. 60
Organic functional groups	Table 15.5, p. 592
Polyatomic ions	Table 2.5, p. 62

Properties of the Elements

Group 1A(1): Alkali metals	p. 529
Group 2A(2): Alkaline earth metals	p. 532
Group 3A(13): Boron family	p. 534
Group 4A(14): Carbon family	p. 538
Group 5A(15): Nitrogen family	p. 544
Group 6A(16): Oxygen family	p. 551
Group 7A(17): Halogens	p. 556
Group 8A(18): Noble gases	p. 562
Period 4 transition metals, atomic properties	Figure 23.3, p. 948
Period 4 transition metals, oxidation states	Table 23.2, p. 950

Miscellaneous

Rules for assigning an oxidation number	Table 4.3, p. 155
SI-English equivalent quantities	Table 1.4, p. 18
Solubility rules for ionic compounds in water	Table 4.1, p. 143
Vapor pressure of water	Table 5.2, p. 200